MATERIALS
HANDBOOK

OTHER McGRAW-HILL HANDBOOKS OF INTEREST

MATERIALS HANDBOOK

An Encyclopedia for Purchasing Managers,
Engineers, Executives, and Foremen

GEORGE S. BRADY

TENTH EDITION

McGRAW-HILL BOOK COMPANY

New York   St. Louis   San Francisco   Düsseldorf   Johannesburg
Kuala Lumpur   London   Mexico   Montreal   New Delhi   Panama
Paris   São Paulo   Singapore   Sydney   Tokyo   Toronto

Sponsoring Editor Daniel N. Fischel
Director of Production Stephen J. Boldish
Editing Supervisor Lila M. Gardner
Editing and Production Staff Gretlyn Blau,
Teresa F. Leaden, George E. Oechsner

MATERIALS HANDBOOK

07–007068–7

567890 KPKP 798765

Preface
to the Tenth Edition

Materials Handbook, Tenth Edition, is the cumulative development of an idea that took root when the author was the first Trade Commissioner sent to Latin America by the United States Government. The problem was to be in a position to discuss intelligently the important characteristics and economics of all types of industrial materials without involvement in details. It began with a card index, but a handy desk tool was needed, a ready-reference volume to present the gist of the vast store of data on industrial materials without the time-consuming study of innumerable texts.

The great strides of science, with consequent overwhelming accumulation of data, has intensified the need for condensation of information for government officials and industrial executives. The First Edition, published when the author was Managing Editor of a trade paper for the metal-working industries, was limited in scope to those industries, but the demand was for an ever-widening viewpoint, with the precisions of the electronics, aerospace, and nuclear industries requiring more exacting analysis of data.

In Materials Science it is said that to take from one source is plagiarism but to take from a thousand sources is research. Science knows no race or international boundary line. Even the chance remark of a nontechnical observer may be the key that aids in unlocking a puzzling research, for "Ideas," wrote Herodotus, "are not born new but are taken from the eternity of positiveness when the mind is made ready to receive them." Every new discovery is but a very small step in a long chain of prior events.

The sources of information for *Materials Handbook* are too numerous to give credit to all who furnished data and counsel, but acknowledgment is made of the ready and willing cooperation of producers, manufacturers, technical authorities, industrial-paper editors, and government bureaus in this country and abroad.   A deep sense of appreciation is felt for the encouragement and advice given to the work by the many members of the National Association of Purchasing Management and the American Ordnance Association.   The Introduction to Part II, originally prepared with the assistance of the NAPM, is retained because its theme is still the basic concept of the materials-educative work of the Association.   This final edition from my hand was made possible by the organizing, tabulating, and coordinating assistance given by Jeanne Brady Moulton, and finally, for the ten editions, credit is due to Adeline Brady, the companion of my life-long wanderings.

George Stuart Brady

Tupá-Sïpé

Foreword to the User

All materials, infinite in possible numbers, derive from only 92 natural elements. It is as basically simple as that, but the varying forms and usages are so intertwined in all of the industries that the executive can have no real comprehension of the characteristics and economics of any one of the materials which he procures for his own industry unless he has an intelligent over-all grasp of its varying forms and usages in other industries. Nor can the executive have a real perspective of the whole economy unless he has that over-all comprehension of materials, for our entire material civilization is built on the products derived from materials.

However, there are definite natural laws of derivation and combination, and the selection of data and of examples in *Materials Handbook* has been made with a view toward giving the reader an intelligent over-all insight. It is not the purpose of the book to provide an exhaustive treatise on any material, as it is assumed that purchasers and products designers will consult producers of the materials for detailed specifications.

General information, with the most commonly accepted comparative figures, is given on materials in their group classifications in order to give a general picture; selected processed materials and patented and trade-named materials are then described to give a more specific understanding of commercial applications. The relative position and the length of description of proprietary materials are for purposes of illustration and bear no relation to the relative merits of the products of any one producer.

Statements regarding characteristics of the materials and nomenclature are not the personal opinions of the author.   They are backed by the most competent authorities in each case, or they constitute the most common usage among successful manufacturers.   Names are selected by the greatest and most reasonable use.   Local, slang, and colloquial names are omitted unless they represent particular grades or uses.   Need for brevity has limited historical background, but some descriptions of commercially superseded materials are retained because they may indicate important steps of development still useful.

MATERIALS HANDBOOK

PART ONE

Materials, Their Properties and Uses

ABLATIVE AGENTS. Materials used for the outward dissipation of extremely high heats by mass removal. Their most common use is as an external heat shield to protect supersonic aerospace vehicles from an excessive build-up of heat caused by air friction at the surface. The ablative material must have a low thermal conductivity in order that the intense heat may remain concentrated in the thin surface layer. As the surface of the ablator melts or sublimes, it is wiped away by the frictional forces that simultaneously heat newly exposed surfaces. The heat is carried off with the material removed. The less material that is lost, the more efficient is the ablative material. Ablation by liquid flow is relatively wasteful and the use of the higher heat of vaporization for heat absorption is preferred. The ablative material, therefore, in addition to low thermal conductivity, should have a high thermal capacity in the solid, liquid, and gaseous states; a high heat of fusion and evaporation; and a high heat of dissociation of its vapors. The ablative agent, or **ablator,** is usually a carbonaceous organic compound, such as a plastic. As the disassociation products are lost as liquid or vapor, the char is held in place by the refractory filler fibers, still giving a measure of heat resistance. The effective life of an ablative is short, calculated in seconds per millimeter of thickness for the distance traveled in the atmosphere.

In the selection of an ablative material all of the factors must be calculated and balanced. For example, it may be desirable to utilize reflective power for the dissipation of the heat. But to obtain the full benefit of radiation the surface temperature should be high, while to get the full benefit of evaporation the surface temperature should be low. As most metals have a long melt range before evaporation, materials that sublime directly from the solid would be desirable, but such materials are non-metallic or organic, as plastics, with low strength. Single ablative materials seldom have all of the desirable factors and thus composites are used. Phenolic or epoxy resins are reinforced with asbestos fabric, carbonized cloth, or refractory fibers such as asbestos, fused silica, and glasses. The refractory fibers are incorporated not only for mechanical strength but have a function in the ablative process, and surface active agents may be added to speed the rate of evaporation. For rockets and some industrial purposes the ablator may require good structural strength. A simple laminate of this type is **Tayloron** of the Taylor Fibre Co. It consists of alternate layers of asbestos and nylon fabrics impregnated with phenolic resin. The sheet has a tensile strength of 12,000 psi. It requires 300 sec to burn through a $1/4$-in. thickness with a 5000°F flame. **Ablative paint,** for protecting woodwork, may be organic silicones which convert to silica at temperatures above 2000°F. **Pyromark,** of Tempil Corp., is a paint of this type.

The **thrust ablator** for the Apollo moon rocket consisted of a fiber glass laminate covered with cork having a white reflective coating which also served as a moisture barrier.   Greatest thickness at the top was $\frac{7}{8}$ in. for a maximum temperature of 1200°F.   This outer structure was jettisoned at 295,000 ft.   The **reentry ablator** consisted of an aluminum honeycomb structure filled with a phenolic-epoxy compound.   Maximum thickness at the base was 2 in., giving safety factors for possible multiple reentries at a temperature of 5000°F.   This structure, developed by NASA and the Avco Corp., also served as a part of the temperature-regulating shield for temperatures from 280°F on the sun side to −280°F on the dark side on the long space flight.

For thermal protection under less severe conditions other methods of heat shielding may be used.   Metals can resist temperatures higher than their melting point by **convection cooling,** or **thermal cooling,** which is heat protection by heat exchange with a coolant.   Thus, tungsten can be arc-melted in a copper kettle which is cooled by circulating water.   The container metal must have high thermal conductivity, and the heat must be quickly carried away and stored or dissipated.   When convection cooling is difficult or not possible, cooling may be accomplished by a heat sink. **Heat-sink cooling** depends on the heat absorption capability of the structural material itself or backed up by another material of higher heat absorption.   Copper, beryllium, graphite, and beryllium oxide have been used.   A heat-sink material should have high thermal conductivity, high specific heat and melting point, and for aerodynamic applications, a low specific gravity.

ABRASIVES. Materials used for surfacing and finishing metals, stone, wood, glass, and other materials by abrasive action.   The natural abrasives include the diamond, emery, corundum, sand, crushed garnet and quartz, tripoli, and pumice.   **Artificial abrasives,** or **manufactured abrasives,** are generally superior in uniformity to natural abrasives, and are mostly silicon carbide, aluminum oxide, boron carbide, or boron nitride, marketed under trade names.   The diamond is also manufactured.   The massive natural abrasives, such as sandstone, are cut into grinding wheels from the natural block, but most abrasive material is used as grains or built into artificial shapes.

For industrial grinding, artificial abrasives are preferred to natural abrasives because of their greater uniformity.   Grading is important because uniform grinding requires grains of the same size.   The abrasive grains are used as a grinding powder, are made into wheels, blocks, or stones, or are bonded to paper or cloth.   **Abrasive cloth** is made of cotton jean or drills to close tolerances of yarns and weaves, and the grains are attached with glue or resin.   But the **Fabricut cloth** of the 3M Co. is an open-weave fabric with alumina or silicon carbide grains of 100 to 400 mesh.   The open weave permits easy cleaning of the cloth in an air blast.

Abrasive paper has the grains, usually aluminum oxide or silicon carbide, glued to one side of 40- to 130-lb kraft paper. The usual grain sizes are No. 16 to No. 500.

Abrasive powder is usually graded in sizes from 8 to 240 mesh. Coarse grain is to 24 mesh; fine grain is 150 to 240. **Blasting abrasive** for blast cleaning of metal castings is usually coarse grain. **Arrowblast,** of the Norton Co., is aluminum oxide with grain sizes 16 to 80 mesh. **Grinding flour** consists of extremely fine grains separated by flotation, usually in grain sizes from 280 to 600 mesh, used for grinding glass and fine polishing. **Levigated abrasives** are fine powders for final burnishing of metals or for metallographic polishing, usually processed to make them chemically neutral. **Green rouge** is levigated chromic oxide, and **mild polish** may be levigated tin oxide; both are used for burnishing soft metals. **Polishing powder** may be aluminum oxide or metal oxide powders of ultrafine particle size down to 600 mesh. **Micria AD,** of the Monsanto Co., is alumina; **Micria ZR** is zirconia; and **Micria TIS** is titania. **Gamal,** of the Fisher Scientific Co., is a fine aluminum oxide powder, the smaller cubes being 1.5 microns, with smaller particles 0.5 micron, or 0.0000197 in. **Cerox,** of the Lindsay Div., is cerium oxide used to polish optical lenses and automobile windshields. It cuts fast and gives a smooth surface. **Grinding compounds** for valve grinding are usually aluminum oxide in oil.

Hardness of abrasives is measured roughly on the Mohs scale, but this scale is inadequate for very hard materials. The hardness of silicon carbide is given as 9.5 on the Mohs scale, but measures 2,500 on the Knoop scale, compared with 6,500 for the diamond which is rated as 10 on the Mohs scale. Garnet is one of the softest of the so-called hard abrasives. Rouge is one of the hardest of the soft abrasives, with a hardness of 5.5 to 6.5. The **mild abrasives,** used in silver polishes and window-cleaning compounds, such as chalk and talc, have a hardness of 1 to 2 Mohs. The milder abrasives for dental pastes and powders may be precipitated calcium carbonate, tricalcium phosphate, or combinations of sodium metaphosphate and tricalcium phosphate. Abrasives for metal polishes may also be pumice, diatomite, silica flour, tripoli, whiting, kaolin, tin oxide, or fuller's earth. This type of fine abrasive must be of very uniform grain in order to prevent scratching. **Cuttle bone,** or **cuttlefish bone,** is a calcareous powder made from the internal shell of a Mediterranean marine mollusk of the genus *Sepia,* and is used as a fine polishing material for jewelry and in tooth powders. **Ground glass** is regularly marketed as an abrasive for use in scouring compounds and in match-head compositions. **Lapping abrasives,** for finish grinding of hard materials, are diamond dust or boron carbide powder.

Aluminum oxide wheels are used for grinding materials of high tensile strength. The toughness and nature of the fracture depend on the crystal size and the impurities.   Silicon carbide is harder but is not as strong as aluminum oxide.   It is used for grinding metals that have dense grain structure and for stone.   The first artificial **grinding wheels** were introduced in 1825 from India where they had been made for centuries by binding natural corundum grains with gum resin or shellac.   There are five processes for making **abrasive wheels,** each giving different characteristics: **Vitrified wheels** are made by molding under heat and pressure. They are used for general and precision grinding where the wheel does not exceed a speed of 6,500 surface ft per min.   The rigidity gives high precision, and the porosity and strength of bond permit high stock removal. **Silicate wheels** have a silicate binder and are baked.   The silicate bond releases the grains more easily than the vitrified, and is used for grinding edge tools to reduce burning of the tool.   Synthetic resins are used for bonding where greater strength is required than is obtained with the silicate, but less openness than with the vitrified.   Resinoid bonds are used up to 16,000 surface ft per min, and are used especially for thread grinding and cutoff wheels.   Shellac binder is used for light work and for high finishing.   Rubber is used for precision grinding and for centerless-feed machines.

Grading of abrasive wheels is by grit size number from No. 10 to No. 600, which is 600 mesh; by grade of wheel, or strength of the bond, which is by letter designation, increasing in hardness from A to Z; and by grain spacing or structure number.   The ideal condition is with a bond strong enough to hold the grains to accomplish the desired result, and then release them before they become too dull.   Essential qualities in the abrasive grain are: penetration hardness, body strength sufficient to resist fracture until the points dull and then break to present a new edge, and an attrition resistance suitable to the work.   Some wheels are made with a porous honeycombed structure to give free cutting and cooler operation on some types of metal grinding.   The **Open-structure wheel** of the Norton Co. is a wheel of this type.   Some diamond wheels are made with aluminum powder mixed with a thermosetting resin, and the diamond abrasive mix is hot-presed around this core wheel.   Norton diamond wheels are of three types: metal bonded by powder metallurgy, resinoid bonded, and vitrified bonded.

ABRASIVE SAND. Any sand used for abrasive and grinding purposes, but the term does not include the sharp grains obtained by crushing quartz and used for sandpaper.   The chief types of abrasive sand include sandblast sand, glass-grinding sand, and stone-cutting sand.   Sand for stone sawing and for marble and glass grinding is usually ungraded, with no preparation other than screening, but it must have tough, uniform grains. **Chats** are sand tailings from the Missouri lead ores, used for sawing stone.

Banding sand is used for the band grinding of tool handles, and for the grinding of plate glass, but is often replaced by artificial abrasives. Banding-sand grains are fine, 95% being retained on a 150-mesh screen. **Burnishing sand,** for metal polishing, is a fine-grained silica sand with rounded grains. It should pass a 65-mesh screen, and be retained on a 100-mesh screen.

ACAROID RESIN. A gum resin from the base of the tufted trunk leaves of various species of *Xanthorrhoea* trees of Australia and Tasmania. It is also called **gum accroides** and **yacca gum. Yellow acaroid** from the *X. tateana* is relatively scarce, but a gum of the yellow class comes from the tree *X. preissii* of Western Australia, and is in small hollow pieces of yellow to reddish color. It is known as **black boy resin,** the name coming from the appearance of the tree. **Red acaroid,** known also as **red gum** and **grass tree gum,** comes in small dusty pieces of reddish-brown color. This variety is from the *X. australis* and about 15 other species of the tree of southeastern Australia. The resins contain 80 to 85% resinotannol with **coumaric acid,** which is an hydroxy cinnamic acid, and they also contain free cinnamic acid. They are thus closely related chemically to the balsams. Acaroid resin has the property unique among natural resins of capacity for thermosetting to a hard, insoluble, chemical-resistant film. By treatment with nitric acid it yields picric acid; by treatment with sulfuric acid it yields fast brown to black dyes. The resins are soluble in alcohols and in aniline, only slightly soluble in chlorinated compounds, and insoluble in coal-tar hydrocarbons. Acaroid has some of the physical characteristics of shellac, but is difficult to bleach. It is used for spirit varnishes and metal lacquers, in coatings, in paper sizing, in inks and sealing waxes, in binders, for blending with shellac, in production of picric acid, and in medicine.

ACETIC ACID. Also known as **ethanoic acid.** A colorless, corrosive liquid of pungent odor and composition $CH_3 \cdot COOH$, having a wide variety of industrial uses as a reagent, solvent, and esterifier. It is employed as a weak acid for etching and for soldering, in stain removers and bleaches, as a preservative, in photographic chemicals, for the manufacture of cellulose acetate, as a solvent for essential oils, resins, and gums, as a precipitant for latex, in tanning leather, and in making artificial flavors. Acetic acid is found in the juices of many fruits, and in combination in the stems or woody parts of plants. It is the active principle in **vinegar,** giving it the characteristic sour taste, acid flavor, and pungent odor. It is made commercially by the oxidation of ethyl alcohol, and also produced in the destructive distillation of wood. It is also made by the reaction of methanol and carbon monoxide. Its specific gravity is 1.049, its boiling point is 118°C, and it becomes a colorless solid below 16.6°C. The pure 99.9% solid is known as **glacial acetic acid.** Standard and laundry special grades contain 99.5% acid, with water the chief impurity. Standard strengths of water solution are 28, 56, 70, 80, 85, 90%.

Acetic anhydride, $CH_3COOCOCH_3$, a colorless liquid with boiling point 139.5°C, is a powerful acetylating agent, and is used in making cellulose acetate. It forms acetic acid when water is added. **Hydroxyacetic acid,** $HOCH_2COOH$, or **glycolic acid,** is produced by oxidizing glycol with dilute nitric acid and is intermediate in strength between acetic and formic acids. It is soluble in water, is nontoxic, and is used in foodstuffs, dyeing, tanning, electropolishing, and in resins. Its esters are solvents for resins. **Diglycolic acid,** $O(CH_2CO_2H)_2$, is a white solid melting at 148°C. It is stronger than tartaric or formic acids, and is used for making resins and plasticizers. **Thioacetic acid** has the formula of acetamide but with HS replacing the NH_2. It is a pungent liquid used for making esters for synthetic resins.

Chloroacetic acid, $CH_2ClCOOH$, is a white crystalline powder melting at 61.6°C and boiling at 189°C. It is used for producing carboxy methyl cellulose, dyes, and drugs. **Sequestrene,** used as a clarifying agent and water softener in soaps and detergents, and to prevent rancidity in foods and sulfonated oils, is ethylene bisamino diacetic acid, $(HOOCCH_2)_2$-$NCH_2CH_2N(CH_2COOH)_2$. It is a liquid, but in the form of its sodium salt is a water-soluble white powder. **Trifluoroacetic acid,** CF_3COOH, is one of the strongest organic acids. It is a colorless, corrosive liquid, boiling at 71.1°C and freezing at −15.3°C. It is used in the manufacture of plastics, dyes, pharmaceuticals, and flame-resistant compounds.

Paracetic acid, $CH_3 \cdot O \cdot COOH$, is a colorless liquid of strong odor with the same solubility as acetic acid. It has 8.6% available oxygen and is used as a bleaching agent, a polymerization catalyst, for making epoxy resins, and as a bactericide. **Acetin** is an ester of acetic acid made from glycerin and acetic acid, used as a solvent for basic dyes and tannins. It is a neutral straw-colored liquid of specific gravity 1.20 and boiling point 133 to 153°C. It is also used in low-freezing dynamites and smokeless powder. The triacetic ester, **triacetin,** is a water-white liquid of specific gravity 1.16 and flash point 271°F, soluble in aromatic hydrocarbons. It is used as a plasticizer.

Phenyl acetic acid, $C_6H_5CH_2COOH$, is a white flaky solid melting at 74.5°C. The reactive methylene group makes it useful for the manufacture of fine chemicals. **Cyanoacetic acid,** $CN \cdot CH_2 \cdot COOH$, has an active methylene group and an easily oxidized cyano group, and is used for producing caffeine, while the derivative **ethyl cyanoacetate,** $NC \cdot CH_2COO \cdot CH_2 \cdot CH_3$, a liquid boiling at 207°C, is used for making many drugs. **Malonic acid,** $CH_2(COOH)_2$, is a very reactive acid sometimes used instead of acetic acid for making plastics, drugs, and perfumes. It decomposes at 160°C, yielding acetic acid and carbon dioxide. **Methyl acetic acid,** CH_3CH_2COOH, is **propionic acid** or **propanoic acid,** a by-product in the extraction of potash from kelp. Modifications of this acid are used for cross-linking plastics.

ACETONE. An important industrial solvent, used in the manufacture of lacquers, plastics, smokeless powder, for dewaxing lubricating oils, for dissolving acetylene for storage, for dyeing cotton with aniline black, and as a raw material in the manufacture of other chemicals. It is a colorless, inflammable liquid with a mintlike odor and is soluble in water and in ether. The composition is $CH_3 \cdot CO \cdot CH_3$, specific gravity 0.790, boiling point 56°C, and solidification point −94°C. Acetone is made from isopropyl alcohol, or by a special fermentation of grain. The oily residue from the distillation is called **acetone oil** and is used as a denaturant of alcohol. **Diacetone,** or **diacetone alcohol,** is a colorless liquid of the composition $CH_3 \cdot CO \cdot CH_2 \cdot COH(CH_3)_2$ with a pleasant odor. It is used as a solvent for nitrocellulose and cellulose acetate, for gums and resins, in lacquers and thinners, and in ink removers. Because of its low freezing point and miscibility with castor oil it is used in hydraulic brake fluids. The specific gravity is 0.938, boiling point 166°C, and freezing point −54°C. Synthetic **methyl acetone** is a mixture of about 50% acetone, 30 methyl acetate, and 20 methanol, used in lacquers, paint removers, and for coagulating latex. **Dihydroxy acetone,** a colorless crystalline solid produced from glycerin by sorbose bacteria reaction, is used in cosmetics, and in preparing foodstuff emulsions, plasticizers, and alkyd resins. It is soluble in water and in alcohol.

ACETYLENE. A colorless gas of the composition $HC\!:\!CH$, used for welding torches, and for producing other chemicals. It contains 92.3% carbon, and is therefore nearly gaseous carbon. When pure, it has a sweet odor, but when it contains hydrogen sulfide as an impurity, it has a disagreeable odor. Acetylene burns brightly in the air, and was widely used for theater stage lighting before the advent of the electric light. When mixed with oxygen as **oxyacetylene** for welding, it gives a temperature of 3500°C. In air it is an explosive gas. The maximum explosive effect is with a mixture of 7.7% gas with 92.3 air. Acetylene has a specific gravity of 0.92. It is nontoxic, and is soluble in water, alcohol, or acetone. It liquefies under a pressure of 700 psi at 70°F. It is easily generated by the action of water on calcium carbide, but is also produced from petroleum. It is marketed compressed in cylinders, dissolved in acetone to make it nonexplosive. One volume of acetone will dissolve 25 volumes of acetylene at atmospheric pressure, or 250 volumes at 10 atm.

Prest-O-Lite is a trade name of Union Carbide Corp. for acetylene dissolved in acetone.   **Acetylene snow,** or solid acetylene, is produced by cooling acetylene below the melting point and compressing.   It is insensible to shock and flame, and is thus easier to transport.   A replacement for acetylene for producing plastics is **methyl acetylene propadiene,** which contains 70% methyl acetylene and 30% of the isomer **propadiene.**   It has the reactions of both acetylene and its isomer.   **Mapp,** of the Dow Chemical Co., for metal cutting, is **methyl acetylene,** $CH:C \cdot CH_3$.   It is safer to handle and gives about the same flame temperature.

ACRYLIC RESINS. Colorless, highly transparent, thermoplastic, synthetic resins made by the polymerization of acrylic derivatives, chiefly from the esters of **acrylic acid,** $CH_2:CH \cdot COOH$, and **methacrylic acid,** $CH_2:C-(CH_3) \cdot COOH$, **ethyl acrylate** and **methyl acrylate.**   **Glacial acrylic acid** is the anhydrous monomer with less than 2% moisture.   It can be esterified directly with an alcohol.   **Vinyl acrylic acid,** $CH_2:CHCH:CHCOOH$, with a melting point of 80°C, is made from acrolein and malonic acid. It polymerizes on heating.

The resins vary from soft, sticky semisolids to hard, brittle solids, depending upon the constitution of the monomers and upon the polymerization.   They are used for adhesives, protective coatings, finishes, laminated glass, transparent structural sheet, and molded products.   Acrylic resins, or **acrylate resins,** are stable and resistant to chemicals.   They do not cloud or fade in light when used as a laminating material in glass and are used as air-curing adhesives to seal glass to metals or wood. Water-based acrylics are used for the formulation of caulks and sealants. They have better adhesion and weather resistance than butyl rubbers and dry more quickly.   The sealants usually contain about 80% solids. **Methyl methacrylate** is a hard, rigid resin of the acrylic series.   In sheet form the density is 1.185, tensile strength 5,800 to 9,000 psi, compressive strength 15,000 psi, flexural strength 15,000 psi, refractive index 1.49, Brinell hardness 18 to 20, softening point 203°F, and dielectric strength 480 volts per mil.   It is superior to ordinary glass in the transmission of ultraviolet light, transmitting the rays down to 250 millimicrons wavelength.   The direct transmission of white light is 93%, and the flat sheet has optical homogeneity.   It is free of benzene rings and chlorine, and resists outdoor oxidation and light radiation.   It is subject to crazing, but cross-linking the resin improves craze resistance and thermal stability.   It is resistant to acids and to common solvents.   Sheet can be molded and bent by heating to 220 to 300°F, and is easily sawed, drilled, or machined. The powder can be injection- or compression-molded.   Because of its transparency, it is adapted for molded products such as costume jewelry, handbag frames, and novelties.   Tough molding resins are made by copolymerizing methyl methacrylate with styrene. **Zerlon 150,** of the Dow Chemical Co., is such a molding resin with a flexural strength of 17,600 psi.   **Thiacril,** of the Thiokol Chemical Corp., is an **acrylate rubber** having a tensile strenth of 2,500 psi and an elongation of 350%.   It is used for gaskets, wire insulation, and hose.

Allyl methacrylate is a liquid of the empirical formula $C_7H_{10}O_2$, boiling at 63°C, and insoluble in water.   It can be polymerized to form liquid or hard solid resins, but is used chiefly as a cross-linking agent for other resins to raise the softening point and increase hardness.   **Gafite,** of the General Aniline & Film Corp., is polymethyl alphachloro acrylate, $(CH_2:CCl \cdot COOCH_3)_x$.   It is a transparent and craze-resistant resin used for aircraft windows.   The heat distortion point is 260°F, and it has higher tensile and flexural strength than other acrylics.   **Cyclohexyl methacrylate** has optical properties similar to crown glass, and is used for cast lenses, where its softness and low softening point, 160°F, are not objectionable.

Lucite is methyl methacrylate of E. I. du Pont de Nemours & Co., Inc., marketed as molding powder and in rods, tubes, and cast and molded sheets.   **Lucitone** is this material molded in dentures in pink and translucent.   **Lucite HM-140** is this material compounded for high-temperature injection molding.   **Acrylic syrup** is a liquid Lucite for use as a low-pressure laminating resin.   It produces strong, stiff, tough laminates adaptable to translucent or bright colors.   Reinforced with glass fibers, a panel with contact cure has a flexural strength of 25,000 psi, elongation 1.5%, distortion point at 233°F, Rockwell hardness R121, and light transmission up to 65%.   **Crystalite,** of Rohm & Haas Co., is an acrylic molding powder.   **Plexiglas,** of this company, is transparent methyl methacrylate in sheets and rods.   **Perspex** is a similar English acrylic resin.   All of these plastics are used for aircraft windows.   **Plexiglas V** is for injection molding, while **Plexiglas VM** is a molding powder to resist heat distortion to 174°F.   **Vernonite,** of Rohm & Haas Co., is an acrylic denture resin. The **Acryloid resins,** of the same company, are acrylic copolymer solid resins, and the **Acrysol resins** are solutions for coatings.   **Plexene M,** of the same company, is a styrene-acrylic resin for injection molding.   The specific gravity of the molded resin is 1.08, the dielectric strength is 350 volts per mil, and tensile strength 15,000 psi.   **Acryloid A-10,** used for coatings and finishes, is a solution of the resin in cellosolve actetate, and **Acryloid B-7** is a solution in ethylene dichloride.   **Rhoplex resins,** of the same company, and **Crilicon,** of the Jersey State Chemical Co., are acrylic resin emulsions for paints, textile finishes, and adhesives.   **Polyco 296,** of the American Polymer Corp., is a water-soluble acrylic copolymer used for thickening natural or synthetic rubber latex for paper and textile coatings. Coatings made with acrylics have good adhesion and gloss, are resistant to oils and chemicals, and have good dielectric strength.   **Carboset 511,** of the B. F. Goodrich Chemical Co., is a water solution of acrylic resin for protecting polished metal surfaces and precision parts against scratching. It is resistant to water, but can be washed off with soap and water.   **Cavalon,** of Du Pont, is a polyacrylic resin for coatings that has high hardness and resistance to abrasion.

Volan, of the same company, is a methacrylate-chromic oxychloride, $CH_2:C(CH_3)C(OH)(OCrCl_2)_2$, in which methacrylic acid is joined with two $CrCl_2$ groups to form **resonant bonds.**   It is a dark-green liquid with a specific gravity of 1.02, boiling at 180°F.   When applied to negatively charged surfaces such as cellulose, polyamides, or silica materials, the chromium complex is strongly held while the chlorine is lost.   In attaching to glass, the CrO forms a chemical bond to the silica of the glass, $Cr \cdot O \cdot Si$. With polyamides, the CrO attaches to a carbon atom, $Cr \cdot O \cdot C$.   It is thus used to obtain strong bonds in plastic laminates.

ACRYLONITRILE. Also called **vinyl cyanide** and **propene nitrile.**   A liquid of the composition $CH_2:CHCN$, boiling at 78°C, used in insecticides and for producing plastics and other chemicals.   It is made by the addition of hydrocyanic acid to acetylene, by using propylene as the starter and reacting with ammonia, or from petroleum.   **Acrylonitrile fiber,** originally developed in Germany as a textile staple fiber and as a monofilament for screens and weaving, and known as **Redon,** has good dimensional stability and high dielectric strength, and is resistant to water and to solvents.   The polymerized acrylonitrile has a molecular structure that can be oriented by drawing to give fibers of high strength.   **Orlon,** of Du Pont, is a polymerized acrylonitrile fiber.   It is nearly as strong as nylon, and has a softer feel.   It can be crimped to facilitate spinning with wool.   It is used for clothing textiles and for filter fabrics.   **Dynel,** of Union Carbide Corp., is an acrylonitrile–vinyl chloride copolymer staple fiber.   It produces textiles with a warmth and feel like those of wool.   It has good strength, is resilient, dyes easily, and is mothproof.   **Verel,** of the Eastman Chemical Products, Inc., is a similar acrylic fiber produced from acrylonitrile and vinylidene chloride, and **Creslan,** of the American Cyanamid Co., called **Exlan** in Japan, is an acrylic fiber.   **Acrilan,** of the Chemstrand Corp., is a similar textile fiber, and is an acrylonitrile–vinyl acetate copolymer.   **Bakelite C-11** is an **acrylonitrile-styrene** copolymer for injection molding and extruding that produces rigid thermoplastic parts of higher tensile strength than those of the methacrylates, and has good dimensional stability and scratch resistance.   **Saran F-120,** of the Dow Chemical Co., is a similar material.

Zefran, of the Dow Chemical Co., is an acrylonitrile polymerized with vinyl pyrrolidone or other dye-receptive monomer.   The fiber has a molecular structure called a **nitrile alloy,** with a continuous polyacrylonitrile backbond with close-packed hydrophilic groups which hold the dye molecules.   It resists heat to 490°F.   **Fostacryl,** of the Foster Grant Co., Inc., is a crystal-clear **styrene-acrylonitrile** copolymer used for molding such articles as dinnerware and food containers.   Acrylonitrile-styrene copolymers are also combined with alkyl-substituted phenolic resins to produce hard, glossy, flexible coatings.   **Itaconic acid,** or **methylene succinic acid,** $CH_2:CCH(COOH)_2$, is also polymerized with acrylonitrile to produce fibers.   When this acid is polymerized with styrene it produces transparent plastics of good optical properties.   For jet aircraft tires an extremely wear-resistant rubber is made of **acrylonitrile-butadiene** with an organometallic catalyst that has alternating groups in the copolymer.

Acrylonitrile reacts with cellulose to form a wide range of resins from soluble ethers useful for textile finishes to tough, resistant materials useful for fibers.   It can be reacted directly with cotton to improve the fiber. **Krilium,** of the Monsanto Co., and **Agrilon,** of the Borden Chemical Co., are sodium salts of acrylonitrile used as soil conditioners.   They are more efficient than peat moss.

ACTIVATED CHARCOAL.   A nearly chemically pure amorphous carbon made by carbonizing and treating dense material such as coconut shells, peach pits, or hardwood.   When made from coal, or in the chemical industry, it is more usually called **activated carbon,** or **filter carbon.**   It may be made by dry distillation, or by leaching the charcoal with steam or by treatment with zinc chloride or potassium thiocyanate.   It is used as an adsorbent material for gas masks, for cigarette filters, and for purifying acids, recovering solvents, and decolorizing liquids.   **Coconut charcoal,** valued for gas masks, is an activated charcoal usually made by heating coconut shells in a closed retort, crushing, and steam treating.   An activated charcoal made from coconut shell will adsorb 68% of its weight of carbon tetrachloride.   Activated charcoal made in Germany for gas masks was produced from ground peat by mixing with zinc chloride and heating to 700°C to drive off moisture, $ZnCl_2$, and HCl, and then leached.   A requirement of activated charcoals, besides high adsorbing power, is that they possess strength to retain a porous structure to pass the air or liquid. **Activated carbon CXC4-6,** of Union Carbide Corp., produced from petroleum and used as a catalyst support, is in $3/16$-in. pellets of high hardness and strength.   Powdered activated charcoal is usually ground to 300 mesh.   For water purification it should be fine enough to wet easily, but not so light that it will float on the top.   For decolorizing or deodorizing oils and chemicals it is mixed in the liquid and settles out in a few hours. A single drop of water will hold 10,000 particles of powdered charcoal. In sugar and oil refining it removes color but does not bleach like chemicals.

Color removal is measured by the **molasses number,** which is the index of color removed per gram of carbon when tested on a standard molasses solution.

Hydrodarco, of the Atlas Chemical Industries, is a powdered activated carbon. **Norit,** of the American Norit Co., Inc., is a group of highly adsorptive activated carbons. **Kelpchar** is activated carbon made from seaweed. **Tec-Char,** of the Tennessee Eastman Co., is a by-product charcoal obtained in wood distillation, and in graded grains for various uses. **Nuchar** is an activated carbon of the West Virginia Pulp & Paper Co. The activated carbon of the Masonite Corp. is made by subjecting wood chips to high steam pressure and disintegrating by sudden release of the pressure. The doughy mass is briquetted and carbonized.

Activated carbon derived from coal is harder than organic carbons and does not crumble easily, permitting a higher flow of liquid to be filtered. It has a high density and high activity. **SGL carbon,** of the Pittsburgh Coke & Chemical Co., has a density of 0.46, and an iodine number of 1,000 compared with 650 for ordinary carbons. Its color-removal index is about 40% higher than that of organic carbons. **Filt-o-cite,** of the Shamokin Filter Co., is finely ground anthracite used to replace sand as a filtering agent for industrial wastes.

ADHESIVES. Materials, usually liquid solutions, employed for sticking, or adhering, one surface to another. The commercial adhesives include pastes; glues; pyroxylin cements; rubber cements; latex cement; special cements of chlorinated rubber, synthetic rubbers, or synthetic resins; and the natural mucilages. Adhesives are characterized by degree of tack, or stickiness, by strength of bond after setting or drying, by rapidity of bonding, and by durability. Adhesives for rapid machine application must have good initial tack. Tack is often increased by adding rosin or ester gum, while the speed of drying may be altered by changing the solvent. The strength of bond is inherent in the character of the adhesive itself, particularly in its ability to adhere intimately to the surface to be bonded. Adhesives prepared from organic products are in general subject to disintegration on exposure. The life of an adhesive depends usually upon the stability of the ingredient that gives the holding power, although otherwise good cements of synthetic materials may disintegrate by the oxidation of fillers or materials used to increase tack. Plasticizers usually reduce adhesion. Some fillers such as mineral fibers or walnut-shell flour increase the thixotropy and the strength, while some such as starch increase the tack but also increase the tendency to disintegrate.

Pastes are usually water solutions of starches or dextrines, sometimes mixed with gums, resins, or glue to add strength, and containing antioxidants. They are the cheapest of the adhesives, but deteriorate on exposure unless made with chemically altered starches.   They are widely employed for the adhesion of paper and paperboard.   Much of the so-called **vegetable glue** is **tapioca paste.**   It is used for the cheaper plywoods, postage stamps, envelopes, and labeling.   It has a quick tack, and is valued for pastes for automatic box-making machines.   **Latex pastes** of the rub-off type are used for such purposes as photographic mounting as they do not shrink the paper as do the starch pastes.   **Glues** are usually water solutions of animal gelatin, and the only difference between animal glues and edible gelatin is in the degree of purity.   Hide and bone glues are marketed as dry flake, but fish glue is liquid.   **Mucilages** are light vegetable glues, generally from water-soluble gums.

Rubber cements for paper bonding are simple solutions of rubber in a chemical solvent.   They are like the latex pastes in that the excess can be rubbed off the paper.   Stronger rubber cements are usually compounded with resins, gums, or synthetics.   An infinite variety of these cements is possible, and they are all waterproof with good initial bond, but they are subject to deterioration on exposure, as the rubber is uncured.   This type of cement is also made from synthetic rubbers which are self-curing.   **Uba-pol,** of the UBS Chemical Co., is a synthetic rubber solvent cement.   Curing cements are rubber compounds to be cured by heat and pressure or by chemical curing agents.   When cured, they are stronger, give better adhesion to metal surfaces, and have longer life.   **Latex cements** are solvent solutions of rubber latex.   They provide excellent tack and give strong bonds to paper, leather, and fabric, but they are subject to rapid disintegration unless cured.

In general, natural rubber has the highest cohesive strength of the rubbers, with rapid initial tack and high bond strength.   It also is odorless. Neoprene has the highest cohesive strength of the synthetic rubbers, but it requires tackifiers.   Gr-S rubber is high in specific adhesion for quick bonding, but has low strength.   Reclaimed rubber may be used in cements, but it has low initial tack and needs tackifiers.

Pyroxylin cements may be merely solutions of nitrocellulose in chemical solvents, or they may be compounded with resins, or plasticized with gums or synthetics.   They dry by the evaporation of the solvent, and have little initial tack, but because of their ability to adhere to almost any type of surface they are called **household cements.**   Cellulose acetate may also be used.   These cements are used for bonding the soles of women's shoes. The bonding strength is about 10 psi, or equivalent to the adhesive strength of the outer fibers of the leather to be bonded.   For hot-press lamination of wood the plastic cement is sometimes marketed in the form of thin sheet.   **Tego resin film,** of the Rohm & Haas Co., is a phenol resin sheet of this class.   **Uformite 507,** of the same company, is a precatalyzed urea-formaldehyde resin powder for dispersion in water as a hot-pressing adhesive for plywood.   **Urac 110 resin,** of the American Cyanamid Co., is a urea-formaldehyde resin powder for adding to starch adhesives to make them waterproof.   **Pressal** was a German adhesive made with 30% melamine resin and 70 starch.   **Norelite glue,** developed by the U.S. Department of Agriculture, is a water-soluble phenol resin with soybean meal and corn gluten.   Polyvinyl acetate–crotonic acid copolymer resin is used as a hot-dip adhesive for book and magazine binding.   It is soluble in alkali solutions and thus the trim is re-usable.   Synthetic resin adhesives may be thermoplastic, or they may be thermosetting, not softened by heat.   Polyvinyl alcohol, with fillers of clay and starch, is used for paperboard containers.   **Desmophen,** a German adhesive, is made with a polyhydric alcohol reacted with adipic acid.   **Polybond,** of Polymer Industries, Inc., is a polyvinyl adhesive for food containers.   Vinyl emulsions are much used as adhesives for laminates.

Epoxy resin cements give good adhesion to almost any material and are heat-resistant to 450°F.   An epoxy resin will give a steel-to-steel bond of 3,100 psi, and an aluminum-to-aluminum bond to 3,800 psi.   When electrical conductivity is required in the bond a metal powder filler is used.   **Isoduct 1205,** of the Isochem Resins Co., is an epoxy-silver paste, giving a shear strength of 3,000 psi.   **Casophen,** of the Borden Chemical Co., is an epoxy adhesive.

Some **pressure-sensitive adhesives** are mixtures of a phenolic resin and a nitrile rubber in a solvent, but adhesive tapes are made with a wide variety of rubber or resin compounds.   The pressure-sensitive adhesives of the Dow Chemical Co. are silicone resins in a solvent.   **Silastic RTV 735** of this company is a thixotropic silicone cement suited for adhering nameplates or ornamental trim to vertical surfaces.   An adhesive of the Bell Telephone Laboratories for bonding polyethylene to rubber and to nonferrous metals, requiring a low degree of unsaturation, is based on a hydrogenated polybutadiene rubber.   It gives a tensile strength of 1,000 psi.   **Adhesive 78,** of Du Pont, is a water-soluble vinyl resin powder. Mixed with water and cooked at 185°F, it makes an adhesive of fast tack. Thin films give grease- and water-resistant bonds to fiberboard.   The strong adhesives, of the same company, originally called **Fairprene cements,** are based on Neoprene, usually compounded with resins to increase tack, and with fillers, and an activator to be added separately.   **Furan cements,** usually made with furfural-alcohol resins, are strong and highly resistant to chemicals.   They are valued for bonding acid-resistant brick and tile. **Furan cement S,** of the Pennsalt Chemicals Corp., has a furfural-ketone resin with a silica powder filler, while **Furan cement C** has a carbon filler. These cements give a bond of 500 psi to brick.   **Eastman 910,** of Eastman Chemical Products, Inc., is a cyanoacrylate that adheres well to almost any material and gives a steel-to-steel bond with a shear strength of 2,800 psi. The softening point of the bond is 165°C.

A **ceramic adhesive** developed by the Air Force for bonding stainless steel to resist heat to 1500°F is made with a porcelain enamel frit, iron oxide, and stainless-steel powder.   It is applied to both parts and fired at 1750°F, giving a shear strength of 1,500 psi in the bond.   But ceramic cements that require firing are not generally classed with ordinary adhesives. **Wash-away adhesives** are used for holding lenses, electronic crystal wafers, or other small parts for grinding and polishing operations.   They are based on acrylic or other low-melting thermoplastic resins.   They can be removed with a solvent or by heating.   **Crystalbond 509,** of Aremco Products, Inc., is such an adhesive.   It melts at low temperatures or can be washed away with acetone.

ADIPIC ACID. Also called **butane dicarboxylic acid.**   A white crystalline solid of the composition $HOOC(CH_2)_4COOH$, used as a plasticizer in synthetic resins and coatings, and in the production of nylon.   It is made by the treatment of fatty acids with nitric acid, or can be made by oxidizing cyclohexanol.   The melting point is 152°C.   It is soluble in alcohol and slightly soluble in water.   Many other dibasic acids useful for making synthetic resins are produced readily from fatty oils.   **Suberic acid,** $HOOC(CH_2)_6COOH$, is made by the oxidation of castor oil.   It is the same as the **octane-dioic acid** made from butadiene.   **Sebacic acid,** $HOOC(CH_2)_8COOH$, is produced by heating castor oil with sodium hydroxide.   **Azelaic acid,** $HOOC(CH_2)_7COOH$, is a strong dibasic acid with melting point at 106°C, made by the oxidation of oleic acid, and is used as a substitute for phthalic anhydride to react with glycerin to form alkyd resins less hard and brittle than those made with phthalic anhydride. It is also used instead of sebacic acid for producing the high-temperature lubricant **ethylhexyl sebacate.**   Another substitute for this acid is pelargonic acid.   **Petroselic acid,** which is an isomer of oleic acid with the double bond in a different position, is made by the hydrogenation of the ricinoleic acid of castor oil, and is then oxidized to produce adipic acid. Adipic acid can be used as a substitute for citric acid for the acidulation of beverages, but is less water-soluble.   It is also used in protein foods to control the gelling action.

ADMIRALTY METAL. An alloy containing about 70% copper, 1 tin, and the remainder zinc, sometimes termed **admiralty bronze.**   This composition is listed by the American Brass Co. as **admiralty alloy.**   The tin increases the hardness and strength but decreases the ductility.   Admiralty metal of Revere Copper & Brass, Inc., has 71% copper, 28 zinc, and 1 tin.   The hard-drawn tube has a tensile strength of 100,000 psi and elongation 3%.   Federal specifications permit up to 0.06% iron and 0.075 lead as impurities.   The weight is 0.305 lb per cu in.   It machines readily, especially when it contains lead.   The alloy has been standard for condenser tubes, but for condenser tubes and other uses where there may be fouling from algae or dezincification from biotic attack, a 70-30 cartridge brass with a small amount of mercury may be used.   **Alloy 77,** of the Bridgeport Brass Co., is a 70-30 brass with 0.05% mercury for condenser tubes.

ADSORBENT. A material used to remove odor, taste, haze, and color from oils, foods, pharmaceuticals, or chemicals by selective adsorption of the impurities.   Such materials are also called **adsorbates.**   Adsorption is distinct from absorption in that it is the process of adhesion of the molecules of the substance to the surface of the adsorbent.   The common adsorbents are activated carbon, or activated clays, alumina, magnesium silicate, or silica gel.   The noncarbonaceous adsorbents are used for decolorizing vegetable, animal, or mineral oils, but activated carbon may also be used in conjunction with clays to adsorb color bodies not removed by the clay.   Granular adsorbents are employed as filter beds, but powdered adsorbents are stirred into the liquid and are usually more effective.   Adsorption from a gas is usually done with activated carbon.   Silica gel is usually employed for removing trace quantities of water from water-insoluble liquids, while activated carbon is used for removing trace quantities of oils or chemicals from water.   Adsorbents are normally recovered and are regenerated for re-use by heating, steaming, or burning off the adsorbed material.

Adsorbents are also used to separate chemicals of different molecular diameters without regard to their boiling points.   A double hydrated aluminum calcium silicate marketed by the Union Carbide Corp. as a zeolite will pass chemicals with molecular diameters less than 5 angstroms and retain larger ones by selective adsorption.   Such adsorptives are called **molecular sieves.**   However, a material used in the separation of liquid mixtures whose components boil too close together for simple fractional distillation is called an **azeotrope.**   It is a solvent added to the mixture to increase the relative volatility of one of the components so that it can be separated.   The solvent may be alcohols, glycols, or nitrobenzene.

The adsorbents used in vacuum tubes to adsorb or combine with residual gases are called **getters.**   **Flash getters** are pellets or strips of barium or barium alloy used to shorten the exhaust period.   The getter is evaporated by induction heating during tube exhaust, and condenses on the tube walls, adsorbing the gas residues.   Later, at operating temperatures of 300 to 400°F, the getter formed on the tube wall traps gases liberated during tube life.   Bulk getters are sheets or wires of zirconium, tantalum, or columbium mounted on the hot electrode to trap gases at temperatures of 900 to 2200°F.   Thorium or **thorium-misch metal** may be used as getters for high temperatures by a coating sintered on the tube anode.

AGAR-AGAR. The dried bleached gelatinous extract from various species of seaweed, *Algae,* mostly species from the Pacific and Indian Oceans. It is the only one of the seaweed products classed as a strategic material because of its use in medicine, but its use is small compared with the use of the products from other seaweeds.   The word agar means seaweed. Translations of double words from the primordial languages, such as Malay, Carib, or Gaelic, must be made by taking the first word as a superlative adjective or the second word as a cognate verb.   Thus, agar-agar means best-quality agar.

When dissolved in hot water, agar forms a transparent jelly, and is used for fixing bacteria for counts, as a stabilizer in toilet lotions, and in medicines.   It has high thickening power but, unlike most other seaweed extracts, it is indigestible and is not used in foodstuffs.   **Kantan** is a variety of agar from the **tengusa seaweed,** *Gelidium corneum,* of Japan.   **Australian agar** is from the abundant seaweed *Gracilaria confervoides.*   Commercial agar is colorless, yellowish, or pink to black.   It is marketed in strips, blocks, or shredded, and is obtained by boiling the dry seaweed and straining out the insoluble matter.

Most of the American production of agar, as distinct from the algins of the Atlantic, is from the giant **kelp,** *Macrocystia pyrifera* and *Gelidium cartilagineum* of the coast of California and Mexico, but it is not valued as highly for bacteriologic use as the Asiatic.   The kelp grows straight up in water 60 to 100 ft deep and then spreads out on the water another 60 to 80 ft.   It is cut about 3 ft below the surface, and three crops are harvested annually.   The plant is 90% water.   The dried kelp is washed with boiling water, cooked with soda ash, filtered, sterilized, and treated with muriatic acid to extract the agar.

Agar constitutes a small part of an extensive plant division known as **algae,** varying from tiny zooidal cell plants to the giant kelp, known as **seaweed.**   About 17,000 varieties of seaweed are listed, but only a few are exploited commercially.   Algae are nonseed-bearing plants containing photosynthetic pigments.   They have no vascular or food-conveying system, and must remain submerged in the medium from which they acquire their food.   They occur in both fresh and salt waters.

The **brown seaweeds,** which are the true kelps, grow in temperate and polar waters.   They produce **algin, fucoidin,** and **laminarin.**   The red seaweeds are the **carrageens** which produce **carrageenin,** and the **agarophytes** which yield **agar** and **agaroid.**   They grow in warm waters.   But color is an indefinite classification; the chlorophyll in the green Irish moss is often so masked by other pigments that the weed may be purplish black. All of the seaweed colloids, or phycocolloids, are polysaccharides, having galactose units linked in long chains of molecular weights from 100,000 to 500,000, varying in their chemical structure. They are anionic polyelectrolytes, with negative radicals on each repeating polymer unit. **Irish moss,** also called **chondrus** (pronounced chone-droosh), **pearl moss,** and carrageen, is a dwarf variety of brown seaweed, *Chondrus crispus,* and *Gigantina mamillosa,* found off the west coast of Ireland and in New England. The weed used mostly for alginic acid is the brown kelp *Laminaria saccharium, L. ditata,* and other species, found off the Hebrides. It is a cold-water plant.

The seaweed *G. stellata,* of the North Atlantic, is also used to produce agar and algin. It is bleached and treated to produce gelatin used in foodstuffs, as a clarifying agent, and as a sizing for textiles. It is a better suspending and gelatinizing medium than agar for foodstuffs and cosmetic emulsions. At least 25 mineral salts are known to be present in seaweed as well as several vitamins. In the utilization of the seaweed as gelatin or alginate these are left in the **kelp meal** which is marketed as poultry and stock feed. In Asia the whole plant is cooked and eaten. **Seaweed flour,** made in Germany from **Iceland seaweed,** *Phaeophyceen,* is the ground dry seaweed containing all the minerals and vitamins. It is mixed with wheat and rye flours to make **algenbrot,** a bread with higher food value and better keeping qualities than ordinary wheat bread. But more than 8% gives a peculiar flavor to the bread. The Irish name **dulse** is applied to the dried or cooked seaweed, *Rhodymenia palmata,* used in the Canadian Maritime Provinces for food. It is purple in color and rich in iodine and mineral salts. Other species, known as **laver** and **murlins,** are also used in Iceland, Ireland, and Scotland for food. When used for producing iodine in Scotland, the seaweed goes under the general name of **tangle.** Much of the 4,500 miles of coastline of Scotland contains brown kelps. The kelp found along the Chilean and Peruvian coasts, when dried for making algin products, is called by the Quechua name **cochayuyo.** **Kombu,** used by the Japanese for food, is a brown seaweed from the coast of Hokkaido.

Dry seaweed contains up to 30% **alginic acid;** the water-soluble salts of this acid are called algin. It belongs to the group of complex open-chain **uronic acids** which occur widely in plant and animal tissues and are related to the proteins and pectins. All the algins are edible, but they pass unchanged through the alimentary tract and add no food value. Carrageenin is much used as a stabilizer for chocolate in milk. Laminarin is used as **laminarin sulfate** as a blood-clotting agent. **Sodium alginate** is used as a stabilizer and ice-crystal retarder in ice cream, as an emulsifier in medicines, and to replace gum arabic. It is a colorless water-soluble gum made by dissolving algin in sodium carbonate solution and neutralizing with hydrochloric acid.   **Protan jelly,** used for coating fish for freezing, is algin in a dilute edible acid.   When frozen, the jelly is impervious to air and prevents oxidation.   It can be washed off with water.

Kelgin, of the Kelco Co., is sodium alginate used as a foodstuff stabilizer, and **Keltrex** is the material in granular form for textile coating. **Kelset,** of the same company, is an algin used as a suspending agent for foodstuffs.   It does not alter flavor or texture and is stable up to 200°F. **Dariloid** is sodium alginate to replace gelatin in ice cream; **Kelcosol** is an alginate to replace starch in foodstuffs.   One part of algin can replace six parts of starch, and it does not smother flavor as starch does.   **Protakyp K,** of Croda, Inc., used as a thickener for textile printing inks, is an alginate compatible with gums.   **Viscobond,** of Stein, Hall & Co., is a modified sodium alginate for finishing cellulosic textiles.   **Kim-Ko gel,** of the Krim-Ko Corp., is a light-buff scaly powder easily soluble in water, made from Irish moss, used as a collodial gelling agent.   It has a pH of 6.4 to 7.2.   **Carrigar** is a purified alginate for pharmaceuticals and foodstuffs. It contains the natural mineral salts and has food value.   It has high capacity for water absorption, making rigid sugar-free jellies with less than 2% in solution.   **Algaloid** and **Agagel,** of T. H. Duche & Sons, Inc., are algins of this type.

Alginic fibers are silklike fibers made by forcing a sodium alginate solution through spinnerets into a calcium chloride bath and insolubilizing with beryllium acetate, but the fiber is soluble in sodium soaps and the fabrics must be dry-cleaned.   Soluble alginic yarns are used for making fancy fabrics where uneven spacing of threads is desired without change in the loom.   The alginate yarn is washed out of the fabric after weaving, leaving the desired spacing.

AGATE. A natural mixture of crystalline and colloidal silica, but consisting mainly of the mineral chalcedony.   It usually occurs in irregular banded layers of various colors derived from mineral salts, and when polished has a waxy luster.   The specific gravity is about 2.6, and the mineral is sometimes harder than quartz.   Agate is used for knife-edges and bearings of instruments, for pestles and mortars, for textile rollers, and for ornamental articles, and the finer specimens are employed as gemstones. The finest of the massive agates come from Uruguay and Brazil.   Much agate encloses dendritic, or fernlike, patterns of manganese oxide or iron oxide, suggestive of moss.   The **moss agates** of Montana, and the yellow-green moss agate of California known as **amberine,** are used as gemstones. Agate is a water-deposited stone, and often occurs in the form of stalactites and in petrified wood.   **Agatized wood** of Wyoming and Arizona has a green fluorescence.   It is cut into ornaments.   Clear translucent yellow agates are called **sard,** while the clear reddish ones are **carnelian.** Both are cut as gemstones. **Sardoine** is a brownish carnelian. **Iris agate,** with rainbow colors, from Montana and Oregon, is highly prized. **Moss opal** of Nevada and California is moss agate intergrown with opal. **Blue moonstone** of California is not a true moonstone but is a blue agate of opalescent luster. Commercial agates may be artificially stained with mineral salts, dyed, or treated with acids to bring out color differences. **White agate** is a cream-colored chalcedony with a more waxy appearance than agate.

AJOWAN OIL. Also called **ptychotis oil.** A yellow essential oil distilled from **ajwan seed** of the herbaceous plant *Carum copticum,* or *Ptychotis ajowan,* of India. The seed yields 3 to 4% oil containing up to 50% **thymol** and some **cymene,** most of the thymol separating out on distillation. Thymol is known as **ajwan ka phul,** meaning flowers of ajwan, and the latter part of the name is Anglicized to thymol. Ajowan oil has a specific gravity of 0.900 to 0.930. It is used in pharmaceuticals. Thymol, $(CH_3)_2CHC_6H_3(CH_3)OH$, is a white crystalline solid with a strong thyme odor, soluble in alcohol, and melting at 50°C. It is used in antiseptics and as a deodorant for leather. Thymol is also obtained from horsemint oil and from eucalyptus oil, or can be made synthetically from meta cresol. It was originally distilled from the **thyme plant,** *Thymus vulgaris,* of the Mediterranean countries, the dried leaves of which are used as a condiment. **Cymene,** $(CH_3)_2CHC_6H_4CH_3$, is used as a scent in soaps, and has high solvent properties. It is also obtained from spruce turpentine. It is a liquid of specific gravity 0.861, boiling at 177°C.

ALBUMIN. The water-soluble and alcohol-soluble protein obtained from blood, eggs, or milk, and used in adhesives, textile and paper finishes, leather coatings, varnishes, as a clarifying agent for tannins, and in oil emulsions. Crude **blood albumin** is a brown amorphous lumpy material obtained by clotting slaughterhouse blood and dissolving out the albumin. The remaining dark-red material is made into **ground blood** and marketed as a fertilizer. Blood albumin is sold as clear, pale, amber, and colored powders. Blood albumin from human blood is a stable, dry, white powder. It is used in water solution for treatment of shock. The material of **egg white** is sometimes spelled **albumen.** Egg white is a complex mixture of at least eight proteins, with sugar and inorganic salts. More than half of the total is the protein **ovalbumin,** a strong coagulating agent, and another large percentage consists of **conalbumin** which forms metal complexes and unites with iron in the human system. Two of the proteins not so desirable in the human body are **ovomucoid,** which inhibits the action of the digestive enzyme trypsin, and **avidin,** which combines with and destroys the action of the growth vitamin biotin. **Egg albumin** is prepared from the dried egg white, and is marketed in yellowish amorphous lumps or powdered. The complexity of proteins is illustrated by the fact that the formula for egg albumin is $C_{1428}H_{2244}N_{462}S_{14}$. The heat of pasteurization damages the proteins of the egg white. A small amount of lactic acid and an aluminum salt will stabilize it and allow pasteurizing at 143°F. **Milk albumin** is made by coagulating casein. **Soybean albumin** is used to replace egg albumin in confectionery. **Synthetic egg white,** or albumin, was made in Germany from fish by extracting the soluble proteins with acetic acid, removing the fat with trichlorethylene, and hydrolyzing with sodium hydroxide. After neutralization, it is obtained as a white powder. **Fish albumin** is a good emulsifier, and can be whipped into a stiff foam for bakery products.

ALCOHOL. The common name for ethyl alcohol, but the term properly applies to a large group of organic compounds that have important uses in industry, especially as solvents and in the preparation of other materials. A characteristic of all alcohols is the monovalent —OH group. In the primary alcohols there is always a $\cdot CH_2OH$ group in the molecule. The secondary alcohols have a $:CHOH$ group, and the tertiary alcohols have a distinctive $:COH$ group. Alcohols with one OH group are called **monohydroxy alcohols;** those with more than one OH group are known as **polyhydroxy alcohols** or **polyhydric alcohols.** Another method of classification is by the terms saturated and unsaturated. The common alcohols used in industry are ethyl, methyl, amyl, butyl, isopropyl, and octyl. The alcohols vary in consistency. Methyl alcohol is like water, amyl alcohol is oily, and melissyl alcohol is a solid. Many of the alcohols are easiest made by fermentation; others are produced from natural gas or from petroleum hydrocarbons. Much of the production of ethyl alcohol is from blackstrap molasses. **Solidified alcohol,** marketed in tins and used as a fuel in small stoves, is a jellylike solution of nitrocellulose in methyl alcohol. It burns with a hot flame. **Sterno,** of Sterno, Inc., is this material, while **Trioxane,** employed for the same purpose, is an anhydrous formaldehyde trimer, but has the disadvantage of being water-soluble.

Butyl alcohol is a colorless liquid used as a solvent for paints and varnishes, and in the manufacture of dyes, plastics, and many chemicals. There are four forms of this alcohol, but the normal or primary butyl alcohol is the most important. **Normal butyl alcohol,** $CH_3(CH_2)_2CH_2\cdot OH$, has a specific gravity of 0.814, and boiling point of 117°C. This form, known as **butanol,** has strong solvent power and is valued where a low evaporation rate is desired. It is also used for organic synthesis.

Fluoro alcohols are alcohols in which fluorine is substituted for hydrogen in the nonalcoholic branch. They have the general composition $H(CF_2CF_2)_xCH_2OH$, with high specific gravities, 1.48 to 1.66, and high reactivity.   As solvents they dissolve some synthetic resins that resist common solvents.   Some of the esters are used as lubricants for temperatures to 500°F.   **Acetylenic alcohols** are **methyl butynol,** $CH:C \cdot C(CH_3)_2OH$, with a specific gravity of 0.8672, boiling at 104°C, and used as a solvent, and **methyl pentynol,** $CH:C \cdot C(CH_3)_2CH_2OH$, boiling at 121°C.   It is a powerful solvent.   It has hypnotic qualities, and is also used for tranquilizing fish in transport.

Fatty acid alcohols, made from fatty acids or synthetically, have the general formula $CH_3(CH_2)_xOH$, ranging from the C_8 of **octyl alcohol** to the C_{18} of **stearyl alcohol.**   They are easily esterified, oxidized, or ethoxilated, and are used for making cosmetics, detergents, emulsifiers, and other chemicals.   **Lorol 24,** of Du Pont, is **cetyl alcohol.**   **Elaidyl alcohol,** made from methyl oleate, is an 18-carbon alcohol.   It is a solid, melting at 75°F.   The fatty acid alcohols vary from water-white liquids to waxy solids.   The **Dytols,** of Rohm & Haas, are fatty alcohols, and the **Alfols,** of the Continental Oil Co., are straight-chain primary fatty alcohols made from ethylene and containing even numbers of carbon atoms from 6 to 18.   **Polyols** are alcohols containing many hydroxyl, —OH, radicals.   They react easily with isocyanates to form urethane.

ALDEHYDE. A group name for substances made by the dehydrogenation or oxidation of alcohols, such as formaldehyde from methyl alcohol.   By further oxidation the aldehydes form corresponding acids, as formic acid. The aldehydes have the radical group —CHO in the molecule, and because of their ease of oxidation are important reducing agents.   They are also used in the manufacture of synthetic resins and many other chemicals. Aldehydes occur in animal tissues and in the odorous parts of plants.

Acetaldehyde is a water-white inflammable liquid with an aromatic penetrating odor, used as a reducing agent, preservative, and for silvering mirrors, and in the manufacture of synthetic resins, dyestuffs, and explosives.   Also called **ethanal,** it has the composition $CH_3 \cdot CHO$, and is made by the oxidation of alcohol, by catalytic hydration of acetylene, or from ethylene.   The specific gravity is 0.801 and the boiling point is 20.8°C. It is soluble in water, alcohol, and naphtha.   **Paraldehyde,** $(CH_3 \cdot CHO)_3$, may be used instead of acetaldehyde in resin manufacture, has a higher boiling point, 124°C, and a higher flash point, but is not as reactive and will not reduce silver solutions to form a mirror.   It is used for fulling leather.   **Propion aldehyde,** or **propanal,** CH_3CH_2CHO, is made in the same way by oxidation of propyl alcohol.   It has a boiling point at 48.8°C, and has reactions similar to acetaldehyde.

When acetaldehyde is condensed by reaction with a dilute alkali, it forms **acetaldol,** called also **aldol,** a viscous pale-yellow liquid of the composition $CH_3 \cdot CH(OH):CH_2CHO$, with a specific gravity of about 1.10, soluble in hot water and in alcohol.   It is used to replace formaldehyde for synthetic resins, and for cadmium plating baths and dye baths, and for making butadiene rubber.   **Paraldol,** the double molecule of aldol, is a white crystalline material melting at 82°C.   When crude aldol is slightly acidified with acetic acid and heated, it yields **croton aldehyde,** also called **crotonic aldehyde** and **propylene aldehyde,** $CH_3 \cdot CH:CH \cdot CHO$, with a specific gravity of about 0.855 and a boiling point of 99 to 104°C.   It is soluble in water, alcohol, and hydrocarbons, and is used as a solvent for resins, gums, and rubber, and in tanning leather.   It has a pungent, suffocating odor, and is used in tear gases.   Small quantities are sometimes used in city gas mains as a warning agent on the escape of poisonous fuel gas, as even tiny quantities will awaken a sleeping person.

Acrolein is **acrylic aldehyde,** $CH_2:CH \cdot CHO$, a colorless volatile liquid of specific gravity 0.8389, boiling at 52.7°C.   The vapor is irritating to the eyes and nose, and the unpleasant effect of scorching fat is due to the acrolein formed.   Acrolein is made by oxidation of propylene with a catalyst.   It polymerizes easily, and can be copolymerized with ethylene, styrene, epoxies, and other resins to form various types of plastics.   Its reactive double bond and carbonyl group make it a useful material for chemical synthesis.   **Acrolein cyanohydrin,** $CH_2:CHCH(OH)CN$, a water-soluble liquid, boiling at 165°C, is also used to modify synthetic resins by introducing a nitrile group and a free hydroxyl into the molecular chain.   It will copolymerize with ethylene and with acrylonitrile.

ALDER. The wood of several species of tree of the genus *Alnus* of the same family as the birch and beech.   The **red alder** is from the *A. rubra,* or *A. oregona,* growing in the northwestern United States.   The wood has a reddish-brown color and a fine even grain, is tough and resilient, can be worked easily, and takes a good polish. It has been much used for furniture, cabinetwork, and interior finish, as it rivals mahogany and walnut in appearance.   **Black alder** is from the tree *A. glutinosa,* widely distributed in the Northern Hemisphere.   It is of a reddish-white color, and has a smooth, fine grain, with a weight of about 35 lb per cu ft.   It is used for plywood, cabinetwork, and toys.   The wood of the alder is also used to produce smoke for curing kippered fish.   The smoke is cooled to remove creosote, and is filtered.   **Formosan alder** is from the *A. maritima* of Asia. The wood is light yellow streaked with reddish lines and has a fine texture.

ALKALI. A caustic hydroxide characterized by its ability to neutralize acids and form soluble soaps with fatty acids.   Fundamentally, alkalies are inorganic alcohols, with the monovalent hydroxyl group —OH in the molecule, but in the alkalies this group is in combination with a metal or an ammonia group; and alkalies have none of the characteristics of alcohols. All alkalies are basic and have a pH value from 7 to 14. They neutralize acids to form a salt and water. The common alkalies are sodium hydroxide and potassium hydroxide, which are used in making soaps, soluble oils, and cutting compounds, in cleaning solutions, and for etching aluminum. All of the alkalies have a brackish taste and a soapy feel; most of them corrode animal and vegetable tissues.

ALKALI METALS. A name given to lithium, sodium, potassium, rubidium, strontium, cesium, calcium, and barium because of the basic reaction of their oxides, hydroxides, and carbonates. Carbonates of these metals are called **fixed alkalies.** The metals show a gradation in properties and increase in chemical activity with increase in atomic weights. All are silvery white and very soft. They tarnish rapidly in the air and decompose water at ordinary temperatures. In the alkali metals the electron bonding is so weak that even the impact of light rays knocks electrons free. All have remarkable affinity for oxygen. Rubidium and cesium ignite spontaneously in dry oxygen. Calcium, strontium, and barium are also called **earth metals.** Thin films of the alkali metals are transparent to ultraviolet but opaque to visible light.

ALKYD RESINS. A group of thermoplastic synthetic resins known chemically as hydroxycarboxylic resins, of which the one produced from phthalic anhydride and glycerol is representative. They are made by the esterification of a polybasic acid with a polyhydric alcohol, and have the characteristics of homogeneity and solubility that make them especially suitable for varnishes and enamels, resistant coatings, calking compounds, adhesives, and plasticizers for other resins. The resins have high adhesion to metals; are transparent, easily colored, tough, flexible, heat- and chemical-resistant; have good dieletric strength; and are the most readily blended of the synthetic resins. They vary greatly with the raw materials used and with varying percentage compositions, from soft rubbery gums to hard brittle solids. Phthalic anhydride imparts hardness and stability. Maleic acid makes a higher melting-point resin. Azelaic acid gives a softer and less brittle resin. The long-chain dibasic acids, such as adipic acid, give resins of great toughness and flexibility. In place of glycerol the glycols yield soft resins, and sometimes the glycerol is modified with a proportion of glycol. The resins are reacted with oils, fatty acids, or other resins such as urea or melamine, to make them compatible with drying oils and to impart special characteristics. They bake to a high gloss, and are resistant to oils, light, and weathering. The oil-modified resins are used as waterproof coatings for textiles. When mixed with urea-formaldehyde or melamine resin, the alkyd resins give harder and more resistant baked coatings.

Blended with ethyl cellulose they are used as tough flexible coatings for electrical cable.   Emulsions of the alkyd resins are used in some resistant water paints.   One of the first of these resins was **Glyptal,** of General Electric, a phthalic anhydride glycerol for lacquers and insulation.

Amberlac and **Duraplex** are alkyd resins of the Rohm & Hass Co. in a wide range of formulations.   The **Paraplex resins** are oil-modified soft resins used for coatings for textiles and paper, and for blending with cellulose plastics to give better adhesion in lacquers.   **Paraplex, P-43HV,** however, is a polyester-styrene copolymer supplied as a clear liquid for laminating, molding, or casting at low pressure.   **Aquaplex,** of the same company, is a group of oil-modified resins for use in water paints.   **Teglac resins,** of the American Cyanamid Co., used for indoor finishes and clear-coat varnishes, are hard alkyd resins made with natural resin acids as blending agents.   **Cycopol,** of the same company, is an alkyd-styrene copolymer resin for fast-drying enamels, giving high gloss and durability.   **Beckosol 1341,** of Reichhold Chemicals, Inc., is a phenol-modified alkyd resin for fast-drying enamels.   **Petrex resin,** of Hercules, Inc., is a series of alkyd resins used in lacquers, varnishes, adhesives, and inks. **Aroplaz 1248-M,** of U.S. Industrial Chemicals, Inc., is a high-gloss phthalic alkyd resin, soluble in mineral spirits, for industrial finishes.   The **Iso Burnok 32-0,** of the T. F. Washburn Co., used as a vehicle for thixotropic paints, is a soybean oil isothalic alkyd.   It has high clarity and is odorless.   **Dyal,** of the Sherwin-Williams Co., is an alkyd resin for finishes, as are also **Amalite** and **Amavar,** of the American Alkyd Industries.

Plaskon Alkyd, of the Allied Chemical Corp., is a mineral-filled alkyd molding powder used for electrical parts having good arc resistance and heat resistance to 350°F.   **Neolyn resins,** of Hercules, Inc., are alkyd resins produced from rosin.   They are used as modifiers for nitrocellulose and for vinyl resins in lacquers and adhesives to add toughness to the film. **Cellolyn 501,** of the same company, is a lauric acid–pentaerythritol alkyd used in durable, color-stable nitrocellulose lacquers.   When maleic anhydride or fumaric acid is reacted with rosin and then esterified with glycerol or other polyhydric alcohol, a series of alkyd resins is produced. **Isocyanate resins** are linear alkyds lengthened by isocyanates and then treated with a glycol or a diamine to cross-link the molecular chain. Plastics made from them are noted for good abrasion resistance.

Since alkyd resins are basically esterification products of innumerable polybasic acids and polyhydric alcohols, and can be modified with many types of oils and resins, the actual number of different alkyd resins is unlimited, and the users' specification is normally by service requirements rather than composition.   **Short-oil alkyds,** with 30 to 45% nonoxidizing oils, are used in baking enamels, while the **long-oil alkyds,** with 56 to 70% oxidizing oils, are soluble in mineral spirits and are used for brushing enamels.   Wide variations in air drying by oxidation, gloss, toughness, and other properties are obtainable by varying oil modification.

ALLIGATOR LEATHER.   A light, tough leather with platelike scales on the surface.   It is made from the skins of large saurians, or lizards, of the order *Crocodilia,* abounding in muddy tropical streams.   The species *Alligator mississippiensis* inhabits the swamps of the southeastern United States. When hatched from the egg, an alligator is about 8 in. long and weighs about 2 oz.   It gains only half a pound the first year, but at 3 years it measures 3 ft and weighs about 15 lb.   Maximum length is about 14 ft. Formerly, the catch from Florida and Louisiana exceeded 200,000 annually, but the animal is now scarce and is protected by law.   Alligator leather is valued for luggage, pocketbook, and shoe leathers.   It is much imitated with embossed split sheepskins, but sheepskin is soft and easily scuffed.   **Lizard leather,** from the **Java ring lizard,** is another reptile leather valued for women's shoes.

ALLOY.   A very old term for the admixture of a precious metal with a metal of lesser value, or with a base metal.   The admixing metal, usually copper, was originally needed in gold or silver to add hardness and to prevent wear erosion of the soft metals, but it also debased the value of the coinage metal.   Now the term applies more generally to any combination of metals.   The term **base metal** now refers to the chief ingredient of the alloy, and the admixing metals may be rare and costly.   The physical properties of the base metal can be altered, improved, or added to by the alloying elements.   Silicon and nickel each give added properties to copper when added alone, but give an additional separate property when used together because of the formation of a nickel silicide compound.

All early alloys were developed by the trial and error of different compositions, but alloying now is a physical science, with consideration given to the atomic interrelations of the elements, crystal formation, and other factors.   An alloy may be a simple solution of one or more metals in the base metal, or it may be a mechanical mixture of metals that do not dissolve in each other.   Lead, for example, does not dissolve in copper but forms separate particles, and in steel the lead forms strings in the steel matrix.   Some elements, such as boron, combine in different ways, the same element forming carbides, nitrides, or silicides, or simply remaining as interstitial constituents under different conditions of alloying or temperature control.   An **intermetal** is an alloy in which the metals are in chemical combination within the crystal.

The so-called "creep" of the alloy is a change in dimension of the metal due to change in shape of the crystals at different temperatures or energy levels.   These changes are referred to as **phase changes.**   This is often prevented or reduced by dispersion of small amounts of elements that block the free electrons of the crystal or form interstitial chemical combinations.   **Superalloys** are structural materials developed especially for extremely high temperatures and high stress conditions.

The number of possible alloys is infinite.   The most common general groups of alloys are brass, bronze, babbitt, alloy steels, nickel silver, and aluminum alloy.   Alloys of various compositions are sold under many trade names, but some trade names may be used to designate the quality of the alloy of a particular maker rather than composition.

Sintered alloys are made by compressing metal powders under hydraulic pressure and then heating in a furnace to obtain a fusion of the metals. **Metal powders** are made in a wide range of high-purity metals, intermetals, or alloys.   They may also be made with individual grains coated with another metal, which will chemically combine during processing.   The process is called **powder metallurgy,** and the parts made are generally stronger than castings and nearly as strong as rolled metals.   Parts can be made to great uniformity, and require little or no machining.   By control of the powder size and the pressure, various degrees of porosity can be obtained for parts such as bearings where oil impregnation is desired, or the metal powders can be combined with graphite for self-lubricating parts, or with abrasives for wear resistance.   **Sinterforged alloys** of the Sintercast Corp. are sintered alloys made by a one-step hot-pressing operation.   **Sintering gases** used for furnace atmospheres are called **endothermic gases,** or **endo gases.**   A typical gas for sintering steel powders with carbon added contains 40% hydrogen, 39 nitrogen, 20 carbon monoxide, 0.5 methane, and 0.5 water vapor.   Steel parts without added carbon are sintered in a reducing atmosphere.

A **technic alloy** is a low-cost alloy used in laboratories or dental schools to avoid the use of expensive alloys of gold or platinum in practice working.   It may be copper or aluminum with tin, nickel, silver, and iron, to give the approximate working characteristics of the expensive metal. **Nimonic alloy** is a general name for any of the precipitation-hardenable chromium-nickel steels.   **Cryogenic alloys** are alloys containing elements, usually nickel, that enable them to retain strength and toughness at subzero temperatures.

A **master alloy,** or **foundry alloy,** is an alloy used for adding elements to metals in the foundry.   Some of these may not be metallic alloys in the true sense.   **Carburite,** for example, is a high-graphite iron master alloy containing 55% carbon and only 26 iron, bonded with fluxing material into blocks for adding to steel to increase the carbon content.   **Nisiloy,** of the International Nickel Co., is an alloy of 60% nickel, 30 silicon, and 10 iron for ladle additions to cast iron to improve uniformity and machinability of the castings.   **Foundry alloy V-5,** of the Vanadium

Corp. of America, used for reducing chill and improving the physical qualities of cast iron, contains 40% chromium, 18 silicon, and 10 manganese, marketed in 8-mesh size for addition to the ladle.   An **aluminum master alloy** of Kawecki Chemical Co., Inc., contains 1.2% boron and 5.5 titanium, and is used for adding these metals to aluminum alloys to refine the grain and increase the hardness.

ALLOY STEEL. A general name for steels that owe their distinctive properties to elements other than carbon.   Alloy steels usually take the name of the element or elements having the greatest influence on the characteristics of the alloy, regardless of the percentage of the element contained in the steel.   These alloy steels include vanadium steel, nickel steel, nickel-chromium steel, manganese steel, and silicon steel.   The American Iron & Steel Institute defines alloy steel as a steel in which a minimum limit is specified or guaranteed for alloying elements.   These minimum percentages are chromium, 0.25%; copper, 0.60; manganese, 1.65; nickel, 0.25; silicon, 0.60; or any amounts of titanium, tungsten, or molybdenum. Steels having casual amounts of these elements, less than those specified above, are not rated as alloy steels, although vanadium steel may be any carbon steel that has been cleansed with vanadium.   Alloy steels are also marketed under a variety of trade names, covering a particular steel made into rough castings, such as **Tufaloy,** a high-strength cast steel of the Fort Pitt Steel Casting Div., or covering a group of steels marketed in rods and sheets such as **Carilloy** of United States Steel Corp.   Some alloy steels owe their particular properties to refinements of manufacture and selection of small amounts of alloying elements.   The alloy steels are used for automotive and machinery parts where high strength or special characteristics are required.   Most tool steels and structural steels with special properties are now alloy steels.   High-speed steels are alloy steels, but are classed as a separate group.   **Universal steel** is a name applied to alloy steels containing a low percentage of carbon to give them a wide range of utility.   They are usually nickel-chromium steels, as these steels can be used with carbon as low as 0.15% without losing their heat-treating properties.   **High-alloy steels** are steels containing very large percentages of elements, usually to obtain some special property such as corrosion resistance.   They are often not steel in the true sense, but are iron alloys.

ALLYL PLASTICS. A group of water-white casting plastics, related to the alkyds, produced by the polymerization of the ester of allyl alcohol or from allyl chloride, both produced from propylene.   **Allyl alcohol,** $CH_2:CH \cdot CH_2OH$, is a colorless liquid also known as **propenol,** which can be made by heating glycerol with formic or oxalic acid.   The specific gravity is 0.849, boiling point 96°C, and freezing point −129°C.   **Allyl**

chloride, $CH_2:CH \cdot CH_2Cl$, is a liquid of specific gravity 0.937, boiling point 45°C, and flash point −25°F.   **Allyl ester** is a clear syrupy liquid of specific gravity 1.26 which polymerizes with a peroxide catalyst to form allyl plastics.   The liquid monomer can be poured into molds and hardened by polymerization.   The polymerized castings are hard and crystal clear.   Allyl plastics have a specific gravity of 1.34 to 1.40, dielectric strength of 1,275 volts per mil, refractive index 1.57, Rockwell M hardness 116, and compressive strength 19,600 psi.   As the plastic has high clarity and less light dispersion than most optical glass, it is used for lenses, prisms, and reflectors.   It can be colored easily with dyes, and is also used for mechanical and electrical parts.   **Kriston,** of the B. F. Goodrich Chemical Co., **Allite,** of the Arol Chemical Prod. Co., and **Vibron 103,** of the Naugatuck Chemical Div., are allyl plastics.   **Allymer CR-39,** of the Cast Optics Corp., is an optically clear, hard, thermosetting casting resin for clock and instrument faces, windows, and lenses.   It is made from diallyl diglycol carbonate and triallyl cyanurate.   The sheet material transmits 92% of ordinary light, has a high heat-distortion point, 130°C, a tensile strength of 5,500 psi, a compressive strength of 22,800 psi, and a Rockwell hardness of M100.   It can be machined with carbide tools.   It is craze-resistant, and has only half the weight of glass.   **V-Lite,** of the Victor Chemical Works, is a **diallyl phenyl phosphate** monomer that polymerizes with a catalyst to form a transparent, hard, strong, flame-resistant thermosetting resin.   It can also be copolymerized with the thermoplastic vinyl acetate or methyl methacrylate to produce thermosetting resins.   **Selectron CR-39,** of the Pittsburgh Plate Glass Co., is an **allyl diglycol carbonate** casting resin.   The cast plastic has good abrasion resistance, is resistant to the action of chemicals, and is noncrazing.   It is also used to modify other plastics.   **Diallyl phthalate** is a thermosetting resin cured by polymerization without water formation.   The molded material, depending on the filler, has a tensile strength from 4,500 to 7,000 psi, a compressive strength up to 30,000 psi, a Rockwell hardness to M108, dielectric strength to 430 volts per mil, and heat resistance to 450°F.   The heat-resistant asbestos-filled resin has a specific gravity of 1.70.   **Dapon resin,** of the FMC Corp., is diallyl phthalate marketed as a white powder.   **Diall resin,** of the Mesa Products Div., is a diallyl phthalate molding compound.

Methallyl alcohol, $CH_2:C \cdot CH_3 \cdot CH_2OH$, also forms esters which can be used for the production of plastics.   It is a liquid boiling at 114.5°C. The allyl radical will combine with starch or sugar to form shellaclike resins.   **Allyl sucrose,** made by combining sugar and allyl chloride, is a resin that produces varnishes which will withstand temperatures to 400°F, and are chemical-resistant.   **Allyl starch** is a resinous material made by treating sweet-potato or grain starches with allyl chloride or allyl bromide.

It is soluble in varnish solvents and is a substitute for shellac as a varnishing agent, forming an adherent, resistant film on paper, fabric, wood, or metal.   It will withstand temperatures to 400°F.

ALMOND OIL. An essential oil distilled from the ground macerated kernels of the bitter almond, *Prunus amygdalus,* of the Mediterranean countries, and from the kernels of the **apricot,** *P. armeniaca.* The two oils are identical and contain the glucoside **amygdalin.**   The American production is mostly from the by-product pits of the apricot-canning industry of California.   The almond is a small tree closely resembling the peach. The fruit is inedible, but the seed inside the pit is marketed as roasted and salted nuts and is made into a paste for confections.   Oil of bitter almonds is used in perfumery and as a flavor.   For flavoring use, the poisonous hydrocyanic acid is extracted.   Synthetic almond oil is **benzaldehyde,** C_6H_5CHO, a colorless volatile oil with an almond flavor, produced from benzol or from toluol, and used for producing **triphenyl methane dyes** and many chemicals.

ALPACA. A fabric made from the fine woollike hair of the alpaca, an animal of the llama family of the mountains of Bolivia, Peru, Chile, and Argentina.   **Alpaca fiber** is long and fine, with a downy feel, but it does not have the strength or elasticity of fine wool, and is more closely allied to hair than to wool.   The alpaca animal is known only in the domesticated state.   There are two breeds, Huacaya and Suri, the latter having the longest and finest wool, reaching a fiber length up to 30 in.   From 3 to 10 lb of fiber are obtained per animal.   **Llama hair** (pronounced lyah-mah) from the llama of Bolivia is marketed as coarse alpaca.   In Incan times llama wool was used by the common people for clothing while the finer wool from the alpaca and vicuña was reserved for the upper classes.   The llama is sheared every two years when the wool reaches a length of about 12 in.   A considerable amount of stiff guard hairs occur in the fiber.

Vicuña, another animal of the llama family, is almost extinct, and the commercial vicuña cloth is made of alpaca or fine wool, or mixtures. There is a limited production of true vicuña from domestic herds in Bolivia and Peru, raised at an altitude of about 14,000 ft.   It is the softest of all animal weaving fibers.   Alpaca and vicuña cloths are used for shawls, jackets, and fine goods.   Imitation **alpaca fabric** for clothing linings is a lustrous, smooth, and wiry fabric plain-woven with a cotton warp and a worsted mohair filling.   When made with a rayon filling, it is called **rayon alpaca.**

ALUM. A colorless to white crystalline **potassium aluminum sulfate,** $KAl(SO_4)_2 \cdot 12H_2O$, or $[KAl(H_2O)_6]SO_4 \cdot 6H_2O$, occurring naturally

as the mineral **kalunite,** and also in combination as the mineral **alunite.**
It is also called **potash alum** to distinguish it from other forms. It has a
sweetish taste and is very astringent. It is used as an additive in the
leather and textile industries, in sizing paper, as a mordant in dyeing, in
medicines as an astringent, and in baking powder. It is an important
water-purifying agent. From a water solution it crystallizes out, forming
positively charged particles which attract the negatively charged organic
impurities, thus purifying the water as they settle out. Alum has a specific gravity of 1.757, melts in its water of crystallization at 92°C, and
when heated to redness is converted to **burnt alum,** a porous, friable
material which dissolves slowly in water. Alum is marketed as USP,
lump, pea, nut, ground, and powdered. The rice crystal alum of the
General Chemical Co. is from 10 to 30 mesh, and the granular is from
30 to 60 mesh.

Alumstone is a gray or pinkish massive form of alunite found in volcanic rocks. A pure variety from Italy is called **Roman alum,** or **roche
alum.** The alunite of Australia is used to produce **potassium sulfate,**
K_2SO_4, for fertilizer, and the residue, containing 50% alumina, is used
for aluminum production. **Soda alum,** in which the potassium is replaced
by sodium, occurs in the South American Andes as the mineral **mendozite.**
It is more soluble than alum, but is more difficult to purify. **Filter alum,**
also called **patent alum** and **aluminous cake,** used for waterworks filtration, is **aluminum sulfate,** $Al_2(SO_4)_3$, plus a varying amount of water of
crystallization. The anhydrous form is used as a dehydrating agent for
gases. It is a white crystalline solid readily soluble in water. When
filter alum contains a slight excess of alumina it is called basic. The
hexahydrate aluminum sulfate of the Allied Chemical Corp. has the composition $Al_2(SO_4)_3 \cdot 6H_2O$, and is used for chemical processing.

Commercial aluminum sulfate is also called **concentrated alum,** and
replaces potash alum for many uses because of its cheapness. It comes
in colorless crystals having a strong astringent taste, and is used as a
mordant in dyeing, in water purification, sizing papers, tanning, in printing inks, and in dry colors. For use in pickling and tanning leathers, it
contains not more than 0.01% iron oxide. **Ammonia alum,** used in tanning sheepskins and fur skins, and in fireproofing and dyeing textiles, is
ammonium-aluminum sulfate, $NH_4Al(SO_4)_2 \cdot 12H_2O$, a colorless or white
crystalline powder soluble in water and, like other alums, insoluble in
alcohol. It is valued for water purification because it forms chloramine,
and is also used in vegetable glues and porcelain cements. For uses
where an alkaline instead of an acid solution is required, **sodium phospho-
aluminate** is employed. It is a white, water-soluble powder, and is a
double salt containing about 70% sodium aluminate and 20 sodium orthophosphate, with the balance water. The **Alkophos** of the Monsanto Co.

is **aluminum phosphate,** $AlPO_4$, a white powder used as a bonding agent for high-temperature cements, and as an alkaline flux for ceramics.

ALUMINA. The oxide of aluminum, Al_2O_3. The natural crystalline mineral is called corundum, but the synthetic crystals used for abrasives are designated usually as **aluminum oxide** or marketed under trade names. For other uses and as a powder it is generally called alumina. It is widely distributed in nature in combination with silica and other minerals, and is an important constituent of the clays for making porcelain, bricks, pottery, and refractories. The **alumina clay** from the large deposits in western Idaho contains an average of 28% Al_2O_3, 5.6 iron oxide, and a high percentage of titanium oxide. Such clays are used for ceramics, but the oxide, alumina, is obtained commercially chiefly by high-temperature fusing of bauxite. It is also produced from alunite with a by-product fertilizer, and obtained from the oil shales of Colorado.

The crushed and graded crystals of alumina when pure are nearly colorless, but the fine powder is white. Off colors are due to impurities. The German **Bikorit** was a white lump material made by the fusion of calcined impure alumina. **Diburin** was a pink abrasive containing chromic oxide, while the black **Redurit** was made by the fusion of bauxite without any reduction. The latter was used in wartime for abrasive paper and cloth. American aluminum oxide used for abrasives is at least 99.5% pure, in nearly colorless crystals melting at 2050°C. The chief uses for alumina are for the production of aluminum metal and for abrasives, but it is also used for ceramics, refractories, pigments, catalyst carriers, and in chemicals.

Aluminum oxide crystals are normally hexagonal, and are minute in size. For abrasives, the grain sizes are usually from 100 to 600 mesh. The larger grain sizes are made up of many crystals, unlike the single-crystal large grains of silicon carbide. The specific gravity is about 3.95, and the hardness is up to 2,000 Knoop. Titanium oxide as an impurity tends to add hardness. For high-grade refractory ceramics the **alumina powder** is free of silica. The ultrafine alumina abrasive powder of Union Carbide Corp. is of two kinds. Type A is **alpha alumina** with hexagonal crystals with particle size of 0.3 micron, density 4.0, and hardness 9 Mohs. Type B is **gamma alumina** with cubic crystals with particle size under 0.1 micron, density 3.6, and hardness 8. Type A cuts faster, but Type B gives a finer finish. At high temperatures gamma alumina transforms to the alpha crystal. The aluminum oxide most frequently used for refractories is the **beta alumina** in hexagonal crystals heat-stabilized with sodium. It has the composition $Na_2O \cdot 11Al_2O_3$, but stabilized alumina is also produced with oxides of calcium, potassium, or magnesium. The alpha and gamma alumina powders of the J. T. Baker Chemical Co. for lapping, grinding, and in dentifrices are of 99.96% purity in controlled particle sizes from 0.02 to 0.4 micron.

The aluminum oxide abrasives in all forms are sold under trade names. **Alundum,** of the Norton Co., **Aloxite,** of the Carborundum Co., and **Lionite,** of the General Abrasives Co., are aluminum oxides.   **Alundum 32,** of the Norton Co., is aluminum oxide with each abrasive grain in a single crystal and, unlike the crushed and ground oxide, having the natural edges of the crystal as the cutting edges.   It is made by growing the crystals in a matrix of chemically unstable glass and then dissolving out this calcium sulfate glass to leave the crystals free.   It is about 96% Al_2O_3, and is brown.   The white **Alundum 38,** of 99.5% purity, is crushed from large crystals.   **Dynablast,** of the same company, has high-purity crystals agglomerated into grain sizes from 16 to 60 mesh.   The 16 grit is used for metal cleaning, the 40 to 60 for granite cutting, and a finer powder, from 100 to 240 mesh, is used for glass and metal polishing.

Activated alumina is partly dehydrated alumina trihydrate, which has a strong affinity for moisture or gases and is used for dehydrating organic solvents.   **Hydrated alumina** is **alumina trihydrate,** $Al_2O_3 \cdot 3H_2O$, used as a catalyst carrier.   At elevated temperatures it becomes active, and the fine powder is an auxiliary catalyst.   It is also used as a filler in plastics and in cosmetics, and comes in various particle sizes for use in glass and vitreous enamels to increase the strength and luster.   **Hydrated alumina C-741** is this material with particles coated with stearic acid for use as a reinforcing pigment in rubber.

Activated alumina F-1, of the Aluminum Co. of America, is a porous form of alumina, Al_2O_3, used for drying gases or liquids.   It will remove moisture up to 15% of the dry weight of the alumina.   **Activated alumina F-6** is this material impregnated with cobaltous chloride which will change color from blue through pale pink to white with progression of the adsorption of moisture.   Activated alumina is also used as a catalyst for many chemical processes.   **Aluminum hydroxide** is a white bulky water-insoluble fine powder of specific gravity 2.42 and refractive index 1.535, used as a base for lake pigments, for making gloss white, as a water repellent in textile and paper coatings, and as an antacid in medicine.   **Boehmite,** of Du Pont, used in cosmetics, is called **colloidal alumina,** but it is an **aluminum monohydrate,** AlOOH, made by polymerizing aluminum cations in a water solution.   **Baymal** of this company, used for coatings, adhesives, paints, and for making dense ceramics, is similar.   The powder is in the form of tiny fibrils, 50 angstroms in diameter and 1,500 angstroms long.   These are dimensions too small to be expressed in inch measurements (10,000 angstroms equals 1 micron).   In coatings the fibrils interlock the molecules into a tight adherent film.   In paints the powder acts as a **thixotropic material** to prevent sagging or running on vertical walls.   The powder is both a **hydrophilic material,** that is, water-soluble, and an **organophilic material** soluble in oils and organic solvents.   **Dispal,** of Continental Oil Co., is an aluminum monohydrate used as a filler in coatings and will give a hydrophilic coating on normally hydrophobic surfaces.   It is in crystals 0.005 micron in size, agglomerated into particles of about 44 microns.   It has very high bulking properties and is used also in cosmetics.

Calcined alumina is made by calcining aluminum hydroxide, and the commercial product is 99.1% Al_2O_3, with no more than 0.5% adsorbed water, and not over 0.4% silicon, iron, sodium, and titanium oxides. The powder, in particle size as small as 10 microns, is used for abrasives, glassmaking, and for refractory ceramics.   The molded material has little porosity or shrinkage, and retains its strength and electrical resistance at high temperatures.   **Alumina A-14,** of the Aluminum Co. of America, is a calcined alumina for electrical insulators with a particle size of 2 to 3 microns and containing not more than 0.08% soda.   For electronic and nuclear ceramic parts, a 99.95% pure alumina is produced by this company.   It has less than 0.01% sodium oxide.   The alumina powder of Reynolds Metals Co. has an average particle size down to 1 micron and has low soda content.   It is made by calcining the powder with silica sand at high temperature.   Sintered parts have a service use to 3500°F with tensile strength to 60,000 psi.   **Alumina Al-200,** of the Coors Porcelain Co., for high-frequency insulators, gives a molded product with a tensile strength of 25,000 psi, compressive strength of 290,000 psi, and specific gravity of 3.36.   The coefficient of thermal expansion is half that of steel, and the hardness about that of sapphire.   **Alumina AD-995,** of this company, is a dense vacuum-tight ceramic for high-temperature electronic use. It is 99.5% alumina with no silica.   The hardness is Rockwell N80, and dielectric constant 9.27.   The maximum working temperature is 3200°F, and at 2000°F it has a flexural strength of 29,000 psi.

Tabular alumina is alumina converted to the corundum form by calcining at temperatures below the fusing point, and the tabular crystals are larger than those of calcined alumina.   It comes as a fine powder or as coarse granules for making refractory ceramics and electrical insulators. **Alumina balls** are marketed in sizes from ¼ to ¾ in. for reactor and catalytic beds.   They are usually 99% alumina, having high resistance to heat and chemicals.   **Alumina fibers** in the form of short linear crystals, called **sapphire whiskers,** have high strength up to 200,000 psi for use as a filler in plastics to increase heat resistance and dielectric properties. **Fumed alumina** powder of submicron size is made by flame reduction of aluminum chloride.   It is used in coatings and for plastics reinforcement and in the production of ferrite ceramic magnets.

Alfrax is the trade name of the Carborundum Co. for alumina as a catalyst carrier and as a refractory.   **Stupalox,** of the same company, for ring and plug gages, is alumina hot-pressed to a density of 3.95.   It is tough and wear-resistant, with a transverse rupture strength of 100,000 psi and compressive strength of 450,000 psi.   **Hi-Supertite,** of Englehard Industries, Inc., is a vitreous ceramic in tube form, composed of 96% alumina, used for protecting thermocouples.   It is gastight at 1450°C.   **Lucalox,** of the General Electric Co., is a translucent ceramic pressed from high-purity fine alumina powder and fired at high temperature.   It transmits 90% of visible light rays, and will withstand temperatures to 3600°F. It is polycrystalline with pores removed in the firing.   The transverse strength is 50,000 psi, and dielectric strength 1,700 volts per mil.   It is used for high-intensity lamps, missile nose cones, and instrument parts. **Alite,** of the U.S. Stoneware Co., used for bearings, valves, nozzles, and extrusion dies, is a white ceramic made by molding or extruding alpha alumina and sintering at 3400°F.   The bonding is by crystal growth, producing nearly a single crystal.   The tensile strength is up to 32,500 psi, compressive strength up to 290,000 psi, and dielectric strength 250 volts per mil.   It is used for temperatures to 1600°F.   **Aluminum oxide film,** or **alumina film,** used as a supporting material in ionizing tubes, is a strong, transparent sheet made by oxidizing aluminum foil, rubbing off the oxide on one side, and dissolving the foil in an acid solution to leave the oxide film, 0.000001 in. thick, from the other side.   It is transparent to electrons.   **Alumina bubble brick** is a lightweight refractory brick for kiln lining, made by passing molten alumina in front of an air jet, producing small hollow bubbles which are then pressed into bricks and shapes.   **Alumina foam** bricks and blocks for high-temperature insulation are made by Pittsburgh Plate Glass Co.   The foam has a density of 28 lb per cu ft and porosity of 85%.   The thermal conductivity at 2000°F is 3.7 Btu per hr pr sq ft per deg F per in.

ALUMINUM. Called **aluminium** in England.   A white metal with a bluish tinge, symbol Al, atomic weight 26.97, obtained chiefly from bauxite.   It is the most widely distributed of the elements next to oxygen and silicon, occurring in all common clays, but it is difficult to extract.   The metal was discovered in 1727, but was obtained only in small amounts until it was reduced electrolytically in 1885.   It has a specific gravity of 2.70 and a melting point of 658.7°C, is resistant to corrosion and to many chemicals, but is attacked by alkalies and hydrochloric acid.   Above 400°F, however, corrosion of the metal is vigorous, and at 600°F it converts to the oxide unless alloyed.   The metal is nonmagnetic, even when highly alloyed with iron.   Its physical properties are greatly affected by even slight additions of other elements.   Pure aluminum is next to gold in order of malleability.   The metal has a face-centered cubic crystal structure and is easy to cold-roll, but aluminum alloys are not as plastic as steel at the forging temperatures and require heavier passes. On a volume basis aluminum has about 60% of the thermal conductivity of copper. The tensile strength of cast aluminum is 12,000 psi, with elongation of 30%, and Brinell hardness 30.

The chief impurities in commercial aluminum are copper, iron, and silicon, but sheet aluminum averages 99.3% pure. It can be produced by reacting aluminum trichloride with aluminum to form aluminum subchloride, AlCl, which is decomposed at 1400°F to obtain the aluminum metal. **Alcoa 2S,** of the Aluminum Co. of America, is commercially pure aluminum. The tensile strength, annealed, is 13,000 psi, with elongation of 35%, and Brinell hardness 23. When cold-rolled to a Brinell hardness of 44 it has a tensile strength of 24,000 psi with elongation of 5%. **High-conductivity aluminum,** called **EC aluminum,** contains 99.45% min aluminum, and has an electrical conductivity 62% that of copper. The tensile strength is 12,000 psi with elongation of 23%. In the H17 hardness, with 66% cold reduction, it has a tensile strength of 20,000 psi and elongation of 2%. **Cond-Al,** used by the General Electric Co. for generator field windings where high strength and low creep at high temperatures are required, contains 0.43% iron, 0.32 magnesium, and 0.10 silicon.

Most of the aluminum used for structural products is in the form of alloys. Because of its high strength-weight factor a large part of the production of aluminum goes into transportation equipment and moving parts of machinery. It is also used for ornamental architectural work, containers, cooking utensils, chemical equipment, electrical conductors, and packaging. But because the yield strength of the metal declines drastically above 375°F, it does not replace steel for large structures where there is danger of fire or locally applied heat. The metal is transparent to X-rays and is used in thin sheets as ray filters. It extrudes easily, and is used to replace tin alloys for collapsible tubes. In powder and flake form it is used in paints and fireworks, thermit welding, and as a catalyst. **Aluminum shot,** for deoxidizing steel, comes in slightly flattened spheroids with maximum size of $\frac{1}{2}$ in. The reflectivity of polished aluminum is high for all wavelengths, and it is used for both heat and light reflectors.

Foamed aluminum, or **aluminum foam,** used as a core material for lightweight structures, is made by foaming the metal with zirconium hydride or other metal hydride. The released hydrogen expands the metal into a cellular structure of good strength with controlled densities from 12 to 40 lb per cu ft. A foam of aluminum-magnesium alloy used for insulated roofing and for building panels, with a density of 12 lb per cu ft, has only 7% the weight of solid aluminum. **Foamalum,** of the Foamalum Corp., is an aluminum foam. **Spangle sheet,** of the Aluminum Co. of America, is aluminum sheet with a glittering finish, used for appliances, novelties, and architecture. An aluminum alloy with a large grain is used, and the sheet is etched with an acid to cause individual grains to stand out in relief with mirrorlike facets on each of the irregularly positioned grains. The sheet reflects light in varying degrees and appears as a spangle of continuously changing patterns.

Anodized aluminum, originally called **Eloxal** in Germany, is aluminum with a hard surface of aluminum oxide produced by electrolysis with the metal as the anode. Coatings are from 0.0001 to 0.008 in. thick, are wear-resistant, and also protect the metal from further oxidation. The coating is a nonconductor of electricity and may be used as an insulator. Oxalic acid was used in the bath for the original Eloxal process, but sulfuric and chromic acids are also used. Colors are obtained either by dyeing the coating or by adding various metals to the bath to produce the colors. The natural oxide film on aluminum is less than a millionth of an inch thick. An anodized film of 0.0004 in. is necessary for corrosion and wear resistance, and for dye coloring a coating of 0.0008 in. is necessary. Heavy coatings for wear and electrical resistance may be 0.006 in. thick. The wear-resistant coatings of Anodic, Inc., are 0.002 in. thick, above and below the surface of the aluminum, increasing the sheet thickness 0.001 in. **Alumilite** is anodized aluminum of the Aluminum Co. of America, and **Alzak** is a bright anodized sheet for reflectors with the thickness of coating less than 0.0002 in., giving a light reflectance of 79%. Aluminum is difficult to electroplate by ordinary methods because it is far removed from hydrogen in the electromotive series, and water solutions always contain ionic hydrogen. Aluminum plating baths may contain lithium hydride or lithium aluminum hydride in an ethyl ether solution of anhydrous aluminum chloride, and the anodes are always of aluminum metal.

ALUMINUM ALLOY. Originally the term aluminum alloy, when not further qualified, referred to **aluminum-copper alloys** with or without small amounts of other alloying elements. The original **Duralumin,** of the Durener Metallwerke, contained 4% copper, 0.5 magnesium, and 0.5 manganese. Copper hardens and strengthens aluminum, and also gives age-hardening properties, especially when a small amount of magnesium is present. This alloy rolls well, but is subject to intercrystalline corrosion unless anodized or clad with pure aluminum. The annealed alloy has a tensile strength of 28,000 psi, elongation 22%, and Brinell hardness 50. Federal specifications for aluminum alloy in wrought form call for 3.5 to 4.5% copper, 0.2 to 0.75 magnesium, and 0.4 to 1 manganese. **Alcoa 17S,** of the Aluminum Co. of America, has a nominal composition similar to Duralumin, with tensile strength when annealed of 26,000 psi, and 62,000 psi when rolled hard and heat-treated.

The influence of even very small amounts of other elements on aluminum makes possible an infinite variety of alloys.   Many of the first compositions still remain as basically standard.   **Anticorodal,** a German aircraft alloy, had 1% silicon, 0.5 manganese, and 0.5 magnesium.   **Aerolite** had only 1.15% copper, with magnesium, silicon, and zinc in small amounts.   The **Hiduminium alloys** developed by the Rolls-Royce laboratories were originally improvements on the German alloys and contained titanium and nickel.   The English **Fairey metal** and the German **Aeron** and **Ultralumin** were variants of Duralumin.   Most of these alloys contain considerable copper.

Aluminum alloys are now classified by their general use characteristics rather than by composition groups, as wrought alloys for construction and manufacturing uses, sand-casting alloys, permanent-mold casting alloys, and die-casting alloys.   These alloys are usually given a number with letter symbols to designate the physical condition and treatment, accompanied by the name of the company, or a company trade name, such as **Alcoa alloys,** of the Aluminum Co. of America, and **Bohnalite,** of the Bohn Aluminum & Brass Co.   The whole range of aluminum alloys is marketed by the Scovill Mfg. Co. under the name of **Truspec alloys.**   The temper of the metal is shown by symbols after the alloy number, F being for the as-fabricated condition, O for annealed and recrystallized, and H for strain-hardened, with numbers added to indicate the degrees of hardness.   **Londal,** of the London Aluminium Co., Ltd., **Hyblum,** of the Sheet Aluminum Corp., and **Weisalloy,** of the Henry Weis Mfg. Co., are group names for aluminum alloys.

The numbering system adopted by the Aluminum Assoc. for aluminum and aluminum alloys is by group classification.   The 1000 series is for aluminum of over 99% purity, the last two digits indicating the minimum aluminum percentage.   Thus, **aluminum 1030** is an aluminum of 99.30% min purity, and **aluminum 1085** is an aluminum of 99.85% min purity. The 1100 and 1200 series consist of 99% min aluminum alloys with small addition of silicon, copper, or other elements.   **Aluminum alloy 1100** is thus the older aluminum alloy 2S, and **aluminum alloy 1235** is the older **aluminum alloy R995,** used for foil.   It contains 99.35% aluminum, 0.65 silicon and iron, and 0.05 copper.   The 2000 series contains copper as the chief alloying element; the 4000 series is silicon alloys; the 5000 series is magnesium alloys; the 6000 series is magnesium and silicon alloys; and the 7000 series is zinc alloys.   When the second digit of the number is used it indicates a modification of the alloy.   **Aluminum alloy 2017** is thus the older **aluminum alloy 17S,** and **aluminum alloy 2117** is the older **aluminum alloy A17S.**   Standard aluminum alloys for various uses are listed in engineering books under ASTM and Association numbers, but aluminum alloying has such tremendous possibilities by even slight changes in composition that alterations are continuously made and trade names still persist.

Zinc and tin in aluminum alloys cause hot-shortness, but zinc adds strength, and when balanced with other elements good physical properties are obtained. Magnesium forms a silicide with the silicon present, and gives age-hardening. Titanium in small amounts refines the grain. Iron in small amounts increases strength, but causes hot-shortness and inter-crystalline corrosion. Beryllium may be used to control the iron and add age-hardening, while nickel is used to reduce hydrogen pickup which causes corrosion in steam or hot-water environments. A small amount of lead gives good machining characteristics for screw-machine work. **Alcoa 11S** is an alloy of this kind, with 5.5% copper, 0.5 lead, and 0.5 bismuth. It has a tensile strength of 55,000 psi, with elongation 15% and Brinell hardness 95. Indium in small amounts increases the strength and hardness of heat-treatable alloys. Cerium metals are added to refine the grain and increase strength.

Alcoa 24S, aluminum alloy 2024, is used in sheet form, and comes in various tempers and treatments. It contains 4.5% copper, 1.5 magnesium, and 0.6 manganese. **Alclad 24S-T4** has a tensile strength of 64,000 psi, and elongation 19%. **Alcoa 61S,** used for forging aircraft and marine parts, has 0.25% copper, 0.6 silicon, 1 magnesium, 0.25 chromium, and 0.15 titanium. It is corrosion-resistant, and has a tensile strength of 45,000 psi, elongation 17%, and Brinell hardness 95. This alloy has been used for precision extruded seamless tubing for such parts as mechanical pencils. It is also used for impact forgings for aircraft parts. **Alcoa 14S, aluminum alloy 2014,** with 4.4% copper, 0.8 silicon, 0.8 manganese, and 0.4 magnesium, will give a tensile strength of 55,000 psi in impact forged parts, with an elongation of 7% and a Brinell hardness of 125. **Reynolds alloy R-301** contains 4.5% copper, 1 silicon, 0.8 manganese, 0.4 magnesium, and may have up to 1% iron and 0.1 chromium. It has a tensile strength of 65,000 psi. It is marketed as a clad metal with a coating containing 1% magnesium and 0.5 manganese for added corrosion resistance. **Aluminum alloy 150S,** for drawing and forming, has 1.5% magnesium, 0.50 silicon, 0.80 iron, and small amounts of copper, chromium, zinc, and manganese. In the soft state it has a tensile strength of 21,000 psi and elongation 25%. It gives a lustrous buffed finish, or a satin anodized finish. **Alcoa 63S,** which has been used for tubing, oil pipelines, and architectural extrusion, has up to 0.85% magnesium, 0.2 to 0.6 silicon, 0.35 max iron, and 0.10 max each of copper, zinc, chromium, and titanium. It has a tensile strength of 30,000 psi, elongation 20%, and Brinell hardness 42. When both titanium and nickel are present the two metals combine to form very hard crystals.

Aluminum-chromium alloys are used for wrought applications. An alloy developed by the Stockholm Metallographic Institute under the name of **Cromal** contained 2 to 4% chromium with small amounts of nickel and manganese. The alloy designated as aluminum-chromium alloy in Federal specifications contains 1.1 to 1.4% magnesium and 0.30 chromium. But present commercial alloys contain only small amounts of chromium as a balancing element rather than as a main constituent. For marine and architectural applications, **Alcoa 52S** may be used as a stronger metal than commercial aluminum. In the $\frac{3}{4}$-hard condition it has a tensile strength of 39,000 psi, elongation 10%, and Brinell hardness 74, but the sheet metal comes with forming characteristics similar to commercial aluminum. It contains 1.3% magnesium, 0.7 silicon, and 0.25 chromium. **Alcoa 51S** and **Bohnalite S51,** for such uses as drawn tubing, have 1% silicon, 0.6 magnesium, and 0.25 chromium, but **Alcan B51S,** of Aluminium Ltd., has 1.3% silicon, 0.8 magnesium, 0.8 manganese, and 0.10 copper. It is resistant to stress corrosion cracking, and in the T6 temper has a tensile strength of 46,000 psi, yield strength of 43,000 psi, and elongation of 13%. Alcoa 51S has a tensile strength of 48,000 psi, elongation 17%, and Brinell hardness 100. **Alcoa 56S** has a high proportion of magnesium, and is used for wire and for rivets for joining magnesium alloys. It contains 5.2% magnesium, 0.1 manganese, and 0.1 chromium. It is very ductile in the soft state. In the hard condition it has a tensile strength of 62,000 psi, and elongation of 6%.

Alloys designated as **aluminum-manganese alloy** in ASTM and Federal specifications contain 1 to 1.5% manganese, with small allowable percentages of copper, iron, silicon, and zinc. Many aluminum alloys contain some manganese, but **Alcoa 3S** contains 1.2% manganese and no other alloying element. This alloy, in the $\frac{3}{4}$-hard condition, has been used for making cans. The tensile strength is 25,000 psi, and elongation 14%. **Bohnalite S53** is a similar alloy. The Swiss alloy called **Aluman,** used for corrugated roofing, is also similar. **Alcoa 4S** has 1.2% manganese and 1 magnesium. This is a very ductile alloy in the soft condition, and the tensile strength is increased about 50% in the hard temper. The tensile strength, soft, is 26,000 psi, with elongation 25% and Brinell hardness 45. **Acieral** is a European alloy of this class. **Navalium** is a name given by the British Institute of Naval Architects for Al-Mn-Mg alloys. The alloys containing magnesium form an anodic film on the outside which retards further corrosion. The German **Seewasser alloy** had 2.25% magnesium and 0.2 antimony, and formed a protective coating of antimony oxychloride on the surface. **Alcoa 50S** contains 1.3% magnesium. In the soft condition it has a tensile strength of 21,000 psi with elongation of 24%, while the hard-drawn metal has a tensile strength of 32,000 psi with elongation of 6%.

The most commonly used sand-casting alloys have about 7% copper with silicon or magnesium, or both, and sometimes zinc. They are made by adding a **hardener alloy** to the aluminum melt, the hardener alloy containing nominally 50% copper and 50 aluminum, but with an allowable content of zinc, silicon, or other elements. **SAE alloy 33** and **BES alloy 3-L-11** are made in this way. The English alloys **BES No. 362** and **BES No. L8** have 11 to 13% copper. **Alcoa 112** has 7% copper and 1.7 zinc. These alloys have a tensile strength of 24,000 psi, elongation 1.5%, and Brinell hardness 70.

For strong heat-treated castings, alloys with about 4% copper and a small amount of silicon or magnesium are used. **Bohnalite B** has 4.5% copper and 0.3 magnesium. **Alcoa 195,** with 4.5% copper and 0.8 silicon, develops a tensile strength of 32,000 psi with 8.5% elongation, or 40,000 psi with 2% elongation. **Alcoa 212,** with 8% copper and 1.2 silicon, is a general-purpose casting alloy. **Alcoa 122** and **Bohnalite J** have 10% copper with a slight amount of magnesium. This type of alloy has a good balance of physical properties and is used for pistons. **Aluminum-magnesium alloys,** with a high percentage of magnesium, have a high combination of tensile and yield strengths, elongation, and resistance to impact. The original German alloy, invented by Dr. Ludwig Mach and called **Mach's metal,** contained 5% magnesium, and his **Magnalium** contained 10%. **Ulmal** was a German alloy with 10% magnesium, 1 silicon, and 0.50 manganese. **Alcoa 220** and **SAE alloy 324** have 10% magnesium. Tensile strength is 46,000 psi, elongation 14%, and Brinell hardness 75. **Aluminum alloy MG-7,** of High Duty Alloys, Ltd., is a strong, corrosion-resistant alloy with 7% magnesium, 0.60 manganese, and 0.75 iron. **Birmabright** is a similar English alloy for salt-water resistance. Small amounts of lead may be added to this type of alloy for free-machining qualities, but it lowers the strength and ductility. **Alcoa 214,** with 3.8% magnesium, is used for architectural castings because of its good white color when anodized. With a small amount of silicon added, it casts more easily in difficult sections, but the color is not as white.

Apex 417, of the Apex Smelting Co., is a free-machining alloy of good dimensional stability. It contains 7% magnesium, 0.2 each of titanium and manganese, and small amounts of copper, silicon, zinc, and iron. The tensile strength is 40,000 psi, with elongation of 13% and Brinell hardness of 70. A corrosion-resistant sheet for welded chemical-processing vessels is **Kaiser alloy 5086.** It has 4% magnesium, 0.45 manganese, and 0.10 chromium. The tensile strength is from 38,000 to 47,000 psi with elongation from 10 to 22%. **Aluminum alloy 6061** is also a strong weldable alloy for sheet and plate construction, containing a maximum of 1.20% magnesium. Another structural alloy, **aluminum alloy 5456,** contains 5.1% magnesium, 0.8 manganese, and 0.10 chromium. It has a tensile strength in the soft temper of 42,000 psi with elongation of 16%. **Aluminum alloy 5083,** with 4.5% magnesium, has less strength, 40,000 psi, but is more easily worked.   A high-strength structural alloy, **Alcoa 7075-T6,** contains 2.5% magnesium, 1.6 copper, 5.6 zinc, and 0.3 chromium.   It has a tensile strength of 77,000 psi with elongation of 7%, giving 5 times the yield strength of hot-rolled structural steel of equal weight.   But these aluminum alloys are not used to replace steel for large structures because the yield strength drops drastically above 375°F and they cannot be used where there is danger of fire or locally applied heat.

Lurium alloys, of the Fromson Co., Inc., are wrought metals which take a brilliant polish and do not oxidize easily.   They are chemically pure 99.99% aluminum alloyed with magnesium.   **Lurium 5** contains 0.50% magnesium and has a tensile strength of 25,000 psi and a Brinell hardness of 40 to 50, almost double the hardness of the original aluminum. **Lurium 10** contains 1% magnesium, and **Lurium 20** has 2% magnesium. It has a tensile strength to 50,000 psi with Brinell hardness to 80.   The magnesium is in solid solution, and the hardness is obtained by cold working.   These materials in sheet form are used for reflectors, costume jewelry, and appliances.   **Kaiser alloy K155,** of Kaiser Aluminum & Chemical Sales, Inc., is a similar alloy containing 0.9% magnesium, with a bright color and high corrosion resistance.

Aluminum-nickel alloys are favored for such uses as pistons and cylinder heads because of a low coefficient of thermal expansion.   A very early alloy called **Bersh metal** was high in nickel and was used for bearings. **Batterium metal,** developed by the British National Physical Laboratory, was an aluminum alloy with copper and nickel.   The **Y-alloy** developed by this laboratory had 4% copper, 2 nickel, and 1.5 magnesium.   **Alcoa 142,** also called **Lo-Ex alloy,** has approximately this composition.   Tensile strength is 28,000 psi, with elongation 2% and Brinell hardness 75. **Bohnalite Y** has about the same composition as Y-alloy, and an alloy called **Nickeloy** by the Western Electric Co. has a similar composition.   **Neonalium** and **Meral** were German and Swiss alloys of this type.   **Magnalite,** of the Walker M. Levett Co., and **BES alloy L-24** are Y-alloy types.   The modified Y-alloys developed by the Rolls-Royce laboratories contained less copper with some titanium.   **R-R 50 alloy** has 1.2% copper, 1.3 nickel, 0.1 magnesium, 0.18 titanium, and 2.2 silicon.   **R-R 53 alloy** has 2.2% copper, 1.3 nickel, 1.6 magnesium, 0.08 titanium, 1.2 silicon, and 1.4 iron.   This alloy was used for die castings.   **Alcoa 750** has 1% copper, 1 nickel, and 6.5 tin, and is used for engine bearings and bushings. The permanent-mold castings have a tensile strength of 20,000 psi, elongation 10%, and Brinell hardness 45.   The nickel adds creep resistance and lowers the thermal expansion.   **Alcoa X-8001,** for cladding in nuclear reactors to resist hydrogen pickup and corrosion deterioration in high-pressure water at 400°F, contains 1.3% nickel, 0.17 silicon, 0.5 iron, and 0.15 copper.

ALUMINUM BRASS. There are two distinct types of aluminum brass. The first is a casting brass in which a small amount of aluminum acts as a flux to eliminate impurities and give the brass greater fluidity for intricate castings. The excess of aluminum remaining in the alloy is usually not more than 0.50%. The addition of aluminum also permits the use of higher percentages of lead up to about 5%, making the castings easy to machine. The second type is wrought brass modified with aluminum, producing alloys with properties between the brasses and the aluminum bronzes. Even slight additions of aluminum, dispersed as metal in the alloy and not as oxide, improve the oxidation resistance of brasses, and brass with as little as 0.10% of aluminum will have a bright color when extruded or forged. Larger amounts increase the strength and hardness, but decrease the ductility.

A 60-40 brass containing 1% aluminum has its strength increased about 30% and its hardness about 25%. **Revalon,** of Revere Copper & Brass, Inc., contains 76% copper, 22 zinc, and 2 aluminum, and is used for condenser tubes. The soft alloy has a tensile strength of 62,000 psi, elongation 50%, Rockwell B hardness 33, while the hard-drawn material has a tensile strength of 83,000 psi, elongation 15%, and hardness 86. It has 22.5% of the electrical conductivity of copper, and is very corrosion-resistant. **Ambraloy 927,** of the American Brass Co., has the same composition and properties. This alloy is known in England as **high-tensile brass. Ad-aluminum,** of the Chase Brass & Copper Co., has 82% copper, 15 zinc, 2 aluminum, and 1 tin. **Alcunic,** of the Scovill Mfg. Co., is a 70-30 brass modified by replacing some zinc with 2% aluminum and 1 nickel.

ALUMINUM BRONZE. A copper-aluminum alloy with aluminum as the chief alloying element, with or without other alloying materials. Plain additions of aluminum to copper increase the strength up to three times that of the original copper, and change the color from red to pale gold. The commercial alloys usually contain from 5 to 10% aluminum. Single-phase alpha alloys up to 7% aluminum have the structure of pure copper with the aluminum in solid solution, and the alloy is tough and ductile. At about 7.5% aluminum the structure changes from homogeneous to duplex, and the alloy becomes increasingly hard and difficult to cold-work. Chemical control of the alloy is important, as free aluminum oxide may make hard spots. Deoxidizers refine the grain size. Iron is the most common metal used for refining the grain, but nickel, manganese, and zinc affect it in varying degrees.

All of the alloys are resistant to corrosion.   They can be cast or forged, but the high-aluminum alloys are difficult to machine because of free aluminum oxide present.   The duplex alloys can be hardened by quenching from a high temperature, and drawn.   Aluminum bronze is used for high-strength and nonmagnetic parts, condenser tubes, and corrosion-resistant chemical equipment.   The hard crystals in a soft matrix made it useful for bearings.   The alloys high in aluminum are used for architectural castings to contrast in color with aluminum-silicon alloys.

Standard aluminum bronze for castings contains 8% aluminum.   It has a tensile strength, annealed, of 76,000 psi, elongation 55%, and Brinell hardness 125.   When hardened, the tensile strength is 134,000 psi, elongation 13%, and hardness 240.   The weight is 0.293 lb per cu in., and the melting point 1940°F.   **Ambraloy 298,** of the American Brass Co., and **Revere alloy 430,** of the Revere Copper & Brass, Inc., have this composition but are wrought alloys.   The hard-drawn rod has a tensile strength of 125,000 psi, with elongation 5%.   **Revere alloy 429** has 95% copper and 5 aluminum.   In hard-drawn condenser tubes it has a tensile strength of 70,000 psi, and elongation 25%.   **Atlas 90,** of Ampco Metal, Inc., contains 10% aluminum, and has a tensile strength of 90,000 psi min.

Additions of iron to aluminum bronze increase the strength, refine the grain and reduce the tendency to self-anneal, and improve forging qualities.   The copper-aluminum-iron alloys are used for cast dies, gears, and strong wear-resistant parts.   They have a hardness up to 325 Brinell. **McGill metal,** of the McGill Mfg. Co., Inc., is the name of a group of these alloys.   A typical analysis is 89% copper, 9 aluminum, and 2 iron. This alloy has a tensile strength up to 90,000 psi, elongation 10 to 20%, and Brinell hardness 160.   It is a casting metal, but can be forged, and it machines about the same as medium-carbon steel.   A casting alloy used for aircraft engine parts, with 10% aluminum and 1 iron, has a tensile strength of 75,000 psi and Brinell hardness 100.   This is **Lumen alloy 11-C,** of the Lumen Bearing Co., and Grade B in Federal specifications, Grade A having more iron and less aluminum.   **Navy bronze 46B-186** has 7 to 9% aluminum and 2.5 to 4.5% iron.   This is **SAE alloy 68,** and has a tensile strength of 80,000 psi.   **Daraloy 437,** of the Darling Valve & Mfg. Co., is a standard Grade A aluminum bronze used for valve stems, facings, and pressure castings.   The tensile strength is 80,000 psi, elongation 18%, and Brinell hardness 90.   **Resistac,** of the American Manganese Bronze Co., has 9% aluminum and 1 iron.   When heat-treated, the tensile strength is 90,000 psi, and Brinell hardness 90.   **Avialite,** a similar composition of the American Brass Co., is used for die-pressed parts and for heat-resistant parts for aircraft engines.   **Atlas 89,** of Ampco Metal, Inc., is also this alloy. **Ampco metal 12** has 8.5 to 9.3% aluminum and 2.5 to

3.25 iron. The annealed metal has a tensile strength of 80,000 psi, elongation 40%, and Brinell hardness 131. **Ampco metal 8** is a wrought metal in sheet and rods. It contains 6.5% aluminum, 2.3 iron, 0.25 tin, 0.25 manganese, nickel, and silver, and the balance copper. The tensile strength is 82,000 psi, elongation 35%, and Brinell hardness 179. A harder bronze is **Ampco Metal 18-22** with 10.3 to 11% aluminum and 3 to 4.25 iron. The tensile strength is 100,000 psi, elongation 6%, and Brinell hardness 223. **Amcoloy 46-40,** of the same company, is an extruded aluminum-iron bronze with tensile strength up to 105,000 psi, elongation 8 to 12%, and hardness 207 to 229. **Superston 40,** of this company, is a high-strength alloy for both casting and rolling. It has 8% aluminum, 12 manganese, 2 nickel, 3 iron, and the balance copper. It has a two-phase structure, and a light gold color. The tensile strength of the cast metal is 98,000 psi with elongation of 26%, and that of the wrought metal is up to 135,000 psi with hardness from 180 to 230 Brinell. **Ambraloy 930,** of the American Brass Co., is a wrought metal with 8% aluminum and 2.5 iron, having a tensile strength of 125,000 psi. The **Tuf-Stuf alloys** of the Mueller Brass Co. have from 1 to 3% iron with 10 to 11 aluminum, but **Tuf-Stuf K** contains 80% copper, 10 aluminum, 2.5 iron, 5 nickel, and 1 manganese.

Nickel is also used in aluminum bronzes, especially in those containing iron. It increases the corrosion resistance and produces dense castings suitable as hydraulic castings, but the alloys require more care in casting. **Auromet 55,** of the Aurora Metal Co., contains 76 to 80% copper, 10 to 12 aluminum, 4 to 6 iron, and 4 to 6 nickel. The wrought metal has a tensile strength of 110,000 psi, elongation 2%, and Brinell hardness 250. Small additions of titanium give strength to the aluminum bronzes and act as a deoxidizer. The bronzes containing manganese are classed with the superbronzes. Lead is sometimes added for bearing bronzes, or for free-cutting casting alloys. It reduces the strength rapidly, and only 1.5% is needed for free cutting, though larger additions may be made to increase frictional qualities. **Atlas 10 bronze,** of Ampco Metals, Inc., has 9% aluminum and 9 lead. The tensile strength is 50,000 psi, and Brinell hardness 55.

Calsun bronze, of the American Brass Co., has 2.5% aluminum and 2 tin. When soft, the tensile strength is 50,000 psi and elongation 30%; when hard-drawn into wire, the tensile strength is 135,000 psi and elongation 4%. **Alloy 712,** of the Bridgeport Brass Co., is a strong resilient wrought alloy used for flat springs, diaphragms, and small tubing for instruments. It is an aluminum-silicon bronze containing 3.5% aluminum, 1 silicon, and the balance copper. Rolled to spring temper it has a tensile strength of 114,000 psi, elongation 3%, and Rockwell B hardness 97. The electrical conductivity is 12% that of copper. When annealed, it has a tensile strength of 65,000 psi with elongation 55%.

ALUMINUM PALMITATE. One of the important metallic soaps. A yellow, massive salt, or a fine white powder of the composition $Al(C_{16}H_{31}O_2)_3 \cdot H_2O$, made by heating a solution of aluminum hydroxide and palmitic acid. It is soluble in oils, alkalies, and benzol, but insoluble in water, and is used in waterproofing fabrics, paper, and leather, and in paints as a drier. In finishing leather and paper it adds to the gloss. It is also used to increase viscosity in lubricating oils. Another material of the same class is **aluminum resinate,** $Al(C_{14}H_{63}O_5)_3$, a brown mass made by heating rosin and aluminum hydroxide. **Aluminum oleate,** $Al(C_{18}H_{33}O_2)_3$, is a white salt of oleic acid used as a drier. **Aluminum stearate,** $Al(C_{18}H_{35}O_2)_3$, is a salt of stearic acid. It is repellent to water and is valued for waterproofing fabrics and as a drier, and in waterproofing concrete and stucco. It is also used to give adherence to dyes, and as a flux in soldering compounds. It is a white fluffy powder of 200 mesh, soluble in oils and in turpentine. Grades high in free fatty acid, up to 22%, do not gel readily and are useful as a flatting agent and suspending medium in paints. Grades low in free fatty acid have a thickening effect on solvents. Those with 5 or 6% are used in lubricating grease, and those with about 8% are used in paints.

ALUMINUM POWDER. Called **aluminum-bronze powder** when alloyed. The flaked powder used for paints is more properly termed **aluminum flake.** Flake powder is made by a stamping process, and used as a pigment in paints and printing inks, in silvering rubber articles, and in plastics. The powder has a high ratio of surface to volume, and the dry powder will ignite easily. All of the grades used for paint contain a major proportion of "very fine," 300 to 400 mesh, with flakes 0.000005 in. thick, and they are revolved in a drum with a lubricant to give luster and also leafing properties to form a metallic surface in the paint by capillary attraction. Aluminum powder burns with an intense heat, but the powder used in calorizing and for pyrotechnics and explosives is not flaked and polished, but consists of particles of spherical shape free from grease. This powder is called **granulated aluminum,** although this designation is also given to larger **aluminum pellets** marketed for metallurgical purposes. Aluminum powder of Union Carbide Corp., used to increase thrust in solid-fuel rockets, has a particle size from 20 to 150 microns. The ultrafine spherical powder of the National Research Corp. has particles smaller than the wavelength of visible light. The average diameter is 0.03 micron, and the maximum diameter is 0.1 micron.   The high surface area gives the powder high reactivity. Aluminum powders of Aluminum Metallurgical Granules, Inc., are in the form of 99.9% pure fine granular powder to 300 mesh or fibrous "whiskers" with more than a million particles per pound. Some aluminum powders not in leafing form are also marketed for paints and enamels where a uniform dispersion rather than a concentrated surface coat of metal is desired.   **Aluminum pigment 584,** of the Metals Disintegrating Co., Inc., is such a powder. **Aluminum grain,** for fast reaction in fuels and incendiaries, consists of irregularly shaped particles in sizes from 0.01 to 0.132 in. Aluminum forgings and extrusions capable of resisting temperatures to 900°F, or 300° higher than unalloyed aluminum, are made by the Aluminum Co. of America by powder metallurgy from unalloyed aluminum powder in which each flake is coated with aluminum oxide.

ALUMINUM-SILICON ALLOY. Many aluminum alloys contain some silicon, but the term aluminum-silicon alloy usually refers to casting alloys with from 5 to 22% silicon.   These high-silicon alloys are characterized by their ease of casting, corrosion resistance, lightness, and ease of welding. They cast well even in thin sections, but the strength decreases and they become more difficult to machine as the silicon increases.   Additions of copper increase the strength and improve the machinability, and also add the property of age-hardening, but decrease corrosion and wear resistance. Slight additions of magnesium also give age-hardening by the formation of Mg_2Si.   The high-silicon alloys also have good thermal conductivity and a low expansion factor, and are used for engine cylinders and pistons. High-silicon casting alloys, such as **aluminum alloy 356,** with 7% silicon and 0.3 magnesium, have large needle-shaped crystals which make the alloy brittle, but adding up to 0.04% sodium refines the crystals and improves the physical properties.

The first high-silicon alloys contained 13% silicon.   The alloy has a specific gravity of 2.64, being lighter than aluminum.   Tensile strength is 24,000 psi and elongation is 5%.   Modification by the addition of a small amount of sodium or lithium increases the tensile strength of the 13% alloy to 32,000 psi, and the elongation to 10%.   **Modified aluminum alloys** were developed in Europe and were covered by patents.   **Alpax,** developed by Aladar Pacz and produced by Light Alloys, Ltd., is a 13% alloy treated with sodium during the casting.   The modified alloys were known in Germany as **Silumin,** and in Italy as **Italsil.**   **Telectal** was a German alloy modified with lithium.   **Wilmil,** of William Mills, Ltd., **Birmasil,** of the Birmingham Aluminium Casting Co., Ltd., and **MVC aluminum alloy,** of Metropolitan-Vickers, were English alloys of this class.

Improvements in alloying and modification now make possible alloys of high silicon content that are machinable. **Hi-Si alloy,** of the Aluminum Co. of America, has 20% silicon. When heat-treated it has a hardness up to 740 Brinell. **Vanasil,** of Gillett & Eaton Plant Div., contains 22% silicon, 2.25 nickel, and 0.10 vanadium. It has a coefficient of expansion about equal to that of cast iron, and is used for pistons.

Aluminum die-casting alloys are usually high in silicon because of the casting qualities. **Alcoa 13,** with 12% silicon, has a tensile strength, die-cast, of 39,000 psi with elongation 2%. A modification of this type of high-silicon alloy is used for forgings. **Alcoa 32S,** for forgings, has 12.2% silicon, 0.9 copper, 1.1 magnesium, and 0.9 nickel. The tensile strength of the heat-treated forging is 55,000 psi, elongation 9%, and Brinell hardness 120. **Alcoa A132,** for permanent-mold castings, has 12% silicon, 1.2 magnesium, 0.8 copper, and 2.5 nickel. The treated castings have a tensile strength of 47,000 psi, elongation 0.5%, and hardness 125. This type of alloy retains its strength well at high temperatures, and for many uses is preferred to the sodium-modified alloys.

Tens-50, of Navan, Inc., used for permanent-mold castings to replace forgings for aircraft pylons, impeller blades, and missile fins, contains 8% silicon, 0.5 magnesium, 0.2 titanium, and 0.3 beryllium. Iron, copper, and zinc are kept at low maximums to avoid embrittlement, and the alloy is treated with 0.04% sodium. The tensile strength is 50,000 psi, yield strength 44,000 psi, and Rockwell hardness E88. **Reynolds alloy 357,** for high-strength castings, has 7% silicon, 0.5 magnesium, and 0.15 titanium, with the iron, copper, manganese, and zinc kept low. Castings with a T6 treatment have a tensile strength of 50,000 psi and elongation of 8%. The two most used die-casting alloys for commercial castings are **ASTM alloy S12B** and **ASTM alloy SC84B.** The first contains 12% silicon, 2 iron, 0.6 copper, 0.5 zinc, 0.35 manganese, 0.1 magnesium, 0.5 nickel, 0.15 tin, and the balance aluminum. The tensile strength is 43,000 psi and elongation 2.5%. The second has less silicon, 8.5%, more copper, about 3.5%, and more zinc, about 1%. It has a tensile strength of 46,000 psi, and it machines more easily.

Alcoa 384 is a 12% silicon die-casting alloy with also 3.8% copper. Its tensile strength is 46,000 psi, and elongation 1%. **Alcoa 360,** a die-casting alloy, has 9.5% silicon with 0.5 magnesium. Tensile strength is 44,000 psi with elongation 3%. **Alcoa 380** has 9% silicon with 3.5 copper. Its tensile strength is 45,000 psi with elongation 2%. **Alcoa 43** is a die-casting alloy with 5% silicon. It has a tensile strength of 30,000 psi with elongation 9%. This alloy in wrought form is widely used for architectural applications. It is similar to **ASTM alloy No. 3** and **Bohnalite S43.** For architectural work it has an attractive white color. **Navy alloy 2** is this material with small additions of other elements.

ALUMINUM STEEL. Any steel containing aluminum as an effective element. Aluminum in small quantities was first used in the Hadfield steels as a deoxidizer and to restrict grain growth by forming dispersed nitrides and oxides. It also increases the strength of the steel, but, if the residual aluminum remaining in the steel is considerable, the steel becomes brittle. Aluminum is much used for deoxidizing steel, but it does not usually remain in the steel. Low-alloy steels containing a small amount of aluminum will develop high strength and hardness when heat-treated, but the steels are normally used only as nitriding steel for casehardening by the nitriding process.

A composition range of **Nitralloy** steel is 0.20 to 0.45% carbon, 0.75 to 1.5 aluminum, 0.9 to 1.8 chromium, 0.4 to 0.70 manganese, 0.15 to 0.60 molybdenum, 0.3 max silicon. Nitralloy is marketed by various steel companies. **Nitrard,** of the Firth-Sterling Steel Co., is also the name of a nitriding steel. Nitralloy steel is used for tools, gages, gears, and shafts. Unlike the soft core of ordinary casehardened steels, it will have a tough core with high hardness. **Nitralloy 135** contains 0.35% carbon, 0.55 manganese, 0.30 silicon, 1.20 copper, 1 aluminum, 0.20 molybdenum, and has a tensile strength, hardened, of 138,000 psi with elongation of 20% and Brinell hardness of 280. **Nitralloy N** is similar but with about 3.5% nickel, higher chromium, and less carbon. It gives a Brinell hardness of 415.

Steels containing aluminum are heat-resistant and are used for engine valves, but at low temperatures they are weak. Small amounts of aluminum may be added to the chromium steels for greater resistance to oxidation at high temperatures. A cast steel, **Circle L18,** of the Lebanon Steel Foundry, contains 7.5% aluminum, 37.5 chromium, and little carbon, but this class of heat-resistant alloy is not usually classed with the steels. **Alumetized steel** is not an alloy steel, but is sheet steel having aluminum sprayed or dipped on the surface and the metal subsequently heated to 1600°F to produce an **iron aluminide** on the surface. But some alumetized steels have a base of alloy steel. **Valve steel,** for automobile intake valves, contains about 2% chromium, 3.75 silicon, 0.30 manganese, and 0.40 carbon, and the steel for exhaust valves has up to 24% chromium, 5 nickel, 3 molybdenum, 1 each of manganese and silicon, and 0.40 carbon. These steels are hot-sprayed with aluminum, and heated to 1450°F to diffuse the aluminum into the surface to give an iron-aluminum compound about 0.001 in. thick which is resistant to hot corrosive gases.

Aluminum-coated steel is made by subjecting the heated steel to the action of a reducing gas and then passing it through an aluminum bath. Coatings up to 0.002 in. thick are made by hot dipping. **Alplate,** of the Reynolds Metals Co., is such a steel. Hot-dip and aluminized steel are now used as replacements for galvanized steel for fence wire and corrugated sheet, and give better resistance to industrial and marine atmospheres than galvanized steel.   **Aluminum-clad wire** for electrical coils is copper wire coated with aluminum to prevent deterioration of the enamel insulation caused by copper oxide.   The wire of the Westinghouse Electric Corp. is made by silver-plating the wire bar to improve adhesion, inserting the bar in a thin-walled aluminum tube, and drawing to size.   The aluminum skin is about 0.0025 in. thick.

Aluminized steel, or alumetized steel, was originally called **calorized steel,** and the **Insuluminum** of the General Electric Co. was a calorized steel used for lead pots and chemical equipment.   The process consists in dip-coating and diffusing the aluminum into the steel at a temperature of about 1600°F to form an aluminum-iron alloy coating.   It is resistant to oxidation and scaling at temperatures to about 1650°F.   The process is now used for wire, sheet, and marine hardware.   Variations in smoothness, brightness, depth, and color can be obtained by varying the aluminum alloy employed for the dip.   Addition of silicon prevents excessive growth of the brittle FeAl alloy.

ALUMINUM-ZINC ALLOY.   An alloy containing a considerable proportion of zinc, although important characteristics may depend upon elements other than zinc.   The casting alloys have found greater use in Europe than in the United States.   Zinc is a hardener of aluminum, but the alloys are likely to be hot-short, to be subject to intercrystalline corrosion unless modified with other elements, and they are more difficult to cast than most other aluminum alloys.   With high zinc they may be brittle.   **Skleron,** a German alloy, contained 12% zinc, 3 copper, 0.6 manganese, 0.25 silicon, and a slight amount of lithium.   **Alneon** contained 7% or more zinc, 2 to 3 copper, and some nickel.   British Engineering Standards alloy **BES 2L5** had 13% zinc and 2.7 copper.   The wrought alloy **Alcoa 72S, aluminum alloy 7072,** with 1% zinc, is used as a coating for Alclad products rather than as a structural material.   The permanent-mold casting alloy **Alcoa A214** has 1.8% zinc and 3.8 magnesium.   Its tensile strength is 27,000 psi, elongation 7%, and Brinell hardness 60.   It is tarnish-resistant, and is used for cast cooking utensils.   **Alcoa 113,** with 1.7% zinc, 2 silicon, and 7 copper, is used to replace some silicon alloys where higher strength is needed.   The tensile strength is 28,000 psi with elongation 2% and hardness 70 Brinell.   Under the newer system of designation the wrought alloys containing zinc as the major ingredient belong to the 7000 series.   **Aluminum alloy 7001** has up to 8% zinc, about 3 copper, 2 magnesium, with small amounts of silicon, iron, manganese, chromium, and titanium.   This alloy has a tensile strength of 37,000 psi with elongation of 17%, and in the T6 temper has a tensile strength of 98,000 psi with elongation of 9%.   **Aluminum alloy 7039,** of the Kaiser

Aluminum and Chemical Corp., for weldable tank plate, has 4% zinc and 2 to 3 magnesium. It has a tensile strength of 60,000 psi. For space-systems applications where corrosion resistance is important, **Alloy X7002,** of the same company, has a composition of 3.5% zinc, 2.5 magnesium, and 0.8 copper.

Tenzaloy, of the American Smelting & Refining Co., has 8% zinc, 0.8 copper, 0.4 magnesium, and 0.1 nickel. This is similar to **ASTM alloy ZC81A.** The castings have good strength and machinability with heat-treatment. The French wrought alloy known as **Zircral** contains 7 to 8.5% zinc, 1.75 to 3 magnesium, 1 to 2 copper, 0.1 to 0.4 chromium, 0.1 to 0.6 manganese, and 0.7 iron and silicon. This alloy is corrosion-resistant and has been used in aircraft construction. The tensile strength of drawn bars is about 80,000 psi, with elongation 9%.

Frontier 40E alloy, of the Frontier Bronze Corp., contains 5.5% zinc, 1 iron, 0.5 magnesium, 0.5 chromium, 0.4 copper, 0.2 titanium, 0.3 manganese, and 0.3 silicon. This is essentially **ASTM alloy ZG61A.** It is corrosion-resistant, has a tensile strength of 35,000 psi, elongation 4%, and Brinell hardness 70 to 80. The wrought structural alloys containing zinc have good strength and working qualities. **Alcoa 75S, aluminum alloy 7075,** of the Aluminum Co. of America, contains 5.1 to 6.1% zinc, 1.2 to 2 copper, 2.1 to 2.9 magnesium, 0.1 to 0.3 manganese, 0.15 to 0.4 chromium, 0.2 max titanium, 0.5 max silicon, and 0.7 max iron. In heat-treated sheet form it has a tensile strength of 77,000 psi, yield strength 67,000 psi, and elongation 12%. **Alcoa X7079** is a development of this alloy for aircraft forgings. It gives greater uniformity of physical properties in heavy sections and increased ductility across the grain. The tensile strength parallel to forging flow lines is 78,000 psi, with elongation of 14%. Corrosion resistance is high.

AMALGAM. A combination of a metal with mercury. The amalgams have the characteristic that when slightly heated they are soft and easily workable, and they become very hard when set. They are used for filling where it is not possible to employ high temperatures. A native **silver amalgam** found in South America contains 26 to 95% silver. Native **gold amalgams** are found in California and Colombia, and contain about 40% gold. Although native amalgams are chemical combinations of the metals, some of the artificial amalgams are alloys and others are compounds. **Dental amalgams** are prepared by mixing mercury with finely divided alloys composed of varying proportions of silver, tin, and copper.

Cadmium amalgam was formerly employed for filling holes in metals and was called **Evans' metallic cement.** It is a silvery-white compound of the composition Cd_5Hg_8, with about 74% mercury, the excess mercury separating out on standing. It softens at about 100°F, and can be kneaded like wax, remaining soft for a considerable time and then becoming hard and crystalline. Tin or bismuth may be added. Amalgams with an excess of cadmium are ductile and can be hammered into sheet. **Bismuth amalgams** are lustrous, very fluid combinations of mercury and bismuth, used for silvering mirrors. They are also added to white bearing metals to make them more plastic, and to fusible alloys to lower the melting point. **Crilley metal** was a self-lubricating bearing alloy containing bismuth amalgam. The binary amalgams of mercury and bismuth are usually too fluid for ordinary use.

The usual quaternary alloy has equal parts of bismuth, mercury, tin, and lead, with the proportion of mercury increased to give greater fluidity. A bismuth amalgam containing bismuth, lead, and mercury was used for lead pencils. A **thallium amalgam,** with 8.5% thallium, which freezes at $-76°F$, is used for thermometers for low readings. **Mackenzie's amalgam** is a two-part amalgam in which each part is a solid but becomes fluid when the parts are ground together in a mortar at ordinary temperatures. One part contains bismuth and mercury, and the other part contains lead and mercury. **Sodium amalgam** contains from 2 to 10% sodium. It is a silvery-white mass which decomposes water and can be used for producing hydrogen. **Potassium amalgam,** made by mixing sodium amalgam with potash, is a true chemical compound, used for amalgamating with other metals.

AMBER. A fossil resin found buried in the countries along the Baltic Sea and in Malagasy. It is employed for making varnishes and lacquers and for ornaments. The original German name for the material was **Glassa,** and in early writings it is referred to by the Greek word **elektron** and the Persian name **karaba.** It was called **vernice** by the Italian painters who used it as a varnish resin. Amber came from a coniferous tree, *Pinus succinifera,* now extinct. It is hard, brittle, tasteless but with an aromatic odor, and dissolves in acids. It is sometimes transparent, but usually semitransparent or opaque with a glossy surface, yellow or orange in color. It takes a fine polish. When rubbed, it becomes electrically charged. Amber contains succinic acid in a complex form, and the finest specimens are known as **succinite,** although this is the name of an amber-colored garnet. The amber of Malagasy was prized for necklaces and pipe mouthpieces. It is semitransparent, wave-streaked, and honey-colored. Synthetic amber is plasticized phenol-formaldehyde or other synthetic resin. **Amberoid** is reclaimed scrap amber pieces compressed into a solid, sometimes mixed with pieces of copal or other resin. It has the same uses as amber. **Amber oil,** distilled from scrap amber, is a mixture of terpenes, and is used in varnish. **Succinic acid,** $(CH_2COOH)_2$, a solid melting at $183°C$, is obtained by distilling scrap amber, but is now made by fermentation of tartaric acid, or synthetically from benzene and called **butane diacid.**   It is used in foods as an acidifier and taste modifier, and **succinic aldehyde** is used for making plastics.   The small, highly polar molecule gives crystalline resins of high strength.   The dioctyl sodium sulfo salt of succinic acid is used in the foodstuffs industry to prevent agglomeration of colloids.   **Complemix,** of American Cyanamid Co., is this material.   **Maleic acid,** $(HCCO_2H)_2$, formed by heating succinic acid, is made commercially from benzene and is used widely for plastics production.   It can be obtained by the dehydration of **malic acid** which is a hydroxy succinic acid.   **Pomalius acid,** of Allied Chemical Corp., is a food grade of malic acid used to replace acetic acid as a more powerful acidulating agent, stabilizer, and flavor enhancer.

AMBERGRIS. A solid, fatty, inflammable substance of grayish to black color found in the intestines of some sperm whales or found floating in the ocean.   It consists of a paste of indigestible matter from the octopus eaten by the whale.   **White amber,** formed by aging in the ocean, is the finest quality.   When dried it pulverizes to a fine dust.   Ambergris has a peculiar sweet fragrance and is highly valued as a fixative in perfumes. In Asia it is used as a spice, and in Egypt for scenting cigarettes.   Lumps weigh from a few ounces up to 600 lb.   Synthetic ambergris, of the Swiss company Firmenick & Co., is a gamma-dihydro ionone, $C_{13}H_{22}O$, which gives the odor, with also **ambreinolide,** a gamma lactone, $C_{17}H_{28}O$, which has fixative power.   **Ambropur** is a German synthetic ambergris.   When the terpene alcohol **manool,** of the wood of the *Dacrydium* trees, is oxidized it yields an acetal which also has the ambergris odor.

AMETHYST. A violet or purple transparent quartz.   The color is due to manganese and iron oxides, and becomes yellow on heating.   It has a density of 2.65, and hardness of 7 Mohs.   Amethyst is composed of alternate right- and left-hand crystals, and breaks with a rippled fracture instead of the conchoidal fracture of ordinary quartz.   The crystals are doubly refractive.   It is used for making pivot bearings for instruments, and for recording needles.   It is the most esteemed of the quartzes for cutting into gemstones, but only deep and uniformly colored stones are used as gems and they are not common.   Any large amethyst of deep and uniform color is likely to be synthetic.   The chief production of natural amethyst is in Brazil and Uruguay.

AMINES. A large group of chemicals derived from ammonia, NH_3, in which one or more of the hydrogen atoms has been replaced by an organic radical.   A **primary amine,** such as **methyl amine,** CH_3NH_2, has one ammonia hydrogen substituted.   It is used in the tanning industry for unhairing skins, and as a catalyst and solvent in the manufacture of synthetic resins.   It is a gas and, like ammonia, is soluble in water and handled in water solution.   It is flammable, a 40% solution having a flash point of 20°F, and the vapors are explosive in air.   A **secondary amine,** dimethyl amine $(CH_3)_2NH$, is more effective for unhairing.   In water solution it forms a hydrate, $(CH_3)_2NH \cdot 7H_2O$, which has a low freezing point, $-16.8°C$.   The **tertiary amine,** trimethyl amine, or **secaline,** $(CH_3)_3N$, is a gas liquefying at 2.87°C.   The methyl amines are used widely as a source of nitrogen.   **Isopropyl amine,** $(CH_3)_2 CNNH_2$, is used as a replacement for ammonia in many chemical processes, and as a solvent for oils, fats, and rubber.   It is a clear liquid of specific gravity 0.686, boiling point 31.9°C, freezing point $-101°C$, and flash point $-15°F$. The **Sipenols,** of Alcolac Chemical Co., are a group of amines used as textile lubricants and softeners.   They are clear to light yellow liquids and are dimethyl ethanol amines or dibutyl ethanol amines.

Changes in characteristics are obtainable in the amines by altering the position of the **amino group,** NH_2, in the carbon chain.   **Hodag Amine 50,** of the Hodag Chemical Corp., is amino ethyl ethanol amine, $HO \cdot CH_2 \cdot CH_2 \cdot NH \cdot CH_2 \cdot CH_2 \cdot NH_2$, a clear liquid with specific gravity of 1.027.   It has both primary and secondary amino groups which give versatility for production of plastics, plasticizers, agricultural chemicals, and textile wetting agents.

Fatty acid amines are used as flotation agents, oil additives to prevent sludge, and rubber-mold release agents.   **Alamine,** of the General Mills Co., is **lauryl amine, palmityl amine,** or other amines of the composition RNH_2, where R is the fatty acid radical.   **Delamin,** of Hercules, Inc., is a series of fatty acid amines produced from tall oil.   The **Armeens,** of Armour & Co., are fatty acid amines with a wide range of uses.

Amino acids have an amino group attached to the carbon atom adjacent to the carboxyl group of an organic acid.   More than 30 natural amino acids have been isolated from proteins.   Proteins are natural **polyamides** of various amino acids linked together by amide groups, also called **peptide linkages.**   An **amide** is formed by replacing the hydroxyl group, OH, of an organic acid by an amino group to form $CONH_2$.   The ease with which even complex radicals can be attached to introduce nitrogen into compounds makes the amines useful for the production of plastics, dyes, pharmaceuticals, explosives, detergents, and other chemicals.

Acetamide, also called **acetic acid amine** and **ethanamide,** is a grayish-white crystalline solid with a melting point of 77 to 81°C, specific gravity 1.139, composition $CH_3 \cdot CO \cdot NH_2$, and slight mousy odor.   It is soluble in water and in alcohol.   It is used as a liquid flux for soldering on painted or oily surfaces, as an antacid in lacquers and explosives, as a softening agent in glues and leather coatings, and as a nonhazing plasticizer in cellulose nitrate and acetate films. Its ability to dissolve starch and dextrine makes it useful in adhesives for waxy papers. With added corrosion inhibitors, it is used as an antifreeze, a 50% solution in water having a freezing point of $-27.5°C$.

AMMONIA. A gas of the formula NH_3, originally called **alkaline air** and **volatile alkali** and later in water solution called **spirits of hartshorn.** It is a by-product in the distillation of coal, but is easily made by passing nitrogen and hydrogen and a catalyst through an electric arc. Ammonia is readily absorbed by water, which at 60°F takes up 683 times its own volume of the gas, forming the liquid commonly called ammonia, but which is **ammonium hydroxide,** a colorless, strongly alkaline, and pungent liquid of the composition NH_4OH with a boiling point of 38°C. At 80°F it contains 29.4% ammonia in stable solution. It is also known as **ammonium hydrate** and **aqua ammonia,** and is used for the saponification of fats and oils, as a deodorant, for cleaning and bleaching, for etching aluminum, and in chemical processing.

Ammonia gas is used in refrigeration, in nitriding steels, and in the manufacture of chemicals. Chlorine unites with it to form **chloramines** which are used as solvents, chlorinating agents, and disinfectants. The gas does not burn in the air, but a mixture of ammonia and oxygen explodes when ignited. **Anhydrous ammonia** is the purified gas liquefied under pressure, marketed in cylinders. At 20°C the liquid has a vapor pressure of 122.1 psi. The anhydrous ammonia used for controlled atmospheres for nitriding steel, bright annealing, and for sintering metals contains 90% NH_3 and is oxygen-free. When disassociated by heat each pound yields 45 cu ft of hydrogen and 11 cu ft of nitrogen.

Smelling salts, sometimes referred to as ammonia, and in solution as **aromatic spirits of ammonia,** is **ammonium carbonate,** $(NH_4)_2CO_3 \cdot H_2O$, forming in colorless or white crystals. It was also called **hartshorn salts.** **Ammonium bicarbonate,** NH_4HCO_3, or **acid ammonium carbonate,** is a water-soluble white crystalline powder used as a source of pure ammonia and carbon dioxide and to decrease density in organic materials by creating voids such as for making foamed rubber and in the food-baking industry. It gasifies completely at 140°F. **Ammonium gluconate,** $NH_4C_6H_{11}O_7$, is a water-soluble white crystalline powder used as an emulsifier for cheese and mayonnaise and as a catalyst in textile printing.

Hydrazine, NH:NH, is a colorless liquid boiling at 113.5°C and freezing at 2°C. It is used as a propellant for rockets, yielding exhaust products of high temperature and low molecular weight. With a nickel catalyst it decomposes to nitrogen and hydrogen. It is a strong reducing agent, and is used in soldering fluxes. Reacted with citric acid it produces the antituberculosis drug **cotinazin,** which is isonicotinic acid hydrazine. It is also used as a blowing agent for foamed rubber, and for the production of plastics. For industrial applications it may be used in the form of **dihydrazine sulfate,** $(N_2H_4)_2 \cdot H_2SO_4$, a white crystalline water-soluble flake decomposing at 180°C and containing 37.5% available hydrazine. **Hydrazine hydrate,** $N_2H_4 \cdot H_2O$, is a colorless, water-miscible liquid boiling at 120.1°C, and freezing at −51.7°C. Hydrazine is made by reacting chlorine and caustic soda and treating with ammonia.

The **ammonium radical,** $-NH_4$, has the chemical reaction of an alkali metal and forms many important chemicals. **Ammonium nitrate** is made by the action of nitric acid on ammonium hydroxide. It is a colorless to white crystalline hygroscopic powder of the composition NH_4NO_3, specific gravity 1.725, melting point 170°C, decomposing at 210°C, and soluble in water, alcohol, and alkalies. It is also used in fertilizers, pyrotechnics, dental gas, insecticides, freezing mixtures, and explosives. For use as a slow-burning propellant for missiles it is mixed with a burning-rate catalyst in a synthetic rubber binder and pressed into blocks. **Riv,** marketed by the Harrison Laboratories as a vapor-phase rust inhibitor, is ammonium nitrate. The British explosive **amatol** is a mixture of ammonium nitrate and TNT, which explodes violently on detonation. The 50–50 mixture can be melted and poured, while the 80–20 mixture is like brown sugar and was used for filling large shells. **Macite,** for tree-trunk blasting, is ammonium nitrate coated with TNT, with a catalyst to make it more sensitive. **Akremite,** of the Maumee Chemical Co., is ammonium nitrate and carbon black, used as an explosive in strip mining.

Ammonium perchlorate is another explosive made by the action of perchloric acid on ammonium hydroxide. It is a white crystalline substance of the composition NH_4ClO_4, specific gravity 1.95, is soluble in water, and decomposes on heating. **Nitrogen trichloride,** NCl_3, which forms in reactions of chlorine and ammonia when there is an excess of chlorine, is a yellow oil of specific gravity 1.653, which is highly explosive. **Ammonium sulfate,** $(NH_4)_2SO_4$, is a gray crystalline water-soluble material obtained in the distillation of coal and used as a fertilizer and for fireproofing.

Ammonium chloride, or **sal ammoniac,** NH_4Cl, is a white crystalline powder of specific gravity 1.52, used in electric batteries, in textile printing, as a soldering flux, and in making other compounds. Many salts and metallic soaps are also formed in the same manner as with the alkali metals. **Ammonium vanadate,** NH_4VO_3, is a white to yellow crystalline powder used as a paint drier, in inks, as a mordant for textiles, and in pottery mixes to produce luster. The specific gravity is 2.326, and it decomposes at 210°C. **Ammonium chromate,** $(NH_4)_2CrO_4$, is a bright-yellow water-soluble granular powder used as a textile mordant, in inks, and for the insolubilization of glues. On boiling, the water solution liberates ammonia. At 180°C the powder decomposes to the dichromate. **Ammonium lactate,** $CH_3CHOHCOONH_4$, is a yellowish syrupy liquid with a slight odor of ammonia, used in leather finishing. **Ammonium stearate** is obtainable as a tan-colored waxlike solid, melting at 74°F. It can be dispersed in hot water, but above 190°F it decomposes to ammonia and stearic acid.

AMYL ALCOHOL. A group of monohydroxy, or simple, alcohols, which are colorless liquids and have the general characteristic of five carbon atoms in the molecular chain. **Normal amyl alcohol,** $CH_3(CH_2)_4OH$, called also **fusel oil, grain oil, pentanol,** and **fermentation amyl alcohol,** has a specific gravity of 0.82 and boiling point of 137°C. It is only slightly soluble in water. It is used as a solvent for oils, resins, and varnishes; in the manufacture of amyl acetate; and in rubber vulcanization. **Secondary amyl alcohol** has a differently arranged molecule, $CH_3CHOH(C_3H_7)$. The specific gravity is 0.82 and flash point 80°F. It is used in the manufacture of secondary amyl acetate for lacquers, and in chemical manufacture. **Tertiary amyl alcohol** has the formula $(CH_3)_2C(OH)C_2H_5$, and a camphorlike odor. The specific gravity is 0.81 and boiling point 102°C. It is highly soluble in water, and soluble in alcohol and ether. It is used as a flavor, and as a plasticizer in paints, varnishes, and cellulose plastics. **Isoamyl alcohol,** or **isobutyl carbinol,** $(CH_3)_2CHCH_2CH_2OH$, has a flash point above 80°F. It is used in pharmaceutical manufacture. **Amyl acetate,** $CH_3COOC_5H_{11}$, called **banana oil** because of its odor of bananas, is an ester made by the action of acetic acid on amyl alcohol. It is a colorless oily liquid of specific gravity 0.896 and boiling point 141°C. It is insoluble in water but soluble in alcohol. It is a good solvent and plasticizer for cellulose plastics, and is used in cellulose lacquers and adhesives. It is also used in linoleum and oilcloth, and as a banana flavor.

ANILINE. Also known as **aminobenzene, phenylamine, aminophen,** and **aniline oil** and, when first made, **krystallin** and **kyanol.** A yellowish, oily liquid of the composition $C_6H_5 \cdot NH_2$, boiling at 184.4°C, freezing at -6.2°C, and soluble in alcohol, benzene, and hydrochloric acid. The specific gravity is 1.022. It turns brown in the air, finally oxidizing into a resin. The vapor is toxic, and it is poisonous in contact with the skin, requiring protective handling. Its largest uses are in the making of dyes and rubber chemicals, but it is also used for the production of plastics, drugs, explosives, perfumes, and flavors. With nitric acid as an oxidizer it has been used as a rocket fuel. **Aniline salt** is **aniline hydrochloride,** $C_6H_5NH_2HCl$, coming in white crystalline plates of specific gravity 1.2215, melting at 198°C and soluble in alcohol.

ANNATTO. One of the chief **food colors.** It is a salmon-colored dye made from the pulp of the seeds of the tree *Bixa orellana* of the West Indies and tropical America and Africa. It contains **bixin,** $C_{25}H_{30}O_4$, a dark-red crystalline carotenoid carboxylic acid, and also **bixol,** $C_{18}H_{30}O$, a dark-green oily alcohol. It is more stable than carotene and has more coloring power. Annatto is sometimes called **bixine,** and in West Africa it is called **rocou.** It is soluble in oils and in alcohol. **Annatto paste** is used as a food color especially for butter, cheese, and margarine, but has a tendency to give a slightly mustardy flavor unless purified. It is also used as a stain for wood and silk. Water-soluble colors are made by alkaline extraction, giving orange to red shades. For coloring margarine yellow a blend of annatto and turmeric may be used. **Anattene,** of S. B. Penick & Co., is a microcrystalline powder produced from annatto, giving a range of colors from light yellow to deep orange. It comes either oil-soluble or water-soluble.

A substitute for annatto for coloring butter and margarine, having the advantage that it is rich in vitamin A, is **carrot oil** obtained from the common carrot. The concentrated oil has a golden-yellow color and is odorless and tasteless. **Carex** is a name for carrot oil in cottonseed oil solution used for coloring foods. Many of the fat-soluble coloring matters found in plant and animal products are terpenes that derive their colors from conjugated double bonds in the molecule. The yellow **carotene** of carrots and the red **lycopene** of tomatoes both have the formula $C_{40}H_{56}$, and are tetra terpenes containing 8 isoprene units but with different molecular structures. **Beta carotene,** produced synthetically from acetone by Hoffmann-La Roche, is identical with the natural food color. Any colors used commercially for products for human consumption in the United States must be approved by the Food and Drug Administration and are known as **certified colors.** They are in three classes: those used for foods, drug and cosmetic colors, and those for external application only in drugs and cosmetics. They must have no toxic effects in the quantities used. In general, the quantities used are small; $1/4$ lb of color will color 100 lb of confectionery or 12,000 bottles of soft drink.

A beautiful water-soluble yellow dye used to color foods and medicines is **saffron,** extracted from the dried flowers and tips of the saffron crocus, *Crocus sativas,* of Europe, India, and China. It is expensive, as about 4,000 flowers are required to supply an ounce of the dye. Saffron contains **crocin,** $C_{44}H_{70}O_{28}$, a bright-red powder soluble in alcohol. Both red and yellow colors are obtained from the orange thistlelike heads of the safflower, which are dried and pressed into cakes.

ANODE METALS. Metals used for the positive terminals in electroplating. They provide in whole or in part the source of the metal to be plated, and they are as pure as is commercially possible, uniform in texture and composition, and have the skin removed by machining.   They may be either cast or rolled, with the manufacture controlled to obtain a uniform grade and to exclude impurities, so that the anode will corrode uniformly in the plating bath and will not polarize to form slimes or crusts.   In some plating, as for white bronze, the anode efficiency is much higher than the cathode efficiency, and a percentage of steel anodes is inserted to obtain a solution balance.   In other cases, as in chrominum plating, the metal is taken entirely from the solution, and insoluble anodes are employed. Chromium-plating anodes may be lead-antimony, with 6% antimony, or tin-lead, with 7% tin.   In addition to pure single metals, various alloys are marketed in anode form.   The usual brass is 80% copper and 20 zinc, but other compositions are used, some containing 1 to 2% tin.   **Brass anodes** are called **platers' brass.   Abaloy anodes,** of the Hanson-Van Winkle-Munning Co., for silvery-white plating, are of copper, tin, and zinc.   **Nickelex,** used in England as a plating undercoat for aluminum, contains 90% copper and 10 tin.   **Copper anodes** for metal plating are usually hot-rolled oval-shaped bars, 99.9% pure, while those for electro-type deposits may be hot-rolled plates, electrodeposited plates, or cast plates.   The **copper ball anodes** of the Udylite Corp. are forged instead of cast to give a finer and more even grain.   **Zinc anodes** are 99.99% pure.   **Nickel anodes** are 99+% rolled or cast in iron molds, or 97% sand-cast.   **Bright nickel** anodes may have 1% or more of cobalt.   **Lead anodes** have low current-carrying capacity, and may be made with a saw-tooth or multiple-angled surface and ribs to provide more area and give greater throwing power.   Anodes of other metals are also made with sections gear-shaped, fluted, or barrel-shaped to give greater surface area and higher efficiency.   **Rhodium anodes** are made in expanded-mesh form.   **Platinum anodes,** also made in mesh form, have the platinum clad on tantalum wire.   Special anode metals are marketed under trade names, usually accenting the color, hardness, and corrosion resistance of the deposited plate.

ANTHRACITE.   Also called **hard coal.**   A variety of mineral coal found in Wales, France, and Germany, but in greatest abundance in an area of about 500 sq mi in northeastern Pennsylvania.   It is distinguished by its semimetallic luster, high carbon content, and high specific gravity, which is about 1.70.   The carbon content may be as high as 95%, but the usual fixed carbon content is from 78 to 84%.   It should give 13,200 Btu per lb.   In theory the best grades of anthracite should have 90% carbon, 3 to 4.5 hydrogen, 2 to 5.5 oxygen and nitrogen, and only 1.7 ash.   Anthracite, when pure and dry, burns without smoke or smell, and is thus preferred to bituminous coal for household furnaces.   But the coal will absorb a high proportion of water, and commercial coal may be wetted down to add to the weight, thus lessening its efficiency. Hard coal is graded as anthracite and **semianthracite,** depending upon the ratio of fixed carbon to volatile matter. When the ratio is 10:1, it is anthracite.

The commercial gradings of anthracite are chiefly by size, varying from three sizes of very fine grains called silt, rice, and buckwheat, to the large size of furnace, or lump, coal. Standard ASTM sizes for anthracite are: broken, $4\frac{3}{8}$ to $3\frac{1}{4}$ in.; egg, $3\frac{1}{4}$ to $2\frac{7}{16}$ in.; stove, $2\frac{7}{16}$ to $1\frac{5}{8}$ in.; chestnut, $1\frac{5}{8}$ to $1\frac{3}{16}$ in.; pea, $1\frac{3}{16}$ to $\frac{9}{16}$ in.; No. 1 buckwheat, $\frac{9}{16}$ to $\frac{5}{16}$ in.; No. 2 buckwheat (rice), $\frac{5}{16}$ to $\frac{3}{16}$ in.; No. 3 buckwheat (barley), $\frac{3}{16}$ to $\frac{3}{32}$ in. As the coal comes from the breaker, the proportions are about 8% silt, 9 rice, 15 buckwheat, 10 pea, 24 chestnut, 23 stove, and 8 egg. **Artificial anthracite,** used extensively in Europe, is briquetted coals with a waterproof coating. It burns uniformly.

ANTIFREEZE COMPOUNDS. Materials employed in the cooling systems and radiators of internal-combustion engines to ensure a liquid circulating medium at low temperatures to prevent damage from the formation of ice. The requirements are that the compound must give a freezing point below that likely to be encountered without lowering the boiling point much below that of water, that it must not corrode the metals or deteriorate rubber connections, that it must be stable up to the boiling point, and that it must be readily obtainable commercially. Calcium chloride was early used for automobile radiators but corroded the metals. It is still used in fire tanks, sodium chromate being added to retard corrosion. Oils were also used, but the high boiling points permitted overheating of the engine, and the oils softened the rubber. Denatured ethyl alcohol may be used, but methanol is less corrosive and less expensive. A 30% solution of ethyl alcohol in water has a freezing point of about 5°F, and a 50% solution freezes at −24°F. Alcohol, however, must be renewed frequently because of loss by evaporation.

Glycerol is also used as an antifreeze, a 40% solution in water lowering the freezing point to about 0°F, and a 50% solution to −15°F. It has the disadvantage of high viscosity, requiring forced circulation at low temperatures, but it does not evaporate easily. Ethylene glycol lowers the freezing point to a greater extent than alcohol and has a high boiling point so that it is not lost by evaporation, but it has a higher first cost and will soften ordinary natural rubber connections. Acetamide in water solution may also be used as an antifreeze. Antifreezes are sold under various trade names. **Zerone,** of Du Pont, has a methanol base, while **Zerex** has a base of ethylene glycol. **Prestone,** marketed by the Union Carbide Corp., is ethylene glycol antifreeze. **Pyro** is an antifreeze of the U.S. Industrial Chemicals, Inc., with a low freezing point. **Ramp,** of the

Antara Chemical Co., is ethylene glycol with anticorrosion and antifoam agents added.   **Antifreeze PFA55MB,** of the Phillips Petroleum Co., used in jet-engine fuels, is ethylene glycol monoethyl ether with 10% glycerine. **Dowtherm 209,** of Dow Chemical Co., is an antifreeze material of inhibited methoxy propanol which boils off without forming gum.

ANTIMONIAL LEAD. An alloy containing up to 25% antimony with the balance lead, used for storage-battery plates, type metal, bullets, tank linings, pipes, cable coverings, bearing metals, roofing, collapsible tubes, toys, and small cast articles.   The alloy is produced directly in the refining of some lead ores, but much is also made by adding antimony to soft lead. The alloy is also known as **hard lead,** and in England is called **regulus metal.**   Much of the lead used in the United States is in the form of antimonial lead.   The antimony hardens the lead and increases the tensile strength.   The usual alloy contains 4 to 8% antimony and has about twice the tensile strength of pure lead.   Up to about 0.10% arsenic stabilizes and hardens the alloy, and from 0.25 to 1% tin may be added to improve the casting properties.   Antimonial lead, of the National Lead Co., for chemical linings contains 6 to 8% antimony, weighs 0.398 lb per cu in., and melts at 475 to 555°F.   An antimonial lead with 6% antimony has a tensile strength of 4,100 psi with elongation of 47%, as rolled.   After heat-treatment at 235°C and aging one day, the tensile strength is 12,600 psi with elongation of 3%.

A hard lead with 10% antimony and 90% lead has a tensile strength of 8,800 psi, elongation 17%, Brinell hardness 17, and melting point 486°F.   **Cable lead,** or **sheathing lead,** used to cover telephone and power cables to protect against moisture and mechanical injury, contains about 1% antimony.   The alloy for collapsible tubes usually contains 2% antimony.   Antimonial lead may be used for machine bearings, but for this purpose it usually contains considerable tin and is classed with the babbitt metals.   **Hoyt metal,** used for bearings, contains 6 to 10% antimony. Alloys containing from 70 to 90% lead, 5 to 20 antimony, and 2 to 20 tin have been used for railway-car bearings under the name of **lining metal.**   **Dandelion metal,** used for locomotive crosshead linings, had 72% lead, 18 antimony, and 10 tin.

ANTIMONY. A bluish-white metal, symbol Sb, having a crystalline scalelike structure.   It is brittle and easily reduced to powder.   It is neither malleable nor ductile and is used only in alloys or in its chemical compounds.   Like arsenic and bismuth, it is sometimes referred to as a **metalloid,** but in mineralogy it is called a **semimetal.**   It does not have the free cloudlike electrons that occur in metal atoms, and thus it lacks plasticity and is a poor conductor of electricity.   In the semimetals each atom is more strongly bonded to three neighboring atoms than to the other three, and the structure is in sheets of atoms with a weakly bonded cleavage between the sheets. The chief uses of antimony are in alloys, particularly for hardening lead-base alloys. The specific gravity of the metal is 6.62, melting point 824°F, and Brinell hardness 55. It burns with a bluish light when heated to redness in the air. Antimony imparts hardness and a smooth surface to soft-metal alloys, and alloys containing antimony expand on cooling, thus reproducing the fine details of the mold. This property makes it valuable for type metals. When alloyed with lead, tin, and copper it forms the babbitt metals used for machinery bearings. It is also much used in white alloys for pewter utensils. Its compounds are used widely for pigments. **Antimony red** is the common name of **antimony trisulfide,** Sb_2S_3, also known as **antimony sulfide** and **antimony sulfuret,** found in the mineral stibnite, but produced by precipitation from solutions of antimony salts. It comes in orange-red crystals with a specific gravity of 4.56 and melting point 546°C. It is used as a paint pigment, for coloring red rubber and in safety matches. **Antimony pentasulfide,** Sb_2S_5, an orange-yellow powder, was once used for vulcanizing rubber, and it colored the rubber red. It breaks down when heated, yielding sulfur and the red pigment antimony trisulfide.

ANTIMONY ORES. The chief ore of the metal antimony is **stibnite,** an impure form of antimony trisulfide, Sb_2S_3, containing theoretically 71.4% antimony. The usual content of the ore is 45 to 60%, which is concentrated to an average of 92% for shipment as matte. Sometimes gold or silver is contained in the ore. Stibnite occurs in slender prismatic crystals of a metallic luster and lead-gray color with a hardness of 2 Mohs. The metal is obtained by melting the stibnite with iron, forming FeS and liberating the antimony, or by roasting the ore to produce the oxide which is then reduced with carbon. For pyrotechnic uses stibnite is liquated by melting the mineral and drawing off the metal which on cooling and solidifying is ground. Stibnite comes from China, Mexico, Japan, Germany, Bolivia, Alaska, and the western United States.

Senarmorite, found in Mexico, Nevada, and Montana, is **antimony oxide,** Sb_2O_3, occurring in cubic crystals with a yellow color. The specific gravity is 5.2, hardness 2.5, and theoretical metal content 83.3%. **Valentinite,** also found in the same localities, has the same theoretical formula and antimony content as senarmorite, but has a rhombic crystal structure, a hardness of 3, and a specific gravity of 5.5. These oxides are used as opacifiers in ceramic enamels. **Cervantite,** found in Mexico, Nevada, and Montana, is **antimony tetraoxide,** Sb_2O_4. It has a grayish-yellow color, specific gravity of 5, and hardness of 4.5, and it contains theoretically 79.2% antimony. **Stibiconite,** from the same area, is a massive pale-yellow mineral, $Sb_2O_4 \cdot H_2O$, with a specific gravity 5.1, hardness 4.5, and antimony content 71.8%.

Kermesite, known as **red antimony,** or **antimony blend,** found in Mexico and Italy, is a mineral resulting from the partial oxidation of stibnite. The composition is Sb_2S_2O, and when pure it contains 75% antimony and 20 sulfur.   It occurs in hairlike tufts, or radiating fibers of a dark-red color and metallic luster, with hardness 1.5 and specific gravity 4.5.   Another sulfide ore of antimony is **jamesonite,** $Pb_2Sb_2S_5$, found in Mexico and the western United States.   It has a dark-gray color, specific gravity 5.5, hardness 2.5, and contains 20% antimony.   When the ore is silver-bearing, it can be worked profitably for antimony.   **Stephanite** is classed as an ore of silver, but yields antimony.   It is a **silver sulfantimonite,** Ag_5SbS_4, containing 68.5% silver and 15.2 antimony.   It occurs massive or in grains of an iron-black color with a hardness of 2 to 2.5 and specific gravity 6.2 to 6.3.   It is found in Nevada, Mexico, Peru, Chile, and central Europe.   Much antimony is in lead ores and is left in the lead as hard lead.   Antimony is marketed in flat cakes or in broken lumps.   The highest grade of pure refined antimony is known as **star antimony** because of the glittering spangled appearance on the surface, but starring can be done with lower grades of antimony by special cooling of the ingots. **Crude antimony** is not antimony metal, but is beneficiated ore, or ore matte, containing 90% or more of metal.   High-grade antimony is +99.8% pure, Standard grade is 99 to 99.8% pure, and Chinese is 99% pure.

ANTIOXIDANT. A material used to retard oxidation and deterioration of vegetable and animal fats and oils, rubber, or other organic products. Antioxidants embrace a wide variety of materials but in general for antioxidant activity the hydroxy groups must be substituted directly in an aromatic nucleus.   In the phenol group of antioxidants the hydrogen atoms must be free.   In the naphthol group the alpha compound is a powerful antioxidant.   Usually, only minute quantities of antioxidants are used to obtain the effect.   **Ionol,** an antioxidant, or **oxidation inhibitor,** of the Shell Chemical Co., is a complex butyl methyl phenol used in gasoline, oils, soaps, rubber, and plastics.   It is an odorless, tasteless, nonstaining granular powder, insoluble in water, melting at 70°C.   In gasoline the purpose of an antioxidant is to stabilize the diolefins that form gums.   **Norconidendrin,** an antioxidant for fats and oils, is produced from the high-phenol **confidendrin,** obtained from hemlock pulp liquor.   The **Tenox antioxidants,** of Eastman Chemical Co., used for meats and poultry, are mixtures of butyl hydroxy anisole, butyl hydroxy toluene, propyl gallate, and citric acid, in solution in corn oil, glyceryl mono-oleate, or propylene glycol.   **Tenox 2** contains 20% BHA, 6 propyl gallate, 4 citric acid, and 70 propylene glycol.   **Tenox 4** contains 20% BHA, 20 BHT, and 60 corn oil.

Tenox HQ, used to prevent rancidity in margarine, dried milk, and cooking fats, is a purified hydroquinone.   **Tenamene,** of the same company, used in rubber, is a complex phenylene diamene.   Most of the antioxidants for rubber and plastics are either phenols or aromatic amines.

A **synergist** may be used with an antioxidant for regeneration by yielding hydrogen to the antioxidant.   Synergists are acids such as citric or maleic, or they may be ferrocyanides.   The presence of small quantities of metallic impurities in oils and fats may deactivate the antioxidants and nullify their effect.   **Phytic acid** is not only an antioxdant for oils and foodstuffs, but it also controls the metallic contaminations. It does not break down as citric acid does or impart a taste to edible oils as phosphoric acid does.   It occurs in the bran of seeds as the salt **phytin,** $CaMg(C_2H_6P_2O_9)_2$, and is obtained commercially from corn steep liquor. Chemicals used to control metallic ions and stabilize the solutions are called **sequestering agents.   Pasac,** of the Sanders Chemical Co., is such an agent. It is **potassium acid saccharate,** $KHC_6H_8O_8$, in the form of a water-soluble white powder.   **Sequelene,** of the A. E. Staley Mfg. Co., for treating hard and rusty waters, is a **sodium glucoheptonate.**

Since odor is a major component of flavor, and the development of unpleasant odors in edible fats arises from oxidation, the use of antioxidants is generally necessary, and in such use they are called **food stabilizers.**   But degradation of some organic materials may not be a simple oxidation process.   In polyvinyl chloride plastics the initial stage of heat degradation is a dihydro chlorination with hydrogen chloride split out of the molecular chain to give a conjugated system subject to oxidation. Materials called **stabilizers** are thus used to prevent the initial release. Traces of iron and copper in vegetable oils promote rancidity, and citric acid is used as a stabilizer in food oils to suppress this action.   **Densitol,** of Abbott Laboratories, for stabilizing citrus-fruit beverage syrups, is a brominated sesame oil.   It also enhances the flavor, although it has no taste.

Light stabilizers may be merely materials such as carbon black to screen out the ultraviolet rays of light.   Most commercial antioxidants for foodstuffs are mixtures, and all the mixtures are synergistic with the total antioxidant effect greater than the sum of the components.   **Sustane 3,** of the UOP Chemical Co., is a mixture of butylated hydroxy anisole, propyl gallate, citric acid, and propylane glycol.   **Inhibitors** for controlling color in the chemical processing of fats and oils are usually organic phosphates, such as the liquids **tri-iso-octyl phosphate** and **chloro ethyl phosphate.**   They are mild reducing agents and acid acceptors, and they complex with the metal salts.   **Ultraviolet absorbers,** to prevent yellowing and deterioration of plastics and other organic materials, are substituted hydroxy benzo phenones.   The photons of the invisible ultraviolet rays of sunlight have great energy and attack organic materials photochemically.   Ultraviolet absorbers are stable in this light and absorb the invisible rays.   **Antirads** are antioxidants that increase the resistance of rubber or plastics to deterioration by gamma rays.   Such rays may break the valence bonds and soften a rubber, or cross-link the chains and harden the rubber.

The term **corrosion inhibitors** usually refers to materials used to prevent or retard the oxidation of metals.   They may be elements alloyed with the metal, such as columbium or titanium incorporated in stainless steels to stabilize the carbon and retard intergranular corrosion, or they may be materials applied to the metal to retard oxygen attack from the air or from moisture.   Many paint undercoats, especially the phosphate and chromate coatings applied to steel, are corrosion inhibitors.   They may contain a ferrocyanide synergist.   **Propargyl alcohol,** C_2H_4CO, a liquid boiling at 115°C, is used in strong mineral acid pickling baths to prevent hydrogen embrittlement and corrosion of steel.   **VPI 260,** of the Shell Chemical Co., is dicyclohexyl amine nitrite, a white crystalline powder which sublimes to form a shield on steel or aluminum to passivate the metal and make it resistant to moisture corrosion.   VPI means **vapor-phase inhibitor.**   **VPI paper** is wrapping paper impregnated with the nitrite, used for packaging steel articles.

ANTISLIP METALS. Metals with abrasive grains cast or rolled into them, used for floor plates, stair treads, and car steps.   They may be of any metal, but are usually iron, bronze, or aluminum.   The abrasive may be sand, but it is more usually a hard and high-melting-point material such as aluminum oxide.   In standard cast forms antislip metals are marketed under trade names.   **Alumalun** is the name of an aluminum alloy cast with abrasive grains, made by the American Abrasive Metals Co.   **Bronzalum** is a similar product made of bronze.   The **Algrip steel** of the Alan Wood Steel Co. is steel plate $\frac{1}{8}$ to $\frac{3}{8}$ in. thick, with abrasive grains rolled into one face.   It is used for loading platforms and ramps.

ANTLER. The bony, deciduous horns of animals of the deer family, used for making handles for knives and other articles but now replaced commercially by plastic moldings.   Antlers are true outgrowths of bone, and are not simply hardenings of tissue as are the horns of other animals.   Unlike horn, antlers are solid, and have curiously marked surfaces.   They are of various shapes and sizes, and are usually found on the male during the mating season, although both sexes of reindeer and American caribou possess them.   They grow in from 3 to 4 months, and are shed annually.

ARGENTITE. An important ore of silver, also called **silver glance.**   It has the composition Ag_2S, containing theoretically 87.1% silver.   It usually occurs massive, streaked black and lead gray, with a metallic luster and a hardness of 2 to 2.5. It is found in Nevada, Arizona, Mexico, South America, and Europe. **Argyrodite** is another silver ore found in Bolivia, and is a source of the rare metal germanium. When pure, it has the composition $4Ag_2S \cdot GeS_2$, and contains 5 to 7% germanium. A similar mineral, **canfieldite,** found in Bolivia, has 1.82% germanium and some tin.

ARGOLS. Also called **wine lees.** A reddish crust or sediment deposited from wine, employed for the production of tartaric acid, cream of tartar, and rochelle salts. It is crude **potassium acid tartrate, or cream of tartar,** $KH(C_4H_4O_6)$. When grape fermentation is complete, the wine is drawn off and placed in storage tanks where the **lees** settle out. The amount of tartrate varies in different types of wine, from 0.1 to 1.0 lb of cream of tartar per gallon. From wines clarified by refrigeration, as much as 1 to 3 lb per gal of tartrate crystallizes out. Cream of tartar is also obtained from **grape pomace,** which is the residue skins, seeds, and pulp, containing 1 to 5% tartrate. **Wine stone** is cream of tartar, 70 to 90% pure, which crystallizes on the walls of wine storage tanks. Purified cream of tartar is a colorless to white crystalline powder of specific gravity 1.956, soluble in water, and used in baking powders.

Tartaric acid is a colorless crystalline product of the composition $HOOC(CHOH)_2COOH$, which has a melting point of 170°C and is soluble in water and in alcohol. It has a wide variety of uses in pharmaceuticals, in effervescent beverages, and as a mordant in dyeing. The pods of the tamarind tree, *Tamarindus indica,* of India, contain 12% tartaric acid and 30 sugars. They are used in medicine and for beverages under the name of **tamarind. Rochelle salts** is **potassium sodium tartrate,** $KNa(C_4H_4O_6) \cdot 4H_2O$, a colorless to bluish-white crystalline solid of specific gravity 1.79 and melting point 75°C, which is soluble in water and in alcohol. It is used in medicines and in silvering mirrors. Like quartz, it is doubly refractive, and is used in piezoelectric devices where the water solubility is not a disadvantage.

ARSENIC. A soft, brittle, poisonous element of steel-gray color and metallic luster, symbol As. The melting point is 850°C, and specific gravity 4.8. In atomic structure it is a semimetal, lacking plasticity, and is used only in alloys and in compounds. When heated in the air, it burns to **arsenious anhydride** with white odorous fumes. The bulk of the arsenic used is employed in insecticides, rat poisons, and weed killers, but it has many industrial uses, especially in pigments. It is also used in poison gases for chemical warfare. The white, poisonous powder commonly called arsenic is **arsenic trioxide, or arsenious oxide,** As_2O_3, also known as **white arsenic.**   When marketed commercially, it is colored pink to designate it as a poison.   White arsenic is marketed as Refined, $+99\%$ pure, High-grade, 95 to 99%, and Low-grade, -95%.   Arsenic is added to antimonial lead alloys and white bearing metals for hardening and to increase fluidity, and to copper to increase the annealing temperature for such uses as radiators.   It is also used in lead shot to diminish cohesion, and small amounts are used as negative electron carriers in rectifier crystals.

Arsenic acid is a white crystalline solid of the composition $(H_3AsO_4)_2 \cdot$ H_2O, produced by the oxidation of white arsenic with nitric and hydrochloric acids.   It is soluble in water and in alcohol, has a specific gravity of 2 to 2.5, and a melting point of 35.5°C.   Arsenic acid is sold in various grades, usually 75% pure, and is used in glass manufacture, in printing textiles, and in insecticides.   The **arsines** comprise a large group of alkyl compounds of arsenic.   They are **arsenic hydrides,** AsH_3, a colorless gas.   The primary, secondary, and tertiary arsines are not basic but the hydroxides are strongly basic.   The arsines are easily oxidized to **arsonic acid,** $RAsO_3H_2$, and related acids.   **Arsenic disulfide,** also known as **ruby arsenic, red arsenic glass,** and **red orpiment,** is an orange-red, poisonous powder with specific gravity 3.5, and melting point 307°C, obtained by roasting arsenopyrite and iron pyrites.   The composition is As_2S_2.   It is employed in fireworks, as a paint pigment, and in the leather and textile industries.   Another arsenic sulfur compound used as a pigment is **orpiment,** found as a natural mineral in Utah, Peru, and central Europe. It is an **arsenic trisulfide,** As_2S_3, containing 39% sulfur and 61 arsenic. The mineral has a foliated structure, a lemon-yellow color, and a resinous luster.   The specific gravity is 3.4, hardness 1.5 to 2, and melting point 300°C.   Artificial arsenic sulfide is now largely substituted for orpiment, and is referred to as **king's yellow.**

ARSENIC ORES. Arsenopyrite, also called **mispickel,** is the most common ore of arsenic.   It is used also as a source of white arsenic, and directly in pigments and as a hide preservative.   The composition is FeAsS.   It occurs in crystals or massive, of a silvery-white to gray-black color and a metallic luster.   The specific gravity is 6.2 and hardness 5.5 to 6.   Arsenic is usually not a primary product from ores, but is obtained as a by-product in the smelting of copper, lead, and gold ores.   A source of white arsenic is the copper ore **enargite,** $Cu_2S \cdot 4CuS \cdot As_2S_3$, containing theoretically 48.3% copper and 19.1 arsenic.   It occurs in massive form with a hardness of 3 and specific gravity of 4.45, and is gray, with a pinkish variety known as **luzonite.**   The mineral is commonly intertwined with **tennantite,** $5Cu_2S \cdot 2(CuFe)S \cdot 2As_2S_3$, a mineral of a gray to greenish color.   **Realgar,** known also as **ruby sulfur,** is a red or orange arsenic disulfide, As_2S_2, occurring with ores of lead and silver in monoclinic crystals. The hardness is 1.5 and specific gravity 3.55. It is used as a pigment. Another ore is **smaltite,** or **cobalt pyrites,** $CoAs_2$, occurring in gray masses of specific gravity 6.5 and hardness 5.5. It occurs with ores of nickel and copper. It may have nickel and iron replacing part of the cobalt, and is a source of cobalt, containing theoretically 28.1% cobalt.

ASBESTOS. A general name for several varieties of fibrous minerals, the fibers of which are valued for their heat-resistant and chemical-resistant properties, and are made into fabrics, paper, insulating boards, and insulating cements. The long fibers are used for weaving into fire-proof garments, curtains, shields, and brake linings. The short fibers are compressed with binders into various forms of insulating boards, shingles, pipe coverings, paper, and molded products. The original source of asbestos was the mineral actinolite, but the variety of **serpentine** known as chrysotile now furnishes most of the commercial asbestos. **Actinolite** and **tremolite,** which furnish some of the asbestos, belong to a great group of widely distributed minerals known as **amphiboles** which are chiefly metasilicates of calcium and magnesium, with iron sometimes replacing part of the magnesium. They occur granular, in crystals, compact such as **nephrite** which is the jade of the Orient, or in silky fibers as in the iron amphibole asbestos mined in the United States. This latter type is more resistant to heat than chrysotile. Its color varies from white to green and black.

Jade occurs as a solid rock and is highly valued for making ornamental objects. Jade quarries have been worked in Khotan and Upper Burma for many centuries, and large pebbles are also obtained by divers in the Khotan River. The most highly prized in China was white speckled with red and green and veined with gold. The most valued of the **Burma jade** is a grass-green variety called **Ayah kyauk.** Most jade is emerald green, but some is white and others are yellow, vermilion, and deep blue. This form of the mineral is not fibrous.

The molecular structure of asbestos determines the nature of the fibers. Asbestos is a hydrated metal silicate with the metal and hydroxyl groups serving as lateral connectors of the molecular chain to form long crystals which are the fibers. The formula for **chrysotile** is given as $Mg_6Si_4O_{11}$ $(OH)_6 \cdot H_2O$. Each silicon atom in the Si_4O_{11} chain is enclosed by a tetrahedron of four oxygen atoms so that two oxygen atoms are shared by adjacent tetrahedra to form an endless chain. When the crystal orientation is perfect, the fibers are long and silky and of uniform diameter with high strength. When the orientation is imperfect, the Si_4O_{11} chain is not parallel to the fiber axis and the fibers are uneven and harsh. In chrysotile the metal connector is magnesium with or without iron, but there are at least 30 other different types of asbestos.

Chrysotile is highly fibrous, and is the type most used for textiles.   The fiber is long and silky, and the tensile strength is from 80,000 to 200,000 psi.   The color is white, amber, gray, or greenish.   The melting point is 2770°F.   The fibers from different mines vary in diameter and flexibility, but the very thin flexible ones can be separated out readily for weaving into light fabrics.   Chrysotile is mined chiefly in Vermont, California, Quebec, Arizona, Turkey, and Rhodesia.   Only about 8% of the total mined is long spinning fiber, the remainder being too short for fabrics or rope.   The Turkish fiber is up to $3/4$ in. in length.   Asbestos produced in Quebec is chrysotile occurring in serpentized rock in veins $1/4$ to $1/2$ in. wide, though veins as wide as 5 in. occur.   The fibers run crosswise of the vein, and the width of vein determines the length of fiber. **Calidria asbestos,** of Union Carbide Corp., is short-fiber chrysotile from California marketed as fibrils or pellets for use as a reinforcing agent in plastic laminates, thickening agent, and opacifier in coatings and adhesives. Chrysotile fiber has about 14% water of crystallization. At temperatures near 1800°F, it loses its water, and the dehydration has a cooling effect. Thus **chrysotile felt** is used as a heat sink in missile and space construction laminates.

Blue asbestos, from South Africa, is the mineral **crocidolite,** $NaFe(SiO_3)_2 \cdot FeSiO_2$. The fiber has high tensile strength, averaging .600,000 psi, is heat-resistant to 1200°F, and is resistant to most chemicals. The fibers are $1/8$ to 3 in. long with diameters from 0.06 to 0.1 in.   It is compatible with polyester, phenolic, and epoxy resins, and is available in all standard forms for reinforcement of plastics and insulating uses. A molding powder is made by mixing the fibers with epoxy and, after partial curing, grinding the mixture to a free-flowing powder.   **Form Pack 2,** of Devcon Corp., is this fiber impregnated with Teflon for packing valves and pistons for use at temperatures to 500°F.

The classes of **cape asbestos** from South Africa are chrysotile, **amosite,** and **Transvaal blue.**   Amosite has a coarse, long, resilient fiber, and is used chiefly in insulation, being difficult to spin.   It comes in white and dark grades, and the fibers are graded also by length from $1/8$ to 6 in.   It has a chemical resistance slightly less than crocidolite and tensile strength of 200,000 psi.   The name amosite was originally a trade name for South African asbestos, but now refers to this type of mineral. Transvaal blue is a whitish, iron-rich, **anthophyllite** $(MgFe)SiO_3$, noted for the length of its fiber.   The best grades are about $1\frac{1}{2}$ in. long.   The fibers are resistant to heat and to acids, and the stronger fibers are used for making acid filter cloth and fireproof garments.   This type of asbestos is also found in the Appalachian range from Vermont to Alabama.   Canadian, Vermont, and Arizona asbestos is chrysotile; that from Georgia and the Carolinas is anthophyllite.   More than 90% of the world production of asbestos is chrysotile in silky to harsh fibers in green, gray, amber, and white colors, and with a specific gravity of 2.4 to 2.6.   Canadian asbestos is graded as crude, mill fibers, and shorts. Crudes are spinning fibers $\frac{3}{8}$ in. or longer, hand-cobbed.   Mill fibers are obtained by crushing and screening.   Shorts are the lowest grades of mill fibers.   **Rhodesian asbestos** is graded in five C & GS grades separated by screen boxes.   Kenya asbestos is anthophyllite, and that from Tanganyika is largely amphibole.   **Nonspinning asbestos** is graded as shingle stock, $\frac{1}{4}$ to $\frac{3}{8}$ in.; paper stock, $\frac{1}{8}$ to $\frac{1}{4}$ in.; and shorts, $\frac{1}{16}$ to $\frac{1}{8}$ in.   The shorts are washed and ground for use as resistant filler in molded plastics.   In England this material is known as **micro asbestos.**

Asbestos fabrics are often woven mixed with some cotton.   For brake linings and clutch facings the asbestos is woven with fine metallic wire. **Asbeston,** of the U.S. Rubber Co., is full asbestos fabric in various weaves and weights.   The 8-oz open-weave fabric is used for cable insulation. The close-woven 16-oz cloth is used for aircraft air ducts.   The 20-oz fabric is used for fireproof clothing.   An **absorbent fabric** used for wiping cloths is made from 20% asbestos fiber and 80 cotton.   The dyed fabric shows color only in the cotton since the asbestos does not absorb the dye. The **Colorbestos** drapery fabric of Johns-Manville has the warp of cotton with the asbestos surrounding the warp threads so that the fabric is flameproof.   It weighs 0.92 lb per yd in plain weave, and 1.1 lb in pattern. **Asbestos wick,** used for calking, is made of strands of carded long asbestos fiber twisted in the form of a soft rope, usually $\frac{1}{4}$ in. in diameter. **Asbestos rope** is larger-diameter material made by twisting or braiding several strands of wick.   **Caposite,** of the North American Asbestos Corp., is rope $\frac{1}{2}$ to 2 in. in diameter made of twisted rovings of long-staple asbestos covered with a braided jacket of asbestos yarn.   It is used for pipe, valve, and joint insulation, and for furnace door packing.   **Asbestos felt,** used for insulation, is usually made by saturating felted asbestos with asphalt, although synthetic rubber or other binder may be used.   The **Pyrotex felt** of Raybestos-Manhattan, Inc., has no binder but is made from a mixture of long-fiber chrysotile and a ceramic fiber.

Asbestos shingles, for fireproof roofing and siding of houses, are normally made of asbestos fibers and portland cement formed under hydraulic pressure.   They are in the natural gray color or are colored with black or green pigments.   Another type of asbestos used for some insulation is **paligorskite,** known as **mountain leather,** found in Alaska.   It is a complex mineral which may be an alteration product of several asbestos minerals.   It absorbs moisture and is thus not suited to the ordinary uses of asbestos, but it can be reduced to a smooth pulp which is molded with a resistant plastic binder into a lightweight insulating board.

ASBESTOS BOARD. A construction or insulating material in sheets made of asbestos fibers and portland cement molded under hydraulic pressure. Ordinary board for the siding and partitions of warehouses and utility buildings is in the natural mottled-gray color, but pigmented boards are also marketed in various colors. The specific gravity of asbestos board is about 2.0, and it will withstand temperatures to about 1000°F. The boards are dense and rigid, but can be worked easily with carpenters' tools. Usual thicknesses are $\frac{3}{16}$, $\frac{1}{4}$, and $\frac{3}{8}$ in. **Asbestos millboard** is also made with an organic binder with sometimes a filler of diatomaceous earth, in soft or hard grades, useful as insulation for temperatures from 800 to 1000°F. Asbestos board is marketed under trade names such as **Industal, Apac board,** and **Linabestos,** of the Keasbey & Mattison Co., and **Transite** of Johns-Manville. **Marinite,** of the same company, is a construction board useful for fire-resistant insulation, consisting of asbestos fiber, diatomaceous silica, and an inorganic binder. The density is 23 to 65 lb per cu ft. The hardest grade, Marinite 65, has a tensile strength of 750 psi. Grade 36 has a hardness equal to that of yellow pine. **Sheetflextos,** of Keasbey & Mattison Co., is a flexible asbestos-cement wallboard in $\frac{1}{8}$-in. thickness in natural gray or waxed decorative colors. **Corrugated asbestos,** used for roofing and siding of industrial buildings, has a thickness of $\frac{3}{8}$ in., and the usual corrugation has a pitch of 4.2 in. The weight is 3.75 lb per sq ft.

Asbestos lumber is asbestos-cement board molded in the form of boards for flooring and partitions, usually with imitation wood grain molded into the surface. **Asbestos siding,** for house construction, is grained to imitate cypress or other wood and is pigmented with titanium oxide to give a clear white color. Asbestos roofing materials may also be made with asphalt or other binder instead of cement. **Fiberock,** of the Philip Carey Co., is a roofing board composed of asbestos fibers impregnated with asphalt. **Copperclad,** of Johns-Manville, is a roofing material consisting of 2-oz Electro-sheet copper bonded to asbestos felt. **Asbestos ebony,** of this company, is an electrical panel board made of asbestos cement bonded under high pressure with an insulating compound. It has good dielectric strength, will withstand temperatures to 300°F, and has a specific gravity of 2.05. **Ebonized asbestos,** of the Ambler Asbestos Shingle & Sheathing Co., is asbestos molded into sheets with an asphalt binder, and used for panels.

ASBESTOS PAPER. A thin asbestos sheeting made of asbestos fibers bonded usually with a solution of sodium silicate. It is strong, flexible, and white in color, and is fireproof and a good heat insulator. For covering steam pipes and for insulating walls, it is made in sheets of two or three plies.   For wall insulation it is also made double with one corrugated sheet to form air pockets when in place.   Thin sheets, 6 lb per 100 sq ft, up to 32 lb, or $\frac{1}{16}$ in. thick, are employed for gaskets and electrical insulation.   The 6-lb paper is 0.015 in. thick, and the 8-lb is 0.019 in. thick.   Crimped asbestos paper is also used for pipe insulation to give dead air spaces between layers.   **Amblerite,** of Keasbey & Mattison Co., is thin sheet made of asbestos fibers with a resilient binder, used for packing for superheated steam and chemical· fittings.   **Uni-Syn** sheet packing, of this company, is made by treating long asbestos fibers with synthetic rubber and felting under pressure.   It is resilient and resistant to chemicals.   **Prenite,** of the B. F. Goodrich Co., is Neoprene-bonded asbestos sheet used for chemical packings.   **Cohrlastic,** of the Connecticut Hard Rubber Co., is asbestos paper coated with white silicone rubber. The thickness is 0.024 in.   It has a dielectric strength of 400 volts per mil, withstands temperatures to 500°F, and is resistant to acids and alkalies.   But the **Cohrlastic 3500,** used for high-strength flexible diaphragms for operation between −75 and 300°F, is not asbestos, but is Orlon fabric coated with a silicone resin.   **Novabestos,** of the Irvington Varnish & Insulator Co., is electrical insulating sheet, 0.003 in. thick, made from asbestos fibers saturated with a silicone resin.   The dielectric strength is 350 volts per mil, and the tensile strength is 10 lb per in. of width. **Terratex,** of the General Electric Co., is asbestos paper with a clay binder in very thin sheets for high-voltage insulation.   **Quinterra,** of Johns-Manville, is flexible asbestos paper in thickness from 0.0015 to 0.020 in., made by a pulping process and used for insulation.   Treated with silicone resin, it has high dielectric strength.   **Quinterra 71** is the asbestos paper saturated with about 45% of epoxy resin in tape and sheets 0.004 in. thick, used for slot lining and other insulation.   The dielectric strength is 700 volts per mil.

ASH.   The wood of a variety of species of ash trees valued for uses where strength, hardness, stiffness, and shock resistance are important.   Most of the species give dense, elastic woods that polish well, but they do not withstand exposure well.   The color is yellowish, which turns brown on exposure.   The woods from the different species vary in their qualities, and are likely to be mixed in commercial shipments, but the general quality is high.   Ash is used for quality cooperage such as tubs, flooring, veneer, vehicle parts, tool handles, bearings, and trim lumber.   **American ash** and **Canadian ash,** also called **cane ash, white ash,** and **Biltmore ash,** come chiefly from the tree *Fraxinus americana* which grows over a wide area east of the Mississippi River.   **Arkansas ash** is from *F. platycarpa;* **Japanese ash,** also called **tamo,** is from *F. mandschurica;* and European ash is from *F. excelsior.*   **European ash** is heavier than American ash, and is tough and elastic.   It is valued for hockey sticks, tennis rackets, and tool handles. Japanese ash is a close-grained wood, but browner in color.

White ash weighs 41 lb per cu ft dry; **red ash,** F. *pennsylvanica,* 39 lb per cu ft; and **green ash,** F. *pennsylvanica lanceolata,* also called **water ash** and **swamp ash,** 44 lb.   This latter tree grows over the widest area throughout the states east of the Rockies, and is commercially abundant in the Southeast and Gulf states.   It is a hardy tree, and has been used for farm windbreaks in the Great Plains area.   All of these woods vary in tensile strength from 11,000 to 17,000 psi.   White ash has a compressive strength perpendicular to the grain of 2,250 psi.   **Mountain ash** and **black ash,** F. *nigra,* are also species of American ash.   The latter, also called **brown ash** and **hoop ash,** is a northern tree and was formerly used in aircraft construction.   It has a specific gravity of 0.53 when oven-dried, a compressive strength perpendicular to the grain of 1,260 psi, and a shearing strength parallel to the grain of 1,050 psi.   **Oregon ash,** F. *oregona,* is somewhat lighter and not as strong as white ash.   It grows along the west coast of Canada.   **Blue ash,** F. *quadrangular,* grows in the central states.   **Pumpkin ash,** F. *profunda,* grows in the lower Mississippi Valley and in Florida.   A wood that has similar uses to ash, for handles, levers, and machine parts, but is harder than ash, is **hornbeam.**   It is from the tree *Ostrya virginiana* of the eastern states of the United States.   The wood is very hard, tough, and strong, but is available only in limited quantities.

ASPEN. The wood of the aspen tree, *Populus tremula,* used chiefly for match stems and for making excelsior, but also for some inside construction work.   The color is yellowish, and it is tough and close-grained. The tree is native to Europe.   The American aspen is from the tree *P. tremuloides,* called also **American poplar,** and from the **largetooth aspen,** *P. grandidentata.*   Both species are also called poplar, and the lumber may be mixed with poplar and cottonwood.   The trees grow in the Lake and northeastern states and in the West.   The heartwood is grayish white to light brown with a lighter-colored sapwood.   It is straight-grained with a fine and uniform texture, but is soft and weak.   It has a disagreeable odor when moist.   The wood is used for excelsior, matches, boxes, and paper pulp.   The pulp is easily bleached.   **Salicin** is extracted from the bark.

ASPHALT. A bituminous, brownish to jet-black substance, solid or semisolid, found in various parts of the world.   It consists of a mixture of hydrocarbons, is fusible and largely soluble in carbon disulfide.   It is also soluble in petroleum solvents and in turpentine.   The melting points range from 32 to 38°C.   Large deposits occur in Trinidad and Venezuela.   Asphalt is of animal origin as distinct from coals of vegetable origin.   Native asphalt usually contains much mineral matter, and crude

Trinidad asphalt has a composition of about 47% bitumen, 28 clay, and 25 water. **Artificial asphalt** is a term applied to the bituminous residue from coal distillation mechanically mixed with sand or limestone. Asphalt is used for roofings, road surfacing, insulating varnishes, acid-resistant paints, and cold-molded products. The material has been known and used since earliest times, the clay bricks of the buildings of Babylon having been cemented with asphalt. The Greek word for native asphalt was **asphaltos,** and the Latin word **bitumen.** The latter word now means the asphalt clean of earthy matter. The word comes from the original Sanskrit word gwitu-men, applied to the native asphalts used as fuel. It is obtained at Athabasca, Canada, in tar sands which are strip-mined. The Tartar word pitch, meaning fuel, now applies chiefly to tars used as roofing or coating materials. In general, bitumens have the characteristics that they are fusible and are totally soluble in carbon disulfide, as distinct from the **pyrobitumens,** albertite, elatarite, and coals, which are infusible and relatively insoluble in carbon disulfide. **Pyrogenous asphalts** are the residues from the distillation of petroleum or from the treatment of wurtzilite. **Asphaltite** is a general name for the bituminous asphaltic materials which are fusible with difficulty, such as gilsonite and grahamite. It is thought that **benzopyrene,** or **carcinogen,** $C_{20}H_{11}$, of coal-tar pitch and asphalt will produce cancer in living tissues. This material also occurs in shale oil, soot, and tobacco smoke.

   Rock asphalt, or **bituminous rock,** is a sandstone or limestone naturally impregnated with asphalt. The asphalt can be extracted from it, or it may be used directly for paving and flooring. **Kyrock** is a rock asphalt from Kentucky consisting of silica sand of sharp grains bound together with a bituminous content of about 7%. The crushed rock is used as a paving material. **Albertite** is a type of asphalt found originally in Albert County, New Brunswick, and first named **Albert coal.** It belongs to the group of asphalts only partly soluble in carbon disulfide, infusible, and designated as **carboids,** although they are true asphalts and not of vegetable origin. The commercial albertite is a type called **stellarite** from Nova Scotia. It is jet black, brittle, contains 22 to 25% fixed carbon, and yields oil and coke when distilled. It is easily lighted with a match, and burns with a bright, smoky flame, throwing off sparks. The albertite found in Utah is called **nigrite** and contains up to 40% fixed carbon. A species found in Angola is called **libollite.** These materials are weathered asphalts. **Ipsonite** is a final stage of weathered asphalt. It is black in color, infusible, only slightly soluble in carbon disulfide, contains 50 to 80% fixed carbon, and is very low in oxygen. It is found in Oklahoma, Arkansas, Nevada, and in various places in South America. The **rafaelite** found in large beds on the eastern slopes of the Andes Mountains in Argentina is a form of ipsonite.

Cutback asphalt is asphalt liquefied with petroleum distillates, used for cementing down floor coverings and for waterproofing walls. Protective coatings based on asphalt cutback form economical paints for protection against salts, alkalies, and nonoxidizing acids at temperatures up to 110°F. They are black in color, but may be pigmented with aluminum flake. They are often marketed under trade names such as **Atlastic,** of the Atlas Mineral Products Co., and **Protek-Coat,** of the Davison Chemical Co. Many corrosion-resistant coatings for chemical tanks and steel structures are asphalt solutions compounded with resins and fillers. **Perfecote,** of the Esbec Corp., for steel and concrete, contains an epoxy resin. The color is black, but it will accept a cover coat of colored plastic paint.

Modified asphalt, for laminating paper and for impregnating flooring felts, is asphalt combined with a rosin ester to increase the penetration, tack, and adhesion, but asphalt for paints and coatings may also be modified with synthetic resins. **Emulsified asphalt** is an asphalt emulsion in water solution, used for floor surfacing, painting pipes, and waterproofing concrete walls. Emulsified asphalts may be marketed under trade names such as **Elastex,** of the Truscon Laboratories, and **Ebontex,** of the Philip Carey Co. **Thermotex,** of the latter company, is an emulsified asphalt mixed with asbestos fibers, used for painting steam pipes. **Brunswick black** is a mixture of asphaltite with fatty acid pitch in a volatile solvent, used for painting roofs. **Amiesite,** of the Amiesite Asphalt Co., is asphalt mixed with rubber latex, or is a premixed asphalt with an aggregate employed for road filling. Rubbers are sometimes incorporated into paving asphalts to give resilience. The natural or synthetic rubber is mixed into the asphalt either in the form of powder or as a prepared additive. **Catalyzed asphalt** is asphalt treated with phosphoric anhydride, P_2O_5, used for road construction to resist deterioration of the pavement from weathering. An asphalt mix developed by the Shell Chemical Co. for aircraft runways to resist the action of jet fuels is petroleum asphalt with an epoxy resin and a plasticizer. **Flooring blocks** and **asphalt tiles** are made in standard shapes and sizes from mixtures of asphalt with fillers and pigments. They are sold under many trade names, such as **Elastite** of the Philip Carey Co. and **Accotile** of the Armstrong Cork Co.

Oil asphalt, petroleum asphalt, petroleum pitch, or **asphalt oil,** is the heavy black residue left after removing the tar tailings in the distillation of petroleum. It contains 99% bitumen, is not soluble in water, and is durable. As it adheres well to metals, wood, or paper, and forms a glossy surface, it is used in roofings, or mixed with natural asphalt for paints and coatings. It is also used for roads. **Vanadiset,** of the Wilson Carbon Co., Inc., is a series of resin fractions of petroleum asphalt with small amounts of vanadium pentoxide, varying from semisolids to a brittle solid. They are used as softeners for rubber and in bitumen paints.

AVOCADO OIL. An oil obtained from the ripe, green-colored, pear-shaped fruit of the avocado, *Persea americana,* a small tree of which more than 500 varieties grow profusely in tropical America.   The oil is also called **alligator pear oil.**   In California, where the fruit is grown for market, it is also known as **Calavo.**   The fruits weigh up to 3 lb, and the seeds are 8 to 26% of the fruit.   The fresh pulp contains 71% water, 20 oil, and 2.37 proteins.   The seeds contain about 2% of an oil, but the avocado oil is extracted from the fruit pulp, the dehydrated pulp yielding 70% oil.   In Central America the oil is extracted by pressing in bags, and the oil has been used by the Mayans since ancient times for treating burns and as a pomade.   It contains 77% oleic acid, 10.8 lin-oleic, 6.9 palmitic, and 0.7 stearic, with a small amount of myristic and a trace of arachidic acid.   It is also rich in lecithin, contains **phyto-stearin,** and is valued for cosmetics because it is penetrating, as lanolin is. It also contains **mannoketoheptose,** a high nonfermentable sugar.   The oil has good keeping qualities and is easily emulsified.   The oil-soluble vitamins are absorbed through the skin, and the oil for cosmetics is not wintered in order to retain the sterols.   The specific gravity is 0.9132. Another oil used in cosmetics and for lubricating fine mechanisms is **ben oil,** a colorless to yellow oil obtained from the seeds of trees of the genus *Moringa,* notably *M. aptera, M. oleifera,* and *M. pterygosperma,* of Arabia, Egypt, India, and the Sudan.   The latter species is also grown in Jamaica. The seeds contain 25 to 34% oil varying from a liquid to a solid, with specific gravity 0.898 to 0.902 and saponification value 179 to 187.

BABASSU OIL. An oil similar to coconut oil obtained from the kernels of the nut of the palm tree *Attalea orbignya* which grows in vast quantities in northeastern Brazil.   There are 2 to 5 long kernels in each nut, the kernel being only 9% of the heavy-shelled nut, and these kernels con-tain 65% oil.   A bunch of the fruits contains 200 to 600 nuts.   The oil is very high in lauric acid, and is a direct substitute for coconut oil for soaps, as an edible oil, and as a source of lauric, capric, and myristic acids. The melting point of the oil is 22 to 26°C, specific gravity 0.868, iodine value 15, and saponification value 246 to 250.   **Tucum oil,** usually classed with babassu but valued more in the bakery industry because of its higher melting point, is from the kernels of the nut of the palm *Astrocaryum tucuma* of northeastern Brazil.   The oil is similar but heavier with melting point up to 35°C.   In Colombia it is called **guere palm.**

Another similar oil is **murumuru oil,** from the kernels of the nut of the palm *A. murumuru,* of Brazil.   The name is a corruption of the two Carib words marú and morú, meaning bread to eat.   The oil contains as much as 40% lauric acid, with 35% myristic acid, and some palmitic, stearic, linoleic, and oleic acids. It is usually marketed as babassu oil. The **awarra palm,** *A. janari,* of the Guianas, yields nuts with a similar oil. **Cohune oil** is a white fat from the kernels of the nut of the palm *Attalea cohune* of Mexico and Central America. It is a small tree yielding as many as 2,000 nuts a year. The oil has the appearance and odor of coconut oil, and contains 46% lauric acid, 15 myristic, 10 oleic, with also stearic, capric, and linoleic acids. All of these oils yield a high proportion of glycerin. Cohune oil has a melting point of 18 to 20°C, saponification value 252 to 256, iodine value 10 to 14, and specific gravity 0.868 to 0.971. The cohune nut is much smaller than the babassu but is plentiful and easier to crack. **Curua oil** is from the nut of the palm *A. spectabilis* of Brazil. It is similar to cohune oil and is used for the same purposes in soaps and foods. **Mamarron oil** is a cream-colored fat with the odor and characteristics of coconut oil, obtained from another species of *Attalea* palm of Colombia. Another oil high in lauric acid, and similar to babassu oil, is **corozo oil,** obtained from the kernels of the nuts of the palm *Corozo oleifera* of Venezuela and Central America. **Macanilla oil** is a similar oil from the kernels of the nuts of the palm *Guilielma garipaes* of the same region. **Buri oil** is from the nuts of the palm *Diplothemium candescens* of Brazil.

BABBITT METAL. The original name for tin-antimony-copper white alloys used for machinery bearings, but the term now applies to almost any white bearing alloy with either tin or lead base. The original babbitt, named after the inventor, was made by melting together 4 parts by weight of copper, 12 tin, and 8 antimony, and then adding 12 parts of tin after fusion. It consisted, therefore, of 88.9% tin, 7.4 antimony, and 3.7 copper. This alloy melts at 462°F. It has a Brinell hardness of 35 at 70°F, and 15 at 212°F. As a general-utility bearing metal, the original alloy has never been improved greatly, and makers frequently designate the tin-base alloys close to this composition as **genuine babbitt.** Some of the early competitive alloys varied in composition, but usually for the purpose of conserving tin. **Thurston's metal** contained 9 to 10% copper, 20 antimony, and the balance tin. **Jacna metal** had 70% lead, 10 tin, 19 antimony, and a small amount of bismuth. **Husman's alloy,** used originally on the German railways, had about 74% tin, 11 antimony, 4 copper, 10 lead, and 0.4 zinc. **Karmash's alloy** contained considerable zinc. **Parsons' white brass** was a hard tin-base alloy with both SnSb and SnCu crystals in the matrix. One of the oldest of the American lead-base babbitts, **Magnolia metal,** of the Magnolia Metal Co., contained about 80% lead with a small amount of arsenic to hold the lead in solution and to improve the bearing qualities. It has a tensile strength of 17,500 psi, Brinell hardness 21.8, pouring range 825 to 900°F, and coefficient of friction about one-third that of regular babbitt metal.   **Adamant alloy,** of this company, is a genuine babbitt, somewhat harder and with higher melting point, but with lower strength, 12,850 psi.

Commercial white bearing metals now known as babbitt are of three general classes: tin-base, with more than 50% tin hardened with antimony and copper, and used for heavy, pounding service; intermediate, with 20 to 50% tin, having lower compressive strength and more sluggish as a bearing; lead-base, made usually with antimonial lead with smaller amounts of tin together with other elements to hold the lead in solution. These **lead-base babbitts** are lower in cost and also serve to conserve tin in times of scarcity of that metal, but they are suitable only for light service, although many ingenious combinations of supplementary alloying elements have sometimes been used to give hard, strong bearings with little tin.   The high-grade babbitts, however, are usually close to the original babbitt in composition.   **SAE babbitt 11,** for connecting-rod bearings, has 86% tin, 5 to 6.5 copper, 6 to 7.5 antimony, and not over 0.35 lead.   A babbitt of this kind will have a compressive strength up to 20,000 psi, while the high-lead alloys have only 15,000 psi.

Copper hardens and toughens the alloy and raises the melting point. Lead increases the fluidity and raises the antifriction qualities, but softens the alloy and decreases its compressive strength.   Antimony hardens the metal and forms hard crystals in the soft matrix which improves the alloy as a bearing metal.   Only 3.5% of antimony is normally dissolved in tin.   In the low-antimony alloys copper-tin crystals form the hard constituent, and in the high-antimony alloys antimony-tin cubes are also present.   Alloys containing up to 1% arsenic are harder at high temperatures and are fine-grained, but arsenic is used chiefly for holding lead in suspension.   Zinc increases hardness but decreases frictional qualities, and with much zinc the bearings are inclined to stick.   Even minute quantities of iron harden the alloys, and iron is not used except when zinc is present.   Bismuth reduces shrinkage and refines the grain, but lowers the melting point and lowers the strength at elevated temperatures.   Cadmium increases the strength and fatigue resistance, but any considerable amount lowers the frictional qualities, lowers the strength at higher temperatures, and causes corrosion.   Nickel is used to increase strength but raises the melting point.   The normal amount of copper in babbitts is 3 ot 4%, at which point the maximum fatigue-resisting properties are obtained with about 7% antimony.   More than 4% copper tends to weaken the alloy, and raises the melting point.   When the copper is very high, tin-copper crystals are formed and the alloy is more a bronze than a babbitt.   All of the SAE babbits contain some arsenic, ranging from 0.10% in the high-tin **SAE babbitt 10** to about 1% in the high-lead **SAE babbitt 15.**   The first of these contains 90% tin, 4.5 antimony,

4.5 copper, and 0.35 lead, while the babbitt 15 has 82% lead, 15 antimony, 1 tin, and 0.60 copper.

Because of increased speeds and pressures in bearings and the trend to lighter weights, heavy cast babbbitt bearings are now little used in spite of the low cost and ease of casting. The alloys are mostly employed as **antifriction metals** in thin facings on steel backings, the facing being usually less than 0.010 in. thick, in order to increase the ability to sustain higher loads and to dissipate the heat.

Babbitts are marketed under many trade names, the compositions generally following the six SAE alloy standards but varying in auxiliary constituents, the possibilities for altering the physical qualities by composition rearrangement being infinite. Some of the trade names which have been used for babbitt-type alloys marketed in ingots are: **Leantin** and **Cosmos metal** of the Lumen Bearing Co., for high-lead alloys; **stannum metal** for high-tin alloys; and **Lubeco metal** and **Lotus metal** for medium-composition alloys. **Hoo Hoo metal** and **Nickel babbitt,** of the American Brake Shoe Co., are high-tin alloys containing nickel, while **Silver babbitt** of the same company has no tin but contains a small amount of silver to aid retention of the lead and to give hardness at elevated temperatures. **Glyco** is the name of a group of lead-base alloys of Joseph T. Ryerson & Son, Inc. **Satco,** of the National Lead Co., is a high-melting-point alloy for heavy service. It melts at 788°F. **Tinite,** of the Ajax Metal Co., is a tin-base metal hardened with copper. **Ajax bull,** of this company, contains 76% lead, 7 tin, and 17 antimony, modified with other elements.

BAGASSE. The residue left after grinding sugarcane and extracting the juice, employed in making paper and fiber building boards. In England it is called **megass.** The fiber contains 45% cellulose, 32 pentosan, and 18 lignin. It is marketed as dry and wet separated, and as dry fiber. The dry-separated fibers bulk 4.5 lb per cu ft, with 62 to 80% passing a 100-mesh screen. The dry fiber bulks 6 to 8 lb per cu ft, and is about 14 mesh. The fibers mat together to form a strong, tough, light, absorptive board. The finer fibers in Cuba and Jamaica are soaked in molasses and used as a cattle feed under the name of **molascuit.** **Celotex** is the trade name of the Celotex Corp. for wallboard, paneling, and acoustical tile made from bagasse fibers. **Ferox-Celotex** is the material treated with chemicals to make it resistant to fungi and termites. **Celo-Rock** is the trade name for Celotex-gypsum building boards. **Acousti-Celotex** is Celotex perforated to increase its sound-absorbing efficiency. In India, the Philippines, and some other countries where sugarcane is plentiful, paper is made from the bagasse. Newsprint is made with a mixture of mechanical and chemical bagasse pulp, and writing papers may be made by delignifying the bagasse and digesting with soda.

Aconitic acid, $HOOCCH:C(COOH)CH_2COOH$, occurs in bagasse and is extracted from Louisiana cane. The acid is esterified for use as a plasticizer for vinyl resins, or sulfonated for use as a wetting agent. This acid is also produced as a white powder of melting point 195°C by the dehydration of citric acid.

BALATA. A nonelastic rubber obtained chiefly from the tree *Manilkara bidentata* of Venezuela, Brazil, and the Guianas. It is similar to gutta percha and is used as a substitute. The material contains a high percentage of gums and is more tacky than rubber, but it can be vulcanized. It differs from rubber in being a transisomer of isoprene with a different polymerization. Balata has been used principally for transmission and conveyor belts. For conveyor belts heavy duck is impregnated with balata solution and vulcanized. The belts have high tensile strength, good flexibility, and wear resistance. The wood of the balata tree is used for cabinetwork and for rollers and bearings. It is called **bulletwood** in the Guianas, but this name is also applied to the wood of the gutta-percha trees of Asia. The wood is extremely hard, durable, and weighs 66 lb per cu ft. It has a deep-red color and a fine, open grain.

BALSA WOOD. The wood of large and fast-growing trees of the genus *Ochroma* growing from southern Mexico to Ecuador and northern Brazil. It is the lightest of the commercial woods and combines also the qualities of strength, stiffness, and workability. It is about one-fourth the weight of spruce, with a structural strength half that of spruce. The crushing strength is 2,150 psi. The wood is white to light yellow or brownish and weighs about 8 lb per cu ft from a 4-year-old tree. Wood from a 6-year-old tree weighs 10 to 12 lb per cu ft. Its peculiar cellular structure makes it valuable as an insulating material for refrigeration. It is also used for life preservers, buoys, floats, paneling, vibration isolators, insulating partitions, and inside trim of aircraft. The small pieces are used for model airplanes. **Balsa sawdust** may be used as a lightweight filler for plastics.

Much of the commercial wood is from the tree *O. grandiflora* of Ecuador. **Barrios balsa,** *O. concolor,* grows from southern Mexico through Guatemala and Honduras. **Limon balsa** is from the tree *O. limonensis* of Costa Rica and Panama, and **Santa Marta balsa** is the *O. obtusa* of Colombia. **Red balsa** is from the *O. velutina* of the Pacific Coast of Central America. The balsa known in Brazil as **Sumaúma** is from a kapok tree *Ceiba pentandra*. It is used for life preservers and rafts, and is quite similar to balsa. A Japanese lightweight wood used for floats, instruments, and where lightness is required is **Kiri,** from the tree *Paulownia tomentosa*. It weighs 14 to 19 lb per cu ft, has a coarse grain, but is strong and resists warping.   Grown as a shade tree since 1834 under the names of **paulownia** and **empress tree,** it is now common in the United States, and the wood is used as a lightweight crating lumber.

BALSAM FIR. The wood of the coniferous tree *Abies balsamea* of the northeastern states and Canada.   It is brownish white in color, soft, and has a fine, even grain.   It is not strong and not very durable, and is used chiefly for pulpwood and for packing boxes and light construction.   The weight is 26 lb per cu ft.   Liquid pitch comes from blisters on the outer bark.   It was formerly used as a transparent adhesive.   **Canada balsam,** or **Canada turpentine,** is a yellowish, viscous oleoresin liquid of pleasant odor and bitter taste, obtained from the buds of the tree.   The specific gravity is 0.983 to 0.997.   It is a class of turpentine, and is used as a solvent in paints and polishes, in leather dressings, adhesives, and perfumes.   It is also referred to as **balm of Gilead** for medicinal and perfumery use, but the original balm of Gilead, marketed as buds, was from the small evergreen tree *Balsamodendron gileadense* of the Near East. **Southern balsam fir** is **Frazer fir,** from the tree *A. fraseri* of the Appalachian Mountains.   The wood is similar to balsam fir.

BAMBOO. A genus of gigantic treelike grasses, of the order *Graminaceae,* of which the *Bambusa arundinacea* is the most common species. It grows most commonly in Indonesia, the Philippines, and southern Asia, but many species have been brought to Latin America and to the southern United States.   The stems of bamboo are hollow, jointed, and have an extremely hard exterior surface.   They sometimes reach more than 1 ft in diameter and are often 50 ft high, growing in dense masses.   Nearly 1,000 species are known.   The *B. spinosa* of the Philippines grows as much as 10 ft in one week.   Bamboo is a material which has had innumerable uses.   The stalks are used for making pipes, buckets, baskets, walking sticks, fishing poles, rug-winding poles, lance shafts, window blinds, mats, arrows, and for building houses and making furniture. The weight is about 22 lb per cu ft.   **Tonkin bamboo** is strong and flexible, and is used for making fishing poles.   **Tali bamboo** of Java, *Gigantochloa apus,* is used for construction.   **Betong bamboo,** *G. asper,* is one of the largest species.   **Giant bamboo,** *Dendrocalamus gigantea,* of Ceylon, grows to a height of 100 ft.   The fast-growing **eeta bamboo** is used in India as a source of cellulose for rayon manufacture.

BARITE. Sometimes spelled **baryte,** and also called **heavy spar,** and in some localities known as **tiff.**   A natural **barium sulfate** mineral of the theoretical composition $BaSO_4$, used chiefly for the production of lithopone, in chemical manufacture, and in oil-drilling muds.   Mixed with synthetic rubber it is used as a seal coat for roads. For chemicals it is specified 90 to 95% pure $BaSO_4$, with not more than 1% ferric oxide. Prime white and floated grades are used for coating paper. **Baroid,** of the National Lead Co., used in oil wells, is barite ore crushed, dried, and finely ground. **Artificial barite, permanent white,** and **blanc fixe** are names for white, fine-grained precipitated paint grades. **Micronized barite,** for rubber filler, is a fine white powder of 400 to 1,000 mesh. Barite is widely distributed and especially associated with ores of various metals or with limestones. It occurs in crystals or massive. It may be colorless, white, or light shades of blue, red, and yellow, and transparent to opaque. Its hardness is 3 to 3.5, and its specific gravity 4.4 to 4.8. It is insoluble in water. The mineral is produced in the western states and from Virginia to Georgia. The barite of Cartersville, Ga., contains 96% $BaSo_4$, 0.6 iron, with silica, alumina, and traces of calcium, strontium, and magnesium. Large deposits of high-grade barite occur in Nova Scotia. In the West much ground crude barite is used as a drilling mud in oil wells. The white pigment marketed by the American Zinc Sales Co. under the name of **Azolite** is 71% barium sulfate and 29% zinc sulfide in 325-mesh powder. **Sunolith,** of Wishnick-Tumpeer, Inc., is a similar product. A substitute for barite for some filler uses is **witherite,** an alteration mineral of the composition $BaCO_3$, which is **barium carbonate,** found associated with barite. Precipitated barium carbonate is a white, tasteless, but poisonous powder used in rat poisons, optical glass, ceramics, and pyrotechnics, as a flatting agent in paints, and as a filler for paper. With ferric oxide it is used for making ceramic magnets. **Barium oxide,** BaO, of 99.99% purity, is made by the reduction of barite. It is used as an additive in lubricating oils.

BARIUM. A metallic element of the alkaline earth group, symbol Ba. It occurs in combination in the minerals witherite and barite, which are widely distributed. The metal is silvery white in color and can be obtained by electrolysis from the chloride, but it oxidizes so easily that it is difficult to obtain in the metallic state. Powdered or granular barium is explosive in contact with carbon tetrachloride, fluoro chloro metanes, and other halogenated hydrocarbons. Its melting point is 850°C, and its specific gravity 3.78. The most extensive use of barium is in the form of its compounds. The salts which are soluble, such as sulfide and chloride, are toxic. An insoluble, nontoxic barium sulfate salt is used in radiography. Barium compounds are used as pigments, in chemical manufacturing, and in deoxidizing alloys of tin, copper, lead, and zinc. Barium is introduced into lead bearing metals by electrolysis to harden the lead. When barium is heated to about 200°C in hydrogen gas it forms **barium hydride,** BaH_2, a gray powder which decomposes in contact with water and can be used as a source of nascent hydrogen for life rafts.

BARIUM CHLORIDE. A colorless crystalline material of the composition $BaCl_2 \cdot 2H_2O$, or in anhydrous form without the water of crystallization. The specific gravity is 3.856, and the melting point 860°C. It is soluble in water to the extent of 25% at 20°C and 37% at 100°C. In the mechanical industries it is used for heat-treating baths for steel either alone or mixed with potassium chloride. The molten material is free from fuming and can be held at practically any temperature within the range needed for tempering steels. It is also used for making boiler compounds, for softening water, as a mordant in dyeing and printing inks, in tanning leather, in photographic chemicals, and in insecticides. **Barium chlorate,** $Ba(ClO_3)_2 \cdot H_2O$, is a colorless crystalline powder soluble in water. The melting point of the anhydrous material is 414°C. It is used in explosives as an oxygen carrier, and in pyrotechnics for green-colored light. **Barium fluoride,** BaF_2, is used in crystal form for lasers. When "doped" with uranium it has an output wavelength of 26,000 angstroms. Doping with other elements gives diffused wavelengths for different communication beams. **Barium cyanide,** $Ba(CN)_2$, is a poisonous, colorless, crystalline material melting at 600°C. It is marketed by the Koppers Co. as a 30% water solution for adding to cyanide plating baths, in which it removes carbonates and increases the current efficiency.

BARIUM NITRATE. Also called **nitrobarite.** A white, crystalline powder of the composition $Ba(NO_3)_2$, with specific gravity of 3.24, melting at 592°C, and decomposing at higher temperatures. It is a barium salt of nitric acid obtained by roasting barite with coke, leaching out the precipitated barium sulfide, precipitating as a carbonate by the addition of soda ash, and then dissolving in dilute nitric acid. It has a bitter metallic taste and is poisonous. Barium nitrate is used in ceramic glazes, but its chief use is in **pyrotechnics.** It gives a pale-green flame in burning, and is used for green signals and flares, and for white flares in which the delicate green is blended with the light of other extremely luminous materials. It is also used as an oxygen carrier in **flare powders** and to control the time of burning of the aluminum or magnesium. **Sparklers** are composed of aluminum powder and steel filings with barium nitrate as the oxygen carrier. The steel filings produce the starlike sparks. **Barium nitrite,** $Ba(NO_2)_2$, decomposes with explosive force when heated. **Barium oxalate,** BaC_2O_4, is used in pyrotechnics as a combustion retarder.

BARLEY. The seed grains of the annual plant *Hordeum vulgare* of which there are many varieties. It is one of the most ancient of the cereal grains. The plant is hardy, with a short growing season, and can be cultivated in cold latitudes and at high altitudes, giving high yields per acre. The grains grow in a dense head with three spikelets, and the six-rowed variety has a high protein content, but has low gluten, thus making a poor breadstuff. **Pearl barley** is the husked and polished grain. When used for cattle feed, barley produces lean meats. The chief industrial use is for making **malt,** for which the two-rowed varieties with low protein and thin husk are used. Malt is barley that has been germinated by moisture and then dried. Malting develops the diastase enzyme, which converts the insoluble starch into soluble starch and then into sugars. It is used for brewing beer and for malt extracts. **Caramel malt** is browned with high-temperature drying, and is used for the dark-colored **bock beer. Barley straw** is employed in Europe and Asia for making braided plaits for hats. In America it is used for packing material, especially for glassware.

BASALT. A dense, hard, dark-brown to black igneous rock, consisting of feldspar and augite and often containing crystals of green olivine. It occurs as trap or as volcanic rock. The specific gravity is 2.87 to 3, and it is extremely hard. Masses of basalt are frequently found in columns or prisms, as in the celebrated basalt cliffs of northern Ireland. It differs from granite in being a fine-grained extrusive rock, and in having a high content of iron and magnesium. Basalt is used in the form of crushed stone for paving, as a building stone, and for making rock wool. A Russian cast basalt used for electrical insulators is called **angarite.** In Germany cast basalt has been used as a building stone, for linings, and for industrial floors. It is made by melting the crushed and graded basalt, and then tempering by slow cooling. The structure of the cast material is dense with needlelike crystals, and has a hardness of 8 to 9 Mohs. **Basalt glass** is not basalt, but is pumice.

BASSWOOD. The wood of several species of lime trees, *Tilia americana, T. heterophylla, T. glabra,* and *T. pubescens,* all native to the United States and Canada. The European **limewood,** from the tree *T. cordata,* is not called basswood. The wood of the *T. glabra,* called in the eastern states the **lime tree** and the **linden,** and also the **white basswood,** *T. heterophylla,* is used for containers, furniture, and such millwood as blinds. It is soft, light in weight, and has a fine, even grain, but is not very strong or durable on exposure. The white sapwood merges gradually with the yellow-brown heartwood. The specific gravity is 0.40 when oven-dried, and the compressive strength perpendicular to the grain is 620 psi.

BATE. Materials used in the leather industry to remove lime from skins and to make them soft and flaccid before tanning by bringing the collagen into a flaccid or unswollen condition.   Since ancient times dung has been used for this purpose, and until very recently the American tanning industry imported dog dung from Asia Minor for bating leather.   **Artificial bates** are now used because of their greater uniformity and cleanliness. Boric acid is sometimes used for deliming, and gives a silky feel to the leather, but most bates have both a deliming and an enzyme action. **Trypsin** is a group of enzymes from the pancreatic glands of animals, and its action on skins is to dissolve the protein.   They are generally used with ammonium chloride or other salt.   **Oropon,** of Rohm & Haas Co., Inc., is this material carried in wood flour and mixed with a deliming salt.   Sulfamic acids are also used as bates.   The lime compounds used for dehairing are called **depilating agents.**

BAUXITE. A noncrystalline, earthy-white to reddish mineral, massive or in grains, having a composition $Al_2O_3 \cdot 2H_2O$, containing theoretically 74% alumina.   It is the most important ore of aluminum, but is also used for making aluminum oxide abrasives, for refractories, white cement, and for decolorizing and filtering.   The chief production in the United States is in Arkansas, Georgia, and Alabama, but only a small amount of the world output is in the United States.   The important producing countries are the Guianas, Hungary, France, and Italy, but large deposits are found in Indonesia, Brazil, Jamaica, Haiti, the Pacific Islands, and Northwest Africa.   Bauxite is graded on the Al_2O_3 content.   High-grade bauxite, Grade A, contains a minimum of 55% alumina and a maximum of 8 silica.   Grade B contains a minimum of 50% alumina with a silica content from 8 to 16%.   Chemical grades should have less than 2.5% Fe_2O_3. Grades appearing in price quotations with up to 84% alumina content are calcined and are based on the dehydrated alumina content of the ore. One long ton of crude bauxite yields 0.87 long ton of dried bauxite.   To produce one short ton of aluminum metal requires 4,000 lb of alumina, which requires 8,000 lb of bauxite.   Normally, it requires about 1.2 lb of soda ash to remove 1 lb of silica from the bauxite, and thus bauxite with less than 8% silica is preferred for aluminum production, but much of the Arkansas bauxite contains 13% silica.   Alumina is also produced directly from bauxite by reacting the ore with carbon and nitrogen to aluminum nitride and then disassociating the nitride by heat to produce the metal and nitrogen.   Or, bauxite can be reacted with carbon and chlorine to form aluminum monochloride, and then heat-reducing to obtain the metal.   The plentiful **alumina clays** of Idaho and other areas are also workable by special methods.   The red and white clays of the Carolinas contain 17% alumina, the red clays being high in iron.

Bauxite has a high melting point, 1820°C, and can be used directly as a refractory.   Cement-making white bauxite from Greece ranks very high in alumina content. Brazilian, Arkansas, and Indian ores also contain some titanium oxide, and the Surinam ore has as high as 3% TiO_2. Two kinds af bauxite are found in Italy, a dark-red variety containing 54 to 58% Al_2O_3, and only 2 to 4 SiO_2, but having 22 to 26% Fe_2O_3, and 2 to 3 TiO_2, and a light-red variety containing 60 to 66% Al_2O_3, 5 to 9 silica, 10 to 16 iron oxide, and 3 to 5 titanium oxide. The best French white bauxite contains 66 to 74% alumina, 6 to 10 silica, 2 to 4 iron oxide, and 3 to 4 titanium oxide. It is preferred for ceramic and chemical purposes, while the best grade of the red variety is used for producing aluminum, and the inferior grade for refractories and for cement manufacture. Malayan and Indonesian bauxite averages 57 to 60% Al_2O_3, 6.7 Fe_2O_3, 3 to 5 SiO_2, and 0.9 to 1 TiO_2. The large deposits on Ponape and other Pacific islands average 50 to 52% alumina, 3 to 6 silica, and 10 to 20 Fe_2O_3, but the bauxite of Hawaii contains only 35% alumina with up to 15% silica. **Phosphatic bauxite,** from the island of Trauhira off the coast of Brazil, is a cream-colored porous rock containing 31.5% alumina, 25.2 P_2O_5, 7.3 iron oxide, 6.8 silica, and 1.3 titania. **Diaspore,** $Al_2O_3 \cdot H_2O$, mined in Missouri, and **gibbsite,** $Al_2O_3 \cdot 3H_2O$, from the Guianas, are bauxites also used for refractories. Gibbsite is also called **wavellite. Filter bauxite,** or **activated bauxite,** is bauxite that has been crushed, screened, and calcined, and is usually in 20- to 60- and 30- to 60-mesh grades. It may be sold under trade names such as **Porocel** and **Floride.** It is preferred to fuller's earth for oil-refinery filtering because it can be revivified indefinitely by calcining. **Calcined bauxite** for the abrasive industry is burned bauxite and contains 78 to 84% alumina. **Laterite,** or **ferroginous bauxite,** has been used in Europe to produce alumina and iron. The laterite of Oregon contains 35% alumina, about 35 iron oxide, and about 7 silica. Low-alumina, high-silica bauxites can be lime-sintered to release the sodium aluminate which goes back into the process while the silicate goes out with the calcium, thus giving high alumina recovery with low soda loss. **Anorthosite,** an abundant **aluminum silicate** mineral containing up to 50% silica, is also used to produce aluminum. The anorthosite of Wyoming is sintered with limestone and soda ash and calcined to yield alumina and a by-product portland cement base of dicalcium silicate. To every pound of alumina produced, 5 lb of cement raw material is obtained.

BEARING BRONZE. Any bronze used for bearing purposes, but usually referring to bronzes containing considerable lead. As an element in bearing metals lead has been called the wax of metals, forming the soft matrix or foundation for the hard crystals, but lead is not easy to keep in solution and the alloys require controlled casting. A high lead content in bronzes improves the antifriction qualities, but reduces the strength

and hardness.   Bronzes with about 30% lead are called **plastic bronze.**
They are superior in strength to the babbitt metals, and are used for heavy
mill bearings.   The so-called **bearing brasses,** formerly much used for
railway-car journals, are not brasses, but are lead bronzes with about 65%
copper, 5 to 10 tin, and up to 30 lead.   They seldom contain zinc, but
the railway bearing metal called **bush metal** in England contains 72%
copper, 14 tin, and 14 yellow brass ingot metal.   The **journal bronze** of
the U.S. Navy contains 82 to 84% copper, 12.5 to 14.5 tin, 2.5 to 4.5
zinc, and 1 lead.   The **ASTM bearing bronzes** have from 70 to 85%
copper, 5 to 10 tin, and 5 to 25 lead, with the zinc kept below 0.50%
as an undesirable element.   The 85–10–5 bronze has a tensile strength
of 28,000 psi, a compressive deformation limit of 18,000 psi, and a
Brinell hardness of 60.   The 70–5–25 bronze has a tensile strength of
15,000 psi, and a hardness of 40.   Zinc is used, however, where higher
strengths are needed, if the copper-tin is high and the zinc remains alloyed
with the copper in the softer matrix.   **SAE alloy 660,** and **Bunting bronze
72,** used for electric motor bearings, contain 83% copper, 7 tin, 7 lead,
and 3 zinc.   This alloy has a tensile strength of 34,000 psi, compressive
limit 22,000 psi, and Brinell hardness 58.   **Asarcon 773,** of the American Smelting & Refining Co., has a similar composition, but the bars and
cylinders are produced by continuous casting through graphite dies from
a nitrogen-atmosphere furnace to give a dense, even-grained structure.
The tensile strength is 44,000 psi, elongation 16%, and hardness 72.

Bearing bronzes owe much of their quality to grain structure, uniformity, and other physical properties which depend upon methods of manufacture, and they are marketed under a variety of trade names such as
Ajax metal, of the Ajax Metal Co., and **Johnson bronze,** of the Johnson
Bronze Co.   **Tiger bronze,** of the National Bearings Div., American
Brake Shoe Co., is a copper-tin bronze with particles of lead evenly dispersed to give low coefficient of friction.   It comes in cast bars and cylinders with tensile strength 30,000 psi and Brinell hardness 53.   **Magnolia
isotropic bronze,** of the Magnolia Metal Co., is die-cast in bars and cylinders to produce a homogeneous structure that gives longer wear life than
a sand-cast bronze.   Tensile strength is 30,000 psi, elongation 8.5%,
and Brinell hardness 70.   **Promet bronze,** of the American Crucible Products Co., contains 11.5 to 15.5% lead, 4.5 to 6.5 tin, 1.25 to 2 nickel,
and the balance copper.   It has a fine dense structure, and needs little
lubrication.   The tensile strength is 33,000 psi with elongation of 8 to
13%.   **Johnson bronze 40,** for sheet bearings, is **SAE bronze 795.**   It
contains 90% copper, 9.5 zinc, and 0.5 tin, giving a Rockwell B hardness
of 65 to 71.   **Johnson bronze 44** is **SAE bronze 791,** with 86 to 90%
copper, 3 to 4.5 tin, 3.5 to 4.5 lead, and 3.5 to 5 zinc, having a Rockwell
B hardness of 65 to 71.

An addition of small amounts of nickel to bearing bronzes helps to keep the lead in solution and improves the resistance to compression and shock. Iron up to 1% increases the resistance to pounding and hardens the bronze, but reduces the grain size and tends to segregate the lead. Some early bearing bronzes were made with antimony instead of lead, but the binary **copper-antimony alloys** are highly crystalline, and the crystalline purple-colored material called by the alchemists **regulus of Venus** was a 50–50 copper-antimony alloy. An early bearing bronze contained 16% lead, 7 antimony, and small amounts of nickel and tin. A copper-antimony alloy used for worm gears contains 7 to 8% antimony, 1.5 to 2.5 nickel, and the balance copper. It casts well and has a triplex structure that makes a good bearing metal. The tensile strength, sand-cast, is 32,000 psi, with elongation 7%. A white alloy used in France under the name of **Palium Z** for heavy-duty bearings contains 4.5% copper, 4 lead, 2.6 tin, 0.6 magnesium, 0.3 manganese, 0.3 zinc, and the balance aluminum.

BEARING MATERIALS. White metals and bronzes are most frequently used for machine bearings, but wood, glass, plastics, and other materials are also employed. Wood is one of the oldest of bearing materials, and is still considered an excellent material for large, low-pressure, and slow-speed bearings. The hardwoods are used, and since they absorb oil and grease little attention is required for lubrication. Lignum vitae was widely used for large marine main-shaft bearings until the introduction of molded, laminated, plastic bearings. The guaiac gum contained in lignum vitae softens at the bearing temperature and provides a good lubricant. **Plastic bearings** are employed where electrical insulation is required. These materials have a compressive strength up to 36,000 psi. Plastic bearings are not easily wetted by water, and a small amount of alkaline sodium oleate is added to the water lubricant. For food-processing equipment where lubricating oil is not desired, ball bearings are made with plastic races and steel balls. The ball bearings of the General Bearing Co. have Delrin races and Type 316 steel balls. **Nylon bearings** require no lubricant for light loads at high speed, and are suitable for textile machinery where oil might soil the fabrics. **Rubber bearings** are used where resilience is needed. Water may be used as the lubricant.

Almost any commercial metal can be used for bearings, but certain metals and alloys are particularly suited for bearings, chiefly because of the fact that a proportion of hard crystals occurs in a background, or matrix, of softer metal, thus supporting the shaft and permitting the free circulation of the lubricant. In the soft babbitt metals these crystals are formed largely by the antimony, while in the bronzes the crystals consist of a chemical compound of copper and tin. One of the metals must have wettability or affinity for lubricants because metal-to-metal contact usually results in high heat, scoring, and galling, or the tearing out of pieces of metal. To form a good bearing, one of the surfaces must slide on minute projecting irregularities. Immissible metals that do not alloy are not as likely to gall as alloys that form welded junctions of the particles. A good bearing metal should support a load up to 1,200 psi without galling.

Cast iron is an excellent bearing metal because of the hard carbides, a soft background of iron, and considerable graphitic carbon which acts as a lubricant. The stainless steels are poor bearing metals and tend to stick and seize. Brass is not much used for bearings since zinc causes sticking, but a bearing alloy known as **Tissier's metal** was a high-copper brass with 1% arsenic to give a crystalline structure. The alloy **Hy Speed** marketed by the Buckeye Brass & Mfg. Co. contained 88% copper, 7 tin, and 5 zinc. In white metals the formation of the structure is affected by the melting times, and a well-cast alloy of inferior composition may result in a better bearing than a high-grade alloy that is poorly cast.

Aluminum bearings have high corrosion resistance against organic acids, good thermal conductivity, and higher strength than other white-metal alloys, and they are equal to babbitts in antiseizure properties. They have the disadvantage of high coefficient of expansion. Aluminum alloys for bearings must have a matrix of aluminum through which are dispersed undissolved constituents. An alloy with 4% silicon and 4 cadmium is used. Other alloys have tin, nickel, and copper or silicon. **Aluminum-tin alloys** are used for heavily loaded high-speed bearings, usually with steel backings to add strength and conserve tin. The alloys contain 20 to 30% tin. A 70–30 alloy has a Vickers hardness of 22. Adding 1% copper raises the hardness to 27 and improves the physical qualities. Usually no more than 3% copper is used. The copper is alloyed with the aluminum, but the tin remains in an almost continuous intercrystalline network in the cast metal. **Alcan Alloy AA 8280,** of Alcan Aluminum Corp., has only 6% tin for high-duty bearings. The bearing known as **Moraine 400,** of the General Motors Corp., contains 4% silicon, 1 cadmium, and the balance aluminum. The alloy is made in strips with a steel backing, and has a thin electrodeposit bearing surface of a lead-tin-copper babbitt-type alloy. The trimetal combination offers the antifrictional advantages of a babbitt bearing, with up to 10 times the service life. **Alloy 750,** also used for automotive engine bearings, does not require a steel backing. It contains 6.5% tin, 2.5 silicon, 1 copper, 0.5 nickel, and the balance aluminum. **Magnesium bearings** are used on such products as small pumps where the die-cast metal is employed without inserts or bushings to operate with a hardened steel shaft. Alloys used are 94% magnesium and 6 tin, or 70 magnesium, 20 cadmium, and 10 lead.

Unlike metals are invariably used for shaft and bearing, and the wear is taken in the bearing. The choice of a bearing metal is usually a compromise of hardness, compressive strength, coefficient of friction, and degree of lubrication. In general, the tin-base alloys have low coefficients of friction and are tough and capable of withstanding shocks, but the copper bronzes are capable of withstanding heavier loads. Between the two, almost any desired combination can be obtained, depending upon the proportions of copper, tin, antimony, and lead. Load-carrying capacity is figured on the projected area surface. Babbitts are usually limited to 300°F operating temperatures, and the tin and lead bronzes to 500°F. Nickel or silver in small amounts improves the hardness and strength of babbitts at higher temperatures. Some constituents of the alloys have a catalytic action on the lubricants. Tin in a bearing metal reduces the tendency of the lubricating oil to sludge, but the presence of an alkali metal may have an injurious effect on the oil. **Indium bearings,** for aircraft, are made by plating the steel backing with silver and then with lead, over which is plated the indium, and then diffused by heating. A lead-indium alloy results, which gives a strong, hard surface with good bearing properties and resistance to the corrosion of oils.

Self-lubricating bearings, or **oilless bearings,** may be porous metals impregnated with oil or graphite, or they may be oil-impregnated wood. **Oilite bearings,** of the Amplex Div., Chrysler Corp., are of porous iron or bronze with a content of 18 to 23% oil. The porous iron is for low speeds at medium to heavy loads, and the bronze for high-speed bearings for appliances, motors, and power tools. The iron has a specific gravity of 6.1 to 6.5, and a tensile strength of 10,000 psi, and the bronze has a density of 6.4 to 6.7 and a tensile strength of 18,000 psi.

Copper sponge, used for bearings, is made by molding a mixture of copper powder and a volatile organic material, sintering to drive off the volatile matter and adhere the copper particles, and then impregnating the porous copper with lead. Molded carbon is also used for bearings where there is need for resistance to corrosive chemicals. **Purabon 5,** of the Pure Carbon Co., is a carbon-graphite mixture molded in the form of bearings and bushings for use in chemical and food equipment.

Trade names are used to designate bearing materials. **Ryertex** is the name of a laminated plastic bearing material, and **Aqualite,** of the National Vulcanized Fibre Co., is the name of laminated plastic marine bearings. **Parock,** of Raybestos-Manhattan, Inc., is an oilless bearing made with graphite bonded with 20% vulcanized rubber. The coefficient of friction is 0.1 to 0.13 dry and 0.05 to 0.08 wet. **Fluoroglas,** of the Fluorolon Laboratories, Inc., is a compound of fluorocarbon resin with glass particles and a mineral pigment, used for oilless marine bearings. The coefficient of friction is 0.04. It has high resistance to wear, and will withstand operating temperatures to 500°F. The Durometer hardness is D50 to D65. **Nolu** is an oil-impregnated **wood bearing** of the Nolu Oilless Bearing Co., and **Woodex** is a similar bearing of the Neveroil Bearing Co. These woods are normally maple, but lignum vitae may be used. **Phosphor lignum,** of the latter company, is a hardwood, oil-impregnated bearing. **Powdiron,** of the Bound Brook Oil-Less Bearing Co., is a porous iron sintered bearing that will hold up to 25% lubricant.

BEECH. The wood of several species of beech trees, *Fagus atropunicea, F. ferruginea,* and *F. grandifolia,* common to the eastern parts of the United States and Canada. The wood is strong, compact, fine-grained, durable, and of a light color similar in appearance to maple. The weight is 47 lb per cu ft. It is employed for tool handles, shoe lasts, gunpowder charcoal, veneer, cooperage, pulpwood, and for small wooden articles such as clothespins. The beech formerly used for aircraft, *F. grandifolia,* has a specific gravity, oven-dried, of 0.66, a compressive strength perpendicular to the grain of 1,670 psi, and a shearing strength parallel to the grain of 1,300 psi. The wood may be obtained in large pieces, as the tree grows to a height of 100 ft and a diameter of 4 ft. It grows from the Gulf of Mexico northward into eastern Canada. **White beech** refers to the light-colored heartwood. **Red beech** is from trees with dark-colored heartwood. The sapwood of beech is white tinged with red and is almost indistinguishable from the heartwood. The wood is noted for its uniform texture and its shock resistance.

Antarctic beech, *F. antarctica,* known locally as **rauli,** grows extensively in southern Chile. It is commonly called by the Spanish word **roble,** or oak, in South America, and is used for cooperage to replace oak. It has a coarser grain than American beech. **European beech,** *F. sylvatica,* is reddish in color, has a close, even texture, is not as heavy as American beech, but is used for tools, furniture, and small articles. **New Zealand beech,** known as **red beech** and **tawhai,** is from the very large tree *Nothofagus solandri.* The wood weighs 44 lb per cu ft, is brown in color, and has high strength and durability. **Silver beech,** of New Zealand, is *N. menziesii.* The trees grow to a height of 80 ft and a diameter of 2 ft. The wood is light-brown, straight-grained, strong, and weighs 34 lb per cu ft. It is used for furniture, implements, and cooperage.

BEEF. The edible meat from full-grown beef cattle, *Bos taurus.* The meat from the younger animals that have not eaten much grass is called **veal** and is lighter in color and softer. The production of beef and beef products is one of the great industries of the world. In the industrial countries, much of the beef is prepared in organized packing plants, but also the production from city slaughterhouses is important. After slaughter and preparation of the animal, the beef is marketed in animal quarters either chilled or frozen.   Fresh-killed beef from local slaughterhouses is also chilled to remove animal heat before marketing.   The amount of marketable beef averages 55 to 61% of the live weight of the animal. The hide is from 5 to 7%, the edible and inedible fat and tallow are 3.5 to 7.5%, and the bones, gelatin, and glue material are 2.8 to 4.9%.   The average live weight of cattle slaughtered in American packing plants is 980 lb.   From 10 to 17% of the live weight may be shrinkage and value-less materials, although the **tankage,** which includes entrails and scraps, is sold as fertilizer.   **Offal** includes tongues, hearts, brains, tripe (stomach lining), livers, tails, and head, and may be from 3 to 5.5% of the live weight.   The **glands** are used for the production of insulin.   **Lipids** is the name for a yellow waxy solid melting at 100°C, extracted from beef spinal cord after removal of cholesterol.   It contains phosphatides and complex acids, and is used in medicine as an emulsifier and anticoagulant. **Cortisone,** used in medicine, is a steroid produced from ox bile, but now made synthetically.

Canned beef, which includes **corned beef, canned hash** (beef mixed with potatoes), and various **potted meats,** is not ordinarily made from the beef of animals suitable for sale as chilled or frozen beef, but is from tough or otherwise undesirable meat animals, or from animals rejected by government inspectors as not suitable for fresh beef.   In the latter case the beef canned is held at high temperature for a sufficient length of time to destroy any bacteria likely to be in the fresh meat.   Federal specifications for canned corned beef require freedom from skin, tendons, and excessive fat, and a maximum content of not more than 3.25% salt and 0.2 saltpeter.   Government inspection of beef for health standards is rigid, but the Federal grading of beef is little more than a rough price evaluation.

Beef extract was first made by Prof. Justus von Liebig in 1840 as a heavy concentrated paste that could be kept indefinitely.   It is now made on a large scale in both paste and cube forms, and used for soups and hot beverages, but much of the extract marketed in bouillon cubes is highly diluted with vegetable protein.   The so-called nonmeat beef extract is made with corn and wheat hydrolysates and yeast.   Pure **nonfat beef extract** is used in the food-processing industry for soups, gravies, and prepared dishes.   The extract of International Packers, Ltd., is a paste of 17% moisture content.   It contains thiamine, niacin, riboflavin, pyrodoxine, pantothenic acid, vitamins B_1 and B_{12}, purine, creatine, and the nutrient proteins found only in meat.   **Dehydrated beef** is lean beef dried by mechanical means into flake or powder forms.   It is semicooked and, when wet with water, resumes its original consistency but has a somewhat cooked taste.   Its advantage is the great saving in shipping space.   Beef is also marketed in the form of **dried beef,** usually sliced and salted.   **Jerked beef,** or **tasajo,** is beef that has been cut into strips and dried in the sun.   It is used in some Latin American countries, but has a strong taste.

BEESWAX. The wax formed and deposited by the honey bee, *Apis mellifica.*   The bees build combs for the reception of the honey, consisting of two sheets of horizontal, six-angled prismatic cells formed of wax. After the extraction of the honey, the wax is melted and molded into cakes.   New wax is light yellow, but turns brown with age.   It may be bleached with sunlight or with acids.   It is composed largely of a complex long-chain ester, **myricil palmitate,** $C_{15}H_{31}COOC_{30}H_{61}$, and **cerotic acid,** $C_{25}H_{51}COOH$.   The specific gravity is 0.965 to 0.969, and the melting point 63°C.   It is easily colored with dyes, and the Germans marketed powdered beeswax in various colors for compounding purposes.   Beeswax is used for polishes, candles, leather dressings, adhesives, cosmetics, molded articles, as a protective coating for etching, and as a filler in thin metal tubes for bending.   It is frequently adulterated with paraffin, stearin, or vegetable waxes, and the commercial article may be below 50% pure.   The standards for the Toilet Goods Assoc. require that it shall contain no carnauba wax, stearic acid, paraffin, or ceresin, and shall not show more than 0.01% ash content.   Beeswax is produced in many parts of the world as a by-product of honey production from both wild and domesticated bees, the honey being used as a sweetening agent or for the making of alcoholic beverages.   **Honey** varies greatly in flavor owing to the different flowers upon which the bees feed, but the chemical properties of both the honey and the wax vary little.   Honey is composed largely of fructose.   In the food industry small proportions are added to the sugar to enhance the flavor of cookies and bakery products.   Honey, normally 82% solids, is also dehydrated to a free-flowing **honey powder** used in confectionery.   Sugar may be added to raise the softening temperature and make the powder more resistant to caking.   West Africa produces much wax from wild bees.   Abyssinia is a large producer of beeswax, where the honey is used for making **tej,** an alcoholic drink.   The ancient drink known as **mead** was fermented honey.   **Scale wax** is produced by removing the combs from the hives, thus forcing production of wax which is dropped in scales or particles by the bees and prevented from being picked up by a screen.

BELL METAL. A bronze used chiefly for casting large bells.   The composition is varied to give varying tones, but the physical requirements are that the castings must be uniform, compact, and fine-grained.   The standard is 78% copper and 22 tin, which alloy weighs 0.312 lb per cu in., is yellowish red, has a fine grain, is easily fusible, and gives a clear tone. Increasing the copper slightly increases the sonorous tone. Large bells of deeper tone are made of 75% copper and 25 tin. Big Ben, at Westminster, cast in 1856, contains 22 parts copper and 7 tin. Another bell metal, containing 77% copper, 21 tin, and 2 antimony, is harder, giving a sharper tone. An alloy for fire-engine bells contains 20% tin, 2 nickel, 0.1 silicon for deoxidation, and the balance copper. The nickel reduces the tendency to embrittlement from pounding. A bell metal marketed by the Lumen Bronze Co. contains 80% copper and 20 tin, deoxidized with phosphorus. **Silver bell metal,** for bells of silvery tone, is a white alloy containing 40% copper and 60 tin. This type of alloy, with tin contents up to as high as 60%, is also used for valves and valve seats in food machinery.

BENTONITE. A **colloidal clay** which has the property of being hydrophilic, or water-swelling, some clay absorbing as much as 5 times its own weight of water. It is used in emulsions, adhesives, for oil-well drilling mud, to increase plasticity of ceramic clays, and as a bonding clay in foundry molding sands. In combination with alum and lime it is used in purifying water as it captures the fine particles of silt. Because of its combined abrasive and colloidal properties it is much used in soaps and washing compounds. It is also used as an absorbent in refining oils, as a suspending agent in emulsions, and in lubricants.

Bentonite occurs in sediment deposits from a few inches to 10 ft thick. It is stated to have been formed through the devitrification and chemical alteration of glassy igneous materials such as volcanic ash, and is a secondary mineral composed of deposits from the mineral **leverrierite,** $2Al_2O_3 \cdot 5SiO_2 \cdot 5H_2O$, crystallizing in the orthorhombic system, though some of the bentonite marketed may be montmorillonite. The finely powdered bentonite from Wyoming was originally called **wilkinite.** Wyoming bentonite is characterized by a very sticky nature and soapy feel when wet, and it is highly absorbent. Bentonites are usually light in color, from cream to olive green. Some have little swelling property, and some are gritty. The material from Otay, Calif., has been called **otaylite.** It is brownish and not as highly colloidal as **Wyoming bentonite.** Analyses of bentonites from various areas vary from 54 to 69% silica, 13 to 18 alumina, 2 to 4 ferric oxide, 0.12 to 3.5 ferrous oxide, 1 to 2.2 lime, 1.8 to 3.6 magnesia, 0.1 to 0.6 titania, 0.5 to 2 soda, and 0.14 to 0.46 potash. The material known as **hectorite** from California is lower in silica and alumina, and higher in magnesia and lime. In general, the highly colloidal bentonites contain the highest percentages of soda which have been adsorbed by the clay particles. Most crude bentonites contain impurities, but are purified by washing and treating.

Bentonites are marketed under various trade names such as **Volclay** of the American Colloid Co., **Refinite** of the Refinite Zeolite Co., and **Eyrite** of the Baroid Division, National Lead Co. **Bentone,** produced in various grades by the National Lead Co., is purified montmorillonite. It is a fine white powder of 200 mesh, and is used as a gelling agent for emulsion paints, adhesives, and coatings. **Bentone 18-C** is an organic compound of the material used for gelling polar organic materials such as cellulose lacquers and vinyl solutions.

BENZENE. Also called **benzol.** A colorless, highly inflammable liquid of the composition C_6H_6. It is an aromatic hydrocarbon obtained as a by-product of coke ovens or in the manufacture of gas, and also made synthetically from petroleum. Its molecular structure is the closed **benzene ring** with six CH groups in the linkage, which forms a convenient basic chemical for the manufacture of styrene and other chemicals. It is also an excellent solvent for waxes, resins, rubber, and other organic materials. It is also employed as a fuel or for blending with gasoline or other fuels. Industrially pure benzene has a distillation range from 78.1 to 82.1°C, a specific gravity of 0.875 to 0.886, and a flash point below 60°F. The pure nitration grade, used for nitrating and for making organic chemicals, has a 1°C boiling range starting not below 79.2°C, and a specific gravity of 0.882 to 0.886. Benzene has a characteristic odor, is soluble in alcohol but insoluble in water, and all of its combinations are toxic. The terms **aromatic chemicals** and **aromatics** refer to all of the chemicals made from the benzene ring.

Nitrobenzene, $C_6H_5NO_2$, is a highly poisonous and inflammable liquid made by the action of nitric and sulfuric acids on benzene, used in soaps and cosmetics. It is called **myrbane oil** as a perfuming agent. The nitrated derivative called **benzedrine,** or **amphetamine,** originally used by wartime pilots to combat fatigue, is **phenyl amino benzine,** $C_6H_5 \cdot CH_2 \cdot CH(NH)_2 \cdot CH_3$. It is used in medicine to control obesity, but it is a stimulant to the central nervous system and is habituating. The isomer dextroamphetamine is d-phenyl amino propane sulfate, commonly called **Dexedrine.** It causes a rise in blood pressure and stimulates cerebral activity which lasts several hours, but it has a depressant effect on the intestinal muscles, causing loss of appetite and delayed activity of the stomach with other side effects.

Diphenyl carbonate, $(C_6H_5)_2CO_3$, is much used for the manufacture of chemicals where two benzene rings are desired. It is a white crystalline water-insoluble solid melting at 78°C. **Benzyl alcohol,** $C_6H_5CH_2OH$, is a colorless liquid soluble in water, having a boiling point of 205.2°C and a freezing point of -15.3°C. It is also called **phenylcarbinol,** and is used as a solvent for resins, lacquers, and paints. **Benzyl chloride,**

$C_6H_5CH_2Cl$, is a colorless liquid of specific gravity 1.103 and boiling point 179°C, which was used as a lachrymatory gas, and is employed in the production of plastics. **Benzyl cellulose** is a thermoplastic plastic of the Imperial Chemical Industries, Ltd., produced by the action of benzyl chloride and caustic soda on cellulose. The plastic is noninflammable, resistant to acids, can be molded easily, and is produced in various grades by different degrees of benzylation. **Benzyl dichloride,** $C_6H_5CH \cdot Cl_2$, is a liquid heavier than benzyl chloride and has a higher boiling point, 212°C, but was also used as a war gas. It is also called **benzylidene chloride** and is used for producing dyestuffs.

BERYLLIUM. A steel-gray, lightweight, very hard metallic element, symbol Be, formerly known as **glucinum.** The specific gravity is 1.847, melting point 1285°C, and hardness 170 Brinell. The metal is produced in small crystalline lumps by chemical reduction, remelted, and converted to **beryllium powder** of 100 to 325 mesh, 99.6% pure. The wrought metal, obtained by powder metallurgy and hot rolling, has a tensile strength up to 90,000 psi with elongation of 15%.

Beryllium is not a tonnage metal, and the cost of finished sheet and forms ranks it almost as a precious metal. Its chief commercial use is for hardening copper and nickel for beryllium bronzes. It will also harden 18-carat gold to 300 Brinell. However, the pure metal has many uses where its high cost is permissible, chiefly in military, electronic, and atomic applications. As a structural metal the strength-weight ratio is equal to a steel that would have a tensile strength of 450,000 psi. Its stiffness is also much greater than that of steel. It resists oxidation to 1500°F, forming a protective film of oxide, and will retain 50% of its yield strength at 1000°F. But at 1750°F its strength drops to 200 to 300 psi. **Beryllium wire** is used for high temperature electronic circuits and small-instrument motor windings. The 0.005-in. wire has a tensile strength of 185,000 psi.

The low atomic number and low density of beryllium make it highly pervious even to long X-rays, the permeability to X-rays being about 17 times that of aluminum. It has also the lowest neutron cross section of any metal melting above 500°C. It is valued for X-ray windows and for atomic applications. It is a good source of neutrons when bombarded by alpha rays. It has a high capacity for conducting and absorbing heat, its specific heat factor being more than four times that of titanium, and it is thus used for heat sinks in missiles to absorb the frictional heat. The metal is nonmagnetic. It is not resistant to mineral acids, and above 900°C it is attacked by nitrogen to form **beryllium nitride,** Be_3N_2. The atom of beryllium is not spherical, and the unit molecule appears to be a flat hexagon. The structure of the metal grains is thus cryptocrystalline.

BERYLLIUM ALLOYS. Beryllium bronze refers to alloys of copper and beryllium containing usually not more than 3% beryllium. They are sometimes designated as **beryllium copper,** although this term is more generally used to mean the master foundry alloys. The alloys are tough, and have a bronzelike crystalline structure. They are noted for their fatigue resistance, and were first employed in Germany for locomotive bearings and for springs. Beryllium bronze is now employed for springs, nonsparking tools, plastic molds, and strong mechanical parts. Its fatigue resistance is utilized in setting diamonds in drill bits. Silicon in small amounts is added to beryllium bronze to harden and strengthen the alloy further by the formation of Be_2Si. Nickel and cobalt also form chemical compounds with beryllium. A small amount of nickel refines the grain and increases the ductility. It is especially useful for this purpose in castings. A very small amount of iron, 0.25%, improves the structure and increases the hardness. A cast beryllium bronze produced by Ampco Metals, Inc., has 2.5% beryllium, and has a hardness of 325 to 375 when heat-treated. **Berylco alloy 165,** produced by the Beryllium Corp. in rods and strip, contains 1.7% beryllium. The No. 1 hard alloy has a tensile strength of 100,000 psi, can be bent 180° without fracture, and has an electrical conductivity 23% that of copper. **Beryldur,** of this company, is a lower-cost alloy with 1% beryllium. In thin sheet it has good formability and a tensile strength, when age-hardened, of 135,000 psi. The electrical conductivity is 18 to 26% that of copper. It is employed for such uses as switch gear, as it is corrosion- and erosion-resistant. Alloys for plastic molds usually have about 2% beryllium, and will harden to 365 Brinell. These alloys are also used for dies for drawing alloy steels, as they do not pick up metal on the drawing radius.

The wrought alloy called beryllium copper by the American Brass Co. has 2 to 2.5% beryllium and 0.25 to 0.50 nickel. The soft material has a tensile strength of 70,000 psi, elongation 45%, and hardness 110 Brinell, while the heat-treated alloy has a tensile strength of 193,000 psi, elongation 2%, and hardness 365 Brinell. It is valued for springs. Beryllium copper of this kind is also used for spot-welder contacts, and about 1.5% titanium may be added to give hardness stability at elevated temperatures. Wrought beryllium bronze is marketed regularly in the form of rods, wire, and strip as a product of the brass mills. A standard alloy contains 2% beryllium, 0.60 nickel plus cobalt, and the balance copper. The annealed alloy has a tensile strength of 60,000 psi, and a Rockwell B hardness of 70. When precipitation-hardened, the tensile strength is 160,000 psi, and the Rockwell C hardness is 40. Or the alloy can be cold-rolled to a hardness of Rockwell B95 with a tensile strength of 100,000 psi, and then precipitation-hardened to Rockwell C45 with a tensile strength of 185,000 psi. **Berylco 717C,** of the Beryllium Corp., has 68.8% copper, 30 nickel, and 0.5 beryllium. The heat-treated castings have a tensile strength of 118,000 psi, elongation of 12%, and a hardness of Rockwell C23. **Viculoy** is the name of a group of beryllium bronzes of the Akron Bronze & Aluminum Co. for high-strength castings to replace aluminum bronze and manganese bronze for gears and marine parts.

Wrought alloys of high electrical conductivity, 50% that of copper, have no more than 0.50% beryllium, with 1.5% cobalt to give a heat-treated strength up to 130,000 psi. **Ampcoloy 91,** of Ampco Metal, Inc., **Tuffalloy 55,** of the Welding Sales & Engineering Co., and **Trodaloy 1,** of the General Electric Co., are **beryllium-cobalt alloys** with 2.6% cobalt, 0.40 beryllium, and the remainder copper. The cast metal has a tensile strength of 90,000 psi, elongation 10%, and electrical conductivity 45% that of copper. The hardness is 96 Rockwell B. The wrought metal, used for springs and tips for soldering irons, has a tensile strength of 60,000 psi, and will withstand higher temperatures than regular beryllium bronze. This alloy, of the Wilber B. Driver Co., for resistance wire, is called **Beraloy C.** The **Trodaloy 7,** of the General Electric Co., contains 0.40% chromium, 0.10 beryllium, and the balance copper. It is used for high-strength electrical parts. A high-conductivity beryllium bronze for electrical parts has 0.50% beryllium and a small amount of silver. Tensile strength is 90,000 psi, and the electrical conductivity is 60 to 65% that of copper.

A beryllium-cobalt alloy intermediate in physical characteristics between beryllium bronze and phosphor bronze contains only 0.5% beryllium, with 2 to 3 cobalt, and the balance copper. The heat-treated alloy has a hardness of 92 to 98 Rockwell B, and an electrical conductivity 50 to 60% that of copper. **Beryllium alloy 50,** of the Beryllium Corp., contains 0.35% beryllium, 1.55 cobalt, and 1 silver. The tensile strength is up to 130,000 psi, and the electrical conductivity is 50% that of copper. **Silvercote wire,** of the Little Falls Alloys, contains 0.5% beryllium, 2.5 cobalt, and the balance copper. The electrical conductivity is 65 to 70% that of copper, and the strength and fatigue resistance are comparable with higher beryllium alloys. The wire is lightly silver-plated for easy soldering.

A **beryllium-nickel alloy** for springs has 1.9% beryllium, 0.50 manganese, and the remainder nickel. The tensile strength, cold-rolled and heat-treated, is 200,000 psi, with elongation of 6%. It is noted for high torsional endurance. **Beryllium-nickel 260-C,** of the Brush Beryllium Co., has 2.55 to 2.8% beryllium, 0.40 carbon, and the balance nickel. The cast metal has a tensile strength up to 125,000 psi and Rockwell hardness C30. After heat treatment the strength is up to 210,000 psi. The alloy is magnetic. Its electrical conductivity is less than 3% that of copper.   It is used for valves, turbine blades, and molds for glass.   **Lock-alloy,** of the Beryllium Corp., for lightweight structural use, is a beryllium-aluminum alloy with 62% beryllium and 38 aluminum.   It has a specific gravity of 2.09, tensile strength of 55,000 psi, yield strength of 40,000, and a service temperature up to 800°F.

BERYLLIUM ORES. Beryllium occurs widely distributed in possibly re-coverable quantities in more than 30 minerals, but the chief ore is **beryl,** $3BeO \cdot Al_2O_3 \cdot 6SiO_2 \cdot H_2O$.   This mineral is usually in pale-yellow rhombic crystals in pegmatic dikes.   The crystals are $\frac{1}{4}$ to $\frac{1}{2}$ in. in diameter, with a specific gravity of 2.63 to 2.90, and a Mohs hardness of 7.5 to 8. The ore is resistant to acid attack and requires calcining to make it reac-tive, though the ore of Utah, called **vitroite,** is of simpler composition and can be acid-leached.   Beryl ore may contain up to 15% beryllium oxide, but most ore averages below 4%.   The Indian ore contains a minimum of 12% BeO, and the beryl of Ontario has 14% BeO, or 5% metallic beryl-lium.   The ore of Nevada contains only 1% BeO, but can be concentrated to 20%.

The secondary ores of beryllium, **bertrandite, herderite,** and **beryllonite,** usually have only small quantities of BeO disseminated in the mineral, but Utah clay from Topaz Mountain, Utah, in which the bertrandite is associated with pyrolusite, fluorspar, opal, and mixed with montmoril-lonite and other clays, is concentrated by flotation, acid-leached, and chem-ically processed to 97% BeO.   Other ores of beryllium are **chrysoberyl,** $BeO \cdot Al_2O_3$, and **phenacite,** which is a **beryllium silicate,** Be_2SiO_4. **Helv-ite,** $(MnFe)_2(Mn_2S)Be_2(SiO_2)_3$, is in cubical crystals of various colors from yellow through green to dark brown, associated with garnet and having the appearance of garnet.   The specific gravity is 3.3, and the hard-ness 6.5.

Choice crystals of beryl, colored with metallic oxides, are cut as gem-stones.   The **emerald** is a flawless beryl colored green with chromium. High-grade natural emeralds are found in Colombia, but occur in the United States only in North Carolina.   The rose-pink, rose-red, and green beryl crystals of Malagasy, called **morganite,** are cut as gemstones, and the dark-blue stone is made by heating the green crystals.   The pale blue-green crystals are **aquamarines** and the **heliodor** is **golden beryl** from Southwest Africa.   But the yellowish-green gemstone of Brazil, called **brazilianite,** is not beryl, but is a hydrous sodium-aluminum phosphate, and is softer.   Crystals of chrysoberyl of lemon-yellow color found in Brazil are valued as gemstones.   Synthetic emerald of the composition $3BeO \cdot Al_2O_3 \cdot 6SiO_2$ was first made in Germany by heat and pressure under the name of **Igmerald.**   Synthetic emeralds are now grown from high-purity alumina, beryllia, and silica, with traces of Cr_2O_3 and Fe_2O_3 to give the green color.   Synthetic beryl is used for bearings in watches and instruments.

BERYLLIUM OXIDE.   A colorless to white crystalline powder of the composition BeO, also called **beryllia,** and known in mineralogy as **bromellite.**   It has a specific gravity of 3.025, a high melting point, about 2585°C, and a Knoop hardness of 2,000.   It is used for polishing hard metals and for making hot-pressed ceramic parts.   Its high heat resistance and thermal conductivity make it useful for crucibles, and its high dielectric strength makes it suitable for high-frequency insulators.   Single-crystal **beryllia fibers,** or whiskers, developed by the National Beryllia Corp., have a tensile strength above 1,000,000 psi.

Hot-pressed and machined parts of beryllium oxide, produced by the Beryllium Corp., for electronic, aircraft, and missile applications, have a density 95% of the theoretical density, a melting point of 4658°F, a dielectric constant of 5.8, and a neutron-absorption cross section of 0.010. Parts have a tensile strength of 15,000 psi and compressive strength of 150,000 psi, and at a temperature of 2000°F they retain a tensile strength of 8,000 psi.

Beryllia is also used in ceramics to produce gas-tight glazes, and for this purpose was called **Degussit** in Germany.   Thin films of the oxide are used on silver and other metals to protect the metal from discoloration. Very thin films are invisible, but heavier films give a faint iridescence. Two other beryllium compounds used especially in chemical manufacturing are **beryllium chloride,** $BeCl_2$, a water-soluble white powder melting at 440°C, and **beryllium fluoride,** BeF_2, melting at 800.   Another beryllium compound, useful for high-temperature, wear-resistant ceramics, is **beryllium carbide,** Be_2C.   The crystals have a hardness of 9 Mohs, and the compressed and sintered powder has a compressive strength above 100,000 psi.   **Berlox,** of the National Beryllia Corp., is a beryllium oxide powder in particle sizes from 80 to 325 mesh for flame-sprayed heat- and wear-resistant coatings.   The powder melts at 4650°F.

BESSEMER STEEL.   Steel made by blowing air through molten iron. The process, developed by Henry Bessemer in England in 1860, made possible for the first time the production of steel on a large scale.   The process is now employed extensively as a preliminary step in the production of other steels, but much bar steel is made by this process.   Ferromanganese and sometimes steel scrap are added to the steel when pouring into the ladle in order to regulate the content.   In the blowing process the chemical action between the oxygen of the air and the molten mass increases the temperature, and the air then forms the chief fuel as the carbon is oxidized and driven off.   The blowing requires only a few minutes, and the carbon is reduced to 0.04% or less. The carbon desired in the steel is then regulated by the addition of carbon to the melt. The two processes, known as acid and basic, differ in the type of refractories employed for lining the converters, and there is a difference in the resulting steel since the acid process does not remove as much sulfur and phosphorus. The acid process is used principally in the United States, and the basic process is employed in Europe where the product is called **Thomas steel.** The lining of an acid converter may be ganister or other refractory acid material. The Brassert process, invented in Austria, makes a high-quality bessemer steel by blowing oxygen through the molten steel. The oxygen must be pure, 99.5%, and nitrogen-free.

Acid **bessemer pig iron** should contain about 1% silicon, but the sulfur and phosphorus must be low. An acid bessemer steel to be free-cutting has a content of 0.09 to 0.13% phosphorus and 0.075 to 0.15 sulfur, but these amounts are too high for structural steels, so that bessemer steel is mostly employed in rod form for making screw-machine products. A good-quality acid bessemer steel contains about 0.15% carbon, 0.40 to 0.80 manganese, and up to 0.08 each of sulfur and phosphorus. For basic bessemer steel the converter has a basic lining of burned dolomite, and the basic bessemer iron has less silicon to avoid the production of much silica. The high-phosphorus pig irons of Europe are made into steel by this process, as the basic lining aids in the elimination of the phosphorus and sulfur, although lime is also added at the beginning of the blow. Low-carbon, low-manganese, basic bessemer steel, deoxidized with aluminum and called **killed steel,** is used to replace open-hearth steels for cold-forming applications. The tensile strength is 47,000 to 57,000 psi, with elongations from 28 to 37%. **Synthetic steel scrap** to replace ordinary steel scrap for open-hearth steel can be made in bessemer converters by partly blowing and then casting into ingots for the furnace charge.

BIRCH. The wood of the birch trees, of which more than 15 varieties grow in the northeastern and Lake states of the United States and in Canada, and other varieties in Europe and north Asia. The birch of north Europe is called **Russian maple.** The wood of the American birches has a yellow color, is tough, strong, hard, and close-textured, and polishes well. It has a fine wavy grain sometimes beautifully figured, and can be stained to imitate cherry and mahogany. Birch is used in construction work for trim and paneling, for furniture, and for turned articles such as handles, shoe pegs, clothespins, toys, and woodenware. The lumber usually includes the wood of several species. It has a specific gravity, oven-dried, of 0.68, a compressive strength perpendicular to the grain of 1,590 psi, and a shearing strength parallel to the grain of 1,300 psi. **Yellow**

birch, *Betula lutea,* highly prized for furniture, is now getting scarce. It is also called **silver birch** and **swamp birch.** The commercial wood includes that from the **gray birch,** *B. populifolia.* **Sweet birch,** *B. lenta,* ranks next in importance. It is called **black birch, cherry birch,** and **mahogany birch,** and may be marketed together with yellow birch. Sweet birch may also include **river birch,** *B. nigra,* but sweet birch is a heavier and stronger wood. **Paper birch,** *B. papyrifera,* is the variety known as **canoe birch** because the silvery-white flexible bark was used by the Indians in making canoes. It is also referred to as silver birch, and is much used for pulpwood. It is similar to and mixed with **white birch,** *B. alba,* the wood of which is strong, elastic, and uniform, and is much used in Vermont and New Hampshire for making spools, bobbins, handles, and toys. Yellow birch of the Canadian border reaches a height of 60 to 80 ft and a diameter up to 2 ft. A 50-year-old tree has a diameter of about 15 in. and a height of 40 ft.

Birch oil is a viscous, yellowish, poisonous oil of specific gravity 0.956, with a characteristic birch odor, obtained by distilling **birch tar,** a product of the dry distillation of the wood of the white birch. It contains phenols, cresol, and xylenol, and is used in disinfectants and in pharmaceuticals. It also called **birch tar oil,** and in pharmacy is known as **oil of white birch.** **Sweet birch oil,** also known as **betula oil,** is a lighter volatile oil distilled from the steeped bark of the *B. lenta,* or sweet birch. It contains methyl salicylate, and is used as a flavoring agent, in perfumes, in dressing fancy leathers, in cleaning solutions and soaps, and as a disinfectant to neutralize odors of organic compounds.

BISMUTH. An elementary metal, symbol Bi, sometimes occurring native in small quantities. American bismuth is obtained chiefly as a by-product in the refining of lead and copper. Foreign bismuth comes largely from the mineral bismuthinite. The chief production of bismuth is in the United States, Peru, Canada, Bolivia, and Mexico. The metal has a grayish-white color with a reddish tinge, is very brittle, and powders easily. It is highly crystalline in rhombohedral crystals. Its cleavage is due to its sixfold coordination structure in which each atom is closer and more strongly attached to three of its neighbors than to the other three. It has few uses in its pure state. The specific gravity is 9.75, melting point 271°C, and hardness 73 Brinell. The thermal conductivity is less than that of any other metal except mercury, and the coefficient of expansion is 0.00000731 per deg F. It is the most diamagnetic of all the metals. It has the property of expanding 3.32% when changing from the liquid to the solid state, which makes it valuable in type-metal alloys and in making small castings where sharp impressions of the mold are needed. The metal imparts to lead and tin alloys hardness, sonorousness, luster, and a lowered melting point.   By regulating the amount of bismuth, it is possible to cast the alloys to fill the mold without expansion or contraction on cooling.   It is used in white alloys for molds for casting plastics, and because of the property of lowering the melting point it is valued in fusible alloys and in soft solders.   Very fine **bismuth wire** used for thermocouples is drawn in glass tubes, but extruded bismuth wire is marketed in diameters from 0.003 to 0.039 in., ductile enough to be wound on its own diameter without fracture.

Bismuth steel, with a very small content of bismuth, is used for transformer sheets.   It has increased electrical resistance without diminished electrical permeability and lowered hysteresis.   About 0.5% bismuth is used in some 18–8 stainless steels instead of selenium to add machinability without impairing the corrosion resistance.   Bismuth is also used in amalgams, and is employed in the form of its salts in pigments, in pharmaceuticals as an antacid, and in many chemicals.   For medicinal purposes bismuth must be completely free of traces of arsenic.   The paint pigment known as **pearl white** is **bismuth oxychloride,** BiOCl, a white crystalline powder of specific gravity 7.717, insoluble in water.   Another bismuth pigment is **bismuth chromate,** $Bi_2O_3 \cdot 2CrO_3$, a water-insoluble orange-red powder.   The material known in medicine as bismuth is **bismuth phosphate,** $BiPO_4$, a white powder insoluble in water.

BISMUTHINITE. An ore of the metal bismuth, found in Bolivia, Peru, central Europe, Australia, and western United States.   It is **bismuth trisulfide,** Bi_2S_3, containing theoretically 81.3% bismuth.   The richest Bolivian ores contain more than 25% bismuth, and concentrates from northwest Argentina contain 40 to 48% bismuth.   The mineral has a massive foliated structure with a metallic luster, a lead-gray streaked color, and a hardness of 2.   The concentrated ore is roasted and smelted with carbon, and the resulting impure bismuth is refined by an oxidizing fusion. Other bismuth ores are **bismite,** or **bismuth ocher,** $Bi_2O_3 \cdot 3H_2O$, containing theoretically 80.6% bismuth, and **bismutite,** $Bi_2O_3CO_3 \cdot H_2O$, containing theoretically 78.3% bismuth, both of which are widely distributed minerals.

BITUMINOUS COAL. Also called **soft coal.**   A variety of coal with a low percentage of carbon, and easily distinguished from anthracite by the property of losing moisture and breaking up into small pieces.   Because of its cheapness it is the coal used most extensively for industrial fuel, but is not preferred for household use because of its smoke and odor.   However, considerable of the fine or powdered coal called **slack coal** is used in making fuel briquettes.   Bituminous coal is widely distributed in many countries, and is found in 28 states of the United States.   The Bureau of

Mines estimated that the coalfields of the United States cover 350,000 sq mi, or one-ninth of the total area of the country.   Much bituminous coal is used for the production of coke, coal tar, liquid fuels, and chemicals. The bituminous coals vary in quality from near lignite to the hard grades near anthracite, called **semibituminous coal,** depending upon their geologic age.   They are not true bitumens.   The specific gravity of clean bituminous coal is 1.75 to 1.80.   The best steam coals are the semibituminous grades from West Virginia, Virginia, Pennsylvania, and some parts of the Middle West.   The latter is very compact and is extracted in large blocks, called **block coal.**   Good coals for industrial use should give 13,500 to 14,500 Btu per lb, and should have from 55 to 60% fixed carbon and 30 to 37 volatile matter.   The best grades are in lumps.   **Coking coals** are the higher-carbon grades low in sulfur, and with capacity to leave the residue coke in large firm lumps.   **Sea coal** is a name for finely ground bituminous coal used in sand mixtures for molds for cast iron to prevent fusing of the sand to the castings.

BLACKFISH OIL.   A pale-yellow waxy oil extracted from the pilot whale, porpoise, or blackfish, *Globicephala melas,* found off the North Atlantic Coast as far south as New Jersey, and the *G. ventricosa* of other seas. The blackfish averages 15 to 18 ft in length, with a weight of about 1,000 lb.   The oil has a saponification value of 290, iodine value 27, and specific gravity 0.929.   The **dolphin oil,** of the common dolphin, *Delphinus delphis,* of all seas, is also classed as blackfish oil, as is also the oil of the killer whale, *Grampus orca,* of all seas.   The oil is used as a lubricant for fine mechanisms, in cutting oils, and for treating leather.   The product from the head and jaw is of the best quality, and is known as **jaw oil,** although the best grade of sperm oil is also called jaw oil.   The jaw oil from blackfish does not oxidize easily, and is free-flowing at low temperatures, having a pour point of $-20°F$.   It consists of 71% mixed acids, of which 86% is **valeric acid,** $C_2H_5(CH_3)CHCOOH$, and 13% oleic and palmitic acids.   Normal valeric acid is methyl ethyl acetic acid, and can be made by the oxidation of amyl alcohol.   It is produced in the human system by the action of enzymes on amino acids.   **Arginine,** of General Mills, Inc., used for treatment of shock and for reducing the toxic effects of ammonia in the blood, is a **guanidine valeric acid.**   A variant of valeric acid is **levulinic acid,** a liquid boiling at 245°C, used for making synthetic resins.   It is produced as a by-product in the production of furfural from corncobs, and has the composition $CH_3COCH_2CH_2COOH$ with reactive methylene groups that undergo condensation readily.   It can also be produced from starches and sugars.

BOILER PLATE.   Originally, a high-grade plain iron or steel plate of $\%_{64}$ in. thickness or heavier, used for making steam boilers, but the term came to mean plate of this kind for any purpose, and plates ¼ in. thick or thinner are referred to as sheet.   Actually, boiler plates for boilers, tanks, and chemical equipment, and **flange plates** for dished ends, are now made in various alloy steels to incorporate high strength, corrosion resistance, and creep resistance, and also in clad steels.   Ordinary boiler plate is divided into firebox, flange, and extra-soft.   A plain steel **firebox plate** contains not more than 0.30% carbon, 0.30 to 0.50 manganese, and not more than 0.40 each of sulfur and phosphorus.   Flange plates contain less carbon.   The tensile strength is about 60,000 psi.   **Boiler-tube steel** may be carbon steel or alloy steels, and may be hot-rolled or cold-drawn. But the tubes are given an internal hydrostatic test and marked with the test pressure used.

Some of the **Croloy alloys** of the Babcock and Wilcox Co. are standard grades of stainless steels.   **Croloy 12** is Type 410 stainless, and **Croloy 18** is Type 430 stainless.   **Croloy 15–15N** will retain a tensile strength of 60,000 psi at 1200°F.   It contains 15% each of chromium and nickel, 1.5 molybdenum, 1.5 tungsten, 2 manganese, 0.75 silicon, and 0.15 carbon, with about 1.2 columbium-tantalum for stabilizing.   **Croloy 16–6PH,** for extruded shapes, has about 16% chromium, 6 nickel, up to 1 each manganese and silicon, with not over 0.12 carbon.   It has a tensile strength of 220,000 psi and Rockwell hardness C45.   **Croloy 16–1** is a low-nickel stainless steel.   It has 16% chromium, 1 nickel, 1 manganese, 0.75 silicon, and a maximum of 0.03 carbon.   The tensile strength is up to 95,000 psi with elongation of 28 to 38%.   Stainless-steel plate is much used for chemical boilers and pressure vessels for food and chemical plants, but copper and aluminum are also employed for these purposes.   The allowable pressure stress of pure aluminum is low, but some aluminum alloys have allowable pressure stresses higher than that of copper.   **Alcoa alloy A54S,** used for pressure vessels and truck tanks, has an ASTM allowable pressure stress of 7,350 psi compared with 6,700 psi for copper.   The alloy contains 3.1 to 3.9% magnesium, 0.15 to 0.35 chromium, with maximums of 0.10 copper, 0.10 manganese, 0.20 zinc, and 0.45 silicon plus iron.   As this alloy has high strength at subzero temperatures, it is also used for oxygen equipment.

BONES.   The dried bones from cattle and from Asiatic buffalo form an important item in international commerce.   In general, organized packing plants do not ship much bone, but utilize it for the production of glue, gelatin, bone meal, and fertilizer.   The bones shipped from packing plants are called **packer bones,** but the source of much commercial bone is from slaughterhouses, local retail meat shops, and the bones from farms and fields known as **prairie bones** and **camp bones,** the latter name being from the Argentine word campo, meaning field.   American imported bone comes from Argentina, Canada, Uruguay, Brazil, South Africa, and India. Large quantities were formerly used for making brush handles, buttons, knife handles, and other novelties, but for these uses plastics are now employed. **Raw bone meal** was the term for the scrap pieces and sawdust from the manufacture of these articles.

Case-hardening bone, for carbonizing steel, and **bone meal,** for animal feed, are processed to remove fats and prevent rancidity, and also steam-sterilized. **Fertilizer bone** is bone meal that is of too fine mesh for carbon-izing use or for making bone black, but it is not cooked or processed, and has an analysis of about 45% ammonia and 50 phosphate of lime. Knucklebones, and also the hard shinbones, are preferred for gelatin manufacture. **Dissolved bone,** used for fertilizer, is ground bone treated with sulfuric acid, or the residue bone after dissolving out the gelatin with acid. The **steamed bone meal** produced as a residue by-product of the glue factories and soup factories is suitable only for fertilizer, but it contains only 1% ammonia. The steamed bone meal for animal feed is merely steam-sterilized raw bone.

Bone black, also called **animal charcoal** and **bone char,** is charred bone ground to a fine silky powder for use as a pigment or as a decolorizing agent for sugar and oils. It has a deep, dense, bluish-black color valued for engraving inks of depth and tone, and to give a dull velvety-black finish to coated paper. Its covering power, however, is inferior to that of carbon black, as it has only about 10% carbon, is largely calcium phosphate, and has a very high ash content. The best blacks may be treated with acid to remove the lime salts. Federal specifications for bone black for pigment require that 97.5% shall pass through a 325-mesh screen. For filtering, the material used is from 4 to 16 mesh. The specific gravity is 2.6 to 2.8. Bone black is made by calcining ground, fat-free, dried bones in airtight retorts. One short ton of dried bones yields about 700 lb of bone black. About 75% of the bone-black production is used for refining sugar and syrups. It may be sold under trade names such as **Filt-char.** **Drop black** is the spent bone black from the decolorizing of sugar, which has been washed and reground for pigment use. **Ivory black,** having the same uses as bone black, is made by heating the refuse of ivory working in a closed retort and then grinding to a fine powder. **Aquablak No. 1,** of the Binney & Smith Co., is a water dispersion of bone black used to give a velvety-black color to inks, water paints, and leather finishes.

Bone oil, used in sheep dips and disinfectants, and in insecticides and fungicides, is a chemically complex oil with a pungent disagreeable odor derived as a by-product in the destructive distillation of bones. It contains nitrides, pyrroles, pyridine, and aniline.

BORAX. A white or colorless crystalline mineral used in glass and ceramic enamel mixes, as a scouring and cleansing agent, as a flux in melting metals and in soldering, as a corrosion inhibitor in antifreeze liquids, as a constituent in fertilizers, in the production of many chemicals and pharamaceuticals, and as a source of boron.   Borax is a hydrous **sodium borate,** or tetraborate, first obtained from Tibet under the Persian name **borak,** meaning white.   **Tincal** is the natural borax, $Na_2O \cdot 2B_2O_3 \cdot 10H_2O$, obtained originally through Iran from Tibet, and later found in quantity in western United States.   The specific gravity is 1.75, hardness 2 to 2.5, and melting point 1125°F.   It contains 47.2% water, and is readily soluble in water.   The borax from California and Nevada known as **colmanite** is **calcium borate,** $2CaO \cdot 3B_2O_3 \cdot 5H_2O$.   That known as **kernite,** or **rasorite,** is another variety of **sodium borate** of the composition $Na_2O \cdot 2B_2O_3 \cdot 4H_2O$. **Ulexite,** or **boronatrocalcite,** is found in western United States, Chile, Bolivia, and Peru, and has the composition $Na_2O \cdot 2CaO \cdot 5B_2O_3 \cdot 16H_2O$, but the ulexite of Chile and Bolivia is also mixed with sodium and calcium sulfates and sodium and magnesium chlorides.   The dried mineral contains 45 to 52% boric acid.   **Priceite,** or **pandermite,** chiefly from Asia Minor, is $5CaO \cdot 6B_2O_3 \cdot 9H_2O$.   All of these minerals are **boron ores** suitable for producing the metal.

Borax is found in great quantities in the desert regions of the western states, and in the Andean deserts of South America, where the borate deposits are in land-locked basins at altitudes above 11,000 ft.   The colmanite is usually associated with ulexite, shale, and clay, and is concentrated to 40% B_2O_3.   Kernite ore from Kern County, California, contains about 29% B_2O_3 and is concentrated to 45%.   Federal specifications for borax call for not less than 99.5% hydrous sodium borate in grades from large crystals to fine white powder.   **Pyrobar** is a crystalline anhydrous borax of the American Potash & Chemical Co., produced from the brine of Searles Lake.   **Puffed borax,** of this company, is an expanded borax powder with bulking density as low as 2 lb per cu ft which is very soluble and is used for detergents.

Boric acid, also called **boracic acid** and **orthoboric acid,** is a white, crystalline powder of the composition $B_2O_3 \cdot 3H_2O$, derived by adding hydrochloric or sulfuric acid to a solution of borax and crystallizing.   It is also obtained from the boron ores of California, Chile, Bolivia, and Peru as one of a number of chemicals.   It occurs naturally in volcanic fissures in Italy as the mineral **sassolite,** $B_2O_3 \cdot 3H_2O$.   The specific gravity is 1.435 and melting point 1050°F.   It is soluble in water and in alcohol. Boric acid is used as a preservative and weak antiseptic in glass and pottery mixes, in the tanning industry for deliming skins by forming calcium borates soluble in water, and as a flux in soldering and brazing.   **Anhydrous boric acid** is nearly pure **boric oxide.**   It is used in glass and ceramic enamels.

BORNEO TALLOW. A hard, brittle, yellowish-green solid fat obtained from the seed nuts of trees of the family *Dipterocarpaceae* of Borneo, Java, Sumatra, and Malaya.   They include the *Shorea aptera, S. robusta, S. stenoptera, Hopea aspera,* and *Pentacme siamensis,* which trees also produce copals and valuable woods.   The kernels of the nuts of the *S. stenoptera* contain 45 to 60% fat.   It contains 39% stearic acid, 38 oleic, 21.5 palmitic, and 1.5 myristic acid.   The specific gravity is 0.852 to 0.860, saponification value 185 to 200, iodine value 29 to 38, and melting point 34 to 39°C.   The seeds are exported as **Sarawak illipé** nuts or **Pontianak illipé,** but they are not the same as the **illipé nuts** and **illipé tallow** from the species of *Bassia* of India.   **Illipé butter,** also called **mowrah butter** and **bassia butter,** is from the seed nuts of the trees *B. longifolia* and *B. latifolia,* of India.   The oil content of the seeds is 50 to 60%.   The crude fat is yellow to green in color, but the refined product is colorless with a pleasant taste.   It is used as a food, and in soaps and candles. **Phulwa butter,** or **Indian butter,** is from the seed nuts of the *B. butyracea* of India.   It is white, stiffer than lard, and is used as a food.   **Siak tallow** is from the *Palanquium oleosum* of Malaya and various species of *Dipterocarpaceae* of Indonesia.   The nuts are smaller than the illipé, and are known as **calam seeds** in Sumatra.   The fat is yellow to greenish, and was used as a substitute for cocoa butter.   **Jaboty fat** is a similar heavy oil from the kernels of the fruit of the tree *Erisma calcaratum* of Brazil.   It contains 44% palmitic acid, 28 myristic, and 4 stearic acid, and has a melting point of 40 to 46°C.   The tropical forests of Brazil, Africa, and southern Asia abound in trees that produce a great variety of nuts from which useful fats and oils may be obtained.

BORON. A metallic element, symbol B, closely resembling silicon. When pure, it is in the form of red crystals or a brownish amorphous powder.   Crystalline boron in lumps of 99.5% purity is extremely hard, has a metallic sheen, is not hygroscopic and resists oxidation, and is a semiconductor.   It has a specific gravity of 2.31, a melting point of about 2200°C, and a Knoop hardness of 2,700 to 3,200, equal to a Mohs hardness of about 9.3.   At about 600°C boron ignites and burns with a brilliant green flame.   It is obtained by the electrolysis of fused boric oxide from the mineral borax, but it is used mostly in its compounds, especially borax and boric acid.   Minute quantities of boron are used in steels for case hardening by the nitriding process to form a boron nitride, and in other steels to increase strength and hardness penetration.   In these steels as little as 0.003% is beneficial, forming an iron boride, but with larger amounts the steel becomes brittle and hot-short unless it contains titanium or some other element to stabilize the carbon.   **Boron steels** are now much used, but close temperature control is necessary since the boron atom is much smaller than the atoms of iron, nickel, and chromium, and may be present as an interstitial element to increase strength and hardness without combining as a carbide.   In cast steels for tools, as much as 1.5% boron may be used, but these steels cannot be forged or machined.   In cast iron, boron inhibits graphitization and also serves as a deoxidizer.   It is added to iron and steel in the form of **ferroboron.**   **Electromet ferroboron,** of the Electro Metallurgical Co., has 18 to 25% boron and 3 max each of silicon and aluminum.

Boron 10, an isotope that occurs naturally in boron in the proportion of 10 to 12%, is 10 times more effective than lead in stopping neutrons, and is used for neutron shielding, but it does not stop gamma rays.   **Boron 11,** which comprises 88 to 90% of natural boron, is transparent to neutrons.   **Boron steel foil** and sheet for neutron shielding, marketed by the Chromalloy Corp. under the name of **Bo-Stan,** has the composition of a stainless steel with 2% boron evenly distributed.   It is made by the sinter-wrought process from exact amounts of the metal powders, compacted under pressure, sintered at below the melting point to bond the metals, and hot-rolled.   A similar foil called **Binal** is aluminum with 2% boron.

Boron fibers for reinforced structural composites are continuous fine filaments.   The fiber of National Standard is 0.004 in. in diameter and contains about 70,000 ft per lb.   **Borsic,** of this company, is the boron filament with a coating of silicon carbide for heat resistance.

Boron compounds are employed for fluxes and deoxidizing agents in melting metals, and for making special glasses.   Boron, like silicon and carbon, has an immense capacity for forming compounds, although it has a different valence.   The boron atom appears to have a lenticular shape, and two boron atoms can make a strong electromagnetic bond, the B_2 acting like carbon but with a double ring.

Typical of a complex boron compound is the natural mineral **danburite** which occurs in orthorhombic crystals that will fuse to a colorless glass. The composition of the mineral is given as $CaB_2(SiO_4)_2$, but each silicon atom is at the center of a group of four oxygen atoms, two such groups having one oxygen atom in common.   The eighth oxygen atom forms another tetrahedral group with one oxygen atom from each of the three Si_2O_7 groups, and in the center of such groups are the boron atoms.   Thus, even tiny amounts of boron can affect alloys greatly.   Boron is used in specialty refractories, electronics, borane fuels, and high-temperature carborane plastics.

Boron trichloride, BCl_3, is used as a catalyst, and to control magnesium ions.   Above 12.5°C it is a gas, but it is also used as the dihydrate, a fuming liquid.   **Boron trifluoride,** BF_3, is a gas used for polymerizing epoxy resins, usually in the solid form of **boron ethyl amine,** $BF_3 \cdot C_2H_5$-NH_2, which releases the BF_3 at elevated temperatures.   **Boron tribromide,**

BBr$_3$, is also a highly reactive compound, used to produced boron hydrides as sources of hydrogen. **Hydrazine diboride,** $BH_3 \cdot NH_2 \cdot NH_2 \cdot BH_3$, used as a source of hydrogen in rocket fuels, is a white crystalline free-flowing powder. **Trimethyl boroxine,** $(CH_3O)_3B \cdot B_2O_3$, is a liquid used for extinguishing metal fires. Under heat it breaks down and the molten coating of boric acid smothers the fire.

BORON CARBIDE. A black crystalline powder of high hardness used as an abrasive, or pressed into wear-resistant products such as drawing dies and gages, or into heat-resistant parts such as nozzles. The composition is either B_6C or B_4C, the former being the harder but usually containing an excess of graphite difficult to separate in the powder. It can be used thus as a deoxidizing agent for casting copper, and also for lapping, since the graphite acts as a lubricant. **Boroflux,** of the General Electric Co., is boron carbide with flake graphite, used as a casting flux.

The boron carbide marketed by the Norton Co. under the name of **Norbide** is B_4C, over 99% pure. It is used as a hard abrasive, and for molding. Parts molded without a binder have a compressive strength of 400,000 psi, a tensile strength of 22,500 psi, and a Knoop hardness of 2,800. The coefficient of expansion is only one-third that of steel, and the density is 2.51, or less than that of aluminum. The melting point is 4450°F, but above 1800°F it reacts with oxygen. The material is not resistant to fused alkalies. **Boron carbide powder** for grinding and lapping comes in standard mesh sizes to 240, and in special finer sizes to 800. The usual grinding powders are 220 and 240, and the finishing powder is 320. Boron carbide powder is also added to molten aluminum and then rolled into sheets for use in shielding against neutrons. **Boral,** of the Aluminum Co. of America, is this sheet containing 35% by weight of carbide and clad on both sides with pure aluminum. A $1/4$-in. sheet is equal to 25 in. of concrete for neutron shielding.

BORON NITRIDE. A light fluffy white powder of the composition BN, used as a lubricant for high-pressure bearings, and for compacting into mechanical and electrical parts. Its X-ray pattern and platy crystal structure are almost identical with those of graphite, and it is called **white graphite.** Boron nitride has a very low coefficient of friction, but unlike carbon, it is a nonconductor of electricity, and it is attacked by nitric acid. It sublimes at 3000°C. It reacts with carbon at about 2000°C to form boron carbide. It is used for heat-resistant parts by molding and pressing the powder without a binder to a density of 2.1 to 2.25.

Sintered parts have an ivorylike appearance, a tensile strength of 3,500 psi, compressive strength to 45,000 psi, and dielectric strength of 1,000 volts per mil. They are soft, with a hardness of Mohs 2, and can be machined easily.   But when compressed at very high pressure and high heat, the hexagonal crystal structure is converted into a cubic structure, and the pressed material has great hardness and strength and is stable up to about 3500°F.   This molded material is resistant to molten aluminum, is not wetted by molten silicon or glass, and is used for crucibles.   Cubical crystal boron nitride equaling the diamond in hardness is produced by the General Electric Co. as an abrasive powder under the name of **Borazon.** It is produced at extremely high pressure and temperature, and the tiny crystals are reddish to black, although chemically pure crystals should be colorless to white.   The cubic crystal structure has the same pattern as that of the diamond, but with greater atomic spacing.   An advantage over the diamond is that it will not disintegrate at temperatures below 3500°F.   **Boron nitride fibers** are produced in diameters as small as 5 to 7 microns and in lengths to 15 in.   The fibers have a tensile strength of 200,000 psi.   They are used for filters for hot chemicals, and as reinforcement to plastic lamination.   **Boron nitride HCJ,** of Union Carbide, is a fine powder, 99% pure, used as a filler in encapsulating and potting compounds to add thermal and electrical conductivity.

Another boron compound used for the production of high-temperature ceramic parts by pressing and sintering is **boron silicide,** B_4Si.   It is a black, free-flowing crystalline powder.   The powder offered by the Allis-Chalmers Mfg. Co. is microcrystalline, with particles about 75 microns diameter, and the free silicon is less than 0.15%.   This compound normally reacts at 2190°F to form B_6Si and silicon, but when compacted and sintered, the ceramic forms a boron silicate oxygen protective coating, and the parts have a serviceable life in air at temperatures to 2550°F.   Molded parts have high thermal shock resistance, and can be water-quenched from 2000°F without shattering.

BOXWOOD. The wood of the **Turkish boxwood** tree *Buxus sempervirens,* native to Europe and Asia but also grown in America.   It is used for rulers, instruments, engraving blocks, and inlay work.   The wood is light yellow, hard, and has a fine grain and a dense structure that does not warp easily.   The weight is about 65 lb per cu ft.   **African boxwood,** or **cape boxwood,** comes from the tree *B. macowani,* of South Africa, and is similar to boxwood but is softer.   **Kamassi wood** is a hard, fine-grained wood from the tree *Gonioma kamassi,* of South Africa, sometimes substituted for boxwood, but it does not have the straight grain of boxwood. It is valued for loom shuttles.   **Coast gray boxwood,** or the **Gippsland boxwood** of New South Wales, is from the tree *Eucalyptus bosistoana.* It is a durable wood of uniform texture but it has an interlocking grain. **Maracaibo boxwood,** or **zapatero,** which comes chiefly from Venezuela, is from the tree *Casearia praecox.*   It comes in straight knotless logs 8 to 10 ft long and 6 to 10 in. in diameter. The light-yellow wood has a fine uniform texture and straight grain. It replaces Turkish boxwood for all purposes except for wood engravings. The **ginkgo wood** used in China for making chessmen and chessboards is from the large tree *Ginkgo biloba* which appears to be the sole survivor of a family of trees with fernlike leaves once very abundant. The wood is white to yellowish, light in weight, fine-textured, and easy to work.

BRAKE LINING. A term generally referring to the treated and compressed fabric materials for lining the brake bands of motor vehicles and machinery, and not including wood-block linings. Brake linings may be impregnated woven fabrics, or they may be compressed fibers cemented together with a heat-resistant binder. The binder may be rubber, synthetic rubber, plastic, or a silicate. The coefficient of friction of asbestos fabric against steel is from 0.27 to 0.38, as compared with 0.16 for cast iron against steel. This coefficient may be increased still further with treated binders, or it may be reduced with interwoven wire. A typical brake lining is made by twisting asbestos yarns with fine wire strands, treating with silicate solution, and then weaving into a fabric which is impregnated with rubber or other frictional binder and subjected to heat and pressure. In Germany, aluminum or steel wire of a diameter of 0.03 mm was used as a substitute for asbestos and bonded with synthetic rubber. Brake linings are marketed under trade names. **Raybestos,** of Raybestos-Manhattan, Inc., is a brake lining and **clutch lining** of various grades made of asbestos fibers and fine wire impregnated and bonded under pressure. The coefficient of friction is 0.45. **Autobestos,** of the Keasbey & Mattison Co., is made of chrysotile fiber molded with a binder.

BRASS. An alloy of copper and zinc, although some brasses also contain other elements. The brasses constitute one of the most important groups of alloys because of their ease of working, corrosion resistance, and attractive appearance. They are more ductile than corresponding copper-tin alloys, or bronzes, but are not as hard and do not contain the hard crystals that make bronzes valuable as bearing metals. Zinc added to copper causes a progressive lowering of the melting point from the 1949°F of the 95–5 brass to the 1616°F of the 50–50 brazing metal. Ten percent of zinc gives a bronze color; 15%, golden; from about 20 to 38% the color is yellow. When the zinc exceeds 45%, the color becomes silvery white, and the alloy is brittle, rapidly losing the characteristics of brass. The maximum tensile strength is reached at 55% copper, and the maximum ductility at about 70% copper content.

Alpha brass is the form of brass having less than 36% zinc all dissolved in the copper, and the alloy has the same structure as copper. It is easily cold-worked. **Beta brass,** with the zinc between 36 and 45%, contains the compound CuZn. It is the best brass for hot working. **Gamma brass,** with the zinc above 45%, has Cu_2Zn_3 in the alloy, and is not easily worked either hot or cold. Much of the commercial wrought brass is the alpha brass known as high brass with 65% copper and 35 zinc, but the 70–30 alpha alloy called cartridge brass is widely used for deep drawing. The standard red brass of the mills, containing 85% copper and 15 zinc, is much used for hot-water pipes for corrosive conditions. The 80–20 alloy known in the mills as low brass is very ductile, easily drawn, and has a fine golden-yellow color. It is much used for jewelry and novelties. **Formbrite brass** of the American Brass Co. is not a special-composition alloy but is brass specially processed to give a metal of very fine grain size, not over 0.012 mm. It gives a better finish with less polishing, and also has higher tensile strength and better ductility than ordinary brass of the same composition. It comes in all standard compositions.

Although the tensile strength of cold-worked brass is high, 85,000 psi for the 60–40 muntz metal, the modulus of elasticity is much lower, proportionally, than that of steel. Brass is annealed for drawing and bending by quenching in water from a temperature of about 1000°F. Simple copper-zinc brasses are made in standard degrees of temper, or hardness. This hardness is obtained by cold-rolling after the first annealing, and the degree of hardness depends upon the percentage of cold reduction. When the thickness is reduced one number of the Brown & Sharp gage, or about 10.9% reduction, the resulting sheet is known as ¼ hard. The other grades are ½ hard, hard, extra hard, spring, and finally extra spring, which is a reduction of 10 numbers on the Brown & Sharp gage, or about 68.7% reduction without intermediate annealing. Degrees of softness in annealed brass are measured by the grain size, and annealed brass is furnished in grain sizes from 0.010 to 0.150 mm. The ASTM standard grain sizes are: 0.015 to 0.025 mm for light anneal, 0.035 mm for drawing or rod anneal, 0.050 mm for intermediate anneal, 0.70 mm for soft anneal, and 0.120 for dead-soft anneal. Brasses with smaller grain sizes are not as ductile as with larger grain sizes, but they have smoother surfaces and require less polishing.

Even slight additions of other elements to brass alter the characteristics drastically. Slight additions of tin change the structure, increasing the hardness but reducing the ductility. Small amounts of tin, arsenic, or antimony are added to the **naval brasses** used for condenser tubes in order to inhibit dezincification from the corrosive salts in the water. **Admiralty metal** usually has 0.01% arsenic to prevent corrosion, and some tin to increase strength and hardness. Lead in small amounts improves the cutting qualities of brass, but reduces the ductility and the impact strength.

The alloys known as **clock brass** contain lead. Iron hardens the alloy and reduces the grain size, making it more suitable for forging, but making it difficult to machine. Manganese increases the strength, increases the solubility of iron in the alloy, and promotes the stabilization of aluminum, but makes the brass extremely hard. Such alloys are called manganese bronze rather than brass. Slight additions of silicon increase the strength of brass, but large amounts promote brittleness, loss of strength, and danger of oxide inclusion. Nickel increases strength and toughness, but when any silicon is present the brass becomes extremely hard and more a bronze than a brass.

Casting brasses are usually made from brass ingot metal and are seldom plain copper-zinc alloys. The most widely used alloy is the one usually designated as **composition metal,** containing 85% copper, 5 tin, 5 zinc, and 5 lead. In melting brass for casting, any overheating causes loss of zinc by vaporization, thus lowering the zinc content. Small amounts of antimony, or some arsenic, are used to overcome this dezincification. The casting brasses are roughly divided into two classes as red casting brass and yellow casting brass, which are various compositions of copper, tin, zinc, and lead to obtain the required balance of color, ease of casting, hardness, and machining qualities.

BRASS INGOT METAL. Commercial ingots made in standard composition grades and employed for casting various articles designated as brass and bronze. They are seldom true brasses, but are composition metals intermediate between the brasses and the bronzes, and their selection for any given purpose is based on a balance of the requirements in color, strength, hardness, ease of casting, and machinability. Brass ingot metal is usually made from secondary metals, but, in general, the grading is now so good that they will produce high-grade uniform castings. In producing the ingot metal there is careful sorting of the scrap metals, and the impurities are removed by remeltings. An advantage of ingot metal over virgin metals is the ease of controlling mixtures in the foundry. The ASTM designates eight grades for brass ingot metal. No. 1 grade, the highest in copper, contains 88% copper, 6.5 zinc, 1.5 lead, and 4 tin, with only slight percentages of impurities. The No. 8 grade contains 63.5% copper, 34 zinc, 2.5 lead, and no tin. The **red brass ingot,** of H. Kramer & Co., contains 80 to 82% copper, 3 to 4 tin, 5 to 7 lead, and the balance zinc. **Yellow ingot,** for plumbing fixtures, contains 65% copper, 1 tin, 2 lead, and the balance zinc. The most widely used ingot metal is the **ASTM alloy No. 2,** which is the 85–5–5–5 alloy known as composition metal. Yellow brass, or **yellow casting brass,** is frequently cast from **ASTM alloy No. 6,** which contains 72% copper, 22 zinc, 4 lead, and 2 tin. It has a tensile strength of 20,000 to 25,000 psi, elongation 15 to 20%, and Brinell hardness 40 to 50.   It is yellow in color, and makes clean, dense castings suitable for various machine parts except bearings.

BRAZIL NUTS. Also called **Pará chestnut.**   The nuts of the large tree *Bertholletia excelsa* growing wild in the Amazon Valley.   The trees and nuts are called **tacarí** in Brazil and **toura** in French Guiana.   The tree begins to bear in 8 years and yields up to 1,000 lb of large round fruit pods containing 18 to 24 hard-shelled kernels which are the commercial nuts.   The shelled kernels are several times the size of the peanut, and have a pleasant nutty flavor.   The kernels contain 67% of a pale yellow oil of specific gravity 0.917, saponification value 192 to 200, and iodine value 98 to 106.   The oil contains 51% oleic acid, 19 linoleic, 2 myristic, 3 stearic, and 12 palmitic.   It is a valuable food oil, and is also a good soap oil, but is normally too high in price for this purpose as the nuts are more valued for eating.

BRAZILWOOD. The wood of the trees *Caesalpinia brasiliensis, C. crista,* and *C. echinata,* of tropical America, and *C. sappan,* of Ceylon, India, and Malaya.   The latter species is called **sappanwood.**   Brazilwood formerly constituted one of the most valuable exports from Brazil to Europe as a dyewood.   It produces purple shades with a chrome mordant and crimson with alum.   **Brazilwood extract** is still valued for silk dyeing, wood staining, and for inks.   The wood is prized for such articles as violins and fine furniture.   It has a rich bright-red color, and takes a fine, lustrous polish.

BRAZING METAL. A common name for high-copper brass used for the casting of such articles as flanges that are to be brazed on copper pipe. Federal specifications for brazing metal call for 84 to 86% copper and the balance zinc.   **Brazing brass,** of the American Brass Co., has 75% copper and 25 zinc.   Some alloys also contain up to 3% lead for ease of machining.   It also makes the metal easier to cast.

The term brazing metal is also applied to **brazing rods** of brass or bronze used for joining metals.   The joining of iron or steel by brazing is essentially different from welding in that the brazing metal has a lower fusion point than iron, and the base metal is not fused.   It is a type of high-temperature soldering, although there is some surface alloying between the brazing metal and the base metal.   A common brazing rod is the 50–50 brass alloy with a melting point of 1616°F.   The SAE designates this alloy as **spelter solder.**   The joints made with it are inclined to be brittle. **Brazing wire,** of the Chase Brass & Copper Co., contains 59% copper and 41 zinc, while the **brazing solder,** for brazing high-zinc brasses, has 51% copper and 49 zinc.   **Phos-copper,** of the Westinghouse Electric Corp., is a phosphor copper which gives joints with 98% the electrical conductivity of copper. It flows at 1382°F. **Tri-Metal,** of the D. E. Makepeace Co., is a brazing metal consisting of sheet brass with a layer of silver rolled on each side. It is used for brazing carbide tips to steel tools. The silver ensures a tightly brazed joint, while the brass center acts as a shock absorbent for the cutting tool.

Brazing rods for brazing brasses and bronzes are usually of a composition similar to that of the base metal. For brazing cast iron and steel, various bronzes, naval brass, manganese bronze, or silicon bronze may be used. Brass rods may contain some silicon. Small amounts of silver added to the high-copper brazing metals give greater fluidity and better penetration into small openings. A series of brazing alloys of varied compositions to give a range of colors, hardnesses, and strengths is marketed by the Eutectic Welding Alloys, Inc., as **Eutechrom, Eutecrod,** and **Bronzochrom.**

BRICK. The most ancient of all artificial building materials, consisting of clay molded to standard shape, usually rectangular, and burned to a hard structure. In some areas bricks, known as **adobe bricks,** are still made by baking in the sun, and a modern adaptation of sun-baked brick, called **bitudobe,** has a binder of emulsified asphalt. Commercial bricks in the United States and in Europe are all of hard-burned clay. They are used for buildings, walls, and paving, and are classified apart from the bricks of fireclays used for refractories. **Brick clays** are of two general classes. The first consists of noncalcareous clays or shales composed of true clay with sand, feldspar grains, and iron compounds, which when fired become buff or salmon in color. The second class comprises calcareous clays containing up to 40% calcium carbonate, called **marls.** When fired, they are yellowish. Brick clays of the first type are widely distributed. Iron oxide in them varies from 2 to 10%, and the red color of common brick depends largely on this content. In practice the composition of bricks varies widely, but much of the difference is also in the burning as well as in the method of pressing. **Pressed brick** is a stiff mud brick made under high pressure. It is homogeneous, and has increased density and strength. **Building brick** made by machine of ground and tempered clay has great uniformity of strength and color. Such brick is made by pressing soft, stiff, or dry. The burning is done in kilns at temperatures from 900 to 1250°C. The calcareous clays require a temperature of 1200°C to bring about chemical combination. The bricks are sorted according to hardness and color, both largely resulting from their position in the kiln. **Paving brick** is usually a hard-burned common brick. **Floor brick** is highly vitrified brick. The common hard brick for building has a crushing strength of 5,000 to 8,000 psi, and weighs 125 lb per cu ft. The common standard for building-brick size is 8¼ by 4 by 2½ in.;

other sizes are also used, especially 8 by 3⅞ by 2¼. Specially sized paving bricks are 8½ by 4 by 3 or 8½ by 4 by 3½ in. **Sand-lime bricks** for fancy walls are of sand and lime pressed in an atmosphere of steam. They are not to be confused with the sand-lime bricks used for firebrick, which are of refractory silica sand with a lime bond. Ceramic glazes and semiglazes are used on some building bricks, especially on the yellow.

BRISTLES. The stiff hairs from the back of the hog, used chiefly in making brushes. The very short bristles, rejects, and scrap pieces are used for filler in plastics. The best brush bristles do not include hair from the sides of the animals, nor the product from the fat-meat animals killed in the slaughterhouses. They come mostly from types of semiwild swine grown in cool climates, notably northern China and Russia. Bristles are in form similar to a tiny tube outwardly covered with microscopic scales and filled with a fatty substance. The so-called flag, or split end, gives the valuable paint-carrying characteristic for brushes. The taper of the bristle gives the brush stiffness at the base and resiliency toward the end. Quality varies according to the type of animal, climate, and feeding. The colors are white, yellow, gray, and black. They are graded by locality, color, and length, and in normal times the name of the place at which they are graded, such as Tsingtao, Hankow, and Chungking, is an indication of the grade. The best fibers are more than 3 in. in length. The Chinese natural black bristles are sometimes sold at a premium. American bristles from Chester hogs are light in color and are of high quality. Bristles from the Duroc hog are bronze in color, are stiff, and are superior to most Chinese grades. Those from the Poland China hogs are black and stiff, but they have a crooked flag and are of poor quality. **Artificial bristles** are made from various plastics, the **nylon bristles** being of high quality and much used. **Exton,** of DuPont, was one of the original nylon monofilament non-tapered bristles. **Tynex,** of this company, now comes both tapered and level. They are more durable than natural bristles. **Casein bristles** are made by extruding an acid solution of casein, stretching the fiber, and insolubilizing with formaldehyde or other chemicals. They have good paint-carrying capacity and good wear resistance, but are dissolved by some paint solvents. **Keron bristle,** of the Rubberset Co., is produced from the protein extracted from chicken feathers. It is nearly identical in composition to natural bristle.

BROMINE. An elementary material, symbol Br. It is a reddish-brown liquid having a boiling point of 58°C. It gives off very irritating fumes, and is highly corrosive. It is one of four elements called **halogens,** a name derived from Greek words meaning salt producer. They are fluorine, chlorine, iodine, and bromine. They are all chemically active, combining with hydrogen and most metals to form **halides.**   Bromine is less active than chlorine but more so than iodine.   It is soluble in water.   It never occurs free in nature, but is obtained by electrolysis of salt solutions.   It occurs in seawater to the extent of 65 to 70 parts per million, and is extracted.   It is marketed 99.7% min purity with specific gravity not less than 3.1, but dry elemental bromine, Br_2, is marketed 99.8% pure for use as a brominating and oxidizing agent.   For these uses, also, bromine is available as a crystalline powder as **dibromo dimethyl hydantoin,** containing 55% bromine.   **Brom 55,** of McKesson & Robbins, is this material.

A pound of bromine is obtained from 2,000 gal of seawater.   It is also produced as a by-product from the brine wells of Michigan, and from the production of chemicals at Searles Lake, Calif., where the bromine concentration is 12 times that of seawater.   It is used in the manufacture of dyes, photographic chemicals, poison gases for chemical warfare, pharmaceuticals, ethyl fluid for gasoline, disinfectants, and many chemicals.   It is also employed in the extraction of gold.

BRONZE.   Usually a **copper-tin alloy,** but the name is now also applied to many copper alloys that have crystalline, bronzelike structure, such as silicon bronze, aluminum bronze, and manganese bronze.   In the true bronzes, tin is the predominating alloying element with the copper, but some brasses are called bronzes because of their color, or because they contain some tin.   Most commercial copper-tin bronzes are now modified with zinc, lead, or other elements.   Bronze is essentially a casting metal, while brass is used mostly in wrought forms.   Unlike zinc, the tin forms a crystalline structure valued for bearing metals.   But tin does not deoxidize copper, and the tin oxide stays in the melt.   Small amounts of phosphorus are used to reduce the oxide to give stronger castings.   Aluminum is sometimes used as a deoxidizer, but not more than 0.25% can be added without increasing the hardness and reducing the working properties.   Small amounts of zinc are added to give sharper castings free from blowholes.   Small amounts of lead make the castings easier to machine, but even a small quantity of lead reduces the strength.

Copper-tin bronze is hard in proportion to the amount of Cu_4Sn crystals it contains, which depends upon the amount of tin and the rate of solidification.   The hard crystals are formed at high temperatures and by chilling; softer Cu_2Sn_2 crystals are formed at low temperatures.   Bronzes containing more than 90% copper are reddish; below 90% the color changes to orange-yellow which is the typical bronze color.   The maximum strength is with 80% copper and 20 tin.   Ductility rapidly decreases with the increase of tin up to 20%, after which it practically disappears until 80% is reached, when it again increases.   Above 20% tin the alloy rapidly becomes white in color and loses the characteristics of bronze. The **high-tin alloys** are also subject to what is known as tin sweat. The amount of tin used in bronzes seldom reaches 20%. The copper-tin alloy known as **Cothias metal,** containing 67% copper and 33 tin, is a master alloy used for adding copper and tin to zinc-base alloys. Bronzes have a lower thermal conductivity than brasses. The average coefficient of expansion is 0.0000098. A 90–10 bronze weighs 0.317 lb per cu in.; an 80–20 bronze weighs 0.315 lb per cu in. The 80–20 bronze melts at 1868°F, and a 95–5 bronze melts at 2480°F. Copper-tin alloys that contain elements other than zinc and lead are designated by group names such as aluminum bronze.

Gear bronze may be any bronze used for casting gears and worm wheels, but usually means a tin bronze of good strength deoxidized with phosphorus and containing some lead to make it easy to machine and lowering the coefficient of friction. A typical gear bronze contains 88.5% copper, 11 tin, 0.25 lead, and 0.25 phosphorus. It has a tensile strength up to 40,000 psi, elongation 10%, and Brinell hardness from 70 to 80, or up to 90 when chill-cast. The weight is 0.306 lb per cu in. This is **SAE bronze No. 65.** A **hard gear bronze,** or **hard bearing bronze,** of the U.S. Navy, contains 84 to 86% copper, 13 to 15 tin, up to 1.5 zinc, up to 0.75 nickel, and up to 0.5 phosphorus. Hard and strong bronzes for gears are now often silicon bronze or manganese bronze.

In a modified 90–10 type of bronze, the zinc is usually from 2 to 4%, and the lead up to 1%. A cast bronze of this type will have a tensile strength of about 40,000 psi, an elongation 15 to 25%, and a hardness 60 to 80 Brinell, those high in zinc being the stronger and more ductile, those high in lead being weaker. Bronzes of this type are much used for general castings and are classified as composition metal in the United States. In England they are called **engineer's bronze.** An alloy designated as **hard bronze** by one automotive company contains 88% copper, 7 tin, 3 zinc, and 2 lead. It makes clean, dense castings and machines well. The tensile strength is 30,000 psi, and elongation 12%. An alloy designated as special hard bronze contains 88% copper, 10 tin, and 2 zinc. It is stronger and harder, and is used for gears and heavy-duty castings, but it is difficult to machine. **Merco bronze,** of the Merco Nordstrom Valve Co., has 88% copper, 10 tin, and 2 lead, deoxidized with phosphorus. It machines well, and has a tensile strength of 42,000 psi and elongation 17%. The **free-cutting bronze** marketed by the Riverside Metal Co. as Mixture 44 contains 92% copper, 4 lead, and 4 tin. It machines to close tolerances at high speed. Cast **bronze bar** for making bearings is produced by a continuous process by passing the molten alloy through a water-cooled die.

Architectural bronze, or **art bronze,** is formulated for color and is very high in copper.   One foundry formula for art bronze of a dull-red color calls for 97% copper, 2 tin, and 1 zinc.   For ease of casting, however, they are more likely to contain lead, and a **gold bronze** for architectural castings contains 89.5% copper, 2 tin, 5.5 zinc, and 3 lead.   In leaded bronze the hard copper-tin crystals aid in holding the lead in solution. These bronzes are resistant to acids and are grouped as valve bronze, or as bearing bronze because of the hard crystals in a soft matrix.   Federal specifications for bronze give 10 grades in a wide variation in tin, zinc, and lead.   The ASTM designates 5 grades of **bronze casting alloys.   Alloy No. 1** contains 85% copper, 10 tin, and 5 lead; **Alloy No. 5** contains 70% copper, 5 tin, and 25 lead.   The British **coinage copper** is a bronze containing 95.5% copper, 3 tin, and 1.5 zinc.

BRONZE POWDER. Pulverized or powdered bronze or brass made in flake form by stamping from sheet metal.   It is used chiefly as a paint pigment and as a dusting powder for printing.   In making the powder the sheets are worked into a thin foil which becomes harder under the working and breaks into small flakes.   Lubricant keeps the flakes from sticking to each other.   Usually stearic acid is used, but in the dusting powder hot water or nonsticky lacquers are used.   The powder is graded in standard screens, and is then polished in revolving drums with a lubricant.   This gives it the property of leafing, or forming a metallic film in the paint vehicle.   The leaf is also called **composition leaf,** or **Dutch metal leaf,** when used as a substitute for gold leaf.   **Flitters** are made by reducing thin sheets to flakes, and are not as fine as bronze powder.

The compositions of bronze powder vary, and seven alloys form the chief commercial color grades from the reddest, called pale gold, which has 95% copper and 5 zinc, to the rich gold which has 70% copper and 30 zinc.   Colors are also produced by heating to give oxides of deep red, crimson, or green-blue.   The powder may also be dyed in colors, using tannic acid as a mordant, or treated with acetic acid or copper acetate to produce antique finish.   The color or tone of bronze powders may also be adjusted in paints by adding a proportion of mica powder.   A **white bronze powder** is made from aluminum bronze, or the silvery colors are obtained with aluminum powder.   The bronze powder of 400 mesh used for inks is designated as extra fine.   The fine grade, for stencil work, is 325 mesh.   Medium fine, for coated paper, has 85% of the particles passing through a 325-mesh screen and 15% retained on the screen. Near mesh, for paint pigment, has 30% passing through a 325-mesh screen.   A 400-mesh powder has 500 million particles per gram.   The old name for bronze powder is **gilding powder.** It is also called gold powder when used in cheap gold-colored paints, but bronze powders cannot replace gold for use in atmospheres containing sulfur, or for printing on leather where tannic acid would corrode the metal.   **Gold pigments** used in plastics are bronze powders with oxygen stabilizers.

BROOMCORN. A plant of the sorghum family, *Holcus sorghum,* grown in the Southwest, in Illinois and Kansas, and in Argentina and Hungary. It is used for making brushes and brooms, and for the stems of artificial flowers.   The jointed stems of the dwarf variety grown in the semiarid regions are 12 to 24 in. long, but the standard brush corn is up to 30 in. long.   The fibers are yellow in color and, when dry, are coarse and hard. They are easily cleaned and readily dyed.   As a brush material they have the objection that they break easily, and are therefore unsuited for mechanical brushes for hard service.   **Broom root,** or **rice root,** is similar to broomcorn, and is suitable for mixing with it or for coarse brushes.   It is from a type of grass, *Epicampes macroura,* of Mexico and Guatemala. The fiber is from the tough, crinkly, yellowish roots.   After removal of the outer bark, the dry root is treated with the fumes of burning sulfur to improve the color.   The fibers are 8 to 18 in. long.   In Mexico it is called raiz de Zacaton, or **Zacaton root,** and its American name rice is a corruption of the Spanish word for root.

BRUSH FIBERS. Industrial brushes are made from a wide variety of fibers, varying from the fine and soft camel's hair to the hard, coarse, and brittle broomcorn.   Bristles are the most commonly used, but tampico and piassava fibers are important for polishing brushes.   The vegetable fibers used for brushes are tough and stiff as compared with the finer flexible and cohesive fibers used for twine and for fabrics.   They may, however, come from the same plant, or even from the same leaf, as the textile fibers, but be graded out for stiffness.   **Palmetto fiber** is from the **cabbage palm** tree, *Sabal palmetto,* of Florida.   Whiskbrooms and brushes are made from the young leafstalks, and stiff floor sweeps from the leaves.

A fiber finer than palmetto is obtained from the twisted roots of the **scrub palmetto,** *S. megacarpa.*   **Arenga fiber** is a stiff, strong fiber from the stems of the **aren palm** tree, *Arenga saccharifera,* of Indonesia.   The finest grades resemble horsehair.   **Kittool** is a similar strong, elastic fiber from the large leaves of the palm tree, *Caryota urens,* of India and Ceylon. It is very resistant, and is valued for machine brushes.   **Gomuti fiber** and **Chinese coir** are fibers from other species of this palm.   **Bass,** or **raphia,** is a coarse fiber used for hard brushes and brooms.   The heavier piassava fibers are also known as bass, but bass is from the leaves of the palm tree, *Raphia vinifera,* of West Africa.   **Darwin fiber,** used for brooms and scrubbing brushes in Australia, is from the *Gahnia trifida.*   **Crin** is from the leaves of a palm tree of Algeria, although the word crin originally referred to horsehair.   **Crin vegetal,** or **vegetable crin,** is fiber from the leaf of the **yatay palm,** *Diplothemium littorale,* of Corrientes Province, Argentina.   **Horsehair,** from the manes and tails of horses, is used for some paintbrushes.

Red sable hair is used for fine-pointed and knife-edged brushes for show-card and water-color use.   It is from the tail of the **kolinsky,** *Mustela siberica,* of Siberia, and the pale red hair has strength and resiliency and very fine points.   **Russian sable hair,** used for artists' brushes, is stronger than red sable hair, but is less pointed and is not as elastic for water painting.   It is from the tail of the **fitch,** *Putorius putorius,* of Central Asia, but the so-called **fitch hair** used for ordinary flowing brushes is usually **skunk tail hair.**   It is stiffer and coarser than fitch hair.   **Badger hair,** also used for flowing brushes, is a resilient hair with fine points, and is from the back of the badger of Turkey and southern Russia.   **Black sable hair,** used for signwriter brushes, is not from a sable, but is the trade name for mixtures of marten hair, bear hair, and some other Siberian hairs.

Vegetable and animal fibers are not resistant to alkalies or acids and cannot be wetted with them.   The artificial fibers of plastics such as nylon are resistant to many chemicals.   For hard-service mechanical brushes, and for resistance to strong chemicals, brush fibers are of steel, brass, or aluminum wire.   **Brush wire** for rotary-power brushes for metal brushing is soft to hard-drawn steel wire usually 0.005 in. in diameter, but finer wire is used to give a soft brush.   Brush wire used by the Osborn Mfg. Co. for soft rotary brushes is a soft steel wire 0.0025 in. in diameter with 242,144 wires in a $1\frac{1}{2}$ in. diameter brush 2 in. long.

BUFFING COMPOSITIONS. Materials used for buffing or polishing metals, originally consisting of dolomitic lime with from 18 to 25% saponifiable grease as a bond.   The lime acts as the abrasive, and in some compositions is partly replaced by other abrasives such as emery flour, tripoli, pumice, silica, or rouge.   Harsher abrasives are used in the compositions employed for the cutting-down or buffing operations.   Abrasive grains are selected for combinations of hardness, toughness, and sharpness, from the soft iron oxide to the hard and sharp aluminum oxide.   Buffing compositions are usually sold under trade names for definite uses rather than by composition.   **Metal polishes** for hand use are now usually liquids. The pastes, formerly known as **Putz cream** and **brass polish,** contained tripoli or pumice with oxalic acid and paraffin.   The liquid polishes now generally contain finer abrasives such as pumicite or diatomite, in a detergent, together with a solvent, and sometimes pine oil or an alkali.

BUILDING SAND. Selected sand used for concrete, for mortar for laying bricks, and for plastering.   Early specifications called for sand grains to be sharp, but rounded grains are now preferred because of fewer voids in the mixture. Building sand is normally taken from deposits within a reasonable haul of the site of building, and is not usually specified by analysis, but should be a hard silica sand that will not dissolve. Pure white sand for finish plaster is made by grinding limestone. Building sand is required to be clean, with not more than 3% clay, loam, or organic matter. ASTM requirements are that all grains must pass through a $\frac{3}{8}$-in. sieve, 85% through a No. 4 sieve, and not more than 30% through a No. 50 sieve. For brick mortar all of the sand should pass through a $\frac{1}{4}$-in. sieve. For plaster, not more than 6% should pass through a No. 8 sieve. **Flooring sand** for mastic flooring is a clean sand passing through a No. 3 sieve, with 7% passing through a No. 100 sieve. **Roofing sand** is a fine white silica sand. **Paving sand** is divided into three general classes: that for concrete pavements, for asphaltic pavements, and for grouting.

The United States Bureau of Public Roads requires that sand for concrete pavements should all pass through a $\frac{1}{4}$-in. sieve, 5 to 25% should be retained on a No. 10 sieve, from 50 to 90% on a No. 50 sieve, and not more than 10% should pass through a No. 100 sieve. Not more than 3% of the weight should be matter removable by elutriation. For asphaltic pavements small amounts of organic matter are not objectionable in the sand. All should pass through a $\frac{1}{4}$-in. sieve, 95 to 100% through a No. 10 sieve, and not more than 5% through a No. 200 sieve. **Grouting sand** should all pass through a No. 20 sieve, and not more than 5% through a No. 200 sieve. **Chat sand,** used for concrete pavements, is a by-product of zinc and lead mines. It is screened through a $\frac{3}{8}$-in. sieve.

BUILDING STONE. Any stone used for building construction may be classed as building stone, but the stones, in order of importance, used in the United States for building are limestone, granite, sandstone, basalt, and marble. Granite and limestone are among the most ancient of building materials and are extremely durable. Two million limestone and granite blocks, totaling nearly 8 million long tons, were used in the pyramid of Ghizeh built about 2980 B.C., the granite being used for casing. Availability, or a near supply, may determine the stone used in ordinary building, but for public buildings stone is transported long distances. Some sandstones, such as the **red sandstone** of the Connecticut Valley, weather badly, and are likely to scale off with penetration of moisture and frost. Granite will take heavy pressures and is used for foundation tiers and columns. Limestones and well-cemented sandstones are employed extensively above the foundations. Nearly half of all the limestone used in the United States in block form is **Indiana limestone.** Marble has a low crushing strength and is usually an architectural or facing stone.

Crushed stone is used for making concrete, for railway ballast, and for road making.   The commercial stone is quarried, crushed, and graded. Much of the crushed stone used is granite, limestone, and **trap rock.** The latter is a term used to designate basalt, gabbro, diorite, and other dark-colored fine-grained igneous rocks.   Graded crushed stone usually consists of only one kind of rock and is broken with sharp edges.   The sizes are from ¼ to 2½ in., although larger sizes may be used for massive concrete aggregate.   Screenings below ¼ in. are employed largely for paving.   **Granite granules** for making hard terrazzo floors are marketed in several sizes, and in pink, green, and other selected colors.   **Roofing granules** are graded particles of crushed rock, slate, slag, porcelain, or tile, used as surfacing on asphalt roofing and shingles.   Granules have practically superseded gravel for this purpose.   Black **amphibole ryolite** may be used, or gray basalt may be colored artificially for granule use.   The **suzorite rock** of Quebec contains feldspar, pyroxenite, apatite, and mica, and is treated to remove the mica.   **Ceramic granules** are produced from clay or shale fired and glazed with metallic salts.   They are preferred because the color is uniform.

BURLAP. A coarse, heavy cloth made of plain-woven jute, or jutelike fibers, and used for wrapping and bagging bulky articles, for upholstery linings, and as a backing fabric for linoleum.   Finer grades are also used for wall coverings.   The standard burlap from India is largely from jute fibers, but some hibiscus fibers are used.   For bags and wrappings, the weave is coarse and irregular, and the color is the natural tan.   The coarse grades such as those used for wrapping cotton bales are sometimes called gunny in the United States, but **gunny** is a general name for all burlap in Great Britain.   Dundee, Scotland, is the important center of burlap manufacture outside of India, but considerable quantities are made from native fibers in Brazil and other countries.   Burlap is woven in widths up to 144 in., but 36, 40, and 50 in. are the usual widths.   **Hessian** is the name of a 9½-oz plain-woven finer burlap made to replace an older fabric of the same name woven from coarse and heavy flax fibers.   When dyed in colors, it is used for linings, wall coverings, and upholstery.   **Bithess** was a name for Hessian fabric coated with bitumen used in India to spread over soft-earth areas as a seal for a top coating to form airplane runways. **Brattice cloth** is a very coarse, heavy, and tightly woven jute cloth, usually 20 oz per sq yd, used for gas breaks in coal mines, but a heavy cotton duck substituted for the same purpose is called by the same name.   Most burlap for commercial bags is 8, 9, 10, and 12 oz, feed bags being 8 oz and grain bags 10 oz.

BUTADIENE. Also called **divinyl, vinyl ethylene, erythrene,** and **pyrrolylene.**   A colorless gas of the composition $CH_2:CH \cdot CH:CH_2$ used in the production of neoprene, nylon, latex paints, and resins. The Columbian Carbon Co. is using it to produce intermediate chemicals such as **cyclododecatriene,** the prime material for nylon 6 and 12. In contact with air or oxygen it forms peroxides that are explosive, and must be safeguarded with inhibitors when shipped. Butadiene has a boiling point of $-3°C$, and a specific gravity of 0.6272. Commercial butadiene is at least 98% pure, with normal butane and butenes as the impurities. It contains 0.01% of phenyl beta naphthylamine or other oxidation inhibitor. It is easily produced by the dehydrogenation of butane from natural gas or petroleum, but may also be made from alcohol. **Butadiene rubber,** or **polybutadiene,** can be made with close regulation of the molecular weight to give uniform rubbers of definite characteristics. The rubbers have less resilience and a higher heat buildup than natural rubber, but they are more resistant to oxidation and abrasion, and they give much greater wear life in automotive tires. They are oil-extendable. **Plioplex 5001** is an easily dissolved emulsion of high-purity polybutadiene used for modifying polystyrene rubbers. **Amerpol CB,** or **cis-polybutadiene,** of Goodrich-Gulf Chemicals, is a polybutadiene rubber polymerized with a cobalt catalyst to keep the detrimental vinyl content below 1%. Carboxy-modified butadiene rubber is highly resistant to ozone, retains elasticity at subzero temperatures, and has good dielectric strength for electrical insulation. Related to butadiene is **propadiene,** a gas of the composition $CH_2:C:CH_2$, called also **dimethylene methane** and **alene.** It also polymerizes easily to form plastics and rubbers.

BUTTER. An edible fat made from cow's milk by curdling with bacterial cultures and churning. The production of butter is one of the large industries of the Western nations, with an annual production exceeding 10 billion pounds, 30% of which is made in the United States. Other important producers are Germany, Holland, the Scandinavian countries, Australia, New Zealand, Canada, Ireland, and Argentina. More than 80% of the butter produced in the United States is made in factories as **creamery butter** subject to Federal inspection, as distinct from **farm butter** not subject to the regulations of interstate trade. Creamery butter is an important raw material in the bakery and confectionery industries. Federal regulations require that creamery butter shall be made exclusively from milk or cream, with or without salt and coloring matter, and shall contain not less than 80% by weight of milk fat, not over 15% moisture, and not over 2.5% salt. Butter varies greatly in color and flavor according to the feed of the animal, the processing, and the storage. The natural color is whitish in winter and yellow in summer when the animal feeds on green pasturage. Commercial butter is usually brought to a uniform yellow by coloring with annatto. Musty, garlicky, and fishy flavors may be caused by noxious weeds eaten by the animal; cheesy or yeasty flavors may be from stale cream; metallic, greasy, scorched, or alkaline flavors may be from improper processing. **Whipped butter** has 50% greater volume in the same weight and has greater plasticity for spreading. American butter is salted, while Argentine butter is usually unsalted.

United States grades for creamery butter range from 93 score for the best butter of fine flavor and body down to 85 score for the lowest grade having pronounced obnoxious weed flavor and defects in body, color, or salt. The grading, or scoring, of butter is done by experts. The flavor is determined by the senses of taste and smell. The flavor, body, color, and salt are rated independently, and points, or scores, are subtracted for defects. Body and texture of the butter are determined by the character of the granules and their closeness. The most common body defects are gumminess, sponginess, crumbliness, and stickiness. The most common defect in color is lack of uniformity, with waves or mottles. Defects in salting are excessive salt and undissolved salt grains. Butter held in storage at improper temperatures is likely to develop rancid or unpleasant flavors and acidity due to chemical changes, or it may absorb flavors from surrounding products. High-grade butter can be held in well-regulated cold storage for long periods without appreciable deterioration.

An important substitute for butter is **margarine**. **Oleomargarine** is a term still retained in old food laws, but the product is no longer manufactured. It was a compound of mutton fat with vegetable tallows and fats, invented by the French chemist Mège-Mouries. Margarine is made from a mixture of about 80% vegetable oils and 20 milk in the same manner as butter. It has a slightly lower melting point than butter, 22 to 27°C, but the melting point and a desired degree of saturation of the fatty acids can be regulated by hydrogenation of the oils. The margarine of lower melting points is used in the bakery industry, and the grades with higher melting points are for table use. From 2.5 to 4% salt is used, together with vitamins A and D, lecithin, annatto coloring, and sometimes phosphatides to prevent spattering when used for frying. **Biacetyl**, $C_4H_6O_2$, a colorless, pungent sweet liquid which gives the characteristic flavor to butter, is also added. The food value is in general higher than that of butter, but because of the competition with butter various Federal and state regulations restrict its use. **Soya buttter** is made from emulsified soybean and, when fortified with butyric acid, the characteristic acid of butter, is practically indistinguishable from butter. It is, however, subject to restrictive regulations. **Butter flavors** are used in confectionery and bakery products. **Butter-Aid**, of Cino Chemical Co., is made by extracting and concentrating the esters of natural butter. It is used as a high-strength flavor in foodstuffs in the form of powder or liquid emulsion. **Butta-Van**, of the Whitehall Food Mfg. Co., is a butter flavor with vanilla. It contains butyric acid, ethyl butyrate, coumarin, vanillin, and glycerin in water solution.   **Ghee butter,** used in India, is made from buffalo milk, sometimes mixed with cow's milk.   It is clarified and the moisture removed by boiling and slow cooling and separating off the opaque white portion.   It is light in color and granular.   **Synthetic butter** was made in Germany in wartime by esterifying with glycerin straight-chain aliphatic synthetic acids of C_{11} and C_{12}, and purifying the resulting esters.

Cheese is an important solid food product made from butterfat by action of cultures of *Lactobacillus*.   It contains all the food value of milk, including the proteins of the casein.   The biotics used in the manufacture produce *n*-butyric acid, with also caproic, caprylic, and capric acids in varying amounts which produce the flavor of the various types of cheese.   In the same manner **lipase enzymes** from the glands of calves and lambs are used for enhancing the flavor of food products containing milk or butterfat. The enzymes hydrolize the butyric or other short-chained fatty acids into the glycerides.   The **Lipolyzed butter** of Marschall Dairy Laboratories, Inc., is made by treating natural butterfat with the enzymes.   It gives intensity and uniformity of flavor to margarine and bakery products.

CADMIUM. A silvery-white crystalline metal, symbol Cd.   It has a specific gravity of 8.6, is very ductile, and can be rolled or beaten into thin sheets.   It resembles tin and gives the same characteristic cry when bent, but is harder than tin.   A small addition of zinc makes it very brittle.   It melts at 608°F and boils at 1409°F.   Cadmium is employed as an alloying element in soft solders and in fusible alloys, for hardening copper, as a white corrosion-resistant plating metal, and in its compounds for pigments and chemicals.   It is also used to shield against neutrons in atomic equipment; but gamma rays are emitted when the neutrons are absorbed, and these rays require an additional shielding of lead.   The metal is marketed in small round sticks 12 in. long, in variously shaped anodes for electroplating, and as foil.   **Cadmium foil** of the American Silver Co. is 99.95% pure cadmium and is as thin as 0.0005 in.   It is used for neutron shielding and for electronic applications requiring high corrosion resistance. Electrolytic cadmium is 99.95% pure.   It is obtained chiefly as a by-product of the zinc industry by treating the flue dust and fumes from the roasting of the ores.   Flue dust imported from Mexico averages 0.66 ton of cadmium per ton of dust.   About half the world production is in the United States.   Other important producers are Germany, Belgium, Canada, and Poland.   The only commercial ore of the metal is **greenockite,** CdS, which contains theoretically 77.7% cadmium.   This mineral occurs in yellow powdery form in the zinc ores of Missouri.   Cadmium occurs in sphalerite to the extent of 0.1 to 1%.

Most of the consumption of cadmium is for electroplating.   For a corrosion-resistant coating for iron or steel a cadmium plate of 0.0003 in. is equal in effect to a zinc coat of 0.001 in. The plated metal has a silvery-white color with a bluish tinge, is denser than zinc and harder than tin, but electroplated coatings are subject to hydrogen embrittlement, and aircraft parts are usually coated by the vacuum process. **Cadmium plating** is not normally used on copper or brass since copper is electronegative to it, but when these metals are employed next to cadmium-plated steel a plate of cadmium may be used on the copper to lessen deterioration. **Cadalyte,** of Du Pont, is a cadmium salt and process for cadmium plating, and **Udylite** is the name of a salt and process of the Udylite Corp.

Small amounts of cadmium added to copper give higher strength, hardness, and wear resistance, but decrease the electrical conductivity. Copper containing 0.5 to 1.2% cadmium is called **cadmium copper** or **cadmium bronze.** **Hitenso** is a cadmium bronze of the American Brass Co. It has 35% greater strength than hard-drawn copper, and 85% the conductivity of copper. The cadmium bronze known in England as **conductivity bronze,** used for electric wires, contains 0.8% cadmium and 0.6 tin. The tensile strength, hard-drawn, is 85,000 psi, and the conductivity is 50% that of copper. **Cadmium nitrate,** $Cd(NO_3)_2$, is a white powder used for making cadmium yellow and fluorescent pigments, and as a catalyst. **Cadmium sulfide,** Cds, is used as a yellow pigment and, mixed with **cadmium selenide,** CdSe, a red powder, gives a bright-orange pigment. The sulfide is used for growing **cadmium sulfide crystals** in plates and rods for semiconductor uses. Crystals grown at 1050°C are nearly transparent, but those grown at higher temperatures are dark amber.

CAFFEINE. An alkaloid which is a white powder when it has the composition $C_8H_{10}N_4O_2$, and occurs in crystalline flakes when it has one molecule of water of crystallization. The melting point is 235°C. It is soluble in water and in alcohol. Caffeine increases muscular contraction and stimulates to lessen fatigue, but in large amounts is highly toxic. Its prime use is in medicine, but most of the production is used in soft drinks. Caffeine does not normally break down in the human body, but passes off in the urine, and the effect is not cumulative, but the sarcosine, which occurs in muscles, is a decomposition product of caffeine though it normally comes from nitrogen metabolism. Caffeine is obtained from coffee, tea waste, kola nuts, or guarana by solvent extraction, or a by-product in the manufacture of such noncaffeine coffees as Sanka, or in the processing of coffee for the production of oil and cellulose. It is made synthetically from **dimethyl sulfat**e, a volatile toxic liquid of the composition $H(CH_2)$-$O(SO_2)O(CH_2)H$, also used for making codeine and other drugs. Synthetic caffeine is also made from urea and sodium cyanoacetate, and is equal chemically to natural caffeine.

Less than 1% caffeine is obtained from coffee, about 2 from **tea waste,** and 1.5 from kola nuts.   In tea it is sometimes called **theine.**   Cocoa waste contains **theobromine,** from which caffeine may be produced by adding one more methyl group to the molecular ring.   The name is a deception, as there is no bromine in the molecule.   Theobromine is a more powerful stimulant than caffeine.   It is a bitter white crystalline powder of the composition $C_7H_8N_4O_2$, also called **dimethyl xanthine,** and used in medicine. **Guarana** contains the highest percentage of caffeine of all the beverage plants, about 3%.   It comes from the seeds of the woody climbing plant *Paullinia cupana,* of the Amazon Valley.   The Indians grind the seeds with water and mandioca flour and dry the molded paste with smoke. For use it is grated into hot water.   **Kola nuts** are the seeds of the fruit of the large spreading tree *Kola acuminata* native to West Africa and cultivated also in tropical America, and the *K. nitida* of West Africa. The nuts of the latter tree contain the higher percentages of theobromine and caffeine.   The white nuts are preferred to the pink or red varieties. **Citrated caffeine,** used in pharmaceuticals, is a white powder produced by the action of citric acid on caffeine, and contains about equal quantities by weight of anhydrous caffeine and citric acid.   It is very soluble in water.

CAJEPUT OIL. A greenish essential oil distilled from the leaves of the tree *Melaleuca leucadendron* growing chiefly in Indonesia.   It contains the cineole of eucalyptus oil and also the **terpinol** which is characteristic of the lilac.   It has a camphorlike odor.   It is used in medicine as an antiseptic and counterirritant, and in perfumes.   **Naouli oil** is a similar oil from the leaves of the tree *M. viridi* of New Caledonia.   **Cajeput bark,** from the same tree, is used as an insulating material in place of cork.   The bark, up to 2 in. thick, is soft, light, resistant, and a good insulator.

CALCITE. One of the most common and widely diffused minerals, occurring in the form of limestones, marbles, chalks, calcareous marls, and calcareous sandstones.   It is a calcium carbonate, $CaCO_3$, and the natural color is white or colorless, but it may be tinted to almost any shade with impurities.   The specific gravity is about 2.72 and Mohs hardness 3.   Calcite is usually in compact masses, but **aragonite,** formed by water deposition, develops in radiating flowerlike growths often twisted erratically.   **Iceland spar,** or **calc spar,** is the name for the perfectly crystallized, water-clear, flawless calcite crystals of optical grade used for the manufacture of **Nicol prisms** for polarizing microscopes, photometers, calorimeters, and polariscopes.   It comes from Iceland, Spain, South Africa, and New Mexico, and some crystals have been found as large as 17 lb.   The common **black calcite,** containing manganese oxide, often also contains silver in proportions high enough to warrant chemical extraction of the metal.

CALCIUM. A metallic element, symbol Ca, belonging to the group of alkaline earths. It is one of the most abundant materials, occurring in combination in limestones and calcareous clays. The metal is obtained 98.6% pure by electrolysis of the fused anhydrous chloride. By further subliming it is obtained 99.5% pure. Calcium metal is yellowish white in color. It oxidizes easily, and when heated in the air burns with a brilliant white light. The specific gravity is 1.55, melting point 810°C, and boiling point 1440°C. Its strong affinity for oxygen and sulfur is utilized as a cleanser for nonferrous alloys. As a deoxidizer and desulfurizer it is employed in the form of lumps or sticks of calcium metal or in ferroalloys and calcium-copper. For the reduction of light-metal ores it is used in the form of the hydride. **Calcium metal** is sold by the New England Lime Co. in $6\frac{1}{2}$-lb ingots. **Crystalline calcium** is also used in the form of a very reactive free-flowing powder of 94 to 97% purity, and containing 2.5% of calcium oxide with small amounts of magnesium and other impurities. The density of the powder is 1.54, and the melting point is 851°C. Natural calcium compounds, such as dolomite, are used directly as a flux in melting iron. Calcium is also used to harden lead, and calcium silicide is used in making some special steels to inhibit carbide formation.

Many compounds of calcium are employed industrially, in fertilizers, foodstuffs, and medicine. It is an essential element in the formation of bones, teeth, shells, and plants. **Oyster shells** form an important commercial source of calcium for animal feeds. The shells are dredged in the Gulf of Mexico where vast quantities of oysters are killed by tidal shifts of fresh water. They are crushed, and the fine flour is marketed for stock feeds and the coarse for poultry feeds. The shell is calcium carbonate. **Edible calcium,** for adding calcium to food products, is **calcium lactate,** a white powder of the composition $Ca(C_3H_5O_3)_2 \cdot 5H_2O$, derived from milk. **Calcium lactobionate** is a white powder that readily forms chlorides and other double salts, and is used as a suspending agent in pharmaceuticals. It contains 4.94% available calcium. **Calcium phosphate,** used in the foodstuffs industry and in medicine, is marketed in several forms. **Calcium diphosphate,** known as **phosphate of lime,** is $CaHPO_4 \cdot 2H_2O$, or in anhydrous form. It is soluble in dilute citric acid solutions, and is used to add calcium and phosphorus to foods, and as a polishing agent in tooth pastes. **Calcium monophosphate** is a stable, white, water-soluble powder, $CaH_4P_2O_8 \cdot H_2O$, used in baking as a leavening agent. The anhydrous **monocalcium phosphate,** $CaH_4(PO_4)_2$, of the Victor Chemical Works, for use in prepared flour mixes, is a white powder with each particle having a coating of a phosphate that is soluble only with difficulty, to delay solution when liquids are added. **Calcium triphosphate,** $Ca_3(PO_4)_2$, is a white water-insoluble powder used to supply calcium and phosphorus to foods, as a polishing agent in dentifrices, and as an antacid. **Calcium sulfite,**

$CaSO_3 \cdot 2H_2O$, is a white powder used in bleaching paper pulp and textiles, and as a disinfectant. It is only slightly soluble in water, but it loses its water of crystallization and melts at 100°C. **Calcium silicate,** $CaO \cdot SiO_2$, is a white powder used as a reinforcing agent in rubber, as an absorbent, to control the viscosity of liquids, and as a filler in paints and coatings. It reduces the sheen in coatings. **Silene EF,** of the Columbia Chemical Div., is a precipitated calcium silicate for rubber. **Micro-Cal,** of Johns-Manville, is a synthetic calcium silicate with particle size as small as 0.02 micron. It will absorb up to six times its weight of water, and 3 lb will absorb a gallon of liquid and remain a free-flowing powder.

Calcium metasilicate, $CaO \cdot SiO_3$, is found in great quantities as the mineral **wollastonite** near Willsboro, N.Y., mixed with about 15% of andradite. The thin, needlelike crystals are easy to crush and grind, and the impurities are separated out. The ground material is a brilliant white powder in short fibers, 99.5% passing a 325-mesh screen. It is used in flat paints, for paper coatings, as a filler in plastics, for welding-rod coatings, and for electrical insulators, tile, and other ceramics. **Calcium acetate,** $Ca(C_2H_3O_2)_2 \cdot H_2O$, is a white powder used in liming rosin and for making metallic soaps and synthetic resins. It is also called **lime acetate, acetate of lime,** and **vinegar salts.**

CALCIUM CARBIDE. A hard, crystalline substance of grayish-black color, used chiefly for the production of acetylene gas for welding torches and for lighting. It was discovered in 1892 and was widely employed for theater stage lighting and for early automobile headlights. It is made by reducing lime with coke in the electric furnace. It can also be made by heating crushed limestone to a temperature of about 1000°C, flowing a high-methane natural gas through it, and then heating to 1700°C. The composition is CaC_2, and the specific gravity is 2.26. It contains theoretically 37.5% carbon. When water is added to calcium carbide, acetylene gas is formed, leaving a residue of slaked lime. Pure carbide will yield 5.83 cu ft of acetylene per pound of carbide, but the commercial product is usually only 85% pure. Federal specifications require not less than 4.5 cu ft of gas per pound.

CALCIUM CHLORIDE. A white, crystalline, lumpy or flaky material of the composition $CaCl_2$. The specific gravity is 2.512 and the melting point is 722°C, and it is highly hygroscopic and deliquescent with rapid solubility in water. The commercial product contains 75 to 80% $CaCl_2$, with the balance chiefly water of crystallization. Some is marketed in anhydrous form for dehydrating gases. It is also sold in water solution containing 40% calcium chloride. Calcium chloride has been used on roads to aid in surfacing and absorb dust, and to prevent cracking from freezing.   It is also used for accelerating the setting of mortars, but more than 4% in concrete decreases the strength of the concrete.   It is also employed as an antifreeze in fire tanks, for brine refrigeration, as an anti-ice agent on street pavements, as a food preservative, and in textile and paper sizes as a gelling agent.   Calcium chloride is obtained from natural salt brines, or as a by-product in the Solvay process.   **Temperite,** of the Truscon Laboratories, is calcium chloride for concrete.

CALCIUM-SILICON. An alloy of calcium and silicon used as a deoxidizing agent for the elimination of sulfur in the production of steels and cast irons.   It is marketed as low-iron, containing 22 to 28% calcium, 65 to 70 silicon, and 5 max iron, and as high-iron, containing 18 to 22% calcium, 58 to 60 silicon, and 15 to 20 iron.   It comes in crushed form, and is added to the molten steel.   At the temperature of molten steel all of the calcium passes off and leaves no calcium residue in the steel.   **Calcium-manganese-silicon** is another master alloy containing 17 to 19% calcium, 8 to 10 manganese, 55 to 60 silicon, and 10 iron.

CAMEL'S HAIR. The fine, tough, soft hair from the mane and back of the camel, *Camelus bactrianus,* used for artists' brushes and for industrial striping brushes.   Most of the hair is produced in central Asia and Iran, and the grades preferred for brushes are from the crossbred Boghdi camel. The hair from the dromedary, also called djemel, or camel, is of poor quality.   Much of the camel hair is not cut, but is molted in large patches and is picked up along the camel routes.   The plucked beard hair and the coarse outerguard hair obtained in combing are the brush fibers.   They are tough, silky, and resilient.   The length is 5 to 8 in.   The fine body hair, or **camel wool,** which constitutes about 90% of the total fiber, is 1.5 to 2 in. long, has a fine radiance, a pale tan color, and a downy feel.   It is the textile fiber.   The beard hair from the Cashmere goat is very similar to camel hair and is used for brushes.   Various other hairs are used for making camel's-hair brushes, including ox-ear hair, badger hair, and sable hair.   The camel routes are now in politically disturbed areas and little is known of the amount of true camel hair available.

CAMPHOR. The white resin of the *Cinnamomum camphora,* an evergreen tree with laurellike leaves, reaching a height of 100 ft.   The tree occurs naturally in China and southern Japan, and is also grown in Florida. Taiwan is the center of the industry.   Camphor, $C_{10}H_{16}O$, has a specific gravity of 0.986 to 0.996, and melts at 175°C.   It is soluble in water and in alcohol.   Camphor is used for hardening nitrocellulose plastics, but it is also used in pharmaceuticals, in disinfectants, and in explosives and chemicals.   It is obtained from the trunks, roots, and large branches by steam distillation. From 20 to 40 lb of chips produce 1 lb of camphor. Crude camphor is pressed to obtain the **flowers of camphor** and **camphor oil.** The crude red camphor oil is fractionated into white and brown oils; the white oil is used in soaps, polishes, varnishes, cleaners, and pharmaceuticals, and the brown oil is used in perfumery. **White camphor oil** is a colorless liquid with a camphor odor and a specific gravity of 0.870 to 1.040, and is soluble in ether or chloroform. Camphor oil may also be distilled from the twigs. **Camphor sassafrassy oil** is a camphor-oil fraction having a specific gravity of 0.97. It has a sassafras tone, and is used for scenting soaps and sprays.

Borneo camphor, or **borneol**, is a white, crystalline solid obtained from the tree *Dryobalanops camphora* of Borneo and Sumatra. It is used as a substitute for camphor in cellulose plastics. It has the composition $C_{10}H_{17}OH$ and a specific gravity of 1.01, is soluble in alcohol, and sublimes at 212°C. The wood of this tree, known as **Borneo camphorwood**, or **kapur,** is used for cabinetwork. It weighs 50 lb per cu ft, has an interlocking grain, and a scent of camphor. It is also known as **camphorwood.**

Artificial camphor is **bornyl chloride,** $C_{10}H_{17}Cl$, a derivative of the pinene of turpentine. It has a camphor odor and the same industrial uses as camphor, but is optically inactive and is not used in pharmaceuticals. **Synthetic camphor,** made from turpentine, in refined form is equal to the natural product for medicinal use, and the technical grade is used in plastics. The camphor substitute **Lindol,** of the Celanese Corp., is **tricresyl phosphate,** or **tolyl phosphate,** $(CH_3C_6H_4)_3PO_4$, a colorless, odorless, viscous liquid which solidifies at $-20°C$. Like camphor, it hardens cellulose nitrate and makes it nonflammable. Tricresyl phosphate is also used as an additive for gasoline to prevent buildup of carbon deposits on the spark plugs and in the engine, thus increasing power by preventing predetonation. Other uses are as a plasticizer for synthetic resins, as a hydraulic fluid, and as an additive in lubricants. It is made from petroleum and from the cresylic acid from coal. **Triphenyl phosphate,** $(C_6H_5)_3PO_4$, is also used as a substitute for camphor in cellulose nitrate, and for making coating compounds nonflammable. It is a colorless solid, melting at 49°C. **Dehydranone,** of Union Carbide Corp., Chemicals Div., is **dehydracetic acid,** $C_8H_8O_4$, a white, odorless solid with some of the properties of camphor, used in nitrocellulose and vinyl resins. **Cyclohexyl levulinate,** $CH_3CO(CH_2)_2COOC_6H_{11}$, is also used as a substitute for camphor in nitrocellulose, and also in vinyl resins and in chlorinated rubber. It is a liquid of specific gravity 1.025, boiling point 265°C, and freezing point $-70°C$. **Adamantine** has the odor of camphor and turpentine. It is obtained from the crude petroleum of Moravia as a stable, crystalline solid, melting at 268°C. It has the empirical formula $C_{10}H_{16}$, and the molecule has four transcyclohexane rings. **Camphorene,** $C_{20}H_{32}$, is made from turpentine by polymerizing two myrcene molecules. It is a raw material for producing geraniol and linalool.

CAMWOOD. The wood of the tree *Baphia nitida,* native to West Africa, used for tool handles and for machine bearings. It will withstand heavy bearing pressures. The wood is exceedingly hard, has a coarse, dense grain, and weighs 65 lb per cu ft. It contains a red coloring matter known as **santalin,** and was once valued as a dyewood for textiles. **Barwood,** from the tree *Pterocarpus santalinus,* of West Africa, is a similar reddish hardwood containing the same dye and used for the same purposes.

CANAIGRE. A tanning material extracted from the roots of the low-growing plant *Rumex hymenosepalus* of northern Mexico and the arid Southwest of the United States. The plant is known locally as **sour dock,** and the roots contain up to 40% tannin. The cultivated plant yields as much as 20 tons of root per acre. **Canaigre extract** contains 30% tannin. It produces a firm, orange-colored leather. Canaigre was the tanning agent of the Aztec Indians, and is still extensively cultivated.

CANARY SEED. The seeds of the **canary grass,** *Phalaris canariensis,* native to the Canary Islands, but now grown on a large scale in Argentina for export, and in Turkey and Morocco for human food and for export. In international trade it is known by the Spanish name **alpiste.** It is valued as a bird food because it contains phosphates, iron, and other minerals, and is rich in carbohydrates. It is, however, low in proteins and fats, and is usually employed in mixtures. **Birdseed** is an extensive item of commerce, but the birdseed that reaches the market in the United States is usually a blend of canary seed and millet, with other seeds to give a balanced food. Canary seed is small, pale yellow in color, and convex on both sides. The term **Spanish canary seed** is applied to the choice seed regardless of origin. **Niger seed,** also valued as a birdseed, is from the plant *Guizotia abyssinica,* of the thistle, or *Compositae* family, grown in India, Africa, Argentina, and Europe. It is also known as **inga seed, rantil, kala til seed,** and **black sesame.** It is also called **gingelli** in India, although this name and **til** are more properly applied to sesame. The seed is high in proteins and fats.

CANDELILLA WAX. A yellowish amorphous wax obtained by hot water or solvent extraction from the stems of the shrubs *Pedilanthus pavonis* and *Euphorbia antisyphilitica* growing in the semiarid regions of Texas and Mexico. The plants grow to a height of 3 to 5 ft and consist of a bundle of stalks without leaves. The stems yield 3.5 to 5% wax that consists of long-chain hydrocarbons with small amounts of esters. The wax has a specific gravity of 0.983, melting point 67 to 70°C, iodine value 37, and saponification value 45 to 65.   The refined grade is purified by remelting, and contains not more than about 1% water.   It is soluble in turpentine, and is used for varnishes, polishes, and leather finishes; as a substitute for carnauba wax; or to blend with carnauba or beeswax.   About half the production goes into furniture and shoe polishes, but it does not have the self-polishing characteristics of carnauba wax.

CANNEL COAL. A variety of coal having some of the characteristics of petroleum, valued chiefly for its quick-firing qualities.   It consists of coaly matter intimately mixed with clay and shale, often containing fossil fishes, and probably derived from vegetable matter in lakes.   It is compact in texture, dull black in color, and breaks along joints, often having an appearance similar to that of black shale.   It burns with a long, luminous, smoky flame, from which it derives its old English name, meaning candle. On distillation, cannel coal yields a high proportion of illuminating gas, up to 16,000 cu ft per ton, leaving a residue consisting mostly of ash.   At low temperatures it yields a high percentage of tar oils.   The proportion of volatile matter may be as high as 70%.   It is found in Great Britain, and in Kentucky, Ohio, and Indiana.   Cannel coal from Scotland was originally called **parrot coal,** and **boghead coal** was a streaky variety.

CARBOHYDRATES. A group of materials, chiefly of vegetable origin, which are distinguished by the fact that they contain the elements carbon, hydrogen, and oxygen, and no others.   Many chemical compounds, such as alcohols and aldehydes, also have these elements only, but the term carbohydrate refers only to the starches, sugars, and cellulose, which are more properly called **saccharides.**   They are best known for their use as foodstuffs, as carbohydrates compose more than 50% of all American food, but they are also used in many industrial processes.   The digestible carbohydrates are the sugars and the starches.   The indigestible carbohydrates are cellulose and hemicellulose, which form the chief constituents of woods, stalks, and leaves of plants, the outer covering of seeds, and the walls of plant cells enclosing the water, starches, and other substances of the plants.   Much cellulose is eaten as food, especially in the leaves of vegetables and in bran, but it serves as bulk rather than as food, and is beneficial if not consumed in quantity.   The digestible carbohydrates are classified as **single sugars, double sugars,** and **complex sugars,** chemically known as **monosaccharides, disaccharides,** and **polysaccharides.**   The single sugars, glucose, fructose, and galactose, require no digestion and are readily absorbed into the blood stream.   The double sugars, sucrose, maltose, and lactose, require to be broken down by enzymes in the human system. **Lactose,** produced from milk solids, is a nonhygroscopic powder.   It is only 16% as sweet as sugar and not as soluble, but it enhances flavor.   It digests slowly.   It is used in infant foods, in dairy drinks and ice cream to improve low-fat richness, in bakery products to decrease sogginess and improve browning, and as a dispersing agent for high-fat powders.   **Galactose** is derived from lactose by hydrolysis.   **Multisugars** are mixed sugars with the different sugars interlocked in the crystals.   They dissolve rapidly to form clear solutions.

The complex sugars are the starches, dextrines, and glycogen.   These require digestion to the single stage before they can be absorbed in the system.   The common starches are in corn, wheat, potatoes, rice, tapioca, and sago.   **Animal starch** is the reserve food of animals stored in the liver and muscles.   It is **glycogen,** a sweet derivative of glycolic acid.   It is not separated out commercially because it is hygroscopic and quickly hydrolyzed.   **Dextran,** related to glycogen, is a **polyglucose** made up of many molecules of glucose in a long chain.   It is used as an extender of blood plasma.   It can be stored indefinitely and, unlike plasma, can be sterilized by heat.   It is produced commercially by biotic fermentation of common sucrose sugar.

The **hemicelluloses** are agar-agar, algin, and pectin.   They differ chemically from cellulose and expand greatly on absorbing water.   The hemicelluloses of wood, called **hexosan,** consist of the **wood sugars,** or **hexose,** with 6 carbon atoms, $(C_6H_{10}O_5)_n$.   They were used in Germany during the war to produce alcohol and glycerin, and are now used to make many chemicals.   The water-soluble hemicellulose of the Masonite Corp., known as **Masonex** in water solution and **Masonoid** as a powder, is a by-product of the steam-exploded wood process.   It is used to replace starch as a binder for foundry cores and for briquetting coal, and for emulsions.   It contains 70% wood sugars, 20 resins, and 10 lignin.   **Lichenin,** or **moss starch,** is a hemicellulose from moss and some seeds.

The **pentosans** are gums or resins occurring in nutshells, straw, and the cell membranes of plants.   They may be classed as hemicellulose and on hydrolysis yield **pentose,** or **pentaglucose,** a sugar containing 5 carbon atoms.   **Pectin** is a yellowish, odorless powder soluble in water and decomposed by alkalies.   It is produced by acid extraction from the inner part of the rind of citrus fruits and from apple pomace.   In East Africa it is obtained from sisal waste.   **Flake pectin** is more soluble and has longer shelf life than the powdered form.   It is produced from a solution of apple pomace containing 5% pectin by drying on steam-heated drums, and the thin film obtained is flaked to 40 mesh.   Another source is **sugarbeet pulp,** which contains 20 lb of pectin per ton.

Pectin has a complex structure, having a lacturonic acid with methanol in a glucoside chain combination.   It is used for gelling fruit preserves, and the gelling strength depends on the size of the molecule, the molecular weight varying from 150,000 to 300,000.   It is also used as a blood coagulant in treating hemorrhage, and for prolonging the effect of some drugs by retarding their escape through the body.   **Sodium pectate** is used for creaming rubber latex, and in cosmetics and printing inks. Hemicellulose and pectin are valuable in the human system because of their ability to absorb and carry away irritants, but they are not foods in the normal sense of the term.   **Oragen,** of the Consumer Drug Co., is a pectin-cellulose complex derived from orange pulp.   It is used in weight-reduction diets, increasing bulk and retaining moisture, thus suppressing desire for excess food.   Each of the saccharides has distinctive characteristics of value in the system, but each also in excess causes detrimental conditions.   The metabolism, or energy-yielding process, of carbohydrates as food is complex and varies greatly in the presence of, or lack of, various minerals, vitamins, nitrogen compounds, absorption of oxygen, and the acids and glycerides of fats.   Carbohydrates are used in many industries.   The sugars are employed for the manufacture of alcohols, the starches for adhesives and sizing, the celluloses for plastics and explosives, and the hemicelluloses as thickening agents.

CARBON. A nonmetallic element, symbol C, existing naturally in several allotropic forms, and in combination as one of the most widely distributed of all the elements.   It is quadrivalent, and has the property of forming chain and ring compounds, and there are more varied and useful compounds of carbon than of all other elements.   Carbon enters into all organic matter of vegetable and animal life, and the great branch of **organic chemistry** is the chemistry of carbon compounds.   The black amorphous carbon has a specific gravity of 1.88; the black crystalline carbon known as graphite has a specific gravity of 2.25; the transparent crystalline carbon, as in the diamond, has a specific gravity of 3.51. **Amorphous carbon** is not soluble in any known solvent.   It is infusible, but sublimes at 3500°C, and is stable and chemically inactive at ordinary temperatures.   At high temperatures it burns and absorbs oxygen, forming the simple oxides CO and CO_2, the latter being the stable oxide present in the atmosphere and a natural plant food.   Carbon dissolves easily in some molten metals, notably iron, exerting great influence on them.   Steel, with small amounts of chemically combined carbon, and cast iron, with both combined carbon and graphitic carbon, are examples of this.

Carbon occurs as hydrocarbons in petroleum, and as carbohydrates in coal and plant life, and from these natural basic groupings an infinite number of carbon compounds can be made synthetically.   Carbon, for chemical, metallurgical, or industrial use, is marketed in the form of compounds; or in master alloys containing high percentages of carbon; or as activated carbons, charcoal, graphite, carbon black, coal-tar carbon, petroleum coke; or as pressed and molded bricks or formed parts with or without binders or metallic inclusions. Natural deposits of graphite, coal tar, and petroleum coke are important sources of elemental carbon. Charcoal and activated carbons are obtained by carbonizing vegetable or animal matter. **Carbon 13** is one of the isotopes of carbon, used as a tracer in biologic research where its heavy weight makes it easily distinguished from other carbon. **Carbon 14,** or **radioactive carbon,** has a longer life. It exists in the air, formed by the bombardment of nitrogen by cosmic rays at high altitudes, and enters into the growth of plants. The half-life is about 6,000 years. It is made from nitrogen in a cyclotron.

Carbon fibers are made by the Pittsburgh Coke & Chemicals Co. by pyrolizing methane at temperatures to 1500°F and passing over a silica surface to yield masses of long and short fibers of 0.1 to 0.4 micron diameter. The carbon has a mesomorphic two-dimensional crystallite form, and the fibers are strong and flexible with a density of 1.991. Carbon fibers are produced as continuous filaments, 0.002 in. in diameter, with tensile strength of 200,000 psi. **Thornel,** of Union Carbide Corp., is a yarn made from these filaments for high-temperature fabrics. It retains its strength to temperatures above 2800°F. **Carbon yarn,** of the Basic Carbon Corp., is 99.5% pure carbon. It comes in plies from 2 to 30, with each ply composed of 720 continuous filaments of 0.0003 in. diameter. Each ply has a breaking strength of 2 lb. The fiber has the flexibility of wool and maintains dimensional stability to 5700°F. **Ucar,** of Union Carbide Corp., is a conductive **carbon fabric** made from carbon yarns woven with insulating glass yarns with resistivities from 0.2 to 30 ohms for operating temperatures to 550°F. **Carbon wool,** of Atomic Laboratories, Inc., for filtering and insulation, is composed of pure-carbon fibers made by carbonizing rayon. The fibers, 5 to 50 microns in diameter, are hard and strong, and can be made into rope and yarn, or the mat can be activated for filter use. **Avceram RS,** of FMC Corp., is a composite rayon-silica fiber made with 40% dissolved sodium silicate. A highly heat-resistant fiber, **Avceram CS,** is woven into fabric and then pyrolized to give a porous interlocked mesh of **carbon silica fiber,** with a tensile strength of 165,000 psi. **Dexsan,** of C. H. Dexter & Sons Co., for filtering hot gases and liquids, is a **carbon filter paper** made from carbon fibers pressed into a paperlike mat, 0.007 to 0.050 in. thick and impregnated with activated carbon.

Carbon brushes for electrical motors and generators, and **carbon electrodes,** are made of carbon in the form of graphite, petroleum coke, lampblack, or other nearly pure carbon, sometimes mixed with copper powder to increase the electrical conductivity, and then pressed into blocks or shapes and sintered. The carbon-graphite brushes of the Pure Carbon Co.

contain no metals but are made from **carbon-graphite powder** and, after pressing, are subjected to a temperature of 5000°F which produces a harder and denser structure permitting current densities up to 125 amp per sq in.   **Carbon brick,** used as a lining in the chemical processing industries, is carbon compressed with a bituminous binder and then carbonized by sintering.   If the binder is capable of being completely carbonized, the bricks are impervious and dense.   **Graphite brick,** made in the same manner from graphite, is more resistant to oxidation than carbon bricks and has a higher thermal conductivity, but it is softer.   The binder may also be a furfural resin polymerized in the pores.   **Karbate No. 1,** of the National Carbon Co., Inc., is a carbon-base brick, and **Karbate No. 2** is a graphite brick.   Karbate has a crushing strength of 10,500 psi, and a weight of 110 to 120 lb per cu ft.   **Impervious carbon** is used for lining pumps, for valves, and for acid-resistant parts.   It is carbon or graphite impregnated with a chemically resistant resin and molded to any shape.   It can be machined.   **Karbate 21** is a phenolic impregnated graphite, and **Karbate 22** is a modified phenolic-impregnated graphite. Molded impervious carbon has a density of 1.77, tensile strength of 1,800 psi, and compressive strength of 10,000 psi.   **Impervious graphite** has a higher tensile strength, 2,500 psi, but a lower compressive strength, 9,000 psi.   The thermal conductivity is 8 to 10 times that of stainless steel.   **Graphitar,** of the U.S. Graphite Co., is a strong, hard carbon molded from amorphous carbon mixed with other forms of carbon.   It has high crushing strength and acid resistance, and is used for sealing rings, chemical pump blades, and piston rings.   **Porous carbon** is used for the filtration of corrosive liquids and gases.   It consists of uniform particles of carbon pressed into plates, tubes, or disks without a binder, leaving interconnecting pores of about 0.001 to 0.0075 in. in diameter. The porosity of the material is 48%, tensile strength 150 psi, and compressive strength about 500 psi.   **Porous graphite** has graphitic instead of carbon particles, and is more resistant to oxidation but is lower in strength.   **Carbocell** and **Graphicell** are trade names of the National Carbon Co., Inc., for these materials.

The so-called carbons used for electric-light **arc electrodes** are pressed from coal-tar carbon, but are usually mixed with other elements to bring the balance of light rays within the visible spectrum.   Solid carbons have limited current-carrying capacity and begin hissing about 40 amp per sq cm.   But when the carbon has a center of metal compounds such as the fluorides of the rare earths, its current capacity is greatly increased.   It then forms a deep positive crater in front of which is a flame five times the brilliance of that with the low-current arc.   The **sunshine carbon,** used in electric-light carbons to give approximately the same spectrum as sunlight, is molded coal-tar carbon with a core of cerium metals to introduce more blue into the light.   **Arc carbons** are also made to give other types of light, and to produce special rays for medicinal and other purposes. **B carbon,** of the National Carbon Co., Inc., contains iron in the core and gives a strong emission of rays from 2,300 to 3,200 angstrom units, which are the antirachitic radiations.   The light seen by the eye is only one-fourth the total radiation since the strong rays are invisible.   **C carbon** contains iron, nickel, and aluminum in the core, and gives powerful lower-zone ultraviolet rays.   It is used in light therapy and for industrial applications.   **E carbon,** to produce penetrating infrared radiation, contains strontium.   **Electrode carbon,** used for arc furnaces, is molded in various shapes from carbon paste.   When calcined from petroleum coke the electrodes contain only 0.2% moisture, 0.25 volatile matter, and 0.3 ash, and have a density of 2.05.   The carbon is consumed both in the production of light and of furnace heat.   For example, from 500 to 600 kg of carbon is consumed in producing a metric ton of aluminum.

CARBON BLACK. An amorphous powdered carbon resulting from the incomplete combustion of a gas, usually deposited by contact of the flame on a metallic surface, but also made by the incomplete combustion of the gas in a chamber.   The carbon black made by the first process is called **channel black,** taking the name from the channel iron used as the depositing surface.   The modern method, called the impingement process, uses many small flames with the fineness of particle size controlled by the flame size.   The air-to-gas ratio is high, giving oxidized surfaces and acid properties.   No water is used for cooling, keeping the ash content low. The supergrade of channel black has a particle size as low as 13 microns and a pH of 3 to 4.2.   Carbon black made by other processes is called **soft black** and is weaker in color strength, not so useful as a pigment. **Furnace black** is made with a larger flame in a confined chamber with the particles settling out in cyclone chambers.   The ratio of air is low, and water cooling raises the ash content.   The particle surface is oily, and the pH is high.

Carbon black from clean artificial gas is a glossy product with an intense color, but all the commercial carbon black is from natural gas.   To remove H_2S the sour gas is purified and water-scrubbed before burning. **Thermotomic black,** a grade made by the thermal decomposition of the gas in the absence of oxygen, is preferred in rubber when high loadings are employed because it does not retard the vulcanization, but only a small part of the carbon black is made by this process.   This thermal process black has large particle size, 150 microns, and a pH of 8.5.   It gives a coarse oily carbon.

The finer grades of channel black are mostly used for color pigment in paints, polishes, carbon paper, and in printing and drawing inks.   The largest use of carbon black is in automotive tires to increase wear resistance of the rubber.   The blacker blacks have a finer particle size than the grayer blacks, hence have more surface and absorptive capacity in compounding with rubber.   Channel black is valued for rubber compounding because of low acidity and low grit content.   The high pH of furnace black may cause scorching unless offsetting chemicals are used, but some furnace blacks are made especially for tire compounding.   **SAF black,** of the Phillips Petroleum Co., is such a furnace black.   In general, the furnace black with particle sizes from 28 to 85 microns and a pH from 8 to 10, and the channel blacks with particle size of about 29 and pH of 4.8, are used for rubber.   **Micronex EPC,** an impingement channel black of the Binney & Smith Co., has a particle diameter of 29 microns, a surface area of 10 acres per lb, and a pH of 4.8, while **Thermax MT,** a thermal process black, has a particle size of 274 microns, a surface area of 1 acre per lb, and a pH of 7.

In rubber compounding the carbon black is evenly dispersed to become intimately attached to the rubber molecule.   Fineness of the black determines the tensile strength of the rubber, the structure of the carbon particle determines the modulus, and the pH determines the cure behavior. Furnace blacks have a basic pH which activates the accelerator, and delaying-action chemicals are thus needed, but fine furnace blacks impart abrasion resistance to the rubber.   Furnace black made with a confined flame with limited air has a neutral surface and a low volatility.   Fineness is varied by temperature, size of flame, and time.   Carbonate salts raise the pH.   Most of the channel black for rubber compounding is made into dust-free pellets less than $1/8$ in. in diameter with a density of 20 to 25 lb per cu ft.   **Color-grade black** for inks and paints is produced by the channel process or the impingement process.   In general, carbon black for reinforcement has small particle size, and the electrically conductive grades, **CF carbon black** and **CC carbon black,** conductive furnace and conductive channel, have large particle size.

Carbon black from natural gas is produced largely in Louisiana, Texas, and Oklahoma.   About 35 lb of black is available per 1,000 cu ft of natural gas, but only 2.2 lb is recovered by the channel process and 10 lb by the furnace method.   By using gas from which the natural gasoline has been stripped, and by controlled preheating and combustion, as much as 27 lb can be recovered.   **Acetylene black** is a carbon black made by heat decomposition of acetylene.   It is more graphitic than ordinary carbon black with colloidal particles linked together in an irregular lattice structure and has high electrical conductivity and high liquid-absorption capacity.   Particle size is intermediate between that of channel black and furnace black, with low ash content, nonoiliness, and a pH of 6.5.   It is valued for use in dry cells and lubricants.   **Ucet,** of Union Carbide Corp., is in the form of agglomerates of irregular fine crystals. The greater surface area gives higher thermal and electrical conductivity and high liquid absorption.

For electrically **conductive rubber,** the mixing of the black with the rubber is regulated so that carbon chain connections are not broken.   Such conductive rubber is used for tabletops, for conveyor belts, and for coated filter fabrics to prevent static buildup.   Carbon blacks are also made from liquid hydrocarbons, and from anthracite coal by treatment of the coal to liberate hydrogen and carbon monoxide and then high-temperature treatment with chlorine to remove impurities.   The black made from anthracite has an open-pore structure useful for holding gases and liquids.

Carbon-black grades are often designated by trade names for particular uses.   **Kosmovar,** of the United Carbon Co., is a black with a slight bluish top tone used as a pigment for lacquers.   The specific gravity is 1.72, and the mesh is 325.   **Gastex** and **Pelletex** are carbon blacks of the General Atlas Carbon Co. used for rubber compounding.   **Statex,** of the Columbian Carbon Co., is a colloidal furnace black for synthetic rubber compounding.   **Kosmos 60,** of United Carbon Co., Inc., is a furnace black of high density and structure, while **Continex FF** of this company is a finely divided furnace black.   Both are used in rubber compounding, the first giving easier extrusion of the rubber, and the second giving better abrasion resistance.   **Aquablak H,** of the Binney & Smith Co., is a colloidal water dispersion of channel black to give a jet-black color. **Aquablak M** is a water dispersion of furnace black to give a blue-gray tone.   They are used as pigments in casein paint, inks, and leather finishes. **Liquimarl-Black,** of H. B. Taylor Co., is a stable colloidal dispersion of pure food-grade carbon black for use in coloring confectionery and for modifying colors in bakery products.

CARBON DIOXIDE. Also called **carbonic anhydride,** and in its solid state, **dry ice.**   A colorless, odorless gas of the composition CO_2, which liquefies at $-65°C$ and solidifies at $-78.2°C$.   It is obtained as a by-product of distilleries, from burning lime, and from natural gas.   In liquid form it is marketed in cylinders, and is used in fire extinguishers, in spray painting, in refrigeration, for inert atmospheres, for the manufacture of **carbonated beverages,** and in many industrial processes.   It is also marketed as dry ice, a white snowlike solid used for refrigeration in transporting food products.   About 1,000 lb of dry ice will refrigerate a car for a trip from California to New York, compared to 10,000 lb of water ice and salt.   **Cardox** is a trade name of the Cardox Corp. for liquid carbon dioxide in storage units at 30 psi pressure for fire-fighting equipment.

Carbon monoxide, CO, is a product of incomplete combustion, and is very reactive. It is one of the desirable products in synthesis gas for making chemicals, the synthesis gas made from coal containing 37% min CO. It is also recovered from top-blown oxygen furnaces in steel mills. Carbon monoxide is an intense poison when inhaled, as it captures instantly the oxygen of the red blood corpuscles, and is extremely toxic even in the small amounts from the exhausts of internal-combustion engines.

CARBON PAPER. Paper used for duplicating typewriting, pencil, or pen writing. It is made by coating the paper with a mixture of a pigment and a medium. The pigments include carbon black, Prussian blue, and organic red, or blue and green lakes. The medium is likely to be a blend of waxes and oils to give a composition of the desired consistency and melting point but, to make a good carbon paper that will not be gummy and will not smear, a proper proportion of a high-melting, nongreasy wax, such as carnauba, must be used. Papers of special texture, preferably rag papers, are employed. Smudgeproof carbon paper has a coating of plastic lacquer.

CARBON STEEL. Any steel owing its distinctive properties to carbon chemically combined with the iron. If other elements in influencing proportions are in the steel, it is designated as an alloy steel, except that up to 1.65% manganese, 0.60 silicon, and 0.60 copper may be included without the steel being considered as alloyed. Likewise, small amounts of sulfur to give free-machining properties may be added without changing the name. When the carbon is below 0.15%, the metal may be called iron; when the carbon exceeds 0.60%, the steel is usually considered to be tool steel. However, there is no fixed dividing line, and carbon steels for general use may be high or low in carbon. The old shop names **machine steel** and **machinery steel,** for open-hearth carbon steel having a low-carbon range, are still used to mean any easily worked low-carbon steel up to the tool-steel range that requires only simple heat treatment. Such steels of low carbon have tensile strengths from 35,000 to 45,000 psi, and those with 0.40 to 0.60% carbon have strengths up to 60,000 psi, or up to 120,000 psi when hard-drawn.

SAE steel 1020, with 0.15 to 0.25% carbon, when cold-rolled or hard-drawn, has a tensile strength from 40,000 to 60,000 psi, with elongation 30 to 40%. These steels do not contain enough carbon to harden fully, but they can be carburized and case hardened. When properly heat-treated, they have a fine grain, good wearing qualities on the outside, and a tough core. They will not withstand repeated shocks or stresses. Those with low carbon are ductile and are useful for deep drawing. The control of microstructure is important in this type of steel, since steels with large crystals tend to be brittle, and fine grains, produced by heat treatment or electron-beam melting, do not readily align along common planes and thus reduce the directionality of the steel. Since carbon raises the transition temperature and the notch toughness of steel, while manganese lowers them, a balancing treatment is needed. **Stressproof steel,** of the La Salle Steel Co., is a high-tensile steel containing about 0.45% carbon, 0.25 silicon, 1.5 manganese, and 0.30 sulfur. The tensile strength is 90,000 psi, but when heat-treated to 285 Brinell it has a tensile strength of 135,000 psi and elongation of 13%. It is resistant to warpage, and is used for such parts as long lead screws. It also comes with the addition of a small amount of copper uniformly distributed in the steel to improve fatigue strength and wear resistance and to increase machinability. The **GLX-W steels** of the Great Lakes Steel Co. are carbon steels, a typical steel having 0.16% carbon and 0.68 manganese, but with 0.01 to 0.04% columbium to refine the grain and improve the formability and welding properties. The tensile strength is 75,000 psi, with elongation of 27%. This type of steel is known as **columbium steel.** The carbon steels are used for shafts, forgings, gears, machine parts, and dies and gages for small runs. They forge and machine easily. Up to 0.15% sulfur, or 0.045 phosphorus, makes them free-cutting and keeps the chips from curling, but reduces the strength.

Rail steel, for railway rails, is characterized by an increase of carbon with the weight of the rail. Railway engineering standards call for 0.50 to 0.63% carbon and 0.60 manganese in a 60-lb rail, and 0.69 to 0.82% carbon and 0.70 to 1.0 manganese in a 140-lb rail. Rail steels are produced under rigid control conditions from deoxidized steels with phosphorus kept below 0.04%, and silicon 0.10 to 0.23%. Guaranteed minimum tensile strength of 80,000 psi is specified, but it is usually much higher.

Sometimes a machinery steel may be required with a small amount of alloying element to give a particular characteristic and still not be marketed as an alloy steel, although trade names are usually applied to such steels. **Crow steel,** of the Allegheny Ludlum Steel Corp., is a carbon steel with 0.50% chromium to give greater depth of hardness. When annealed, it machines the same as the straight carbon **Corinth steel** of this company. **Economo steel,** of Wheelock, Lovejoy & Co., Inc., is a low-carbon steel containing 0.18% molybdenum to produce a tough core when case hardened. **Max-El 1B steel,** of the Crucible Steel Co., has 0.20% carbon, high manganese, and a small amount of molybdenum. **Carilloy FC steel,** of the Carnegie-Illinois Steel Corp., is a free-cutting manganese-chrome-molybdenum steel giving tensile strengths to 175,000 psi without heat treatments. The **Rytense AA** machinery steel, of Joseph T. Ryerson & Sons, Inc., is a special-analysis steel with a tensile strength up to 115,000 psi, elongation 20%, and Brinell hardness 229. **Precision-ground steel** of the L. S. Starrett Co., for toolmaking, is an 0.18-carbon steel in flat ground strips in thicknesses from $\frac{1}{16}$ in.

Hobbing steels, used for making plastic molds by pressing the hard model into the steel, may be plain carbon steel for case hardening, or they may be low-alloy steels. **Press E-Z steel,** of the Jessop Steel Co., is a hobbing steel containing 0.40 to 0.50% carbon and 0.15 to 0.20 manganese with no alloying elements. It is marketed annealed to 100 Brinell, and when carburized and hardened has a hardness of 60 Rockwell C. **SAE steel 3110** is a hobbing steel containing 0.50% manganese, 0.60 chromium, and 1.25 nickel. It takes deep impressions, and when hardened has high core strength. **SAE steel 3312** is a hobbing steel with 3.5% nickel and 1.5 chromium. After air hardening, the core strength is 160,000 psi and core hardness 360 Brinell. **Speed Alloy,** of W. J. Holliday & Co., is a mold steel that machines easily and gives deep hardening and high core strength when hardened. It is a 0.30% carbon steel with some chromium and molybdenum. Tensile strength, annealed, is 107,000 psi, elongation 26%, and Brinell hardness 207. These materials, however, are low-alloy steels rather than plain carbon steels.

CARBON TETRACHLORIDE. A heavy colorless liquid of the composition CCl_4, also known as **tetrachloro methane,** which is one of a group of chlorinated hydrocarbons. It is an important solvent for fats, asphalt, rubber, bitumens, and gums. It is more expensive than the aromatic solvents, but it is notable as a noninflammable solvent for many materials sold in solution, and is widely used as a degreasing and cleaning agent in the dry-cleaning and textile industries. Since the fumes are highly toxic it is no longer permitted in compounds for home use. It is used as a chemical in fire extinguishers such as **Pyrene,** but when it falls on hot metal it forms the poisonous gas phosgene. It is also used as a disinfectant, and because of its high dielectric strength has been employed in transformers. It was first produced in 1839 and used in Germany as a grease remover under the name of **Katharin.** Carbon tetrachloride is obtained by the chlorination of carbon bisulfide. The specific gravity is 1.595, boiling point 76.0°C, and freezing point 23°C. **Chlorobromo methane,** $Br \cdot CH_2 \cdot Cl$, is also used in fire extinguishers as it is less corrosive and more than twice as efficient as an extinguisher. It is a colorless, heavy liquid with a sweet odor, a specific gravity of 1.925, boiling point of 67°C, and freezing point of -65°C. It is also used as a high-gravity flotation agent. **Chlorocarbene,** CCl_2, a yellowish liquid boiling at -20°C, is made by carbonizing carbon tetrachloride, and is used for making insecticides and perfumes.

CARNAUBA WAX. A hard, high-melting lustrous wax from the fanlike leaves of the palm tree *Copernica cerifera* of the arid region of northeastern Brazil, sometimes referred to as **Brazil wax,** or **ceara wax.** It is composed largely of **ceryl palmitate,** $C_{25}H_{51}COOC_{30}H_{61}$. The trees grow up to 60 ft in height with leaves 3 ft in length. The wax forms a protective coating on the leaves, and when the leaves are dried it flakes and is beaten off and melted into cakes. The wax comes in hard, vitreous, yellowish cakes or lumps that melt at about 85°C, and have a specific gravity of 0.995. It is soluble in alcohol and in alkalies. **Olho wax** is the wax from young yellow leaves and is whitish gray. **Palha wax,** from older green leaves, is of a deeper grayish-yellow hue. In melting, water is added to the palha to make the **chalky wax.** No. 3 chalky contains up to 10% water. Olho wax without water yields the prime yellow wax. **Flora wax** is the highest quality and is clear yellow. Fully 70% of the production of carnauba goes into the manufacture of floor waxes and carbon paper. It has the property of being self-polishing in liquid floor waxes. In carbon paper it is nongreasy and nonsmearing. Other uses are in shoe polishes, in leather finishes, and for blending with other waxes in coating compounds. **Burnishing wax,** in the shoe industry, is carnauba wax blended with other waxes.

A wax quite similar to carnauba is **guaruma,** or **cauassu wax,** from the leaves of the *Calathea lutea,* a small plant with large leaves like those of the banana, growing in the lower Amazon Valley. Its melting point is 80°C. Another similar wax is from the trunk of the **wax palm,** *Ceroxylon andicola,* growing on the Andean slopes. A wax that is very similar to carnauba in properties and is more plentiful, but which contains the green leaf coloring difficult to bleach out, is **ouricury wax.** The name is also spelled **urucury** (uru, the Carib name for a shell; o means leaf). The wax is from the leaves of the palm tree *Syagrus coronata,* or *Cocos coronata,* of northeastern Brazil. It is beaten off or boiled off the dried leaves and melted into blocks. The green color results largely from the method of preparation of the wax as it does not flake off the leaves as carnauba does. Ouricury wax has a melting point of about 85°C, acid number 10.6, iodine value 16.9, and saponification value 78.8. It has the same uses as carnauba where color is not important, or it is used to blend with carnauba to increase the gloss. The nuts of the tree are called **licurí nuts,** and are used to produce **licurí oil** employed in soaps. The name **licurí wax** is sometimes erroneously given to ouricury.

Cotton wax, which occurs in cotton fiber to the extent of about 0.6%, is very similar to carnauba wax. It is a combination of C_{28} to C_{32} primary alcohols with C_{24} to C_{32} fatty acids. It has not been produced commercially. **Sugarcane wax** is a hard wax similar to carnauba occurring on the outside of the sugarcane stalk. A ton of cane contains 2 to 3 lb of wax, which concentrates in the filter press cake after clarification of the cane juice. The filter cake contains as high as 21% wax, which is solvent-extracted, demineralized with hydrochloric acid, and distilled to remove the low-molecular-weight constituents. It is used in floor and furniture polishes. The wax has a tan color, a melting point at about 176°F, and acid number 23 to 28. **Duplicane wax,** of the Warwick Wax Co., Inc., is a grade of sugarcane wax for carbon paper, and **Technicane wax** is a grade for polishes. Sugarcane wax is miscible with vegetable and petroleum waxes, and has greater dispersing action than carnauba wax. **Henequen wax,** extracted from the waste pulp of the henequen plant, has a melting point of 185°F, and is similar to carnauba. **Moss wax,** used for polishes, is extracted from Spanish moss which contains up to 4% wax. **Spanish moss** is the fiber from the plant *Tillandsia usneoides,* which grows throughout tropical and subtropical America, and along the southeastern coast of the United States, hanging from branches of trees. It is used for packing fragile articles, and for mattresses.

CARNOTITE. A mineral found in Utah and Colorado and employed as a source of uranium, radium, and vanadium. It is a vanadate of uranium and potassium, $V_2O_5 \cdot 2U_2O_3 \cdot K_2O \cdot 3H_2O$. It is found as a powder with other sands and gives them a pale-yellow color. The ore may contain 2 to 5% uranium oxide and up to 6 vanadium oxide, but it usually runs 2% V_2O_5. The vanadium is produced by roasting the ore, leaching, precipitating the oxide with acids, and sintering. The production of radium from the residue ore is a complex process, and 400 tons of ore produces only a gram of radium. **Patronite,** mined in Peru as a source of vanadium, is a greenish mineral, V_2S_9, mixed with pyrites and other materials. Carnotite ore may contain up to 2,500 parts per million of selenium and is a source of this metal.

CAROA. Pronounced car-o-áh. The fiber from the leaves of the plant *Neoglaziovia variegata* of northeastern Brazil. It is more than twice as strong as jute and is lighter in color and lighter in weight, but is too hard to be used alone for burlap. It is employed as a substitute for jute in burlap when mixed with softer fibers and also for rope, and in mixtures with cotton for heavy fabrics and suitings. Some suiting is made entirely of the finer caroa fibers. **Fibrasil** is a trade name in Brazil for fine white caroa fibers used for tropical clothing.

CARTRIDGE BRASS. One of the standard alloys of the brass mills, containing 70% copper and 30 zinc. Because of the general use of the alloy for making cartridges and for other deep drawing, the highest-purity zinc is used and all lead is excluded. It has high ductility and an attractive yellow color, and is used for deep-drawn or spun articles such as lamp bases, horns, and cornets. It brazes well and electroplates easily.

Hard-rolled sheet has a tensile strength of 84,000 psi with elongation 5%, while the annealed sheet has a strength of 49,000 psi with elongation 55%.   The coefficient of expansion is 0.0000103 per deg F, weight 0.308 lb per cu in., and electrical conductivity 27% that of copper.   **Revere alloy No. 160,** of the Revere Copper & Brass, Inc., is this alloy.   This composition of brass is also marketed as **brass powder** for making parts by molding and sintering, and when used with 1% phosphor-copper powder produces strong and tough parts, but most copper-alloy powders are bronze powders.   A slightly harder alloy, used for wire goods, is **eyelet brass,** containing 68% copper and 32 zinc.   A grade produced by the American Brass Co. under the name of **spinning brass** contains 67% copper and 33 zinc.   **Lubaloy,** of the Winchester-Western Div., contains some tin.   A typical composition of the **cartridge brass strip** of the Scovill Mfg. Co. is 68.94% copper, 0.01 lead, 0.01 iron, and the balance zinc.   **Primer brass,** for cartridge primers, may be the 70–30 alloy, or it may be cap copper.

Brass alloy 77, of the Bridgeport Brass Co., is a **mercurial brass** used for condenser tubes to resist algae growth.   It is a 70–30 brass with 0.05% mercury.   The mercury also inhibits dezincification.   **Hi-Strength brass,** of the Chase Brass & Copper Co., is a 70–30 brass processed to give a fine grain, 0.025 mm compared with 0.070 mm in regular cartridge brass.   It has a tensile strength of 53,000 psi, yield strength of 21,000 psi, and elongation 21%.   **Nebaloy,** of the New England Brass Co., is a low-cost cartridge brass for drawn and stamped products.   It has 63% copper and 37 zinc, and is mill-processed to give a very fine grain.   The annealed metal has a tensile strength of 45,000 psi with elongation 40%, and the half-hard has a tensile strength of 61,000 psi with elongation 15% and Rockwell hardness of B71.

CASE-HARDENING MATERIALS.   Any materials employed for adding carbon to the outside of low-carbon steels or to iron so that upon quenching a hardened case is obtained, the center of the steel remaining soft and ductile.   The material may be plain charcoal, raw bone, or mixtures marketed as **carburizing compounds.**   A common mixture is about 60% charcoal and 40 barium carbonate.   The latter decomposes, giving carbon dioxide which is reduced to carbon monoxide in contact with the hot charcoal.   If charcoal is used alone, the action is slow and spotty.   Coal or coke can be used, but the action is slow, and the sulfur in these materials is detrimental.   Salt is sometimes added to aid the carburizing action.   By proper selection of the carburizing material the carbon content may be varied in the steel from 0.80 to 1.20%.   The carburizing temperature for carbon steels is 1600°F, but for alloy steels this may vary.   The articles to be carburized for case hardening are packed in metallic boxes for heating in a furnace, and the process is called **pack hardening** as distinct from the older method of burying the red-hot metal in charcoal.

The principal liquid carburizing material is sodium cyanide, which is melted in a pot and the articles dipped in, or the cyanide rubbed on the hot steel.   **Cyanide hardening** gives an extremely hard but superficial case. Nitrogen as well as carbon is added to the steel by this process.   Gases rich in carbon, such as methane, may also be used for carburizing, by passing the gas through the box in the furnace.   When ammonia gas is used to impart nitrogen to the steel, the process is not called carburizing but is referred to as **nitriding.**   Aluminum steel is nitrided with hot ammonia gas, and the liberated nitrogen combines with the steel, forming nitrides of aluminum, chromium, and molybdenum.   The surface hardness of **nitrided steel** may be as high as 1,200 Brinell, and the steel has a tensile strength up to 190,000 psi.   Nitrided steels can be softened, or denitrided, by heating in a fused mixture of potassium and sodium chlorides, which frees the nitrogen as a gas.

Any steel will absorb some nitrogen under special conditions and carbon steels and alloy steels without aluminum can be nitrided by treatment in a molten bath of cyanide and cyanate salts at about 1000°F.   Iron carbides form on the surface but the nitrogen penetrates to form iron nitrides at depths up to 0.040 in.   The hardness is about Rockwell C55 at the surface but decreases in the diffused zone.   **Tufftride,** of Kolene Corp., is a nitriding process using molten potassium cyanate with a small amount of sodium ferrocyanide in titanium-lined melting pots.   **Carbonitrided steel** is produced by exposing the steel at about 1500°F in a carbon-nitrogen atmosphere and then quenching in oil.   The depth of the case depends on the length of time of treatment.   The surface is harder and more wear-resistant than carbon case-hardened steel.

Malcomized steel, of the Crane Co., is stainless steel surface-hardened to a Rockwell hardness of 92 by heat-treating with nitrogen.   The chromium of the steel is the hardening element, and no aluminum is needed in the steel as in nitriding. Borax may also be added to carburizing compounds to give the hardening effect of boron.

Case-hardening compounds are marketed under a wide variety of trade names.   These may have a base of hardwood charcoal or of charred bone, with sodium carbonate, barium carbonate, or calcium carbonate.   **Char,** of the Char Products Co., is a carburizing material in which the particles of coal-tar carbon are surrounded by an activator and covered with a carbon coating.   **Accelerated Salt WS,** of Du Pont, for heat-treating baths, has a content of 66% sodium cyanide, with graphite to minimize fuming and radiation losses.   For selective case hardening on steel parts a stiff paste of carburizing material may be applied to the surfaces where a carbon impregnation is desired.   **Carburit,** of the Denfis Chemical Laboratories, is a carburizing paste of this kind. **Aerocarb** and **Aerocase,** of the American Cyanamid Co., are mixtures of sodium and potassium nitrates and nitrides for use in carburizing baths over a temperature range up to 1850°F.

CASEIN. A whitish to yellowish granular or lumpy protein precipitated from skim milk by the action of a dilute acid, or coagulated by rennet, or it is precipitated with whey from a previous batch. The precipitated material is then filtered and dried. Cow's milk contains about 3% casein. It is insoluble in water or in alcohol, but soluble in alkalies. Although the casein is usually removed from commercial milk, it is a valuable food accessory because it contains **methionine,** a complex mercapto butyric acid, which counteracts the tendency toward calcium hardening of the arteries. This acid is also found in the ovalbumin of egg white. Methionine, $CH_3 \cdot S \cdot CH_2CH_2CHNH \cdot COOH$, is one of the most useful of the amino acids, and is used in medicine to cure protein deficiency and in dermatology to cure acne and falling hair. It converts dietary protein to tissue, maintains nitrogen balance, and speeds wound healing. It is now made synthetically for use in poultry feeds. Some casein is produced as a byproduct in the production of lactic acid from whole milk, the casein precipitating at a pH of 4.5. It is treated with sodium hydroxide to yield **sodium caseinate.**

Most of the production of casein is by acid precipitation, and this casein has a moisture content of not more than 10%, with no more than 2.25% fat, and not over 4 ash. The casein made with rennet has up to 7.5% ash content, less than 1% fat, and is less soluble in alkalies. It is the type used for making plastics. **Rennet** used for curdling cheese is an extract of an enzyme derived from the stomachs of calves and lambs and is closely related to pepsin. Rennet substitutes produced from pepsin and other vegetable sources are only partial replacements and often have undesirable off-flavors. But **Sure-Curd,** of Chas. Pfizer and Co., is derived from a strain of *Endothia parasitica* and is similar to true rennet in coagulating and proteolytic properties. **Whey** is the thin sweet watery part separated out when milk is coagulated with rennet. Whey solids are used in prepared meats and other foods to enhance flavor, and in pastries to eliminate sogginess. **Tekniken,** of the Western Condensing Co., is a dry whey for use in margarine, chocolate, and cheese. **Orotic acid,** $NH(CO \cdot NH \cdot CO \cdot CH):C \cdot COOH$, produced synthetically, is identical with the biotic *Lactobacillus bulgaricus* of **yogurt,** the fermented milk whey used as food. It is a vitaminlike material.

Argentina and the United States are the most important producers of casein, but production drops in the United States at times when milk products are in greater demand for food. France, Norway, and Holland are also large producers. Casein is employed for making plastics, adhesives, sizing for paper and textiles, washable interior paints, leather dressings, and as a diabetic food.   **Casein glue** is a cold-work, water-resistant paste made from casein by dispersion with a mild base such as ammonia. With a lime base it is more resistant but has a tendency to stain.   It is marketed wet or dry, the dry powder being simply mixed with water for application.   It is used largely for low-cost plywoods and in water paints, but is not waterproof.   Concentrated **milk protein,** available as **calcium caseinate** or **sodium caseinate,** is for adding proteins and for stabilizing prepared meats and bakery products.   It contains eight amino acids and is high in lysine.   **Sheftene,** of the Sheffield Chemical Co., is this material.

CASEIN PLASTICS. A group of thermoplastic molding materials made usually by the action of formaldehyde on rennet casein.   The process was invented in 1885, and the first commercial casein plastic was called **Galalith,** meaning **milkstone.**   Casein plastics are easily molded, machine easily, are noninflammable, will withstand temperatures up to 300°F, and are easily dyed to light shades.   But they are soft, have high water absorption, 7 to 14%, and soften when exposed to alkalies.   They are thus not suitable for many mechanical or electrical parts.   They are used for ornamental parts, buttons, and for such articles as fountain-pen holders.   The specific gravity of the material is 1.34, and the tensile strength is 8,000 psi.   They were usually marketed under trade names. Some of these are **Aladdinite,** of the Aladdinite Co., Inc.; **Inda,** of the American Machine & Foundry Co.; **Erinoid,** of the Erinoid Co.; **Lactoid,** of the British Xylonite Co., Ltd.; **Lactonite,** of the British Lactonite Co.; **Ameroid,** of the American Plastics Corp.; and **Karolith,** of the Karolith Corp.   **Sicalite** is a French casein plastic.   **Casein fiber** is made by treating casein with chemicals to extract the albumen and salts and forcing it through spinnerets, and again treating it to make it soft and silklike.   The fiber is superior to wool in silkiness and resistance to moth attack, but is inferior in general properties.   It is blended with wool in fabrics and in hat felts.   **Lanitol** was an early Italian casein fiber.   **Aralac fiber,** of Aralac, Inc., is a translucent, white, silky casein fiber.   **Caslen,** of the Rubberset Co., is a resilient curled casein fiber used as a substitute for horsehair.

CASHEW SHELL OIL. An amber-colored, poisonous, viscous oil obtained by extraction from the by-product shells of the cashew-nut industry of India and Brazil.   For every pound of shelled nuts there are 3.55 lb of by-product shells.   The cashew nut grows on the distal end of the fruit of the tree *Anacardium occidentale.*   The thin-skinned, yellow, pear-shaped fruit may be eaten or used in preserves.   The kernel of the seed nut, known as the **cashew nut,** is roasted and widely used as an edible nut or in confections.   The kernel is crescent-shaped, and the nuts are graded by sizes from 200 per lb to 400–450 per lb.   On crushing, the nuts produce 45% of an edible oil, but the nuts are more valuable as a confection than for oil, and there is no commercial production of **cashew-nut oil.** One pound of shells yields 0.335 lb of cashew-nut shell oil, which contains 90% **anacardic acid,** a carboxy penta-dica-dienyl phenol, very blistering to the skin.   It is used for the production of plastics, drying oils, and insulating compounds.   The oil reacts with formaldehyde to give a drying oil.   With furfural it produces a molding plastic.   Reacted with other chemicals it forms rubberlike masses used as rubber extenders and in electrical insulating compounds.   The other 10% of cashew-nut shell oil is **cardol,** a dihydroxy penta-dica-dienyl benzene.   When decarboxylated the anacardic acid yields **cardanol,** a light oily liquid of the composition $C_6H_4 \cdot OH(CH_2)_6CH:CH(CH_2)_6CH_3$, with boiling point at 360°C and freezing point of about $-20°C$.   Cardanol polymerizes with formaldehyde to form a heat-resistant, chemical-resistant, flexible resin of high dielectric strength valued for wire insulation.   Small amounts of this resin also improve the chemical and electrical properties of the phenol resins. **Cardolite,** of the Irvington Varnish & Insulator Co., is a high-molecular-weight, straight-chain bisphenol derived from cashew-nut shell oil.   It is used for making flexible epoxy resins, supplanting about half the normal amount of epichlorhydrin used in the resin.

CASHMERE.   A fine, soft, silky fabric made from the underhair of the Cashmere goat raised on the slopes of the Himalayas in Asia.   The hair is obtained by combing the animals, not by shearing, and only about 3 oz are obtained from a goat.   The hair is straight and silky, but not lustrous, and is difficult to dye.   The fabrics are noted for warmth, and the production now goes mostly into the making of shawls and fine ornamental garments.   **Cotton cashmere** is a soft, loosely woven cotton fabric made to imitate cashmere, or it may be a cotton and wool mixture, but it lacks the fineness of true cashmere.   **Cashmere hair,** used for fine paintbrushes, is from the beard of the Cashmere goat.   It is similar to camel hair.   **Qiviut,** the underwool of the musk ox of northern Canada, is a finer and longer fiber than cashmere, and about 6 lb may be obtained from each animal. It is shed in May or June.   One pound of qiviut will make a 40-strand thread 26 miles long.   It dyes easily, and does not shrink even when boiled.   It is used for fine gloves and sweaters.

CASSITERITE.   Also called **tin stone.**   It is the only commercial **tin ore,** and is a **tin dioxide,** SnO_2, containing theoretically 78.6% tin.   It is a widely distributed mineral, but is found on a commercial scale in only a few localities, notably in Malaya, East Indies, Bolivia, Cornwall, England,

Nevada, Isle of Pines, and Australia. The mineral occurs granular massive with a specific gravity of 6.8 to 7.1, a hardness of 6 to 7, and a brown to black color. It is present in the ore usually in amounts of from 1 to 5%, and is found in veins, called **lode tin,** or in placer deposits. The concentrated ore averages 65 to 70% tin oxide. It is roasted to eliminate sulfur and arsenic, and then smelted in reverberatory furnaces.

CAST IRON. A combination of iron with from 2 to 6% carbon, receiving its name from the fact that it is readily cast into almost any desired shape in an ordinary sand mold. The ASTM definition is an iron containing so much carbon that it is not malleable at any temperature. The low limit is about 1.7%. Cast iron is of two kinds: **white cast iron** and **gray iron.** The first is a chemical compound of most of the carbon with the iron; the second contains most of the carbon in the form of graphite mechanically mixed with the iron. Ordinary cast iron is brittle and not malleable. It is low in cost, easy to machine, and has a higher proportional fatigue than steel. It is used for the massive bodies of machines and for intricate castings that do not require high strength. Ordinary gray iron will also withstand much higher operating temperatures than common steels, and is used for carbonizing boxes. White iron is made by chilling gray iron, but it will revert to gray iron with prolonged heating to 1850°F. But superior cast irons are also made by control of the analysis. A cast iron of the General Motors Corp., called **Centra steel,** has a compacted carbon structure similar to that of malleable iron, giving the strength of a cast steel. It contains 1.7% carbon, 2.25 silicon, 0.40 manganese, 0.01 boron, 0.10 sulfur, and 0.05 phosphorus. **Centrifugal cast iron,** cast in a spinning mold for hollow cylindrical parts, has a dense homogeneous structure free from porosity, with the impurities tending to segregate on the inside of the cylinder. It is stronger and has better impermeability to hydraulic pressure than ordinary cast iron.

Cast iron is usually made by melting pig iron and scrap in a cupola in contact with the fuel, which is normally coke. Pouring temperature, which varies with the analysis, is important, especially to prevent **cold shut,** which is a discontinuity in the structure caused by two streams of metal meeting and failing to unite. With an electric furnace, scrap iron may be employed alone with carbon without pig iron, and the furnace may be operated continuously. The product is called **synthetic cast iron.**

The specific gravity of gray iron is 7.10, and that for white iron is 7.50. The coefficient of expansion is 0.0000056. Tensile strengths of plain gray irons vary from 18,000 to 25,000 psi, and compressive strength from 60,000 to well over 100,000 psi.

Gun iron, formerly used for casting cannon, was a fine-grained iron of uniform texture, low in sulfur and in total carbon, made with charcoal in an air furnace, and had tensile strengths equal to some modern high-test cast irons.   Ordinary gray iron now made with some steel scrap will have a tensile strength from 30,000 to 45,000 psi, with Brinell hardness from 187 to 235.   A typical gray iron of this kind contains about 3% total carbon, 2 silicon, 0.60 manganese, 0.20 phosphorus, and 0.12 sulfur, with about 0.80 combined carbon as iron carbide.   Gray cast iron with a ferrite matrix in which graphite flakes are dispersed machines easily, but when the combined carbon is high or the structure shows free carbides and free pearlite the machinability is reduced drastically.   Various degrees of structure change may be due to differences in cooling rates in different section sizes.

The combined carbon structure of cast iron is known as **austenite.**   It is a solid solution in which gamma iron is the solvent, and it is the structure of soft steel.   The structure with the compound Fe_3C, which forms when the austenite changes on cooling, is called **cementite,** and is a structure in hard steel.   **Martensite** is an unstable constituent formed without diffusion in quenching.   The term **ferrite** is used for the iron crystals having no carbon.   **Pearlite,** the most desirable structure of cast iron, consists of alternate layers of ferrite and cementite.   The tensile strength of such a structure, if it could be obtained throughout, would be 100,000 psi, but a good average for plain gray iron is 22,000 psi, with a compressive strength of 100,000 psi.   **Bainite** is a decomposition product of austenite and consists of an aggregate of ferrite and carbides.

Graphite is a weakening element in cast iron, and the high-graphite irons are desired only because of their ease of casting and machining.   The lower the carbon, the stronger the cast iron.   To obtain this result, steel scrap is used in the mix.   Low-carbon steel of known chemical content, such as plate and rod ends and rail croppings, is used.   The amount of steel varies from 15 to 60%, and the product resulting from the larger additions is called **semisteel.**   Tensile strengths as high as 40,000 psi can be obtained without great reduction in the casting and machining qualities of the cast iron.   Semisteel castings can be softened and made more ductile by annealing at a temperature of about 800°F, but they then lose 25 to 35% of the tensile strength.   In cast iron the graphite occupies 11 to 17% of the volume, and by control of its distribution and the size of the flake it is possible to vary the tensile strength from 10,000 to 60,000 psi.   An important factor in the control is the rate at which the molten iron cools down to about 1000°F.

Nodular cast iron, or **ductile iron,** is cast iron in which the graphite has a nodular or spheroid shape distributed through a ferritic matrix instead of the usual flat flakes in a matrix of pearlite and ferrite.   Nodular iron is produced by treating the molten iron with magnesium, usually in the form of a magnesium-copper-ferrosilicon or other master alloy, leaving up to 0.08% residual magnesium in the iron.   A high-strength pearlitic nodular iron has a tensile strength of 100,000 psi, elongation of 4%, and Brinell hardness of 245, while a high-ductility, ferritic, nodular iron has a tensile strength of 75,000 psi, elongation 18%, and Brinell hardness 160. The ductile iron of the Howard Foundry Co. is a pearlitic iron of this type in the form of cast bar stock for bushings, pins, and shafts.   It has good antifriction qualities.   A **nodulizing alloy,** marketed by the Union Carbide Corp., for adding magnesium to cast iron contains 7 to 10% magnesium, 43 silicon, and the balance iron.   **Cecolloy,** of the Chambersburg Engineering Co., is a nodular cast iron having a tensile strength of 80,000 psi and elongation 15%.   The **Flex-Iron** of the Crane Co. is a nodular iron made with yttrium instead of magnesium.   The ductile irons containing large amounts of nickel are classed as iron alloys.

Phosphorus in cast iron increases fluidity, but more than 0.6% makes the iron hard.   Sulfur is an undesirable impurity.   Silicon goes into solid solution in iron to form iron silicides and precipitates graphite.   Small amounts make the iron soft, but large amounts make it glassy hard. Copper is also used as a graphitizer and to increase the heat conductivity. Engine cylinder blocks of high heat conductivity and good strength contain about 0.75% copper.   Lithium-treated cast irons make sound, dense, and hard castings.   The lithium cleans the iron and disperses the carbon. Nickel, chromium, and other elements are added to cast irons while molten to give additional strength, toughness, or hardness, but the iron is then generally known as **alloy cast iron.**   Manganese decreases the magnetic properties of cast iron.   **Nomag,** an English **nonmagnetic cast iron,** contains 6% manganese.   Adding nickel makes this iron machinable without changing its nonmagnetic quality.   Small amounts of tungsten increase the tensile and transverse strength of cast iron, but reduce its hardness. **Tungsten cast iron,** with 1.2% tungsten, has a tensile strength of about 40,000 psi.   Case hardening of cast iron is done by using powdered ferromanganese on the mold surface.   **Nitrided cast iron,** hardened by nitrogen treatment to give great wear resistance, usually has a special composition. A typical composition for the **Nitricastiron,** as given by the Electro Metallurgical Co., is 2.9% total carbon, 0.6 combined carbon, 2.7 silicon, 0.75 manganese, 1.3 chromium, 1 aluminum, 0.16 vanadium, 0.25 molybdenum, with sulfur and phosphorus below 0.07.   It can be hardened to 800 to 1,000 Brinell to a depth of 0.004 to 0.006 in.   Cast iron deteriorates rapidly when subjected to temperatures above 800°F, and the **heat-resistant cast irons** for firebox castings and stove grates contain some chromium to stabilize the pearlite and cementite.   A cast iron containing 1.25% chromium will withstand temperatures up to 1400°F.   Trade names are used to designate cast iron made by special processes.   **Pomoloy,** of the Pomona Pump Co., is an unalloyed cast iron with a tensile strength of 40,000 psi, and hardness 215 Brinell.   **DeLavaud metal,** of the U.S. Cast Iron Pipe & Foundry Co., is made by a centrifugal process in rotating steel molds. After annealing, the pipe has an outer layer of malleable iron, a center layer resembling steel, and an inner surface of gray iron.   **Hi-Tem iron,** of the Bethlehem Foundry & Machine Co., is a corrosion-resistant cast iron used for processing vessels.   **Hi-Tem S** is a high-manganese iron used for retorts.

High-test cast iron was originally cast iron that was superheated in the melting for pouring, poured in chilling molds, and then heat-treated, the only change in composition being to keep the silicon and manganese high. The term now means high-strength irons that are processed to give a careful balance of ferrite, pearlite, cementite, and carbon by the treatment, by additions of steel scrap, and by additions of nickel, chromium, and other elements that give strength to the metal by balancing the structure, but are not in sufficient quantities to classify the iron as an alloy cast iron.   Tensile strengths above 50,000 psi are obtained, and all of the high-test irons are fine-grained, and are not spongy like gray iron.   Steel scrap gives a stronger and finer structure; nickel gives ease of machining and aids in the chilling; chromium gives hardness and resistance to growth; molybdenum raises the combined carbon and adds strength and hardness.   **Oxygenized iron** is high-test cast iron made by blowing air through a part of the metal and then returning the blown metal to the cupola.   There is no sharp dividing line between some of these processed irons and steel, and when the combined carbon is high and the graphitic carbon is well distributed in even flakes the metal is called **graphitic steel.**   High-test cast irons are used for brake drums, cams, rolls, and high-strength parts.   In many cases they are substitutes for malleable iron.   They are marketed under many trade names.   **Ermal** is a pearlitic cast iron of the Erie Malleable Iron Co. with a tensile strength up to 70,000 psi.   **Perlit,** of the Durson Corp., is another pearlitic cast iron.   **Aremite** is a synthetic cast iron of Robbins & Myers, Inc.   **Jewell alloy,** of the Jewell Steel & Malleable Co., is the name of a group of high-strength and heat-resistant irons.   **Ermalite,** of the Erie Malleable Iron Co., and **Wearloy,** of the Frank Foundries Corp., are high-strength, wear-resistant cast irons.   **Gunite,** of the Gunite Corp., is a graphitic steel which, when quenched to a hardness of 477 Brinell, has a compressive strength of 200,000 psi.   **Arma steel,** of the Saginaw Malleable Iron Div., General Motors Corp., is a graphitic steel, or arrested malleabilized iron of high strength and shock resistance, used for connecting rods, gears, and camshafts where both high strength and bearing properties are required.   **Meehanite metal,** produced under license of the Meehanite Research Institute of America, is made in a wide range of high-strength, wear-resisting, corrosion-resisting, and heat-resisting castings for dies, hydraulic cylinders, brake drums, pump parts, and gears.   The normal strengths range from 35,000 to 55,000 psi, compressive strengths from 135,000 to 175,000 psi, and hardnesses from 193 to 223 Brinell.

Cast irons are standardized by composition, but procurement of castings for quantity production of parts is usually by physical properties for the intended use.   Quality in a casting depends greatly on careful control of pouring temperature, proper surfacing and venting of molds, and other foundry techniques.   **Cylinder iron** is a general term for cast iron for engine and compressor cylinders, but also used for a variety of mechanical parts.   The iron must be easily cast into a dense structure without hard spots or blowholes.   Combined carbon must be sufficient to give wear resistance without brittleness, and the content of free graphite must be high enough to give a low coefficient of friction without great loss of strength. A plain cylinder iron for internal-combustion engines may have 3 to 3.25% total carbon with 2 to 2.25 silicon and 0.75 manganese to increase hardness. But cylinder irons now are usually made with up to 20% steel scrap which introduces other balancing elements.   Nickel decreases the tendency of low-silicon irons to chill in the thin sections.   Copper increases heat conductivity.   Molybdenum refines the grain and increases strength.   A truck **engine iron** containing 3% total carbon, 0.75 combined carbon, 2 silicon, 1.7 nickel, and 0.7 chromium has a tensile strength of 38,000 psi and a Brinell hardness of 2.29.

CASTOR OIL.   A light-yellow to brownish viscous oil obtained from the seed beans of the castor plant, *Ricinus communis.*   In the tropics the plant grows to the proportions of a sturdy tree, but in temperate climates it is small with a poor yield.   Besides its original use as a purgative in medicine, castor oil is one of the most widely used industrial vegetable oils.   When pure and fresh, the oil is nearly colorless and transparent.   The hot-pressed oil is brownish.   It has a characteristic acrid, unpleasant taste.   The specific gravity is 0.960 to 0.970, iodine value 82 to 90, saponification value 147, and solidifying point $-10\degree$C.   The oil is chiefly composed of the glyceride of **ricinoleic acid,** which has a complex double-bonded molecular structure that can be polymerized easily.   **Castor seeds** have the appearance of mottled colored beans and are enclosed in hard husks which are removed before crushing.   The chief commercial production has been in Brazil, where two types are grown.   The large Zanzibar type has seeds 16 mm long containing 30 to 35% oil, and the sanguineous type has seeds 10 mm long containing up to 60% oil.   They are usually mixed in shipments, and the average yield is calculated as 0.45 lb of oil from 1 lb of beans.   In the southwestern states of the United States, dwarf disease-resistant hybrid varieties are grown that give high oil yields.   Cold-pressed oil is used in medicine and in lubricants, but the industrial oil is usually hot-pressed. Castor oil is used in paints, as a hydraulic oil, for treating leather and textiles, in soaps, and for making urethane resins. It increases the lathering power of soaps and their solubility in cold water. In lubricating oils and in cutting oils it has excellent keeping qualities and does not gum on exposure.

When castor oil is chemically dehydrated by removing the hydroxyl groups in the form of water by means of a catalyst, a double bond is formed giving an oil of heavy viscosity, light color, and with iodine value 116, acid value 3.5, and saponification value 191. **Dehydrated castor oil** gives a better gloss in varnishes than tung oil with a softer and less brittle film, but it has less alkali resistance than tung oil unless mixed with synthetic resin. **Sulfonated castor oil,** known as **Turkey red oil** in the textile industry, is made by treating crude hot-pressed castor oil with sulfuric acid and neutralizing with sodium sulfate. It is miscible with water and lathers like a solution of soap. It is used for the preparation of cotton fibers to be dyed, and gives clearer and brighter colors. It is also employed in soaps and in cutting compounds. Sulfonated dehydrated castor oil is used in nonalkaline water-washable skin ointments. It has a softening point of 30°C and an SO_2 content of 10%. **Synthenol,** of Spencer Kellogg & Sons, Inc., is a dehydrated castor oil for paints and varnishes. **Castung,** of the Baker Castor Oil Co., and **Isoline,** of the Woburn Degreasing Co., are dehydrated castor oils. **Copolymer 186** is a polymerized dehydrated castor oil which adds flexibility and improved general qualities to paints and outside enamels. **Mannitan drying oil,** of Atlas Chemical Industries, is an ester of dehydrated castor oil that dries faster than linseed oil and has better resistance in paints.

Hydrogenated castor oil is a hard, nongreasy, white solid melting at 82°C, used as an extender for waxes in coating compositions, and as a hard grease for making resistant lithium-type lubricating greases. Hydrogenated castor oil is odorless and tasteless, and is valued for coatings. **Castorwax,** of the Baker Castor Oil Co., **Emery S-751-R,** of the Emery Industries, Inc., and **Cenwax G,** of the W. C. Hardesty Co., Inc., are hydrogenated castor oil. In general these materials are white, nongreasy, waxlike solids melting at about 85°C. **Primawax,** of the U.S. Cotton Oil Co., Inc., is a flaked form of hydrogenated castor oil used as a plasticizer in vinyl and cellulose plastics.

The hydrogenated ricinoleic acid, known as **hydroxy stearic acid,** may also be separated and used for making waxy esters for pharmaceutical ointments, or for reacting with amines to make white, waxy solids useful as water repellents. By reacting castor oil with sodium hydroxide under heat and pressure, **sebacic acid,** $HO_2C(CH_2)_8CO_2H$, is produced. It is a powder melting at 129°C, and is a versatile raw material for alkyd resins, fibers, and heat-resistant plasticizers. It is also used for making nylon polymers and for **sebacate esters** for cold-weather lubricants, although the lower-cost azelaic and adipic acids may be substituted.   Both sebacic acid and isosebacic acid are now produced synthetically from butadiene.   **Isosebacic acid** is a mixture of sebacic acid with the isomers of this acid, **diethyl adipic acid** and **ethyl suberic acid.**   It can replace sebacic acid for resin manufacture.   Also similar in chemical properties to the ricinoleic acid of castor oil is **dimorphecolic acid,** obtained naturally from **daisy oil** from the seeds of the Cape marigold, of the genus *Dimorphotheca,* grown in California.

A substitute for castor oil in medicine is **croton oil,** a yellow-brown oil obtained from the dried ripe seeds of the small tree *Croton tiglium* of India and Ceylon.   It has a burning taste and unpleasant odor, and is a more violent purgative than castor oil.   The leaves and flowers of the tree are used like derris to kill fish.   **Curcas oil** is a yellowish oil from the kernels of the seeds of the *Jatropha curcas* which grows in Central America.   The kernels yield 50% oil with a specific gravity 0.920, iodine value 98 to 104, and saponification value 192.   It is also a good soap oil but has an unpleasant odor.   The ethyl and methyl esters of **crotonic acid** are used as monomers for flexible plastics for coatings.   The acid with a composition $CH_3CH:CHCOOH$ is now made synthetically from acetylene and aldol.

CAST STEEL. Steel that has been cast into sand molds to form finished or semifinished machine parts or other articles.   **Steel castings** are used to replace forgings where only small quantities are required that would not justify the cost of forging dies, and for large parts that could not be forged easily, but the most general use of steel castings is for intricate parts that would usually require much machining by other methods of production. The electric furnace is most commonly used in the melting process because of the ease of changeover for the production of a variety of grades of steel in small or large tonnages.   The open-hearth process is used by foundries that have large runs or very large castings.   With controlled methods practically any type of steel may be cast, and some steels, such as those with a high boron content, can only be cast.   Thus, cast steel is actually not a type of steel.

There are five general classes of commercial steel castings: **low-carbon steels,** with carbon content below 0.20%; **medium-carbon steels,** with carbon between 0.20 and 0.50%; **high-carbon steels,** with carbon above 0.50%; **low-alloy steels,** with alloy content totaling less than 8%; **high-alloy steels,** with alloy content totaling more than 8%.   Federal specifications for cast steel call for 0.35% carbon in the soft grade, 0.45 in the medium grade, and 0.50 in the hard grade.   The tensile strength of the soft is 60,000 psi, and of the hard 80,000 psi.   The yield point is taken as 45% of the tensile strength.   The shrinkage allowed for cast steel is $1/4$ in. per ft.   British engineering standard specifications call for cast steel for general purposes to have 0.30% carbon, and a tensile strength of 26 tons per sq in., with elongation 15 to 20%. Most carbon-steel castings produced in the United States are of medium-carbon steel, and these range from 65,000 to 100,000 psi, depending on the carbon and the heat treatment. High-carbon steels, with tensile strengths from 100,000 to 125,000 psi, are produced for parts requiring hardness and wear resistance, such as metal-working dies and rolls. **Boron cast steels** contain 0.006% max boron, which hardens and strengthens the steel without impairing the ductility and impact properties when the sulfur, phosphorus, and nitrogen contents are controlled. These steels replace some alloy steels. Cast steel, if not produced under controlled conditions, has the disadvantage in comparison with forged steel that it may contain blowholes, slag, sand holes, shrinkage cavities, or cold shuts, the last from pouring at too low a temperature. Thus, companies usually feature careful metallurgical control rather than merely chemical content of the steel, and the cast steels are generally sold under trade names.

Aluminom, titanium, or other elements in the form of master alloys are used to deoxidize and degasify alloy steels to produce homogeneous castings. Alloy steels for heavy-duty castings may be chromium steel, with 0.80 to 1.10% chromium; vanadium, with 0.15 to 0.20 vanadium; chrome-vanadium; 1.50 to 3.50 nickel; nickel-chromium; or manganese, with either high or medium manganese content. One of the simplest alloy cast steels for parts subject to shock and fatigue stresses is the standard low-carbon and medium-carbon steel with 2% nickel. It is used for mining and other heavy-machinery parts, locomotive frames, and ship castings. The tensile strength is up to 85,000 psi, with yield point up to 55,000 psi, and elongation 25 to 32%. The nickel, with manganese up to 0.90%, gives the steel greater shock resistance at low temperatures, as ordinary steel is brittle in cold climates or when used on refrigerating equipment. A 3 to 3.50% nickel steel used for cast gears for rolling mills has a tensile strength of 110,000 psi, elongation 20%, and hardness 200 Brinell as cast. A nickel-chromium-molybdenum cast steel for heavy gears contains 1.5% nickel, 0.75 chromium, 0.35 molybdenum, 0.70 manganese, and 0.35 carbon. The tensile strength is 145,000 to 160,000 psi.

CATALYST. A material used to cause or accelerate chemical action without itself entering into the chemical combination. Catalysts are chosen for selectivity as well as activity, mechanical strength, and life. They should give a high yield of product per unit and be capable of regeneration whenever possible for economy. In the cracking of petroleum, activated carbon breaks the complex hydrocarbons into the entire range of fragments; activated alumina is more selective, producing a large yield of C_3 and C_4; and silica-alumina-zirconia is intermediate. **Contact catalysts** are the ones chiefly used in the chemical industry, and they may be in various forms. For bed reactors the materials are pelleted. **Powdered catalysts** are used for liquid reactions such as for the hydrogenation of oils. **Chemical catalysts** are usually liquid compounds, especially such acids as sulfuric or hydrofluoric.

Various metals, especially platinum and nickel, are used to catalyze or promote chemical action in the manufacture of synthetics. Nitrogen in the presence of oxygen can be "fixed" or combined in chemicals at ordinary temperatures by the use of ruthenium as a catalyst. Acids may be used to aid in the polymerization of synthetic resins. Mineral soaps are used to speed up the oxidation of vegetable oils. Cobalt oxide is used for the oxidation of ammonia. Cobalt and thorium are used for synthesizing gasoline from coal. All of these are classed as **inorganic catalysts.** Sometimes more complex chemicals are employed, silicate of soda being used as a catalyst for high-octane gasoline. In the use of **potassium persulfate,** $K_2S_2O_8$, as a catalyst in the manufacture of some synthetic rubbers, the material releases 5.8% active oxygen, and it is the nascent oxygen that is the catalyst. **Sodium methylate,** called also **sodium methoxide,** $CH_3 \cdot O \cdot Na$, used as a catalyst for ester-exchange reactions in the rearrangement of edible oils, is a white powder soluble in fats but violently decomposed in water.

Aluminum chloride, $AlCl_3$, in gray granular crystals which sublime at 950°C, is used as a catalyst for high-octane gasoline and synthetic rubber, and in the synthesis of dyes and pharmaceuticals. **Antimony trichloride,** $SbCl_3$, is a yellowish solid, melting at 73.4°C, used as a catalyst in petroleum processing to convert normal butane to isobutane. This chemical is also used for antimony plating and as a cotton mordant. **Aluminosilicates** are used in fluid catalyst cracking of gasoline. They bear a negative charge even at high temperatures. **Bead catalysts** of activated alumina have the alumina contained in 3-mm beads of silica gel. **Catasil** is alumina adsorbed on silica gel, used for polymerization reactions.

Catalyst carriers are porous inert materials used to support the catalyst, usually in a bed through which the liquid or gas may flow. Materials used are generally alumina, silicon carbide, or mullite, and they are usually in the form of graded porous granules or in irregular polysurface pellets. High surface area, low bulk density, and good adherence of the catalyst are important qualities. Pellets are bonded with a ceramic that fuses around the granules with minute necks that hold the mass together as complex silicates and aluminates with no trace elements exposed to the action of the catalyst or chemicals. Catalyst carriers are usually bonded to make them about 40% porous. The pellets may be 50 mesh or finer, or they may be in sizes as large as 1 in. Refractory filters known as **porous media,** used for filtering chemicals and gases at high temperatures, are essentially the same materials as catalyst carriers with ceramic bonds fired at about 1250°C, but they are usually in the form of plates or tubes, and the porosity is usually about 35%. They may be used directly as filters, or as underdrain plates for filter powders.

Sunlight or ultraviolet rays are also used as catalysts in some reactions. For example, chlorine and hydrogen combine very slowly in the dark, but combine with great violence when a ray of sunlight is turned on. **Biologic catalysts** are the **enzymes,** which are **organic catalysts** that are a form of life. They are sensitive to heat and light and are destroyed at 100°C. Enzymes are soluble in water, glycerin, or dilute saline solutions, and water must always be present for enzyme action. Their action may be stimulated or checked by other substances. When dehydrated vegetables lose their flavor by destruction of the enzymes, the flavor may be restored by adding small percentages of enzymes from the same or similar vegetables. **Fermenting agents** comprise a wide range of yeasts, bacteria, and enzymes which break down molecules to form other products.

Enzymes have various actions. **Diastase,** found in the seeds of barley and other grains, converts starch to maltose and dextrin. **Diastase 73,** of Rohm and Haas Co., is an enzyme chemical for converting gelatinized starches to dextrose. It is **amylo glucosidase** modified to remove the bitter taste. One pound will convert 100 pounds of starch. **Cytase,** found in seeds and fruits, decomposes cellulose to galactose and mannose. **Zymose,** found in yeast, hydrolyzes glucose to alcohol. **Thiaminase,** an enzyme which occurs in small amounts in salmon, cod, rockfish, and some other fish, destroys the vitamin thiamine, and if taken in high concentration in the human diet causes ventritional polyneuritis. **Rhozyme LA,** of the Rohm & Haas Co., is a diastatic enzyme concentrate in liquid form for desizing textiles. **Bromelin,** an enzyme used in breweries, is produced from pineapples by alcohol precipitation from the juice. **Fermcozyme** is a liquid glucose-oxidase-catalase used in carbonated beverages to remove dissolved oxygen which would combine with glucose to form gluconic acid resulting in loss of color and flavor. It is also used in egg powders to remove undesirable glucose.

Yeasts are important in foodstuffs manufacture. A yeast is a fungus, and the life organisms produce carbon dioxide gas to raise doughs. These are called **leavening yeasts. Fermenting yeasts** produce alcohols by action on sugars. Many of the yeasts are high in proteins, vitamins, and minerals, and as dry, inactive powders are used to raise the nutritional values of foodstuffs. **Torula yeast,** *Torulopsis utilis,* used as an additive in processed foods, is a by-product of the sulfite paper mills, growing on the 5- and 6-carbon wood sugars. It contains more than 50% proteins, and has 10 different vitamins and 15 minerals. The dry powder is inactive, and does not cause raising in baked foods. **Prostay,** of St. Regis Paper Co., is this material.

CATECHU. An extract obtained from the heartwood and from the seed pods of the tree *Acacia catechu* of southern Asia. It is used in tanning leather, and as a dyestuff, giving brown, drab, and khaki colors. It is used in medicine as an astringent for diarrhea and hemorrhage. The name is sometimes applied to gambier, which also contains catechu tannin, $C_{15}H_9(OH)_5$. Catechu, or **cutch,** comes either as a liquid which is a water solution, or as brownish, brittle, glossy cakes. The liquid contains 25% tannin, and the solid 50%. A ton of heartwood yields, by hot-water extraction, 250 to 300 lb of solid cutch extract. It is a powerful astringent. When used alone as a tanning agent, the leather is not of high quality, being of a dark color, spongy, and water-absorbent. It is normally employed in mixtures. **Burma cutch** is from the *A. catechuoides*. **Indian cutch** is from the *A. sundra.* The latter is frequently adulterated with starch, sand, and other materials. **Wattle** is an extract from Australian and East African acacia, *A. dealbata,* and other species. The wattle tree is called **mimosa** in Kenya. **Wattle bark** contains 40 to 50% tannin. It gives a firm pinkish leather and is employed for sole leathers. The solid extract contains 65% tannin. **Golden wattle,** used for tanning in New Zealand, is the tree *A. pycantha.* Much wattle extract is produced in Brazil from the **black wattle. Turwar bark,** or **avarem,** used in India for tanning cattle hides, is from the tree *Cassia auricula,* and is similar to wattle.

CATGUT. String made from the intestines of sheep, used for violin strings, and for tough, durable cords for rackets and other articles. After cleansing and soaking in an alkali solution, the intestines are split, drawn through holes in a plate, cured in sulfur or other material, and graded according to size. Sheep intestines are also used for making surgical sutures, but for this purpose they are not called catgut, but simply **gut.** The sutures are encased in tubes and bombarded by electron-beam radiation for sterilization. In the meat-packing industry the intestines of sheep and goats are referred to as **casings** and are employed as the covering of sausage and other meat products. They are graded by diameter, freedom from holes, strength, color, and odor. Intestines of hogs and beef cattle are also used as casings, but they are not as edible as those from sheep.

CEDAR. A general name that includes a great variety of woods. The true cedars comprise trees of the natural order of *Coniferae,* genus *Cedrus,* of which there are three species: **Lebanon cedar,** *Cedrus libani;* **Himalayan cedar,** *C. deodora;* and **Atlas cedar,** *C. atlantica.* The differences are slight, and all of the species are sometimes classed as *C. libani.* The Himalayan cedar is also known as **deodar.** All are mountain trees, and are native to southern Europe, Asia, and northern Africa. The true cedar is yellow in color, fragrant in odor, takes a beautiful polish, and is very durable.   It is used in construction work, and timbers in temples in India more than 400 years old are still in perfect preservation.   The wood weighs about 36 lb per cu ft.   Numerous species of *Cedrela* occur in tropical America, Asia, and Africa, and are also called cedar, but the wood has greater resemblance to mahogany.   In the United States and Canada the name cedar is applied to woods of species of *Thuya, Juniperus,* and *Cupressus,* more properly classified as thuya, juniper, and cypress.

Spanish cedar, or **Central American cedar,** used in the United States as a substitute for mahogany in patternmaking, and for cigar boxes, furniture, carving, cabinetwork, and interior trim, is a softwood from numerous species of *Cedrela,* called in Spanish America by the name of **Cedro.**   It is a light-red color sometimes beautifully figured with wavy grain, has an agreeable odor, is easily worked, seasons well, and takes a fine polish. The weight is 28 to 33 lb per cu ft.   The trees grow to a large size, logs being available 40 in. square.   The imports come chiefly from Central America and the West Indies, but the trees grow as far south as northern Argentina.   **Paraguayan cedar** is the wood of the tree *C. braziliensis,* of Paraguay, Brazil, and northern Argentina, employed locally for cabinetwork, car building, and interior building work.   It is similar in appearance to Spanish cedar but is denser, harder, and redder in color.   The wood known as **southern white cedar,** and called juniper in the Carolinas, is from the tree *Chamaecyparis thyoides,* growing in the coastal belt from Maine to Florida.   The heartwood is light brown tinged with pink, and the thin sapwood is lighter in color.   The wood is light in weight, straight-grained, durable, and fragrant.   The more plentiful **white cedar** of the West Coast, known also as **Port Orford cedar, Oregon cedar, ginger pine,** and in England as **Lawson cypress,** is from the tree *C. lawsoniana* of California and Oregon, mostly from a narrow coastal strip in Oregon to an altitude of about 5,000 ft.   Mature trees reach a height of 160 ft and a diameter of 6 ft.   The wood is white with a yellow tinge and a trace of red.   It is rather hard, tough, with a fine straight grain, and is very durable.   It has an agreeable aromatic odor, and is free from pitch.   The wood is used for doors, sash, boats, matches, patterns, and where a light, strong, straight-grained wood is required.   **Toon,** the wood of the tree *Cedrela toona* of India, southeast Asia, and Australia, resembles Spanish cedar but is somewhat harder, heavier, 35 lb per cu ft, and deeper red in color.   It has a beautiful grain, and takes a high polish.   It is durable, does not warp, and is used for furniture and cabinetwork.

CELLULOSE. The main constituent of the structure of plants, which, when extracted, is employed for making paper, plastics, and in many combinations.   Cellulose is made up of long-chain molecules in which the complex unit $C_6H_{10}O_5$ is repeated as many as 2,000 times.   It consists of glucose molecules with three **hydroxyl groups** for each glucose unit.   These OH groups are very reactive, and an almost infinite variety of compounds may be made by grafting on other groups, either repetitively or intermittently, such as reaction with acetic or nitric acids to form acetates or nitrates, reaction with ethylene oxide to form hydroxy ethyl cellulose, reaction with acrylonitrile to form cyanoethylated cellulose, or reaction with vinyls. Cellulose is the most abundant of the nonprotein natural organic products. It is highly resistant to attack by the common microorganisms, but the enzyme **cellulase** digests it easily, and this organism is used for making paper pulp, for clarifying beer and citrous juices, and for the production of citric acid and other chemicals from cellulose.   **Takamine 4000,** of the Miles Chemical Co., is this enzyme.   Cellulose is a white powder insoluble in water, sodium hydroxide, or alcohol, but dissolved by sulfuric acid.   The highly refined insoluble cellulose with all the sugars, pectin, and other soluble matter removed is called **alpha cellulose,** or **chemical cellulose,** used for the production of chemicals.   It was formerly made only from cotton linters, but is now largely made from wood pulp.   **Avicel,** of the American Viscose Corp., is such a cellulose marketed as a white crystalline powder for use in foodstuffs to give body and gel stability to such products as peanut butter, cheese spreads, and prepared puddings.   It forms a firm gel in water and absorbs oils easily.   It is odorless and tasteless, and has no calorie content.

One of the simplest forms of cellulose used industrially is **regenerated cellulose,** in which the chemical composition of the finished product is similar to that of the original cellulose.   It is made from wood or cotton pulp digested in a caustic solution.   The viscous liquid is forced through a slit into an acid bath to form a thin sheet, which is then hardened and bleached.   **Cellophane,** of Du Pont, is a regenerated cellulose in thin sheets for wrapping.   It is transparent, or is dyed in colors or embossed.   It is up to 0.0016 in. thick, with tensile strengths from 8,000 to 19,000 psi. It chars at about 375°F.   The thinnest sheets, 0.0009 in. in thickness, have 21,500 sq in. per lb.   The three-digit gage system used for cellophane indicates the total film yield.   Thus, 180 gage has a film yield of 18,000 sq in. per lb.   The waterproofed material is coated with a thin film of cellulose lacquer, or the cellophane may be laminated with a film of a synthetic resin.   **Cellothene,** of the Chester Packaging Products Co., is a heat-sealable film of laminated cellophane and polyethylene, the polyethylene thickness being at least 0.0005 in.   Cellophane has greater transparency than polyethylene, but is not as strong nor as chemically resistant. For food packaging, the printing is done on the reverse side of the cellophane before laminating.

Purocell, of the Eastern Corp., was a highly purified and bleached cellulose produced from wood pulp and used for making high-grade writing papers.

Barcote, of the Foote Mineral Co., is a nearly pure cellulose used in plastics or for carbonizing. It is a buff-colored, odorless powder or granular material with residual ash content of 1.6%. Some cellulose is obtained from potatoes as a by-product in the production of starch. It is pure white and is used in plastics. **Solka-Floc,** of the Brown Co., is 99.5% pure wood cellulose in the form of tough, white fibers 1 to 2 microns in diameter and 35 to 165 microns long, bulking 9 to 34 lb per cu ft. It is used as a filler for plastics requiring a fine surface finish and dimensional stability, such as for buttons, knobs, trays, and vinyl floor tile. It is also used in welding rod coatings, in adhesives, and for cellulose chemicals. Water-soluble cellulose, or **cellulose gum,** used as a substitute for gum arabic and carob-bean flour as a stabilizer, thickener, or emulsifier, is **sodium cellulose glycollate,** or **sodium carboxy methyl cellulose,** in powder form. It is also used to increase the effectiveness of detergents. Water-soluble film is also made from this material. **Carbose,** of the Wyandotte Chemicals Corp. and **Cellocel S,** of the Dow Chemical Co., are sodium carboxy methyl cellulose. **CMC gum,** of the Dow Chemical Co., is **carboxy methyl cellulose,** used as a temporary binder for ceramic glazes. It burns out in the firing. A purified grade of this gum is used as a stabilizer in pharmaceuticals and low-acid foodstuffs. **Cellocel A** is **aluminum cellulose glycollate,** a water-soluble brownish powder used for waterproofing paper. **Natrosol,** of Hercules, is **hydroxy ethyl cellulose,** a white powder used for textile finishes and as a thickener for water-base paints. **Ethylose,** of Rayonier, Inc., is a hydroxy ethyl cellulose with a low degree of substitution of ethylene oxide in the molecular chain. It is insoluble in water, but is alkali-soluble. It is used in paper coating to add gloss and water resistance. **Cellosize QP-4400,** of the Union Carbide Corporation, is a hydroxy ethyl cellulose powder easily soluble in water but nongelling. It is used as a thickener in latex paints, inks, cosmetics, and pharmaceuticals. **Ceglin,** of the Sylvania Corp., is an alkali-soluble **cellulose ether** marketed as a white fibrous powder. When dissolved in a water solution of caustic soda, it forms a viscous liquid used for sizing textiles. **Sodium cellulose sulfate** is a water-soluble granular powder used as a thickener in emulsion paints, foods, and cosmetics, and for sizing paper and textiles. It produces a clear, tough, greaseproof coating. It is the sodium salt of cellulose acid sulfate produced by sulfuric acid treatment of wood pulp, with the sulfate groups in ester-type linkages on the cellulose chain. **SCS gum,** of the Tennessee Eastman Corp., used to replace gum arabic, is this material.

Ethyl cellulose is a colorless, odorless ester of cellulose resulting from the reaction of ethyl chloride and cellulose. The specific gravity is 1.07 to 1.18. It is noninflammable, very flexible, stable to light, and forms durable alkali-resistant coatings. It is used as a thin wrapping material, for protective coatings, as a hardening agent in resins and waxes, and for molding plastics.   **Ethyl cellulose plastics** are thermoplastic and are noted for their ease of molding, light weight, and good dielectric strength, 400 to 520 volts per mil, and retention of flexibility over a wide range of temperature from −70 to 150°F, the softening point.   But they are softer and lower in strength than cellulose-acetate plastics.   **Lumarith EC,** of the Celanese Corp., is ethyl cellulose in the form of sheet, films, and molding powder.   **Celcon** is a name applied by this company to ethyl cellulose plastics.   **Hercocel E,** of Hercules, is a compounded ethyl cellulose molding powder in several formulations to give tensile strengths from 3,750 to 7,400 psi, with elongation from 6 to 16%.

Ethocel is ethyl cellulose of the Dow Chemical Co., and **Stripcoat** is a solution of ethyl cellulose used for dipping automotive and aircraft replacement parts or other metal products to form a thin, waterproof protective coating to prevent corrosion.   The coating strips off easily when the part is to be used.   The same material is marketed by a number of other companies for the same purpose under a variety of trade names. **Methyl cellulose** is a white, granular, flaky material, which is a strong emulsifying agent, and is used in soaps, floor waxes, shoe cleaners, in emulsions of starches, glues, waxes, and fats, and as a substitute for gum arabic.   It gives colorless, odorless solutions resistant to fermentation.   It dissolves in cold water, but is stable to alkalies and dilute acids.   In soaps it lowers the surface tension of the water and aids lathering.   It is also used for tree-wound dressings, and as a moisture-conserving soil conditioner.   **Colloresin,** of the General Drug Co., is methyl cellulose, and **Methocel HB,** of the Dow Chemical Co., is a hydroxy butyl methyl cellulose for use in paint removers.   **Cyanoethylated cellulose** is a white fibrous solid used to produce thin transparent sheets for insulating capacitors and as carriers for luminescent phosphors.   It has a high dielectric constant and low dissipation factor.   A 0.002-in. film has a tensile strength of 5,300 psi, and is flexible.   **Cyanocel,** of the American Cyanamid Co., is this material.

CELLULOSE ACETATE.   An amber-colored, transparent material made by the reaction of cellulose with acetic acid or acetic anhydride in the presence of sulfuric acid.   In Germany it was made by treating beechwood pulp with acetic acid in the presence of an excess of zinc chloride.   It is employed for lacquers and coatings, molding plastics, rayon, and photographic film.   Cellulose acetate may be the triacetate $C_6H_7O_2(OOCCH_3)_3$, but may be the tetracetate or the pentacetate, or mixtures.   It is made in different degrees of acetylation with varying properties.   Unlike nitrocellulose, it is not flammable, and it has better light and heat stability.   It has a refractive index of 1.47 to 1.50, and a sheet ⅛ in. thick will transmit 90% of the light.   The specific gravity is 1.27 to 1.37, hardness 8 to 15

Brinell, tensile strength 3,500 to 8,000 psi, compressive strength up to 20,000 psi, elongation 15 to 80%, dielectric strength 300 to 600 volts per mil, and softening point 122 to 205°F.   It is thermoplastic, and is easily molded.   The molded parts or sheets are tough, easily machined, and resistant to oils and to many chemicals.   In coatings and lacquers the material is adhesive, tough, and resilient, and does not discolor easily.   In fiber form for rayons it can be made in fine filaments that are strong and flexible, noninflammable, mildewproof, and easily dyed.   Standard cellulose acetate for molding is marketed in flake form.   The high acetyl type of the Hercules compound contains 56 to 58.5% combined acetic acid, and it makes plastics of high dimensional stability.   **Cellulose triacetate,** with 60 to 61.5% combined acetic acid, is more insoluble, has higher dielectric strength, and is more resistant to heat and light than other types. It is cast into sheets, and is also used for resistant coatings and for textile fibers.   **Cellulose acetate film,** used for wrapping, is somewhat lighter in weight than regenerated cellulose, giving 14,500 sq in. per lb for the 0.0015-in. film.   **Kodapak,** of the Eastman Co., is cellulose acetate film for packaging.

Lumarith is a cellulose acetate of the Celanese Corp. in the form of rods, sheets, tubes, and molding powder.   **Lumarith X** is a high acetyl cellulose acetate for molding.   The tensile strength is up to 8,000 psi, and Brinell hardness up to 12.5.   **Vuelite,** of the Monsanto Chemical Co., is transparent cellulose acetate for fluorescent light fixtures.   **Cellomold** is a cellulose-acetate molding powder of F. A. Hughes & Co., Ltd., and **Celastoid** is an extrusion acetate of the British Celanese, Ltd.   **Tenite** is a cellulose-acetate molding material of the Tennessee Eastman Corp.   **Estron** is a name adopted by this company to designate cellulose ester yarns and staple fiber.   **Protectoid** is Lumarith in the form of noninflammable motion-picture film.

Cellulose acetate lacquers are sold under many trade names.   They are the acetate in solvents with plasticizers and pigments.   **Vimlite,** of the Celanese Corp., is a Saran screen filled with cellulose acetate.   It transmits ultraviolet light, and is used for glazing.   **Miramesh,** of the National Research Corp., is this material with one side coated with a film of aluminum. It is used for light diffusers and radiant-heat reflectors.   **Masuron,** of John W. Masury & Son, **Nixonite,** of the Nixon Nitration Works, and **Plastacele,** of Du Pont, are cellulose-acetate materials.   **Acele,** of the latter company, is a name for acetate yarns. **Celanese** is the name of cellulose-acetate yarns and fabrics of the Celanese Corp. of America.   **Celairese,** of the same company, is a fluffy acetate fiber used for interlinings.   **Lanese** is a fine fluffy acetate fiber used to blend with wool.   **Fortisan,** of the same company, is a specially processed strong acetate fiber of extreme fineness, 0.0001 in. diameter, originally developed for parachutes but now also used for fine fabrics.   **Forticel,** of the same company, is a cellulose propionate plastic for injection molding.   It has a flow point at 161°C, has high impact resistance, and requires less plasticizer than cellulose acetate.   **Arnel,** of the Celanese Corp., is a cellulose tricetate fiber resistant to shrinkage and wrinkling in fabrics.   **Arnel 60** is a cellulose acetate fiber with a circular cross section instead of the normal crenelated cross section, giving higher strength and better spinning qualities.   **Hercocel A,** of Hercules, is cellulose acetate molding powder that will produce moldings with tensile strengths from 4,000 to 7,000 psi, and elongations from 14 to 22%.   The flow temperature is from 285 to 355°F, depending on the formulation.   **Avcocel,** of the American Viscose Corp., used as a filler in plastics to increase the impact strength, is a by-product of cellulose acetate production.   It contains 50% cellulose acetate and 50% white cotton.

Cellulose-acetate butyrate is made by the esterification of cellulose with acetic acid and butyric acid in the presence of a catalyst.   It has the same appearance and approximately the same range of properties as cellulose acetate, but can be used with fewer plasticizers, has less water absorption, and is more stable to heat and light.   It is particularly valued for coatings, insulating tapes, varnishes and lacquers, and electrical parts.   **Tenite II** is this material.   **Tenite III** is **cellulose-acetate propionate** for extrusion rod and moldings of high impact strength.   **Hercose C,** of Hercules, is cellulose-acetate butyrate used for cable coverings and coatings.   It is more soluble than cellulose acetate and more miscible with gums. It forms durable and flexible films.   **Ester EAB-171,** of Eastman, is a liquid cellulose acetate butyrate for glossy lacquers, chemical-resistant fabric coatings, and wire-screen windows.   It contains 17% butyl with 1 hydroxyl group per 4 anhydro glucose units.   It transmits ultraviolet light without yellowing or hazing and is weather-resistant.

CELLULOSE NITRATE PLASTICS.   Materials made by treating cellulose with a mixture of nitric and sulfuric acids, washing free of acid, bleaching, stabilizing, and dehydrating.   For sheets, rods, and tubes it is mixed with plasticizers and pigments and rolled or drawn to the shape desired.   The cellulose molecule will unite with from 1 to 6 molecules of nitric acid.   The lower nitrates are very inflammable, but they do not explode like the high nitrates, and they are the ones used for plastics, rayons, and lacquers, although their use for clothing fabrics is restricted by law. The names **cellulose nitrate** and **pyroxylin** are used for the compounds of lower nitration, and the term **nitrocellulose** is used for the explosives.   **Collodion** is a name given to the original solution of cellulose nitrate in a mixture of 60% ether and 40 alcohol for making fibers and film, and the name is still retained in pharmacy.   The name **soluble cotton** is used to designate batches of cellulose nitrate wet with alcohol for storing for the production of lacquers, but the soluble cotton gauze, used for surgical dressings, is cotton oxidized with nitrogen dioxide.

Cellulose nitrate was first used as a plastic in England in 1855 under the name **Parkesine.** It consisted of nitrocellulose mixed with camphor and castor oil for hardening and making it nonexplosive. Later, in 1868, an improved cellulose nitrate and camphor plastic was called **Celluloid,** now the trade name of the Celanese Corp. of America for cellulose nitrate plastics. **Xylonite** was the name used in England for the nitrocellulose hardened with camphor made by Daniel Spill in 1868. The name is still used by the British Xylonite Co. for cellulose nitrate plastics. Cellulose nitrate is the toughest of the thermoplastics. It has a specific gravity of 1.35 to 1.45, tensile strength of 6,000 to 7,500 psi, elongation 30 to 50%, compressive strength 20,000 to 30,000 psi, Brinell hardness 8 to 11, and dielectric strength 250 to 550 volts per mil. The softening point is 160°F, and it is easy to mold and easy to machine. It also is readily dyed to any color. It is not light-stable, and is therefore no longer used for laminated glass. It is resistant to many chemicals, but has the disadvantage that it is inflammable. The molding is limited to pressing from flat shapes. It burns with a smoky flame, and the fumes are poisonous. Methyl or amyl alcohols are the usual solvents for the material, and various plasticizers are used, some of which aid in reducing the flammability. Camphor is the usual hardener and plasticizer, from 24 to 30% being the usual amount. Cellulose nitrate plastics in rod, sheet, and the tube forms have been marketed under many trade names. Some of these are **Pyralin** and **Viscoloid,** of Du Pont; **Nitron,** of the Monsanto Chemical Co.; **Nixonoid,** of the Nixon Nitration Works; **Amarith,** of the Celanese Corp. of America; and **Fiberloid,** of the Fiberloid Corp. **Cellulose nitrate lacquers,** which are solutions with pigments and plasticizers, are quick-drying on evaporation of the solvent, and they give good adhesive films that are tough, flexible, and resistant. They are sold under many trade names such as **Duco, Zapon,** and **Arcozon.**

CEMENT. A material, generally in powder form, that can be made into a paste usually by the addition of water and, when molded or poured, will set into a solid mass. Numerous organic compounds used for adhering, or fastening materials, are called cements, but these are classified as adhesives, and the term cement alone means a construction material. The most widely used of the construction cements is **portland cement.** It is a bluish-gray powder obtained by finely grinding the clinker made by heating strongly an intimate mixture of calcareous and argillaceous minerals. The chief raw material is a mixture of high-calcium limestone, known as **cement rock,** and clay or shale. Blast-furnace slag may also be used in some cements.   American specifications call for five types of portland cement.   Type I, for general concrete construction, has a typical analysis of 63.2% CaO, 21.3 SiO$_2$, 6 Al$_2$O$_3$, 2.7 Fe$_2$O$_3$, 2.9 MgO, 1.8 SO$_3$.   Type III, for use where high early strength is required, has 64.3% CaO, 20.4 SiO$_2$, 5.9 Al$_2$O$_3$, 3.1 Fe$_2$O$_3$, 2 MgO, 2.3 SO$_3$.   The color of the cement is due chiefly to iron oxide.   In the absence of impurities the color would be white, but neither the color nor the specific gravity is a test of quality. The specific gravity is at least 3.10.   Good cement is always ground fine, with 98.5% passing a 200-mesh screen.

White cement is from pure calcite limestone, such as that found in eastern Pennsylvania.   It is ground finer and used for a better class of work, but the physical properties are similar to those of ordinary cement. A typical analysis of white cement is: 65% CaO, 25.5 SiO$_2$, 5.9 Al$_2$O$_3$, 0.6 Fe$_2$O$_3$, 1.1 MgO, 0.1 SO$_3$.   The white cements of France and England are made from the chalky limestones, and have superior working qualities, as they are usually ground finer.   White cement is also made from inferior iron-bearing limestone by treatment with fluorspar.

Aluminous cement, or **aluminate cement,** sometimes referred to as **high-speed cement,** will set to high strength in 24 hr, and is thus valued for laying roads or bank walls.   It is made with bauxite, and contains a high percentage of alumina.   A typical analysis is: 39.8% Al$_2$O$_3$, 33.5 CaO, 14.6 Fe$_2$O$_3$, 5.3 SiO$_2$, 1.3 MgO, 0.1 SO$_3$.   **Lumnite cement,** of the Universal-Atlas Cement Co., is a cement of this type.   **Accelerated cements** are intermediate cements that will set hard in about 3 days.   The raw mixture for making portland cement is controlled to give exact proportions in the final product, and some quartz or iron ore may be added to balance the mix.   The temperature of the rotary kiln is raised gradually to about 2650°F.   The burned clinker is then ground with a small amount of gypsum which controls the set.

The amount of portland cement used in the United States exceeds 200 million tons annually.   But a number of other construction cements not classed as portland cement are also used.   **Natural cement** is made by heating to complete decarbonation, but not fusion, a highly argillaceous soft limestone.   This is the most ancient of the manufactured cements, and is still called **Roman cement.**   It is low in cost and will set more quickly than portland cement, but is softer and weaker.   It is sometimes called **hydraulic lime.**   When used for laying brick and stone it is called **masonry cement,** but ordinary **mortar** for laying brick is not this product, but is slaked lime and sand.   **Cement mortar** is made with portland cement, sand, and water, with sometimes lime to aid spreading.

Oxychloride cement, or **Sorel cement,** is composed of **magnesium chloride,** MgCl$_2$, and calcined magnesia.   It is strong and hard and, with various fillers, is used for floors and stucco.   **Magnesia cement** is magnesium oxide, prepared by heating the chloride or carbonate to redness. When mixed with water it sets to a friable mass but of sufficient strength for covering steam pipes or furnaces. It is usually mixed with asbestos fibers to give strength and added heat resistance. The term 85% magnesia means 85% magnesia cement and 15 asbestos fibers. The cement will withstand temperatures up to 600°F.

Keene's cement, also known as **flooring cement** and **tiling plaster,** is a **gypsum cement.** It is made by burning gypsum at about 1100°F, to drive off the chemically combined water, grinding to a fine powder, and adding alum to accelerate the set. It will keep better than ordinary gypsum cement, has high strength, is white in color, and takes a good polish. **Parian cement** is similar, except that borax is used instead of alum. **Martin's cement** is made with potassium carbonate instead of alum. These cements are also called **hard-finish plaster,** and they will set very hard and white. They are used for flooring and to imitate tiling. An ancient natural cement is **pozzuolana cement.** It is a volcanic material found near Pozzuoli, Italy, and in several other places in Europe. It is a volcanic lava modified by steam or gases so that it is powdery and has acquired hydraulic properties. The chief components are silica and alumina, and the color varies greatly, being white, yellow, brown, or black. It has been employed as a construction cement since ancient times. **Trass** is a similar material found in the Rhine district of Germany. **Santorin** is a light-gray volcanic ash with somewhat similar characteristics from the Greek island of Santorin. Artificial pozzuolana cements and trass cements are made in the United States by intergrinding pumicite, tufa, or shale with portland cement. **Slag cement** is made by grinding blast-furnace slag with portland cement. **Pozzolans** are siliceous materials which will combine with lime in the presence of water to form compounds having cementing properties. **Fly ash** in an artificial pozzolan composed principally of amorphous silica with varying amounts of the oxides of aluminum and iron and traces of other oxides. It is a fine dark powder of spheroid particles produced as the by-product of combustion of pulverized coal, and collected at the base of the stack. As an admix it improves the workability of concrete, and in large amounts its pozzolanic action adds to the compressive strength.

CERAMIC CLAYS. Clays used for making pottery, tiles, brick, and pipes, but more particularly the better grade of clays for pottery and molded articles not including the fireclays and fine porcelain clays. **Clay** is a general name for all earths that form a paste with water and harden when heated. The U.S. Department of Agriculture distinguishes clay as having small grains, less than 0.002 mm in diameter, as distinct from **silt** with grains from 0.002 to 0.05 mm. Most clays are composed chiefly of silica and alumina. Kaolins are the purest forms of clay. The clayey mineral in all clays is kaolinite, or minerals closely allied, as **anauxite,** $Al_2O_3 \cdot 3SiO_2 \cdot 2H_2O$, and **montmorillonite,** $Al_2O_3 \cdot 4SiO_2 \cdot 2H_2O$, the latter having an expanding lattice molecular structure which increases the bond strength of ceramic clays. When the aluminum silicates are in colloidal form, the material is theoretically true clay, or **clayite.** Some clays, however, derive much of their plasticity from colloids of organic material, and since all clays are of secondary origin from the weathering or decomposition of rocks, they may vary greatly in composition. Hardness of the clay depends upon the texture as well as on the cohesion of the particles. Plasticity involves the ability of the clay to be molded when wet, to retain its shape when dry, and to have the strength to withstand handling in the green or unfired condition. The degrees of plasticity are called fat, rich, rubbery, and waxy, or the clays may be termed very plastic, which is waxy, sticky plastic, medium plastic, and lean, which is nonplastic. Clays that require a large amount of water for plasticity tend to warp when dried. Those that are not easily worked may be made plastic by **ceramic binders** such as alkaline starch solutions, ammonium alginate, or lignin. For making pressed or cast whiteware, methyl cellulose is used as a binder for the clay. It gives good binding strength, and it fires out of the ceramic with an ash residue of only 0.5%.

Clays with as much as 1% iron burn red, and titanium increases this color. Yellow ochres contain iron as a free hydrate. Most clays contain quartz sand and sometimes powdered mica. **Calcareous clays** are known as **marls.** Pyrites burn to holes in the brick bordered by a ring of magnetic iron oxide, and a clay should be free of this mineral. Limestone grains in the clay burn to free lime which later slakes and splits the ceramic. Most of the common brick clays are complex mixed earths likely to have much undesirable matter that makes them unsuitable for good tile, pipe, or pottery. **Kingsley clay** of Georgia, used for artware, wall tile, dishes, and refractories, has only 0.4% iron oxide, 0.15 Na_2O, 0.1 K_2O, and 0.05 CaO. It contains about 45% silica, 40 alumina, and 1.15 titanium oxide. The **seito ware** of Japan is made with the **Gaerome clay** found near Nagoya. It is a granite with quartz particles, and when used with a high percentage of zirconium oxide produces ceramics of close density and brilliant whiteness. Alumina clay of western Idaho contains on a dry basis 28.7% alumina, 5.6 iron oxide, and a high percentage of titania.

In firing clays, the moisture is driven off when the temperature is raised from 100 to 150°C, and the chemically combined water is lost at 400 to 700°C. Incipient fusion ranges from 900 to 1200°C, at which point the fluxes begin to be viscous. **Common brick** is usually finished at this point. Above this temperature the pores are filled with vitreous semi-molten material, and the ware will cool to a vitreous luster. **Stoneware** and paving brick are fired to this condition. At higher temperatures the clay body fuses. **Chemical stoneware** may range from 30 to 70% clay, 5 to 25 feldspar, and 30 to 60 silica. The vitrified and glazed product will have a tensile strength up to 2,500 psi and a compressive strength up to 80,000 psi. **Clinker brick** is fired to the fusion point. Bright and true colors are obtained when the wares are muffled during the firing to prevent oxidation of the impurities. **Industrial stoneware** is made from specially selected or blended clays to give desired properties, and these may be marketed under trade names. Actually, the possible compositions in making ceramics are infinite, and ceramics for industrial uses are now not likely to be made with natural clays alone. One company, the Glascote Products, Inc., has more than 3,000 different formulas for ceramic coatings. The American Ceramic Society defines a ceramic simply as a material in which silicon and its oxide have a predominant position.

Ceratherm, of the U.S. Stoneware Co., is an acid-resistant and heat-shock-resistant ceramic having a base of high-alumina clay. It is strong and nonporous, and is used for pump and chemical-equipment linings. The chemical stoneware of the General Ceramics Corp., made with a mullite-zircon body, is white, dense, strong, and thermal-shock-resistant. The ceramic marketed under the name of **Prestite** by the Westinghouse Electric Corp. for insulators and molded electrical parts is blended of flint, feldspar, kaolin, and ball clay. It is nonporous and moistureproof without a glaze, has high dielectric strength, a tensile strength of 5,000 psi, and a compressive strength of 48,000 psi. The ceramic produced by the Rostone Corp. under the name of **Rosite,** for molded electrical parts and panels, is a calcium-aluminum-silicate mixed with asbestos. It will withstand temperatures to 900°F, is resistant to akalies, and has a compressive strength up to 15,000 psi.

CERARGYRITE. An ore of the metal silver, found in the upper zone of silver veins in Nevada, Colorado, Idaho, Peru, Chile, and Mexico. It is sometimes called **horn silver,** owing to its hornlike appearance. It is a **silver chloride,** AgCl, containing theoretically 75.3% silver, with sometimes some mercury. The hardness is 2.3 and specific gravity 5.8. It is massive, resembling wax, with a pearl-gray color.

CERIUM METALS. A group of trivalent metallic elements that occur together and have been called **rare-earth metals,** or **rare earths,** because of the difficulty of extracting them rather than because of their rarity. They include the elements 57 through 71, from lanthanum to lutetium, and also **yttrium, element 39,** and **thorium, element 90,** since these are also found together in monazite, the chief ore. The true cerium metals are the light-metal elements 57 to 63, together with **ytterbium, element 70.** All of these metals have the xenon atom core and three outer electrons. They differ only in the number of electrons in the intermediate levels.

Thorium is separated by a relatively easy process, and the others remain grouped as the cerium metals, to be extracted as metals or compounds for special purposes justifying high costs.   The separate metals are regularly marketed in pellets and in 325-mesh powder of 99.9% purity for pyrophoric and electronic uses, and as oxides of 99.9% purity.   Cerium metal has an iron-gray color, is only slightly harder than lead, and is malleable. It has a specific gravity of 6.77, and a melting point at 1480°F.

After extraction of the thorium oxide from monazite the residual matter is reduced by converting the oxides to chlorides and then removing the metals by electrolysis.   The product obtained is an alloy containing about 50% cerium together with lanthanum, didymium, and the other rare metals.   It is usually called **misch metal,** the German name for mixed metal, and its original use was for making pyrophoric alloys.   **Cerium standard alloy** of the Cerium Metals Corp. is a misch metal containing 50 to 55% cerium, 22 to 25 lanthanum, 15 to 17 neodymium, and the balance a mixture of yttrium, terbium, illinium, praseodymium, and samarium, with 0.5 to 0.8% iron.

Misch metal is used in making aluminum alloys, and in some steels and irons.   In cast iron it opposes graphitization, and produces a malleableized iron.   It removes the sulfur and the oxides, and completely degasifies steel.   In stainless steel it is used as a precipitation hardening agent. An important use of misch metal is in magnesium alloys for aircraft castings.   From 3 to 4% of misch metal is used with 0.2 to 0.6% zirconium, both of which refine the grain and give sound castings of complex shapes.   The cerium metals also add heat resistance, and castings have service temperatures to 500°F.   **Magnesium alloy EK30A** is an alloy of this type with 3% cerium metals, 0.55 zirconium, and the balance magnesium.   The tensile strength is 23,000 psi with elongation of 3%, and the specific gravity is 1.76.   **Magnesium alloy EZ33A** is a modification containing also 3% zinc.

Ceria, cerium oxide, or **ceric oxide,** CeO_2, is a pale-yellow heavy powder of specific gravity 7.65, used in coloring ceramics and glass and for producing distortion-free optical glass.   It is used also for decolorizing crystal glass, but when the glass contains titania it produces a canary-yellow color. **Cerious oxide,** Ce_2O_3, is a greenish powder of specific gravity 7.0, and refractive index 2.19.   About 3% of the oxide in glass makes the glass completely absorbent to ultraviolet rays.   It is also an excellent opacifier for ceramics.   **Cerium fluoride,** CeF_3, is used in arc carbons to increase brilliance. **Cerious nitrate,** $Ce(NO_3)_3 \cdot 6H_2O$, is a red crystalline powder used in gas-mantle manufacture.   Cerium salts are used for coloring glass.

Ceric titanate, $Ce(TiO_3)_2$, gives a golden-yellow color, and **ceric molybdate** gives a blue color.

Neodymium has a specific gravity of 7.01 and a melting point of 1875°F. It is used in magnesium alloys to increase strength at elevated temperatures, and is used in some glasses to reduce glare. **Neodymium glass,** containing small amounts of neodymium oxide, is used for color television filter plates since it transmits 90% of the blue, green, and red light rays and no more than 10% of the yellow. It thus produces truer colors and sharper contrasts in the pictures and decreases the tendency toward gray tones. **Praseodymium** has a specific gravity of 6.77, and a melting point at 1715°F. **Lanthanum** is a white metal, malleable and ductile, with a specific gravity of 6.16, melting at 1688°F. Like the other cerium metals, it oxidizes easily in the air and is easily soluble in acids. **Lanthanum oxide,** La_2O_3, is a white powder used for absorbing gases in vacuum tubes. **Lanthanum boride,** LaB_6, is a crystalline powder used as an electron emitter for maintaining a constant, active cathode surface. It has high electrical conductivity.

Didymium is not an element, but is a mixture of rare earths without cerium. It averages 45% La_2O_3, 38% **neodymium oxide,** Nd_2O_3, 11% **praseodymium oxide,** Pr_6O_{11}, 4% **samarium oxide,** Sm_2O_3, and other oxides. It is really the basic material from which the rare metals are produced. In glass it gives a neutral gray color, and it is used in glass for welders' goggles as it absorbs yellow light and reduces glare and eye fatigue. It is available as **didymium carbonate,** a pink powder soluble in acids, as **didymium oxide,** a brown acid-soluble powder, and as **didymium chloride** in pink lumps soluble in water and in acids.

Dysprosium has a specific gravity of 8.56 and a melting point of 2700°F. Its corrosion resistance is higher than that of other cerium metals. It also has good neutron-absorption ability, with a neutron cross section of 1,100 barns. It is used in nuclear-reactor control rods, in magnetic alloys, and in ferrites for microwave use. The metal is paramagnetic. It is also used in mercury vapor lamps. With argon gas in the arc area it balances the color spectrum and gives a higher light output. **Samarium** has a higher neutron cross section, 5,500 barns, and is used for neutron absorption in reactors. Samarium has a specific gravity of 7.54, and a melting point at 1925°F.

Ytterbium metal is produced in lumps and ingots. It has a specific gravity of 6.96 and a melting point at 1515°F. **Yttrium** is more abundant in nature than lead, but is difficult to extract. It is found associated with the elements 57 to 71, although its atomic number is 39. It has a silvery luster, a specific gravity of 4.47, and a melting point at 1550°F. It is the lightest of the cerium metals except scandium. The metal is corrosion-resistant to 400°C. It has a hexagonal close-packed crystal structure. **Ytterbium oxide,** Yb_2O_3, and **yttrium oxide,** Y_2O_3, are the usual commercial forms of these metals. The two metals occur in the mineral **gadolinite,** or **ytterbite,** $4BeO \cdot FeO \cdot Y_2O_3 \cdot 2SiO_2$, which also contains **gadolinium, erbium, europium, holmium** and rhenium. The mineral is found in Greenland, Sweden, Norway, and Colorado. Erbium has been obtained only in small quantities as a dark-gray powder. The metal has a specific gravity of 9.06 and a melting point at about 2700°F. It forms the rose-red **erbium oxide,** or **erbia,** Er_2O_3, and other highly colored reddish salts. At high temperatures erbia glows with a greenish light.

Yttrium also occurs in the scarce mineral **nuevite** found in California. The mineral also carries titanium, tantalum, iron, and quartz, and is similar to the **keilhauite** found in Norway. **Fergusonite,** a brown mineral with a vitreous fracture, found sparsely in the Appalachian hills from New England to South Carolina, is a columbate and tantalate of yttrium with cerium, erbium, and uranium. In Europe it is known as **bragite** and **tyrite.** The mineral known as **bastnasite** in California is a fluorocarbonate of cerium and lanthanum, and the deposit at Mountain Pass, Calif., is sufficient to supply commercial needs of all the cerium metals. About 0.01% of rare-earth metals remain in the waste after apatite ores are processed in the making of phosphoric acid fertilizer. These metals are extracted by solvent or ion-exchange methods. Yttrium oxide is available as a fine white powder. **Yttralox,** of General Electric Co., is a transparent ceramic made from yttrium oxide and has a melting point above 4000°F. It is used for special high-temperature lenses, infrared windows, lasers, and high-intensity lamps. For the brilliant reds for television phosphors small amounts of europium are added to **yttrium vanadate.**

Gadolinium oxide, or **gadolinia,** G_2O_3, has high neutron absorption, and is used for shields in atomic-power plants. As a molded ceramic it has a density of 7.0, low thermal conductivity, and a melting point of 2350°C. **Lutetium** is a heavy, refractory metal with a density of 9.85 and a melting point at about 3100°F. **Lutetium oxide,** Lu_2O_3, of 99% purity, is produced for atomic uses. **Holmium** has a specific gravity of 8.8 and a melting point at about 2700°F. It is used in glass to transmit radiant energy for wavelength-calibration instruments. **Thulium** is a heavy metal with a density of 9.32 and a melting point at about 2800°F. It is used for radiographic applications. **Thulium 170** is a soft-gamma-ray emitter and is used as a radiation source. **Thulium oxide,** Tm_2O_3, is radioactive and is used as a power source for small thermoelectric devices. **Scandium** is a silvery-white metal found in the mineral **thortveitite,** $(ScYt)_2Si_2O_7$, of Norway, which contains 42% **scandium oxide,** Sc_2O_3. It also occurs in small amounts in the fergusonite of Montana, and in lepidolite, muscovite, beryl, and the amphiboles. The metal has a melting point of 1400°C, and a specific gravity slightly higher than aluminum.

CERMETS. Mixtures of refractory metal powders and ceramic oxides which are pressed or cast to shape and then sintered. They do not include the chemically combined metals known as hard metals, nor the hard carbides with cobalt or nickel binders. The possible variety of cermets is very extensive, but the usual base metal is chromium, and the most usual oxide is alumina. They are used for rocket nozzles, inserts, pouring spouts, seals, and refractory tool parts. **Haynes cermet LT-1,** of the Stellite Division, has 77% chromium and 23 alumina. Sintered parts have a melting point of 3362°F, and will resist oxidation to 2200°F. The tensile strength is 21,000 psi, compressive strength 110,000 psi, and it will retain a tensile strength of 12,000 psi at 2000°F. The hardness is Rockwell C37. A modification, **Cermet LT-1b,** contains 60% chromium, 20 molybdenum, 2 titanium, and 18 alumina. This material has higher tensile and rupture strength, but is lower in oxidation resistance. The term cermet, although employed frequently, is very indefinite, and could include practically any ceramic containing metal oxides, but it may be considered as indicating molded metal-oxide ceramics for high-temperature or special atomic uses, although molded aluminum oxide is not called a cermet while gadolinium oxide is thus designated.

CESIUM. Also spelled **caesium.** A rare metal, symbol Cs, obtained from the mineral **pollucite,** $2Cs_2O \cdot 2Al_2O_3 \cdot 9SiO_2 \cdot H_2O$, of Southwest Africa and Canada. The metal resembles rubidium and potassium, is silvery white and very soft. It oxidizes easily in the air, ignites at ordinary temperatures, and decomposes water with explosive violence. It can be kept only in a vacuum. The specific gravity is 1.903, melting point 28.5°C, and boiling point 670°C. It is used in low-voltage tubes to scavenge the last traces of air. It is usually marketed in the form of its compounds such as **cesium nitrate,** $CsNO_3$, **cesium fluoride,** CsF, or **cesium carbonate,** Cs_2CO_3. In the form of **cesium chloride,** CsCl, it is used on the filaments of radio tubes to increase sensitivity. It interacts with the thorium of the filament to produce positive ions. In photoelectric cells cesium chloride is used for a photosensitive deposit on the cathode, since cesium releases its outer electron under the action of ordinary light, and its color sensitivity is higher than that of other alkali metals. The high-voltage rectifying tube for changing alternating current to direct current has cesium metal coated on the nickel cathode, and has cesium vapor for current carrying. The cesium metal gives off a copious flow of electrons and is continuously renewed from the vapor. Cesium vapor is also used in the infrared signaling lamp, or **photophone,** as it gives infrared waves without visible light. **Cesium 137,** recovered from the waste of atomic plants, is a gamma-ray emitter with a half-life of 33 years. It is used in teletherapy, but the rays are not as penetrating as cobalt 60, and twice as much is required to produce equal effect.

CHALK. A fine-grained limestone, or a soft, earthy form of **calcium carbonate,** $CaCO_3$, composed of finely pulverized marine shells. The natural chalk comes largely from the southern coast of England and the north of France, but high-calcium marbles and limestones are the sources of most of the American chalk and precipitated calcium carbonate. Chalk is employed in putty, crayons, paints, rubber goods, linoleum, calcimine, and as a mild abrasive in polishes. **Whiting** and **Paris white** are names given to grades of chalk that have been ground and washed for use in paints, inks, and putty. **French chalk** is a high grade of massive talc cut to shape and used for marking. The color of chalk should be white, but it may be colored gray or yellowish by impurities. The commercial grades depend on the purity, color, and fineness of the grains. The specific gravity may be as low as 1.8.

Precipitated calcium carbonate is the whitest of the pigment extenders. **Kalite,** of the Diamond Alkali Co., is a precipitated calcium carbonate of 1-micron particle size, and **Suspenso, Surfex,** and **Nonferal** are grades with particle sizes from 5 to 10 microns. **Witcarb RC,** of the Witco Chemical Co., for rubber compounding, is a fine-grained grade, 0.065 micron, coated to prevent dusting and for easy dispersion in the rubber. **Purecal SC,** of the Wyandotte Chemicals Corp., is a similar material. **Limeolith,** of the Kansas City Limeolith Co., **Calcene,** of the Pittsburgh Plate Glass Co., and **Kalvan,** of R. T. Vanderbilt Co., Inc., are precipitated calcium carbonates. A highly purified calcium carbonate for use in medicine as an antacid is **Amitone,** of Winthrop-Stearns, Inc.

CHAMOIS. A soft, pliable leather originally made from the skins of the chamois, *Antilopa rupicapra,* a small deer inhabiting the mountains of Europe but now nearly extinct. The leather was of a light-tan color, with a soft nap. All commercial chamois is now made from the skins of lamb, sheep, goat, or from the thin portion of split hides. The Federal Trade Commission limited the use of the term chamois to oil-dressed sheepskins mechanically sueded, but there are no technical precedents for such limitation. The original **artificial chamois** was made by tanning sheepskins with formaldehyde or alum, impregnating with oils, and subjecting to mechanical sueding, but chamois is also made by various special tannages with or without sueding. Those treated with fish oils have a distinctive feel. Chamois leather will withstand soaking in hot water and will not harden on drying. It is used for polishing glass and plated metals. **Buckskin,** a similar pliable leather, but heavier and harder, was originally soft-tanned, oil-treated deerskin, but is now made from goatskins.

CHARCOAL. An amorphous form of carbon, made by enclosing billets in a retort and exposing them to a red heat for 4 or 5 hr.   It is also made by covering large heaps of wood with earth and permitting them to burn slowly for about a month.   Much charcoal is now produced as a by-product in the distillation of wood, a retort charge of 10 cords of wood yielding an average of 2,650 gal of pyroligneous liquor, 11,000 lb of gas, and 6 tons of charcoal.   **Wood charcoal** is used as a fuel, for making black gunpowder, for carbonizing steel, and for making activated charcoal for filtering and absorbent purposes.   **Gunpowder charcoal** is made from alder, willow, or hazelwood.   Commercial wood charcoal is usually about 25% of the original weight of the wood, and is not pure carbon.   The average composition is 95% carbon and 3 ash.   It is an excellent fuel, burning with a glow at low temperatures, and with a pale-blue flame at high temperatures.   Until about 1850 it was much used in blast furnaces for melting iron, and it produces a superior iron with less sulfur and phosphorus than when coke is used; 200 bushels are required to smelt 1 ton of iron.   **Red charcoal** is an impure charcoal made at a low temperature, and retaining much oxygen and hydrogen.

CHARCOAL IRON. Originally, all iron was made with charcoal, but because of the relative scarcity of wood and the greater expense, charcoal is now seldom used in the blast furnace, the desired qualities being obtained by metallurgical control.   Charcoal iron has less sulfur and phosphorus than iron made with coke, and cast iron made from it has a dense structure and a tendency to chill.   **Elverite,** of the Fuller Lehigh Co., is a charcoal type of cast iron which gives a hard chill with a soft, gray-iron core.   **Charcoal pig iron** was formerly imported from Sweden and Norway, and was used for such purposes as car wheels, magnet cores, and for making high-grade steels for boiler tubes.   **Stora** was a name for Swedish charcoal iron used for making malleable iron.

CHAULMOOGRA OIL. A brownish semisolid oil from the seeds of the fruit of the tree *Taraktogenos kurzii* and other species of Thailand, Assam, and Indonesia.   It is used chiefly for skin diseases and for leprosy.   A similar oil is also obtained from other genera of bushes and trees of the family *Flacourtiaceae,* and that obtained from some species of *Hydnocarpus* is superior to the true chaulmoogra oil.   The tree *H. anthelminthica,* native to Thailand, is cultivated in Hawaii.   This oil consists mainly of chaulmoogric and hydnocarpic acids.   **Sapucainha oil,** from the seeds of the tree *Carpotroche brasiliensis,* of the Amazon Valley, contains chaulmoogric, hydnocarpic, and **gorlic acids,** and is a superior oil.   **Gorliseed oil,** from the seeds of the tree *Onchoba echinata* of tropical Africa, and cultivated in Costa Rica and Puerto Rico, contains about 80% chaulmoogric acid and 10 gorlic acid.   **Dilo oil** is from the kernels of the nuts of the tree *Calophyllum inophyllum* of the South Sea Islands.   In Tahiti it is called **tamanu.**   The **chaulmoogric acids** are cyclopentenyl compounds, $(CH)_2(CH)_2CH(CH_2)_xCOOH$, made easily from cyclopentyl alcohol.

CHEESECLOTH. A thin, coarse-woven cotton fabric of plain weave, 40 to 32 count, and of coarse yarns.   It was originally used for wrapping cheese, but is now employed for wrapping, lining, interlining, filtering, as a polishing cloth, and as a backing for lining and wrapping papers.   The cloth is not sized, and may be either bleached or unbleached.   It comes usually 36 in. wide.   The grade known as **beef cloth,** originally used for wrapping meats, is also the preferred grade for polishing enameled parts.   It is made of No. 22 yarn or finer.   For covering meats the packing plants now use a heavily napped knitted fabric known as **stockinett.** It is made either as a flat fabric or in seamless tube form, and is also used for covering inking and oiling rolls in machinery.   Lighter grades of cheesecloth, with very open weave, known as **gauze,** are used for surgical dressings, and for backings for paper and maps.   **Baling paper** is made by coating cheesecloth with asphalt and pasting to one side of heavy kraft or Manila paper.   **Cable paper,** for wrapping cables, is sometimes made in the same way but with insulating varnish instead of asphalt.   **Buckram** is a coarse, plain-woven open fabric similar to cheesecloth but heavier and highly sized with water-resistant resins.   It is usually of cotton, but may be of linen, and is white or in plain colors.   It is used as a stiffening material, for bookbindings, inner soles, and interlinings.   **Cotton bunting** is a thin, soft, flimsy fabric of finer yarn and tighter weave than cheesecloth, used for flags, industrial linings, and decorations.   It is dyed in solid colors or printed.   But usually the word **bunting** alone refers to a more durable, nonfading lightweight worsted fabric in plain weave.

CHEMICAL INDICATORS. Dyestuffs that have one color in acid solutions and a different color in basic or alkaline solutions.   They are used to indicate the relative acidity of chemical solutions, as the different materials have different ranges of action on the acidity scale.   The materials are mostly weak acids, but some are weak bases. The best known is **litmus,** which is red below a pH of 4.5 and blue above a pH of 8.3, and is used to test strong acids or alkalies.   It is a natural dye prepared from several varieties of lichen, *Variolaria,* chiefly *Rocella tinctoria,* by allowing them to ferment in the presence of ammonia and potassium carbonate. When fermented, the mass has a blue color and is mixed with chalk and made into tablets or papers.   It is used also as a textile dye, wood stain, and as a food colorant.   **Azolitmin,** $C_7H_7O_4N$, is the coloring matter of litmus, and is a reddish-brown powder.   **Orchil,** or **cudbear,** is a red dye from another species.   **Alkanet,** also called **orcanette, anchusa,** or **alkanna,** is made from the root of the plant *Alkanna tinctoria* growing in the Mediterranean countries, Hungary, and western Asia.   The coloring ingredient, **alkannin,** is soluble in alcohol, benzene, ether, and oils, and is produced in dry extract as a dark red, amorphous, slightly acid powder. It is also used for coloring fats and oils in pharmacy and in cosmetics, for giving an even red color to wines, and for coloring wax.

Some coal-tar indicators are: **malachite green,** which is yellow below a pH of 0.5 and green above 1.5; **phenolphthalein,** which is colorless below 8.3 and magenta above 10.0; and **methyl red,** which is red below 4.4 and yellow above 6.0.   A **universal indicator** is a mixture of a number of indicators that gives the whole range of color changes, thereby indicating the entire pH range.   But such indicators must be compared with a standard to determine the pH value.

The change in color is caused by a slight rearrangement of the atoms of the molecule.   Some of the indicators, such as **thymol blue,** exhibit two color changes at different acidity ranges because of the presence of more than one chromophore arrangement of atoms.   These can thus be used to indicate two separate ranges on the pH scale.   **Curcumin,** a crystalline powder obtained by percolating hot acetone through turmeric, changes from yellow to red over the pH range of 7.5 to 8.5, and from red to orange over the range of 10.2 to 11.8.   **Test papers** are strips of absorbent paper that have been saturated with an indicator and dried.   They are used for testing for acidic or basic solutions, and not for accurate determination of acidity range or hydrogen-ion concentration such as is possible with direct use of the indicators.   **Alkannin paper,** also called **Boettger's paper,** is a white paper impregnated with an alcohol solution of alkanet. The paper is red, but it is turned to shades from green to blue by alkalies. **Litmus paper** is used for acidity testing.   **Starch-iodide paper** is paper dipped in starch paste containing potassium iodide.   It is used to test for halogens and oxidizing agents such as hydrogen peroxide.

CHERRY.   The wood of several species of cherry trees native to Europe and the United States.   It is brownish to light red in color, darkening on exposure, and has a close, even grain.   The weight is about 40 lb per cu ft. It retains its shape well, and takes a fine polish.   The annual cut of commercial cherry wood is small, but it is valued for instrument cases, patterns, paneling, and cabinetwork.   **American cherry** is mostly from the tree *Prunus serotina,* known as the **black cherry,** although some is from the tree *P. emarginata.*   The black cherry wood formerly used for airplane propellers has a specific gravity of 0.53 when oven-dried, compressive strength perpendicular to the grain 1,170 psi, and shearing strength parallel to the grain 1,180 psi.   This tree is found only thinly scattered through the eastern part of the United States. The wood is light to dark reddish with a beautiful luster and silky sheen, but has less figure than mahogany. **English cherry** is from the trees *P. cerasus* and *P. avium*.

CHESTNUT. The wood of the tree *Castanea dentata,* once growing plentifully along the Appalachian Range from New Hampshire to Georgia, but now very scarce. The trees grow to a large size, but the wood is inferior to oak in strength though similar in appearance. It is more brittle than oak, has a coarse, open grain often of spiral growth, and splits easily in nailing. The color is light brown or yellowish. It was used for posts, crossties, veneers, and some mill products. The wood contains from 6 to 20% tannin, which is obtained by soaking the chipped wood in water and evaporating. **Chestnut extract** was valued for tanning leather, giving a light-colored strong leather. The seed nuts of all varieties of chestnut are used for food and are eaten fresh, boiled, or roasted. The **European chestnut,** *C. sativa* and *C. vesca*, also called the **Spanish chestnut** and the **Italian chestnut,** has large nuts of inferior flavor. The wood is also inferior. The **horse chestnut** is a smaller tree, *Aesculus hippocastanum,* grown as a shade tree in Europe and the United States. The nut is round and larger than the chestnut. It is bitter in taste, but is rich in fats and starch and, when the saponin is removed, it produces an edible meal with an almondlike flavor used in confections in Europe. The nuts of the American horse chestnut, **buckeye,** or **Ohio buckeye,** *A. glabra,* and the **yellow buckeye,** *A. octandra,* are poisonous. The trees grow in the central states, and the dense, white wood is used for furniture and artificial limbs.

CHICLE. The coagulated latex obtained from incisions in the trunk of the evergreen tree *Achras zapota* and some other species of southern Mexico, Guatemala, and Honduras. The crude chicle is in reddish-brown pieces, and may have up to 40% impurities. The purified and neutralized gum is an amorphous white to pinkish powder insoluble in water, which forms a sticky mass when heated. The commercial purified gum is molded into blocks of 10 to 12 kilos for shipment. It contains about 40% resin, 17 rubber, and about 17 sugars and starches. Under the name of **txixtle** the coagulated latex was mixed with asphalt and used as **chewing gum** by the Aztec Indians, and this custom of chewing gum has been widely adopted in the United States. Chicle is used chiefly as a base for chewing gum, sometimes diluted with gutta gums. For chewing it is compounded with polyvinyl acetate, microcrystalline wax, and flavors.

CHLORIDE OF LIME. A white powder, a **calcium chloride hypochlorite,** of the composition $CaCl(OCl)$, having a strong chlorite odor. It decomposes easily in water and is used as a source of chlorine for cleaning and bleaching.   It is produced by passing chlorine gas through slaked lime.   Chloride of lime, or **chlorinated lime,** is also known as **bleaching powder,** although commercial bleaching powder may also be a mixture of calcium chloride and calcium hypochlorite, and the term **bleaches** is used for many chlorinated compounds.   The dry bleaches of the Food Machinery & Chemical Corp. are chlorinated **isocyanuric acids,** the CDB-85 being a fine white powder of the composition $ClNCO_3$, containing 88.5% available chlorine.   **Perchloron,** of the Pennsylvania Salt Mfg. Co., is **calcium hypochlorite,** $Ca(OCl)_2$, containing 70% available chlorine.

CHLORINATED HYDROCARBONS.   A large group of materials used as solvents for oils and fats, for metal degreasing, dry cleaning of textiles, as refrigerants, in insecticides, and in fire extinguishers.   They are hydrocarbons in which hydrogen atoms were replaced by chlorine atoms.   They range from the gaseous methyl chloride to the solid **hexachloro ethane,** CCl_3CCl_3, with most of them liquid.   The increase in the number of chlorine atoms increases the specific gravity, boiling point, and some other properties.   They may be divided into four groups: the methane group, including methyl chloride, chloroform, and carbon tetrachloride; the ethylene group, including dichlorethylene; the ethane group, including ethyl chloride and dichlorethane; and the propane group.   All of these are toxic, and the fumes are injurious when breathed or absorbed through the skin.   Some decompose in light and heat to form more toxic compounds. Some are very inflammable, while others do not support combustion.   In general, they are corrosive to metals.

Chloroform, or **trichloro methane,** is a liquid of the composition $CHCl_3$, boiling point 61.2°C, and specific gravity 1.489, used industrially as a solvent for greases and resins, and in medicine as an anesthetic.   It decomposes easily in the presence of light to form phosgene, and a small amount of ethyl alcohol is added to prevent decomposition.   **Ethyl chloride,** also known as **monochlorethane, kelane,** and **chelene,** is a gas of the composition CH_3CH_2Cl, used in making ethyl fluid for gasoline, as a local anesthetic in dentistry, as a catalyst in rubber and plastics processing, and as a refrigerant in household refrigerators.   It is marketed compressed into cylinders as a colorless liquid.   The specific gravity is 0.921, freezing point − 140.8°C, and boiling point 12.5°C.   The condensing pressure in refrigerators is 12.4 lb at 6°F, and the pressure of vaporization is 10.1 lb at 5°F.   Its disadvantage as a refrigerant is that it is highly inflammable, and there is no simple test for leaks.   **Methyl chloride** is a gas of the composition CH_3Cl, which is compressed into cylinders as a colorless liquid of boiling point − 10.65°F and freezing point − 144°F. Methyl chloride is one of the simplest and cheapest chemicals for methylation.   In water solution it is a good solvent.   It is also used as a catalyst in rubber processing, as a restraining gas in high-heat thermometers, and as a refrigerant. **Monochloro benzene,** C_6H_5Cl, is a colorless liquid boiling at 132°C, not soluble in water. It is used as a solvent for lacquers and resins, as a heat-transfer medium, and for making other chemicals. **Trichlor cumene,** or **isopropyl trichloro benzene,** is valued as a hydraulic fluid and dielectric fluid because of its high dielectric strength, low solubility in water, and resistance to oxidation. It is a colorless liquid, $(CH_3)_2CHC_6H_2Cl_3$, boiling at 260°C, and freezing at − 40°C. **Halane,** of the Wyandotte Chemicals Corp., used in processing textiles and paper, is dichloro dimethyl hydantoin, a white powder containing 66% available chlorine.

CHLORINATED RUBBER. An ivory-colored or white powder produced by the reaction of chlorine and rubber. It contains about 67% by weight of rubber, and is represented by the empirical formula $(C_{10}H_{13}Cl_7)x$, although it is a mixture of two products, one having a CH_2 linkage instead of a $CHCl$. Rubber was first chlorinated in 1846 to improve its aging qualities, but was not marketed until about 75 years later. The first commercial chlorinated rubber was the **Duroprene** of the United States Alkali Co. Chlorinated rubber is used in acid-resistant and corrosion-resistant paints, in adhesives, and in plastics. It was of prime importance before the advent of low-cost synthetic rubbers.

The uncompounded film is brittle, and for paints chlorinated rubber is plasticized to produce a hard, tough, adhesive coating, resistant to oils, acids, and alkalies. The specific gravity of chlorinated rubber is 1.64, and bulking value 0.0735 gal per lb. The tensile strength of the film is 4,500 psi. It is soluble in hydrocarbons, carbon tetrachloride, and esters, but insoluble in water. The unplasticized material has a high dielectric strength, up to 2,300 volts per mil. **Tornesit** and **Parlon** are chlorinated rubbers of Hercules Inc. **Paratex,** of the Truscon Laboratories, and **Roxaprene,** of the Roxalin Flexible Lacquer Co., Inc., are chlorinated-rubber coating materials. **Pliofilm,** of the Goodyear Tire & Rubber Co., is a rubber hydrochloride made by saturating the rubber molecule with hydrochloric acid. It is made into transparent sheet wrapping material which heat-seals at 105 to 130°C, or is used as a coating material for fabrics and paper. It gives a tough, flexible, water-resistant film. **Pliolite,** of this company, is a cyclized rubber made by highly chlorinating the rubber. It is used in insulating compounds, adhesives, and protective paints. It is soluble in hydrocarbons, but is resistant to acids and alkalies. **Pliowax** is this material compounded with paraffin or ceresin wax. **Pliolite S-1** is this material made from synthetic rubber. **Dartex** and **Alloprene** are German chlorinated rubbers, and **Rulahyde** is Dutch. Resistant fibers have also been made from chlorinated rubbers.

Tensolite, of the Tensolite Corp., for filter cloth, was one of these. **Betacote 95,** of Essex Chemical Corp., is a maintenance paint for chemical processing plants which is based on chlorinated rubber. It adheres to metals, cements, and wood and is rapid-drying; the coating is resistant to acids, alkalis, and solvents.

Cyclized rubber can be made by heating rubber with sulfonyl chloride or with **chlorostannic acid,** $H_2SnCl_6 \cdot 6H_2O$. It contains about 92% of rubber hydrocarbons, and has the long straight chains of natural rubber joined together with a larger ring-shaped structure. The molecule is less saturated than ordinary natural rubber, and the material is tougher. It is thermoplastic, somewhat similar to gutta percha or balata, and makes a good adhesive. The specific gravity is 1.06, softening point 80 to 100°C, and tensile strength up to 4,500 psi. It has been used in adhesives for bonding rubbers to metals, and for waterproofing paper.

CHLORINE. An elementary material, symbol Cl, which at ordinary temperatures is a gas, Cl_2, but which is marketed in pressure cylinders as a liquid. Its name comes from its greenish-yellow color. It occurs in nature in great abundance in combinations, in such compounds as common salt. It has a powerful suffocating odor, and is strongly corrosive to organic tissues and to metals. During the First World War it was used as a poison gas under the name of **Bertholite.** An important use for liquid chlorine is for bleaching textiles and paper pulp, but it is also used for the manufacture of many chemicals. For bleaching, it is also widely employed in the form of compounds easily broken up. **Chlorine dioxide,** ClO_2, is a reddish-yellow gas which is more than twice as effective as a bleach as chlorine, but it is unstable and must be made just before use, from chlorine and sodium chlorite. The other two oxides of chlorine are also unstable. **Chlorine monoxide,** or **hypochlorous anhydride,** Cl_2O, is a highly explosive gas. **Chlorine heptoxide,** or **perchloric anhydride,** Cl_2O_7, is an explosive liquid. The **chlorinating agents,** therefore, are largely limited to the more stable compounds. Dry chlorines are used in cleansing powders and for detinning steel, where the by-product is tin tetrachloride.

Chlorine may be made by the electrolysis of common salt. The specific gravity of the gas is 3.214, or 2.486 times heavier than air. The boiling point is -33.6°C, and the gas becomes liquid at atmospheric pressure at a temperature of -24.48°F. The vapor pressure ranges from 39.4 lb at 0°C to 602.4 lb at 100°C. The gas is an irritant and not a cumulative poison, but breathing large amounts destroys the tissues. Commercial chlorine is produced in making caustic soda, by treatment of salt with nitric acid, and as a by-product in the production of magnesium metal from sea water or brines.   The chlorine yield is from 1.8 to 2.7 times the weight of the magnesium produced.

CHLOROPHYLL. A complex chemical which constitutes the green coloring matter of plants and the chief agent of their growth.   It is obtained from the leaves and other parts of plants by solvent extraction and is used as a food color and as a purifying agent.   When extracted from alfalfa by hexane and acetone, 50 tons of alfalfa yields 400 lb of chlorophyll.   A higher yield is obtained in California from the cull leaves of lettuce.   It is one of the most interesting of chemicals, and is a sunlight-capturing, food-making agent in plants.   It has the empirical formula $C_{55}H_{72}O_5N_4Mg$, having a complex ring structure with **pyrrole,** $(CH:CH)_2NH$, as its chief building block, and a single magnesium atom in the center.   It is designated as a **magnesium-porphyrin** complex.   The **iron-porphyrin** complex, **hematin,** of blood, is the same structure with iron replacing magnesium.   The **vanadium-porphyrin** complex of fishes and cold-blooded animals, and found also in petroleum, is the same thing with vanadium replacing the magnesium.   Under the influence of sunlight and the pyrrole complex, carbon dioxide unites with water to produce formaldehyde and oxygen, and enables plant and animal bodies to produce carbohydrates and proteins.   Failure of the pyrrole ring to link up with NH, connecting with sulfur instead, completely suspends the functioning of the blood.

Chlorophyll is obtained as a crystalline powder soluble in alcohol and melting at 183°C.   It combines with carbon dioxide of the air to form formaldehyde which is active for either oxidation or reduction of impurities existent in the air, changing such gases to methanol, formic acid, or carbonic acid.   It is thus used in household air-purifying agents such as **Air Wick** and **Wizard Wick.**   In plants, some of the formaldehyde is given off to purify the air, but most of it is condensed in the plant to form **glycollic aldehyde,** $HOCH_2CHO$, the simplest carbohydrate, and also **glyceric aldehyde,** another simple carbohydrate.   Although chlorophyll is used as an odor-destroying agent in cosmetics and foods, its action when taken into the human body in quantity in its nascent state is not fully understood, and the magnesium in the complex is capable of replacing the iron in the blood complex.

The **porphyrins,** each having a nucleus of 4 pyrrole rings and a distinctive metal such as the magnesium of the chlorophyll of plants, are termed pigments in medicine, and the disease of unbalance of porphyrin in human blood is called porphyria.   In addition to photosynthesis they have catalytic and chelating actions and may be considered as the chief growth agents in plant and animal life.   For example, the **zinc porphyrin** of the eye is formed in the liver, and a lack of supply to the fluid of the eye may cause loss of vision.

Pyrrole can be obtained from coal tar and from bone oil, or can be made synthetically, and is used in the production of fine chemicals. **Pyrrolidine,** used as a stabilizer of acid materials and as a catalyst, is a water-soluble liquid, $(CH_2CH_2)_2NH$, made by the hydrogenation of pyrrole, or by treating tetrahydro furan with ammonia. **Polyvinyl pyrrolidine,** $H_2C \cdot H_2C \cdot NH \cdot CH_2 \cdot CH_2$, is a cyclic secondary amine made from formaldehyde and acetylene. It is used as a supplementary blood plasma, and for making fine chemicals. Small amounts are added to fruit beverages such as prune juice, as a color stabilizer. It combines with the phenols which cause the oxidation, and the combination can be filtered off.

Chelating agents, used for eliminating undesirable metal ions in water solutions, for increasing color intensity in organic dyes, and for treating water and organic acids, are chemically similar to chlorophyll in having a single polyvalent metal ion surrounded by straight-chain carboxylic or amino compounds in a ring structure, but are unlike chlorophyll in that their metal-alkyl linkage depends on electron resonance instead of electron sharing. The **Versenes,** of Versenes, Inc., are chelating agents used in agriculture to correct iron deficiency and stimulate plant growth. In medicine they are used to remove poisonous lead or mercury from the blood. The **Mullapons,** of the General Aniline & Film Corp., are chelating agents. **Potassium acid saccharate,** $HOOC(CHOH)_4COOK$, is marketed by the Sanders Chemical Co. as a chelating agent for metal cleaning and plating solutions.

CHROME-MOLYBDENUM STEEL. Any alloy steel containing chromium and molybdenum as the predominating alloying elements. Chromium gives hardness and toughness to the steel, while molybdenum improves the forging and machining properties and increases the strength. Chrome-molybdenum, or chromium-molybdenum, steels are noted for high strength and toughness. Only small amounts of alloying elements are used in the standard steels. A chrome-molybdenum steel used for airplane tubing contains 0.80 to 1.10% chromium, 0.15 to 0.25 molybdenum, 0.40 to 0.60 manganese, and 0.25 to 0.35 carbon. It has a tensile strength of 95,000 psi min, with elongation 10%, and is slightly air-hardening. It draws well, and tubes with a wall thickness of only 0.035 in. are made. Molybdenum adds red hardness to steel to a greater degree than tungsten, and the amounts used in these steels are sufficient to make them slightly red-hard and air-hardening. **SAE steel 4140,** which has the same composition as the airplane tubing but with 0.40% carbon, has a tensile strength up to 260,000 psi, elongation 8%, and Brinell hardness 490 when oil-quenched and drawn. This type of steel, with 0.30% carbon, **AISI steel**

4130, is used for structural parts where welding is to be done. The chrome-molybdenum steels marketed by the Crucible Steel Co. under the name of **Almo steel** for automotive and ordnance work have tensile strengths up to 167,000 psi, with elongation 18%. **Croloy 2,** of the Babcock & Wilcox Co., used for boiler tubes for high-pressure superheated steam, contains 2% chromium and 0.50 max molybdenum, and is for temperatures to 1150°F. **Croloy 5** has 5% chromium and 0.50 max molybdenum, for temperatures to 1200°F and higher pressures. **Croloy 7** has 7% chromium and 0.50 molybdenum.

Chrome-molybdenum steels, with high carbon, have great resistance to wear at high heat, and are used for die blocks for forging. **Cromo steel,** of the Michigan-Standard Alloy Casting Co., is a cast steel with a strength of 100,000 psi and elongation 15 to 25%, used for large die blocks. **Albor die steel,** of Wm. Jessop & Sons, Inc., used for dies for stamping hard metals, contains 0.90% chromium, 0.30 molybdenum, and 0.90 carbon. It is tough and deep-hardening. **Atlas No. 93,** of the Allegheny Ludlum Steel Co., is a shock-resistant steel with 0.65% chromium, 0.35 molybdenum, and 0.55 carbon.

Chrome-molybdenum steels air-harden from a relatively low temperature, about 1550° F, thus minimizing distortion, and since they are less costly than most tool steels, are often used in modified compositions for tools and strong forgings. **Lo-Air steel,** of the Universal Cyclops Steel Corp., contains 1.35% molybdenum, 1 chromium, 2 manganese, 0.30 silicon, and 0.70 carbon. It hardens to about Rockwell C62, and when tempered to Rockwell C58 has a tensile strength of about 300,000 psi with elongation of 1%. **Hi Shock 60 steel,** of Carpenter Technology, for punches, hobs, coining dies, and shear blades, contains 1% molybdenum, 1 chromium, 2.5 copper, 0.5 nickel, 0.5 manganese, 0.3 silicon, 0.15 vanadium, and 0.68 carbon. It has high strength and toughness. **Lesco BG 41 steel,** of the Latrobe Steel Co., used to replace stainless-steel Type 440C for aircraft engine parts where high-compression stresses at temperatures above 800°F are encountered, has 14.5% chromium, 4 molybdenum, 0.30 manganese, 0.30 silicon, and 1.10 carbon. At 800°F the hardness is Rockwell C58, and it is above Rockwell C50 at 1000°F, while the hardness of **AISI Type 440C steel** falls off rapidly at 800°F. This latter steel contains about 17% chromium, 0.75 molybdenum, 0.5 nickel, 1 manganese, 1 silicon, and 1 carbon. Chrome-molybdenum steels with carbon to 1% are used for castings for bucket lips, crusher parts, and other heavy-duty parts. They have tensile strengths up to 150,000 psi, with elongation 12 to 14%.

CHROME-VANADIUM STEEL. A chromium alloy steel containing a small amount of vanadium which has the effect of intensifying the action of the chromium and the manganese in the steel. It also aids in the formation of carbides, hardening the alloy, and also increasing the ductility by the deoxidizing effect. The amount of vanadium is usually 0.15 to 0.25%. These steels are valued where a combination of strength and ductility is desired. They resemble those with chromium alone, with the advantage of the homogenizing influence of the vanadium. A chrome-vanadium steel having 0.92% chromium, 0.20 vanadium, and 0.25 carbon has a tensile strength of 100,000 psi, and when heat-treated has a strength up to 150,000 psi and elongation 16%. Chrome-vanadium steels are used for such parts as crankshafts, propeller shafts, and locomotive frames. High-carbon chrome-vanadium steels are the mild-alloy tool steels of high strength, toughness, and fatigue resistance. The chromium content is usually about 0.80%, with 0.20 vanadium, and with carbon up to 1%. **Milwaloy,** of the Milwaukee Steel Foundry Co., is a casting steel. Grade 7 contains 1.5 to 1.75% chromium, 0.60 to 0.70 vanadium, and 0.30 to 0.50 carbon. It is used for high-strength parts.

Many high-alloy steels also contain some vanadium, but where the vanadium is used as a cleansing and toughening element and not to give the chief characteristics to the steel, these alloys are not classed as chrome-vanadium steel. **H.Y.C.C. steel** of the Crucible Steel Co., for example, is an oil-hardening steel of high wear resistance containing 12% chromium and 2.25 carbon with 0.25 vanadium. It is a hard, deep-hardening steel for dies. Some modified chrome-vanadium steels for high-temperature, high-strength parts are in the class of tool steels except that they may have less carbon. **Viscount 44,** of the Latrobe Steel Co., contains 5% chromium, 1 vanadium, 1.2 molybdenum, 1 silicon, 0.75 manganese, 0.40 carbon, and a small percentage of sulfides to give free machining. The tensile strength is 200,000 psi, elongation 12%, and Rockwell hardness C45. **Vascojet 1000,** of the Vanadium Alloy Steel Co., also for heat-resistant parts, contains 5% chromium, 1.3 molybdenum, 0.5 vanadium, and 0.4 carbon. The tensile strength is 285,000 psi with elongation of 8%.

CHROMIC ACID. A name given to the red, crystalline, strongly acid material of the composition CrO_3 known also as **chromium trioxide** or as **chromic anhydride.** It is in reality not the acid until dissolved in water, forming a true chromic acid of the composition H_2CrO_4. It is marketed in the form of porous lumps. The specific gravity is 2.70, melting point 196°C. It is produced by treating sodium or potassium dichromate with sulfuric acid. The dust is irritating, and the fumes of the solutions are injurious to the nose and throat as the acid is a powerful oxidizing agent. Chromic acid is used in chromium-plating baths, for etching copper, in electric batteries, and in tanning leather. **Chromous chloride,** $CrCl_2$, is used as an oxygen absorbent and for chromizing steel. **Chromic chloride,**

$CrCl_3$, is a volatile white powder used for tanning and as a mordant, for flame metalizing, and in alloying steel powders.

Chrome oxide green is a **chromic oxide** in the form of dry powder or ground in oil, used in paints and lacquers and for coloring rubber. It is a bright-green, crystalline powder of the composition Cr_2O_3, with specific gravity 5.20 and melting point 1990°C, insoluble in water. The dry powder has a Cr_2O_3 content of 97% min, and is 325 mesh. The paste contains 85% pigment and 15 linseed oil. Chrome oxide green is not as bright in color as chrome green but is more permanent.

CHROMITE. An ore of the metal chromium, called **chrome ore** when used as a refractory. It is found in the United States, chiefly in California and Oregon, but most of the commercial production is in South Africa, Rhodesia, Cuba, Turkey, the Philippines, Greece, and New Caledonia. The theoretical composition is $FeO \cdot Cr_2O_3$, with 68% chromic oxide, but pure **iron chromate** is rare. Part of the iron may be replaced by magnesium, and part of the chromium by aluminum. The silica present in the ore, however, is not a part of the molecule. Chromite is commonly massive granular, and the commercial ores contain only from 35 to 60% chromic oxide. The hardness is 5.5 and the specific gravity 4.6. The color is iron black to brownish black, with a metallic luster. The melting point is about 3900°F, but when mixed with binders as a refractory the fusion point is lowered. New Caledonia ore has 50% chromic oxide, Turkish ore averages 48 to 53%, Brazilian ore runs 46 to 48%, and Cuban ore averages only 35%. The high-grade Guleman ore of Turkey contains 52% Cr_2O_3, 14 Al_2O_3, 10.4 FeO, 4.4 Fe_2O_3, 16 magnesia, and 2.5 silica. Most of the domestic ore in the United States is low grade.

Cuban ore is rich in spinel and deficient in magnetite, and this type is adapted for refractory use even when the chromic oxide is low. Ore from Baluchistan is also valued for refractory use, as are other hard lumpy ores high in Al_2O_3 and low in iron. For chemical use the ores should have more than 45% chromic oxide and not more than 8 silica, and should be low in sulfur. Metallurgical ore should have not less than 48% chromic oxide, and the ratio of chromium to iron should not be less than 3:1. Chromite is used for the production of chromium and ferro chromium, in making **chromite bricks** and refractory linings for furnaces, and for the production of chromium salts and chemicals. For bricks the ground chromite is mixed with lime and clay and burned. Chromite refractories are neutral and are resistant to slag attack. A chrome-ore high-temperature cement marketed by the General Refractories Co. under the name of **Grefco** has a fusion point of 3400°F.

CHROMIUM. An elementary metal, symbol Cr, used in stainless steels, heat-resistant alloys, high-strength alloy steels, for wear-resistant electroplating, and in its compounds for pigments, chemicals, and refractories. The specific gravity is 6.92, melting point 2750° F, and boiling point 3992°F. The color is silvery white with a bluish tinge. It is an extremely hard metal, the electrodeposited plates having a hardness of 9 Mohs. It is resistant to oxidation, is inert to nitric acid, but dissolves in hydrochloric acid and slowly in sulfuric acid. At temperatures above 1500°F it is subject to an intergranular corrosion known as **green rot.**

Chromium occurs in nature only in combination. Its chief ore is chromite, from which it is obtained by reduction and electrolysis. It is marketed for use principally in the form of master alloys with iron or copper. The term **chromium metal** usually indicates a pure grade of chromium containing 99% or more of chromium. A grade marketed by the Shieldalloy Corp. has 99.25% min chromium, with 0.40 max iron and 0.15 max silicon. **High-carbon chromium** has 86% min chromium and 8 to 11% carbon with no more than 0.5% each of iron and silicon. **Isochrome** is a name given by the Battelle Memorial Institute for chromium metal, 99.99% pure, made by the reduction of chromium iodide. Chromium metal is used for making alloys, particularly resistance metals, and for chemical use, in which case it comes as a fine powder. Nozzles and tubing for jet engines are extruded from pure chromium powder. But chromium metal lacks ductility and is susceptible to nitrogen embrittlement, and is not used as a structural metal requiring flexural strength. **Chromium plating** is widely used where extreme hardness or resistance to corrosion is required. When plated on a highly polished metal, it gives a smooth surface that has no capillary attraction to water or oil, and chromium-plated bearing surfaces can be run without oil. For decorative purposes chromium plates as thin as 0.0002 in. may be used; for wear resistance, plates up to 0.050 in. are used. Increased hardness and wear resistance in the plate are obtained by alloying 1% molybdenum with the chromium. **Alphatized steel,** of the Alloy Surfaces Co., is steel coated with chromium by a diffusion process. The deposited chromium combines with the iron of the steel and forms an adherent alloy rather than a plate. Less penetration is obtained on high-carbon steels, but the coating is harder.

CHROMIUM CAST IRON. Cast iron containing chromium as the chief alloying element. It is used where hardness and high strength are required. Chromium in cast iron is a carbide-forming element. The free carbides begin to form in the iron at about 0.60% chromium. Small amounts of chromium refine the graphite structure, but at about 1% chromium content, the cementite builds up rapidly. At about 3% chromium, the graphite disappears and the matrix consists of oriented cementite. At 5% chromium, there is much massive carbide in the structure. Chromium also prevents the decomposition of iron silicide, and unless modified with other alloying elements the iron may reach a hardness of 700 Brinell.   Usually, nickel is used in combination with chromium to balance the chromium by acting as a graphitizer and preventing the formation of hard carbide spots. The proportion of nickel to chromium is generally about 3 to 1.   **Ni-Hard,** of the International Nickel Co., is a chromium-nickel white iron containing 4 to 6% nickel and 1 to 1.25 chromium.   It is tough, and when chilled has a surface hardness up to 700 Brinell.   For greater wear resistance it may contain manganese up to 1.5%.   Sometimes very high carbon is used in these irons for wear resistance.   **Flintmetal,** of the Taylor-Wharton Iron &.Steel Co., contains 4 to 4.5% nickel, 1.25 to 1.75 chromium, and 3 to 3.5 carbon.   It has a Brinell hardness of 600.   Chromium cast irons are used for automotive body dies, rolls, and various wear-resistant castings, but most of them are high in nickel and are classified with the nickel-chromium irons.   **Chromium-molybdenum irons** are white irons with a martensitic structure.   They combine high wear resistance with strength and toughness.   **Climax 15-3,** of the Climax Molybdenum Co., has a nominal composition of 15% chromium, 3 molybdenum, and 3 to 4 carbon. Its hardness is Rockwell C55.

CHROMIUM COPPER.   A name applied to master alloys of copper with chromium used in the foundry for introducing chromium into nonferrous alloys, or to **copper-chromium alloys,** or **chrome copper,** which are high-copper alloys containing a small amount of chromium with or without other alloying elements.   When they also contain tin, silicon, or iron, they may be referred to as **chromium bronze.**   A chromium-copper master alloy marketed under the name of **Electromet chromium copper** by the Electro Metallurgical Sales Corp. contains 8 to 11% chromium, 88 to 90 copper, and a maximum of 1 iron and 0.50 silicon.   Chrome copper in wrought form has high impact strength, and the electrical conductivity is higher than when the copper is hardened with silicon.   Chrome copper with 0.50% chromium has a thermal conductivity about 85% that of high-conductivity copper, which is about twice that of aluminum alloy, or seven times that of cast iron.   A wrought chrome copper of the American Brass Co. contains 0.85% chromium and 0.10 silicon, and has a tensile strength of 92,000 psi with elongation 3%.   Chromium bronze, used for bearings, is a cast metal containing 1% chromium, 1 iron, and from 2 to 10 tin.   It has high strength and good wearing qualities.   **Kumium,** of the Imperial Chemical Industries, Ltd., is a copper-chromium alloy containing a high percentage of chromium, used for electrodes for spot-welding machines. It retains its hardness and conductivity at 400°C.   **Copper alloy PD-135** of the Phelps Dodge Corp. is oxygen-free copper with small percentages of chromium and cadmium and is a **chromium-cadmium bronze.**   The extruded metal has a tensile strength of 36,000 psi and an electrical conductivity 60% that of copper.   It can be cold-worked and heat-treated to strengths up to 80,000 psi and will retain its strength to above 1000°F. It is used for electrical switches and contacts, high-flex wire and springs, and commutator bars.

CHROMIUM STEEL. Any steel containing chromium as the predominating alloying element may be termed chromium steel, but the name alone usually means the hard, wear-resisting steels that derive the property chiefly from the chromium content.   Chromium combines with the carbon of steel to form a hard chromium carbide, and it restricts graphitization. When other carbide-forming elements are present, double or complex carbides are formed.   Chromium refines the structure, gives deep-hardening, increases the elastic limit, and gives a slight red-hardness so that the steels retain their hardness at more elevated temperatures.   Chromium steels have great resistance to wear.   They also withstand quenching in oil or water without much deformation.   Up to about 2% chromium may be included in tool steels to add hardness, wear resistance, and nondeforming qualities.   When the chromium is high, the carbon may be much higher than in ordinary steels without making the steel brittle.   Steels with 12 to 17% chromium and about 2.5 carbon have remarkable wear-resisting qualities and are used for cold-forming dies for hard metals, for broaches, and for rolls.   However, chromium narrows the hardening range of steels unless balanced with nickel.   Such steels also work-harden rapidly unless modified with other elements.   The high-chromium steels are corrosion-resistant and heat-resistant but are not to be confused with the high-chromium stainless steels which are low in carbon, although the nonnickel Type 400 stainless steels are very definitely chromium steels.   Thus, the term is indefinite but may be restricted to the high-chromium steels used for dies, and to those with lower chromium used for wear-resistant parts such as ball bearings.

Carbide precipitation occurs in chromium-nickel steels at 800 to 1550°F, and the carbon in solution precipitates out at the grain boundaries, making the alloy brittle and susceptible to corrosion.   Thus, chromium-nickel steels must be kept low in carbon, or modified with a powerful carbide-forming element such as columbium.   Chromium steels are not corrosion-resistant unless the chromium content is at least 4%.   Plain chromium steels with more than 10% chromium are corrosion-resistant even at elevated temperatures and are in the class of stainless steels, but are difficult to weld because of the formation of hard brittle martensite along the weld.

Chromium steels with about 1% chromium are used for gears and shafts. **Uma steel No. 1,** of the Republic Steel Corp., has 0.55 to 0.75% chromium, 0.35 to 0.65 manganese, and 0.15 carbon.   It is a case-hardening gear steel.   **Uma No. 5** has 0.85 to 1.10% chromium, 0.70 to 0.90 manganese, and 0.50 carbon. It is deep-hardening, with a tensile strength up to 135,000 psi, and is used for transmission gears. This type of steel with higher carbon is deep-hardening and has high compression strength and is used for ball and roller bearings. However, **ball-bearing steel** derives many of its characteristics from the heat treatment. A good ball-bearing steel is one that has uniform undissolved carbides in a matrix of martensite and a Rockwell C hardness of 60 to 64 when quenched in oil and stress-relieved. **Teton steel,** of the Allegheny Ludlum Steel Corp., has 1.25% chromium and 1 carbon, and is used for ball bearings and hard wear-resistant parts. **Bower 315 alloy,** of Federal-Mogul Bower Bearings, Inc., for jet-engine bearings, when carbonized and heat-treated, has a Rockwell C hardness of 58, and will recover its hardness after being exposed to high temperatures. It contains only 1.5% chromium, with 3% nickel, 5 molybdenum, 0.5 manganese, 0.3 silicon, and up to 0.15 carbon. **Vac-Arc Regent steel,** of the Latrobe Steel Co., for high-duty aircraft bearings, has 1.5% chromium, 1 carbon, 0.35 manganese, and 0.3 silicon. It is tempered at 400°F to a hardness of Rockwell C60.

Chromium steels with 3 to 4.5% chromium and 0.80 to 1 carbon are used for dies for hot pressing and forging. **EB alloy,** of the Allegheny Ludlum Steel Corp., has 3.75% chromium, 0.55 vanadium, 0.70 molybdenum, and 0.65 carbon. Another hot-work steel of this company is **Potomac steel** with 5% chromium, 1.75 molybdenum, 1.25 tungsten, and 0.32 carbon. **Uniloy chrome steel,** of the Universal-Cyclops Steel Corp., contains 4 to 6% chromium, 0.1 to 0.25 carbon, up to 0.60 manganese, with either molybdenum 0.40 to 0.60%, or tungsten 1 to 1.25%. A small amount of tungsten, or a smaller amount of molybdenum, refines the grain, increases the elastic limit, and makes the steel more resistant to corrosion at elevated temperatures. **Cyclops 62 steel,** of the same company, for shears, blanking dies, and extrusion rolls, has 3.5% chromium, 2.25 molybdenum, 1.25 vanadium, 1 silicon, 0.55 manganese, and 1 carbon. When air-cooled and tempered it has a tensile strength of 352,000 psi with elongation of 1%. **HWD No. 1 steel,** of Firth Sterling, Inc., for hot-forging dies, has 5% chromium, 1.55 molybdenum, 1.4 tungsten, 1 silicon, 0.3 vanadium, 0.4 manganese, and 0.35 carbon. It is air-hardening, or can be oil-quenched to Rockwell C53 and tempered to as low as Rockwell C40. A variation of this steel, **HWD No. 2 steel,** for die-casting dies and aluminum extrusion dies, has 5.25% chromium, 1.35 molybdenum, 0.5 vanadium, 1 silicon, 0.4 manganese, and 0.38 carbon. It is resistant to softening and to heat checking. Air cooling and long-time tempering to about Rockwell C48 give long wear life in die-casting dies. The **chromium-tungsten steels** are employed where resistance to hot chemicals or petroleum is required, but the steels with high tungsten are usually classed as tungsten steel regardless of the amount of chromium. A steel used for high-strength resistant castings is **Circle L-10** of the Lebanon Steel Foundry. It contains 5.5% chromium, 0.50 molybdenum, 0.65 manganese, 0.40 silicon, and 0.20 carbon. When heat-treated it has a tensile strength of 100,000 psi and elongation 20%. **Nicroman** is an all-purpose tool steel of Henry Disston & Sons, Inc., 1% chromium, 1.65 nickel, 0.35 copper, and 0.70 carbon. **G.S.N. steel,** of this company, is a high-chromium, high-carbon die steel. **Nilstain steel,** of the Wilber B. Driver Co., for spring wire, is an 18-8 steel with 2% manganese and 1 silicon.

A wear-resistant die steel, marketed by Carpenter Technology under the name of **Hampden steel,** contains 12.5% chromium, 0.25 nickel, 0.25 manganese, and 2.1 carbon. It is deep-hardening, has high compressive strength, and is valued for forming rolls and spinning tools. A similar-purpose tool steel with air-hardening properties is **Carpenter No. 610.** It has 12% chromium, 1.5 carbon, 0.80 molybdenum, 0.20 vanadium, and 0.30 manganese. **Huron steel,** of the Allegheny Ludlum Steel Corp., is a wear-resistant steel having 12.5% chromium, 1 vanadium, and 2 carbon. It is used for dies. **O-Hi-O** steel, of the Vanadium Alloys Steel Co., is an air-hardening die steel having 12% chromium, 1.55 carbon, 0.85 vanadium, 0.40 cobalt, and 0.80 manganese. This company also produces **Crocar,** a wear-resistant steel with similar composition but with 2.2% carbon, and **Vasco 1741 CVM,** for high-temperature bearings, pump parts, and seal rings which contains 17% chromium, 4 molybdenum, 1 vanadium, 0.30 manganese, 0.20 silicon, and 1.30 carbon. It retains a hardness of about Rockwell C60 at 1000°F. **Cromovan steel,** of Firth Sterling, Inc., contains 12% chromium, 1 vanadium, 1 molybdenum, and 1.55 carbon. It is a nondeforming, wear-resistant die steel, also used for equipment parts requiring high abrasion resistance, such as brick-mold liners. The hardness ranges from 42 to 64 Rockwell C, depending on the tempering. **Cromovan F.M.** is this steel with 0.12% sulfur to give improved machinability and better surface finish.

CINCHONA. The hard, thick, grayish bark of a number of species of evergreen trees of the genus *Cinchona,* native to the Andes from Mexico to Peru but now grown in many tropical countries chiefly as a source of quinine. The small tree *Remijia pendunculata* also contains 3% quinine in the bark, and quinine occurs in small quantities in other plants and fruits, notably the grapefruit. **Cinchona bark** was originally used by the Quechua Indians of Peru in powdered form and was called **loxa bark.** It derives its present name from the fact that in 1630 the Countess of Cinchon was cured of the fever by its use. In Europe it became known as **Peruvian bark** and **Jesuits' bark.** **Quinine** is one of the most important drugs as a specific for malaria and as a tonic. It is also used as a denaturant for alcohol as it has an extremely bitter taste. Metallic salts of quinine are used in plastics to give fluorescence and glow under ultraviolet light. Quinine is a colorless crystalline alkaloid of the composition $C_{20}H_{24}O_2N_2 \cdot 3H_2O$. It is soluble with difficulty in water, and is marketed in the form of the more soluble **quinine sulfate,** a white powder of the composition $(C_{20}H_{24}O_2N_2)$ $H_2SO_4 \cdot 2H_2O$. **Quinine bisulfate** has the same composition but with 7 molecules of water. During the Second World War **quinine hydrochloride** was preferred by the Navy. It contains 81.7% quinine compared with 74% in the sulfate and is more soluble in water but has a more bitter taste. **Synthetic quinine** can be made, but is more expensive. **Atabrine,** of I. G. Farbenindustrie, is **quinacrine hydrochloride.** It is not a complete substitute, is toxic, and is a dye that colors the skin when taken internally. **Primaquine,** of Winthrop-Stearns, Inc., is an 8-amino quinoline, and as an antimalarial is less toxic than other synthetics. In Germany, copper arsenite has been used as an effective substitute for quinine. The **maringin** of grapefruit is similar to quinine, and in tropical areas where grapefruit is consumed regularly the incidence of malaria is rare.

The bark of the tree *C. ledgeriana* yields above 7% of quinine but it is not a robust tree and in cultivation is grafted on the tree *C. succirubra* which is hardy but yields only 2 to 3% quinine. Ledgeriana trees on plantations in Mindanao and in Peru yield as high as 13% total alkaloids from the bark. Most of the world production is from the *C. officinalis* and *C. calisaya,* which are variations of *C. ledgeriana,* or **yellow bark.** The **red bark,** *C. succirubra,* is grown in India. The trees are grown from seeds, which are small, 75,000 to the ounce. The peak gathering of bark is 10 years after planting of the 2-year seedlings, and the trees are uprooted to obtain bark from both trunk and root. An 8-year-old tree yields 4 kilos of bark, and a 25-year tree yields 20 kilos but of inferior quality. The bark is dried and ground to powder for the solvent extraction of the alkaloids. Besides quinine the bark contains about 30 other alkaloids, chief of which are **cinchonidine, quinidine,** and **cinchonine. Totaquina** is the drug containing all the alkaloids. It is cheaper than extracted quinine, is effective against malaria, and is a better tonic. Quinidine has the same formula as quinine but is of right polarization instead of left. It is used for heart ailments. Cinchonine, $C_{19}H_{22}ON_2$, has right polarization and is 13 times more soluble in water than quinine sulfate. Cinchonidine has the same formula, but has left polarization. **Australian quinine,** or **alstonia,** is not true quinine. It is from **dita bark,** the bark of the tree *Alstonia scholaris* of Australia, and is used as a febrifuge. It contains the water-soluble alkaloid **ditiane,** $C_{22}H_{28}O_4N_2$, and the water-insoluble alkaloid **ditamine,** $C_{16}H_{19}O_2N$. **Fagarine,** used as a substitute for quinidine for heart flutter, is extracted from the leaves of the tree *Fagara coco* of northern Argentina. **Chang shan,** used as an antimalarial in China, is the root of the plant *Dichroa febrifuga.* It contains the alkaloid **febrifugine.**

CINNABAR. The chief ore of the metal mercury.   As a pigment it was originally called **minium,** a name now applied to red lead.   It is a **mercuric sulfide,** HgS, which when pure contains 86.2% mercury.   The ores are usually poor, the best ones containing only about 7% mercury, and the average Italian ore having only 1.1% Hg and American ore yielding only 0.5%.   The chief production is in Italy, Spain, Mexico, and the United States.   Cinnabar has a massive granular structure with a hardness of 2 to 2.5, a specific gravity of about 8, and usually a dull earthy luster.   It is brownish red in color, from which it derives the name **liver ore.   Chinese cinnabar** is ground as a fine scarlet pigment for inks.   Cinnabar is not smelted, the extraction process being one of distillation, made possible by the low boiling point of the metal.   Another ore of mercury found in Mexico is **livingstonite,** $2Sb_2S_3 \cdot HgS$.   It is a massive, red-streaked mineral of specific gravity 4.81 and hardness 2.   **Calomel,** a minor ore in Spain, is a white crystalline mineral of the composition Hg_2Cl_2 with a specific gravity of 6.5.   It is also called **horn mercury.**   It is used in medicine as a purgative, but is poisonous if retained in the system.   The ore found in Colorado and known as **coloradoite** is a **mercuric telluride,** HgTe.   It has an iron-black color and a specific gravity of 8.   **Tiemanite,** found in California and Utah, is a **mercuric selenide,** HgSe, having a lead-gray color and a specific gravity of 8.2.   There are more than 20 minerals classed as **mercury ores.**

CINNAMON. The thin, yellowish-brown highly aromatic bark of the tropical evergreen laurel tree *Cinnamomum zeylanicum,* of Ceylon and southeast Asia.   It is used as a spice, as a flavor in confectionery, perfumery, and medicine.   The bark is marketed in rolls or sticks packed in bales of 112 lb.   **Cassia** is the bark from the *C. cassia* of South China. **Saigon cinnamon,** *C. loureirii,* is cinnamon, but is not as thin or as smooth a bark, and it does not have as fine an aroma and flavor.   **Cassia buds** are small dried flowers of the *C. cassia,* used ground as a spice, or for the production of oil.   They resemble cloves in appearance, and have an agreeable spicy odor and sweet warm taste.   **Cinnamon oil, cinnamon leaf oil,** and **cassia oil** are essential oils distilled, respectively, from the bark, leaf, and bud.   They are used in flavoring, medicine, and perfumery.   Cinnamon oil contains about 70% **cinnamic aldehyde,** 8 to 10% eugenol, and also pinene and linalol.   The specific gravity is 1.03, and the refractive index 1.565 to 1.582.   The pale-yellow color darkens with age.   Cinnamic aldehyde is also made synthetically.   **Flasolee,** of the J. Hilary Herchelroth Co., is **amyl cinnamic aldehyde,** redistilled to remove the unpleasant odor of heptyl aldehyde, for use in perfumes.   The leaf oil is used as a substitute for clove oil.   About 1.9% oil is obtained from cassia buds, but it lacks the delicate fragrance of cinnamon oil.   **Nikkel oil,** a bright-yellow liquid with an odor of lemon and cinnamon, is distilled from the leaves and twigs of the tree *C. laureirii* of Japan. It contains citral and cineol, and is used in perfumery. Some of the cinnamon marketed in the United States is **Padang cassia,** from the tree *C. burmannii* of Indonesia. It does not have the delicate aroma of true cinnamon.

CLOVES. The dried flower buds of the evergreen tree *Caryophillus aromaticus,* grown chiefly in Zanzibar, but also in Malagasy, East Africa, and Indonesia. The buds yield 15 to 19% of a pungent yellowish essential oil, **clove oil,** also called **caryophil oil** and **amboyna.** It contains 85% **eugenol,** and also the terpene **clovene,** $C_{15}H_{24}$. Clove oil is used in medicine as an antiseptic, in toothpastes, in flavoring, and for the production of artificial vanilla. Eugenol is a viscous phenol-type liquid. It is also the basis for carnation-type perfumes. **Clove buds** are chiefly valued as a highly aromatic spice. Lower-grade **Zanzibar cloves** containing only about 5% oil are used in the strootjes cigarettes of Indonesia, in a mixture of 75% tobacco and 25 cloves. Ground clove is also an efficient antioxidant, and is sometimes used in lard and pork products. The clove tree attains a height up to 40 ft, bearing in 7 or 8 years, and continuing to bear for a century, yielding 8 to 10 lb of dried cloves annually. Clove stems are also aromatic, but contain only 5 to 6% oil of inferior value. Clove was one of the most valued spices of medieval times. It grew originally only on five small islands, the Moluccas, in a volcanic-ash soil, and was carried by Chinese junks and Malayan outriggers to India from whence the Arabs controlled the trade, bringing the tree also to Zanzibar. The *Victoria* of Magellan's fleet returned to San Lucar with 26 tons of cloves, enough to pay for the loss of the other four ships and the expenses of the voyage around the world.

COAL. A general name for a black mineral formed of ancient vegetable matter, and employed as a fuel and for destructive distillation to obtain gas, coke, oils, and coal-tar chemicals. Coal is composed largely of carbon with smaller amounts of hydrogen, nitrogen, oxygen, and sulfur. It was formed in various geological ages and under varying conditions, and occurs in several distinct forms. **Peat** is the first stage, followed by lignite, bituminous coal, and anthracite, with various intermediate grades. The mineral is widely distributed in many parts of the world. The value of coal for combustion purposes is judged by its fixed carbon content, volatile matter, and lack of ash. It is also graded by the size and percentage of lumps. The percentage of volatile matter declines from peat to anthracite, and the fixed carbon increases. A good grade of coal for industrial power-plant use should contain 55 to 60% fixed carbon and not exceed 8% ash. The Btu value should be 13,500 to 14,000 per lb. Finely ground coal, or **powdered coal,** is used for burning in an air blast like oil, or may be mixed with oil.   Coal in its natural state absorbs large amounts of water and also, because of impurities and irregular sizes, is not so efficient as a fuel as the **reconstructed coal** made by crushing and briquetting lignite or coal and waterproofing with a coating of pitch.   **Anthracite powder** is used as a filler in plastics.   **Carb-O-Fil,** of the Shamokin Filler Co., is powdered anthracite in a range of particle sizes used as a carbonaceous filler.   It has a plasticizing effect.   It can also be used to replace carbon black in phenolic resins.

Increasing amounts of coal are being used for the production of gas and chemicals.   By the hydrogenation of coal much greater quantities of phenols, cresols, aniline, and nitrogen-bearing amines can be obtained than by by-product coking, and low grades of coal can be used.   The finely crushed coal is slurred to a paste with oil, mixed with a catalyst, and reacted at high temperature and pressure.   **Synthesis gas,** used for producing gasoline and chemicals, is essentially a mixture of carbon monoxide and hydrogen.   It it made from low-grade coals.   The pulverized coal is fed into a high-temperature reactor with steam and a deficiency of oxygen, and the gas produced contains 40% hydrogen, 40 carbon monoxide, 15 carbon dioxide, 1 methane, and 4 inert materials.   It is also made by passing steam through a bed of incandescent coke to form a **water gas** of about equal proportions of carbon monoxide and hydrogen.   It is also made from natural gas.

COATED FABRICS.   The first coated fabric was a rubberized fabric produced in Scotland by Charles Macintosh in 1823 and known as **Mackintosh cloth** for rainwear use.   Since no method of vulcanization was then known, the cloth was made by coating two layers of fabric with rubber dissolved in naphtha and pressing them together, making a double fabric impervious to water.   **Rubberized fabrics** are made by coating fabrics, usually cotton, with compounded rubber and passing between rollers under pressure. The vulcanized coating may be no more than 0.003 in. thick, and the resultant fabric is flexible and waterproof.   But most coated fabrics are now made with synthetic rubbers or plastics, and the base fabric may be of synthetic fibers, or a thin plastic film may be laminated to the fabric.

Coated fabrics now have many uses in industrial applications, and the number of variations with different resins and backing materials is infinite. They are usually sold under trade names, and are used for upholstery, linings, rainwear, bag covers, book covers, tarpaulins, outerwear, wall coverings, window shades, gaskets, and diaphragms.   Vinyl-type resins are most commonly used, but for special purposes other resins are selected to give resistance to wear, oils, or chemicals.   The coated fabric of Reeves Bros., Inc., called **Reevecote,** for gaskets and diaphragms, is a Dacron fabric coated with Kel-F fluorocarbon resin.   An industrial sheeting of the Auburn Mfg. Co. is a cotton fabric coated with urethane rubber. It is tough, flexible, and fatigue-resistant, and gives 10 times better wear resistance than natural rubber.

Vinyl-coated fabrics are usually tough and elastic, and are low in cost, but unless specially compounded are not durable. Many plastics in the form of latex or emulsion are marketed especially for coating textiles. **Rhoplex WN-75** and **WN-80** are water dispersions of acrylic resins for this purpose. **X-Link 2833,** of the National Starch & Chemical Corp., is a vinyl-acrylic copolymer. Coatings cure at room temperature, have high heat and light stability, give softness and flexibility to the fabric, and withstand repeated dry cleaning. **Polectron,** of the General Aniline & Film Corp., is a water emulsion of a copolymer of vinyl pyrrolidone with ethyl acrylate. It forms an adherent, tough, and chemical-resistant coating. **Geon latex,** of the B. F. Goodrich Co., is a water dispersion of a polyvinyl chloride resin. Polyvinyl chloride of high molecular weight is resistant to staining, abrasion, and tearing, and is used for upholstery fabrics.

Upholstery fabrics, for furniture and automobile seat covers, have been called **imitation leather** and **leather fabrics,** but the coated fabrics are more durable, more easily cleaned, and generally lower in cost than split leathers. The base cloth may be of various weights from light sheetings to heavy ducks. They may be embossed with designs to imitate leather. The **Boltaflex cape vinyl,** of the Bolta Co., is a rayon fabric coated with a vinyl resin embossed with a leatherlike grain. It has the appearance, feel, and thickness of a split leather and, when desired, is impregnated with a leather odor. But, in general, coated fabrics are superior in service qualities to natural leather, and the materials are usually marketed by trade names on the basis of service requirements, and not as imitation leather.

One of the first of the upholstery fabrics to replace leather was **Fabrikoid,** of Du Pont. It was coated with a cellulose plastic, and was in various weights, colors, and designs, especially for automobile seating and book covers. **Armalon** is twill or sateen fabric coated with ethylene plastic for upholstery, and **Pontan** is a rubberized fabric made to imitate colored leathers. For some uses, as for draperies or industrial fabrics, the fabric is not actually coated, but is impregnated, either in the fiber or in the finished cloth, to make the fabric water-repellent, immune to insect attack, and easily cleaned. **Tontine** is a plastic-impregnated fabric for window shades. The **Fairprene fabrics,** also of Du Pont, are cotton fabrics coated with chloroprene rubber or other plastics. **Corfam,** of the same company, used as a leather substitute, is a nonwoven sheet of urethane fibers reinforced with polyester fibers, with a porous texture. The fabric can be impregnated or coated.

Pliosheen, of the Goodyear Tire & Rubber Co., is rayon fabric coated with a Chemigum type of synthetic rubber.   **Terson voile,** of the Athol Mfg. Co., for umbrellas, rainwear, and industrial linings, is a sheer-weight rayon coated with a vinyl resin.   It weighs 2 oz per yd.   **Vynside,** of the Columbia Mills, Inc., for book covers, is a heavy buckram cotton fabric coated with a vinyl resin in colors.   **Lantuck fabric,** of the Wellington Sears Co., is a nonwoven fabric with a vinyl coating which permits deeply embossed patterns for upholstery.   Coated fabrics may also be napped on the back, or coated on the back with a flock, to give a more resilient backing for upholstery.   **Kalistron,** of the U.S. Plywood Corp., has such a flock backing.

Impregnated fabrics may have only a thin, almost undetectable surface coating on the fibers to make them water-repellent and immune to bacterial attack, or they may be treated with fungicides or with flame-resistant chemicals or waterproofing resins.   **Stabilized fabrics,** however, are not waterproofed or coated, but are fabrics of cotton, linen, or wool that have been treated with a water solution of a urea-formaldehyde or other thermosetting resin to give them greater resiliency with resistance to creasing and resistance to shrinking in washing.   **Shrinkproof fabrics** are likewise not coated fabrics, but have a light impregnation of resin that usually remains only in the core of the fibers.   The fabric retains its softness, texture, and appearance, but the fibers have increased stability.   Various resin materials are marketed under trade names for creaseproofing and shrinkproofing fabrics, such as **Lanaset,** a methylo melamine resin of the American Cyanamid Co., and **Synthrez,** a methylo urea resin of Synthron, Inc.

Under the general name of **protective fabrics,** coated fabrics are now marketed by use characteristics rather than by coating designation since resin formulations vary greatly in quality.   For example, the low-cost grades of vinyl resins may be hard and brittle at low temperatures and soft and rubbery in hot weather, and thus unsuitable for all-weather tarpaulins.   Special weaves of fabric are used to give high tear strength with light weight, and the plastic may be impregnated, coated on one side or both, bonded with an adhesive or electronically bonded, or some combination of all of these.   Flame resistance and static-free qualities may also be needed.   Many companies have complete lines to meet definite needs. The **Coverlight** fabrics of Reeves Bros., Inc., which come in many thicknesses and colors, are made with specially woven fabrics of continuous filament nylon yarn with coatings of neoprene, Hypalon, or vinyl chloride resin, with weights from 6 to 22 oz per sq yd and widths up to 72 in. The **H.T.V. Coverlight** is a high-tear nylon fabric with specially formulated vinyl coating.   The 22-oz grade for such heavy-duty, all-weather uses as truck-trailer covers and concrete-curing covers has a thickness of 0.027 in. It has a tensile strength of 500×400 lb per in., a tear strength of 800 lb per in., and it remains flexible at temperatures down to $-50°$F.

COBALT. A white metal, Co, resembling nickel but with a bluish tinge instead of the yellow of nickel. Although allied to nickel, it has distinctive differences. It is more active chemically than nickel. It is dissolved by dilute sulfuric, nitric, or hydrochloric acids, and is attacked slowly by alkalies. The oxidation rate of pure cobalt is 25 times that of nickel. Its power of whitening copper alloys is inferior to that of nickel, but small amounts in nickel-copper alloys will neutralize the yellowish tinge of the nickel and make them whiter. The metal is diamagnetic like nickel, but has nearly three times the maximum permeability. Like tungsten, it has the property of adding red-hardness to cutting alloys. It also hardens alloys to a greater extent than nickel, especially in the presence of carbon, and can form more chemical compounds in alloys than nickel.

Cobalt has a specific gravity of 8.756, melting point at 1493°C, hardness 86 Brinell, and electrical conductivity about 16% that of copper. The tensile strength of pure cast cobalt is 34,500 psi, but with 0.25% carbon it is increased to 62,000 psi. The metal is employed in cutting alloys and tool steels, in magnet alloys, in high-permeability alloys, and as a catalyst, and its compounds are used as pigments and for producing many chemicals. The metal has two forms, a close-packed hexagonal crystal form, which is stable below 417°C, and a cubic form stable at higher temperatures to the melting point. Cobalt has valences of 2 and 3, while nickel has only a valence of 2.

The natural cobalt is **cobalt 59,** which is stable and nonradioactive, but the other isotopes from 54 to 64 are all radioactive, emitting beta and gamma rays. Most have very short life except **cobalt 57** which has a half-life of 270 days, **cobalt 56** with a half-life of 80 days, and **cobalt 58** with a half-life of 72 days. **Cobalt 60,** with a half-life of 5.3 years, is used for radiographic inspection, requiring only one-third the exposure time of high-voltage X-rays for steel inspection. It is also used for irradiating plastics, and as a catalyst for the sulfonation of paraffin oils since the gamma rays cause the reaction of sulfur dioxide and liquid paraffin. Cobalt 60 emits gamma rays of 1.1- to 1.3-mev energy which gives high penetration for irradiation. The decay loss in a year is about 12%, the cobalt changing to nickel.

Cobalt metal is marketed in rondels, or small cast slugs, in shot and anodes, and as a powder. Powders with low nickel content for making cobalt salts and catalysts are produced by Sherritt-Gordon Mines, Ltd., in particle size down to 1 micron. About one-quarter of the supply of cobalt is used in the form of oxides and salts for driers, ceramic frits, and pigments. **Cobalt carbonyls** are used for producing **cobalt powder** for use in powder metallurgy, as catalysts, and for producing cobalt chemicals. **Dicobalt octa carbonyl,** $Co_2(CO)_8$, or **cobalt tetra crbonyl,** is a brownish powder melting at 51°C, and decomposing at 60°C to **tetra cobalt**

dodeca carbonyl, $(CoCO_3)_4$, a black powder which oxidizes in the air.

Cobalt is one of the most prolific complex formers of all the metals, and the possible compounds are almost infinite. It combines easily with oxygen, nitrogen, carbon, sulfur, and with the halogens, amines, cyanides, and other groups. Cobalt is a necessary material in human and animal metabolism, and is used in fertilizers in the form of **cobaltous carbonate,** $CoCO_3$, in which form it is easily assimilated. This form occurs in nature in the mineral **cobalt spar** and mixed with magnesium and iron carbonates. **Cobaltous citrate,** $Co(C_6H_5O_7) \cdot 2H_2O$, is a rose-red powder soluble in water, used in making pharmaceuticals. **Cobaltous fluorosilicate,** $CoSiF_6 \cdot H_2O$, is an orange-red water-soluble powder used in toothpastes. It furnishes fluorine and silica as well as cobalt. **Cobaltous hydroxide,** $Co(OH)_2$, has a high cobalt content, 61.25%, is stable in storage, and is used for paint and ink driers, and for making many other compounds. **Cobaltous chloride,** $CoCl_2$, a black powder, is an important cobalt chemical. It is also used as a **humidity indicator** for silica gel and other desiccants. As the **desiccant** becomes spent, the blue of the cobaltous chloride changes to the pink color of the hexahydrate, but when the material is regenerated by heating to drive off the moisture, the blue reappears.

Cobalt metal may be obtained from the sulfur and arsenic ores by melting and then precipitating the cobaltous hydroxide powder which is high in cobalt, has high stability in storage, and is readily converted to the metal or the oxide or used directly for driers and other applications. The chief **cobalt ores** are cobaltite and smaltite. **Cobaltite,** or **cobalt glance,** from Ontario and Idaho, is a sulfarsenide, $CoAsS$, and occurs with **gersdorffite,** $NiAsS$. Another sulfide is **linnaeite,** Co_3S_4, containing theoretically 58% cobalt, but usually containing also nickel and iron. Cobalt is also found with pyrites as the mineral **bieberite,** which is **cobaltous sulfate,** $CoSO_4 \cdot 7H_2O$, but combined with iron sulfate. Some cobalt is extracted from the iron pyrites of Pennsylvania, the concentrated pyrite containing 1.41% cobalt, 42 iron, and 0.28 copper. **Erythrite** is a hydrous cobalt arsenate occurring in the smaltite deposits of Morocco. **Skutterudite** also occurs in Morocco. It is a silvery-gray brittle mineral of the composition $(CoNiFe)As_3$, with a specific gravity of 6.5 and hardness of 6.

Asbolite, an important ore in Katanga and in New Caledonia, is a soft mineral, hardness 2 Mohs, consisting of varying mixtures of cobaltiferous manganese and iron oxides. A number of minerals classed as **heterogenite,** black in color and containing only cobalt and copper, occur in copper deposits, especially in Katanga. Among these are **mindigite,** $2Co_2O_3 \cdot CuO \cdot 3H_2O$, and **trieuite,** $2Co_2O \cdot CuO \cdot 6H_2O$. **Carrollite,** $CuS \cdot Co_2S_3$, a steel-gray mineral with a specific gravity of 4.85 and hardness of 5.5, is an important ore in Rhodesia. The copper ores of the Congo and Rhodesia form one of the chief sources of commercial cobalt. Some of the metal is exported as **white alloy,** containing 40% cobalt, 9 copper, and the balance iron. Cobalt occurs naturally in many minerals, and the metal may be considered as a by-product of other mining. Small quantities are produced regularly as a by-product of zinc production in Australia, although the cobalt content of the concentrate is only 0.015%. Some cobalt is obtained from the silver ores of Ontario, and some comes as a by-product from the lead and zinc ores of Missouri. Its relative scarcity is a matter of cost of extraction.

COBALT OXIDE. A steel-gray to blue-black powder employed as a base pigment for ceramic glazes on metal, as a colorant for glass, and as a chemical catalyst. It gives excellent adhesion to metals and is valued as an undercoat for vitreous enamels. It is the most stable blue, as it is not changed by ordinary oxidizing or reducing conditions. It is also one of the most powerful colorants for glass, 1 part in 20,000 parts of a batch giving a distinct blue color. Cobalt oxide is produced from the cobalt-nickel and pyrite ores, and the commercial oxide may be a mixture of the three oxides. **Cobaltous oxide,** CoO, is called **gray cobalt oxide** but varies in color from greenish to reddish. It is the easiest to reduce to the metal, and reacts easily with silica and alumina in ceramics. **Cobaltic oxide,** Co_2O_3, occurs in the mixture only as the unstable hydrate, and changes to the stable **black cobalt oxide,** or **cobalto-cobaltic oxide,** Co_3O_4, on heating. Above about 900°C this oxide loses oxygen to form cobaltous oxide.

Cobalt dioxide, CoO_2, does not occur alone, but the dioxide is stable in combination with other metals. The blue-black powder called **lithium cobaltite,** $LiCoO_2$, is used in ceramic frits to conserve cobalt, since the lithium adds fluxing and adherent properties. The pigment known as **smalt,** and as **royal blue** and **Saxon blue,** is a deep-blue powder made by fusing cobalt oxide with silica and potassium carbonate. It contains 65 to 71% silica, 16 to 21 potash, 6 to 7 cobalt oxide, and a little alumina. It is used for coloring glass and for vitreous enameled signs, but does not give good covering power as a paint pigment. **Thenaud's blue** is made by heating together cobalt oxide and aluminum oxide. **Rinmann's green** is made by heating together cobalt oxide and zinc oxide.

COBALT STEELS. Cobalt is a much rarer and more expensive metal than nickel, but it has powerful influencing properties in steel and iron alloys, and is used in tool steels, cutting alloys, and magnet steels. Small amounts of cobalt are used in special tool steels to give hardness, but large amounts decrease the impact resistance. The cobalt steels retain hard carbides at high temperatures, and the high-speed steels containing cobalt are harder than the regular tungsten steels and can be operated at higher temperatures, but since they are not plastic at ordinary forging temperatures they require higher heats for forging and more care in heat-treatment. A typical super-high-speed steel is **Braecut steel,** of the Braeburn Alloy Steel Corp. It contains 12% cobalt, 6.25 molybdenum, 5.25 tungsten, 4.25 chromium, 2.25 vanadium, and 1.15 carbon. It develops a hardness of Rockwell C70. Another alloy called a "balanced" high-speed steel, for drills, cutters, and lathe tools, is **Rex 49 steel,** of the Crucible Steel Co. of America. It has 5% cobalt, 6.75 tungsten, 4.25 chromium, 3.75 molybdenum, 2 vanadium, 0.45 manganese, 0.3 silicon, and 1.1 carbon. It hardens by oil quenching to Rockwell C68. The qualities of hardness and heat resistance are developed in the cobalt steels best when considerable amounts of chromium are present.

Cobalt increases residual magnetism in steel and increases the coercive magnetic force, and more than 30% of the cobalt supply is used in magnetic alloys. But the magnetic and permeability alloys may have little or no iron and are high alloys rather than steels, as is also the case with the cobalt alloys used for heat-resistant spring wire, although many such high alloys used for high-temperature applications are called steels. **Ferrovac WD65,** of the Crucible Steel Co. of America, for such uses as aircraft bearings to operate at temperatures to 900°F, contains 5% cobalt, 15 chromium, 4 moybdenum, 2.5 vanadium, 2.25 tungsten, and 1.12 carbon. It is air-hardening, and will harden to Rockwell C65. **Alloy MA-18NiCoMo,** of the International Nickel Co., Inc., contains 7% cobalt, 18 nickel, 5 molybdenum, 0.5 titanium, and not over 0.05 carbon. When heat-treated it has a yield strength of 300,000 psi and retains high strength and resistance to stress corrosion at elevated temperatures. Many tool steels and some low-alloy steels also contain cobalt. **Unimach UCX2,** of the Universal-Cyclops Steel Corp., is a low-alloy steel which can be heat-treated to a tensile strength of 270,000 psi with elongation of 5% and Rockwell hardness of C50, and which is not notch-sensitive. It contains 1% cobalt, 1.1 chromium, 1 silicon, 0.7 manganese, 0.25 molybdenum, 0.15 vanadium, and 0.39 carbon. When annealed it is easily deep-drawn.

COCHINEAL. A dyestuff of animal origin, which before the advent of coal-tar dyes was one of the most important coloring materials. Cochineal is the female of the *Coccus cacti,* an insect that feeds on various species of cactus of Mexico. The insects have no wings, and at the egg-laying season are brushed off the plants, killed by boiling, and dried. They are dark reddish brown in color. Cochineal contains 10 to 20% pure coloring matter, carminic acid, mostly in the eggs, from which the **carmine red,** $C_{11}H_{12}O_7$, is obtained by boiling with mineral acid. Carmine red produces brilliant lake colors of various hues with different metals. Commercial cochineal may be adulterated with starch, kaolin, red lead, or chrome lead.

The brilliant red pigment known as **carmine lake** is made by precipitating a mixture of cochineal and alum.   Salmonella-free cochineal in water solution is now used in foods to give a reddish-purple color.   A species of cochineal insect that feeds on the leaves of the **tamarisk** tree, *Tamarix manifera,* produces **manna,** a viscous, white, sweet substance composed mostly of sugars.   It forms in small balls and falls usually in May to July. When dry, it is hard and stable, and is a good food.   It is native to the Near East.

COCOA BEANS. The seed beans from the large fruit pods of the **cacao tree,** *Theobroma cacao,* native to Mexico, and *T. leiocarpum,* native to Brazil.   The tree was cultivated in Mexico from ancient times, and the beans were used by the Aztecs to produce a beverage called **chocolatl** which contained the whole substance of the fermented and roasted bean flavored with vanilla.   Cocoa beans are now produced in many countries, and the United States imports them from about 40 countries.   Ghana, Nigeria, and Brazil are noted producers.   The tree grows only in the tropics, cannot withstand temperatures below 60°F, but grows best in the highlands.   It begins to bear in 4 or 5 years and continues to bear for as long as 50 years, having fruits and flowers throughout the year.   The fruits are melonlike pods 6 to 9 in. long with a pulp and from 40 to 60 seed beans.   The pulp and seeds are scooped out, fermented, and dried in the sun.   During the curing the beans lose their bitter taste, and become reddish brown in color. Numerous varieties are cultivated.   The flavor and aroma also vary with soil and climate, and differences in curing methods also produce differences in the beans, so that types and grades are best known by the shipping ports and districts in which they grown.   **Mico cocoa** is wild cocoa of Central America.   The beans are smaller and are noted for fine flavor.   Cocoa beans are shipped dried but not roasted.   They are roasted just before use to develop the flavor, to increase the fat content, and to decrease the tannin content.   The hard shells are removed, and the roasted seeds are ground and pressed to produce **bitter chocolate.**   **Sweet chocolate** is made by adding sugar and flavoring, usually vanilla.   **Cocoa,** for beverage purposes, is made by removing about 60% of the fatty oil from chocolate by hydraulic pressing and powdering the residue, to which is usually added ground cocoa shells.   The removed fatty oil is **cocoa butter,** used for bakery products, cosmetics, and pharmaceuticals.   A hundred pounds of cocoa beans yields 48 lb of **chocolate powder,** 32 lb of cocoa butter, and 20 lb of waste.   Also an artificial cocoa butter is made by fractionating palm kernel oil.   **Pakena,** a substitute cocoa butter of the Dura Commodities Corp., contains 53% lauric acid, 21.5 myristic, 12 palmitic, 8 oleic, 3.5 stearic, and 2 capric acids.   Besides fat, chocolate contains much starch and protein and has high food value, but is not as stimulating as the cocoa since the alkaloid is largely contained in the waste and shells.   These contain 1 to 1.5% theobromine and are used for the synthetic production of caffeine.   The chocolate is used in the manufacture of confectionery, chocolate bars, bakery products, and flavoring syrups.   **Microfine cocoa,** of the Cook Chocolate Co., used for bakery products, is ground to 325 mesh, and contains from 9 to 16% cocoa butter.   **Postonal** is a German substitute for cocoa butter for pharmaceuticals.   It is a polymerized ethylene oxide containing chemically combined castor oil.

Cocoa powder, used in the United States for beverages and for adding chocolate flavor to foodstuffs, as distinct from the sweet chocolate used in Latin countries for beverages, was originally made from the shells, but is now made from the residue cake after extraction of the **chocolate liquor** and the pressing out of the cocoa butter.   It is widely used as a flavor for cakes and confectioneries.   Sugar makes the powder easily soluble in water; **instant cocoa** is cocoa powder processed with about 70% sugar and sometimes also with nonfat milk powder.   The fat content of commercial cocoa powders ranges from 6 to 22% with a color range from light brown to reddish black.   The high-fat grade, called **breakfast cocoa,** is more stimulating as a beverage than the Latin-type chocolate since it contains caffeine.   Cocoa powder is usually acidic with the pH as low as 3.3, but **Dutched cocoa,** for nonacid foods, is **stabilized cocoa** with the pH raised to as high as 9.0 by treatment with solutions of sodium or potassium carbonate.

COCOBOLA.   The wood of the hardwood tree *Dalbergia retusa,* of Central America, also known as **Honduras rosewood.**   It is a beautiful wood, extremely hard, and very heavy with a weight of 75 to 85 lb per cu ft.   It has orange and red bands with dark streaks and takes a fine polish.   The thick sapwood is hewn off before shipment, and the heartwood logs are usually not more than 18 in. in diameter.   The wood is used for canes, turnery, inlaying, scientific-instrument cases, and knife handles.   **Cocos wood,** also called **cocoawood** and **West Indian ebony,** used chiefly for inlaying, is from the tree *Brya ebenus* of tropical America.   The sapwood is light yellow, and the heartwood is brown streaked with yellow.   The grain is dense and even, and the wood is hard and tough.

COCONUT OIL.   The oil obtained from the thick-kernel or meat adhering to the inside of the shell of the large nuts of the palm tree *Cocos nucifera* growing along the coasts of tropical countries.   The tree requires salt air, and inland trees do not bear fruit unless supplied with salt.   The name coco is the Carib word for palm.   **Copra** is the dried meat of the coconut from which the oil is pressed.   The dried copra contains 60 to 65% oil. It is an excellent food oil, and is valued as a shortening for crackers, but its use for margarine has declined.   It is also valued for soaps because of its high lathering qualities due to the large percentage of lauric and myristic acids, though these acids are irritating to some skins. It is also employed as a source of lauric acid, but lauryl alcohol is now made synthetically. Coconut oil was once the chief illuminating oil in India, and the oil for burning was exported under the name of **Cochin oil.** This oil was cold-pressed and filtered and was water-clear. Coconut oil has a melting point of 27 to 32°C, specific gravity 0.926, saponification value 251 to 263, and iodine value 8 to 9.6. It contains 45 to 48% lauric acid, 17 to 20 myristic, 10 capric, 5 to 7 palmitic, up to 5 stearic, and some oleic, caprylic, and caproic acids.

In sun-drying coconut meat to make copra there is a loss of some of the oil, sugars and other carbohydrates, and some proteins. The oil from copra contains more free fatty acid than that from fresh dried coconut and is rancid, requiring neutralization, decolorization, and deodorization. The meal and cake are also dirty and rancid but are useful for animal feed or fertilizer. **Dehydrated coconut** meat gives a better yield of oil and is not rancid. The **copra cake** of India is called **poonac.** The chief production of copra and coconut oil is in southern Asia, Indonesia, the Philippines, and in the South Sea Islands. About 5,000 coconuts are required to produce a metric ton of copra, and the average yield of crude oil is 63%. The stearine separated from crude coconut oil by the process of wintering is known as **coconut butter** and is used in confectionery. It has a melting point of 27 to 32°C. Hydrogenated coconut oil is a soft solid with a melting point of 45°C. **Desiccated coconut,** produced by oven drying or dehydration of the fresh coconut meat, is used shredded as a food and also powdered in many bakery products as a food and stabilizer. It has high food value, containing not less than 60% oil, 15 carbohydrates, 14 cellulose, 6 to 7 protein, and various mineral salts and considerable vitamin B. It is easily digested and has antitubercular value, but its characteristic coconut flavor is not universally liked and its use is largely confined to confections.

COFFEE. The seed berries, or beans, of the **Arabian coffee** tree, *Coffea arabica,* the **Liberian coffee,** *C. liberica,* and the **Congo coffee,** *C. robusta,* of which the first species furnishes most of the commercial product. The coffee bean contains the alkaloid caffeine used in medicine as a stimulant and in soft drinks, but most of the commercial coffee beans are used for the preparation of the beverage coffee, with small quantities for flavoring. The alkaloid is stimulating and is harmless in small amounts as it does not break down in the system and is easily soluble in water and thus carried off rapidly, but in large quantities at one time it is highly toxic. In the beverage it is partly neutralized by the sugar used. Coffee contains niacin, and also rubidium and other metallic salts useful in small quantities in the human system. The normal effect of coffee, due to the caffeine, is contraction of the muscles, which relieves tiredness, but causes irritation as the muscles again relax.

The Arabian coffee plant is a small evergreen tree first introduced to Europe through Arabia. The first plants were brought to America in 1723, and the trees are now grown in most tropical countries. It requires a hot, moist climate, but develops best at higher altitudes. There are numerous varieties, and the coffee beans also vary in aroma and taste with differences in climate and cultivation. The Liberian and Congo species, grown on the west coast of Africa, are more hardy plants, but the coffee is different in aroma and is used only for blending. **Mocha coffee** and **Java coffee** are fragrant varieties of Arabian coffee. The fruits are small fleshy berries containing two greenish seeds. They are dried in the sun, or are pulped by machine and cleaned in fermenting baths and oven-dried. After removal of the skin from the dried beans they are graded and shipped as green beans. The general grades are by shipping ports or regions with numbered grades or qualities. Coffee is always roasted for use. This consists in a dry distillation with the formation of new compounds which produce the flavor and aroma. The aroma is from a combination of aldehydes, alcohols, and phenols. Green coffee beans can be stored for long periods, but in the roasted coffee the aldehydes are gradually reduced, and phenols and H_2S are formed which change the flavor. The diacetyl is converted to acetylmethylcarbinol with loss of aroma. Excessive boiling of coffee causes loss of the aromatic volatile oils and also produces phenols and H_2S. The **caffeic acid** in coffee is a complex form of cinnamic acid which changes readily to a complex coumarin. **Coffee-Captan,** of Cargille Scientific, Inc., is alpha furfuryl mercaptan, one of the essential constituents in the aroma of freshly roasted coffee. It is a water-white liquid used in masking agents, and is also a vulcanizer for rubber. **Coffee flavor,** made synthetically for adding to coffee blends, is furfural mercaptan. The **mercaptans** are thioalcohols, or sulfur alcohols, which have compositions resembling those of the alcohols but react differently to give **mercaptals** with aldehydes and **mercaptols** with ketones and produce various flavors from offensive to pleasant.

Brazil produces about half of all coffee, and **Brazilian coffee** is the base for most blends, though the average quality is not high. In blends, **Medellin coffee** from Colombia is used for rich flavor, Mexican **Coatepec** for winey flavor, El Salvador for full body, Costa Rican for fragrance, and Arabian mocha for distinctive flavor. Some coffees, such as Guatemalan, which have a full body and rich flavor, are used without blending, though trade-named coffees are usually blends because of the lack of quantity of superior types. **Powdered coffees** are usually evaporated and crystallized cooked coffee, to which it is only necessary to add hot water. **Chicory,** which is used extensively in Europe for blending with coffee, is the dried, roasted, and ground root of the perennial plant *Cichorium intybus,* native to Europe and growing wild in the United States. It is cultivated in the central states. From 5 to 40% chicory may be used in some blends of coffee. It gives a taste preferred by some. **Caffeine-free coffee** for dietary use has the alkaloid removed by solvent extraction and is sold under trade names such as **Sanka. Kava,** of Borden, Inc., has the tannic acid neutralized to improve digestibility.

COIR. A fiber by-product of the coconut industry. The fiber is retted from the outer husks, hammered with wooden mallets, and then combed and bleached. The coarse and long fibers are used for brushmaking; the finer and curly fibers are spun into coir yarn used for mats, cordage, and coarse cloths. In the West Indies it is mixed with sisal and jute to make coffee-bag cloth. In the Philippines it has been used with cement to make a hard-setting, lightweight board for siding. In India **coir fiberboard** is made by bonding with shellac, pressing, and baking. The boards are hard and have a good finish. Coir is easily dyed. The Ceylon **coir yarn** is sold in two quality grades, Kogalla and Colombo, with subdivisions according to the thickness and texture. The yarn is properly called coir, and the harsh brush fiber is best known as **coconut fiber.** Coir yarn averages 330 meters per kg. The Indian yarn is in 450-yd lengths tied into bundles. A hundred nuts yield 17 or 18 lb of fiber. **Coconut shell,** a by-product of the copra industry, is used for making activated charcoal and for **coconut shell flour** used as a filler in molded plastics. It has a composition similar to walnut shell, being chiefly cellulose with about 30% lignin, 17 pentosan, and 5 methoxyl.

COKE. The porous, gray, infusible residue left after the volatile matter is driven out of bituminous coal. The coal is heated to a temperature of 1200 to 1400°C, without allowing air to burn it, and the volatile matter expelled. The residue, which is mainly fixed carbon and ash, is a cellular mass of greater strength than the original coal. Its nature and structure make it a valuable fuel for blast furnaces, burning rapidly and supporting a heavy charge of metal without packing. Soft, or bituminous, coals are designated as coking or noncoking, according to their capacity for being converted into coke. Coal low in carbon and high in ash will produce a coke that is friable and not strong enough for furnace use, or the ash may have low-melting constituents that leave glassy slag in the coke. Coke is produced in the beehive and by-product ovens, or is a by-product of gas plants. One ton of coal will yield an average of 0.7 ton of coke, 11,500 cu ft gas, 12 gal tar, 27 lb ammonium sulfate, 50 gal benzol, 0.9 gal toluol and naphtha, and 0.5 lb naphthalene, but the product yield varies with the temperature.   When steel production is low and coking ovens are run at lower temperature with a longer cycle, the yield of naphthalene is low.

The fixed carbon of good coke should be at least 86%, and sulfur not more than 1%.   The porosity may vary from 40 to 60%, and the apparent specific gravity should not be less than 0.8.   **Foundry coke** should have an ignition point about 1000°F, with sulfur below 0.7%, and the pieces should be strong enough to carry the burden of ore and limestone.   Coke suitable for foundry use is also made from low-grade coals by reducing them to a semicoke, or char, and briquetting, but **semicoke** and **smokeless fuel** are generally coals carbonized at low temperatures and briquetted for household use.   These fuels are sold under trade names such as **Coalite** and **Carbolux,** and they are really by-products of the chemical industry since much greater quantities of liquids and more lighter fractions in the tar are obtained in the process.

Pitch coke, made by distilling coal tar, has a high carbon content, above 99%, with low sulfur and ash, and is used for making carbon electrodes. **Petroleum coke** is the final residue in the distillation of petroleum, and forms about 5% of the weight of the crude oil.   With the sand and impurities removed it is about 99% pure carbon, and is used for molded carbon products.   **Calcined coke** is petroleum coke that has been calcined at 2400°F to remove volatile matter.   It is used for electrodes.   **Carbonite** is a natural coke found in England and in Virginia.   It is a cokelike mineral formed by the baking action of igneous rocks on seams of bituminous coal.

COLD-MOLDED PLASTICS.   This term applies most properly to products made with bituminous binders such as pitch and gilsonite, with fillers of silica, talc, kaolin, or asbestos fibers to add strength and heat resistance, and sometimes with drying oils or driers.   The color is normally black. The filler content may be as high as 80%, and the plastics may withstand temperatures above 500°F, although the melting point of the original binder may be as little as 200°F.   The plastics are water-resistant and acid-resistant, and are good electrical insulators, but are usually much weaker in strength than hot-molded synthetic resins.   They were once widely used for such parts as battery cases and electrical insulating parts, but their use is now largely restricted to parts where low cost is the prime factor or for short-run items.   They differ from hot-molded plastics in that the powdered or granular material is premixed on the spot, only simple pressure is used in the molding, and no chemical transformation takes place in the molding as with synthetic resins.   Cold-molded plastics have been marketed under many trade names, such as **Ebrok, Aico,** and **Okon.** Products made by cold-molding mixtures of asphalt and asbestos fiber or other material, baking, and then impregnating with a synthetic resin are also sometimes called cold-molded plastics, but they are not plastics in the sense that the term is normally used industrially. The term cold-molded plastics is also sometimes used for products made with premixes containing a phenolic resin binder. These plastics have higher strength than those made with a bituminous binder, but, unlike the ordinary cold-molded plastics, they require much higher pressure.

The **water-fillable plastics** used to replace wood or plaster of paris for ornamental articles such as plaques, statuary, and lamp stands, and for model making, are thermoplastic resins that cure to closed-cell lattices that entrap water. The resin powders are mixed with water and a catalyst and poured into a mold without pressure. They give finer detail than plasters, do not crack or chip, and are light in weight, and the cured material can be nailed and finished like wood. Water content can be varied from 50 to 80%. **Polylite WFP,** of Reichold Chemicals, Inc., is a polyester plastic for this purpose. It is cured with a peroxide catalyst.

COLD-ROLLED STEEL. Almost any steel can be cold-rolled, and some high-alloy and stainless steels are specially rolled to obtain mirrorlike finishes for special purposes. But the old term cold-rolled steel still applies generally to low-carbon, open-hearth steel that has been worked into strips, sheet, or bars by cold rolling, giving a good finish and a grain oriented in one direction. Bar stock is usually drawn to final dimensions through dies, and may be called **cold-finished steel.**

The carbon content of cold-rolled steel is usually from 0.08 to 0.12%, with manganese from 0.30 to 0.80%. After the regular hot rolling has been completed, the steel is annealed and pickled, and then passed cold through finishing rolls which smooth and polish the surfaces and increase the hardness and tensile strength. Only a slight reduction is made by cold-rolling sheet steel. For the making of cold-rolled strip steel the slabs after hot rolling are sheared to length, then hot-rolled into strip which is wound on a coil. The coils are recoiled to loosen the scale, pickled, rolled in breakdown mills, and annealed. The cold rolling is then accomplished until the desired hardness is obtained. It is usually in four tempers, but sometimes in six, from No. 1, hard, to No. 6, dead soft. Dead-soft steel is for severe drawing and cupping work. It has a minimum tensile strength of 37,500 psi and elongation of 40%. Medium soft, or quarter soft, is for forming or light drawing. The minimum tensile strength is 42,500 psi, with elongation 20%. Medium-hard, or half-hard, is for bending at sharp right angles across the grain. The tensile strength is 50,000 psi. Hard-rolled steel is for flat work and easy punching. The tensile strength is 55,000 psi, and elongation 5%. Specifications for cold-rolled sheet steel for automobile bodies call for less than 0.14% carbon, under 0.60 manganese, and under 0.045 each of sulfur and phosphorus.

The average tensile strength of the normalized sheet is 50,000 psi.   **Thin-steel** is the trade name of the Cold Metal Products Co. for cold-rolled strip steel in thin gages made to very close accuracy.   It comes in various tempers from dead soft to full hard in gages down to 0.001 in.   **Stain-stripe,** of the Acne Steel Co., is cold-rolled steel with decorative designs rolled on.   **Cold-drawn steel** is bar or rod steel that has been finished by cold drawing through dies.   Cold drawing doubles the yield point of hot-rolled bars, and imparts a high finish.   The tensile strength of commercial, low-carbon, cold-drawn steel is 70,000 psi and elongation 15%.   **Rycase** is the name of a low-carbon, high-manganese, cold-drawn steel of Joseph T. Ryerson & Son, Inc., used for such parts as spindles to be case hardened.   The tensile strength is 75,000 psi.   **Jalcase 100,** of the Jones & Laughlin Steel Corp., is a free-machining, cold-finished bar steel which is stress-stabilized to prevent distortion after machining.   It has the nominal composition of **AISI steel C-1144,** with 0.45% carbon, 1.5 manganese, and 0.33 max sulfur, but the physical properties are higher.   The minimum yield strength is 105,000 psi, and the Brinell hardness is 248.

COLUMBITE. An ore of the metal columbium. Its composition varies and may be $FeO \cdot Cb_2O_5$ or $(FeMn)Cb_2O_6$, or it may also contain tungsten and other metals. It is produced chiefly in Nigeria and marketed on the basis of the Cb_2O_5 content. But columbium occurs more usually in combination with tantalum. Concentrates generally average 44 to 70% Cb_2O_5 and 0.4 to 7% Ta_2O_5. The combined mineral known as **columbo-tantalite,** mined in South Dakota, Idaho, and the Congo, is marketed on the basis of the total $Ta_2O_5 \cdot Cb_2O_5$ content, and as the tantalum increases and the specific gravity increases, the mineral is called tantalite. The black mineral is associated with pegmatite, and some crystals are up to a ton in weight. Columbite concentrates contain about 60% **columbium pentoxide,** Cb_2O_5.

COLUMBIUM. An elementary metal, symbol Cb. It was called **Niobium** in Germany, with the symbol Nb. It occurs in the minerals columbite and tantalite and, as it closely resembles tantalum, is difficult to separate from it. Columbium has a fine yellowish-white color, a specific gravity of 8.57, a melting point of 2415°C, a tensile strength of 48,000 to 59,000 psi, annealed, and up to 130,000 psi in drawn wire. The electrical conductivity is one-eighth that of copper. It is ductile and malleable when pure, but slight amounts of impurities harden the metal. When free of nitrogen, oxygen, and hydrogen it is extremely ductile, and a 3-in. bar can be rolled into foil 0.0005 in. thick without annealing. The metal can be machined readily with a cutting lubricant. It is insoluble in most acids and not easily attacked by alkalies. The metal oxidizes in the air, but the film of oxide retards further oxidation, and the normal rate is only about 5% that of molybdenum. However, above 750°F there is severe oxidation caused by nucleation and growth of a porous columbium pentoxide which keeps a continuously refreshed surface of metal exposed to corrosion. At high temperatures, also, the metal absorbs gases. Its gas-absorbent properties are greater than those of tantalum, and it is thus used in high-vacuum tubes. The color of the metal is more attractive than that of tantalum, and it is used for jewelry. Columbium is the only metal, other than gold and silver, that can reasonably meet the characteristics needed for a **coinage metal:** intrinsic value, aesthetic value, durability, and widespread availability to prevent a national monopoly. Specimen coins have been made, but usage requires an act of Congress and international acceptance.

Although costly, columbium is not a rare metal, and it is estimated to be 50% more abundant in nature than lead. It is used in stainless steels in small amounts to inhibit intergranular corrosion. In chromium steels it reduces air hardening, increases impact strength, reduces creep, shortens the annealing time, and improves oxidation resistance. Small amounts are added to brass and copper alloys to aid retention of temper hardness at elevated temperatures. **Ferrocolumbium,** for adding columbium to steel, is marketed as an alloy containing 50 to 60% columbium, 7 silicon, and the balance iron.

Columbium alloys are used for high-temperature parts in turbines and missiles. An alloy of 80% columbium, 10 titanium, and 10 molybdenum retains a tensile strength of 11,000 psi at 2500°F. A **columbium-tungsten alloy,** with 11% tungsten, 3 molybdenum, and 2 hafnium, for instrument use, retains a tensile strength of 28,000 psi at 2000°F. **Fansteel 80,** of the Fansteel Metallurgical Corp., is a **columbium-zirconium alloy** for missile and aircraft parts. It has a density of 8.6 and a melting point at 4350°F, and retains a tensile strength of 18,000 psi at 2000°F. **Fansteel 82** is an alloy of columbium, zirconium, and tantalum. It has a density of 10.26 and a melting point at 4550°F. The tensile strength is 55,000 psi, and it retains a strength of about 30,000 psi at 2000°F with high oxidation resistance. **Alloy FS-85,** of the same company, for aerospace parts, contains 28% tantalum, 10.5 tungsten, 0.9 zirconium, and the balance columbium. The melting point is 4695°F. It retains a tensile strength of 15,000 psi above 2500°F and retains ductility at −320°F. **Columbium alloy Cb-65,** of the Union Carbide Corp., contains 7.5% titanium and 0.75 zirconium. It has a tensile strength of 37,000 psi at 1800°F. It can be hot-extruded, forged, or cold-worked. It has high oxidation resistance and a low neutron cross section. **Haynes alloy Cb-752** contains 10% tungsten and 5 zirconium. At ordinary temperatures it has a tensile strength of 125,000 psi with good ductility, and it retains a tensile strength of 50,000 psi at 2000°F. This alloy comes as **columbium foil** in a thickness of 0.002 in. for high-temperature honeycomb structures. **Haynes alloy Cb-753** contains 5% vanadium; 1.25 zirconium; small amounts of carbon, nitrogen, and oxygen; and the balance columbium. Thin sheets retain a tensile strength of 27,400 psi up to 2200°F.

Columbium selenide, $CbSe_2$, is more electrically conductive than graphite and forms an adhesive lubricating film. It is used in powder form with silver, copper, or other metal powders for self-lubricating bearings and gears. Columbium also comes in the form of **columbium oxide,** Cb_2O_5, a white powder melting at 1520°C, and as **potassium columbate,** $4K_2O \cdot 3Cb_2O_5 \cdot 16H_2O$. **Columbium ethylate,** $Cb(OC_2H_5)_5$, has a melting point of 6°C. It is used for producing thin dielectric films and for impregnating paper for dielectric use. Other such **metal alcoholates** are **columbium methylate,** $Cb(OCH_3)_5$, with a melting point of 53°C, and the **tantalum alcoholates** of the same formulas. **Columbium carbide,** CbC, is an extremely hard crystalline powder, which can be molded with a metal binder and sintered for use in cutting tools. The melting point is about 3800°C. It is made by sintering columbium powder and carbon in a hydrogen furnace.

COMPOSITE METALS. Usually, sheet or plate metal having a face of special resistance metal welded to a base of lower-cost metal, used for making tanks, boilers, and chemical processing equipment where it is desired to have an acid-resistant or heat-resistant facing with the more easy-working and lower-cost plain steel plate. But the term also embraces other metal laminates for electrical, atomic, and other uses, sometimes with **fiber-reinforced metals** containing boron, tungsten, or sapphire fibers in a metal matrix.

Laminated metals were used very early in the jewelry and silverware industries, and silver-clad iron was made by the Gauls by brazing together sheets of silver and iron for lower-cost products as substitutes for the Roman heavy silver tableware. An early French **duplex metal** called **doublé,** for costume jewelry, had a thin facing of a noble metal on a brass or copper base, and **Efkabimetal** was a German name for this material. **Gold shell,** used for costume jewelry, is a duplex metal with gold rolled on a rich low brass. **Abyssinian gold, talmi gold,** and other names were used for these duplex metals in traders' jewelry. **Inter-Weld metal,** of the American Silver Co., has a base metal of brass to which is silver-soldered a sheet of nickel over which is welded the gold sheet. When rolled, the gold is extremely thin, but the nickel prevents the color of the base metal from bleeding through.

Composite tool steel, used for shear blades and die parts, is not a laminated metal. The term refers to bar steel machined along the entire length and having an insert of tool steel welded to the backing of mild steel. **Clad steels** are available regularly in large sheets and plates. They are made with coatings of nickel, stainless steel, monel metal, aluminum, or special alloys, on one or both sides of the sheet. Where heat and pressure are used in the processing there is chemical bonding between the metals. For some uses the cladding metal on one side will be 10 to 20% of the weight of the sheet. A composite plate having an 18–8 stainless-steel cladding to a thickness of 20% on one side saves 144 lb of chromium and 64 lb of nickel per 1,000 lb of total plate. The coatings may also be extremely thin.

Pluramelt, of the Allegheny Steel Corp., is composite steel with various types of stainless steels integrally bonded to a depth of 20% by a process of intermelting. **Ingaclad,** of the Ingersoll Steel & Disc Co., consists of stainless steel bonded to carbon-steel plate. **Silver-Ply** is a **stainless-clad steel** of the Jessop Steel Co., made with a stainless coating either 10 or 20% of the thickness of the plate combined with the mild steel backing by hot rolling. **Permaclad,** of the Alan Wood Steel Co., has stainless steel bonded to one side of carbon steel. **SuVeneer steel,** of the Superior Steel Corp., used for automobile bumpers, has a veneer of stainless steel bonded to spring steel. **Bronze-clad steel,** of Ampco Metal, Inc., is sheet steel with high-tensile, corrosion-resistant bronze rolled on one or both sides. The cladding is from 0.031 in. up to 40% of the thickness of the sheet. It is used for tanks and chemical equipment. **Hortonclad,** of the Chicago Bridge & Iron Co., has the stainless steel or other cladding joined to the steel baseplate by a process of heating the assembly of base metal, cladding metal, and brazing material together under vacuum. Since there is no rolling, the clad thickness is uniform, and there is no migration of carbon from the steel plate to the surface of the cladding.

Titanium-clad steel, of the Lukens Steel Co., is produced by sandwich-pack rolling without the use of any interlayer foil between the plate and the cladding. An atmosphere of argon gas is used during the heating, and there is no incorporation of the impurities that normally make the titanium brittle. **Nickel-clad flange steel** is also produced by this company. **Niclad,** of the Flannery Mfg. Co., has the nickel deposited on the steel by a continuous welding process. The duplex metal called **Bronze-on-steel,** of the Johnson Bronze Co., used for bearings, is made by sintering a homogeneous alloy powder of 80% copper, 10 tin, and 10 lead, to strip steel in a hydrogen atmosphere, and then rolling the strip and forming it into bearings and bushings. **Nifer,** of the Metals & Controls Corp., is **nickel-clad steel** with the nickel bonded to both sides of a carbon steel, while **Alnifer** has nickel on one side and aluminum on the other. It comes in thin gages, up to 0.010 in. for electronic uses. **Stainless-clad aluminum,** of the same company, comes in strip for automotive trim.

Stainless-clad copper is copper sheet with stainless steel on both sides, used for making cooking utensils and food-processing equipment. With stainless steel alone, heat remains localized and causes sticking and burning of foodstuffs. Copper has high heat conductivity, is corroded by some foods, and has an injurious catalytic action on milk products. Thus, the stainless-clad copper gives the conductivity of copper with the protection of stainless steel. The internal layer of copper also makes the metal easier to draw and form. **Rosslyn metal,** of the American Clad-metals Co., is this material. **Ferrolum,** of Knapp Mills, Inc., is sheet steel clad with lead to give protection against sulfuric acid in tanks and chemical equipment. **Copper-clad steel** usually has a cladding of copper equal to 10% of the total thickness of the sheet on each side of a soft steel. But **Conflex,** of the Metals & Controls Corp., has the copper laminated to a hardenable carbon steel so that spring characteristics can be given by heat treatment of the finished parts. The electrical conductivity is 30% that of solid copper.

Brass-clad steel, used for making bullet jackets and shell cases, consists of 90–10 brass on one side of a low-carbon-steel sheet, with the brass equal to 20% of the weight of the sheet. **Bronco metal,** of the Metals & Controls Corp., is copper-strip coated on both sides with 25% by weight of phosphor bronze. The bronze gives good resiliency for springs, and the material has an electrical conductivity 55% that of solid copper.

Coppered steel wire is produced by wet-drawing steel wire which has been immersed in a copper sulfate or copper-tin sulfate solution. The tin gives a brass finish or a white finish, depending on the proportion of tin. **Fernicklon,** of the Kenmore Metals Corp., is nickel-coated wire for instrument use, made by nickel-plating steel or copper rod and then drawing into wire. **Copper-clad steel wire,** marketed by the Copperweld Steel Co., for line wires, screens, and staples, has an electrical conductivity 40% that of an equal section of pure copper, and a tensile strength 250% higher than that of copper. **Copperply wire,** of the National-Standard Co., has either 5 or 10% by weight of copper electroplated on hard-drawn or annealed steel wire in 5 to 36 B&S gage. The conductivity of the 10% coated wire is 20% that of copper wire, or 23% when low-carbon soft wire is used. It is employed for electrical installations where high strength is needed. **Nickel-clad copper wire** is used where an electrical conductor is required to resist oxidation at high temperatures. It is made by inserting a copper rod into a nickel tube and drawing. **Kulgrid,** of Sylvania Electric Products, Inc., is a nickel-clad copper wire for lead-in wires. The cladding is 28% of the total weight, and the electrical conductivity is 70% that of solid copper. The tensile strength of the hard-drawn wire is 85,000 psi, and it resists oxidation at high temperatures.

Feran, a German duplex metal, was made by passing strips of aluminum and iron through rolls at a temperature of 350°C and then cold-rolling to sheet.   **Alclad,** of the Aluminum Co. of America, is an aluminum-clad aluminum alloy, with the exposed pure aluminum giving added corrosion resistance, and the aluminum-copper base metal giving strength.   The German **Lautal** with pure aluminum rolled on is called **Allautal.**   **Zinnal** is a German aluminum sheet with tin cladding on both sides, while **Cupal** is a copper-clad aluminum sheet.   **Copper-clad aluminum** is regularly available in sheet, strip, and tubing.   The copper is rolled on as a coating equal to 5% of the total thickness on each side, or 10% on one side, with a minimum thickness of copper of 0.001 in.   It gives a metal with good working characteristics, and high electrical and heat conductivity.   **Alcuplate,** of the Metals & Controls Corp., is aluminum with copper bonded to both sides, used for stamped and formed parts where good electrical conductivity and easy soldering in combination with light weight are desired. **Alsiplate,** of this company, has silver bonded to both sides of aluminum sheet.   **Aluminized steel** of the Sylvania Electric Products, Inc., is cold-rolled steel which has a 0.005-in. coating of an aluminum-silicon alloy rolled into the surface and then annealed in hydrogen.   It has a black surface, and is used for vacuum-tube parts to give thermionic radiation and absorb stray electrons.   **Alfer,** of the Metals & Controls Corp., is **aluminum-clad steel.**   The aluminum cladding is 10% of the total thickness on each side.   It comes in strips of thin gages.   **Aliron,** of this company, is a five-ply strip metal in very thin gages for radio-tube anode plates.   It has a core of copper amounting to 40% of the thickness, with a layer of iron and a layer of aluminum on both sides.   The copper gives good heat dissipation, and the iron-aluminum compound formed when the metal is heated makes it highly emissive.

Black-coated steel is used to give a high thermal emittance in electronic equipment.   **Carbostrip,** of the Sylvania Electric Products, Inc., is this type of steel in the form of sheet 0.006 in. thick.   The base metal is aluminum-deoxidized steel containing 0.13% carbon, 0.45 manganese, 0.04 max phosphorus, and 0.05 max sulfur.   The steel is coated with a 5% by weight layer of nickel oxide, which is reduced in a hydrogen furnace to form a spongy layer of nickel.   This sponge is impregnated with a carbon slurry to form a black carbonized surface.

COMPOSITION METAL.   Also called **composition brass,** although it does not have the characteristics of a true brass.   A general name for casting alloys that are in a mid-position between the brasses and the bronzes.   The most widely used standard composition metal is **ounce metal,** containing 85% copper, 5 zinc, 5 tin, and 5 lead, which derived its name from the fact that originally 1 oz each of the white metals was added to 1 lb of copper.   It makes a good average bearing metal and, as it gives a dense casting that will withstand liquid pressures, is also used for valves, pumps, and carburetor parts.   It casts well, machines easily, and takes a good polish, so that it is widely employed for mechanical castings.   It has about the same coefficient of expansion as copper, and can thus be used for pipe fittings.   **ASTM alloy No. 2** is this metal.   It contains 84 to 86% copper, 4 to 6 zinc, 4 to 6 tin, and 4 to 6 lead, and may also contain up to 0.75% nickel and small amounts of iron, either as intentional additions to increase strength or as impurities.   The minimum tensile strength is 26,000 psi, yield point 12,000 psi, and elongation 15%.   Well-cast alloys may have strengths as high as 32,000 psi, with elongation 20% or higher, and Brinell hardness 50 to 59.   The weight is 0.31 lb per cu in.   This alloy is also called **red casting brass, hydraulic bronze,** and **steam brass,** and has also been used for forgings, producing parts with a tensile strength of 33,000 psi and elongation 25%.

In the high-copper red casting-brass series, for any given content of copper and zinc, the higher the ratio of tin to lead the stronger but less ductile the alloy.   The higher the content of zinc, the more ductile the alloy.   For cast pipe fittings, the alloy may have 80 to 86% copper, 4 to 15 zinc, 2 to 6 lead, and 3 to 6 tin.   This type of alloy is called **valve bronze,** and when the copper content is higher it is called **valve copper.** It should cast readily without cracks, checks, or porous spots.   The **M bronze** of the U.S. Navy, for valves, contains 86 to 91% copper, 6.25 to 7.25 tin, 1.5 to 5 zinc, 1 to 2 lead, and not over 0.25 iron.   It has a tensile strength of 34,000 psi and elongation 17%.   It will withstand continuous temperatures up to 500°F, while the 85–5–5–5 bronze can be used for temperatures only to 400° F.   **ASTM alloy No. 1,** designated as high-grade red casting brass for general castings, contains 85% copper, 1.5 lead, 6.5 tin, and 4 zinc.   It has a tensile strength of 36,000 psi, elongation 25%, and Brinell hardness 50 to 60.

Nickel is added to composition metals for hydraulic and steam castings to densify the alloy and make the lead more soluble in the copper.   One company uses an alloy containing 84.5% copper, 5 lead, 7 zinc, 2.5 tin, and 1 nickel for casting injectors and lubricator parts.   The nickel is added to the melt in the form of nickel shot which contains 5 to 7% silicon to deoxidize the metal and increase the hardness.   For heavy high-pressure hydraulic castings as much as 5% silicon may be added to alloys containing nickel, giving strengths above 40,000 psi.   The alloys for machinery bearings usually contain higher proportions of tin or lead, or both, and are classified as high-lead bronze, but **Johnson bronze No. 44,** for bearings, contains 88% copper, 4 tin, 4 lead, and 4 zinc.   The **hardware bronze** used for casting hardware and automobile fittings to be highly polished and plated is likely to be a true copper-zinc brass or a leaded brass with only a small amount of lead.   **Oreide bronze,** a term still used in the hardware industry, was the metal employed for carriage and harness hardware. It contains 87% copper and 13 zinc, and polishes to a golden color. The hardware bronze of the Chase Brass & Copper Co. contains 86% copper, 12.25 zinc, and 1.75 lead. Aluminum, even in small amounts, is not considered a desirable element in the red casting brasses as it decreases the ductility and requires more care in casting.

CONCRETE. A construction material composed of portland cement and water combined with sand, gravel, crushed stone, or other inert material such as expanded slag or vermiculite. The cement and water form a paste which hardens by chemical reaction into a strong stonelike mass. The inert materials are called **aggregates,** and for economy no more cement paste is used than is necessary to coat all the aggregate surfaces and fill all the voids. The concrete paste is plastic and easily molded into any form or troweled to produce a smooth surface. Hardening begins immediately, but precautions are taken, usually by covering, to avoid rapid loss of moisture since the presence of water is necessary to continue the chemical reaction and increase the strength. Too much water, however, produces a concrete that is more porous and weaker. The quality of the paste formed by the cement and water largely determines the character of the concrete.

Proportioning of the ingredients of concrete is referred to as designing the mixture, and for most structural work the concrete is designed to give compressive strengths of 2,500 to 5,000 psi. A rich mixture for columns may be in the proportion of 1 volume of cement to 1 of sand and 3 of stone, while a lean mixture for foundations may be in the proportion of 1:3:6. Concrete may be produced as a dense mass which is practically artificial rock, and chemicals may be added to make it waterproof, or it can be made porous and highly permeable for such use as filter beds. An air-entraining chemical may be added to produce minute bubbles for porosity or lightweight. Normally, the full hardening period of concrete is at least 7 days. The gradual increase in strength is due to the hydration of the tricalcium aluminates and silicates. Sand used in concrete was originally specified as roughly angular, but rounded grains are now preferred. The stone is usually sharply broken. The weight of concrete varies with the type and amount of rock and sand. A concrete with traprock may weigh 155 lb per cu ft. Concrete is stronger in compression than in tension, and steel bars or mesh is embedded in structural members to increase the tensile and flexural strengths. In addition to the structural uses, concrete is widely used in precast units such as block, tile, sewer and water pipe, and ornamental products.

Concrete blocks may be made from cement, sand, and gravel, or from cement and sand alone. For insulating purposes they may be made with cement and asbestos fibers.   **Careystone,** of the Philip Carey Co., is cement with asbestos pressed into blocks, into corrugated slabs for roofing and siding, or into sheathing and wallboard.   **Reinforced concrete** is a combination of concrete with a steel internal structure generally composed of rods or metal mesh.   The strength of the concrete is thus greatly increased, and it is used for buildings, bridges, telegraph poles, roads, and fences. **Nonslip concrete,** for steps, is made by applying aluminum oxide grains, sizes 3 to 60 mesh, to the concrete before it hardens.

Insulating concrete and lightweight concretes are made by special methods, or by the addition of spongy aggregates.   Slag may be used for this purpose.   **Aerocrete,** of the Aerocrete Corp., is a porous lightweight concrete produced by adding aluminum powder to the cement.   The reaction between the aluminum flakes and the lime in the cement forms hydrogen bubbles.   **Durox,** of the U.S. Durox Co., produced as lightweight blocks, panels, and wall units, is a **foamed concrete** made from a mixture of sand, lime, cement, and gypsum, with aluminum powder which reacts to produce $3CaO \cdot Al_2O_3$ and free hydrogen which generates tiny bubbles.   The set material contains about 80% cells and has only about one-third the weight of ordinary concrete with a compressive strength of 1,000 psi.   **Acid-resistant concrete,** developed by the Dutch firm of Ocrietfabrick, and called **Ocrete,** is made by passing the well-dried concrete products through a treatment tunnel containing **silicon tetrafluoride** gas, SiF_4, which converts the free lime to calcium fluoride.   In the center of the concrete parts where moisture still remains, silicic acid is formed and fills the pores.   The parts have increased density and are more wear-resistant than the original concrete.

Many prepared aggregates are used for special-purpose concretes.   **Haydite** is a lightweight aggregate made by kiln-burning shale to produce a material of expanded cellular structure.   Haydite concrete weighs below 100 lb per cu ft, but is not as strong as gravel concrete.   **Superock** and **Waylite** are trade names for expanded aggregate made by treating molten slag with water or steam.   **Microporite** is a German aggregate made by steam-treating ground silica and lime.   **Calicel,** of the Keasbey & Mattison Co., is a lightweight spongy aggregate made by fusing silicates of lime and alumina and cooling to produce a stone of cellular structure.   **Fluftrok,** of the Fluftrok Corp., is a lightweight aggregate made by heating obsidian in a kiln.   The rock expands to 16 times its original volume, forming a porous material.   Mixed with about 10% portland cement it is made into building blocks that are light and strong.

CONDUCTORS. A term usually applying to materials, generally metals, employed for conducting electric current, though heat conductors and sound conductors have important uses.   Silver is the best conductor of electricity, but copper is the most commonly used, and the current-carrying capacity of all other conductors is measured from pure copper as the standard, although the conductivity of pure copper is only 97.6% that of silver. In copper, where there is no cross-linking of free electrons by oxygen, the conductivity is increased. Because of the low conductivity of zinc, the brasses have low current-carrying capacity, but are widely used for electrical connections and parts because of their workability and strength. The electrical conductivity of aluminum is only 63% that of copper, but it is higher than that of most brasses. **Copper wire** for electrical conductors in high-temperature environments has a plating of heat-resistant metal. The conductors of American Metal Climax, Inc., are made of oxygen-free copper with an outer electroplate of Type 430 steel. The wire has a service temperature to 1300°F. **Aluminum wire,** usually with a steel core, is used for power transmission because of the long spans possible. Steel has a conductivity only about 12% that of copper, but the current in a wire tends to travel near the surface, and the small steel core does not reduce greatly the current-carrying capacity. Aluminum is now much used to replace brass in switches and other parts. Aluminum wire for electrical equipment and to replace copper wire for housing installations is usually commercially pure aluminum with small amounts of alloying elements such as magnesium which give strength without reducing the conductivity. **Alcoa alloy 2EC,** of the Aluminum Co. of America, is such a conductor alloy of high strength and low creep. Plastics, glass, and other nonconductors are given conductive capacity with coatings of transparent lacquer containing metal powder, but **conductive glass** usually is made by spraying on at high temperature an extremely thin invisible coating of tin oxide. Coated glass panels are available with various degrees of resistivity.

CONTACT METALS. Metals used for contact points or surfaces for electrical apparatus. The qualities required are high electrical conductivity, corrosion resistance, and wear resistance. Because of its superior electrical conductivity and corrosion resistance, silver is preferred where great wear resistance is not needed. Fine silver, of 99.9% purity, is used widely as a contact facing, but where greater hardness is required coin silver of 10% copper content is used. Nickel brass is harder, is lower in cost, and has good resistance to corrosion and wear, and the conductivity is sufficiently high for pushbuttons. Nickel silvers are now used for low-cost electrical contacts and conductors although the conductivity is only about 8% that of copper. They have high tensile strengths, are corrosion resistant without plating, and are easily worked. **Silver-zinc alloy,** with 75% silver, is used for telephone jacks. **Spring contacts** have 92.5% silver, 7 copper, and 0.5 tin. **Radio contacts** contain 72 to 92.5% silver and 7.5 to 28% copper. **Internally oxidized alloys,** such as **silver-cadmium,** give good resistance to arc corrosion.   The alloy is heated in an oxidizing atmosphere to disperse cadmium oxide in the silver matrix.   Higher hardness is obtained in the alloy with small amounts of copper, nickel, tin, or manganese.   For current breakers, a high percentage of tungsten carbide may be added.

Where high resistance to arcing is required tungsten is employed, but the conductivity is low.   However, for high-speed equipment it is more important to have a heat-resistant metal than to have high electrical conductivity.   An ordinary low-melting contact metal will last only about 25,000 contacts, while a telegraph relay may operate 6 million times a day. For relays and signal instruments, platinum hardened with iridium, palladium, osmium, or rhenium may be used.   Telephone contacts may be pure palladium, although this metal has only 20% of the conductivity of platinum.   Sensitive relays are of **platinum-palladium alloy** with 25% palladium.   **Ignition contacts** are of **platinum-osmium alloy** with 35% osmium. For low contact pressure and high corrosion resistance an **osmium-rhodium alloy** with 35% rhodium may be used.   It has high hardness.

Silver-tungsten alloys, made by powder metallurgy, combine the conductivity of silver with the arc resistance of tungsten, and are used for contacts.   **Silver-tungsten alloys** of the Gibson Electric Co. contain 20 to 90% silver with hardnesses 80 to 100 Rockwell B and good conductivity. For use in electric-discharge drilling tools the alloys contain only small amounts of silver.   **Tungsten Alloy EDM,** of Firth Sterling, Inc., is such an alloy.   **Gibsiloy M-12** is a **silver-molybdenum alloy** containing a high percentage of molybdenum, used for circuit breakers subject to high arcing. **Gibsiloy KA alloys** are alloys of silver with cadmium oxide to prevent welding and sticking of switches and relays.   The conductivity is from 75 to 80% that of copper.   **Silver-graphite alloys,** with low percentages of graphite, are used for contacts that require rubbing or sliding lubrication and for brushes and collector rings.   **Aeralloy,** of the H. A. Wilson Co., is a **platinum-ruthenium alloy** with high ruthenium content, used for aircraft magneto contacts.   It is hard and gives long wear life.   **Wilco No. 6 alloy,** for automotive magneto contacts, is platinum hardened with ruthenium. **Gibsiloy UW-8,** used for contacts for oil-immersed motor starters, is a copper-tungsten alloy.

COOLANTS.   Liquids employed for quenching steels in heat treating, although this term is also used to designate the cutting oils used on machines to cool the work and improve the cutting.   When water is used for the normal water-hardening steels, it may be modified with soda or other material to give a less drastic and more uniform cooling.   A water bath containing 5% sodium hydroxide gives uniform rapid cooling.   Oils are used in cooling or quenching baths for many alloy steels, as they remove the heat from the steel more uniformly and not as suddenly as water.

Quenching oils are usually compounded, although fish oils alone are sometimes employed. Fish oils, however, have offensive odors when heated. Vegetable oils alone are likely to oxidize and become gummy. Animal oils become rancid. Lard and palm oils give low cooling rates, while cottonseed, neatsfoot, and fish oils give more rapid cooling. Mineral oils compounded with fish, vegetable, or animal oils are sold under trade names and vary considerably in their content. **Oil-quenching baths** are usually kept at a temperature of not over 150°F by providing cooling pipes. **Tempering oils** differ from quenching oils only in that they are compounded to withstand temperatures up to about 525°F.

COPAL. A general name for fossil and other hard resins found in nearly all tropical countries and used in making varnishes and lacquers, adhesives, and coatings, though now largely replaced by synthetic resins. Copals are distinguished by their solubility in chloral hydrate. All of the copals are also soluble in alcohol, linseed oil, and turpentine. The hardest varieties come from Africa. **Zanzibar copal,** from the tree *Trachylobium verrucosum,* or from species no longer existent, is one of the hardest of the varnish resins, with a melting point of 240 to 360°C, compared with 180 to 200°C for **Congo copal** from Guinea. **Madagascar copal** is from the tree *Hymenaca verrucosa,* and is darker than Zanzibar. **Gum benguela** is a semifossil resin from the tree *Gulbourtia copaifera* of West Africa. The melting point is 170°C. Many species of trees of the genus *Hymenaca* of tropical America furnish copals. **Animi gum,** or **gum Zanzibar,** is from the stem of the plant, *H. coubarii* of Zanzibar and East Africa. It belongs to the group called **East African copals,** but is distinguished from other copals by its solubility in alcohol. The specific gravity is about 1.065, and melting point 245°C. The **Brazilian copal** known as **jutahycica resin** is from the jatahy tree which is plentiful in the Amazon Valley. **Jatabó** and **trapucá resins** are fossil copals from species of *Hymenaca* of the state of Bahia, Brazil. **Congo gum,** chiefly from the tree *Copaifera demensi,* is the most insoluble of the natural resins, but after thermal processing, it is soluble in a wide range of solvents. The specific gravity of copals is from 1.04 to 1.13. The colors vary from white through yellow, red, brown, to brownish black.

The commercial copals are classed in five groups: East African, West African, Manila, East Indian, and South American. The name copal is applied in Indonesia to the resin of the tree *Agathis alba,* closely related to the kauri pine. The types include **Manila copal, Loba,** and **Boea.** In Malaya the tree has been classed as *Dammara orientalis* and the copal is known as **white dammar.** In the Philippines the tree is called **almacido,** and the gum, Manila copal. There are seven grades of Manila copal, from No. 1 pale, scraped chunks, to the No. 7 dust. Hard copal is harder than dammar, and has a higher melting point, but the hardness of the resin depends greatly upon the seasoning time in the ground. The semihard and soft copals are produced directly from the trees by tapping. The melting point of copal from *A. alba,* collected 1 day after tapping, averages 85°C, compared with 105°C when collected 3 months after tapping. **Fossil copal,** or **copalite,** of high quality, is obtained by separation from the low-grade coals of Utah, which contain about 5%. The copal has an amberlike appearance of light yellow to red color, with a specific gravity of 1.02 to 1.06, melting point 165°C, and hardness about the same as that of Congo gum.

COPPER. One of the most useful of the metals, and probably the one first used by man. It is found native and in a large number of ores, but it is much less plentiful than nickel and some other metals. Its apparent plentifulness is only because it is easy to separate from its ores and is often a by-product from silver and other mining. It is yellowish red in color, tough, ductile, and malleable, gives a brilliant luster when polished, has a disagreeable taste and a peculiar odor. It melts at 1083°C and boils at 2310°C. The specific gravity is 8.91, and weight 0.321 lb per cu in. It is the best conductor of electricity next to silver, with a conductivity 97% that of silver. The coefficient of expansion is 0.000017 per deg C. The tensile strength of cast copper is from 17,000 to 20,000 psi with elongation 40 to 50%. Annealed wrought copper has a strength of 32,000 psi with elongation 56%, while cold-drawn copper has a tensile strength of 56,000 psi with elongation 6%. The **bus-bar copper** used by the electrical companies has a tensile strength up to 40,000 psi. Copper does not have the ductility of brass for metalworking, but does not work-harden as rapidly as brass. Pure copper is difficult to cast, as the molten metal absorbs oxygen, forming oxides. Copper is used for electrical conductors; for making brasses and bronzes; for sheathing, fittings, and pipe; and for cast articles. Small amounts of copper are added to some steels to give corrosion resistance.

More than half of all copper is sold in **wirebars** of about 200 lb for rolling and drawing. About 25% of the copper used in the United States goes into electrical manufactures, and about 15% into electrical wiring, but besides its use for electrical conductivity, copper is a supplementary metal with a wide variety of uses in all manufacturing. The annual consumption of copper in the United States holds very constantly to about 1.33% that of steel, but in war years when much is used in cartridge and shell cases the percentage is about 1.87. Price is sensitive to industrial conditions. In 1930 the New York average copper price was 17 cents per lb; in 1932 it was 5 cents. During the Second World War the price was fixed at 12 cents, and during the Korean War, 1950–1951, it was set at

24 cents.   It rose to 50 cents in 1956 and dropped to 20 cents in 1958, rising again with increased industrial demand.   Without normal wartime restrictions on nonmilitary usage during the Vietnam War the quoted price in 1970 was 60 cents, with higher prices in what was called the Gray Market.

The United States produces more than half of all copper.   Chilean and Congo copper are next in importance, but Peru, Canada, and other countries are important producers.   **Secondary copper** is a term used to designate copper recovered from smelting scrap and old copper alloys.   The production of secondary copper is about 40% that of new copper.   Copper is marketed in three general grades: electrolytic, lake, and casting.   **Electrolytic copper** has a purity not less than 99.9%.

Commercial wrought copper in bars, wire, sheets, and rods is marketed as **electrolytic tough pitch, oxygen-free copper, phosphorized copper,** and **arsenical copper.   Silver-bearing copper** is 99.9% pure, carrying 8 to 30 oz of silver per ton.   The silver raises the annealing temperature, and the metal is used for high-speed motors, commutators, and semiconductor cases.   **Amsil,** of American Metal Climax, Inc., with 15 oz of silver per ton, has the electrical conductivity at room temperature of pure copper. Electrolytic tough pitch, or **high-conductivity copper,** deoxidized with phosphorus without residue and annealed, has an electrical resistance of 0.67879 microhm per cu in. at 20°C, which is taken as 100% conductivity.   This copper has the disadvantage of becoming brittle when heated and of not giving a high finish.   Much of the copper marketed for commercial use as copper contains slight amounts of silicon or other hardener, but even as little as 0.40% arsenic or other impurity will reduce the electrical conductivity drastically.   Oxygen-free copper is 99.9% pure, has high conductivity, is not subject to brittleness, and will withstand much cold working. Phosphorized copper contains residual phosphorus.   It has high strength, higher hardness and resistance to corrosion than other copper, but has lower conductivity.   **Amphos,** of American Metal Climax, Inc., is phosphorized copper which has enough phosphorus to raise the softening point, giving better workability.   It comes in billets for producing high-strength wrought metals.   Anaconda condenser tubes of arsenical copper contain 0.25% arsenic.   **Lake copper,** from the Lake Superior region, usually contains arsenic.

Hard-drawn wire or sheet arsenical copper has a tensile strength of 60,000 psi, while the annealed material has a strength of 32,000 psi and elongation 45%.   **Cast copper** has only 80 to 90% the conductivity of wrought copper.   A special grade of copper having high ductility, high conductivity, and fatigue resistance is made without melting by converting electrolytic cathode copper directly into rods and strips by rolling at elevated temperature in a reducing atmosphere.   The Phelps Dodge Corp. produces this copper under the name of **PDCP copper.   Electro-sheet copper** is thin sheet copper produced by electrodeposition.   It is marketed by the American Brass Co. in roll sheets of 1 to 7 oz per sq ft (0.0013 to 0.0094 in.), and is used for roofing and dampproofing.   **Rocan copper** is a sheet copper of Revere Copper & Brass, Inc., having high strength and resistance to corrosion fatigue.   It contains 0.50% arsenic.   It is used for roofing and leaders.   **Roofing copper** is hot-rolled soft copper sheet in 14- to 32-oz weights, but **cornice copper** is cold-rolled to a hard temper.   The 16-oz sheet is used for gutters and leaders.   **Braziers' copper** is a term used to designate heavy sheets of copper weighing from 1.5 to 6 lb per sq ft, used for coppersmiths' work.   **Coppersmiths' copper** is hot-rolled, soft-temper, heavy sheets up to $\frac{1}{2}$ in.   **Copper foil** is sheet copper less than 0.005 in. in thickness.   **Free-cutting copper** is deoxidized copper containing up to 0.70% tellurium, marketed in rods for making screw-machine products.

Cupaloy, of the Westinghouse Electric Corp., is nearly pure copper containing small amounts of silver and chromium, the chromium forming a hard crystalline structure and the silver acting as a stabilizer.   When temper-hardened the wrought alloy has a tensile strength of 70,000 psi, elongation 15%, and Rockwell B hardness 80 to 85.   It has 85% the electrical conductivity of copper.   It is used for welding electrodes, commutator bars, and strong electrical parts.   The **copper-silver alloy** developed by the Army Signal Corps for high-strength electrical conductors contains 6.5% silver.   Wire drawn to a tensile strength of 160,000 psi has a conductivity 70% that of copper.   When drawn to a tensile strength of 116,000 psi, it has a conductivity 85% that of copper.   The fine-gage **copper-silver wire** of Handy & Harman contains 94% copper and 6 silver, and has a tensile strength of 150,000 psi and a conductivity 70% that of copper.   **Copper-iron alloy,** with 12.5% iron, has a tensile strength of 150,000 psi and conductivity 50% that of copper.   For this alloy magnesium is used as a deoxidizer in pouring the ingots at high temperature. **Switch copper,** of the Revere Copper & Brass, Inc., is electrolytic copper in shaped bars of close tolerance and burnished finish.   It is used for switchblades and electrical parts.   The minimum tensile strength is 36,000 psi, elongation 15% min, and Rockwell B hardness 35 to 65.

Copper powder is usually chemically reduced copper in noncrystalline form.   It is used in a liquid vehicle for copper coating, or for sintering. The powder produced electrolytically is flaked, suitable for pigment but not for sintering.   Copper powder of the Nichols Copper Co. is 98.3% pure, and all particles pass through a 350-mesh screen.   Copper powder in flake form for paint and ink pigment is produced by the Phelps Dodge Corp. by electrolysis.   The cathodes are coated with oxidized castor oil, and the deposited copper is in crystalline flakes easily reduced to a fine grade of red bronze powder by stamp milling.   **Fernlock,** of Malone Metal Powders, Inc., is **dendritic copper powder,** with dendritic, or fernlike, grains.   The fine grains of large surface area give high green strength and a uniformly dense structure in the sintered molding.   **Copper shot** is copper in the form of round globules, used chiefly in alloying gold and silver. **Leaded copper** is copper in commercial rods and shapes containing a small amount of lead to make it free-machining.   **Sulfur copper** is copper containing about 0.3% sulfur, marketed in rods by the Bridgeport Brass Co., for the production of screw-machine products.   It is free-cutting, but does not machine as easily as tellurium copper, and has higher electrical conductivity, about 96% that of standard copper.   Copper is also marketed in the form of master alloys such as **copper aluminum,** which is an alloy of 50% copper and 50 aluminum melting at 1070°F, used for making aluminum alloys.

COPPER ACETATE. Also known as **crystals of Venus.**   A dark-green crystalline poisonous powder of the composition $Cu(CH_3COO)_2 \cdot H_2O$, of specific gravity 1.882 and melting point 115°C.   It is soluble in water and in alcohol.   It is used as a pigment in paints, lacquers, linoleum, inks, and for making artificial verdigris or patina on copper articles.   It is also used as a catalyst in making phthalic anhydride plastics.   When used for mildewproofing cotton cloth, the copper precipitates out to form the **waxate,** or copper soap coating.   **Verdigris** is an old name for basic copper acetate as a blue-green pigment, but the name is now usually applied to the bluish-green corrosion crust on copper.   The greenish-brown crust known as **patina,** formed on bronze, is esteemed as a characteristic of antiquity.   It is a basic sulfate of copper, usually with oxides of tin, copper, and lead. Another green copper paint pigment is **copper carbonate,** also called **artificial malachite.**   It is a poisonous powder of the composition $CuCO_3 \cdot Cu(OH)_2$, made by adding sodium carbonate to a solution of copper sulfate.   The specific gravity is 3.7.   It is insoluble in water.   As a pigment it is also named **mineral green, Bremen green,** and **mountain green.**

COPPER ORES.   There are about 15 copper ores of commercial importance, and these are widely distributed in almost all parts of the world. More than 40 countries produce copper on a commercial scale.   The average copper content of ores, however, is usually low, and copper would be an expensive metal if it were not for the valuable by-products, silver, gold, nickel, and other metals.   About 80% of the ores in the United States contain only 1.17 to 1.57% copper and are concentrated before smelting. The direct smelting ores average from 4.3 to 6.2% copper.   The most important ore of copper is **chalcopyrite,** also known as **copper pyrites** and **yellow copper ore.**   It occurs widely distributed, associated with other minerals, and may carry gold and silver.   It is the chief copper ore in many parts of the United States, Canada, Chile, Africa, England, and

Spain. Chalcopyrite is a sulfide of copper and iron, $CuFeS_2$, containing theoretically 34.5% copper. It usually occurs massive, with a hardness of 3.5 and a specific gravity of 4.2. The color is brass yellow, with greenish-black streaks. To obtain the copper, the ore is first smelted with enough sulfur to combine with all of the copper, producing a matte which is a mixture of CuS_2 and FeS together with impurities. Air is then blown through the molten matte in a reverberatory furnace, converting the iron sulfide to oxide and the sulfur to sulfur dioxide. The remaining copper is cast into pigs which are called **blister copper**, owing to its blistered appearance. Blister copper contains 96 to 99% copper, with various metals and arsenic and sulfur. It is not used commercially, but is refined in furnaces or electrolytically. The **cement copper** shipped from Cyprus contains about 51% copper.

Chalcocite is another important ore found in Montana, Arizona, Alaska, Peru, Mexico, and Bolivia. It is a **cuprous sulfide,** Cu_2S, containing theoretically 79.8% copper. It usually occurs massive, but crystals are also found. The hardness is 2.5 to 3, and the specific gravity 5.5. It has a shining lead-gray color. But the emerald-green platy mineral **chalcolite** is a **copper-uranium mica,** $CuO \cdot 2UO_3 \cdot P_2O_5 \cdot 8H_2O$, with a high percentage of uranium oxide, U_3O_8. **Tennantite,** or **gray copper ore,** found in Colorado, Wyoming, and Montana, has the composition $3Cu_2S \cdot As_2S_3$, with iron and antimony. When much of the arsenic is replaced by antimony it is called **tetrahedrite.** **Azurite,** also called **blue copper carbonate** and **chessylite,** is found with other copper ores. It is a basic carbonate of copper, $Cu(OH)_2 \cdot 2CuCO_3$, occurring in azure-blue crystals. **Malachite,** or **green copper ore,** is an important carbonate ore, $Cu(OH)_2 \cdot CuCO_3$, containing theoretically 57.4% copper. It has a bright-green color, specific gravity 3 to 4, and hardness 3.5 to 4. **Cuprite,** or **red copper ore,** is a cuprous oxide, Cu_2O, containing theoretically 88.8% copper. It occurs usually massive, but sometimes in crystals. The specific gravity is 6, and the hardness 3.5 to 4. The color may be various shades of red, with an adamantine luster in the clear crystalline form, or a dull earthy luster in the massive varieties. Cuprite is found in the copper deposits in Arizona, and is one of the ores in Chile, Peru, and Bolivia.

Bornite, also known as **horseflesh ore, peacock ore,** and **variegated ore,** is an important ore of copper widely distributed and mined in Chile, Peru, Canada, and the United States. It occurs in massive form, having a bronze color that turns purple on exposure. The composition is Cu_5FeS_4, having theoretically 63.3% copper. It has a metallic luster and a hardness of 3. **Chrysocolla** is a highly refractory ore of copper occurring in the oxidized parts of copper veins of Arizona and New Mexico. It is a hydrous copper silicate of the composition $CuSiO_3 \cdot 2H_2O$. It occurs in compact masses with a specific gravity of 2 to 2.4 and a hardness of 2 to 4.

The color is green to bluish. It was used as a green pigment by the ancient Greeks. Large reserves of this ore occur in the Gambia and other copper regions of Africa, and it is treated by high-temperature methods to obtain the copper. **Atacamite** is an ore found in Bolivia, Arizona, and Australia. It is a copper chloride with copper hydroxide, $CuCl_2 \cdot 3Cu(OH)_2$, generally found in confused crystalline aggregates, fibrous or granular. The hardness is 3 to 3.5, specific gravity 3.75, and the color may be various shades of green. The unique copper ores of Japan, called **kuromono,** are complex sulfide-sulfate replacement minerals.

Much **native copper** metal occurs in the Lake Superior region, particularly in Michigan, but it occurs irregularly and not in continuous veins. The Ontonagon boulder of native copper in the National Museum, weighing 3 tons, came from Michigan. A mass of native copper found in 1847 was 10 ft long and weighed 6 tons. The largest ever found weighed 18 tons.

COPPER OXIDE. There are several oxides of copper, but usually the term refers to **red copper oxide,** or **cuprous oxide,** Cu_2O, a reddish crystalline powder formed by the oxidation of copper at high temperatures. It also occurs naturally in cuprite ore. The specific gravity is 6.0 and the melting point 1235°C. It is insoluble in water but soluble in acids and alkalies. It is used in coloring glass and ceramics red, in electroplating, and in alternating-current rectifiers. **Rextox,** of the Westinghouse Electric Corp., is copper upon which a layer of copper oxide has been formed. Electric current will flow easily from the oxide to the copper, but only with difficulty from the copper to the oxide. It may be used for transforming alternating current into pulsating direct current. **Black copper oxide,** or **cupric oxide,** CuO, is a brownish-black amorphous powder of specific gravity 6.4 and melting point 1065°C. It is used for coloring ceramics green or blue. In its natural ore form it is called **tenorite.** **Copper hydroxide,** formed by the action of an alkali on the oxides, is a poisonous blue powder of the composition $Cu(OH)_2$ and specific gravity 3.37. It is used as a pigment.

COPPER-SILICON ALLOYS. Silicon up to 6.7% is soluble in copper, and forms hard, strong alloys very resistant to corrosion. Above 3% silicon, the alloys are too hard for most uses. The plain copper-silicon alloys are used for springs. Manganese up to about 1% may be added to improve the working qualities, and the ratio of silicon to manganese is kept at 3:1. When hard-drawn these alloys can have tensile strengths up to 150,000 psi. **Webert alloy,** of the American Brass Co., contains small amounts of silicon and manganese, and is used for pressure die castings. Tensile strength is 85,000 psi. **Arcoloy,** of the American Radiator

Co., is a casting alloy containing 97.25% copper, 2.63 silicon, 0.12 iron, and 0.01 phosphorus. **Cusiloy A,** of the Scovill Mfg. Co., has 95.5% copper, 3 silicon, 1 iron, and 0.5 tin. It is marketed in various forms, and the annealed wire has a tensile strength of 60,000 psi and elongation 50%. **Herculoy 418,** of Revere Copper & Brass, Inc., contains 96.5% copper, 3 silicon, and 0.5 tin. The tensile strength of the annealed sheets is 60,000 psi with elongation 50%, and of the cold-rolled sheet 85,000 psi, with elongation 10%. The weight is 0.308 lb per cu in., melting point 1820°F, but the electrical conductivity is only 8.1% that of copper. It is resistant to many chemicals, and is used as a structural metal in the chemical industries.

Alloys of this type but with lower silicon contents are softer and more ductile and are suited to cold heading, spinning, and drawing. **Herculoy 419** has 2% silicon and 0.25 tin. **Herculoy 421** has 1.5% silicon and 0.25 manganese. This alloy in annealed sheet form has a tensile strength of 38,000 psi and elongation 35%, while the cold-rolled sheet has a tensile strength of 60,000 psi and elongation 10%. The copper-silicon alloys are marketed in sheets, rods, bars, shapes, tubes, forgings, and ingots for castings. Both the silicon-tin and the silicon-manganese types are single-phase, and the castings are dense and fine-grained, suitable for such uses as valves.

COPPER STEEL. Steel containing up to 0.25% copper and very low in carbon, employed for construction work where mild resistance to corrosion is needed and where the cost of the higher-resistant chromium steels is not warranted. It is employed in sheet form for culverts, ducts, pipes, and for such manufacturing purposes as washing-machine boilers. The alloy steels containing considerable copper for special purposes are not classed as copper steels. The copper neutralizes the corroding influence of the sulfur in the steel, and also aids in the formation of a fine-grained oxide that retards further corrosion. Copper is not added to unalloyed high-carbon steels because it causes brittleness and hot-shortness. Since the carbon content of copper steel is usually very low, the material is in reality a **copper iron.** Unless balancing elements, especially nickel, are present, more than 0.2% copper in steel may cause rolling defects. Molybdenum in small quantities may also be added to give additional corrosion resistance, and the percentage of carbon may be raised to 0.40% when about 0.05% molybdenum is added. **Toncan iron,** of the Republic Steel Corp., has this composition, and has a tensile strength of 40,000 to 48,000 psi, elongation 32 to 40%, and weight 0.283 lb per cu in.

The copper-bearing iron specified for culverts by the ASTM contains not less than 0.20% copper and not more than 0.10% carbon, manganese, phosphorus, sulfur, and silicon as impurities. But up to 0.20% phosphorus in very-low-carbon copper iron increases the corrosion resistance and the strength.   The German corrosion-resistant copper iron known as **Resista** has 0.10% phosphorus with not more than 0.10% carbon.   The tensile strength is up to 85,000 psi with elongation 20%.   **Cor-Ten,** of the U.S. Steel Corp., is a structural steel containing somewhat more phosphorus with 0.30% copper, 0.5 chromium, 0.10 carbon, and 0.5 silicon. The tensile strength is 70,000 psi, the elongation is 22%, and the corrosion resistance is about 5 times that of plain carbon steel.   **Lyonore metal** is an open-hearth steel of the Lyon Conklin Co. containing small amounts of chromium and nickel.   In the low-alloy steels from 0.5 to 1.5% copper can be added as the copper graphitizes the free carbides, and these steels have excellent drawing characteristics and a high fatigue limit. **Yoloy,** of the Youngstown Sheet & Tube Co., is a high-tensile, corrosion-resistant structural steel with 1% copper, 2 nickel, and up to 0.05 max carbon.   The tensile strength is up to 90,000 psi, with elongation 30%. **Copperoid** is a plain copper steel of this company.   Other copper-bearing steels are **Cop-R-Loy,** of the Wheeling Steel Co.; **Apolloy,** of the Apollo Steel Co.; **Gohi iron,** of the Newport Rolling Mill Co.; **Newaloy,** of the Newton Steel Co.; **Beth-Cu-Loy,** of the Bethlehem Steel Co.; **Copper-Clude,** of Spang, Chalfant & Co., Inc.; and **Weircoloy,** of the Weirton Steel Co.   The **Tri-Ten steel** of the U.S. Steel Corp. is a manganese-nickel-copper low-alloy structural steel balanced to withstand shock at low temperatures.

COPPER SULFATE.   Also called **bluestone** and **blue vitriol.**   An azure-blue crystalline lumpy material of the composition $CuSO_4 \cdot 5H_2O$ and specific gravity 2.286.   It is soluble in water and insoluble in alcohol. When heated, it loses its water of crystallization and melts at 150°C.   It is used for wet electric-battery solutions, for copperplating, in dyestuffs, in germicides, in coppering steel, and in various chemical processes.   In its natural form, called **chalcanthite,** it is a rare mineral found in arid regions and deposited from the water in copper mines.   It is produced as a by-product in copper refineries, or by the action of sulfuric acid on copper or copper oxide.

CORAL.   A shiny, hard, calcareous material valued for jewelry, buckles, beads, and novelties.   It is a growth composed of the skeletons of *Corallium nobile* and other species of aquatic protozoa.   The structures are built up by these creatures into forms like leafless trees or shrubs, fans, mushrooms, or cups.   **White coral** is common and not used commercially. The most valuable is the **red coral,** a twiglike species that grows about 12 in. high with thin stems.   **Pink coral** and **black coral** are also valued. Red and pink corals come from the Indian Ocean and off the coast of

Northeastern Africa.   Black coral is from Southeastern Asia.   The red and black varieties are very hard and take a beautiful polish.   The pink is softer, with a more delicate appearance, and is used for beads.   The rate of growth of coral is very slow.   The gleaming white sand of tropical beaches called **coral sand** is usually not coral, but consists of the disintegrated limy skeletons of the seaweed *Halimeda opuntia*.

CORDAGE. A general term for the flexible string or line of twisted fibers used for wrapping, baling, power transmission, and hauling. **Cordage fibers** are any materials used for making ropes, cables, twine, and cord.   In general, the cordage fibers are hard compared with those used for weaving into fabrics, but cotton and some other soft fibers are used for cord.   **Twine** is cordage less than $\frac{3}{16}$ in. in diameter, and composed of two or more rovings twisted together.   **Rope** is cordage made by twisting several yarns into strands, and then twisting the strands into a line. A **cable** is a strong rope, usually referring to the large sizes of special construction.   **Cord** is an indefinite term for twine, but is, more specifically, the soft cotton twines used for wrapping.   The term **string** is used for the weak cotton cords used for wrapping light packages.   **Seaming twines** are made of flax fibers.   **Seine twine** is a three-strand cotton twine with 2 to 56 plies per strand.   Most of the **binder twine** is made from sisal, but **Indian twine** is made from jute.   Ramie fiber is used for marine twines.   Binder twine has 15 turns to the foot and 500 ft to the pound. **Baler twine,** for heavier work, has 12 turns to the foot and 125 ft to the pound.   Before the advent of synthetics, about half of American strong cordage was from Manila hemp, and about 30% from sisal. Manila hemp is very resistant to seawater.   Sisal is used for the cheaper grades of rope, but it absorbs water easily.   True hemp is considered a superior fiber for strong ropes.   Untarred **hemp rope** is used for elevator cables, and tarred hemp is employed for ship cables.   **Marine rope,** used by the Navy, was formerly true hemp, then Manila hemp, and is now often synthetic fiber. Most industrial rope has at least three strands, each strand having at least two yarns, and may be hard lay, medium lay, or soft lay.   Twisting may be S twist or Z twist, conforming approximately to the shape of these letters. Cable twist has the twists alternating in each successive operation. Hawser twist, to give greater strength and resilience, has the plies twisted SSZ.

Cordage fibers are also obtained from a wide variety of plants.   Generally, after the fibers are retted, the softer and finer fibers are separated out for use in weaving into fabrics and the harder and coarser fibers are marketed as cordage fibers.   **New Zealand hemp,** or **New Zealand flax,** is a strong cordage fiber obtained from the leaves of the swamp lily, *Phormium tenax,* grown in New Zealand and Argentina.   The fibers are white, soft, and lustrous.   One variety of the plant reaches a height of 16 ft and the other variety 6 ft.   **Olona fiber,** grown in Hawaii and used locally for fishnets, is from the nettle plant, *Touchardia latifolia.*   The bast fibers of the bark of the slender branches are soft and flexible, are very water-resistant, and have a tensile strength 3 times that of Manila hemp.   **Gravatá** is a Brazilian name for the very long and resistant fibers from the leaves of the pineapple plant, *Ananas sagenaria.*   The leaves of this species are up to 7 ft in length.   The fiber known as **widuri** of Indonesia is bast fiber from the tree *Calotropis gigantea* which yields the madar kapok.   It has great strength and is resistant to seawater.   It is used for ropes and fishnets.   **Agel fiber** is from the stems and leaves of the **gebang palm** of the Celebes where the various grades are used for sailcloth, rope, and fishnets, and the coarser fibers are woven into Bangkok hats. The fibers from the leafstalks are fine and white. **Caraguatá** is a strong, highly resistant fiber from the plant *Bromelia balansea* of Paraguay.   It was employed by the Indians for making hammocks, and is now used for cordage and burlap fabrics.

Synthetic fibers are also used for cordage.   **Nylon rope** is about twice as strong as **Manila rope,** is lighter, and because of its property of stretching rapidly but recovering slowly it makes a desirable rope for lifting and towing, giving a smooth, shock-absorbing pull.   Nylon ropes are used for pulling airplane gliders and for tugboat lines.   **Mylar rope,** of U.S. Plastics Rope, Inc., is made by slitting Mylar film, and stretching and spinning the strands.   A three-strand rope of 1 in. diameter has a breaking strength of 18,000 psi, compared to 9,000 lb for manila rope of the same size.   Moisture absorption is less than 0.3%.   Elongation at 50% of breaking strength is about 4.75%.   **Saran rope,** made by the Plymouth Cordage Co. for chemical-plant use, is made of three strands of vinylidene chloride monofilament.   The breaking strength is 70% that of manila rope, and it is flexible and chemical-resistant, but it is not recommended for temperatures above 170°F.   The **M-cord** of the same company is a strong wrapping twine made with a core of manila fiber wrapped with a tough, smooth paper.   Nylon and some other plastics have a tendency to fray in cordage, and may be coated with polyvinyl butyral to give abrasion resistance.   **Chemclad** is **rayon cordage** coated with polyvinyl chloride. The nylon rope of Rochester Ropes, Inc., is steel-wire rope with an extruded coating of nylon in various colors, used for automotive brake cables, aircraft control cables, and luggage handles.   **Glass rope,** woven from continuous filaments of glass fiber, is used for chemical and electrical applications where resistance to chemicals or electrical insulation is needed. It is strong, but is expensive and has low flexing strength.   It comes in diameters from $\frac{1}{4}$ to $\frac{3}{4}$ in.   **Fiberglas cordage,** of the Owens Corning Fiberglas Co., is marketed in diameters from $\frac{1}{64}$ to $\frac{1}{8}$ in. and made of continuous filament or staple glass fibers.   The $\frac{1}{8}$-in. untreated continuous-filament cord has a breaking strength of 258 lb.   **Newbroc,** of Hitemp Wires, Inc., is chemical-resistant and heat-resistant thread and cord made with continuous-filament glass fiber impregnated with Teflon plastic, in diameters from 0.0046 to 0.076 in.   It remains flexible at subzero temperatures and is used for lacings and for sewing canvas.   The 0.020-in. fiber has a tensile strength of 70 lb.   Cordage made with high-modulus polyethylene fiber has high tensile strength and elasticity, and is used for tugboat hawsers.

CORE OILS. Liquid binders used for sand cores in foundry work.   The binder should add strength to the core, should bake to a dry bond, should not produce much gas, and should burn out after the metal is poured, so that the sand core will collapse.   Linseed oil is considered one of the best binders, but it is usually expensive and may be mixed with cheaper vegetable oils or with mineral oil.   In some cases fish oil or rosin is also used. Molasses, dextrin, or sulfite liquor may be included in prepared core oils. The specifications of the American Foundrymen's Association call for 50% raw linseed oil, 25 H grade rosin, and 25 water-white kerosene, with no fish oil.   A good core oil should have a specific gravity of 0.9368 max, flash point 165 to 200°F, Saybolt viscosity 155 min, and iodine number 154, and should be of light color.   However, any drying oil or semidrying oil can be used to replace all or part of the linseed oil.   Perilla and corn oils are used, and core oils of linseed- and soybean-oil mixtures have good strength.   The liquor from sulfite pulp mills contains lignin and is used as a core binder.   **Glutrin,** of the Robeson Process Co., is a core oil with sulfite liquor.   **Truline** is a resinous binder in powder form marketed by Hercules Inc.   **Uformite 580,** of the Rohm & Haas Co., is a **core binder** especially for aluminum sand cores.   It is a modified urea-formaldehyde resin which bakes in the core at 325 to 375°F, and will break down in the core at temperatures above 450°F.   **Cycor 191,** of the American Cyanamid Co., is a urea-formaldehyde resin in water solution for sand cores for short-cycle baking in an electronic oven.   **Dexocor** and **Kordex,** of the Corn Products Sales Co., are dextrin binders.

CORK. The thick, spongy bark of a species of oak tree, *Quercus suber,* grown in Spain, Portugal, Italy, Algeria, Morocco, Tunisia, and to a limited extent the United States.   It is used for bottle stoppers, insulation, vibration pads, and floats for rafts and nets.   The scrap cuttings are used for refrigerator insulation, packing for the transportation of fruits, and the manufacture of linoleum and pressed products.   When marketed as **granulated cork,** this material usually comes in sizes of $\frac{1}{2}$ in. and No. 8 mesh.   Cork is also used natural or in the form of pressed composition for gaskets, oil retainers, roll coverings, polishing wheels, and many other articles. The material has a cellular structure with more than 50% of the volume in air cells. The cell structure is peculiar, and each cell is in contact with 14 neighboring cells, and because of lack of capillarity it does not absorb moisture. When dried, cork is light, porous, easily compressed, and very elastic. It is one of the lightest of solid substances, the specific gravity being 0.15 to 0.20. It also has low thermal conductivity. Charring begins at 250°F, but it ignites only with difficulty in contact with flame. The cork tree grows to a height of about 30 ft. After it has attained the age of about 25 years it can be barked in the summer, and this barking is repeated every 8 or 10 years. The quality of the bark improves with the age of the tree, and with proper barking, a tree will live for 150 years or more. The thickness of the bark varies from 1/2 to 2 in. **Cork bark** is shipped in bales of 170 lb, and **cork wastes** in bales of 148 lb.

Brazilian cork is the bark of the tree *Angico rayado,* called **pao santo bark,** and also from the trees *Piptadenia incuriale* and *P. colomurina.* The bark has a cellular structure and, when ground, has the appearance of a low grade of true cork, but is softer. It is suitable for insulation. The trees grow in northeastern Brazil, beginning to produce in 12 to 15 years, and reproducing in about 5 years. A substitute for cork for insulation packings and acoustical panels is marketed by the Palmetex Corp. under the name of **Palmetex.** It is the compressed pith from the internal fibers of the saw-tooth palm, *Cerano repens,* of the eastern Gulf states. It has lower heat conductivity than cork, but without a binder it is more friable.

CORKBOARD. Construction board made by compressing granulated cork and subjecting it to heat so that the particles cement themselves together. It is employed for insulating walls and ceilings against heat and cold, and also as a sound insulator. **Cork tile** is corkboard in smaller, regularly shaped blocks for the same purposes. The natural gum in the cork is sufficient to bind the particles, but other binders may be used. Corkboard produced by the Armstrong Cork Co. is marketed in sheets in thicknesses from 1 to 6 in. The weight is from 6 to 10 lb per cu ft, depending upon the amount of compression and the binder. The heat conductivity is 0.304 Btu per hr per bd ft for 1°F difference in temperature between the sides, or about one-third that of wood. Corkboard retains the properties of cork, being cellular, and without capillarity or tendency to absorb moisture. **Novoid corkboard,** of the National Cork Co., is made with both large and small granules tightly packed to leave only small air spaces. **Joinite,** of L. Mundet & Son, Inc., is a corkboard for use under machinery to deaden vibration and noise. **Corkoustic** is a sound-absorbent corkboard of the

Armstrong Cork Co. for walls and ceilings.   It has a sound-absorbing coefficient of 0.30 compared with 0.032 for brick walls.   **Linotile,** of the same company, is a resilient tile made of powdered cork, oxidized oils, and color pigments.

CORN. One of the most important food grains of the world for both human and animal consumption, but also used industrially for the production of starch, glucose, alcohols, alcoholic beverages, and corn oil.   Corn was unknown to Europe before the discovery of America, where it was one of the chief foods of the Indians from Canada to Patagonia.   In Europe and in foreign trade it is known by its original name of **maize,** and the Incan name of **choclo** still persists in South America for the grains on the cob.   In Great Britain corn means all hard grains including wheat, and the American term corn is an abbreviation of the name **Indian corn.** In South Africa it is called **mealies.**   Corn is the seed grain of the tall leafy plant *Zea mays,* of which there are innumerable varieties or subspecies.   It grows in temperate climates and in the high elevations of the tropics where there is a warm growing season without cold nights, but high commercial yields are limited to areas where there is a combination of well-drained friable soil, plenty of moisture, few cloudy days, and no night temperatures below 66°F during the growing season of 4 months. Corn is an unnatural plant, with seeds not adapted for natural dispersal; it does not revert to a wild species.   It is a product of long selection. No wild plants have ever been found, but it is believed to have been a cultivated selection from the grass **teosinte** of Mexico.

About half the world production of corn is in the United States and Argentina, but large amounts are also grown in southern Europe and northern India.   About the end of the nineteenth century corn constituted 15% of the energy value of the American diet, but the direct use of corn as food is now low, although its derivatives enter largely into prepared foodstuffs.   **Confectionery flakes,** used as an additive and conditioner in candy, cookies, and pastries, is a bland, yellowish, flaky powder made from degerminated yellow corn.   It contains 8% protein, and is pregelatinized to require no cooking.   The **pregelatinized corn flour** of the General Foods Corp., used to improve texture, binding qualities, and flavor of bakery products, is a cream-colored powder which hydrates in cold water and needs no cooking.   It contains 82% starch, 9 protein, 1 corn oil, and 8 moisture, and is a food ingredient rather than an additive, although it may replace 10% of the wheat flour.   In the corn belt of the United States, 40% of the corn grown is used for hog feed, while in the dairy belt the hogs are fed on skim milk, buttermilk, and whey, and most of the corn is fed to poultry or shipped commercially.

Corn grains grow in rows on a cob enclosed by leafy bracts.   They are high in starch and other food elements, and form a valuable stock feed especially for hogs and poultry.   Nearly 90% of the commercial corn in the United States is for animal feed.   But corn is one of the cheapest and easiest sources of starch, and much of the Argentine corn is used for starch and glucose.   The average yield of corn grains is about 24 bu per acre, although yields as high as 50 bu per acre are obtained.

Sweet corn is a type of **soft corn,** Z. *saccharata,* cultivated for direct eating and for canning.   There are about 70 varieties grown widely on farms, but not cultivated for industrial applications.   **Popcorn,** Z. *everta,* has very hard, small, elongated oval grains which, when heated, explode into a white, fluffy, edible mass without further cooking.   It was used by the Indians as a food for journeys, and is now grown for food and confections.   The corns cultivated for stock feeding and for starch and glucose are varieties of **flint corn,** Z. *indurata,* and **dent corn,** Z. *indentata.* Flint corn has long cylindrical ears with hard smooth grains of various colors.   Dent corn has larger and longer ears which are tapering, with white or yellow grains.   About 300 varieties of dent corn are grown in the corn belt of the United States, while the Argentine corn is largely flint varieties which yield high starch.   Much of the corn grown in the United States is **hybrid corn.**   This is not a species, but consists of special seed stocks produced by crossing inbred strains.   It is resistant to disease and gives high yields.   The **waxy corn** grown in Iowa produces a starch comparable with the root starches.   In the wet milling of corn for the production of cornstarch, the germ portion of the grain is separated as a by-product and used for the extraction of **corn oil, or maize oil.**   The germ contains 50% oil which is a bright-yellow liquid of specific gravity 0.920 to 0.925, iodine value 123.   It contains 56% linoleic, 7 palmitic, 3 stearic, and the balance mainly oleic acid.   About 1.75 lb of oil per bushel of corn is obtained by crushing the germ, and another 1.4% is obtained by solvent extraction.   About 1% of oil remains in the **corn oil meal** marketed as feed.   Corn oil is used as an edible oil as a substitute for olive oil and in margarine, and also in soaps, belt dressings, core oils, and for vulcanizing into factice.   Corn syrups and glucose are produced directly from the starchy corns.   **Zein,** of the Corn Products Refining Co., is a protein extracted from corn.   It is dissolved in alcohol to form a lacquerlike solution which will dry to a hard, tough film.   It is used as a substitute for shellac and is more water-resistant than shellac.   **Zein G210** is a water solution of prolamine protein extracted from corn gluten, used to produce hard, tough, grease-resistant coatings, and for formulating polishes and inks.   **Corn tassels** are used for livestock and poultry feed. They are a rich source of vitamins.   About 270 lb of dry tassels are produced per acre.   **Cornstalks** contain up to 11% sugars, usually about 8% sucrose, and 2 other sugars, but little sugar is produced commercially from this source, the stalks being used as cattle feed.   **Corncobs** are used to produce **cob meal** for feeds, and also processed to produce lignin, xylose, furfural, and dextrose.   **Korn-Kob,** of Kube-Kut, Inc., is granular corn cob used as an abrasive material for finishing metal parts in tumbling barrels.   It is tougher than maple and will not absorb water as wood granules do.

Kafir corn is a variety of sorghum grass not related to true corn.   The plant is a tall annual with a stalk similar to corn but with smaller leaves and long cylindrical beardless heads containing small round seed grains. It is widely grown in tropical Africa, and a number of subvarieties are grown on a limited scale in Kansas, Texas, and Oklahoma.   The grain is similar in composition to corn, but has a peculiar characteristic flavor.   It is used as flour in bread mixtures, and in biscuit and waffle flour.

CORROSION-RESISTANT ALLOYS.   Any metals that offer resistance to corrosion, such as the alloys of the noble metals, the stainless steels, and the nickel-copper alloys, but the name usually refers to the highly alloyed, chemical-resistant chromium or chromium-nickel ferrous alloys not otherwise specifically designated as stainless iron or steel.   Many of these alloys are also heat-resistant, or resistant to scaling at high temperatures, and there is no real dividing line between the corrosion-resistant and the heat-resistant alloys.   Corrosion is a gradual disintegration by chemical reaction in the molecule.   Oxygen, for example, reacts with iron to form iron oxides, and the rapidity of action depends upon temperature or other energy factors.   Acids, sulfur compounds, and other chemicals cause such molecular reactions, and terms such as heat-resistant or acid-resistant refer to types of corrosion resistance.   These properties are obtained in an alloy by balancing the composition to form highly stable compounds with a minimum of free electrons.

Chromium-iron alloys and **chromium-nickel alloys** give corrosion-resistant and acid-resistant properties within certain limits as defined by the stainless irons and steels.   Other elements extend the range of these limitations.   Molybdenum gives added resistance to hot oils.   Copper neutralizes the corrosive effects of any sulfur present, and combines with the phosphorus to give an added corrosion-resistant element.   It also graphitizes any free carbides and absorbs any oxygen present to form fine-grained oxides.   With molybdenum in the alloy the copper content can be considerable without making the alloy brittle.   Silicon gives resistance to acids except to hydrofluoric acid.   The nickel gives strength to the alloys and prevents corrosion cracking.   These alloys are white in color and take a brilliant polish even when the iron content is high, and they are thus valued for food-processing equipment.   Those with some cobalt are more silvery in color and have increased resistance.

The use of chromium, nickel, and cobalt in ferrous alloys for acid resistance antedates the invention of the stainless steels. An old alloy under the name of **Borcher's metal** had 30 to 36% chromium, with nickel, cobalt, and sometimes molybdenum. **Sideraphite** was an iron alloy with a high content of nickel, and with copper and tungsten. A complex alloy with high resistance to hot acids and alkalies and to chloride solutions is **Hastelloy,** of Union Carbide Corp., nominally 45.5% nickel, 22 chromium, 6.5 molybdenum, 2.5 cobalt, 2 columbium and tantalum, 1.5 manganese, 1 tungsten, 0.5 titanium, 0.8 max carbon, and the balance iron. The tensile strength of the sheet is 106,000 psi, with elongation of 52% and a Rockwell B hardness of 84. It is easily fabricated and machined, but is expensive and difficult to obtain in times of materials shortages.

Most of the corrosion-resistant alloys are now marketed under trade names. **Lebanon No. 34,** of the Lebanon Steel Foundry, for resistance to sulfuric and hydrochloric acids, has 20% chromium, 30 nickel, 3.25 molybdenum, 5 copper, and 3.25 silicon. The tensile strength is 72,000 psi and elongation 45%. One grade of **Midvaloy,** of the Midvale-Heppenstall Co., contains 60% nickel, 10 chromium, 2 tungsten, and 1.5 manganese. When cast, this alloy has a tensile strength of 65,000 psi and elongation 24%. **Cooper alloy 531,** of the Cooper Alloy Corp., contains 10 to 14% chromium, 27 to 30 nickel, 3 to 4 each of molybdenum and copper, 0.10 max carbon, 0.5 to 0.8 each of silicon and manganese, and 0.4 to 0.6 antimony. The antimony forms an insoluble copper-antimony film that gives added resistance to hydrochloric acid. It is also highly resistant to nitric and sulfuric acids. **Noncorrodite,** of the Millbury Steel Foundry Co., is a high-chromium steel for castings. The silicon irons, containing high percentages of silicon, also form a group of corrosion-resisting metals much used for cast parts for chemical equipment.

Many of the tool steels, especially those used for molds, forging dies, and hot-work tools, are highly corrosion-resistant and heat-resistant, but are classified by their uses rather than as corrosion-resistant materials. Likewise, many construction steels for special uses may be classed as stainless steels but are high alloys and are not steels in the restricted sense of the term. **Armco 21-6-9,** of the Armco Steel Corp., for resistance to oxidation at high temperatures and to the action of leaded gasolines, contains about 21% chromium, 6 nickel, 9 manganese, 1 silicon, 0.3 nitrogen, and 0.08 carbon. The tensile strength is 100,000 psi, and at a temperature of 1200°F it retains a strength of 58,000 psi. **Armco 22-4-9,** for nuclear-reactor construction, has higher strength, 162,000 psi, and higher hardness, 345 Brinell, but its higher carbon content, up to 0.60%, makes it susceptible to intergranular corrosion if used in hot corrosive solutions. **HA alloy,** recommended by the Alloy Casting Institute for cast fittings and headers for handling sour crude oil at temperatures to 1200°F, contains 9% chromium, 1 molybdenum, 1 max silicon, 0.5 manganese, and not over 0.20 carbon.

Vitallium, an alloy of 65% cobalt, 35 chromium, and 5 molybdenum, originally used for surgical straps because of its noncorroding quality and high resistance to body acids and fluids, was adopted during the war for turbosuperchargers for military planes because of its resistance to hot gases at continuous temperatures of about 1500°F. This metal has good precision casting qualities. **Eatonite,** of the Eaton Mfg. Co., used for valve facings to withstand the corrosive action of hot gases and antiknock fuels, is a similar material but with tungsten instead of molybdenum, and part of the cobalt replaced by nickel. **Stellite No. 21,** of Union Carbide Corp., used for buckets for turbosuperchargers, contains 28% chromium, 6 molybdenum, 0.25 carbon, and the balance cobalt. At 1800°F it has a tensile strength of 32,900 psi.

The high cobalt content in this class of alloy is now usually reduced by additions of titanium. An alloy used by the Germans to resist the hot gases of jet aircraft, under the name of **Tinidure,** contained 30% nickel, 15 chromium, 2 titanium, and 0.15 carbon. **Chromadure,** for the same purpose, contained 12% chromium, 18 manganese, 0.65 vanadium, 0.5 silicon, and 0.15 carbon. This alloy was used because of the shortage of nickel, and had poor creep resistance. **Berlaloy** contained 17% chromium, 15 nickel, 2 molybdenum, and 1.15 combined cobalt and tantalum.

CORUNDUM. A very hard crystalline mineral used chiefly as an abrasive, especially for grinding and polishing optical glass. It is aluminum oxide, Al_2O_3, in the alpha, or hexagonal, crystal form, usually containing some lime and other impurities. It is found in India, Burma, Brazil, and in the states of Georgia and the Carolinas, but most of the commercial production is in South Africa. The physical properties are theoretically the same as for synthetic alpha alumina, but they are not uniform. The melting point and the hardness are generally lower because of impurities, and the crystal structure also varies. The hexagonal crystals are usually tapered or barrel-shaped, but may be flat with rhombohedral faces.

The Hindu word corundum was originally applied to gemstones. The ruby and the sapphire are corundum crystals colored with oxides. **Oriental topaz** is yellow corundum containing ferric oxide. **Oriental emerald** is a rare green corundum, but it does not have the composition of the emerald, and the use of the name is discouraged in the jewelry industry. The clear-colored crystals are sorted out as gemstones, and the premium ore is the large-crystal material left after sorting. Some material is shipped in grain. The crude ore is washed, crushed, and graded. There are four grades of abrasive corundum shipped from South Africa: Grade A is over 92% Al_2O_3, Grade B is 90 to 92%, Grade C is 85 to 90%, and Grade D is under 82%.   In the United States most of the natural corundum used for optical-glass grinding is in sizes from 60 to 275 mesh, while the grain sizes for coarse grinding and snagging wheels are 8 to 36 mesh.   Corundum is now largely replaced by the more uniform manufactured aluminum oxide, and even the name **synthetic corundum,** or the German name **Sintercorund,** is no longer used.

COTTON. The white to yellowish fiber of the calyx, or blossom, of several species of plants of the genus *Gossypium* of the mallow family. It is a tropical plant, and the finest and longest fibers are produced in hot climates, but the plant grows well in a belt across southeastern United States and as far north as Virginia.   It requires a growing season of about 200 days with an average summer temperature about 75°F and a dry season during the time of ripening and picking.   Cotton was used in India and China in most ancient times, was described in Greece as a vegetable wool of India, but was not used in Europe until the early Middle Ages.   All of the Asiatic species are short-staple, and the long-staple cottons are from species cultivated by the American Indians.   Cotton has a wide variety of uses for making fabrics, cordage, and padding, and for producing cellulose for plastics, rayon, and explosives.

There are many species and varieties of the plant, yielding fibers of varying lengths, coarseness, whiteness, and silkiness.   Cotton fiber contains 88 to 96% cellulose, dry weight, together with protein, pectin, sugars, and 0.4 to 0.8% wax.   Ordinary treatment does not remove the wax.   When the wax is removed by ether extraction the fiber is stronger but is harsh and difficult to spin.   The most noted classes are Sea Island, Egyptian, American upland, Brazilian, Arabian, and Nanking.   **Sea Island cotton,** *G. barbadense,* was native to the West Indies, and named when brought to the islands off the American coast.   It is grown best in hot moist climates, and is the longest, finest, and silkiest of the fibers.   Its length varies from $1\frac{1}{4}$ to $2\frac{1}{2}$ in., but it is cream-colored.   **Egyptian cotton,** grown in Egypt and the Sudan, came originally from Peruvian seed. **Peruvian cotton,** *G. acuminatum,* is long-staple, silky, has strength and firmness, but is brownish in color.   The **tanguis cotton** from Peru is valued for fine English fabrics.   Egyptian cotton, or **maco cotton,** is next in quality to Sea Island.   The long staple is from $1\frac{1}{8}$ to $1\frac{3}{8}$ in., and the extra-long staple is over $1\frac{3}{8}$ in.   It has a fine luster and great strength. It also has a remarkable twist, which makes a strong, fine yarn.   It is used chiefly in yarns for the production of fine fabrics, thread, and automobile-tire fabrics.   **American-Egyptian cotton** is grown in Arizona.   The fiber has an average length of $1\frac{5}{8}$ in., and has the same uses as the Egyptian. **Upland cotton,** *G. hirsutum,* is the species originally grown by the Aztecs of Mexico.   It is whiter than Egyptian or Sea Island cotton, and is the easiest and cheapest to grow.   There are 1,200 named varieties of this plant.   The short-staple upland has a fiber under $1\frac{1}{8}$ in. in length, and can be spun only into coarse and medium yarns, but it is the most widely grown of cottons in the United States.   Long-staple upland is from $1\frac{1}{8}$ to $1\frac{3}{8}$ in. in length.   The common grades of cotton fiber in the United States vary in diameter from 0.0006 to 0.0009 in.   Sea Island cotton fiber is as fine as 0.0002 in., compared with 0.001 in. for the coarse Indian cotton.   The cotton of India, China, and the Near East is from *G. herbaceum,* and the fiber is short, $\frac{3}{8}$ to $\frac{3}{4}$ in., but strong.

In normal times, in spite of a surplus of cotton in the United States, the Indian cotton is imported for use in blankets and in hard fabrics. The **Chaco cotton** grown in Argentina is from Louisiana seed, and probably 70% of total world cotton is now grown from American upland seed although it varies in characteristics due to differences in climate and soil. Cotton is shipped in bales of 478 lb each.   **Cotton yarn** is put up in 840-yd hanks, and the number, or count, of cotton yarn indicates the number of hanks to the pound.   No. 10 cotton yarn, for example, has 10 hanks, or 8,400 yd, to the pound.

Mercerized cotton, developed in 1851 by John Mercer, is prepared by immersing the yarn in a stretched condition in a solution of sodium hydroxide, washing, and neutralizing with dilute sulfuric acid.   Mercerized yarns have a silky luster resembling silk, are stronger, have less shrinkage, and have a greater affinity for dyes.   The fabrics are used as a lower-cost substitute for silk, or the yarns are mixed with silk.

Absorbent cotton is cotton fiber that has been thoroughly cleaned and has had its natural wax removed with a solvent such as ether.   It is very absorbent and will hold water.   It is marketed in sterilized packages for medical use.   **Cotton batting** is raw cotton carded into matted sheets, and put up usually in rolls to be used for padding purposes.   **Cotton waste,** used in machine shops for wiping under the general name of waste, is usually in mixed colors, but the best grades are usually all white, of clean soft yarns and threads without sizing.   It is very oil-absorbent.   **Comber waste** consists of the lengths of fiber up to 1 in., and is not sold with the waste from yarns, but is sent to mills that produce cheap fabrics.   **Cotton fillers,** used as reinforcing materials in molding plastics to replace wood flour or other fibers, are made by cutting cotton waste or fabric pieces into short lengths.   **Filfloc,** of the Rayon Processing Co., is cotton flock for this purpose; **Fabrifil** is cotton fabric cut into small pieces; **Cordfil** is cotton cord cut into very short pieces.   These fillers give greater strength to the molded product than wood flour.   **Acetylated cotton** is a mildewproof cotton made by converting part of the fiber to cellulose acetate by chemical treatment of the raw fiber.   **Aminized cotton** is produced by reacting the raw cotton with aminoethyl sulfuric acid in an alkaline solution.   Amino groups are chemically combined with the cellulose of the fiber, which gives ion-exchange properties and good affinity for acid wool dyes, and also absorption of metallic waterproofing agents. **Cyanoethylated cotton** is produced by treating the fibers with acrylonitrile, caustic, and acetic acid. The acrylonitrile reacts with the hydrogen of the hydroxyl groups, forming cyano ethyl ether groups in the fiber. The fibers retain the original feel and appearance, but have increased heat strength, better receptiveness to dyes, and strong resistance to mildew and bacteria attack. Another method of adding strength, chemical resistance, and dyeing capacity to cotton fibers is by treating them with anhydrous mono-ethylamine. It forms an amine-cellulose complex instead of the hydrogen bond. Since cotton is nearly pure cellulose, many chemical variations can be made, and even some dyes may alter the fiber.

COTTON FABRICS. Cotton cloth is made in many types of weave and many weights, from the light, semitransparent **voile,** made of two-ply, hard-twisted yarn, and **batiste,** a fine, plain-woven fabric, to the coarse and heavy canvas and duck. They may have printed designs, as in **calico** which is highly sized; or yarn-dyed plain stripes, plaids, or checks, as in **gingham;** or woven figures, as in **madras.** **Muslin,** a plain white fabric widely used for garments, filtering, linings, and polishing cloths, has a downy nap on the surface. The full-bleached cloth is usually of finer yarns than the unbleached. Cheaper grades are usually heavily sized, and the sizing is removed in washing. **Crinoline** is an open-weave fabric of coarse cotton yarn, and is heavily sized to give stiffness. It was originally made as a dress fabric of horsehair and linen. It is now used for inter-linings, and as a supporting medium where a stiff, coarse fabric is needed. **Wigan** is similar to crinoline, but is more closely woven. **Percale** is a softer fabric similar to calico but with a higher yarn count. **Swiss** is a plain-woven, fine, thin muslin, stiff and crisp. **Dotted Swiss** is a very thin, transparent, plain-woven cotton with colored swivel or lappet woven dots. It is sized stiff and crisp. **Dimity** is a plain-woven, sheer fabric with ribs in the form of corded checks or stripes. It comes in white or colors. **Organdy** is a plain-woven, thin, transparent crisp fabric stiffened with shellac or gum, usually in delicate color shades. All of these are plain-woven. **Poplin** is a lateral-ribbed fabric, often mercerized. It is heavier than broadcloth. **Rep** has a rib produced by heavy warp yarns. **Crash** is a rough-texture fabric with effects produced by novelty yarns. **Charmeuse** in the cotton industry designates a soft, fine, satin-weave fabric of Egyptian cotton used industrially as a lining material. **Chambray** is a plain-woven, lightweight cotton similar to gingham but with no pattern and a dyed warp and white filling. It is used for linings, shirtings, and dresses. **Cotton damask** is a type of jacquard-figured fabric having warp sateen figures in a filling sateen ground or vice versa. The surface threads of the figures lie at right angles to those in the ground so that the light is diffusely reflected, causing them to stand out in bold relief. It is usually of coarse or medium yarns, 15's to 30's, bleached and finished to imitate linen. **Cotton crepe** is a cotton fabric having a pebbled surface. The pebble is produced with sulfonated oil, lauric acid ester oil, or other soluble oil which is washed off after the treatment. When the word crepe is used alone, it usually signifies silk crepe. **Domet** is a warp-stripe cotton fabric similar to flannel, used for apparel linings. **Venetian** is a highly mercerized, stout, closely woven fabric with the yarn in reverse twist. It is used as a lining for hats, pocketbooks, and luggage. **Cottonade** is a coarse heavy cotton fabric made to look like woolens and worsteds in weave and finish, and is used for men's suit linings. **Eiderdown** is a cotton fabric of knitted soft-spun yarns, heavily napped on one or both sides. It is used for shoe and glove linings. **Tarlatan** is a thin cotton fabric with a net weave, heavily sized, used for linings. **Cambric** was originally a fine, thin, hard-woven linen but is now a strong cotton fabric of fine weave and hard-twist yarn. It was used as **varnished cambric** and **varnished cloth** with a coating of insulating varnish or synthetic resin. The strength exceeded that of the older **varnished silk** but was less than **varnished rayon.** A 0.003- to 0.008-in.-thick fabric of Irvington Varnish & Insulator Co. made from high-tenacity rayon has a dielectric strength of 1,000 volts per mil.

Strex, developed by the U.S. Rubber Co., is an elastic full-cotton fabric that has 100% elongation without the use of rubber. It is made from yarn that has a twisting like a coiled spring. The fabric is used for surgical bandages, gloves, and wearing apparel. **Glass cloth** is a name given to cotton fabric made of smooth, hard-twisted yarns which do not lint, and is used for wiping glass, but this is now largely replaced by silicone-treated soft papers. It may be of the type known as **sponge cloth,** which is a twill fabric of **nub yarn** or honeycomb effect, or it may be of **terry cloth,** which has a heavy loop pile on one or both sides. Another **wiping cloth** for glass and instruments where a lint-free characteristic is important is made with a cotton warp and a high-tenacity rayon filling. It is strong, soft, and absorbent. The **Nun-Lint cloth** of Rittenbaum Bros., Inc., for polishing glass and fine instruments, is a nonwoven fabric made by binding the cotton fibers with a plastic.

Twill is a fabric in which the threads form diagonal lines. **Tackle twill,** used for football uniforms, is also used in olive-drab color for Army parachute troop uniforms. It is a strong, snag-resistant fabric having a right-hand twill with a rayon warp and combed cotton filling. It is 8.5 oz per sq yd, 180-lb warp, and 80-lb filling. **Cavalry twill** is not a cotton cloth, but is of worsted or rayon twill woven with a diagonal raised cord.   It is similar to **gabardine** except that gabardine has a single cord and cavalry twill has a double cord.   **Bedford cord** has the cord running lengthwise, and the cord is more pronounced than in cavalry twill.   These three are usually woolen fabrics, but **parade twill** is a mercerized cotton fabric of combed two-ply yarns, with the fabric vat-dyed in tan.   It is employed for work clothing.   **Byrd cloth** is a wind-resistant fabric made originally for Antarctic use.   It has a close-twill weave with about 300 threads per in.   It is soft and strong, and comes in light and medium weights.   **Sateen** is fabric made with a close-twill weave of mercerized cotton in imitation of satin.   The wind-resistant sateen used for military garments is a 9-oz cotton fabric in satin weave with two-ply yarn in warp and filling.   The thread count is 112 ends per in., 68 picks per in.   The fabric is singed, mercerized, and given a water-repellent finish. **Foulard** is a highly mercerized twill-woven cotton with a silky feel.   It is plain or printed, and is used for dresses or sportswear.   **Cotton duvetyn** is a twill-woven, mercerized cotton fabric with a fine nap that gives it a soft velvety feel.   It is much used for apparel linings and pocket linings. **Brilliantine** is a lightweight fabric with a cotton warp and a twilled worsted filling, yarn-dyed.   It is used for apparel linings.

Balloon cloth is a plain-woven cotton fabric used originally as a base material in making coated fabrics for the construction of balloons, but now used in many industries under the same name.   The various grades differ in weight, thread count, and strength.   Grade HH, having 120 threads per inch in each direction, is most widely used.   A Navy fabric has a weight of 2.05 oz per sq yd and a tensile strength of 38 psi in each direction.   When several layers are built up and rubberized or plastic-coated, they may be on the bias, and the outside layer coated with aluminum paint to reduce the heat absorption.   **Gas cell fabric** is a single-ply, coated balloon cloth.   **Airplane cloth,** formerly used for fabric-covered training planes, is a plain-woven cotton fabric of two-ply combed yarns mercerized in the yarn.   It is usually 4 oz per yd, but wide fabrics may be 4.5 oz.   The cotton is $1\frac{1}{2}$ in. min staple, and the threads per inch are 80 to 84.

COTTONSEED OIL. One of the most common of the vegetable oils, used primarily as a food oil in salad oils, margarine, cooking fats, and for sardine packing.   It also has a wide industrial use in lubricants, cutting oils, soaps, quenching oils, and in paint oils, although soybean oil is used as a more abundant substitute.   The hydrogenated oil is widely used as a cooking grease.   Its food value is lower than that of lard, but it is often preferred because it is odorless and does not scorch.   Cottonseed oil is expressed from the seed of the cotton plant, *Gossypium,* and is entirely a by-product of the cotton industry, its production depending upon the cotton crops.   The yield of seed is 890 lb per 478-lb bale of cotton, and 100 lb of seed yields 15.5 lb of oil.   When the seeds are crushed whole, the oil is dark in color and requires careful refining.   The American practice is to hull the seeds before crushing.   The oil is colorless, nearly odorless, and has a specific gravity of 0.915 to 0.921.   Upland cottonseed contains about 25% oil, which has 40% linoleic, 30 oleic, and 20 palmitic acids.   The residue is caked and sold as **cottonseed meal** for cattle feed and fertilizer.   About 900 lb of meal and from 450 to 620 lb of hulls are obtained per short ton of seed, the yield of hulls varying inversely with the yield of linters.   The American oil has an iodine value up to 110, and a saponification value of 192 to 200.   Egyptian and Indian oils are inferior in color, and the Indian oil has a fishy odor and a fluorescence.   **Cottonseed stearin** is the solid product obtained by chilling the oil and filtering out the solid portion.   It has an iodine value between 85 and 100, and consists largely of palmitin.   It is used for margarine, soap, and as a textile size.   Winter-yellow cottonseed oil is the expressed oil after the stearin has been removed.

COTTONWOOD.   The wood of the large trees *Populus monilifera, P. deltoides,* and other species of the United States and Canada.   It is a soft wood of a yellowish-white color and a fine, open grain.   It is sometimes caller poplar, or **Carolina poplar,** and **whitewood.**   The weight is about 30 lb per cu ft.   The wood is easy to work, but is not strong and warps easily.   It is used for packing boxes, paneling, and general carpentry.   The *P. deltoides,* or **eastern cottonwood,** used in paneling, has a specific gravity when kiln-dried of 0.43, a compressive strength perpendicular to the grain of 650 psi, and a shearing strength parallel to the grain of 660 psi.   This wood comes from the lower Mississippi Valley.   **Black cottonwood** is from the large tree *P. trichocarpa,* of the Pacific Coast.   The wood is used for boxes, excelsior, and pulpwood.   It has a light color, uniform texture, and fairly straight grain.   **Swamp cottonwood,** *P. heterophylla,* also called **river cottonwood,** grows in the Mississippi and Ohio River valleys.   **Balsam poplar** is from the tree *P. balsamifera,* of the northeastern states.   It is a soft weak wood used chiefly for containers and for making excelsior.   The tree also goes under the Algonquin name of **tacamahac.**   The wood may be marketed as cottonwood even when mixed with aspen.   It is an excellent paper-pulp material.   The name cottonwood is also applied to the wood of the tree *Bombax malabaricum,* native to India, which produces kapok.   The wood is white in color, soft, and weighs about 28 lb per cu ft.   It is much softer than cottonwood.

CREOSOTE.   Also called **dead oil** and **pitch oil.**   A yellowish poisonous oily liquid obtained from the distillation of coal tar.   It has the odor of carbolic acid, a specific gravity of 1.03 to 1.08, and a boiling point of 200 to 300°C.   The crude **creosote oil** is used as a wood preservative and as a harsh disinfectant.   Creosote is also obtained in the distillation of pine wood tar, and is then a yellowish liquid with a smoky odor, a mixture of phenols and derivatives.   Creosote oil contains **acridine,** a dibasic pyridine, used as an insecticide, and is also the source of other complex heterocyclic ring compounds.   The distillation of wood also produces charcoal, gas, and **methyl acetate,** a sweet-smelling liquid of the composition $CH_3COO \cdot CH_3$, and boiling point 54°C, used as a solvent.

Cresol, also known as **cresylic acid** and as **methyl phenol,** obtained in the distillation of coal tar, is a mixture of three isomers of cresol, $CH_3 \cdot C_6H_4 \cdot OH$, and **xylenol,** $(CH_3)_2 \cdot C_6H_3 \cdot OH$.   The crude material is a brownish-yellow liquid solidifying at 11°C.   It is used for making plastics, in ore flotation, in refining petroleum, in soap-emulsion cutting oils as a disinfectant, and in medicine as a strong antiseptic such as **Lysol,** which is a 50% solution of cresols in liquid soap.   It is also used in the production of other chemicals.   **Orthocresol** is a colorless solid with a melting point of 30°C and a boiling point of 191.5°C.   It is soluble in alcohol, but only slightly soluble in water.   It is used in the manufacture of cumerones, disinfectants, and fumigants, and as a plasticizer.   **Metacresol** is a colorless yellow liquid freezing at 12°C and boiling at 202.8°C. It is used in the manufacture of photographic developers, nitrocresols, disinfectant soaps, printing inks, paint and varnish removers, as a preservative in leathers, glues, and pastes, in the reclaiming of rubber, and in making synthetic resins, perfumes, and pharmaceuticals.   **Paracresol** is a colorless solid melting at 36°C and boiling at 202.5°C.   It is the least soluble of the cresols.   It is used in the manufacture of cresotinic acid dyes, disinfectants, and pharmaceuticals.

CRYOLITE. A mineral of the composition Na_3AlF_6, found in commercial quantities in Greenland, and used as a flux in the electric production of aluminum, in the making of special glasses and porcelain, as a binder for abrasive wheels, and in insecticides.   One ton of cryolite is used for flux for 40 tons of aluminum.   For glass batches 30 lb of cryolite is equivalent to 22.7 lb soda ash, 16.3 lb fluorine, and 11 lb aluminum hydrate.   It acts as a powerful flux because of its solvent power on silicon, aluminum, and calcium oxides.   In opal and **milky glasses** it forms a complex AlF_6 anion, retaining the alumina and preventing loss of the fluorine.   Cryolite occurs in masses of a vitreous luster, colorless to white, with a hardness of 2.5.   It fuses easily.   **Kryolith,** of the Pennsylvania Salt Co., is cryolite of 98 to 99% purity, and **Kyrocide** is a grade of 90% purity.   The latter is the dust from the natural ore, and is used as an insecticide.   Synthetic cryolite is made by reacting fluorspar with boric acid to form fluoroboric acid, and then reacting with hydrated alumina and sodium carbonate to form cryolite and regenerate boric acid.

CRYPTOSTEGIA RUBBER. Rubber obtained from the leaves of two species of perennial vines native to Malagasy, *Cryptostegia grandiflora* and *C. madagascariensis.* The former was grown in India, and the rubber was known as **palay rubber.** It was brought to Mexico and Florida as an ornamental plant and now grows extensively in Mexico and the West Indies. The maximum rubber content is found in the leaves 3½ months old, at which time it is 2 to 3% of the dry weight of the leaf. There is also about 8% resin in the leaf which must be separated from the rubber as it makes it soft and tacky. The *C. madagascariensis* contains less rubber, but the leaves of hybrid plants grown from both species give increased yields of rubber. The hybrid does not come true to type from seed, and is propagated from cuttings. When extracted and separated from the resin, cryptostegia has the same uses as ordinary hevea rubber.

Another plant that yields rubber from the leaves is the desert **milkweed,** *Asclepias erosa, A. subulata,* and other species growing in the dry regions of southwest United States. The short and slender leaves are produced only on the young stems and the gathering season is short. The dry leaves are ground, and the rubber is obtained by solvent extraction. The average rubber content is about 2%, but as much as 12% has been obtained from some species of wild plants. As with guayule and cryptostegia a considerable amount of resin is extracted with the rubber. **Goldenrod rubber** is extracted similarly from the leaves of the goldenrod, the dry leaves containing as much as 7% rubber mixed with resin. The species which contains the most rubber is *Solidago leavenworthii.* It does not occur in the plant as a latex, but is in isolated globules in the cells, mostly in the leaf. The **milk bush,** *Euphorbia tirucalli,* of Cuba and Jamaica, also produces rubber of good elasticity, but the crude latex from the bush causes skin blisters, and the extraction requires special treatment.

Dandelion rubber is the gum latex extracted from the roots of the Russian dandelion, which, when separated from the contained resin, has practically the same characteristics as the rubber from the hevea tree. Dandelion rubber, from various species of the genus *Taraxacum,* chiefly the plants known as **kok sagyz, tau sagyz,** and **crim sagyz,** native to Turkmen, is produced in Russia. The plant is grown only on a small scale in the United States and Canada. The roots, which extend 15 to 20 in. into the ground, contain up to 10% rubber after the plant has passed the first-year flowering period. The normal yield is about 6% rubber with also considerable resin. The dry roots also contain a high percentage of inulin.

CUMERONE. A colorless oily liquid of the composition C_8H_6O, used chiefly in making synthetic resins. It occurs in the fractions of naphtha between 165 and 175°C.   It has a specific gravity of 1.096, is insoluble in water, and is easily oxidized.   Another similar product is **indene,** C_9H_{10}, a colorless liquid of specific gravity 0.993, boiling at about 182°C, obtained from coal tar.   When oxidized it forms phthalic acid, and with sulfuric acid it polymerizes readily.   It is a bicyclic ring compound with an active double bond and a methylene group in the five-membered ring fused to the benzene nucleus.   It can be reacted with butadiene to form an indene-butadiene rubber of superior properties.   All of the **cumenes** are variants of benzene.

The **indene resins** are classed with the cumerone resins, but they are lighter in color and are used in varnishes.   The simple polymer, or di-indene resin, is a crystalline solid melting at about 58°C.   The polyindene resins are made by polymerizing indene with ultaviolet light and oxygen. The **cumerone resins,** which are polymers of $C_6H_4 \cdot O \cdot CH{:}CH$, made by the action of sulfuric or phosphoric acid on cumerone, are very soluble in organic solvents, and are used in lacquers, waterproofing compounds, molding, and in adhesives.   The specific gravity of the molded resins is 1.05 to 1.15.   They have high dielectric strength.   **Paracumerone,** called also **paraindene** and **cumar gum,** is a synthetic resin which is a copolymer of cumerone and indene.   The grades vary from a soft gum to a hard brown solid, with melting points from 5 to 140°C.   Varnishes made with it are resistant to alkalies.   **Nevindene,** of the Neville Co., is a cumerone-indene resin of specific gravity 1.08 and melting point 10 to 160°C, used for compounding with rubber and synthetics.   **Nevilloid C-55** is a **cumerone-indene resin** in water emulsion for coatings.   It forms cohesive translucent films of slightly tacky nature.   Blended with melamine resin it forms a clear and hard film.   **Cumar** is the name of a cumerone-indene resin of the Barrett Co., but the name cumar has been applied to a range of pale-yellow to reddish-brown coal-tar resins which are polymers of indene, cumerone, and other compounds, with melting points from 45 to 160°C.   They are used in rubber compounding to increase tensile strength and tear resistance.   **Piccoumaron resins** of the Pennsylvania Industrial Chemical Corp. are paracumerone-indene thermoplastic resins produced by the polymerization of unsaturates in coal-tar oils.   They vary from light liquids to tacky solids with melting points from 10 to 120°C.   The colors vary from pale yellow to reddish brown. They are resistant to alkalies, and are used in paints and waterproofings for concrete, and in adhesives for floor tile.

CUPRONICKEL. Any alloy of copper and nickel, as nickel and copper form solid solutions in all proportions.   Nickel and copper are found naturally alloyed in many copper mines, and as the two metals are difficult to separate, the cupronickel alloys were among the first alloys used.

They are ductile and malleable, are very corrosion-resistant, and have a maximum hardness at about 50% nickel. A 15% nickel alloy can be rolled from a thickness of $1\frac{1}{2}$ in. to about 0.040 in. without intermediate annealing. Nickel whitens copper and gives the alloys a characteristic pinkish-white color sometimes called yellow, which can be whitened by the addition of small amounts of cobalt. At least 10% nickel is needed to obtain a nickel-white color, and this amount gives high corrosion resistance. Cupronickel with 2.5% nickel is used for the driving bands of shells, 15% nickel for bullet jackets and condenser tubes, and 25% for coinage. The higher-nickel alloys are used for resistance wire, for corrosion-resistant equipment, and for parts where strength, toughness, and a white color without plating are required. For the latter use, however, the alloys contain other elements. When color is important, the alloys should not contain zinc because of the change in color by dezincification. Aluminum is also used as a whitener and hardener. An old formula for a silvery-white alloy for silverware, called **minargent,** was for 100 parts copper, 70 nickel, 6 antimony, and 2 aluminum. The standard cupronickels are 5, 15, 20, and 30% nickel.

Supernickel is a name given by the American Brass Co. to the 70–30 alloy for condenser tubes. This alloy and the 80–20 alloy are also marketed by the Revere Copper & Brass, Inc., for condenser tubes. The 80–20 alloy is used to replace nickel-silver for electrical springs. It has strength and flexural endurance comparable to monel metal. The 70–30 alloy has a tensile strength, annealed, of 49,000 psi with elongation 50%, and when hard-drawn the strength is 75,000 psi with elongation 5%. The weight is 0.323 lb per cu in. The white alloy of the Scovill Mfg. Co. known as **Adnic,** used for valve diaphragms and parts for chemical equipment, has 70% copper, 29 nickel, and 1 tin. When hard-drawn it has a tensile strength of 113,000 psi and elongation 10%. The hot-rolled rod has a strength of 65,000 psi and elongation 45%. This is essentially the same alloy marketed by the Revere Copper & Brass, Inc., as **admiralty metal. Revere alloy 508,** originally developed by the British Non-Ferrous Metals Research Association for condenser tubes, contains 88.5% copper, 10 nickel, and 1.5 iron. **Cufenloy 30,** of the Phelps Dodge Copper Products Corp., for heat-exchanger tubes to operate at temperatures to 800°F and pressures to 8,000 psi, contains 29.1% nickel, 0.5 iron, 0.35 manganese, and the balance copper. The tensile strength is 77,000 psi, and at 1050°F the strength is 43,000 psi. This type of alloy is also used for castings, giving a cast strength of 65,000 psi with elongation of 20%.

Small amounts of silicon added to cupronickel form a nickel silicide that gives a **hardenable copper,** which is the ancient tool material of the Incas. But, since the nickel is usually low in these alloys, they are not classed with the cupronickels. An alloy of this type marketed by the

American Brass Co. under the name of **Tempaloy** contains 95% copper, 4 nickel, and 1 silicon.   It is hard and strong, and can be forged or cold-rolled.   Annealing by heating throws the nickel silicide into solid solution and produces a soft and ductile metal, which can be hardened again by holding at a temperature of 450°C for several hours.   The tensile strength is from 50,000 to 150,000 psi with hardness above 200 Brinell. Small amounts of manganese and iron may be added to cupronickel to harden and strengthen the alloy.   **Davis metal,** of the Chapman Valve Mfg. Co., for valves and fittings, contains 67% copper, 29 nickel, 2 iron, 1.5 manganese, and 0.5 carbon and silicon.   The castings are hard and corrosion-resistant.   **Cufenium,** a white alloy used as a base metal in tableware, contains 72% copper, 22 nickel, and 6 iron.   Some chromium may be added for further corrosion resistance.   **Everbrite,** of the American Manganese Bronze Co., has 60% copper, 30 nickel, 3 iron, 3 silicon, and 3 chromium.   It is white in color, has a tensile strength, cast, of 75,000 psi, elongation 14%, and Brinell hardness 170.   **Cataract metal,** of the Niagara Falls Smelting & Refining Corp., is the name of a series of cupro-nickel alloys containing small amounts of other elements.   **Copper-nickel alloy** is the name used for the 75–25 and 50–50 cupronickel slabs, ingots, and shot used for adding nickel to brasses.   Federal specifications for copper-nickel alloy call for a minimum of 65% copper and 25 nickel with other elements allowable.

The high-nickel cupronickel alloys are very corrosion-resistant at high temperatures, and are used for electrical-resistance wire and strip where the temperature does not exceed 1100°F.   **Lucero,** of the Driver-Harris Co., is a 70–30 alloy, and **Copel** is a 55–45 alloy for resistance wire.   The 55–45 alloy has an electrical resistivity of 294 ohms per cu mil ft, tensile strength, cold-drawn, of 140,000 psi.   Because of its constant-temperature coefficient of resistance, it was given the name of **constantan** when used in low-temperature pyrometers.   It has a high thermoelectric effect with either copper or iron, but cannot be used for high-temperature pyrometers as the melting point is 1290°C.   **Advance metal,** of the Driver-Harris Co., and **Cupron,** of the Wilber B. Driver Co., are names for this alloy for pyrometer use.

CURUPAY. The wood of the tree *Piptadenia cebil,* native to Argentina, Paraguay, and Brazil.   In northern Argentina and Paraguay it is also known under the Guarani name **cevil.**   The wood is very hard and heavy, weighing 74 lb per cu ft, and it has a reddish color and a handsome, wavy grain.   It is used as an ornamental hardwood and is much employed locally for construction.   Another wood of the same order is **angico,** from the *Angico rigida* of Brazil, also known as **queenwood,** and the lighter-colored wood is called **angico vermelho,** or **yellow angico.**   It is very hard, with a dense, close grain, a reddish-brown color, and weight of 70 lb per cu ft.   It is employed where a heavy hardwood is required, and in cabinetmaking.

CUTTING ALLOYS. Cobalt-based alloys, usually of complex Co-Cr-W-Fe-Si-C composition, used for lathe and planer tools for cutting hard metals.   They form a class distinct from the cemented carbides which are not true alloys, from the refractory hard metals which are chemical compounds, and from the cobalt high-speed steels which are high in iron and usually have less carbon.   The hardness is inherent in the alloy, and is not obtained by heat treatment as with the cobalt steels.   Cutting alloys are cast to shape and are usually marketed in the form of tool bits and shear blades.   Complex alloys, however, may have heat-transition points at which the metal complexes change structure, limiting the range of use.

Since the development of balanced super-high-speed steels and cermet-type cutting tools, these alloys with a high proportion of the scarcer cobalt have lost their importance as cutting alloys, and, because of their high corrosion, heat, and wear resistance, are used chiefly for weld-facing rods and heat-corrosion applications.   One of the earliest of the alloys, called **Cooperite,** was based on nickel.   The first of the commercial cobalt cutting alloys was **Stellite,** of the Haynes Stellite Co., in various composition grades and with trade names such as **J-metal** and **Star J-metal.**   The hardest alloy, with a Rockwell hardness to C68, contained about 45% cobalt, 32 chromium, 17 tungsten, 1.5 iron, 1.5 silicon, and up to 2.7 carbon.   The tensile strength is above 100,000 psi, and compressive strength about 325,000 psi.   It is silvery white in color.   The **Delloy** of the Penn Rivet Corp. contained a somewhat similar composition.   Other similar alloys were **Speedaloy, Rexalloy, Crobalt,** and **Borcoloy,** the latter two containing also boron for added wear resistance.   This type of alloy is now also used in **surgical alloys** for surgical tools and dental plates since they are not attacked by body acids and set up no electromotive currents.   To make them more workable for this purpose, they usually contain a higher content of cobalt, 60% or more, with a smaller amount of molybdenum instead of tungsten, and with less carbon and silicon.

CUTTING OILS.   Oils used on cutting tools and on work being machined to aid in the cutting action.   The chief object of the oil is to act as a lubricant between the tool and the work, decreasing the friction.   These oils, therefore, are usually heavy oils or compounds distinguished from the thin solutions of soluble oils employed for flooding the work with the object of keeping it cool.   However, the cutting oil also carries off much of the heat and enables the tool to stand up longer under the cutting action.   There is no sharp dividing line between the cutting oils and the coolants which are designated in the mechanical industries as **soluble oils** because they are generally used in the water solution.   These soluble oils also have some lubricating action, but the old coolant known as **soda water** in machine shops is a solution of soap and soda ash in water.

Lard oil is a good cutting oil, but is seldom used alone because of its cost.   It is mixed with mineral and vegetable oils, or with hydrogenated oils.   The mineral-lard oils are used for machining copper alloys or for turning steel where a good surface finish is required.   Lard oil mixed with kerosene is used for cutting aluminum and for monel metal.   Ordinary mineral oils are used for light cutting operations and combine lubrication and cooling.   For cutting brass, an emulsion of oil in soapy solution is often employed.   Carbon tetrachloride mixed with turpentine has been used for cutting hard steels.   For screw cutting, a paraffin oil mixed with a vegetable oil may be used, but for cutting fine threads a heavy oil mixed with white lead is preferred.

In general, the soluble oils are made by treatment of an oil with sodium hydroxide or other alkali; they emulsify easily because of the formation of sodium oleate and sodium palmitate; and they can be mixed with water in all proportions.   Federal specifications for compounded soluble oil permit a maximum of only 10% water, with no separation of the water in 24 hr at 75°F.   Cutting oil, or **cutting compounds,** are marketed under many trade names.   They may vary widely in composition, and contain rosin or rosin oil to improve cutting action, cresol or other disinfectant, corrosion inhibitors, or antioxidants to prevent rancidity, but they are generally based on sulfonated oils, or **sulfurized oils.**   The sulfur adds film strength to the oil and gives better penetration of the cutting tool. **Cleartex, Sultex,** and **Transultex** are grades of sulfurized oils of the Texas Co.   **Sulchlor,** of the Carlisle Chemical Works, is a modified sperm oil with sulfur and chlorine in the molecule.   It is used for high-pressure cutting.   **Aquadag,** of the Acheson Colloids Co., is a solution of about 22% of colloidal graphite in water.   **Antisep,** of E. H. Houghton & Co., is a high-sulfur oil concentrate with an antiseptic and a rust inhibitor.

CYPRESS. A number of different woods are called cypress, but when the name is used alone it is likely to refer to the wood of the **Italian cypress,** *Cupressus sempervirens,* native to the Mediterranean countries but now grown in the Gulf states and in California.   This wood is light in weight, soft, light brown in color, and has a pleasant aromatic odor.   It is very durable, and is used for furniture, chests, doors, and general construction. The **citrus wood,** or **citron board,** from which the massive dining tables of ancient Rome were made, were heavy plates of the wood of this tree cut across the trunk near the roots to show a variegated grain.   The wood was cut in Mauritania.   **Arizona cypress,** *C. arizonica,* is a smaller tree, and the wood is used chiefly for fence posts.   The wood usually referred to in the eastern United States as cypress, and also as **marsh cypress, red cypress, bald cypress, yellow cypress, gulf cypress,** and **southern cypress,** is from the coniferous tree *Taxodium distichum,* and the **pond cypress** is from *T. ascendens,* of the southeastern states.   Southern cypress grows along the coast from Delaware to Mexico, especially in Florida and the lower Mississippi Valley.   The red cypress is along the coast and the yellow is inland, the coastal types being darker in color.   The trees are sometimes very old, reaching a height of 120 ft in 800 years.   The wood is yellowish red or pink in color, and is moderately hard with an open grain.   The weight is about 32 lb per cu ft.   It is very durable, and is valued for shingles, tanks, boatbuilding, or construction where resistance to weather exposure is needed.   The wood called yellow cypress on the West Coast, also known as **Sitka cypress, Alaska cedar,** and **yellow cedar,** is from the tree *chamaecyparis nootkaensis,* or *Cupressus sitkaensis,* growing on the Pacific Coast from Alaska to Oregon.   The trees reach 6 ft in diameter and 120 ft in height in 500 years.   The heartwood is bright yellow, and the sapwood slightly lighter.   The wood has a fine, uniform, straight grain, is light in weight, moderately hard, easily worked and polished, shock-resistant and durable.   It is used for furniture, boatbuilding, and interior finish.   **Monterey cypress,** *C. macrocarpa* of California, is one of the chief trees planted on reforestation projects in New Zealand.

DAMMAR. Also written **damar.**   The resin from various species of trees of the genus *Shorea, Balanocarpus,* and *Hopea,* but the name is also applied to the resins of other trees, especially from the *Agathis alba,* the source of Manila copal.   There is no dividing line between the dammars and the copals, and dammar may be considered as a recent or nonfossil copal, the Malay word damar meaning simply a gum.   The best and hardest dammars are from deposits at the bases of the trees, which are then the seasoned or fossil resins like the copals.   Dammar is obtained by tapping the trees and collecting the solidified gum after several months.   It is used in varnishes, lacquers, adhesives, and coatings.   The usual specific gravity is 1.04 to 1.12, and the melting point up to 120°C.   The average grade of dammar does not have a melting point much higher than 100°C.   Dammar is a spirit varnish resin, gives a flexible film, but is softer and less durable than the copals.   It is noted for its complete solubility in turpentine.   It is also soluble in alcohol, and the Batavia and Singapore dammars are soluble in chlorinated compounds and in hydrocarbons.   Dammar is classified according to color and size, the best grades being colorless and in large lumps. The high-grade pale-colored dammars from Batavia and Sumatra, including the so-called **cat's-eye dammar,** are from species of *Hopea.* Most of the **white dammar** equivalent to Manila copal comes from

Malagasy.   It is semihard to hard, and is used in paints where resistance
to wear is required, as in road-marking paints, but is not as hard as Congo
copal.   In general, the true dammars are from the *Shorea* and *Balanocarpus,* and they are inferior in hardness to the fossilized resins approaching the copals.   The *Shorea* resins are usually dark in color.   The **Malayan
black dammar, dammar hitam,** is from a species of *Balanocarpus*.   The
plentiful **dammar penak** is from the Malayan tree *B. heimii,* which also
yields the important wood known as **chengal** used for furniture and boatbuilding.   **Black dammar** is from the tree *Canarium strictum,* of India, and
comes in black, brittle lumps, easily ground to powder.   The reddish
dammar sengai is also from a species of *Canarium.*These are types of
elemi.   **Dewaxed damar,** for making colorless, glossy lacquers, is highly
purified dammar in xylol solution.

DENATURANTS. Materials used chiefly for mixing with ethyl alcohol to
be employed for industrial purposes to prevent the use of the alcohol as a
beverage and to make it tax-free under the Tax Free Industrial Alcohol
Act.   The qualities desired in a denaturant are that its boiling point should
be so close to that of the alcohol that it is difficult to remove by ordinary
distillation, and that it should be ill tasting.   Some of the denaturants are
poisonous and cause death if the alcohol is taken internally.   The usual
denaturants are methyl alcohol, pyridine, benzene, kerosene, and pine oil.
One or several of these may be employed, but denaturants must be approved
by the Bureau of Internal Revenue.   Completely denatured alcohol is a
term used to designate alcohol containing poisonous denaturants, and these
are employed only for antifreeze, fuels, and lacquers, but not in contact
with the human body.   Special denatured alcohol is alcohol containing
denaturants authorized for special uses, such as pine oil for hair tonics.
Many approved denaturants are marketed under trade names.   **Denol** is
the name of a mixture of primary and secondary aliphatic higher alcohols.
Agadite is a compounded petroleum product.   **Hydronol** is a hydrogenated organic product.   Denaturants are also used in imported oils that
are permitted entry at lowered tax rates for industrial use so that they cannot be diverted for edible use.   Rapeseed oil, for example, is denatured
with brucine.

DERRIS. The root of various species of vines of the bean family, *Derris
uliginosa, D. elliptica,* and *D. trifoliata,* growing in Indonesia.   It is
imported as crude root, and marketed as a fine powder of 200 mesh for
use as an insecticide diluted with dusting clay to a rotenone content of 1%,
or as a spray in kerosene or other liquid.   The root contains **rotenone,** a
colorless, odorless, crystalline solid poison of complex composition,
$C_{22}H_{22}O_6$, and melting point $163°C$.   The value of rotenone as an insecti-

cide is that it is highly toxic to cold-blooded animals, including insects and worms, and nonpoisonous to warm-blooded animals.   It is widely used as an agricultural insecticide as it is harmless to birds.   It is about 30 times more toxic to cutting worms than lead arsenate.

Rotenone is also found in many other plants, and when separated has the same toxic power.   **Cubé** is the root of the vine *Lonchocarpus utilis,* of Peru, containing rotenone and used for the same purposes as derris. **Timbó,** also known as **urucú** and as **tingi** and **conambi,** is the root of the vine *L. urucu,* of Brazil, also containing rotenone and used in the same manner.   **Barbasco** is a name applied to timbó and all other fish-killing plants of the Orinoco Valley.   The Caribs used the root either in shredded or in extract form for catching and killing fish.   A cubic foot of root will poison an acre of water without harming the fish as food.   The tubers of the wild yam called barbasco yield **diosgenin,** a steroidal used in the synthesis of steroids which are oxidized to produce cortisone.   Other plants of the same family are **nicou, nekoe,** and **haiari** of the Guianas, and rotenone sometimes goes under the name of **nicouline.**   The high yield of rotenone from Indonesian derris, up to 12%, is due to careful selection and propagation in cultivation, the semiwild roots of South America sometimes containing only about 2%.   The Brazilian government standard for timbó is 4% rotenone content.   From 1 to 4% rotenone is also obtained from the long leathery shoots of the perennial weed *Tephrosia virginiana,* known as **devil's shoestring,** growing in Texas.   Piperonyl butoxide is sometimes mixed with rotenone to give greater insect-killing power.

DETERGENTS. Materials which have a cleansing action like soap.   Although soap itself is a detergent, as are also the sodium silicates and the phosphates, the term usually applies to the synthetic chemicals, or **soapless soaps,** which give this action.   The detergents may be the simple sulfonated fatty acids such as turkey-red oil; the **monopole soaps,** or highly sulfonated fatty acids of the general formula $(SO_2OH)_xR \cdot COONa$; or the **gardinols,** which are sulfonated fatty alcohols.

All of the synthetic detergents are **surface-active agents,** or **surfactants,** with unsymmetrical molecules which concentrate and orient at the interface of the solution to lower interfacial tension.   They may be **anion-active agents,** with a positive-active ion; **cation-active agents,** with a negative-active ion; or **nonionic agents.**   Most of the household detergents are anion-active, and are powders.   Most of the nonionics are liquids, and are useful in textile processing since they minimize the difference in dye affinity of various fibers.   The cationics have lower detergency power and are usually skin irritants, but they have disinfectant properties and are used in washing machines and dairy cleansers.   They are called **invert soaps** by the Germans.   The synthetic detergents do not break down in the presence of acids or alkalies, and they do not form sludge and scum, or precipitate salts in hard waters like soap.   They do not form quantities of suds like some soaps, but suds contribute little to cleansing, and are not desirable in automatic washing equipment.   **Textile softeners** are different from surface-active agents.   They are chemicals that attach themselves molecularly to the fibers, the polar, or charged end, of the cation orienting toward the fiber, with the fatty tails exposed to give the softness to the fabric. **Arqued 2HT,** of Armour & Co., is a distearyl dimethyl ammonium chloride for this purpose.   A special-purpose surfactant used for dispersing oil slicks on the sea is **Dispersol,** of Imperial Chemical Industries.   It is a polyethanoxy dissolved in isopropyl alcohol.   It is soluble in oil but not in water.   It agglomerates the oil into small blobs that are scattered by the winds and eventually destroyed by marine organisms.

Synthetic detergents have now largely replaced soaps for industrial uses, and the annual volume of detergents used is more than three times that of soaps.   They are employed in textile washing, metal degreasing, paper-pulp processing, and industrial cleansing.   They are also used in household cleansers, soapless shampoos, and toothpastes.   **Biodegradable detergents** are those which can be chemically disintegrated by bacteria so that the discharged wastes do not contaminate the ground waters.   **Millox,** of Millmester Onyx Corp., is a group of biodegradable detergents made by the reaction of sucrose and fatty acids with a linking of ethylene oxide. This type of detergent is more powerful than petroleum-based detergents. **Millox 120** is made from the fatty acids of coconut oil, and **Millox 180** is from tallow.   The detergents produced from straight-chain paraffinic hydrocarbons derived from petroleum cracking are alkyl aryl sulfonates, $R \cdot Ar \cdot SO_3Na$, or alkyl benzene sulfonates.   These detergents do not break down in the wastes and therefore do tend to contaminate the ground waters.   The detergent characteristics vary with the number of carbon atoms in the alkyl chain and the arrangement of atoms in the chain. Detergency increases to a maximum at 12 to 15 atoms and then decreases. These detergents are 10 times as bulky as soda ash, but can be mixed with alkaline or phosphate cleaners.

The household detergent **Dreft,** of Procter & Gamble, is a fatty alcohol sulfonate.   **Lowila,** of the Foster Milburn Co., is a sodium lauryl sulfo-acetate in bar form to replace toilet soap.   **Maprofix PAS,** of Onyx Chemical Co., for bar soaps, is a potassium lauryl sulfate in the form of a white powder.   The detergents are more efficient than toilet soaps, but tend to leave the skin with an alkaline hardness.   Lecithin may be used in detergent bars to reduce tackiness, and starch may be used for hardening. **Nytron,** of the Solvay Process Co., is a sodium sulfonate derived from petroleum hydrocarbons.   It is a buff-colored powder.   **Surfax 1288,** of E. F. Houghton & Co., is an aryl sulfopropionate with only slight detergent power, used in textile processing for rewetting and as a leveling agent for dye baths.   **Clavenol,** of the Dexter Chemical Corp., is a polyethylene glycol condensate of the nonionic class.

The German **Igepons** were made by esterifying oleic acid with iso-ethionic acid and then saponifying.   They were not stable in alkalies, but the more stable **Igepon T** had an amide linkage :CONH: to prevent breaking down by hydrolysis.   The Igepon T of the General Dyestuff Corp. is a sodium amide made by reacting oleic acid with methyl taurine.   **Taurine** is an aminoethyl sulfonic acid, $H_2NCH_2CH_2SO_3H$, which is found in bile but is produced synthetically.   **Igepon TE-42** is a sodium taurate produced from tallow acids.   It is stable in hard waters and in acid or alkaline solutions.   The fatty acids for the German detergents were made from the paraffin obtained in the hydrogenation of brown coal.   The detergent sulfonates were then easily made by the action of sulfuric acid on the hydrocarbons that contain the double bond :CH:CH: or hydroxyl group :CHOH.   The **isoethionic acid** used for the Igepons has the formula $HOCH_2CH_2SO_3H$, and has both alcohol and acid characteristics.   A German detergent, **Comperlan,** which is not soluble in water but is soluble in alcohols and glycols, is an alkyl ethanol amine used for shampoos and cosmetics.

The **Ultrawets** of the Atlantic Refining Co., **Kamenol D** of the Kamen Soap Products Co., **Oronite detergent** of the Standard Oil Co., **Kreelon** of the Wyandotte Chemicals Corp., **Parnol** of Jacques Wold & Co., **Wicamet** of Wica Chemicals, Inc., and **Santomerse** of the Monsanto Chemical Co. are alkyl aryl sulfonates.   This type of chemical is available in powder, bead, or paste forms, and 1 molecule in 40,000 molecules of water gives good detergency.   It is effective in hard water or in acid and alkaline solutions.   **Sulframin E,** of the Ultra Chemical Works, Inc., is this material in liquid form.   The household detergent **Surf,** of Lever Bros., is an alkyl aryl sulfonate containing also phosphates.   **Lensex,** of Shell Chemical Co., is a sodium alkyl sulfate in the form of a paste for wool scouring.

Superonyx, of the Onyx Oil & Chemical Co., is a modified sodium alkyd sulfate and is a neutral detergent and dye assistant for processing textiles. **Maprosyl 30,** of the same company, is called a **modified soap.**   It has the detergent and emollient properties of soap but does not form scum as soap does, and does not cause skin irritation as many detergents do.   Unlike soap, it is soluble in highly alkaline solutions, and unlike most detergents, it has high foaming qualities.   It is a sodium lauroyl sarcosinate produced from fatty acids, and may also be in the form of stearoyl, linoleyl, or derivatives of other fatty acids.   The **sarcosine** is **methyl glycine,** CH_3-$NHCH_2CO_2H$, an amino acid occurring in small amounts in animal muscle, but now made synthetically.   It is a decomposition product of caffeine. **Lauryl pyridium chloride** is also a soaplike detergent.   It is a tan-colored semisolid with a soapy feel and with germicidal properties.   It is used for textile washing.

The **Pluronics** of the Wyandotte Chemicals Corp. are nonionic detergents produced from polyoxy propylene glycol, ethylene oxide, and ethylene glycol.   When the ethylene oxide content is 70% the detergent is a solid which can be flaked.   It is formulated with alkyl sulfonate and sodium carboxymethyl cellulose for laundry work.   Somewhat similar chemicals to the detergents are used as **dispersing agents** for latex, paper coatings, dyestuffs, and agricultural sprays.   **Daxad 11,** of the Dewey & Almy Chemical Co., is a polymerized salt of alkyl naphthalene sulfonic acid.   Its action is to impart an electrical charge to each particle, giving a repelling action to space the particles and prevent agglomeration or settling.   It increases fluidity and permits a higher solids content in dispersions without increasing the viscosity.

DEXTRIN. Also called **amylin.**   A group of compounds with the same empirical formula as starch $(C_6H_{10}O_5)_x$, but with a smaller value of x. The compounds have strong adhesive properties and are used as pastes, particularly for envelopes, gummed paper, and postage stamps, for blending with gum arabic, in pyrotechnic compositions, and in textile finishing. Dextrin is a white, amorphous, odorless powder with a sweetish taste.   It dissolves in water to form a syrupy liquid, and is also distinguished from starch by giving violet and red colors with iodine.   Dextrin is made by moistening starch with a mixture of dilute nitric and hydrochloric acids, and then exposing to a temperature of 100 to 125°C.   Dextrin varies in grade chiefly owing to differences in the type of starch from which it is made.   **British gum** is a name given to dextrins that give high tack for paste use.   **Cartonite,** of Paisley Products, Inc., is a liquid solution of a converted dextrin used as an adhesive in box-sealing machines.   It is also marketed as a brown water-soluble powder.   **Koldrex,** of the A. E. Staley Mfg. Co., is a formulated dextrin which dissolves easily in cold water to produce stable liquid adhesives of uniform viscosity.   It is produced by combining dextrin with borax, preservatives, and defoamers, and then spray-drying the mixture into powder.   The **borated dextrin** of the National Starch and Chemical Corp., for automatic packaging machines, has high initial tack and good adhesion.   It gives 400 sealings per minute.

DIAMOND. A highly transparent and exceedingly hard crystalline stone of almost pure carbon.   When pure, it is colorless, but it often shows tints of white, gray, blue, yellow, or green.   It is the hardest known substance, and is placed as 10 on the Mohs hardness scale.   But the **Mohs scale** is only an approximation, and the hardness of the diamond ranges from 5,500 to 7,000 on the **Knoop scale,** compared with 2,670 to 2,940 for boron carbide which is designated as 9 on the Mohs scale.   The diamond always occurs in crystals in the cubical system, and has a specific gravity of 3.521 and a refractive index of 2.417.   Carbon is normally quadrivalent in flat planes, but in the diamond the carbon atoms are arranged in face-centered lattices forming interlocking tetrahedrons and also hexagonal rings in each cleavage plane.

The diamond has been valued since ancient times as a gemstone, but it is used extensively as an abrasive, for cutting tools, and for dies for drawing wire.   These **industrial diamonds** are diamonds that are too hard or too radial-grained for good jewel cutting.   **Jewel diamonds** have the formation in regular layers, while industrial diamonds are grown in all directions.   Technically these are called feinig and naetig.   **Ballas diamonds,** valued for industrial drilling, are formed with the crystallization starting from one central point.   The stones thus formed do not crack in the tool as easily as those with layer formation.   Stones for diamond dies are examined in polarized light to determine the presence of internal stresses.   They are then drilled normal to the rhombic dodecahedron plane with cleavage planes parallel to the die-hole axis to obtain the greatest die-service life.   The stones for industrial purposes are also the fragments and the so-called **bort** which consists of the cull stones from the gem industry including stones of radiating crystallization that will not polish well.   Bort also includes a cryptocrystalline variety of diamond in brown, gray, or black colors, known as **black diamonds, carbonados,** or **carbons,** found in Brazil in association with gem diamonds.   The carbons have no cleavage planes, are compact, and thus offer greater resistance to breaking forces.   The carbons vary greatly in quality and hardness.   Some rare natural diamonds of South America contain small amounts of aluminum and other elements which give stability to the crystal above the normal disintegrating temperature.   These diamonds are not suitable as gemstones but are efficient semiconductors.

The value of diamonds is based on the gem value and is determined by color, purity, size, and freedom from flaws.   The weight is measured in carats.   Diamond splinters as small as $\frac{1}{500}$ carat may be cut and faceted. Small diamonds are sieved into straight sizes and the tinted stones are separated.   Then each stone is examined for cut, brilliance, and degree of perfection, and diamond merchants who sell by grade are meticulously careful of their reputation for uniform judgment.   The most valued gems are blue-white.   A faint straw color detracts from the value, but deep shades of yellow, red, green, or blue are prized.   The largest diamond found in Brazil, the **Vargas diamond,** was a flawless stone weighing 726.6 carats.   It was cut into 23 stones.   The famous **Kohinoor diamond** weighed originally 793 carats, and the **Jonkers diamond** from South Africa was a blue-white stone weighing 726 carats.   The **Cullinan diamond,** or

Star of Africa, measured 4 by 2.5 by 2 in., and weighed 3,106 carats.   The annual world production of natural diamonds reaches as high as 28 million carats, or about 6 tons, of which 5 tons are industrial diamonds.   An average of 250 tons of ore is processed to obtain 1 carat.   In Angola the average find is 0.14 carat per cu meter of ore.

Most of the diamonds come from South Africa, Brazil, India, and the Congo.   The average diamond content of the Bushimaie deposits of the Congo is 5 or 6 carats per meter.   The diamonds are associated with pebbles of flint, jasper, agate, and chalcedony but diamonds usually occur in **kimberlite,** an intrusive rock with the appearance of granite but with a composition similar to basalt plus much olivine.   It occurs in South Africa, North Carolina, and Arkansas.   Diamonds are formed at very high pressures and heat, and since at ordinary pressure the diamond disintegrates into graphite at 1600°F, the natural diamonds could not have been released until the temperature of the rock was below that point.   The stones found in the beach sands of Southwest Africa and in sandstone in Brazil are not native to the sand, but were washed into it after scattering from the exploded rock.   Diamonds have been found irregularly in Arkansas since their discovery in 1906.   The average weight of the Arkansas diamonds is less than 1 carat, with the largest 40.22 carats.   Some diamonds are found in the Appalachian region, the largest, from West Virginia, weighing 34.46 carats.   Few of the American diamonds are of gem quality, but they are of full hardness.

Synthetic diamonds are produced from graphite at pressures from 800,000 to 1,800,000 psi and temperatures from 2200 to 4400°F.   A molten metal catalyst of chromium, cobalt, nickel, or other metal is used, which forms a thin film between the graphite and the growing diamond crystal. Without the catalyst much higher pressures and temperatures are needed. The shape of the crystal is controllable by the temperature.   At the lower temperatures cubes predominate, and at the upper limits octahedra predominate; at the lower temperatures the diamonds tend to be black, while at higher temperatures they are yellow to white.   The synthetic diamonds produced by the General Electric Co. are up to 0.01 carat in size, and are of industrial quality comparable with natural diamond powders.   The synthetic blocky powder, Grade MBG-11, is harder and tougher than natural diamond powder and is used for cutting wheels.   Synthetic diamonds have been produced in a flame at about 7000°F, but the time element in a torch flame is short and the crystal particle size is extremely small.   With high pressure, larger crystals can be grown at lower temperatures.   **Diamond crystals** are used as temperature-sensitive resistant elements in thermistors for ovens and furnaces and for temperature control in chemical processing.   They are used at temperatures from minus 200°C up to 650°C.

Diamond dust is a powder obtained by crushing the fragments of bort, or from refuse from the cutting of gem diamonds. It is used as an abrasive for hard steels, for cutting other stones, and for making **diamond wheels** for grinding. Grit sizes for grinding wheels are 80 to 400. The coarse, No. 80, for fast cutting, has about 1,400 particles per square inch in the face of the bonded wheel. The National Bureau of Standards designates nine grades of **diamond powder** from No. ¼ to No. 60. The No. ¼ has a particle size of ½ micron, equivalent to a mesh of 60,000. It is used for metallographic polishing. The No. 60 has a particle size of 35 to 85 microns, equivalent to a mesh of 230, and is for rough polishing. The Elgin National Watch Co. grades diamond powder in 10 graduated sieves with from 1,600 to 105,625 openings per inch. The finest sieve grade is then placed in pure water, and as the heavier particles sink first, at intervals the water suspensions are removed to segregate the particles into absolute uniformity. These **Dymo diamond powders,** with particle size to ½ micron for fine polishing, are marketed in various colors for easy selection of grade. **Hyprez,** of the Engis Equipment Co., is also accurately graded diamond powder for fine polishing. **Swarf** is diamond powder obtained by collecting the dust from diamond-wheel grinding operations and separating the diamond dust chemically. The **blocky diamond powder** of Englehard Industries, Inc., used for metal-bonded grinding wheels and saws for stone and ceramics, contains no perfect cubes, but has about 75% of blocks having equal measurement of all three dimensions, 20% rectangles with one side shortened or lengthened, and 5% needles, flats, and slivers. The powder comes in grade sizes from 16–20 mesh to 270–325 mesh, and gives high cutting efficiency. **Abrasive RVG–D,** of General Electric, for use in resin-bonded wheels for high-speed grinding and polishing of tungsten carbide, is a diamond powder of irregularly shaped friable grains coated with a copper-base alloy to give lubricity and heat dissipation. Grain sizes are from 40–60 to 325–400 mesh.

DIATOMACEOUS EARTH. A class of compact, granular, or amorphous minerals composed of hydrated or **opaline silica,** used as an abrasive, for filtering, in metal polishes and soaps, as a filler in paints and molding plastics, for compacting into insulating blocks and boards, and in portland cement for fine detail work and for waterproofing. It is formed of fossil diatoms in great beds and is not earthy. In mineralogy it is called **diatomite,** and an old name for the ground powder is **fossil flour.** Tripoli and kieselguhr are varieties of crystalline diatomite.

The American production of the mineral is mainly in Oregon, California, Washington, Idaho, and Nevada. After mining, the material is crushed and calcined. When pure it is white; with impurities it may be gray, brown, or greenish. The powder is marketed by fineness and chemical purity. The density is usually 12 to 17 lb per cu ft. Its high resistance to heat, chemical inertness, and dielectric strength, and the good surface finish it imparts make it a desirable filler for plastics. For insulating purposes, bricks or blocks may be sawed from the solid or molded from the crushed material, or it may be used in powdered form. **Diatomite block** has a porosity of 90% of its volume and makes an excellent filter. **Celite,** of Johns-Manville, is a 325-mesh uncalcined, amorphous diatomaceous earth for portland-cement mixtures, paper finishes, and for use as a flatting agent in paints. **Sil-O-Cel,** of the same company, is diatomaceous earth in powder or in insulating block to withstand temperatures to 1600°F. **Superex,** of the same company, is calcined diatomite powder bonded with asbestos fibers to resist temperatures up to 1900°F. **Dicalite,** of the Philip Carey Co., is a fine diatomite powder weighing 8 to 8.5 lb per cu ft loose, and 15 to 17 lb tamped, used for heat-insulating cement or as insulation for walls. **Compressible insulation,** to absorb the expansion stresses known as drag stress, between the firebrick and the steel shell of metallurgical furnaces, may be of diatomaceous silica. **Superex SG,** for blast furnaces, is a composite block with Superex on the hot side and a blanket of fine spun-glass fibers on the cold side. It recovers to 97% of its original thickness in cooling from a temperature of 1900°F and a compression of 10%.

DIE-CASTING METAL. Any alloy employed for making parts by casting in metal molds, or dies, in pressure-casting machines as distinct from other permanent-mold castings where no pressure is used. The pressures may be as high as 25,000 psi to give a uniform dense structure and smooth finish in castings of intricate design and varying section thicknesses. The cost of equipment, including heat-resistant dies, thus limits the process economically to high-production quantities. Temperature limits on the tools restrict the process to nonferrous metals. A characteristic of the castings, also, is that they must have a draft of at least 2 deg on all sides to give rapid ejection from the die.

Zinc-base alloys, with melting points below 800°F, constitute the largest single tonnage of die castings, but the high-melting alloys, based on aluminum, magnesium, or copper, with melting points to about 1600°F, are used for a very wide range of mechanical parts. **Lead-base alloys** and low-melting alloys of lead, zinc, tin, and bismuth are also cast in steel or bronze dies, including **slush castings** in which excess metal is poured out after a skin of metal on contact with the die has set, leaving a hollow casting. But these are cast without pressure, and are classed as permanent-mold castings rather than die castings, although the composition of the alloys may be essentially the same.

Die-casting alloys are standardized into relatively small groups with symbol numbers under the zinc, aluminum, magnesium, and copper alloys, but the possibilities of variation, particularly with the minor ingredients, are infinite, and trade names and company numbers are often used to designate uniform quality standards for particular uses.   The aluminum-silicon alloys have superior casting qualities and good strength.   The aluminum-magnesium alloys have higher corrosion resistance, but have inferior casting qualities.   The aluminum-silicon-magnesium alloys give a balance of castability, corrosion resistance, and pressure tightness, but they may be less ductile and shock-resistant.   Most of the alloys have a small amount of nickel, usually 0.5% max, to add strength and improve color. They also contain small amounts of tin, 0.3% max, to improve machining and polishing qualities, but much tin tends to hot-shortness.   Copper and iron add heat-treatable qualities, giving strength and hardness, but decrease the corrosion resistance.

ASTM alloy S12B contains 11 to 13% silicon with 2 iron, and maximums of 0.6 copper, 0.3 manganese, 0.1 magnesium, 0.5 zinc, 0.5 nickel, and 0.1 tin.   It has a tensile strength of 39,000 psi with elongation of 1.8%.   **ASTM alloy SC84B,** or **Reynolds alloy 380,** contains about 8% silicon and 4 copper, with the usual maximums of the other elements.   Its tensile strength of 45,000 psi is the same as that of the aluminum-magnesium alloy **ASTM alloy G8A,** or **Alcoa alloy 218,** which contains 8% magnesium, 1.8 iron, and the lower limits of the other elements, but its elongation is only 2% compared with 8% in alloy G8A.   **Alcoa alloy 85,** or **ASTM alloy SC54B,** is an aluminum-silicon-copper alloy with 5% silicon, 4 copper, and 2 iron.   It casts well, develops high strength and hardness, but is not as corrosion-resistant as the silicon alloys.   **Apex Red X alloys,** of the Apex Smelting Co., designates a series of aluminum die-casting alloys.   **Ruselite,** of the Milwaukee Die Casting Co., and **Renyx,** of the Allied Die Casting Corp., are also aluminum die-casting alloys. The **permanent-mold alloys** are also usually aluminum-silicon alloys, but they frequently have higher copper and zinc, with small amounts of chromium and titanium.   Most of them are, like the die-castings alloys, in the ASTM series of CS and SC alloys.   **ASTM alloy CS104A** has 10% copper and 4% silicon, while **ASTM alloy SC122A** has 12% silicon and 2% copper.   The **Ternaloy alloys** of the Apex Smelting Co. are high in zinc.   **Ternaloy 7,** which is **ASTM alloy ZG42A,** has 4% zinc and 2% magnesium.   It develops a tensile strength of 53,000 psi with elongation of 6.5%.

DIE STEELS. Any tool steels used for dies.   Originally, the term meant high-grade carbon steel with about 0.90 to 1.1% carbon that could be hardened to retain a keen cutting edge and not shrink or warp greatly in the hardening.   Unalloyed tool steels are still widely used for many types of dies. They have the advantage of low cost and ease of machining. Also, they are easy to harden and temper, have high impact strength, and have good fatigue endurance. They are used for cold-header dies, stamping and forming dies and punches, shear blades, small tools, sledges, and for dowels, bushings, shafts, and other machine parts. Often, the die steels now have small amounts of vanadium or other element, not enough to rate them as alloy steels but sufficient to give them added physical properties. The modern die steels are made to a high degree of uniformity, with the manganese and silicon adjusted to give depth of hardening and uniformity of grain structure. Typical of this class of steel is **H-9 Extra Hard,** or **cold-heading die steel,** of Carpenter Technology. It contains 0.90% carbon, 0.40 manganese, and 0.40 silicon, and is used for coining dies, cold-heading dies, and knurls. A water-hardening die steel is **Special A.S.V. steel** of Firth Sterling, Inc., for punching, forming, swaging, and threading dies. It has 1 to 1.10% carbon, 0.30 manganese, 0.30 silicon, with sulfur and phosphorus below 0.015%. This is a shallow-hardening steel, with a very hard surface ranging from Rockwell C66 to C56 according to temper, and a tough, shock-resistant interior.

The **low-alloy die steels** are distinguished from the low-alloy construction steels in that the small percentages of alloying elements are carefully balanced to give certain physical characteristics. They may be classed with the carbon tool steels, but are given trade names. Very small amounts of vanadium refine the grain and give finer cutting edges. As little as 0.30% chromium in the steel increases the pearlite and also refines the graphite, while free hard carbides are formed with about 0.60% chromium. A typical steel of this kind is **Artdie steel** of the Columbia Tool Steel Co., used for high-production jewelry dies. It contains 0.95% carbon, 0.30 chromium, 0.20 vanadium, 0.25 manganese, and 0.25 silicon. **Silvan Star steel,** of Firth Sterling, Inc., is called a carbon steel, but it contains 0.20% vanadium, with 1.03 carbon, 0.25 manganese, and 0.25 silicon. It is suitable for a wide range of dies and tools. It is easily hardened by water quenching to Rockwell C67, and tempered in hot oil or fused salts to Rockwell C62 for keen hardness or to C58 for tough swaging dies.

Small amounts of tungsten or molybdenum add toughness and wear resistance. Water hardening usually requires immediate tempering to remove the stresses of the drastic quenching treatment, and the alloyed steels may call for the less drastic oil quenching. **SAE steel 6150** and **SAE steel 6195,** with about 1% chromium, 0.15 vanadium, 0.45 tungsten, and up to 1% carbon, are used for dies that require a high degree of hardness, toughness, and fatigue resistance. **Albany steel,** of the Allegheny Ludlum Steel Corp., is a steel of this type, and **Alhead steel,** of the same company, for cold-heading dies, has 1.5% tungsten, 1.5 cobalt, and 1 carbon. **Break-die steel,** of the Crucible Steel Co., has 0.20% molybdenum, 1 chromium, 0.70 manganese, 0.30 silicon, with only 0.35 carbon. **Hedervan steel,** of the Latrobe Steel Co., is a 0.90-carbon cold-heading steel with up to 3.5% vanadium carbide particles to increase wear resistance. **BR-3 die steel,** of the same company, for long-run blanking and forming dies, and to withstand the high abrasion in such uses as brick molds, contains 4.5% vanadium in the form of hard carbides, with 5.25 chromium, 1.10 molybdenum, 0.70 manganese, 0.30 silicon, and sufficient carbon, 2.8, to form the carbides. Tools can be operated without cracking at a hardness of Rockwell C65.

The possibilities of variation of physical characteristics of die tool steels by even slight changes in the alloying elements and in the treatment are unlimited, and usually there are many hundreds of these steels offered commercially at any one time, the methods of marketing being on performance in particular uses rather than on composition. Die steels also include alloy steels classified by characteristic types, as nondeforming steel or hot-work steel. They also include the prehardened steel blocks used for making plastic molds, die-casting dies, forging dies, and dies for pressing ceramics. These **die-block steels** usually contain a high percentage of chromium or vanadium with high carbon to form hard carbides, but they may be low-alloy, low-carbon steels for easy die sinking or hobbing, to be face-hardened by carburizing or nitriding. **Ottawa 60 steel,** of the Allegheny Ludlum Steel Corp., contains 12% vanadium, 1 chromium, 1 molybdenum, and 3.25 carbon. **Airdi 225 steel,** of the Crucible Steel Co., is an air-hardening die-block steel with 12% chromium, 1 molybdenum, 0.25 vanadium, and 2.25 carbon. **Prestem 5M21 steel,** of the Heppenstall Co., for die-casting dies and high-pressure press dies, is prehardened to Rockwell C36 to C45. It contains 3.38% molybdenum, 3 nickel, 0.65 manganese, 0.30 silicon, 0.15 chromium, and 0.20 carbon. **Cromoco die steel,** of Firth Sterling, Inc., for forming dies, swages, and metal shears, has 12% chromium, 1 cobalt, 1 molybdenum, and 1.6 carbon. **Select B-FM steel,** of the Latrobe Steel Co., is an air-hardening 15% chromium steel with sulfur added for free machining. **Lo-Air steel,** of the Universal-Cyclops Steel Corp., for dies, punches, and shear blades, is an air-hardening steel containing 2% manganese, 1.35 molybdenum, 1 chromium, 0.30 silicon, and 0.70 carbon. It has a tensile strength of 275,000 psi and Rockwell hardness C55. **Multimold steel,** of the Bethlehem Steel Co., for die-casting dies, which has some red hardness, is a low-alloy steel with 0.80 chromium, 0.30 molybdenum, and 0.35 carbon. But **Thermold AV steel,** of the Universal-Cyclops Steel Corp., is an **ASTM H13 steel,** with 5% chromium, 1.40 vanadium, 1 silicon, 0.40 manganese, and 0.35 carbon. **Thermold 75,** for aluminum casting dies, has less chromium and vanadium with an addition of molybdenum and cobalt.

Pressurmold steel, of the Braeburn Alloy Steel Corp., is also a modified chromium precipitation-hardening steel. These steels are tempered to less than Rockwell C55, but can be nitrided when high hardness is wanted. **Badger steel,** of the Latrobe Steel Co., is a nonshrinking die steel with 1.20% manganese, 0.50 tungsten, 0.50 chromium, 0.30 silicon, and 0.94 carbon. It is tempered to Rockwell C63 for dies. **MGR punch steel** of the same company is tempered to Rockwell C63 for punches. It contains 5% chromium, 1.20 tungsten, 1.20 molybdenum, 0.95 silicon, 0.30 manganese, and 0.55 carbon, and is shock-resistant.

DISINFECTANTS. Materials used for killing germs, bacteria, or spore, and thus eliminating causes of disease or bad odors in factories, warehouses, or in oils and compounds. The term **antiseptic** is employed in a similar sense in medicine, and the term **germicide** is often used for industrial disinfectants. Some disinfectants are also used as preservatives for leather and other materials, especially chlorine and chlorine compounds. Phenol is one of the best-known disinfectants, and the germ-killing power of other chemicals is usually based on a comparison with it. Practically all bacteria are killed in a few minutes by a 3% solution of phenol in water, but phenol has the disadvantage of being irritating to the skin. Industrial disinfectants are usually sold as concentrates to be diluted to the equivalent of a 3 to 5% solution of phenol.

Too large a proportion of disinfectants in oils, solutions, or the air may be injurious to workers, and the advice of health officials is ordinarily obtained before general use. Creosote oil and cresylic acid are employed in emulsions in disinfecting sprays and dips, but continuous contact with creosote may be injurious. Formaldehyde has high germicidal power, and is used for hides and leather, and some air sprays may contain chemicals such as chlorophyll which unite with moisture in the air to produce formaldehyde. But formaldehyde is not generally recommended for odor control as it is an **anesthetizer.** It desensitizes the olfactory receptors so that the individual is no longer able to detect the odor. **Masking agents,** which introduce a stronger, more pleasant odor, are likewise not a recommended method of disinfecting. They do not destroy the undesirable odor, and may permit raising the total odor level to unhealthy proportions. Elimination of odors requires chemicals that neutralize or destroy the cause of the odors without causing undesirable effects.

The silver ion is an effective cleanser of water that contains bacteria which produce sulfur-bearing enzymes, and silver sterilization is done with silver oxides on activated carbon, or with organic silver compounds, but the safe limit of silver in water for human consumption is specified by the U.S. Health Service as 10 parts per billion, and as with many other disinfectants the use requires competent supervision. Antiseptic atmospheres may be produced by spraying chloramine T, iodine, or argyrol.   **Chloramine T** is a white crystalline powder of the composition of $CH_3C_6H_4SO_2NClNa \cdot 3H_2O$, soluble in water and in organic solvents.   Besides its use as an antiseptic and germicide it is also employed as an oxidizing and chlorinating agent.   Thymol is used as a disinfectant in ointments, mouthwashes, soaps, and solutions.   Condensation products of thymol with other materials are also used.   **Thymoform,** $C_{21}H_{28}O_2$, made by condensing thymol with formaldehyde, is a yellow powder used as an antiseptic dusting powder. **Thymidol** is an antiseptic made by condensing thymol with menthol. **Dihydroxyacetic acid,** $CH(OH)_2COOH$, and its sodium salt, both white powders, are used in cosmetics, pharmaceuticals, and in coatings for food-wrapping papers, as they are nontoxic and do not irritate the skin.   **Hexylresorcinol,** $CH_3(CH_2)_5C_6H_3(OH)_2$, is a more powerful antiseptic than phenol and is not injurious to the skin or tissues.   **Caprokol,** of Sharpe & Dohme, is hexylresorcinol.   The antiseptic throat lozenge of this company, known as **Sucret,** has a base of sugar and glucose, with hexylresorcinol and a flavor.   **Pinosylvine** is a natural antiseptic extracted from the heartwood of the pine tree, where it protects the tree against decay and insects.   It is related chemically to resorcinol, and its germ-killing power is 30 times that of phenol.   **Ceresan M,** of Du Pont, is a powder designated as ethyl mercury toluene sulfonanilide, used for disinfecting seeds to protect against soil-borne plant diseases.   **Pittside,** of the Columbia Chemical Div., used as an industrial germicide, is a stabilized calcium hypochlorite, in water-soluble granules.   Disinfectants sold under trade names are usually complex chemicals, and may be chlorinated or fluorinated phenyl compounds not harmful to the skin.

DIVI-DIVI.   The dried seed pods of the tree *Caesalpinia coriaria,* native to tropical America, employed in tanning leather.   Most of the divi-divi is produced in Colombia, Dominican Republic, and Venezuela.   It is used chiefly in blends with other tannins to increase acidity, to give a light color to the leather, and to plump and soften the leather.   The pods are about 3 in. long, and contain up to 45% pyrogallol tannin.   They require to be kept from fermentation, which develops a red coloring matter.   The best pods are the thickest and lightest in color, and they are used to replace gambier, valonia, and myrobalans.   The commercial extract contains 25% tannin.   **Algarobilla,** from the pods of the *C. brevifolia,* of Chile, is a similar tanning agent.   **Cascalote** is from the pods of the tree *C. cacolaco* of Mexico, and is the standard tanning material of Mexico.   It is also used to replace quebracho for oil-well-drilling mud.   **White tan,** or **tari,** is from the pods of the *C. digyna* of the Far East.   **Tara,** or **Bogotá dividivi,** also called **cevalina,** is from the pods of the tree *C. tinctoria* of Colombia and Peru.   The pods contain 32% tannin, and 1,000 lb of tara pods produce 500 lb of **tara powder.** The material makes a soft leather, and is used to replace sumac.

DOGWOOD. A heavy hardwood noted for its ability to stay smooth under long-continued rubbing. Its outstanding use is for shuttles for weaving. The texture is fine and uniform. Other uses of the wood are for small pulleys, golf-club heads, mallet heads, jewelers' blocks, skate rollers, and bobbins. There are 17 known varieties of the plant in the United States, only four of which grow to tree size. The **white dogwood** is *Cornus florida;* the **Pacific dogwood** is *C. nuttalli;* **rough-leaf dogwood** is *C. asperfolia;* and **blue dogwood** is *C. alternifolia.* Dogwood grows widely throughout the eastern states. **Turkish dogwood** was formerly imported for shuttles, as was also the **Chinese dogwood,** or **kousa,** *C. kousa.*

DOLOMITE. A type of limestone employed in making cement and lime. as a flux in melting iron, as a lining for basic steel furnaces, for the production of magnesium metal, for filtering, and as a construction stone. It is a carbonate of calcium and magnesium of the composition $CaCO_3 \cdot MgCO_3$, differentiated from limestone by having a minimum of 45% $MgCO_3$. It occurs widely distributed in coarse, granular masses or in fine-grained compact form known as **pearl spar.** The specific gravity is 2.8 to 2.9 and hardness 3.5 to 4. It is naturally white, but may be colored by impurities to cream, gray, pink, green, or black. For furnace linings it is calcined, but for fluxing it is simply crushed. The raw dolomite, marketed by Basic Refractories, Inc., for open-hearth steelmaking, is washed crushed stone in $\frac{5}{8}$-in. size. When calcinated at a temperature of about 3100°F, dolomite breaks down to MgO and CaO, and it is limited to about 3000°F as a refractory. **Calcined dolomite** used in Germany as a water-filter material under the name of **magno masse** is in grain sizes 0.5 to 5.0 mm. Dolomite for the production of magnesia, some of which is cut as building marble, contains 10 to 20% magnesia, 27 to 33 lime, 1 to 12 alumina, 40 to 46 carbonic acid, 1 to 5 silica, and 0 to 3 iron oxide. The dolomite found in huge deposits in Oklahoma contains 30.7% CaO, 21.3 MgO, and only very small amounts of silica, alumina, and iron oxide. For the production of magnesium metal, calcined dolomite and ferrosilicon are brought to a high temperature in a vacuum and the magnesium is driven off as a vapor. In the ceramic industry dolomite is sometimes called **bitter spar** and **rhombic spar.**

DOUGLAS FIR. The wood of the tree *Pseudotsuga taxifolia,* of the northwestern United States and British Columbia. It is sometimes called **Oregon pine, Douglas pine, Douglas spruce, red fir, fir, yellow fir,** and **Puget Sound pine.** The wood of young trees with wide growth rings is reddish brown, and is the type called red fir, though the true red fir is from the large tree *Abies magnifica* of California and Oregon, the lumber of which is called **golden fir,** and the wood of which is used also for paper pulp. The wood of older trees of slower growth with narrow rings is usually yellowish brown and is called yellow fir.   Both woods may come from the same tree.   The narrow-ringed wood is stronger and heavier.   Douglas fir averages below longleaf pine in weight, strength, and toughness, but above loblolly pine in strength and toughness, though below it in weight. The grain is even and close, with resinous pores less pronounced than in pitch pine.   It is a softwood, and is fairly durable.   The weight is 34 lb per cu ft.   The compressive strength perpendicular to the grain is 1,300 psi; the shearing strength parallel to the grain is 810 psi.

Douglas fir is used for general construction and millwork, plywood, boxes, flooring, and where large timbers are required.   It is also used for pulping, and yields kraft paper of high folding endurance but low bursting strength.   The fibers are large.   The trees grow to great heights, the average being 80 to 100 ft.   The stand is estimated at more than 450 billion bd ft, or about one-fourth of all timber in the United States.   **Douglas fir bark** contains from 7.6 to 18.3% of a catechol tannin, the bark of young trees yielding the higher percentages.   It is suitable for tanning heavy leathers, and yields a pliable, light-colored leather.   **Silvacon 383,** of the Weyerhaeuser Timber Co., is Douglas fir bark in flaky corklike granules used in flooring and acoustical tile.   **Silvacon 490** is the bark as a reddish powder used in dusting powders and paints.   **Silvacon 508** is hard, spindle-shaped small fibers from the tissue of the bark, used as a filler for plastics and in asphalt and fibrous paints.   **Douglas-fir bark wax** is a hard glossy wax extracted from the bark of the Douglas fir, and is a partial replacement for carnauba wax.   A ton of bark yields 150 lb of wax by solvent extraction with 150 lb of tannin and 10 lb of quercetin as by-products.

DRIERS.   Materials used for increasing the rapidity of the drying of paints and varnishes.   The chief function of driers is to absorb oxygen from the air and transfer it to the oil, thus accelerating its drying to a flexible film. They are in reality catalyzers.   Excessive use of driers will destroy the toughness of the film and cause the paint to crack.   Solutions of driers are called liquid driers; it is in this form that **paint driers** are most used. Certain oils, such as tung oil, have inherent drying properties and are classed as drying oils but not as driers.   Driers may be oxides of metals, but the most common driers are metallic salts of organic acids.   **Manganese acetate,** $(CH_3COO)_2Mn \cdot 4H_2O$, is a common paint drier.   It is a pinkish crystalline powder soluble in water and in alcohol.   **Sugar of lead,** used as a drier, is **lead acetate,** $Pb(CH_3COO)_2 \cdot 3H_2O$, a white crystalline powder with a faint acetic acid odor, also used as a mordant in textile printing.

It is also known as **plumbous acetate** and **Goulard's powder**. **Lead oleate,** $Pb(C_{18}H_{33}O_2)_2$, is a drier made by the action of a lead salt on oleic acid. It is also used for thickening lubricants. **Lead linoleate,** $Pb(C_{18}H_{31}O_2)_2$, is a drier made by adding litharge to linseed oil, and heating. Lead and manganese compounds together act more effectively as driers than either alone. **Lead resinate** adds toughness of film as well as drying power. **Zinar,** of Newport Industries, Inc., is a **zinc resinate** with 5.6% zinc content. **Cobalt octoate,** which has about 12% cobalt in combination with hexoic acid, is used as a drier. **Cobalt driers** are twice as rapid in drying power as manganese driers, but too rapid drying often makes a wrinkled film which is desirable for some finishes but not for others.

Naphthenate driers are metallic salts made with naphthenic acids instead of fatty-oil acids. They are usually more soluble in paint solvents, and since the naphthenic acids can be separated into a wide range of molecular weights by distillation, a wider variety of characteristics can be obtained. **Sodium naphthenate,** with 8.6% metal content, and **potassium naphthenate,** with 13.1%, are powders that are good bodying agents and emulsifiers as well as driers. **Tin naphthenate,** with 20% tin, may be added to lubricating oils as an antioxidant. **Mercuric naphthenate,** with 29% mercury, retards the growth of bacteria and mold when added to finishes. **Barium naphthenate,** with 22.6% barium, has binding and hardening properties, and is used in adhesives and in linoleum. **Uversols,** of the Harshaw Chemical Co., are naphthenic acid salts of aluminum, calcium, cobalt, lead, manganese, or zinc, in liquid form for use as paint driers, wetting agents, and catalysts. **Octoic driers,** of the Witco Chemical Co., are metallic salts made with ethyl hexoic acid, and the metal content is lower than that of driers made with naphthenic acids. They are light in color, have no odor, and have high solubility. The **Octasols,** of the Harshaw Chemical Co., are ethyl hexoic acid metal salts. **Drying agents** for resin coatings and inks may act by oxidation or other chemical reaction. **Sulfur dichloride,** S_2Cl_2, speeds the drying action of coatings and inks formulated with alkyd, urea, or melamine resins, and such inks dry almost instantly.

DRILL ROD. Tool-steel round rod made to a close degree of accuracy, generally not over or under 0.0005 in. the diameter size, and usually polished. It is employed for making drills, taps, reamers, punches, or for dowel pins, shafts, and rollers. Some mills also furnish square rods to the same accuracy under the name of drill rod. Common drill rod is of open-hearth high-carbon steel hardened by quenching in water or in oil. The usual commercial sizes are from $1\frac{1}{2}$ in. in diameter down to No. 80, which is 0.0135 in. in diameter. The usual lengths are 1 to 3 ft. The sizes are by the standard of drill gages, with about 200 different diameters. The carbon content is usually from 0.90 to 1.05%, with 0.25 to 0.50

manganese, 0.10 to 0.50 silicon, and a maximum of 0.04 phosphorus or sulfur. It also comes in high carbon with from 1.50 to 1.65% carbon and 0.15 to 0.35 manganese. Drill rod can also be obtained regularly in high-speed steels, and in special alloy steels for dowel pins. **Needle wire** is round tool-steel wire used for making needles, awls, and latch pins. It comes in coils, in diameters varying by gage sizes from 0.010 to 0.105 in. **Needle tubing** for surgical instruments and radon implanters is stainless-steel tubing 0.014 to 0.203 in. in diameter in 6-ft lengths. The **hypodermic tubing** of J. Bishop & Co. is hard-drawn stainless-steel tubing 0.008 to 0.120 in. outside diameter, with wall thicknesses from 0.004 to 0.012 in., in 2-ft lengths, with a fine finish. **Capillary tubing** is also stainless steel, but comes in lengths to 200 ft, with outside diameters from 0.060 to 0.125 in. The inside bore can be had in various diameters from 0.006 to 0.025 in. for the 0.060-in. tubing, and from 0.010 to 0.024 in. for the 0.125-in. tubing. **Stud steel** is an English name for round bar steel made to close limits and hardened and descaled, used for heavy pins and studs. **Pin bar** is small-diameter rod of case-hardening steel used for dowel pins. **Drill steel,** for mine and quarry drills, comes in standard rounds, octagons, squares, and cruciform bars, solid or hollow, usually in carbon steel.

DRUG PLANTS. Known in the trade as **crude drugs** and **botanicals.** The roots, leaves, stalks, flowers, or bark of many plants are used for medicines or for the production of medicinal products, and more than 1,000 distinct botanicals are marketed commercially. Many of these are acute poisons having specific physiological effects on nerves, blood, heart action, or organs of the body. Knowledge of the specific effect of each, with control of the amount to produce a needed effect to correct organic disturbances, constitutes the theory of the use of these. The manufacture and sale of drugs in all civilized countries are controlled by various laws and by recognized and listed standards known as formulary and pharmacopoeia. The term drug has come to have an awesome significance, but many drugs occur in the most common foodstuffs, and it is theoretically possible by a perfect balance of foods and by the taking of the right foods at the right time to obtain balanced physiological effects and perfect health. Conversely, the excessive consumption of some foodstuffs causes toxic conditions because of the contained drugs. Balance is complex and varies within different individuals. Some derangements of the human system are caused by food unbalance, some by germ action, and some by faults in the system that impede metabolism or generate toxic products. It is the purpose of drugs to correct unbalances. Many of the most valuable drug plants contain **alkaloids** which have complex arrangements of carbon, hydrogen, oxygen, and nitrogen. Most of the alkaloids are violent poisons even in small quantities, and with few exceptions, such as quinine, are not employed as medicines except under the direction of trained physicians or pharmacists. The actual amount to produce sufficient effect without injury must be understood before use of a drug. **Pain-killing drugs,** for example, do not kill pain but diminish the conductivity of the nerve fibers, and thus prevent the brain from recording the pain. The alkaloid **hyoscine,** or **scopolamine,** a heavy liquid of the composition $C_{17}H_{21}NO_4$, causes loss of part of the normal inhibition control, and is known as **truth serum,** but what is expressed as truth by a mentally disturbed person may be only the product of imagination, and the drug should be given only by trained operators.

Drug plants are almost unlimited in number. **Belladonna,** used to relieve pain, to check perspiration, and as a dilatant, consists of the leaves, roots, flowers, and small stems of the perennial herb *Atropa belladonna* cultivated chiefly in Yugoslavia and Italy, but also grown in the United States. The plant is called **banewort** and **deadly nightshade.** The leaves are dried in the shade to retain the green color. They contain two alkaloids, **atropine** and **hyoscyamine.** Atropine is used as an antidote for military nerve gas. **Henbane** is the dried leaves and flowering tops of the illsmelling herb *Hyoscyamus niger,* a plant of the nightshade family containing several alkaloids. It is used as a sedative. The plant is grown in southern Europe and Egypt and to some extent in the United States. It is harvested in full bloom and dried in the shade.

Stramonium is the dried leaves, flowers, small stems, and seeds of the **thorn apple** or **jimson weed,** *Datura stramonium,* an annual of the nightshade family which grows as a common weed in the United States. It is shipped from Ecuador under the name of **chamico.** It produces the alkaloids atropine and hyoscyamine, and is used as a nerve sedative, hypnotic, and antispasmodic. Under cultivation, the yield is 1,000 to 1,500 lb of dry leaf or 500 to 2,000 lb of seed per acre. In general, the yield of drug plants in cultivation is high, so that only small acreages are needed. **Aconite** is the dried root of the **monkshood,** a perennial plant, *Aconitum nepullus.* It is grown in Europe and the United States. The root contains the colorless, crystalline, extremely poisonous alkaloid **aconitine,** $C_{34}H_{47}O_{11}N$. It is used as a cardiac sedative, diaphoretic, and to relieve pain and fever. **Matrine,** obtained from the plant *Sophora angustifolia,* is a lupine alkaloid having two piperidine rings. Combined with phenol sulfonate salts under the name of **dysentol,** it is used for amoebic dysentery.

Digitalis, an important heart stimulant, consists of the leaves of the perennial **foxglove plant,** *Digitalis purpurae,* native to Europe but also grown in New England and the Pacific Northwest. The leaves contain the bitter glucoside **digitoxin,** $C_{34}H_{54}O_{11}$. **Peyote** is the root of a cactus, *Lophophora williamsii,* growing wild in the desert region of Mexico. The buttonlike tops of the root, called **mescal buttons,** contain several alkaloids, and were used by the Indians to produce a sense of well-being with visions.

Peyotina hydrochloride, made from the buttons, is used in medicine as a heart stimulant similar to digitalis, and also as an anesthetic to the nervous system.   The **glucosides,** unlike the alkaloids, contain no nitrogen.   They are ethers of single sugars.   The glucoside **rutin,** used for treatment of hemorrhage and for high blood pressure, is a yellow nontoxic powder extracted from flue-cured tobacco and from **Tartary buckwheat** or **rye buckwheat.**   The active ingredient, **quertin,** is extracted and used to prevent hemorrhage in hypertensive persons.   **Ipecac** is the rhizone of the shrub *Cephalis ipecacuamha,* of tropical South America, chiefly Brazil.   It contains **emetine,** $C_{30}H_{40}O_5N_2$, and other alkaloids, and is used as an emetic tonic, and expectorant.   **Gentian,** also known as **bitter root,** is the dried root of the perennial herb *Gentiana lutea* of central Europe.   It contains glucosides and is used in tonics and also in cattle feeds.

Ginseng is the dried root of the plant *Panex ginseng* of China, and *P. quinquefolium* of North America.   It is used as a stimulant and stomachic. **Dog-grass root,** known in medicine as **triticum,** is the powdered dried rhizome of **Scotch grass,** *Agropyron repens,* which abounds in the meadows of the northern United States.   It has a slight aromatic odor and sweet taste and is used as a diuretic.   **Lobelia** is the dried leaves and tops of the small annual plant *Lobelia inflata,* known in the northeastern states as **Indian tobacco.**   It contains the alkaloid **lobinine,** and is used as an emetic and antispasmodic.   **Erigeron** is the herb and seeds of the **fleabane herb,** *Erigeron canadensis,* which grows wild in the north central and western states.   The herb yields 0.35 to 0.65% **erigeron oil** used as an astringent and tonic.   **Hamamelis** is the dried leaves of the witch hazel shrub, *Hamamelis virginiana,* of the eastern United States.   It is used as a tonic and sedative, and the water extract of the leaves and twigs with 14% alcohol and 1% active ingredient is known as **witch hazel.**   It is used as an external astringent.   It is fragrant, and contains also tannic acid from the bark of the twigs.   **Ephedrine,** or **ephedra,** is an alkaloid extracted from the dried twigs of the **mahuang,** *Ephedra sinica,* and other species of mountain shrubs of China and India.   It is also grown in South Dakota.   It is used as an adrenalin substitute to raise blood pressure, and also in throat medicines and nasal sprays.   **Hoarhound** is an extract from the leaves and flowering tops of the small perennial herb *Marrubium vulgare* of North America, Europe, and Asia.   It is used in preparations for colds, and also as a flavor in confections.

Cascara is the bark of the small **buckthorn** tree, *Rhamnus purshiana,* of the northwestern states and Canada.   It was also called **chittem bark.** It was used by the Indians and given the name **cascara sagrada** by the Spaniards.   The word cascara simply means bark; the word sagrada is not translated sacred but is a term applied to medicinal botanicals.   Cascara is used as a laxative and tonic.   The **European buckthorn,** *R. frangula,* also yields cascara.   **Aloe,** used in purgative medicines, is the dried resinous juice from the leaves of the bush *Aloe vulgaris* of the West Indies and *A. perryi* of western Africa.   The cut leaves are placed in troughs where the juice exudes.   It is then evaporated to a viscous black mass which hardens.   Both aloe and cascara contain the glucoside **emodin,** occurring also in senna and in **rhubarb.**   The latter, the stalks of which are much used as a food, is known in medicines as **rheum** and is employed as a laxative and stomach tonic.   **Aloin,** used in skin creams for radiation and sunburns, is an extract from the *A. vera,* a plant of the lily family growing in Florida.   **Aletris root** is a botanical drug from the **stargrass,** *Aletris farinosa,* growing in the eastern United States.   It is also known as **colic root,** and is used as a tonic and uterine stimulant.   **Senega,** used as an emetic and stimulant, is the dried root of the **snakeroot** or **milkwort,** *Polygala senega,* a small perennial herb grown in the eastern United States. **Calumba root** is the yellow root of the woody climbing plant *Coscinium fonestratum* of Ceylon.   It is used as a cure for tetanus.   The wood, which has a bright-yellow color, is used locally as a dye.   **Tanacetum** is the dried leaves and tops of the **silverweed,** *Tanacetum vulgaris* of Michigan and Indiana, used as a vermifuge.   The green herb yields about 0.2% **tansy oil,** or **tanacetum oil,** which contains a terpene **tanacetene,** and borneol.   It is used as an anthelmintic.

Ergot, used to stop hemorrhage, is the dried sclerotium of the fungus *Claviceps purpurea,* which develops on rye and some grasses.   The purple structure that replaces the diseased rye grain contains the alkaloid **clavine** $C_{11}H_{22}O_4N_2$.   Ergot is also used to produce the alkaloids **ergotamine** and **ergonovine,** used for treating high blood pressure and migraine headache, and used for mental-disease research.   It requires 1,000 lb of ergot to yield 1.5 oz of ergonovine, but it is produced synthetically by the Eli Lilly Co. from **lysergic acid,** which is synthesized from **indole propionic acid,** $C_8H_6N(CH_2)_2COOH$.   **Ergot oil,** used in medicinal soaps, is obtained by extraction from the dry ergot.   It was the original source of **ergosterol,** one of the most important **sterol alcohols** from plants, known as **phytosterols,** which, when irradiated, yield vitamin D.   Ergot is produced chiefly in Spain, and its commercial production has not been encouraged in the United States because it is an undesirable disease on grain.   Ergot also contains the amino acid **thiozine** found in blood.

Araroba, or **Goa powder,** is a brownish, bitter, water-soluble powder scraped out of the split logs of the tree *Andira araroba* of Brazil.   The Carib Indians used the powder for skin diseases, and it is now employed for eczema and skin infections.   It contains **chrysarobin,** a complex mixture of reduction products of a complex acid contained in the wood. **Labdanum** is an oleoresin obtained in dark-brown or greenish lumps from the branches of the **rock rose,** *Cistus ladaniferus,* and other species of the

Mediterranean countries. It yields a volatile oil with a powerful sweet characteristic odor which is used as a stimulant and expectorant and also as a basis for lavender and violet perfumes. It was originally obtained in Greece by combing from the fleece of sheep that browsed against the bushes. **Buchu** is the dried leaves of the South African herb *Barosma betulina* used as an anticatarrhal. **Serpasil,** of Ciba Pharmaceutical Products, Inc., is an extract from the root of the plant *Rauwolfia serpentina* of India and *R. heterophylla* of Central America. It is used as a sedative in hypertension cases, and belongs to the class of **tranquilizing agents. Rauwolfia extract** contains the two alkaloids **reserpine** and **rescinnamine,** both having hypotensive activity. They are produced by the Riker Laboratories as **Serpiloid** and **Rauwiloid,** and the product of Squibb is called **Raudixin.** A synthetic material, **meprobamate,** is a complex **propanediol dicarbamate,** and **Singoserp,** of Ciba, is a synthetic reserpine.

DRYING OILS. Vegetable oils which are easily oxidized by exposure to the air and thus suitable for producing a film in paints and varnishes, and known as **paint oils.** The best drying oils are those which contain the higher proportions of unsaturated acids, in which oxidation causes polymerization of the molecules. The drying of an oleoresinous varnish takes place in two stages. First, the reducer or solvent evaporates, leaving a continuous film composed of gums and drying oil. The drying oil is then oxidized by exposure, leaving a tough, hard skin. This oxidation is hastened by driers, but the drying oil itself is responsible for the film. The drying power of oils is measured by their **iodine value,** as their power of absorbing oxygen from the air is directly proportional to their power of absorbing iodine. Linseed oil is the most common of the drying oils, though tung oil and oiticica oil are faster in drying action. Linseed oil alone will take about 7 days to dry, but can be quickened to a few hours by the addition of driers. Linseed oil and other oils may be altered chemically to increase the drying power.

Conjugated oils are oils that have been altered to give conjugated double bonds in place of isolated double bonds in the molecules of the fatty acids. **Conjulinol,** of the Woburn Degreasing Co., is a drying oil of this class made from linseed oil. The iodine value is 154, and the drying time is greatly reduced. Normally, soybean oil is not classed as a drying oil although it may be blended with drying oils for paint use. But by chemical alteration it can be given good drying power. **Conjusoy** is a drying oil made by conjugation of soybean oil. The iodine value is 128, and the drying time is about half that of boiled linseed oil.

Castor oil, which has poor drying properties, is dehydrated to form a good drying oil. Other methods are used to alter oils to increase the drying power, notably polymerization of the linoleic and some other acids in the oils, or oils may be fractionated and reblended to increase the percentage of acids that produce drying qualities.   The **Admerols,** of the Archer-Daniels-Midland Co., comprise a series of drying oils made by treating linseed or soybean oil with butadiene, styrene, or pentaerythritol. **Kel-X-L oil,** of Spencer-Kellogg & Sons, is a modified linseed oil with an iodine value up to 170, used as a substitute for tung oil in quick-drying varnishes.   **Kellin,** of the same company, is a quick-drying blended oil with a linseed-oil base, while **Kellsoy** is a similar oil with a soybean-oil base.   **Cykelin,** of the same company, is a quick-drying oil made by treating linseed oil with **cyclopentadiene,** $(CH:CH)_2 \cdot CH_2$, a low-boiling liquid obtained from coal tar or from cracking petroleum.   **Cykelsoy** is another drying oil made by treating soybean oil with cyclopentadiene.   **Dorscolene,** of Dorward & Sons Co., is a drying oil made from fractionated and blended fish oils.   The German substitute drying oil known as **Resinol** was a liquid obtained by the distillation of the heavy fractions of the benzolated oils derived from scrubbing coke-oven gas.   **Resigum** is the final residue in the distillation of tar-oil benzol which has been washed with sulfuric acid, caustic soda, and water.   It contains a maximum naphthalene content of 5%.   It is miscible with resins or copals, and with vegetable oils, and makes a good paint without other drying oils.   Synthetic drying oil, of Shell Development Co., is **glycerol allyl ether** derived from propylene gas obtained in cracking petroleum.   **C oil,** of the Standard Oil Development Co., is a heavy, sticky liquid with a butadiene base.   In paints it gives high adhesion to metals and masonry, and produces a smooth, hard, glossy coating with good chemical resistance.

Although the great volume of drying oils is produced from linseed, soybean, tung, oiticica, castor, and fish oils, many other oils have drying properties and are used in varying quantities.   **N'gart oil** is from the seed nuts of a climbing plant of Africa, and is equal in drying power to linseed oil.   **Lallemantia oil,** obtained from the seeds of the *Lallemantia iberica,* of southeastern Europe and Asia, resembles linseed oil in physical properties.   **Isano oil,** obtained from the kernel of the nut of the *Ongokea klaineana* of tropical Africa, is a pale-yellow viscous oil that has little drying power, but when heat-treated sets up an exothermic action to produce a varnish oil.   **Anda-assu oil,** also used in Brazil for paints, is from the seeds of the plant *Joannesia princeps.*   The seeds yield 22% of a clear yellow oil with an iodine value of 142 which is bodied by heating. **Manketti oil** is a varnish oil with about two-thirds the drying power of linseed oil.   It is a light-yellow viscous oil from the seed nuts of the tree *Ricinodendron rautanenii,* of southwest Africa.

Chia-seed oil is a clear amber-colored oil extracted from the seeds of the plant *Salvia hispanica* of Mexico.   It has a higher drying value than linseed oil.   The seeds yield about 30% oil, which contains 39% linolenic acid, 45 linoleic, 5 palmitic, 2.7 stearic, with some arachidic, oleic, and myristic acids. The specific gravity is 0.936, iodine value 192, and acid value 1.4. The seeds scatter easily from the pods and are difficult to collect.

DUCK. A strong, heavy cotton fabric employed for sails, awnings, tents, heavy bags, shoe uppers, machine coverings, and where a heavy and durable fabric is needed. It is woven plain, but with two threads together in the warp. It is made in various weights, and is designated by the weight in ounces per running yard 22 in. wide. It is marketed unbleached, bleached, or dyed in colors, and there are about 30 specific types with name designations usually for particular uses such as **sailcloth.** When woven with a colored stripe, it is called **awning duck. Russian duck** is a fine variety of **linen duck.** Large quantities of cotton duck are used for making laminated plastics and for plastic-coated fabrics, and it is then simply designated by the weight. **Belt duck,** for impregnated conveyor and transmission belts, is made in loosely woven soft ducks and in hard-woven, fine-yarn hard fabric. The weights run from 28 to 36 oz. **Conveyor belting** for foodstuff plants is usually of plastic fabric for cleanliness. The **Transilon** of Extremultus, Inc., is a belting of good strength and flexibility to operate over small-diameter rollers. It is made of nylon fabric faced on both sides with polyvinyl chloride sheet. It may have a variety of surface finishes such as tetrafluoro ethylene.

Hose duck, for rubber hose, is a soft-woven fabric of plied yarns not finer than No. 8, made in weights from 10 to 24 oz. The grade of duck known as **elevator duck** for conveyor belts is a hard-woven 36-oz fabric. **Plied-yarn duck** is used for Army tents instead of flat duck as it does not tear easily and does not require sizing before weaving. **Canvas** is duck of more open weave. The term is used loosely in the United States to designate heavy duck used for tarpaulins, bags, sails, and tents. But more properly it is a heavy duck of square mesh weave more permeable than ordinary duck, such as the canvas used for paintings and for embroidery work. The word duck is from the Flemish doeck meaning cloth, originally a heavy linen fabric. The word canvas is from the Latin cannabis, originally a coarse, heavy hempen cloth for tents. **Osnaburg cloth** is a heavy, coarse, plain-woven fabric used for wrapping and bailing, and for inside sacks for burlap flour bags. It is made from lower grades of short-staple cotton and from waste. In colored checks and stripes it is used for awnings.

Drill is a stout, twilled cotton fabric used for linings and where a strong fabric lighter than duck is required. It differs from duck also in that it has a warp-flush weave that brings more warp than filling to the face of the cloth. It comes unbleached, bleached, or piece-dyed, or may be yarn-dyed.

It is made in various weights, and is designated in ounces per yard the same as duck. Tan-colored drill is called **khaki. Denim** is a heavy, twill-woven, warp-flush fabric usually lighter in weight than drill. The warp is yarn-dyed. The filling is made with one black and one white yarn. It is much used for workmen's clothing, and the light weights for sportswear are called **jean.** Denim is also used industrially where a tough fabric is needed. **Art denim,** in plain colors or woven with small figures, is used for upholstery.

DYESTUFFS. Materials employed for giving color to textiles, paper, leather, wood, or other products. They may be either natural or artificial. Many chemicals will stain and color other materials, but a product is not considered a dye unless it will impart a distinct color of some permanence to textiles. The natural dyestuffs may be mineral, animal, or vegetable, but the artificial dyes are derived mainly from coal-tar bases. **Tyrian purple,** from various Mediterranean snails, was in ancient times the most noted of the animal dyestuffs. Cochineal and kermes are other animal dyes. One of the earliest metallic or mineral dyestuffs was called **iron buff.** It was made by allowing pieces of iron to stand in a solution of vinegar to corrode. Fabrics that had been dipped in this solution were rinsed in a solution of wood ashes. **Mineral dyes** now include ochre, chrome yellow, and Prussian blue. **Vegetable dyes** may be water solutions of woods, barks, leaves, fruits, or flowers. The buff and brown textile colors of early New England were made by boiling fresh green butternuts in water, while a dark-red dye was made by boiling the common red beet in water. The yellow to red colors known by the Algonquin name of **puccoon** were from the orange-red juice of the root of the **bloodroot,** a perennial of the poppy family. Vegetable dyes now include brazilwood, barwood, sappanwood, fustic, logwood, madder, henna, saffron, annatto, indigo, and alkanet. The **camphire** of the ancients mentioned in the Bible and Koran was a reddish-orange dyestuff made by grinding to a paste the red, sweet-scented spikes of the small cypress tree, *Lawsonia inermis,* of Egypt and the Near East. It was used by the Eastern and Roman women to stain the fingernails, and is now used under the name of **henna** for dyeing leather and as a hair dye. It gives various shades from yellowish to red or brown. **Argol,** a brilliant red used extensively until replaced by synthetic dyes, is from the **orchilla,** a lichen found in the Canaries and Near East. It was used to produce the brilliant colors of the medieval **Florentine cloth. Chinese green, buckthorn bark,** or **lokao,** is the powdered bark of the buckthorns, *Rhamorus globosa* and *R. utilis,* of China and Russia. It is used in dyeing silk and cotton. **Weld,** from the plant *Reseda luteola* of Europe, produces a very bright-yellow color with an alum mordant. With indigo it produces green.

Woad is the dried fermented leaves of the plant *Isatis tinctoria* of Europe. It gives a blue color, but is now little cultivated.

Synthetic dyes are mostly coal-tar or aniline colors. They are more intense, brighter, faster, and generally cheaper than natural dyestuffs. There are thousands of these dyes, classified by a color index rather than by their chemical composition. The dyes are complex chemicals, but they usually contain characteristic groups of atoms so that the color or change in color can be predicted. They are generally marketed under trade names or company numbers. The chemical names refer to the forms of atom groupings. The **azo dyes,** with an $\cdot N{:}N\cdot$ linkage, constitute about half of the production. **Azo benzene,** $C_6H_5\cdot N{:}N\cdot H_5C_6$, is made from nitrobenzene, and is in crystalline red plates melting at 68°C. This may be converted to **hydrazo benzene,** $C_6H_5NHNHC_6H_5$, a solid of camphor-like odor melting at 131°C. **Substituted azo dyes** constitute a class containing OH and NH groups, made by coupling amines or phenols with the salts. The azo dyes are in general poisonous, but are sometimes used in restricted quantities to color foodstuffs. Some are poisonous in contact with the skin, such as **xylyazo naphthol** and the sodium salt of **sulfophenylazo,** designated by the Food and Drug Administration as Red No. 32, and Orange No. 1, and proscribed for use in coloring lipstick and oranges.

The other three important classes are: **anthroquinone dyes, indigoid dyes,** and **thioindigoid dyes,** the latter being **sulfur dyes.** The sulfur dyes may be made by treating the organic compounds with sodium sulfide. They are fast to washing and to light, but the range of color is limited, and their use is generally limited to fibers where a strongly alkaline bath is tolerable.

Some of the synthetic dyes will color animal fibers well and not vegetable fibers, or vice versa, while some will color all fibers. Some, called **direct dyes,** can be dyed direct, while others require a mordant. Some are permanent, or fast, while others are water-soluble and will fade when the fabric is washed, or some may not be light-fast and will fade when exposed to light. Direct dyes usually have a weak OH bond between the nitrogen in the dye and the fiber. In **reactive dyes** the dye reacts with the fiber to produce both an OH and an oxygen linkage, the chlorine combining with the hydroxyl to form a strong ether linkage. Such dyes are fast and very brilliant. **Acid dyes** contain a carboxylic or sulfonic acid group and operate best in an acid bath. **Basic dyes** have an amino group, and are marketed as salts. **Vat dyes** are insoluble and are applied in the soluble colorless form and then reduced or oxidized to color. They usually have an anthraquinone structure, and are solubilized by the reducing agent, a hydroxyl group, OH, diffusing into the fiber where it is fixed.

Color carriers, used to aid adherence of dyes to synthetic fibers, are usually chemicals that act as swelling agents to open the fiber structure, such as phenylphenol, benzoic acid, or dichloro benzoic acid. The **Ketosol 75,** of Union Carbide, is 75% methylphenyl carbinol and 25% aceto-phenone. Monochloro benzene, used as a color carrier for Dacron fiber, acts to promote a concentrated layer of dye solution around the fiber. **Ring-dyed fiber** is a synthetic fiber not receptive to dyes that has been passed through a bath of a receptive plastic before dyeing. The dye then adheres to the coated surface and encases the fiber.

EBONY. A hard, black wood valued for parts subject to great wear, and for ornamental inlaying. It is the wood of various species of trees of the ebony family, *Ebenaceae,* although the name is also applied to some woods of the genus *Dalbergia,* family *Leguminosae.* **Black ebony,** from the tree *Diospyros dendo* of West Africa, and ebony, from the tree *D. melanoxylos,* of India, are the true ebonies. Black ebony has a black heartwood with brownish-white sapwood. It is next to lignum vitae in hardness, has a fine, open grain, and weighs 78 lb per cu ft. It is used for inlaying, piano keys, and turnery. The ebony of India is also ex-tremely hard, with a fine and even grain. The heartwood is black with brownish streaks. **Marblewood,** or **Andaman marblewood,** is an ebony from the tree *D. kurzii* of India and the Andaman Islands. The wood is black with yellowish stripes. It has a close, firm texture, is hard, takes a fine polish, and weighs 65 lb per cu ft. **Marble ebony** is another species from Malagasy. The ebony from Japan, called **kaki,** is from the tree *D. kaki.* It has a black color streaked with gray, yellow, and brown. The grain is close and even, and the wood is very hard, but the weight is less than that of African ebony. Ebony wood is shipped in short billets, and is graded according to the color and the source, as Niger, Macassar, Cam-eroon. **Green ebony** is a name sometimes given to the cocoswood of the West Indies. **Artificial ebony,** formerly composed of asphaltic com-pounds, is now usually molded plastics. **Partridgewood,** a heavy blackish wood used for fine inlay work, is **acapau,** from the large tree *Voucapapoua americana* of the Amazon Valley. It is valued in Brazil for furniture because of its resistance to insect attack.

ELEMENTS. The basic, or elemental, materials from which all products are produced. They are the elemental building blocks, or **atoms,** of all tangible materials in the universe. There are 92 elements, or material atoms, that are stable under normal earth conditions, from hydrogen, atomic number 1, or **element 1,** to uranium, or **element 92.** Elements of higher atomic weight than uranium are made, but they are unstable, their time decay being measured progressively as half life.

The unit of an element, the atom of that element, gets its name from the Greek word atomos, meaning indivisible, and it is not divisible by

ordinary chemical means.   The elements are used either alone or in combination for the making of useful products.   They combine either as
mechanical mixtures or as **chemical compounds.**   In a **mixture** each element retains its original nature and energy, and the constituents of the
mixture can be separated by mechanical means.   In chemical compounds
of two or more elements the original elements lose their separate identities;
the new substance formed has entirely different properties, and the atomic
energy stored within the compound is not equal to the sum of the elemental
energies.   A chemical compound is bonded by electrons and can be
broken down by chemical means.   An **alloy** is usually a combination of
chemical compounds and mixtures, the metal mixtures in the matrix being
gaged by their maximum fused or liquid solubility, known as the **eutectic
point.**   With the elements the number of different compounds, or useful
substances, that can be made by varying the combinations of elements and
the proportions is infinite.

The atom may be considered chemically the indivisible unit of the
element, and the known atoms are arranged in a **Periodic Table** progressively by **atomic number,** based on the **atomic weight** of the element
with hydrogen as the unit of mass, though oxygen may be taken as the
point of calculation.   The atom is not a solid, but is a region of energy
particles in motion.   At various energy levels the geometrical shape of
the electron orbit changes, and the apparent ring, or **electron shell** structure,
is the energy-level extension of the orbital pattern.   The distances and
space covered are so vast in relation to the size of the particle, and the
speeds are so great, that the interior of the atom might be considered
mostly as empty space.   As a single atom is a billion or more times the size
of an electron, it is estimated that if the space within the atom could
be removed, a thimbleful of atoms would weigh millions of tons.   If the
copper atom were magnified 10 billion times, the electrons that the chemist
employs to connect it with another atom of a molecule would still be too
tiny to be seen.   Thus, a solid metal used for construction is a region
of relatively vast space populated by energy particles in perpetual motion.

The term **space chemistry** was first used at the beginning of the twentieth
century by the Dutch physicist Van't Hoff, the founder of modern
physical chemistry, but the subject was not new.   It may be said that
modern atomic science, equipped with advanced experimental methods
and testing instruments, has taken up where the Greeks, working only
with geometry and the theoretical deductions of metaphysics, left off at
their School of Numbers about 450 B.C.   The Greeks reasoned that all
matter came from one source, made from a qualitatively indeterminable
primordial unit, the **monad,** now known as **energy.**   It was stated to be

incorporeal, composed of No Thing, but vital and always in motion.   This idea of a nonmaterial basis of tangible materials, now necessary for modern scientific analysis of materials, is intrinsic in human logic.   It came to the Greeks from the Ionians, survivors of the Cretan civilization antedating 3000 B.C., and appears in the Hebraic Genesis, in the Sanskrit Vedas, and in the Taoism of ancient China.   Energy is in harmonic motion, in waves or rays, and may be said to become a particle of **mass** when the frequency is 1, that is, a closed unit cycle.   All materials give off light when activated, and **light rays** have the fastest known speed, 186,000 mi per sec.

More than 70 new elements, to element 168, have been projected, though not all have been synthesized.   These are higher elements made by additions to natural elements.   Atoms may also be broken down by the application of high energy.   The process, known as **fission,** is usually by electric energy built up to extremely high voltage by resonant pulsation in a magnetic field in a manner akin to that of the generation of lightning in the clouds.   More than thirty subatomic particles have been isolated. **Fissionable elements** are normally considered to be only those of high atomic weight and radioactivity, and relative unstability, but all elements are fissionable.

A subatomic unit may be considered as both a **ray** and a **particle.**   But present studies of the atomic elements acknowledge the fact that little is yet known of causation in the structure of the atom.   The **nucleus** of the atom is a relative term.   The **proton** is identical with the nucleus of the hydrogen atom, and is one unit of positive electricity.   The proton complex, or **spheron,** contains also a **positron** which is one unit of positive electricity of the same mass as a negative **electron.**   The nuclei of all other elements consist of combinations of protons and neutrons.   The electrons of the various atoms appear to orbit around the nucleus, but the electron, though considered a negatively charged particle, is also a **beta ray,** and the axis of its vortex motion is in calculable relativity to the respective positron. A spheron may contain one or more neutrons, and atoms having different numbers of neutrons are called **isotopes** and are of different atomic weights and have different physical properties.

The **helium atom** of mass 4 and positive charge 2 has two protons and two neutrons with the protons apparently in opposite polarity, and it has zero valence.   This combination is called an **alpha particle.**   Alpha particles are emitted at high velocity from radioactive elements, expelling the detached electrons, and when captured, are deposited as helium.   These usually come from outer-ring spherons and not necessarily from the inner nucleus.   The expelled electrons are beta rays.   When these collide with a nucleus, high-frequency **X-rays** break off.   **Gamma rays** are emitted from some radioactive elements.   The only difference between X-rays and gamma rays is the origin.   Gamma rays come from the nucleus, while X-rays come from electrons striking matter.   Few of the high-energy X-rays coming from the sun penetrate the atmosphere.

A detached positron has only a momentary existence; however, since in collision with an electron it produces a gamma ray, it may be inferred that the gamma ray is an electron in orbital linkage with a positron, and that when gamma rays are emitted, both the positron and its respective electron are stripped off as a unit.   Gamma rays and X-rays may be at various energy levels.

Gamma rays from the sun come only in infrequent bursts, and the **cosmic rays** from space are almost entirely protons, or stripped ions of hydrogen.   Cosmic rays appear to travel at about the speed of light. **Mesons** from cosmic rays appear to carry unit charges as beta rays do, but they have more energy and greater range.   While beta rays are stopped in the human skin, mesons can cause damage throughout the body.   High-energy cosmic rays are stopped by the atmosphere, and only a small proportion penetrate to the earth's surface.

The **neutron** is a particle of neutral charge with a mass approximately that of a proton.   A neutron has a mass 1,838 times that of an electron, while a proton has a mass 1,836 times that of an electron.   High-energy bombardment of nuclei yields electrons and positrons, and a proton thus may be a positron and a neutron in combination, while a neutron may be an electron bound to a proton together with the neutral particle known as the **neutrino.**   Each particle in an atom moves at extremely high speed in precise geometrical shapes.   The three-dimensional figure of the positron is said to be "doughnut shaped," and the shape of the electron is that of a revolving lemniscate which elongates to raise the particle to a higher energy level by the change in speed and angle with the application of energy.   This may account for crystal **phase changes,** which are the precise crystal changes for any given energy environment.

In the technology of producing and processing materials the atom is not subdivided, although in some operations of electrochemistry and electronics the electron is detached, and also particles and rays are employed, especially for activation.   In respect to the combining of the elements, **metallurgy** is high-energy chemistry.   In a solid metal, as in other materials, the atom does not appear alone, and the physical properties of a metal or alloy derive chiefly from the molecular structure.

Elements having one, two, or three outside valence electrons are **metals.** In chemical reactions they can release these electrons and form positive metal ions.   The elements having five, six, or seven outer electrons are **nonmetals.**   An element with four outer electrons is a **semimetal** and can react as either a metal or a nonmetal.   An element with eight outer electrons is said to have **zero valence** and is normally inactive, but by special energy application, or catalyzation, the linkage of the spherons can be broken and the electrons freed for chemical reactions.

The elements that make up all the planets and the stellar systems of the universe appear to be the same as those of the earth. There are many theories for the original formation of the material elements, but the subject pertains to astronomy rather than to materials technology, and involves the mathematics of progressive assembly of energy waves into monoquantic vortices which constitute mass. While elements do not have life in the same sense as the term is used for animals and plants, they do have intrinsic habits that can be controlled and altered by changing the environmental conditions. Elements are gregarious, and atoms separate only when activated by extremes of energy as with high heat, and they tend to congregate even when dissipated in water or in air.

Elements have orderly calculable habits of combining into **molecules,** or geometrically shaped units bonded to their own kind or to atoms of other elements. Compounding the elements into useful materials is done by the addition or subtraction of energy with consideration of time and space. Even the automatic reactions of two elements in proximity, known as **chemical affinity,** and the seeming holding action of **stabilizing agents,** depend upon a transfer of energy. Energy, **time,** and **space** are non-material, and their limits and bounds are not presently comprehensible to the human mind. Thus, most of the knowledge of the internal workings of the extremely minute atoms is analogical, or reasoned by inference from test comparisons of effects. The tools of the technologist in working with the atoms, therefore, are the theories. A **theory** is considered the best available knowledge at any given time, based on the analytical coordination of the results of many tests. A theory, in the light of further test experiments, may prove inadequate for more advanced operations, but old theories are often not discarded because they may be correct within certain bounds and thus may continue to be useful as the easiest way to accomplish limited objectives.

The term **crystal** is usually applied only to molecular structures which at normal temperatures are hard solids that form into pronounced geometric shapes or are capable of being split on precise planes, and solids without apparent planes are termed **amorphous.** But the crystal shapes tabulated for metals usually represent merely the typical position pattern of the atoms. **Single crystals,** used for electronic purposes, may be cut from natural crystals, may be grown by flame melting, or may be grown chemically by application of heat and pressure. **Seed crystals** used to initiate growth are grains or particles made up of many molecules, while a **unit crystal** is the unit molecule or, in some cases, the unit pattern of the lattice, and these determine the shape and nature of the structure. In microscopy the structures of aluminum and silver appear optically as similar cubes, but the unit crystal of aluminum in the solid state forms both a cube and a lattice, while the unit crystal of silver forms no cube and does not lattice, and the metal grains are cryptocrystalline. Usually, the smaller the grain size, the nearer the approach to the physical properties of the single crystal, so that large single crystals are sometimes made by compacting extremely fine powders.

All elements convert progressively from solid to gaseous form by the application of energy, usually by heat application, and vice versa by the extraction of heat. The terms **solid, liquid,** and **gas** are **phase changes** depending on the mobility of the molecule caused by changes in its three-dimensional shape. A **gaseous element** is one that is a gas at ordinary temperatures and pressures, such as hydrogen. At extremely low temperatures a **hydrogen crystal** should be a hard white metal of cryptocrystalline structure with straight planes of cleavage. **Liquid hydrogen** for rocket fuel normally has a molecule of conical shape in spin. When catalyzed by hot platinum it changes to an ovaloid shape which can pass through a smaller molecular sieve, and it also requires 20% less storage space per unit of fuel. These forms are called **ortho hydrogen** and **meta hydrogen,** but are both H_2.

Phase changes often occur within the solid stage, and the change in dimensions of the material, called **creep,** is the effect from change in volume of the molecules. With some materials the liquid stage is so short as to be undetectable, appearing to pass directly from solid to vapor, and this transition is called **sublimation.** All molecules have energy transition points at which they break down to free the original elements or to interact and combine with other available elements to form new compounds. For example, iron molecules, having free electrons, disintegrate easily in the presence of air or moisture to form iron oxides. This process is called corrosion; in organic materials it is called decay. The molecule of gold has no free electrons and, because of its high energy, is not broken down easily by the influence of other elements. Thus it is said to be noncorrosive. In the case of aluminum, oxygen from the air cross-links the free electrons on the surface of the grains and protects the metal from further corrosion.

In metallurgy and the metalworking industries the elements are normally not used alone in a pure state, and as solids and liquids only in molecular forms. In the casting of metals and alloys from a melt the time of solidification is short and, without the application of high energy as in the form of high pressure, there is no growth into large single crystals. Growth is usually into particles, or grains, which may be single crystals or irregular conglomerates of unit crystals. In the contraction of cooling, however, grain boundaries may be so close as to be undetectable even at a magnification of 2 million to 1, and thus the impurities are likely to be in the unmatched open spaces among the crystals, and not interstitial.   But with some latticing molecules, such as copper, there is room within the lattice for smaller atoms or molecules, such as those of beryllium, without interference with the paths of bonding electrons, while in the aluminum lattice there appears to be no such room.

Organic and other chemicals are usually produced from the elements by **synthesis,** that is, built up by progressive steps logically deduced from known data and theories concerning the natural habits and characteristics of the atoms and their elementary groups.   A compound may thus be written as a **chemical formula** which expresses graphically the specific number and locations of the atomic elements in the compound.   In some degree this system is also used in the production of **ceramics,** i.e., compounds or compound mixtures based on metallic oxides, where the resultant material is expressed in percentage proportions of the crystal formulas.   Alloys are usually made by batch-mixing of the elements, and the resultant material is expressed in weight percentages of the contained elements, not in terms of the molecular structure on which the physical properties of the alloy depend.

ELEMI. A soft, sticky, opaque resin with a pleasant odor, obtained from the **Pili tree,** *Canarium luzonicum,* of the Philippines, and employed for giving body and elasticity to lacquers and in lithographic inks.   In medicine it is used in ointments.   It contains **dipentene,** $C_{10}H_{18}$, which is called **limonene** from its lemonlike odor, and is known as **cajeputene** when obtained from cajeput.   **Limonene dioxide,** or **dipentene dioxide,** a colorless liquid of the composition $C_{10}H_{12}O_2$, is a valuable synthetic chemical for making epoxy resins and for cross-linking acrylic and other resins.   Elemi also contains a related terpinene oil, **phellandrene.**   Substitute elemi resins are obtained from various trees of the family *Burseraceae* of tropical Africa and America.   The pili trees are hacked or stripped, and the resin collects on the bark, a tree yielding about 5 lb per year.   **West Indian elemi** is from the tree *Dacryodes hexandra* of the West Indies.   **Nauli gum** is elemi from the tree *C. commune* of the Solomons.   **Elemi oil,** obtained by distilling elemi, is a colorless liquid of specific gravity 0.87 to 0.91, used in perfumes and in medicines.   It has an aniselike odor.

ELKSKIN. The commercial name for soft, pliable, and durable leather made from the bundled rawhides known as kips, or from overgrown calf by a special tanning process and impregnation with oils.   It is used chiefly for children's shoe uppers and for pocketbooks.   A heavier elkskin, or **elk leather,** for sport shoes and boots, is made from cowhides by the same treatment.   Elkskin, like chamois, dries out to its original softness after wetting.   **Smoked elk** is elk leather dyed cream-colored to imitate the original leather of elks, which was smoked over a wood fire.

ELM. The wood of several species of the elm tree, of the eastern United States and Canada, and northern Europe.   The wood of the **American elm,** or **white elm,** *Ulmus americana,* has a fine grain, has a weight of about 40 lb per cu ft, is hard and tough, and is whitish brown in color.   It is the best known commercially of the six species grown in the United States. The American elm is not a forest tree, but is grown as a shade and ornamental tree.   It does not grow in the mountains.   The trees sometimes reach a diameter of 6 ft and a height of 100 ft.   The tough, durable wood is valued for ax handles, and for parts requiring a combination of strength, bending qualities, and ability to withstand rough usage.   The wood of this tree, and also of the rock elm, was formerly used for superstructures of naval ships because it did not sharp-splinter like oak.   It was also the favorite wood for hubs and spokes of heavy wagon wheels.   **Rock elm,** or **hickory elm,** *U. thomasii,* is also native to the United States and Canada. It has a very fine, close grain and is slightly heavier.   It is sometimes called **cork elm,** although this name applies to the **wahoo,** or **winged elm,** *U. alata,* of the southeastern states, because of the corky appearance of the twigs.   The winged elm is grown as a shade tree, but the wood was valued for vehicle parts.   **English elm,** *U. procera,* has a straight trunk and rounded crown more like the oaks.   **Chinese elm,** *U. parvifolia,* has small leaves and is very resistant to disease.   **Slippery elm** is a smaller forest tree, *U. fulva,* of northeastern United States.   Considerable lumber came from this tree under the name of **red elm.**   The inner bark of the tree is mucilaginous with a sweet taste and characteristic odor.   It was used by the Indians as a chewing gum and as a poultice for skin infections.   The dried and powdered bark is now used in medicine for skin infections and for the throat.   It contains **ulmic acid,** or **geic acid,** $C_{20}H_{14}O_6$.

EMERY. A fine-grained, impure variety of the mineral corundum, with the fine crystals of aluminum oxide embedded in a matrix of iron oxide. It usually contains only 55 to 75% Al_2O_3.   The specific gravity is 3.7 to 4.3, and the hardness about 8.   It occurs as a dark-brown granular massive mineral.   It is used as an abrasive either ground into powder or in blocks and wheels.   In the natural block material the grains are irregular, giving a varying grinding performance.   The grains are graded in sizes from 220 mesh, the finest, to 20 mesh, the coarsest.   **Emery paper** and cloth are usually graded from 24 to 120 mesh, and the grains are glued to one side of 9- by 11-in sheets.   **Flour of emery** is the finest powder, usually dust from the crushing.   **Emery cake** as made for buffing and polishing is now not likely to be made of emery, but a graded combination of aluminum oxide and iron oxide, with a higher percentage of the hard alumi-num oxide for buffing, and higher iron oxide for polishing.   It is furnished in various grades of fineness, with grains of 120 to 200 mesh, or flour sizes, F, FF, and FFF.   Emery takes its name from Cape Emery, on the Island of Naxos.   Most of the world supply comes from Greece and Turkey, but some is mined at Peekskill, N.Y.

EMULSIFYING AGENTS.   Materials used to aid in the mixing of liquids that are not soluble in one another, or to stabilize the suspension of non-liquid materials in a liquid in which the nonliquid is not soluble.   The suspension of droplets of one liquid in another liquid in which the first liquid is not soluble is called an **emulsion.**   The emulsion of oil and water, used in machine shops as a cutting lubricant and work coolant, may be made with soap as the emulsifying agent.   The emulsifying agent protects droplets of the dispersed medium from uniting and thus separating out. The oil itself may be treated so that it is self-emulsifying.   Sulfonated oils contain strong negatively charged ester sulfate groups in the molecule, and do not react and conglomerate with the molecules of a weakly charged liquid.   They will thus form emulsions with water without any other agent.

In emulsions of a powder in a liquid an emulsifying agent called a **protective colloid** may be used.   This is usually a material of high molecu-lar weight such as gelatin, and such materials form a protective film around each particle of the contained powder.   Saponin and starches are com-monly used thus as **suspending agents.**   For the suspension of drug mate-rials in pharmaceutical mixtures gum arabic or tragacanth may be used. Starches, egg albumin, and proteins are common emulsifying agents for food preparation.   Alginates are among the best suspending agents for a wide range of emulsions because of the numerous repelling charges in the high molecular weight and the irregular configuration of the chain, but when added to protein-containing liquids such as many foodstuffs, the similar conditions of the algin and the protein molecules cause a neutraliza-tion reaction and a precipitation of the agglomerated particles.   Suspend-ing agents generally increase the viscosity of the liquid, and with high con-centrations of some gums or resins the water molecules may be completely encased in the resin lattice as a semisolid or water-filled plastic.

Sucrose esters, used as emulsifiers for foods, cosmetics, and drugs, are made from sugar and palmitic, lauric, or other fatty acids.   The monoes-ters are soluble in water and in alcohol, and the diesters are oil-soluble. **Sorbester,** of Howards of Ilford, Ltd., for emulsifying fatty foodstuffs, is a diester of sucrose.   **Sucrodet D-600,** of the Millmaster Chemical Corp., is a white, tasteless, and odorless powder made from sugar and palmitic acid. **Myrj 45,** of the Atlas Chemical Industry, is polyoxy ethylene stearate.

Propylene laurate is a light, high-boiling liquid that is self-emulsifying in water, and is employed in foodstuffs and pharmaceuticals to stabilize the mixtures. The sodium salt of **ursolic acid** is a strong emulsifying agent for oil-in-water mixtures. The acid is a complex triterpene obtained from the skins of the cranberry.

Some solid materials may be suspended indefinitely in liquids if ground to such a fineness that the electronegative mutually repelling force, or **zeta potential,** of the particles is greater than the force of gravity. Silica, for example, has only a feeble electronegativity, and if the particles are below about 1 micron in size they will give a permanent suspension in water. These finely ground solids are used as **thickening agents** for paints and coatings. Bentonite is thus used in adhesives and paints. Thickening agents may also add other properties such as giving better adhesion or strengthening the film. Some long-chain chemicals used as emulsifying agents in cutting oils also give antirust properties. **Thickening agent ASE-95,** of the Rohm & Haas Co., has a powerful thickening action on water-base emulsions which can be halted at any desired viscosity by neutralizing the acidity It is an acrylic copolymer of 20% solids containing an organic acid giving a pH of 3. When added to the emulsion to be thickened the solids dissolve in minute particles, and the process is stopped at the desired viscosity by adding an alkali.

ENAMEL. A protective coating which upon hardening has an enameled or glossy face. **Pottery enamels, ceramic enamels,** or **vitreous enamels** are composed chiefly of quartz, feldspar, clay, soda, and borax, with saltpeter or borax as fluxes. The quartz supplies the silica, and such enamels are fusible glasses. In acid-resisting enamels alkali earths may be used instead of borates. To make enamels opaque, opacifiers are used. They may be tin oxide for white enamel, cobalt oxide for blue, or platinum oxide for gray. Enamel-making materials are prepared in the form of a powder which is called **frit.** The frit-making temperature is about 2400°F, but the enamel application temperatures are from 1400 to 1600°F. Each succeeding coat has a lower melting point than the one before it so as not to destroy the preceding coat. It must also have about the same coefficient of expansion as the metal to prevent cracking. Enamels for aluminum usually have a high proportion of lead oxide to lower the melting point, and enamels for magnesium may be based on lithium oxide. Some enamels for low-melting metals have the ceramic frit bonded to the metal with monoaluminum phosphate at temperatures as low as 400°F.

The mineral oxide coatings fused to metals are often called **porcelain enamels,** but they are not porcelain, and the term vitreous enamel is preferred in the industry, although ceramic-lined tanks and pipe are very often referred to as **glass-lined steel.** The composition varies greatly, one company having more than 3,000 formulas.   Vitreous enameled metals are used for cooking utensils, signs, chemical tanks and piping, clock and instrument dials, and siding and roofing.   Ground coats are usually no more than 0.004 in. thick, and cover coats may be 0.003 to 0.008 in. thick. The hardness ranges from 150 to 500 Knoop.   Thick coatings on thin metals are fragile, but thin coatings on heavy metals are flexible enough to be bent.   Standard porcelain-type enamel has a smooth glossy surface with a light reflectance of at least 65% in the white color, but pebbly surfaces that break up the reflected image may be used for architectural applications.

High-temperature coatings may contain a very high percentage of zirconium and will withstand temperatures to 1650°F.   **Refractory enamels,** for coating superalloys to protect against the corrosion of hot gases to 2500°F, may be made with standard ceramic frits to which is added boron nitride with a lithium chromate or fluoride flux.   Blue undercoats containing cobalt are generally used to obtain high adhesion on iron and steel, but some of the **enameling steels** do not require an undercoat, especially when a specially compounded frit or special flux is used.   When **sodium aluminum silicate,** $Na_2O \cdot Al_2O_3 \cdot 6SiO \cdot xH_2O$, is used instead of borax, a white finish is produced without a ground coat.   **Mirac,** of the Pemco Co., is a white enamel which gives good adhesion direct to steel.   Enamels containing titanium oxide will adhere well to steels alloyed with a small amount of titanium.   **Ti-Namel,** of the Inland Steel Co., is an enameling steel containing titanium.

Many trade names are applied to vitreous enamels and to enameled metals.   **Vitric steel,** of the Republic Stamping & Enameling Co., is an enameled corrugated sheet steel for construction.   **Majolica** is an old name for marblelike enamels made by mixing enamels of different colors, but **mottled graywear** is made with cobalt oxide on steel that has a controlled misting on the surface.   **Cloisonné enamel** is an ancient decorative enamel produced by soldering thin strips of gold on the base metal to form cells into which the colored enamel is pressed and fused into place. It requires costly hand methods, and is now imitated in synthetic plastics under names such as **Enameloid.**

The word enamel in the paint industry refers to glossy varnishes with pigments or to paints of oxide or sulfate pigments mixed with varnish to give a glossy face.   In general, they do not have the heavy body of a paint and require undercoats.   **Japan** is a name applied to black baking enamels. The same finish in other colors would not be called japan, as the original oriental lacquer was always black.   Japan consists of a pigment, a gum, a drying oil, and a reducer, the same as any oil enamel.   It is always baked, which drives off the solvent and fuses the gum into a uniform vitreous layer.   Japans give a tough durable finish to small machine parts, but require expensive between-coat rubbing, and are now replaced by synthetic baking finishes.   The modified phenolmelamine and alkyd-melamine synthetic resins produce tough and resistant enamel coatings.   Quick-drying enamels are the cellulose lacquers with pigments.   **Fibrous enamel,** used for painting roofs, is an asphalt solution in which asbestos fibers have been incorporated.   When of heavy consistency and used for calking metal roofs, it is called **roof putty.**

EPOXY RESINS. A class of synthetic resins characterized by having in the molecule a highly reactive **oxirane** ring of triangular configuration consisting of an oxygen atom bonded to two adjoining and bonded carbon atoms.   They are usually made by the reaction of epichlorohydrin with phenol compounds, but epoxidation is also done by the oxidation of a carbon-to-carbon double bond with an organic peracid such as peracetic acid.   **Epichlorohydrin** is produced from allyl chloride, and is a colorless liquid with a chlorine atom and an epoxide ring.   The **dipoxy resins** made by the oxidation of olefins with peracetic acid have higher heat resistance than those made with bisphenol.   Epoxidation is not limited to the making of plastic resins, and **epoxidized oils,** usually epoxidized with peracetic acid, are used as paint oils and as plasticizers for vinyl resins. **Flexol EPO,** of Union Carbide, is such an epoxidized soybean oil.

Epoxy resins are generally more costly than many other resins, but, because of their unusual combinations of high mechanical and electrical properties, they are important, especially for such uses as adhesives, resistant coatings, and for encapsulation of electronic units.   The resins are thermosetting and inert.   For encapsulation, they cast easily with little shrinkage.   They have very high adhesion to metals and nonmetals, heat resistance from 350 to 500°F, dielectric strength to 550 volts per mil, and hardness to Rockwell M110.   The tensile strength may be up to 15,000 psi, with elongation of 2 to 5%, but some resilient encapsulating resins are made with elongation to 150% with lower tensile strengths.   The resins have high resistance to common solvents, oils, and chemicals. **Maraglas 658,** of the Marblette Corp., is an epoxy casting resin for encapsulating which has crystal clarity and a 90% light transmission.

An unlimited variety of epoxy resins is possible by varying the basic reactions with different chemicals or different catalysts or both, by combination with other resins, or by cross-linking with organic acids, amines, and other agents.   To reduce cost when used as laminating adhesives they may be blended with furfural resins, giving adhesives of high strength and high chemical resistance.   Blends with polyamides have high dielectric strength, mold well, and are used for encapsulating electrical components.   The **Epon resins** of the Shell Chemical Corp. are epoxy resins made with epichlorohydrin and bisphenols.   **Kem-Krete,** of the

Sherwin-Williams Co., a coating for ceramic blocks, and **Erkopon,** a coating for tanks, of the Earl Paint Corp., are based on **ethoxyline resins,** or polyaryl ethylene oxide condensates, made from epichlorohydrin and bisphenol with an ethylene diamine catalyst. By using a polyamide curing agent an epoxy can be made water-emulsifiable for use in water-based paints. The **water-soluble epoxy** of General Mills, Inc. is a reaction product of **Genepoxy M195,** a bisphenol epichlorohydrin epoxy resin, and **Versamid 265-WR70,** an ethylene glycol ether acetate. **Resin X-3441,** of the Dow Chemical Co., is an epoxy resin with 19% bromine in the molecule. It is flame-resistant. Another grade, with 49% bromine, is a semisolid, used for heat-resistant adhesives and coatings. **Oxiron resins,** of the FMC Corp., are **epoxidized polyolefins.** They have five or more reactive epoxy groups along each molecule of the chain instead of the usual two terminal epoxy groups on each molecule. With dibasic acids or anhydrides they form strong, hard resins of high heat resistance, or resins of lower viscosity are made for laminating and casting. **Novolac DEN 438,** of the Dow Chemical Co., is an epoxy resin with a high distortion point, 570°F, made by the reaction of epichlorohydrin with a phenol-formaldehyde resin with an anhydride catalyst. As an adhesive for laminates it gives very high strength at elevated temperatures. **Narmco adhesive,** of Whittaker Corp., is an **epoxy adhesive** with a sheer strength of 5,500 psi. Epoxies can be copolymerized with other resins. **Epoxy-acrylate resin,** used for glass fiber laminates, combines the resistance and adhesiveness of the epoxy with the fast cure and strength of the acrylate. **Epoxy resin ERRA-0300,** of Union Carbide, has cyclo pentyl oxide terminal groups instead of diglycidyl ether. The yield strength at 392°F is 18,200 psi and it has a heat deflection temperature of 434°F.

ESSENTIAL OILS. Aromatic oils found in uncombined form in various parts of plants, and employed for flavors, perfumes, disinfectants, medicines, stabilizers; for masking undesirable odors; and as raw materials for making other products. They are usually the esters upon which the odoriferous properties of the plants depend, and are called essential oils because of their ease of solubility in alcohol to form essences. They are also called **volatile oils,** although this term is sometimes also applied to the light and volatile distillates from petroleum. The essential oils are of four general classes: the **pinenes** or **terpenes** of coniferous plants, containing carbon and hydrogen of the empirical formula $C_{10}H_{16}$, such as oil of turpentine; **oxygenated oils** containing carbon, hydrogen, and oxygen, such as oil of cassia; **nitrogenated oils** containing carbon, hydrogen, oxygen, and nitrogen, such as oil of bitter almonds; **sulfurated oils** containing carbon, hydrogen, and sulfur, such as oil of mustard.

Although fixed vegetable oils are obtained by expression, the essential oils are obtained by distilling the buds, flowers, leaves, twigs, or other parts of the plant.   Rose oil is found only in the flowers.   Orange and lemon oils are from both the flowers and the fruits, but are of different compositions.   Sweet birch and cinnamon oils are from the bark.   Valerian and calamus are only in the roots, while sandalwood and cedar oils are only in the wood.   Sometimes the essential oil is not in the plant, but is developed when the plant is macerated with water.   The **alpha pinene** extracted from turpentine is used for paints and varnishes as it has a high evaporation rate.   It is a water-white liquid of pleasant odor boiling at 163°C.   It is also used in the synthesis of camphor.   **Pinic acid** is a complex carboxy cyclobutane acetic acid produced from alpha pinene.   Its esters are used for synthetic lubricants.   **Balsams** are solid or semisolid resinous oils, and are mixtures of resins with cinnamic or benzoic acid, or both, with sometimes another volatile oil.   They are obtained from a variety of trees, and are used in antiseptics, perfumes, flavors, and in medicine.

Some of the essential oils contain alkaloids which have a physiological effect.   **Wormwood oil,** distilled from the dried leaf tops of the perennial herb *Artemisia absinthium,* native to southern Europe but also grown in the United States, is used in medicine for fevers, and also for flavoring the liqueur absinthe.   The drug **santonin,** used for worm treatment for animals, is an alkaloid extracted from the unopened flower heads of the **Levant wormseed,** *A. cina,* of the Near East, but **wormseed oil,** or **Baltimore oil,** used for the same purpose, is an essential oil containing the alkaloid **ascoridole.**   It is distilled from the seeds and leaf stems of the annual plant *Chenopodium anthelminticum,* grown in Maryland.

ESTERS. Combinations of alcohols with organic acids, which form several important groups of commercial materials.   The esters occur naturally in vegetable and animal oils and fats as combinations of acids with the alcohol glycerin.   The natural fats are usually mixtures of esters of many acids, coconut oil having no less than 14 acids.   Stearic, oleic, palmitic, and linoleic acid esters are the common bases for most vegetable and animal fats, and the esters of the other acids such as linolenic, capric, and arachidic give the peculiar characteristics of the particular fat, although the physical characteristics and melting points may be governed by the basic esters.   Esters occur also in waxes, the vegetable waxes being usually found on the outside of leaves and fruits to protect them from loss of water.   The waxes differ from the fats in that they are combinations of monoacids with monohydric, or simple, alcohols, rather than with glycerin.   They are harder than fats and have higher melting points.   Esters of still lower molecular weights are also widely distributed in the essential oils of plants where they give the characteristic odors and tastes.   All of the esters have the characteristic formula ArCOOR or RCOOR, where R represents an **alkyl group,** and Ar an **aryl group,** that is, where R is a univalent straight-chain hydrocarbon having the formula C_nH_{2n+1}, and Ar is a univalent benzene ring $C_6H_5\cdot$. In the esters of low molecular weight which make the odors and flavors, the combination of different alcohols with the same acid yields oils of different flavor. Thus the ester methyl acetate, CH_3COOCH_3, is **peppermint oil;** amyl acetate, $CH_3COOC_5H_{11}$, is banana oil; and isoamyl acetate, $CH_3COO(CH_2)_3(CH_3)_2$, is **pear oil.** Esters are used as solvents, flavors, perfumes, waxes, oils, fats, fatty acids, pharmaceuticals, and in the manufacture of soaps and many chemicals.

Ester alcohols are intermediates that require less acid for esterification. **Texanol,** of Eastman Chemical Co., has both a hydroxy group and an ester linkage with the empirical formula $C_{12}H_{24}O_3$. It produces a wide range of chemicals and compounds with low, minus 57°C, pour point.

ETCHING MATERIALS. Chemicals, usually acids, employed for cutting into, or etching, the surface of metals, glass, or other material. In the metal industries they are called **etchants.** The usual method of etching is to coat the surface with a wax, asphalt, or other substance not acted upon by the acid, cut the design through with a sharp instrument, and then allow the acid to corrode or dissolve the exposed parts. For etching steel, a 25% solution of sulfuric acid in water or a ferric chloride solution may be used. For etching stainless steels a solution of ferric chloride and hydrochloric acid in water is used. For high-speed steels, brass, or nickel, a mixture of nitric and hydrochloric acids in water solution is used, or nickel may be etched with a 45% solution of sulfuric acid. Copper may be etched with a solution of chromic acid. Brass and nickel may be etched with an acid solution of ferric chloride and potassium chlorate. For red brasses, deep etching is done with concentrated nitric acid mixed with 10% hydrochloric acid, the latter being added to keep the tin oxide in solution and thus retain a surface exposed to the action of the acid. For etching aluminum a 9% solution of copper chloride in 1% acetic acid, or a 20% solution of ferric chloride may be used, followed by a wash with strong nitric acid. Sodium hydroxide, ammonium hydroxide, or any alkaline solutions are also used for etching aluminum. Zinc is preferably etched with weak nitric acid, but requires a frequent renewal of the acid. Strong acid is not used because of the heat generated, which destroys the wax coating. A 5% solution of nitric acid will remove 0.002 in. of zinc per minute, compared with the removal of over 0.005 in. per min in most metal-etching processes. Glass is etched with hydrofluoric acid or with **white acid.** White acid is a mixture of hydrofluoric acid and **ammonium bifluoride,** a white crystalline material of the composition $(NH_4)FHF$. Sodium chlorate may be used as the electrolyte in producing **chemical finishes.** The process in which the metal is removed chemically to give the desired finish as a substitute for mechanical machining is called **chemical machining.**

ETHER. The common name for **ethyl ether,** or **diethyl ether,** a highly volatile, colorless liquid of the composition $(C_2H_5)_2O$ made from ethyl alcohol. It is used as a solvent for fats, greases, resins, and nitrocellulose, and in medicine as an anesthetic. The specific gravity is 0.720, boiling point 34.2°C, and freezing point −116°C. Its vapor is heavier than air and is explosive. Actually, ether is a more general term, and an ether is an **alkyl oxide** with two alkyl groups joined to an oxygen atom. The ethyl ether would thus be expressed as $C_2H_5 \cdot O \cdot C_2H_5$, and there are many ethers. **Butyl ether,** $(C_4H_9)_2O$, has a much higher boiling point, 140°C, is more stable, and is used as a solvent for gums and resins. **Isopropyl ether,** $(CH_3)_2CHOCH(CH_3)_2$, is a by-product in the manufacture of isopropyl alcohol from propylene. It has a higher boiling point than ethyl ether, 69°C, and lower solubility in water, and is often preferred as an extractive solvent. **Methyl ether,** or **dimethyl ether,** also known as **wood ether,** is a colorless gas of the composition $(CH_3)_2O$, with a pleasant aromatic odor. The boiling point is −23.5°C. The specific gravity is 1.562 or, as a liquid compressed in cylinders, 0.724. It is used for fuel, as a welding gas, as a refrigerant, and for vapor-pressure thermometers. **Hexyl ether,** $C_6H_{13}OC_6H_{13}$, has a high boiling point, 226.2°C, very low water solubility, and a specific gravity of 0.7942. It is stable and not volatile, with a flash point of 170°F. It is used in foam breakers, and in chemical manufacture where anhydrous properties are desired. A low-boiling chemical used as an extractive solvent and for plastics because of its stability in alkalies and its high water solubility is **methylal,** $CH_3OCH_2OCH_3$. It is a water-white liquid boiling at 42.3°C. Ether reacts slowly with the oxygen of the air to form highly explosive and poisonous compounds, so that long-stored ether is dangerous for use as an anesthetic.

ETHYL ALCOHOL. Also called **methyl carbinol,** and **ethanol** when made synthetically. It is the common beverage alcohol, which when denatured for nonbeverage purposes is called **industrial alcohol.** About 90% of the ethyl alcohol used in the United States is denatured. Ethyl alcohol is a colorless liquid with a pleasant odor but burning taste. The composition is CH_3CH_2OH, specific gravity 0.79, boiling point 78.5°C, and freezing point −117.3°C. It mixes with water in all proportions and takes up moisture from the air. It burns with a bluish flame and high temperature, yielding carbonic acid and water. The ignition temperature is 965°F. It is one of the best solvents, and dissolves many organic materials such as gums, resins, and essential oils, making solutions called **essences.**

Alcohol is sold by the proof gallon, a 100 proof containing 50% alcohol by volume and having a specific gravity of 0.7939.   The term **alcohol,** alone, refers to 188 to 192 proof.   High-purity alcohol, **grain alcohol,** and pure ethyl alcohol are terms for 190 proof.   **Absolute alcohol,** or **anhydrous alcohol,** is 200 proof, free of water.   **Methylated spirits** is a term first used in England to designate the excise-free mixture of 90% ethyl alcohol and 10 wood alcohol for industrial use.   Denatured ethyl alcohol, made unsuitable for beverage purposes, may be marketed under trade names such as **Synasol** of Union Carbide.   **Solox,** of the U.S. Industrial Chemicals, Inc., consists of 100 parts 190-proof alcohol, 5 ethyl acetate, and 1 gasoline, used for lacquers, fuel, and as a solvent.   **Neosol,** of the Shell Chemical Corp., is 190-proof ethyl alcohol denatured with 4 parts of a mixture of tertiary butyl alcohol, methyl isobutyl ketone, and gasoline.

Ethyl alcohol is used as a solvent in varnishes, explosives, extracts, perfumes, pharmaceuticals, as a fuel, as a preserving agent, as an antifreeze, and for making other chemicals.   Up to 15% of alcohol can be used in gasoline motor fuels without change in the carburation.   The German motor fuel **Monopolin** was a mixture of absolute alcohol and benzene. Ethyl alcohol is classed as a poison when pure, but is employed as a beverage in many forms.   In small quantities it is an exhilarant and narcotic.   In all countries large amounts of **beverage alcohol** are made from starches, grains, and fruits, retaining the original flavor of the raw material and marketed directly as wines, whiskies, and brandies.   But **synthetic wines** are made by fermenting sugar and adding vegetable extracts to supply flavor and bouquet.   No methyl alcohol or fusel oil is produced in the process.   Alcohol is produced easily by the fermentation of sugars, molasses, grains, and starch.   It is also made cheaply by hydrating ethylene produced by the cracking of petroleum hydrocarbons.   In Europe it is also made from the waste liquor of pulp mills by fermentation of the wood sugar.   **Sulfite pulp liquor** contains 1.8% fermentable hexose sugar.   It is also made directly from wood waste by fermenting the wood sugar molasses.

A substitute for ethyl alcohol for solvent purposes and as a rubbing alcohol is **isopropyl alcohol,** or **isopropanol,** a colorless liquid of the composition $(CH_3)_2CHOH$, boiling point 82°C, and produced by the hydration of propylene from cracked gasses.   It is also used as a stabilizer in soluble oils, and in drying baths for electroplating.   **Petrohol,** of the Enjay Chemical Co., is isopropyl alcohol.   **Trichloro ethanol,** $CCl_3 \cdot CH_2OH$, is a viscous liquid with an ether odor, boiling at 150°C and freezing at 13°C, slightly soluble in water, used for making plasticizers and other chemicals. The spent grain from alcohol distilleries, called **stillage,** is dried and marketed as livestock feed, and is a better feed than the original grain because of the high concentration of proteins and vitamins, with the starch removed. The **leaf alcohol** which occurs in fruits and many plants is a hexene alcohol. It is made synthetically for blending in synthetic flavors and for restoring full flavor and fragrance to fruit extracts.

ETHYL SILICATE. A colorless liquid of the composition $(CH_2H_5)_4SiO_4$, used as a source of colloidal silica in heat-resistant and acid-resistant coatings and for moldings. The specific gravity is 0.920 to 0.950. It is a **silicic acid ester,** with a normal content of 25% available silica, though the **tetra ethyl orthosilicate** has 27.9% available silica, and the **Ethyl silicate 40** of Union Carbide has 40% silica. The latter is a brown liquid. Water hydrolyzes ethyl silicate to alcohol and **silicic acid,** H_4SiO_2, which dehydrates to an adhesive amorphous silica. For molding, the ester is mixed with silica powder, and for such products as bearings wood flour may be incorporated to absorb and retain the lubricating oil. Ethyl silicate solutions are employed for the surface hardening of sand molds and graphite molds for special casting. Silicic acid ester paints are used to harden and preserve stone, cement, or plaster, and for coating insulating brick. They are resistant to heat and to chemical fumes. **Kieselsol,** a German material for clarifying wine and fruit juices by precipitation of the albumin, is a 15% water solution of silicic acid.

ETHYLENE. Also called **ethene.** A colorless, inflammable gas, CH_2: CH_2, which is produced in the cracking of petroleum. Ethylene liquefies at $-154.8°F$. It was first produced in Holland by dehydrating ethyl alcohol with sulfuric acid, and is now made from cracking petroleum, or by breaking down alcohol by catalytic action. It was originally employed for enriching illuminating gas to give it a more luminous flame, and was called **olefiant gas** because it formed an oil, ethylene dichloride, called **Dutch liquid,** when treated with chlorine. Its nature as a chemical radical was early discovered, and it was believed by the French chemist Wurtz to be the connecting link between organic and inorganic compounds. Ethylene is now used to produce ethyl alcohol, acrylic acid, and styrene, and it is the basis for many types of reactive chemicals. **Ketene,** for example, used as a reactant in connecting polymers to improve physical properties of the plastics, has the basic formula $H_2C:C:O$, which is ethylene modified by substituting oxygen for two of the hydrogens. **Butyl ethyl ketene** of Eastman Chemical Products, Inc., for modifying compounds with active double bonds or active hydrogens, is a yellow liquid of specific gravity 0.826, having the composition $(C_4H_9)(C_2H_5):C:C:O$. **Calorene** is ethylene in pressure cylinders for flame cutting. When burned with oxygen, it gives a flame lower in temperature than acetylene, and it is more stable in storage. For making resins and waxes, and for solvent use, it may be employed in the form of **ethylene diamine,** $NH_2CH_2CH_2$-NH_2, a colorless liquid of specific gravity 0.968, boiling at about 120°C. **Ethylene imene,** C_3H_7N, is a very reactive chemical useful for making a wide range of products.   It is a water-white liquid of specific gravity 0.79, boiling at 66°C, soluble in water and in common solvents.   The **imene ring** in the molecule has two carbon atoms and a nitrogen atom forming a triangle.   The ring is stable with basic chemicals, but is strongly reactive to acid compounds, opening at the carbon-nitrogen bond to receive hydrogen. By acid catalyzation and control with alkaline solutions to avoid violent simultaneous opening of the two carbon bonds, the material can be polymerized or made to receive other chemical groups.

Trichlorethylene is a heavy colorless liquid of pleasant odor of the composition $CHCl:CCl_2$, also known as **westrosol.**   Its boiling point is 87°C and its specific gravity 1.471.   It is insoluble in water and is unattacked by dilute acids and alkalies.   It is not inflammable and is less toxic than tetrachlorethane.   Trichlorethylene is a powerful solvent for fats, waxes, resins, rubber, and other organic substances, and is employed for the extraction of oils and fats, for cleaning fabrics, and for degreasing metals preparatory to plating.   The freezing point is −88°C, and it is also used as a refrigerant.   It is also used in soaps employed in the textile industry for degreasing.   **Tri-Clene** is a trade name of Du Pont for trichlorethylene, marketed for dry cleaning.   **Triad** and **Perm-A-Clor** are trade names of the Detroit Rex Products Co. for trichlorethylene stabilized with a basic organic stabilizer that prevents breakdown of the solvent in degreasing metals.

ETHYLENE GLYCOL.   Also known as **glycol** and **ethylene alcohol.**   A colorless syrupy liquid, CH_2OHCH_2OH, with a sweetish taste, very soluble in water.   It has a low freezing point, −25°C, and is much used as an antifreeze in automobiles.   A 25% solution has a freezing point of −5°F, without appreciably lowering the boiling point of the water.   It has the advantage over alcohol that it does not boil away easily, and permits the operation of engines at much higher temperatures than with water, giving greater fuel efficiency.   It is also used for the manufacture of acrylonitrile fibers, and as a solvent for nitrocellulose.   It is highly toxic in contact with the skin.

Diethylene glycol, $C_4H_{10}O_3$, is a water-white liquid boiling at 244°C, used as an antifreeze, as a solvent, and for softening cotton and wool fibers in the textile industry.   A 50% solution of diethylene glycol freezes at −28°C.   **Cellosolve,** $C_2H_5OCH_2CH_2OH$, of Union Carbide, is the monoethyl ether of ethylene glycol.   It is a colorless liquid boiling at 135.1°C, and is a powerful solvent used in varnish removers, cleaning solutions, and as a solvent for paints, varnishes, plastics, and dyes.   **Car-**

bitol, of the same company, is an ether of diethylene glycol of the composition $CH_3CH_2OCH_2CH_2OCH_2CH_2OH$, used as a solvent for oils, dyes, resins, and gums. The boiling point is 201.9 and freezing point $- 76°C$. **Propylene glycol,** or **propanediol,** $CH_3 \cdot CHOH \cdot CH_2OH$, is a colorless and odorless liquid boiling at 188°C, used in cosmetics and perfumes; in flavoring extracts as a humectant, wetting agent, and color solvent; and in baked foods to maintain freshness. **Methyl carbitol,** with one less CH_2 group, is also a high-boiling solvent for gums and resins, and **carbitol acetate** is used as a high-boiling solvent for cellulose acetate. **Glycol diformate,** $HCOOCH_2CH_2OOCH$, used as a solvent for cellulose acetate and nitrocellulose, is a colorless liquid soluble in water, alcohol, and ether. It hydrolyzes slowly, liberating formic acid.

ETHYLENE PLASTICS. A class of synthetic resins which range from greaselike liquids in the low molecular weights to waxlike materials at molecular weights from about 4,000 to 10,000, to tough white solids at molecular weights above about 12,000, which are thermoplastic resins melting at 210 to 235°F. In the ethylene molecule the two carbon atoms, each of which has two attached hydrogen atoms, are linked together with a straddle bond of the Nos. 1 and 2 electrons of the carbons, which normally form the hexagonal carbon ring. This type of **double bond** is not double in a mechanical sense and is termed a **reactive bond,** that is, a bond that can be broken readily to receive other attachments. It can be polymerized by heat and pressure to form molecular chains, called **polyethylene,** of any desired molecular weight. The melt viscosity is dependent on the molecular weight, and the hardness is a factor of the density, which may be regulated by the pressure.

Polyethylene of low molecular weight is used for extending and modifying waxes, and also in coating compounds especially to add toughness, gloss, and heat-sealing properties. **Epolene N-11,** of the Eastman Chemical Products, Inc., for blending with waxes, has a molecular weight of 1,500, a density of 0.925, and a softening point at 103°C. **Epolene N,** used in paste polishes, has a molecular weight of 2,500 to 3,000. **Epolene LVE,** used in paper and textile coatings, is a low-density polyethylene with a molecular weight of 1,500, but **Epolene HDE,** used for self-polishing floor waxes to add hardness to the film, has the same molecular weight but a high density, 0.956. Such materials are called **polyethylene wax,** but they are not chemical waxes. They can be made emulsifiable by oxidation, and they can be given additional properties by copolymerization with other plastics. **Elvax,** of Du Pont, is such a copolymer of ethylene with vinyl acetate. It is compatible with vegetable and paraffin waxes, and when added to these waxes it increases adhesiveness, gloss, toughness, and heat sealing. Wax polyethylene compounds for paper coatings may be sold

under trade names.   **Ladcote,** of the L. A. Dreyfus Co., is such a compound.   **Chemetron 100,** of the Chemetron Corp., is a modified **ethylene
wax.**   It is an **ethylene stearamide,** and comes as powder or beads.   It
improves luster, pigment dispersion, and mar resistance in lacquers.   The
polymethylene waxes are microcrystalline and have sharper melting points
than the ethylene waxes.   They are more costly, but have high luster
and durability.

Molding and extruding resins with densities from 0.91 to 0.94 have
tensile strengths from 1,500 to 2,500 psi, with elongations to 600% and
Shore hardness D50 to D56.   The dielectric strength is 480 volts per mil,
and softening point not over 235°F.   They are used for a wide range of
mechanical and electrical parts, piping, wire insulation, packaging film,
containers, and bottles.   Higher-density resins, with specific gravities to
0.96, have tensile strengths to 4,500 psi or above, with elongation of 25%,
Shore hardness D68, and dielectric strength to 500 volts per mil.   High-
density polyethylene has a higher softening point, up to 260°F, and dishes
and bottles made from it can be steam-sterilized without warpage.   **Poly-
thene** and **Alathon** are names for polyethylene of Du Pont, in the forms of
molding powder, rod, sheet, tubes, foil for packaging, and paper coatings.
Agilene, of the American Agile Corp., is polyethylene.   The plastic can
be cross-linked by irradiation, and irradiated polyethylene parts become
thermoset and have increased strength, toughness, and higher heat resistance.   **Irrathane,** of the General Electric Co., is irradiated polyethylene.
The plastic can also be cross-linked chemically by heating with carbon
black and a diperoxide.   For piping, this method increases strength, improves weather resistance, and eliminates stress cracking.   **Irrathene tape
SPT,** of this company, is a flexible irradiated polyethylene self-sealing
insulating tape for corona-resistant electric cables.   It withstands temperatures to 260°F.

Fortiflex A, of the Celanese Corp, used for rigid chemical piping, is
polyethylene of specific gravity 0.96, having a linear crystalline structure.
It has a tensile strength of 4,500 psi, flexural strength of 5,500 psi, Rockwell hardness R40, and will withstand operating temperatures above
400°F.   For piping and wire covering, polyethylene is also compounded
with small amounts of carbon black to give high resistance to weathering.
Fortiflex F-087 has a density of 0.938 and transverse elongation of 600%.
It is used for packaging film and takes printing ink well.   **Microthene
ML708,** of U.S. Industrial Chemicals Co., is a high-density powder of
350 mesh for rotational molding of thin-walled parts.

Polyethylenes produced at low pressure with a catalyst have a crystalline
structure and yield moldings and extrusions of higher strength, greater
toughness, and higher heat resistance than ordinary branched-chain polyethylene.   **Dylan,** of the Koppers Co., is such a plastic.   Low-pressure

linear polyethylene used for polyethylene fibers, with a density of 0.95, has a tensile strength of 3,500 psi, elongation of 225%, and softening point at 255°F.   The fibers and fabrics are marketed under trade names. **Reevon,** of Reeves Bros., Inc., is an upholstery fabric woven of polyethylene monofilament.   **Polyethylene foam** is light in weight, has negligible water absorption, and is used in sheet and film for thermal insulation, and for wire insulation.   **Orthofoam** and **Metafoam,** of Ludlow Papers, are polyethylene foams in sheets from 0.016 to 0.035 in. thick. The low-density film has a tensile strength to 1,500 psi, and the high-density material has a tensile strength to 12,000 psi with elongation of 2.5 to 5%.   **Polyethylene DGDA-2580,** of the Union Carbide Corp., for extruded insulation on electric cables, gives uniformly dispersed closed cells so that the material has about 30% gas by volume.   Extruded coatings have a smooth surface, a tensile strength of 2,800 psi, and a dielectric constant of 1.5 to 1.7.

Polyethylene film has high resistance to oils, greases, and fatty acids; it also has good tear strength and fold endurance, and the light weight gives a large area per pound.   It is thus widely used for packaging.   **Tenite 161M,** of Eastman Chemical Products, Inc., is an extruding grade giving a film with a density of 0.923, tensile strength of 2,200 psi, and elongation of 600%.   When polyethylene film is irradiated and stretched biaxially it can be shrunk as much as 20% in all directions by applying a blast of hot air or dipping in water at a temperature of 180°F, and such films are used for packaging meats and poultry where a tight, close fit is desired.   **Cryovac L,** of W. R. Grace & Co., is a film of this kind.   High-density polyethylene has a high concentration of hydrogen atoms which are capable of slowing down or stopping fast neutrons, and sheets made with a small amount of boron to stop also the low-energy neutrons are used for atomic shielding where light weight is necessary.   **Panelyte sheet,** of the St. Regis Paper Co., for this purpose, is made of **Petrothene 100,** of the U.S. Industrial Chemicals Co., a polyethylene containing 2% boron.

Polyethylene rubbers are rubberlike materials made by cross-linking with chlorine and sulfur or are ethylene copolymers.   **Chlorosulfonated polyethylene** is a white spongy material.   It has chlorine atoms and sulfonyl chloride groups spaced along the molecule.   It is used to blend with rubber to add stiffness, abrasion resistance, and resistance to ozone, and also for wire covering.   **Hypalon S-2,** of Du Pont, is this material.   **Plaskon CPF200,** of Allied Chemical Corp., is a chlorinated polyethylene containing about 73% chlorine.   It is used for coatings and has high resistance to acids and alkalis.   **Ethylene-propylene rubber,** produced by various companies, is a chemically resistant rubber of high tear strength.   The **ethylene butadiene resin** of Phillips Petroleum Co. can be vulcanized with sulfur to give high hardness and wide temperature range.   For greater elongation a terpolymer with butene can be made.

A wide variety of plastics is made by copolymerizing polyethylene with vinyls and other resins.   **Zetafax resin,** of Dow Chemical Corp., is an **ethylene-acrylic resin.**   It has good adhesion to metals and high chemical resistance.   **Zetabon** is a Zetafax-coated metal tape for cable shielding. The **Ultrathene UE630-81A,** of U.S. Industrial Chemicals Co., is an **ethylene vinyl acetate** copolymer for rubberlike packaging film.   The **Aircoflex resins,** of Air Reduction Co., are similar copolymers for use as pigment binders, paper and textile coatings, and adhesives.   They have higher molecular weight and better stability than polyethylene.

The **fluorocarbon resins,** or **fluorine plastics,** have the same general structure as polyethylene, but the hydrogen is replaced by fluorine.   Or, a part may be replaced by chlorine, and called a **fluorohalocarbon resin.** Polymerized **tetrafluoro ethylene,** $(CF_2 \cdot CF_2)_n$, which is the **Teflon** of Du Pont, is a white, waxy solid of specific gravity up to 2.3.   The tensile strength is up to 3,500 psi, elongation 250 to 350%, dielectric strength 1,000 volts per mil, and melting point 594°F.   It is water-resistant and highly chemical-resistant.   Its waxy, self-lubricating properties make it useful for bearings and gaskets, and its high electrical properties make it valuable for wire covering and insulation.   **Teflon tape** is used for high-temperature electrical insulation, and **Teflon film** is used for insulation and for such applications as the covering of rolls and tables in food plants so that dough will not stick.   **Teflon S** is a liquid resin of 22% solids, sprayed by conventional methods and curable at low temperatures.   It gives a hard, abrasion-resistant coating for such uses as conveyors and chutes.   Its temperature service range is up to 400°F.   **T-film,** of Eco Engineering Co., is thin Teflon film for sealing pipe threads.   **Teflon fiber** is the plastic in extruded monofilament, down to 0.01 in. in diameter, oriented to give high strength.   It is used for heat- and chemical-resistant filters.   **Teflon tubing** is also made in fine sizes down to 0.10 in. in diameter with wall thickness of 0.01 in.   **Teflon 41-X** is a collodial water dispersion of negatively charged particles of Teflon, used for coating metal parts by electrodeposition.   **Teflon FEP** is fluorinated **ethylene-propylene** in thin film, down to 0.0005 in. thick, for capacitors and coil insulation.   The 0.001-in. film has a dielectric strength of 3,200 volts per mil, tensile strength of 3,000 psi, and elongation of 250%.   **Whitcon,** of the Whitford Chemical Corp., is **fluorocarbon powder** of 1 micron particle size for use as a dry lubricant or for incorporation into rubbers, plastics, and lubricating greases.   **Plaskon Halon,** grade G80, of Allied Chemical Co., is a tetrafluoroethylene powder of fine particle size, 25 to 30 microns, for molded parts that have tensile strengths to 6,500 psi.

Fluorothene plastic, of Union Carbide, has the formula $(CF_2 \cdot CFCl)_n$, differing from Teflon in having one chlorine atom on every unit of the polymer chain, replacing the fourth fluorine atom. It is transparent, and molded parts have a specific gravity of 2.1, a tensile strength of 9,400 psi, and high dielectric strength, and it will withstand temperatures to 300°F. **Kel-F,** of Minnesota Mining & Mfg. Co., is **trifluorochloro ethylene** used for moldings, gaskets, seals, liners, diaphragms, and coatings. The molded parts have high chemical resistance. The compressive strength is 30,000 psi, but it can be heat-treated to increase the compressive strength to 80,000 psi. The tensile strength of the molded material is 5,000 psi, but oriented fibers have tensile strength to 50,000 psi. **Fluorocarbon rubber** produced by this company for tubing, gaskets, tank linings, paints, and protective clothing has a tensile strength of 3,000 psi, elongation of 600%, heat resistance to 400°F, and high resistance to oils and chemicals. It is a saturated fluorocarbon polymer containing 50% fluorine. **Aclar,** of the Allied Chemical Corp., is chloro trifluoro ethylene transparent packaging film which is exceptionally resistant to oils and chemicals, has a moisture-barrier efficiency 400 times that of polyethylene film, has good strength to 390°F, and retains its flexibility to −300°F. It is also used for wire covering. **Polyox resins,** of Union Carbide, are white granular powders of water-soluble **ethylene oxide plastics** with a wide range of molecular weights for films, fibers, and molded articles. **Polyox film** has a tensile strength of 1,800 to 2,400 psi, with elongation from 100 to 2,000%, and heat seals at temperatures from 170 to 265°F. It is used for packaging soaps, detergents, and chemicals to be added in measured amounts without removing the package. The plastic has high adhesive strength, and is also used for adhesives where water solubility is wanted. **Radel,** of this company, is an oriented polyethylene oxide for film and molded parts. The film heat-seals at 135 to 160°F and comes in thicknesses from 0.0015 to 0.010 in. The opaque film has biaxial orientation which allows heat printing and increases its water solubility.

EXPANDED METAL. Sheet metal that has been slit and expanded to form a mesh, which is used for reinforced-concrete work or plaster wall construction, and also for making grills, vents, and such articles as trays, where stiffness is needed with light weight. The expanded metal has greater rigidity than the original metal sheet, and also permits a welding of the concrete or plaster through the holes. It is made either with a plain diamond-shaped mesh, or with rectangular meshes. One type is made by slitting the sheet and stretching the slits into the diamond shape. The other variety is made by pushing out and expanding the metal in the meshes so that the flat surface of the cut strand is nearly at right angles to the surface of the sheet. Expanded metal is made from low-carbon steel, iron, or special metals, in sheets from 8 to 12 ft in length and 3 to 6 ft in width, in several thicknesses. It is also marketed as **metal lath,** usually 96 in. long, and 14 to 18 in. wide. Expanded metal of the U.S. Gypsum Co. is made of stainless steel and aluminum alloys in various thicknesses with openings from $\frac{1}{2}$ to $1\frac{1}{2}$ in. **Rigidized steel** is thin sheet steel that is not perforated, but has the designs rolled into the sheet so that the rigidity of the sheet is increased 2 to 4 times. Thus, extremely thin sheets of stainless steel can be used for novelties, small mechanical products, and paneling. Rigidized steel, of the Rigidized Metals Corp., and previously known as **Rigid-Tex steel,** is made in many ornamental designs, and comes also in vitreous enameled sheets for paneling. **Crimp metal,** of the American Nickeloid Co., has various designs of embossing in either raised or depressed ridges rolled into the polished side of the metal. **Perforated metals** are sheet metals with the perforations actually blanked out of the metal. They are marketed in sheets in carbon steel, stainless steel, or monel metal, with a great variety of standard perforation designs. Those with round, square, diamond, and rectangular designs are used for screens and for construction. **Agaloy,** of the Agaloy Tubing Co., is perforated metal made into tube form.

EXPANSIVE METAL. An alloy which expands on cooling from the liquid state. The expansive property of certain metals is an important characteristic in the production of accurate castings having full details of the mold such as type castings. The alloys are also used for proof-casting of forging dies, for sealing joints, for making duplicates of master patterns, for holding die parts and punches in place, and for filling defects in metal parts or castings. Antimony and bismuth are the metals most used to give expansion to the alloys. **Lewis metal,** one of the original expansive alloys, had one part of tin and one of bismuth, and melted at 138°C. **Matrix alloy** and **Cerromatrix,** of the Cerro Copper and Brass Co., contain 48% bismuth, 28.5 lead, 14.5 tin, and 9 antimony. The melting point is 248°F, tensile strength 13,000 psi, and Brinell hardness 19. **Cerrobase,** of this company, is another alloy balanced to give the exact impression of the mold without shrinkage or expansion in cooling. It is harder than lead, and melts at 255°F.

EXPLOSIVE. A material which, upon application of a blow, or by rise in temperature, is converted in a small space of time into other compounds more stable and occupying much more space. Commercial explosives are solids or liquids that can be instantaneously converted by friction, heat, shock, or spark, into a large volume of gas, thereby developing a sudden rise in pressure which is utilized for blasting or propelling purposes. **Gunpowder** is the oldest form of commercial or military explosive, but this has been replaced for military purposes by more powerfully acting chemicals. **Smokeless powder** was a term used to designate nitrocellulose powders as distinguished from the smoky black gunpowder.   **Blasting powders** are required to be relatively slow acting to have a heaving or rending effect. **Military explosives** used as propellants must not give instantaneous detonation, which would burst the gun, but are arranged to burn slowly at first and the explosion does not reach a maximum until the projectile reaches the muzzle.   This characteristic is also required in explosives used for the explosive forming of hard metals.   The more rapid-acting **high explosives** are generally used for bombs, torpedoes, boosters, and detonators.   The **detonators** are extremely sensitive explosives, such as the fulminates, set off by a slight blow but too sensitive to be used in quantity as a charge.   The **booster explosives** are extremely rapid but not as sensitive as the detonators.   They are exploded by the detonators and in turn set off the main charge of explosive.   Some explosives such as nitroglycerin can be exploded by themselves, while others require oxygen carriers or carbon carriers mixed with them.   Other requirements of explosives are that they should not react with the metal container, should be stable at ordinary temperatures, and should not decompose easily in storage or on exposure to air.

Shaped charges of high explosive give a penetrating effect, known as the Monroe effect, used in armor-piercing charges.   A solid mass of explosive spends itself as a flat blast, but with a conical hole in the charge, having the open end facing the target; a terrific piercing effect is generated by the converging detonation waves coming from the sides of the cone, and drives a jet of hot gases through the steel armor.   **Permissible explosives** are explosives that have been passed by the Bureau of Mines as safe for blasting in gaseous or dusty mines.   Most of the permissibles are of ammonium nitrate or gelatin base.   **Wet-hole explosives,** for oil-well and mining operations, may be ammonium nitrate in plastic containers, or various combinations in containers. **Nitramex 2H,** of Du Pont, is TNT-ferrosilicon-ammonium nitrate in a metal can.   **Lox,** used in mines and quarries, is an explosive consisting of a paper cartridge filled with carbon black or wood pulp soaked in liquid air.   It cannot be tamped as it is very sensitive.   It is fired by electric detonators.   **Cardox,** an explosive used in coal mining, consists of liquid carbon dioxide in a steel cylinder with aluminum powder. The powder is fired by an electric spark, heating and gasifying the carbon dioxide.   **Picric acid,** or **trinitro phenol,** $C_6H_2(OH)(NO_2)_3$, a lemon-yellow crystalline solid melting at 248°F, is a powerful explosive used in shells, and because of its persistent color also used as a dyestuff.   It is called **melanite** by the French, **lyddite** by the English, and **schimose** by the Japanese.   It is made by treating phenol with sulfuric and nitric acids, or can be produced by treating acaroid resin with nitric acid.   It reacts with metals to form dangerous explosive salts, so that the shells must be lacquered. **Cressylite,** used for shells, is a mixture of picric acid and trinitro cresol. It has a lower melting point.

Explosive D, or **dunnite,** made by the neutralization of picric acid with ammonium carbonate, is **ammonium picrate,** $C_6H_2(NO_2)_3ONH_4$. It forms orange-red needles that explode when heated to 300°C, but is not highly sensitive to friction. It is used as a bursting charge in armor-piercing shells. **Trinitrotoluene,** or **trinitrotoluol,** $C_6H_2(CH_3)(NO_2)_3$, also commonly known as **TNT,** and also called **trotyl** and **tolite,** is the principal constituent of many explosives. It resembles brown sugar in appearance, it melts at 80°C, and the fumes are poisonous even when absorbed through the skin. Its detonation velocity is 23,000 ft per sec. It is thus not as powerful as picric acid, but it is stable, not hygroscopic, and does not form unstable compounds with metals. It is safe in handling because it does not detonate easily, but is exploded readily with mercury fulminate, and is used for shrapnel, hand grenades, mines, and depth bombs. TNT is made by the nitration of toluol with nitric and sulfuric acids. The intermediate product, **dinitrotoluol,** is employed with hexanitrodiphenylamine for torpedoes. **Hexanitrodiphenylamine,** $(NO_2)_3C_6H_2 \cdot NH \cdot C_6H_2(NO_2)_3$, is a powder that explodes with great violence. It is highly poisonous, and causes painful blisters and inflammation. The commercial explosive **sodatol** is made by mixing TNT with nitrate of soda.

Trinitro aniline, $(NO_2)_3C_6H_2NH_2$, commonly known as **TNA,** is derived from aniline by nitration, and is one of the strongest of the high explosives. It is a yellowish-green crystalline powder melting at 215°C. It stains the skin yellow but is not poisonous. It is more sensitive to shock than TNT and is more costly. **Trinitro anisol,** used in Japanese Baka planes, has the composition $C_6H_2OCH_3(NO_2)_3$. It is about equal to TNT in power, and has the advantage that it does not attack metals.

Tetryl, or **pyronite,** $(NO_2)_3C_6H_2N(NO_2)CH_3$, is a nitro derivative of benzene. It is a yellow crystalline powder melting at 130°C, and exploding when heated to 186°C. It is more sensitive to shock than TNA, and has a higher rate of detonation than TNT. It is too sensitive to be used as a shell filler, and is employed as a booster and in commercial explosives to replace mercury fulminate for detonators. The high explosive **RDX** is cyclo trimethylene trinitro amine, and has a detonation velocity of 27,500 ft per sec. It is used in bombs, torpedoes, mines, and rockets, but is very sensitive to shock and is mixed with waxes or plasticizers to reduce sensitivity. **PETN** is pentaerythritol tetranitrate, with a detonation velocity of 26,500 ft per sec. **Pentolite** is a 50-50 mixture of TNT and PETN with less sensitivity and a detonation velocity of 25,000 ft per sec. It is used as a booster. When aluminum powder is added to high explosives, the brisance, or blast effect, is increased. A powerful explosive used during the Second World War contained 40% RDX, 40 TNT, and 20 aluminum powder. Various combinations of high explosives are now used in thin sheet form for **explosive welding** of laminated metals.

FAT LIQUORS. Oil emulsions used in tanneries for treating tanned leather to lubricate the fibers, increase the flexibility, and improve the finish. There are two general types of fat liquor emulsions: acid and alkaline. The acid group includes sulfonated oils and some soluble-oil combinations. Alkaline types are emulsions of oils with soaps or alkalies. Leather may be treated first with an alkaline liquor and then with an acid, or borax or soda ash may be added to sulfonated oils to produce alkaline liquors. For suede and white leathers, egg-yolk emulsions may be used. The oils employed in emulsions may be sperm, cod, or castor oil, and those that are neutral have a neatsfoot-oil base. The soaps are usually special for the tannery trade. Prepared fat liquors are marketed under trade names. **Tanners' greases,** used for sponging or milling onto the leather, are also trade-named mixtures of waxes, sulfonated oils, and soaps.

FATS. Natural combinations of glycerin with fatty acids, some fats having as many as 10 or more different fatty acids in the combination. They are derived from animal or vegetable sources, the latter source being chiefly the seeds or nuts of plants. Fats in a pure state would be odorless, tasteless, and colorless, but the natural fats always contain other substances that give characteristic odors and tastes. Fats are used directly in foods and also in the making of various foodstuffs. They are also used in making soaps, candles, and lubricants, and in the compounding of resins and coatings. They are also distilled or chemically split to obtain the fatty acids. The annual world consumption of fats is tabulated at 30 million metric tons, but actual consumption is much higher because of unrecorded consumption in meats, nuts, and other products. In the United States at least 75% of all tabulated consumption of edible fats and oils is in margarine, shortenings, and salad oils.

Fats are most important for food, containing more than twice the fuel value of other foods. They are also important carriers of glycerin necessary to the human system. Metabolism, or absorption of fats into the system, is not a simple process, and is varied with the presence of other food materials. The fats with melting points above 45°C are not readily absorbed into the system. The heavy fats are called tallow. Lack of certain fats, or fatty acids, causes skin diseases, scaly skin, and other affections. Some fatty acids are poisonous alone, but in the glyceride form in the fats they may not be poisonous but beneficial. Fats can be made synthetically from petroleum or coal. **Edible fats** were first made synthetically by the Germans in wartime by the hydrogenation of brown coal and lignite and then esterifying the C_9 to C_{16} fractions of the acids.   But the world resources of natural fats are potentially unlimited, especially from tropical nuts, forming a cheap source of fatty acids in readily available form.   The U.S. Department of Commerce estimated that 300 million tons of palm nuts are ungathered annually in Brazil alone.

FATTY ACIDS. A series of **organic acids** deriving the name from the fact that the higher members of the series, the most common ones, occur naturally in animal fats, but fatty acids are readily synthesized, and the possible variety is almost infinite.   All of these acids contain the **carboxyl group** ·COOH.   The acids are used for making soaps, candles, coating compounds, as plasticizers, and for the production of plastics and many chemicals.   The hydrogen atom of the group can be replaced by metals or alkyl radicals with the formation of salts or esters, and other derivatives such as the halides, anhydrides, peroxides, and amides can also be made.   The **neoacids,** in general, have the formula $R(COOH)$ in which the R is substituted methyl or other groups.   Some of the fatty acids can be polymerized to form plastics.   Various derivatives of the acids are used as flavors, perfumes, driers, pharmaceuticals, and antiseptics.   Certain fatty acids, such as oleic and stearic, are common to most fats and oils regardless of their source, while others, such as arachidic and erucic, are characteristic only of specific fats and oils.

Saturated acids are acids that contain all the hydogen with which they can combine, and they have the type formula $C_nH_{2n+1}COOH$.   They have high melting points.   **Unsaturated acids,** such as oleic, linoleic, and linolenic, are liquid at room temperature, and are less stable than saturated acids.   **Fatty acid glycerides** in the form of animal and vegetable fats form an essential group of human foods.   Fats of the highly unsaturated acids are necessary in the metabolism of the human body, the glycerides of the saturated acids such as palmitic being insufficient alone for food.

Polyunsaturated acids of the linoleic type with more than one double bond lower blood cholesterol, but saturated acids with no double bonds do not.   **Arichidonic acid** with four double bonds lowers blood cholesterol greatly.   It is manufactured in the body from linoleic acid if Vitamin B_6 is present.   **Linoleic acid,** $C_{18}H_{32}O_2$, the characteristic unsaturated food acid, has two double bonds.   **Linolenic acid,** $C_{18}H_{30}O_2$, found in linseed oil, has three double bonds.

The names of the fatty acids often suggest their natural sources, though commercially they may be derived from other sources or made synthetically.   **Butyric acid,** $CH_3CH_2CH_2·COOH$, is the characteristic acid of butter.   Also called **butanoic acid** and **ethylacetic acid,** it is made synthetically as a colorless liquid with a strong odor and completely soluble in water.   With alcohols it forms butyrates of pleasant fruity odors used as flavors.   The cellulose esters of butyric acid are used in lacquers, and have good water resistance and easy solubility in hydrocarbons.   The acid is also used as a starting point for fluoro rubbers.

Some acids, such as linoleic, are found in greater amount in cold-climate products, while some other acids are found in most abundance in hot-climate products.   **Lauric acid,** or **dodecanoic acid,** $CH_3(CH_2)_{10}COOH$, occurs in high percentage in the oil of the coconut and other kernels of tropical palm nuts.   It is a saturated acid much lower in carbon and hydrogen than linoleic acid, and is a semisolid melting at 44°C.   It is one of the chief constituents of coconut oil that gives sudsing properties to soaps.   It is also used for making detergents and plasticizers, and as a modifier for waxes in coatings and polishes.   **Neo-Fat 12,** of Armour & Co., is 95% pure lauric acid.   The ester of lauric acid is used for treating cotton fabrics to give a pebbly surface.   **Lauralene** is a lauric acid of the Beacon Co. with an acid value of 324 and saponification number of 366. **Methyl laurate** is often preferred to lauric acid for all the uses.   It is a stable, noncorrosive, water-white liquid.   **Methyl esters** of other acids are similarly used.   **Methyl stearate** is an economical compounding agent for rubbers, waxes, and textile coatings.   **Myristic acid,** $CH_3(CH_2)_{12}COOH$, is a hard crystalline solid melting at 58°C, obtained from coconut oil.   It is soluble in alcohol and is compatible with waxes and oils.   It is used in cosmetics, and will produce high-lathering soaps that are not irritating to the skin as are the coconut-oil soaps.   **Neo-Fat 14,** of Armour Industrial Chemical Co., is myristic acid 94% pure.

Caprylic acid, $CH_3(CH_2)_6COOH$, obtained from coconut oil, has a melting point of 11°C, acid number of 382, and iodine value of 1.   It is used in cosmetics, as a fungicide, and in the manufacture of pharmaceuticals.   **Capric acid,** or **decanoic acid,** $CH_3(CH_2)_8COOH$, obtained from coconut oil, is a bad-smelling white crystalline solid melting at 31.5°C with an acid value of 321.   It is used for making esters for perfumes and flavors.   **Neo-Fat 10** is capric acid 92% pure, containing 5% lauric acid and 3 caprylic acid.   **Aliphat 2** and **Aliphat 3,** of the General Mills Co., are caprylic acid and capric acid, respectively.   **Caproic acid,** or **hexanoic acid,** $CH_3(CH_2)_4COOH$, occurs in coconut and palm kernel oils, but is produced synthetically on a large scale for the manufacture of hexylresorcinol, hexylphenols, flavors, and high-boiling plasticizers.   It is a liquid boiling at 203°C and has a goatlike odor from which it derives its name. **Oenanthic acid,** or **heptoic acid,** is a homolog of caproic acid with one more carbon atom.   When polymerized with lactam it gives a nylon stronger and more flexible than ordinary nylon 6.   **AB fatty acid,** of E. F. Drew & Co., Inc., used for soaps, is composed of the acids from coconut oil distilled to remove most of the low fractions to improve color and odor. It contains 60% lauric acid, 18 myristic, 7 palmitic, 7 oleic, 3 linoleic,

3 capric, and 1 each of stearic and caprylic. Some fatty acids that occur only occasionally in small amounts in vegetable oils are made synthetically. **Undecylenic acid,** $CH_2:CH(CH_2)_8COOH$, is a highly reactive acid of this kind used for making synthetic resins, fungicides, and perfumes. The **Duomeens,** of the Armour Industrial Chemical Co., are alkyl trimethylene diamenes derived from fatty acids, and are used as pigment dispersants, metalworking lubricants, and flotation agents. They have the general formula $RNHCH_2CH_2NHH$, where R is the alkyl group from the fatty acid. **Duomeen C** is from coconut oil, **Duomeen S** is from soybean oil, and **Duomeen O** is from oleic acid. The **lactams** and **lactones,** used in making plastics, form a wide range of amino–fatty acid ring compounds. They are produced from fatty acids.

FEATHERS. The light fluffy outgrowth or plumage of birds. The industrially important feathers are those from the duck, goose, chicken, and ostrich. Radiantly colored feathers from many other types of birds are used for ornamental and art purposes. An important featherwork art exists in Mexico as a development of the Aztec featherwork. **Down** is the soft feathers of young birds or the soft undergrowth of adult birds, used as a stuffing material. **Eiderdown,** from the eider duck, is highly valued as an insulation in sleeping bags. In Iceland the female duck plucks the down from her breast to line the nest, and this down is gathered commercially after the birds are hatched.

More than 100 million pounds of chicken feathers annually come from the commercial preparation of chickens in the United States. The midrib and quill are made into protein plastic, and the fluffy barbs are used as stuffing, but many of the feathers are processed directly into protein. The inedible protein is used for making brush bristles and insulating fiber, or is split into edible proteins for poultry feed. **Ostrich feathers,** from the domesticated ostriches of Argentina, South Africa, and Australia, are used for ornamental purposes, hats, and dusting brushes. The ostrich has 24 feathers on each wing, some as long as 25 in., and the grade depends upon the color and the length. Male ostrich feathers are black. The female feathers are a soft gray, with white feathers in the wings and tail. The life of the ostrich is 50 to 75 years, and the feathers begin to be clipped at the age of 10 months. **Ostrich eggs,** which weigh 4 lb and are laid every other day, are a valuable food by-product.

FELDSPAR. A general name for a group of abundant minerals used for vitreous enamels, pottery, tile, and glass; in fertilizers; in fluxes; for roofing granules; and as an abrasive in soaps and cleaning compounds. Ground feldspar is also used for extinguishing magnesium fires, as it melts and gives a smothering action. There are many varieties of feldspar, but those of greatest commercial importance are the **potash feldspars, orthoclase** or **microline,** $K_2O:Al_2O_3 \cdot 6SiO_2$, the **soda feldspar, albite,** $Na_2O:Al_2O_3 \cdot 6SiO_2$, and the **calcium feldspar, anorthite,** $CaO:Al_2O_3 \cdot 2SiO_2$.   Orthoclase and microline have the same composition but different crystal structures. Anorthite crystals occur in many igneous rocks, white, gray, or reddish in color.   **Aplite,** used as a flux for ceramics, has more silica and less alumina. **Japanese aplite** has 77.6% silica, 12.8 alumina, 3.7 K_2O, and 3.9 Na_2O, with small amounts of calcia, magnesia, and iron oxide.   Orthoclase is called **sunstone.**   **Adularia** is a pure form of orthoclase with only a little sodium.   Pieces with an opalescent sheen are called **moonstone,** and are used as gemstones.   This stone is white with a bluish adularescence caused by the action of light on the laminations.   The hardness is 6 to 6.5 Mohs, but the cleavage in two directions makes it fragile.   The blue opalescent moonstone of New Mexico is **sanidine,** a quartz mineral.   **Amazon stone,** or **amazonite,** is a beautiful green microline found in Italy, Malagasy, and Colorado, used as a gemstone.   The Amazon stone of Virginia has bluish-green and white streaks, and was formerly shipped to Germany for cutting into ornamental objects.   The colors of feldspar are from mineral oxides and impurities and are white, gray, yellow, pink, brown, and green. Albite is generally white, while microline is more often green.

All of the chemical components of feldspar are glassmaking materials, and in making glass about 150 lb are used to each 1,000 lb of sand.   But the mineral in its natural occurrence varies widely in composition even in the same mine, and thus must be controlled chemically to obtain uniform results in glass and ceramic enamels.   It occurs in pegmatite dikes associated with quartz, mica, tourmaline, garnet, and spodumene.   The mineral is ground to a uniform size, from 80 to 140 mesh, and shipped in bags.   Crude unground feldspar is also marketed in bulk.   The melting point varies from 1185 to 1490°C, but the preferred range is 1250 to 1350°C.   The hardness is 6 to 6.5, and the index of refraction is 1.518 to 1.588, the lowest being orthoclase and the highest anorthite.   The specific gravity is 2.44 to 2.62 for orthoclase and microline, and 2.6 to 2.8 for anorthite.   Tennessee and North Carolina feldspar has about 70% SiO_2 and 17 Al_2O_3, with 9 to 11 K_2O, and 2 to 3 Na_2O.   New England feldspar is lower in silica and higher in potash.   **Potash spar** from New York and New Jersey has about 12% K_2O, and is suited for glass and pottery.   **Soda spar,** with about 7% Na_2O, is preferred for ceramic enamels.   **Cornwall stone,** from England, is a kaolinized feldspar with about 2% CaO.   A similar stone from North Carolina is called **Carolina stone.**   Aplite is a ceramic fluxing stone found in Virginia and used chiefly to supplement feldspar to provide more alkalies.   It is a white massive material of feldspars and other minerals, containing 60% silica, 24 alumina, 6 calcia, 6 sodium oxide, and 3 potassium oxide.   Another feldspar material is **alaskite,** a feldspar and quartz mixture from North Carolina. It is classed as a pegmatitic granite. Ground feldspar for enamels is sometimes called **glass spar.** **Dental spar** is specially selected potash feldspar used in making artificial teeth.

FELT. A fabric of wool, fur, or hair made by matting the fibers together under pressure when thoroughly soaked or steam-heated. The matting may also be accomplished by blowing the wet fibers under a powerful air blast and then pressing. The animal fibers mat together, owing to minute scales on their surface. Cotton and other vegetable fibers do not have the property of felting, but a percentage of vegetable or synthetic fibers may be incorporated to vary the characteristics of the felt. So great is the felting property of wool that only 20% is needed in mixtures. Most commercial felts are mixtures. New and reworked wool and noils are mixed with cotton, rayon waste, ramie, jute, casein fiber, and other fibers. Cotton decreases the density and prevents voids in the felt. Kapok gives lower thermal and sound conductance, and **insulating felt** may contain a high percentage of kapok. Felt is made of staple fibers of about $1\frac{1}{2}$ in. length, and noils of $\frac{3}{4}$ to 1 in. Longer fibers tend to mat. Shorter fibers lack depth of penetration to give necessary strength. Since most of the wool used is secondary or waste, all grades are employed, from the fines to the coarse carpet wools. Grading is by characteristic symbols. Thus, felt No. 26R1 is a felt with a specific gravity of 0.26 in roll form of first quality. But, although true felt is based on wool, most of the roll and sheet felt is now produced from synthetic fibers mechanically or chemically bonded, and they have the chemical resistance and physical properties of the particular synthetic fiber. **Needled felt** is a fabric made of natural or synthetic fibers physically interlocked by the action of a needle loom. It may also be treated chemically, or by heat or moisture, for special effects.

Felt is one of the earliest manufactured materials. It is now used for insulation, sound and vibration absorption, for padding and lining in instrument cases, hats, in roofing, and where a soft resilient fabric is needed. Although the best hat felts are made with nutria or beaver fur, vast quantities of rabbit furs or mixed furs and wool are used. **Hair felt** is made of cattle hair, and is used for insulating cold-water pipes and refrigerating equipment, and for cushioning and padding. The **Ozite felt** of the American Felt Co. is an all-hair felt. Felt comes in thicknesses from $\frac{1}{4}$ to 2 in., the $\frac{1}{4}$ in. weighing 4 oz per sq ft. The **K felt** of this company is made to Army-Navy specifications and weighs 3.24 lb per sq yd per in. of thickness. It has a tensile strength of 12 psi and compressive strength of 3 psi at 50% deflection. It is for sound and thermal insulation. **Filtering felts,** for filtering gases and liquids, are usually made from various synthetic fibers to meet specific chemical-resistant requirements. **Teflon**

felt, of the American Felt Co., for filtering hot strong acids and alkalies, is made from fluorocarbon fibers.   Because of the high chemical and physical properties of this fiber it is called **dragon fur** in the felting industry.   It also has a low friction coefficient, and is repellent to sticky materials, giving high filtering efficiency and easy cleaning.   The **Scottfelt,** of Scott Paper Co., is a **foam filter** made from urethane foam compressed under heat and pressure to $\frac{1}{15}$ of its original thickness.   The tensile strength is increased from 35 to 270 psi, and the porosity may be graduated up to 1,340 per linear in.

Roll felt, for mechanical use, may have a density range from 7 lb per sq yd for soft padding to 16 lb for hard service.   Cattle- and goat-hair felts are also used for glass polishing.   **Baize** is an old name for a thin woolen felt used for desk and table tops, box linings, and for bases of instruments. Its name is derived from the fact that it was originally bay, or brown, in color, but the industrial baize is now usually green.   The name is now used to designate a plain-woven, loose, cotton or woolen fabric with a short, close nap, in plain colors for the same purposes.   **Feltex,** of the Philip Carey Corp., is an asphalt-saturated felt for roofing, and **Mica-kote** is a heavy felt coated with asphalt and finished with mica flakes, used for roofing.   **Unisorb,** of the Felters Co., is a heavy felt in blocks and sheets for isolation pads under machinery to absorb vibration.   **Slaters' felt** is a tarred sheathing felt used in building construction, usually in 25- and 30-lb rolls.   **Fire felt,** of Johns-Manville, is made of asbestos fibers felted into sheets, blocks, or shapes, for boiler and furnace insulation. **Slatekote,** of the same company, is a heavy felt saturated with asphalt and coated with colored crushed slate, used for roofing.   The term **roofing felt** is also applied to the thick asphalt-impregnated papers used for that purpose, and **papermakers' felt** is the woven wool or part-wool belting used in papermaking.

FERRIC OXIDE.   The red **iron oxide,** Fe_2O_3, found in abundance as the ore hematite, or made by calcining the sulfate.   It has a dark-red color and comes in powder or lumps.   The specific gravity is 5.20, and melting point about 1550°C.   It is used as a paint pigment under such names as **Indian red, Persian red,** and **Persian Gulf oxide.**   In cosmetics and in polishing compounds it is called rouge.   The Persian red oxide from the Island of Hormuz contains from 60 to 90% Fe_2O_3, and is marketed on a 75% basis. **Brown iron oxide** is made from ferrous sulfate and sodium carbonate and is not a pure oxide, though its chemical formula is given as Fe_2O_3.   It is also called **iron subcarbonate,** and is used in making green glass, in paints, and in rubber.

The names **metallic red** and **metallic brown** are applied to pigments from Pennsylvania ores containing a high percentage of **red iron oxide.**   Vene-

tian red is a name for red iron oxide pigments mixed with various fillers. The **Tuscan red** pigments are red iron oxide blended with up to 75% of lakes, but may also be barium sulfate with lakes. **Ferric oxide pigments** make low-priced paints, and are much used as base coats for structural steel work. The natural oxides come chiefly from Alabama, Tennessee, Pennsylvania, Iran, and Spain.

The **Mapico colors** of the Binney & Smith Co. are **iron oxide pigments** refined under controlled conditions to give uniformity free of other mineral impurities. **Mapico red** and **Mapico crimson** contain 98% Fe_2O_3, the balance being almost entirely material lost on ignition or water-soluble impurity. The red oxide has a spheroidal particle shape, while the crimson has an acicular, or needle-shaped, particle. **Mapico lemon yellow** contains 87% Fe_2O_3, with 11.85% ignition loss. The particles are acicular and are only half the size of the crimson particles, being only 0.1 to 0.8 micron. **Mapico brown** contains 93.1% Fe_2O_3 and 5% FeO. Its particles are cubical and of sizes from 0.2 to 0.4 micron. **Mapico black** contains 76.3% Fe_2O_3 and 22.5% FeO, with a cubical particle shape. The **Auric brown** of Du Pont, used for giving light-fast shades to paper, is a hydrated ferric oxide ground to an extremely fine particle size.

Yellow iron oxide, known also as **ferrite yellow** and **Mars yellow,** used as a paint pigment, is $Fe_2O_3 \cdot 3H_2O$ plus from 2 to 12% calcium sulfate. It is made by precipitating ferrous hydroxide from iron sulfate and lime and then oxidizing to the yellow oxide. **Black ferric oxide, ferroferric oxide,** or **magnetic iron oxide,** is a reddish-black amorphous powder, $FeO \cdot Fe_2O_3 \cdot H_2O$. It is used as a paint pigment, for polishing compounds, and for decarbonizing steel. The finely ground material used as a pigment is called **magnetic black,** and when used for polishing it is called black rouge. **Hammer scale** is the iron oxide Fe_3O_4, formed in the hot rolling or forging of steel, and is used for decarbonizing steel by packing the steel articles in the scale and raising to a high temperature. It is very hard, 5.5 to 6.5 Mohs, and is also used as an abrasive.

FERROCHROMIUM. A high-chromium iron master alloy used for adding chromium to irons and steel. It is also called **ferrochrome.** It is made from chromite ore by smelting with lime, silica, or fluorspar in an electric furnace. **High-carbon ferrochrome,** of Union Carbide, contains 66 to 70% chromium in grades of 4.5, 5, 6, and 7% carbon. It is used for making tool steels, ball-bearing steels, and other alloy steels. It melts at about 1250°C. It is marketed as crushed alloy in sizes up to 2 in., and as lump alloy in lumps up to about 75 lb. **Low-carbon ferrochrome** of this company and the Vanadium Corp. of America contains 67 to 72% chromium, in grades of 0.06, 0.10, 0.15, 0.20, 0.50, 1, and 2% carbon. It is used for making stainless steels and acid-resistant steels. **Simplex**

ferrochrome, of Union Carbide, contains as little as 0.01% carbon. It comes in pellet form to dissolve easily in the steel, and is used for making low-carbon stainless steels. Low-carbon ferrochrome is also preferred for alloy steel mixtures where much scrap is used because it keeps down the carbon and inhibits the formation of hard chromium carbides. The various grades of ferrochromium are also marketed as **high-nitrogen ferro-chrome,** with about 0.75% nitrogen for use in making high-chromium cast steels which would normally have a coarse crystalline structure. The nitrogen refines the grain and increases the strength. **Foundry-grade ferrochrome,** for making cast irons, contains 62 to 66% chromium and 5 carbon. The **V-5 Foundry alloy** of the Vanadium Corp. has about 40% chromium, 18 silicon, and 9 manganese. It is used for ladle additions to cast iron to give uniform structure and increase the strength and hardness. Addition of 1% of the alloy to a cast iron of 3.40% total carbon, with resultant balance of 1.30% silicon, 0.60 manganese, and 0.35 chromium, gives a dense iron of good hardness.

FERROMANGANESE. A master alloy of manganese and iron used for deoxidizing steels, and for adding manganese to iron and steel alloys and bronzes. Manganese is the common deoxidizer and cleanser of steel, forming oxides and sulfides that are carried off in the slag. Ferromanganese is made from the ores in either the blast furnace or the electric furnace. Standard ferromanganese has 78 to 80% manganese. British ferromanganese contains about 7% carbon, but the content in the American alloy is usually 5 to 6.5%. **Low-carbon ferromanganese** is also marketed containing 0.10 to 1% carbon. Low-phosphorus ferromanganese contains less than 0.10% phosphorus. The alloys are marketed in lumps to be added to the furnace. **Spiegeleisen** is a form of low-manganese ferro-manganese with from 15 to 30% manganese and from 4.5 to 5.5 carbon. The German name, meaning mirror iron, is derived from the fact that the crystals of the fractured face shine like mirrors. Spiegeleisen has the advantage that it can be made from low-grade manganese ores, but the quantity needed to obtain the required proportion of manganese in the steel is so great that it must be premelted before adding to the steel. It is used for making irons and steels by the bessemer process. Grade A spiegeleisen, of Union Carbide, has 19 to 21% manganese, and 1 silicon; Grade B has 26 to 28% manganese and 1 silicon. The melting point is from 1950 to 2265°F.

FERROPHOSPHORUS. An iron containing a high percentage of phos-phorus, used for adding phosphorus to steels. Small amounts of phos-phorus are used in open-hearth screw steels to make them free-cutting, and phosphorus is also employed in tinplate steels to prevent sticking together of the plates in annealing.   Ferrophosphorus is made by melting phosphate rock together with the ore in making the pig iron.   The phosphorus content is about 18% and is chemically combined with the iron.   Another grade, made in the electric furnace and containing 23 to 25% phosphorus, is used for adding phosphorus to bronzes.   A master alloy for adding selenium to steels to give free-machining qualities to steel, particularly the stainless steels, is **ferroselenium.**   A typical ferroselenium, of the American Smelting & Refining Co., contains about 52% selenium and 0.90 carbon.

FERROSILICON. A high-silicon master alloy used for making silicon steels, and for adding silicon to transformer irons and steels.   It is made in the electric furnace by fusing quartz or silica with iron turnings and carbon.   It is marketed in various grades with from 15 to 90% silicon. The silicon forms a chemical combination with the iron, but the alloys having more than about 30% silicon are fragile and unstable.   The silicon also causes the carbon to be excluded in graphite flakes.   The alloys of high silicon content are called **silicon metal.**   One producer markets two grades, 15 and 45% silicon, while another has 15, 50, 75, 85, and 90% grades.   Grades with silicon from 80 to 95% are marketed for use where small ladle additions are made for producing high-silicon steels, and also for producing hydrogen by reaction with caustic soda.   The alloy is marketed in lumps or crushed form.   Silicon is often added to steels in combination alloys with deoxidizers or other alloying elements.   **Ferrosilicon aluminum,** containing about 45% silicon and 12 to 15 aluminum, is a more effective deoxidizer for steel than aluminum alone.   It is also used for adding silicon to aluminum casting alloys.   **Silvaz,** of Union Carbide, is a ferrosilicon aluminum containing also vanadium and zirconium.   The alloy serves as a deoxidizer and fluxes the slag inclusions, and also controls the grain size of the steel.   **Simanal,** of the Ohio Ferro Alloy Corp., is a **deoxidizing alloy** containing 20% each of silicon, aluminum, and manganese.   **Alsifer,** of the Vanadium Corp., contains 40% silicon, 20 aluminum, and 40 iron.   The aluminum and silicon are in the form of an aluminum silicate which forms a slag that is eliminated during the teeming of the steel.   **Alsimin** is a Swiss ferrosilicon aluminum with 50% aluminum. **Silicon aluminum** is a master alloy for adding silicon to aluminum alloys, and it does not contain iron.   A 50–50 silicon aluminum, of Alloys & Products, Inc., has a melting point of 1920°F, but is soluble in aluminum at 1275°F.   It comes in pyramid waffle form for breaking into small lumps.

FERROTITANIUM. A master alloy of titanium with iron used as a purifying agent for irons and steel owing to the great affinity of titanium for oxygen and nitrogen at temperatures above 800°C.   The value of the alloy is as a cleanser, and little or no titanium remains in the steel unless the percentage is gaged to leave a residue. The **ferrocarbon titanium** is made from ilmenite in the electric furnace, and the carbon-free alloy is made by reduction of the ore with aluminum. Ferrotitanium comes in lumps, crushed, or screened. **High-carbon ferrotitanium,** of the Vanadium Corp., has 17% titanium and 7 carbon. It is used for ladle additions for cleansing steel. **Low-carbon ferrotitanium** has 20 to 25% titanium, 0.10 carbon, 4 silicon, and 3.5 aluminum. It is used as a deoxidizer and as a carbide stabilizer in high-chromium steels. **Graphidox,** of the same company, has 10% titanium, 50 silicon, and 6 calcium. It improves the fluidity of steel, increases machinability, and adds a small amount of titanium to increase the yield strength. The **Grainal alloys** of this company, for controlling alloy steels, have various compositions. Grade No. 6 has 20% titanium, 13 vanadium, 12 aluminum, and 0.20 boron. **Tam alloy No. 78,** of the Titanium Alloy Mfg. Div., contains 15 to 18% titanium, 7 to 8 carbon, with low silicon and aluminum. It is used in cast iron and steels. **Tam alloy No. 35** has 18 to 21% titanium, and only 3.5 to 4.5 carbon. Its melting point is 2750°F. Ferrotitaniums with 18 to 22% titanium are used for making fine-grained forging steels. **Carbotam,** of the same company, contains 16 to 17% titanium, 2.5 to 3 silicon, 6.5 to 7.5 carbon, 1.5 to 2 boron, and less than 1 calcium. It is used for cast steels to contain boron for high hardness. **Manganese titanium** is used as a deoxidizer for high-grade steels and for nonferrous alloys. A common grade contains 38% manganese, 29 titanium, 8 aluminum, 3 silicon, 22 iron, and no carbon. **Nickel titanium** is used for hard nonferrous alloys. The low-iron grade contains 15% titanium, 5 aluminum, 4 silicon, 1 iron, and 75 nickel. **Thermocol,** of the Vanadium Corp., is a **ferrocolumbium** for adding columbium to steel. It contains 53% columbium and 0.15 max carbon. It has an exothermic reaction which prevents chilling of the molten metal.

FERROUS SULFATE. Also called **iron sulfate** and **green vitriol.** It is a green crystalline material of the composition $FeSO_4 \cdot 7H_2O$. It occurs naturally as the mineral **melanterite** and is a by-product of the galvanizing and tinning industries. The specific gravity is 1.898, the melting point is 64°C, and it is soluble in water. On exposure to the air it becomes yellowish because of the formation of basic iron sulfate, and on heating to 140°C it becomes a white powder, $FeSO_4 \cdot H_2O$, which also occurs as the mineral **szomolnokite.** Ferrous sulfate, under the name of **copperas,** is an important salt in the ink industry to give color permanence to the inks. It is also employed in water purification, as a disinfectant, in polishing rouge, as a mordant in dyeing wool, and in the production of pigments. **Ferric sulfate** is a grayish amorphous powder of the composition $Fe_2(SO_4)_3 \cdot$

$9H_2O$, or $Fe_2(SO_4)_3$.   The specific gravity of the hydrous is 2.1, and of the anhydrous 3.097.   It is very soluble in water, and is used as a pigment, as a mordant in dyeing, for etching aluminum and steel, and as a disinfectant.   **Ferrisul,** of the Monsanto Co., is anhydrous ferric sulfate used for speeding the action of metal pickling baths and for descaling boilers.   In etching steel, the action of anhydrous ferric sulfate is 30 times more rapid than sulfuric acid.

FERTILIZERS. Materials added to the soil to supply plant food either directly or by chemical reaction with the soil.   The preparation of ferti- lizers is now one of the major industries, and the commercial fertilizers include nitrates, phosphates, potash salts, calcium salts, and mixtures. They may also include the materials which regulate the acidity of the soil for better plant production, such as lime, and the materials which act as **soil conditioners,** which are **synthetic mulches,** such as methyl cellulose or polymeric plasticlike organic chemicals.   **Plant regulators** are fertilizers containing selected metals or minerals for specific plant foods, and are applied either in the soil or to the plant.

Chemicals used as fertilizers must not be of such a nature as to kill earthworms.   It is stated that a minimum of at least 50,000 earthworms per acre are needed for invigorating and loosening the soil.   Also, mil- lions of bacteria are in every pound of good soil, and millions of ants, bugs, and invertebrates in every acre perform a tremendous pattern of inter- dependent chemical conversion.   Thus, fertilizers should not contain drastic chemicals that make the soil sterile.

The value of fertile soils was understood in most ancient times, and natural fertilizers were used, including sulfur in the vineyards of the Romans.   But fertilizers were not understood or used in western Europe, and the lands were strikingly depleted before the introduction of their use from the Indians of America.   The Algonquins employed fish as fertilizer, and the Incas of Peru and Bolivia used vast quantities of guano. **Guano** (Quechua word huano, guttural h) is the excrement of fish-eating sea birds deposited in great amounts on the dry rocky islands of the Peruvian coast.   It contains 12 to 16% nitrogen.   It was formerly imported into the United States, but is now replaced by nitrates.   Some guano from caves, deposited by bats, is recovered in the United States for fertilizer.   During the American Civil War, **bat guano** from the great caves of Virginia was used in the South to produce saltpeter.   Much barn- yard manure is employed as fertilizer, but does not enter the commercial mixed fertilizers except the dried and ground sheep and cow manures. Much local fertilization is also done by the planting and plowing under of legumes that bring nitrogen from the air and also serve as soil condi- tioners.   Conditioning of the soil, for the retention of moisture and to prevent hard-caking so that plants may take deep root and have the needed elements readily available, is a necessary part of fertilization.   Decayed vegetable matter, or peat moss, may thus be added to the soil as **humus.** These materials also often add plant foods to the soil.   **Fersolin,** of the Timber Engineering Co., is such a material produced by heating sawdust with a catalyst below the charring temperature to convert the cellulose to lignin and humus.   It is usually mixed with fertilizers to give greater plant yields.   **Merloam,** a soil conditioner of the Monsanto Co., is a vinyl acetate–maleic acid compound.

Chilean nitrate, phosphate rock, and potash are the chief natural minerals used as fertilizers.   Nitrogen is needed in most soils, and phosphorus is a necessary ingredient in soils.   Large quantities of muriate of potash are used in fertilizers to supply K_2O, while vast quantities of hydrated lime are employed to supply MgO and to reduce the acidity of some soils. Potassium, calcium, and sodium are also supplied in combination forms especially with ammonia to yield nitrogen.   Ammonium sulfate yields both nitrogen and sulfur.   Ground gypsum is a source of sulfur trioxide for cotton, tobacco, grapes, and some other crops.   It also helps to liberate soluble potash and stimulates growth of nitrogen-fixing bacteria in the soil. Calcium cyanamid is employed as a fertilizer to yield nitrogen and calcium. Crude urea is now also used as a fertilizer, and has the nitrogen in the same form as in the natural guanos and manures.   **Uramon,** of Du Pont, is a urea fertilizer in the form of a dark-brown powder easily soluble in water and yielding 42% nitrogen, equivalent to 51% ammonia.   It also contains calcium and phosphorus.   **Ureaform,** developed by the U.S. Department of Agriculture, is a hygroscopic powder made by reacting urea with a small amount of formaldehyde and crushing.   It may also be mixed with ammonium nitrate.   **Fertilizer pellets** that resist the bleaching action of rains and release nitrogen slowly are made in $3/8$-in. granules from ammonium sulfate with a binder of asphalt and wax.

Superphosphate, or **phosphate fertilizer,** is made by treatment of the phosphate rock with sulfuric or nitric acid, reacting with ammonia to neutralize the acid and add nitrogen, and then adding potash salts.   The final ground product contains 12% each of nitrogen, phosphoric acid, and potash.   Or it may be produced by digesting the rock with ammonium sulfate yielding ammonium phosphate and gypsum.   The ammonium sulfate is then treated with sulfuric acid to yield 70% phosphoric acid and ammonium sulfate.   The German fertilizer **Nitrophoska** is a nitrate-phosphate-potash made by treating phosphate rock with nitric acid, neutralizing with ammonia, and then granulating with potassium salts.   The **calcium nitrate tetrahydrate** which is precipitated off is also used as fertilizer.   The calcium nitrate used in Europe is produced by treating phosphate rock with nitric acid.   It is highly alkaline and efficient in release of nitrogen, but is very hygroscopic and sets up in lumps.   Fish meal, castor pomace, cottonseed meal, soybean meal, copra cake, and other residues from oil pressing are used as commercial fertilizers.   Tankage from the meat-packing plants is also an important fertilizer material.   **Whale guano,** from South Georgia and Newfoundland, was a mixture of whale-meat meal and bone meal.   Ground bone meal is used in fertilizers to give phosphorus, calcium, and other mineral salts to the soil.   Some plants require boron, and borax is applied as a fertilizer to some soils.   Many vegetable products obtain their coloring and some characteristic properties from small quantities of copper, manganese, rubidium, iodine, and other elements that do not occur in all soils.   Boron is necessary for sunflower growth, iron is necessary for pineapples, molybdenum is needed for cauliflower, and cobalt oxide is necessary in the soil to prevent salt sickness in cattle.   Lack of manganese in the soil also causes yellow spot on leaves of tomatoes and citrus fruits.   For use as a fertilizer, **manganese sulfate,** $MnSO_4$, comes as a water-soluble powder of porous spherical particles.   Most plants require minute quantities of zinc to promote formation of **auxin,** a complex butyl-cyclopentene ring compound needed for growth of plants.   However, plants require balanced feeding, and indiscriminate use of fertilizers is often injurious.   Too much manganese in the soil, for example, may cause necrosis, or inner bark rot, on apple trees, or excess of some common fertilizers may cause abnormal growth of stalk and leaves in plants.

FIBERBOARD. Heavy sheet material of fibers matted and pressed or rolled to form a strong board, used for making containers and partitions, and for construction purposes.   Almost any organic fiber may be used, with or without a binder.   The softboards are made by felting wood pulp, wood chips, or bagasse, usually without a binder.   **Masonite,** of the Masonite Corp., is produced from by-product wood chips reduced to the cellulose fibers by high steam pressure.   The long fibers and the lignin adhesive of the wood are retained, and no chemicals are used in pressing the pulp into boards.   **Masonite quarter board,** for paneling, is made in boards $1/4$ in. thick.   **Presdwood** is a grainless grade made by compressing under hydraulic pressure, and is dense and strong.

These types belong to the class known as **hardboard,** in the processing of which the carbohydrates and soluble constituents of the original wood are dissolved out and the relative proportion of lignin is increased, resulting in a grainless, hard, stiff, and water-resistant board free from shrinkage. The density of most hardboards is greater than 1.0, and the modulus of rupture is from 5,000 to 15,000 psi.   The lignin acts as a binder for the fibers, but some hardboards are made harder and more resistant by adding a percentage of an insoluble resin.   The usual weights range from 50 to 65 lb per cu ft, but with added resin binder the weight may be as much as

70 lb, and **densified hardboard,** made with high pressure, is 85 lb or above. Hardboards have uniform strength in all directions and have smooth surfaces.   Tensile strengths are up to 7,700 psi, and compressive strength to 26,000 psi.

Irradiated wood is natural wood impregnated with resins of low molecular weight and irradiated with gamma rays from cobalt 60 which crosslinks the resin molecules and binds them to the fibers of the wood.   The resins add strength and hardness without changing the grain structure and color of the wood.   Maple, impregnated with 0.5% by weight of methyl methacrylate and irradiated, is 3 times as hard as the natural wood but can be worked with ordinary tools.   **Particle boards,** made with wood particles, have lower density, about 40 lb per cu ft, and have greater flexibility.   The process is not limited to the making of boards.   **Wood particles** are also used for low-cost molded parts, with up to 90% wood particles and the balance urea, phenolic, or melamine resin.   Birch or maple particles are preferred.   These **Granuplast moldings** are made with low heat and pressure to densities of 45 to 85 lb.

Wood molding powder is made by the same method of treating wood fibers with steam pressure and hydrolizing the hemicellulose, leaving the lignin free as a binder.   Hardboard is used for counter tops, flooring, furniture, and jigs and templates.   **Forall,** of the Forest Fiber Products Co., is a light-colored hardboard in thicknesses from ⅜ to ¾ in., made by compressing Douglas fir free of bark.   It is grain-free, and will not split or splinter.   **Presdply,** of the Masonite Corp., has surfaces of grainless hard Presdwood and a core of soft plywood that will hold screws.

Hardwood, of the Elmendorf Corp., is a hard board made from hardwood waste compressed into sheets under heat and hydraulic pressure. The surface is hard with a high polish.   A hard board, developed by the Scottish Cooperative Wholesale Society and called **heatherwood,** is made by pulping heather and pressing into boards with a synthetic resin binder. **Heather,** or **heath,** is a small flowering shrub, *Ericaceae tetralix* and *E. cinerea,* which grows profusely in Great Britain.   **Wonderwood,** of the Wonderwood Corp., is a development of the **Novopan** made in Switzerland.   It is made by pulping chipped waste wood and compressing with a resin binder.   **Tensilite 300,** of the J. P. Lewis Co., is made of pulp combined with nitrile rubber and a phenolic resin and pressed into sheets. The specific gravity is 1.35, dielectric strength 600 volts per mil, and compressive strength 32,000 psi.   It is suitable for mechanical and electrical applications as well as for paneling.   The **Forest hardboard** of the Forest Fiber Products Co. is made of chipped wood that is pulped and mixed with synthetic resin and wax and then hydraulically pressed.   The board has a smooth glossy face, and is suitable for making furniture and toys and for paneling.   **Prespine,** of the Curtis Co., Inc., is a paneling board of lower hardness and density made by mixing 5 to 15% phenolic resin with sawdust and wood chips and pressing at only 200 psi. These hardboards are used for many construction parts, but the lighter and less dense fiberboards are preferred for insulation and some construction uses. **Granite board,** of National Starch and Chemical Corp., is a strong, nonsplintering **building board** made from fine particles of eastern white pine molded under pressure with a resin binder to a density about equal to natural wood. It has an acoustical value higher than that of natural wood. **Kimflex board,** of the Kimberly-Clark Corp., is a lightweight, pliable fiberboard used for shoe counters. It is made from balsawood pulp, using rubber latex as a binder. **Electrite,** of the West Virginia Pulp & Paper Co., is a wood fiberboard of high strength and high dielectric strength for electrical panels. **Temlok,** of the Armstrong Cork Co., is a fiberboard made from pinewood fibers impregnated with resin and compressed into building boards and tiles. **Temwood,** of the same company, is a lightweight board of wood fibers hydraulically pressed into grainless boards in hard and semihard grades. **Temboard** is a decorative wood fiberboard used for interior paneling. **Veneer fiberboard,** of the Elmendorf Co., is made by cutting veneer waste into fibers of 0.010 to 0.015 in. thickness with strand lengths from 1 to 8 in. The flat side of the strand is edge-grained, and when felted the broad surface lies parallel to the faces of the board. From 10 to 20% phenolic resin is used as a fiber binder. The density of the boards is from 0.60 to 0.80. **Disfico board,** of the Diamond State Fibre Co., for making trunks and boxes, is made of pressed jute and hemp fibers. It comes in sheets in plain colors. **Thermax,** of the Northwest Magnesite Co., is an insulating board made of shredded wood fibers with a fire-resistant cement.

FILTER FABRICS. Any fabric used for filtering liquids, gases, or vapors, but, because of the heat and chemical resistance usually required, they are generally of synthetic or metal fibers. Weave is an important consideration. Plain weave permits maximum interlacings per square inch, and in a tight weave gives high impermeability to particles. Twill weave has lower interlacings in sharp diagonal lines, and gives a more selective porosity for some materials. Satin weave has fewer interlacings, is spaced widely but regularly, and is used for dust collection and gaseous filtration.

Fibers are chosen for their particular chemical resistance, heat resistance, and strength. Dacron has good acid resistance except for concentrated sulfuric or nitric acid. It can be used to 325°F. High-density polyethylene has good strength and abrasion resistance, and its smooth surface minimizes clogging of the filter, but it has an operating temperature only to 230°F. Polypropylene can be used to 275°F. Nylon gives high strength and abrasion resistance.   It has high solvent resistance, but low acid resistance.   Its operating limit is about 250°F.   Teflon is exceptionally resistant to a wide variety of chemicals.   It can be operated above 400°F, and its waxy, nonsticking surface prevents clogging and makes it easy to clean, but the fiber is available only in single-filament form.

FILTER SAND.   A natural sand employed for filtration, especially of water.   Much of the specially prepared filter sand comes from New Jersey, Illinois, and Minnesota, and is from ocean beaches, lake deposits, and sandbanks.   The specifications for filter sand require that it be of fairly uniform size, free from clay and organic matter, and chemically pure, containing not more than 2% combined carbonates.   The grain sizes are specified in millimeters, the most common being from 0.35 to 0.65 mm.   Very fine sand clogs the filter.   **Greensand,** produced from extensive beds in New Jersey, is used as a water softener.   It is a type of marl classed as **zeolite,** and consists largely of **glauconite,** which is a greenish granular mineral containing up to 25% iron, with a large percentage of silica and some potash and alumina.   Synthetic zeolite is a **sodium alumina silicate,** $Na_2O \cdot Al_2O_3 \cdot 6SiO_2 \cdot xH_2O$, made by reacting caustic soda with bauxite to form sodium aluminate and then reacting with sodium silicate.   In addition to filtering, the greensand softener extracts the calcium and magnesium from the water.   It is regenerated for further use by passing common salt brine through it.   The **Zeolex** of J. M. Huber Corp. is **sodium silico aluminate** in extremely fine powder form.   Up to 2% is added to such products as dried egg-yolk powder to prevent caking and to keep dry ingredients in automatic food-processing equipment free-flowing.

Molecular sieves are synthetic crystalline zeolites whose molecules are arranged in a crystal lattice so that there are a large number of small cavities interconnected by smaller pores of uniform size, the network of cavities and pores being up to 50% of the volume of the crystal.   The sieves consist of three-dimensional frameworks of SiO_4 and AlO_4 tetrahedra.   Electrovalence of each tetrahedron is balanced by the inclusion in the crystal of a metal cation of Na, Ca, or Mg.   Firing in a kiln drives out the water, and by exchanging the sodium ion for a smaller or larger ion the pore openings can be varied from 2 to 12 angstroms.   For gasoline upgrading, 4-angstrom openings are used, while 10-angstrom openings serve for removing oil vapor or hydrogen sulfide from gas.   The mean path required for oxygen and nitrogen molecules is about 0.1 micron.   **Filter plates,** for filtering acids and oils, are porous fused alumina with pores from 0.09 to 0.30 mm diameter.   **Zeolon,** of the Norton Co., is a zeolite with a crystal structure known as **nordenite.**   The pore diameter is about 10 angstroms.   **Zeolite 4A,** of Linde, for chemical separations, will pass molecules no larger than 4 angstroms.

FIRECLAY. Clays that will withstand high temperatures without melting or cracking, used for lining furnaces, flues, and for making firebricks and lining tiles. Common fireclays are usually silicate of alumina. Theoretically these clays contain 45.87% alumina and 54.13 silica, but in general they contain considerable iron oxide, lime, and other impurities. Most of the American clays are from New Jersey, Kentucky, Pennsylvania, Ohio, and Missouri. They are largely $Al_2O_3 \cdot SiO_2$, with CaO, Fe_2O_3, and TiO_2. Those low in iron oxide, lime, magnesia, and alkalies are chosen. The clays are grouped as low-duty, intermediate, high-duty, and super-duty. The low-duty has low alumina and silica with high impurities, and is limited to a temperature of 1600°F. Standard types are good for temperatures of 2400 to 2700°F, and the super-duty to temperatures of 2700 to 3000°F. Kiln-burned clay should have a balanced proportion of coarse, intermediate, and fine grain sizes. Clays with an excess of silica are also used. The German **Klingenberg clay** used for crucibles has about 60% silica. The term **refractory clay** embraces nearly all clays having a melting point above 1600°C. But the clays alone are likely to shrink and crack, and they may be mixed with other clays, sand, or graphite. **Firebrick** is made in various shapes and sizes and is usually white or buff in color. Common firebrick from natural clays will melt at from 2800 to 3100°F.

Insulating firebrick is made with fireclay and a combustible material such as sawdust which burns out to leave a porous structure. The weight is 1.25 to 4 lb per brick compared with 8 lb for regular firebrick. Firebrick containing more than 47.5% alumina is not classed as fireclay brick but as **alumina brick.** The **SL firebrick** of Johns-Manville is a **kaolin firebrick** with 62% silica, and can be used up to 2300°F. Spalling is a common failure of fireclay brick, but high-duty should show little spalling under long soaking at 1650°F or alternating periods of heating and cooling at higher temperatures. **Alamo brick** and **Varnon brick,** of the Harbison-Walker Refractories Co., are high-duty firebrick. **Kaosil firebrick,** of the same company, is designated as a **semisilica firebrick.** It is made from low-alkali siliceous kaolin of Pennsylvania, rotary-fired at high temperature. The nominal composition is 75.6% silica, 21.8 alumina, 1.7 titania, 0.5 iron oxide, 0.27 magnesia, 0.15 lime, and 0.10 alkalies. The brick can be used in a soaking heat of 2700°F, is resistant to spalling and to fluxing by alkali slags, and has high load-carrying ability. **Korundal,** of the same company, is a corundum-mullite brick for temperatures to 3425°F. It contains 91% corundum alumina, 8 silica, and less than 1% iron oxide, lime, magnesia, and alkalies. It melts at 2020°C, converting all the mullite to corundum, but slow cooling returns the brick to the original mixture.

Some other materials used in making firebrick are chromite, bauxite, diatomaceous earth, and magnesite, or the artificial materials silicon carbide and aluminum oxide, but brick made of these are designated by the name of the material or by trade names.   **Chromite brick** will withstand temperatures up to 3700°F, and **magnesia brick** up to 3900°F, while silicon carbide brick without a clay binder will withstand heats to 4000°F.   **Firecrete,** of Johns-Manville, is a lightweight refractory consisting of calcined high-alumina clay used for furnace doors and floors.   It will withstand temperatures of 2400°F in continuous operation.   **Insuline,** of the Quigley Co., is a calcined fireclay in small cellular particles.   In insulating brick it is called **Insulbrix,** and as a lightweight concrete it is known as **Insulcrete.** **Allmul firebrick,** of the Babcock & Wilcox Co., for glass furnaces, is mullite with no free silica.

FIRE EXTINGUISHERS. Materials used for extinguishing fires, usually referring to chemicals in special containers rather than the materials, like water, used in quantity for cooling and soaking the fuel with a noncombustible liquid.   There are three general types of fire extinguishers: those for smothering, such as carbon dioxide; those for insulating the fuel from the oxygen supply, such as licorice and protein foams, which class also includes mineral powders which melt and insulate metallic fires; and chemicals which react with the combustion products to terminate the chain reaction of combustion, as **bromo trifluoro methane,** $CBrF_3$, a nontoxic colorless gas liquefied in cylinders.   **Freon FE 1301,** of Du Pont, is this chemical, while **Freon 13Bl** of the same company is **monobromo trifluoro methane** gas pressurized with nitrogen.   The relative effectiveness of extinguishers varies with the type of fuel in the fire, but on an average, with bromo trifluoro methane taken as 100%, dibromo difluoro methane would be about 67%, the dry chemical sodium hydrogen carbonate 66, carbon tetrachloride 34, and carbon dioxide about 33.   **Fire-Trol,** of the Arizona Agrochemical Co., is ammonium sulfate and **attapulgic clay** for fighting forest fires.   It is sprayed in a water solution, and the slurry mixture coats the trees to stop fire spread.

FISHERY PRODUCTS. Fisheries constitute one of the largest industries of the world, the annual commercial catch of fish exceeding 30 million metric tons, exclusive of whale, shells, seaweed, and other marine products. In addition to its use as food, fish is important as the source of fatty oils, animal feeds, fertilizer, vitamin products, fish flour, protein powders, pearl essence, and skins.   More than half of all species of vertebrates (animals with backbones) are fish, and more than 40,000 kinds of fish have been classified, varying from the small goby, weighing less than 0.01 oz, to the whale shark sometimes weighing more than 20 tons.   Varieties of fish live in icy polar waters and in hot desert pools with temperatures above 100°F, in mud flats, in high mountain lakes, and at great pressure depths in the seas, but fish do not live in waters polluted by chemical wastes. Extreme shapes vary from the snakelike eel to the sea horse, but the **marine herring,** *Clupea herengus,* is designated by the U.S. Fish and Wildlife Service as the typical **fish** because of its abundance, its lack of extremes in form, size, and structure, and its water efficiency due to its streamlined shape and fin arrangement.

Japan and China are the leading fishery countries, with about 15% of the world catch, while the commercial catch of the United States is 9% of the world total. But the production of Japanese fisheries is no more than 115 lb per capita, while the annual catch for Iceland is 6,225 lb per capita, for Newfoundland 1,525 lb, and for Norway 680 lb. The consumption of food fish in the United States is relatively low, from 8 to 12 lb per capita annually, and little attention is given to fresh-water fish farming. In some countries, as Thailand, fish constitutes the only important protein element in the people's food. In the American fisheries large quantities of fish are caught only for the oil and meal. However, in the United States and Canada fishing is one of the most widespread of the sports and recreational activities, and large quantities of fish are caught and eaten which are not included in official statistics.

About 90% of all fish caught commercially are from Northern Hemisphere waters, and 95% of all fish taken in the Pacific Ocean, which constitutes more than one-third of the earth area, are caught north of the equator. Little is known yet of life in the depths of the seas. Salmon are not normally caught in the seas, but tagging indicates that they migrate up to 2,500 miles with true homing annually in the original rivers. On the other hand, steelhead trout, which, like salmon, ascend rivers of the Pacific Coast, spend up to 2 years in fresh water. Fishing is intense in some areas, reaching 33 metric tons per trawler per day off the Greenland coast. In some areas, as with pilchard off the California coast, the catch has at times exceeded the reproduction of the fish. In the organized fishing on Great Slave Lake, nets are required to have a mesh of 5½ in. to permit small fish to escape. The **lake whitefish,** shipped to the United States, are of the family *Coregonidae,* related to the salmon and trout, and the mature fish are 18 in. long, weighing 2.5 lb. **Klipfish,** shipped from Iceland, is not a species of fish, but is a term meaning stone fish, referring to dried fish, usually cod, sun-dried in cold air on stone slabs. The fish is whiter and less rancid than fish dried in hot air.

Ocean perch, *Sebastes marinas,* is the chief commercial fish caught in the New England area, and menhaden constitutes the chief catch of the Atlantic coasts. The red **snapper,** *Lutianus aya,* and the red **grouper,** *Epinephelus morio,* constitute the major part of the catch in the Gulf of Mexico. **Smelt,** *Oamerus mordax,* planted in the Great Lakes in 1912, constituted 97% of the commercial catch of fish in Lake Erie before the recent pollution of the lake.

One third of all fresh and frozen packaged fish in the United States is ocean perch, or **rosefish,** compared with 24% for haddock. **Rockfish,** very low in oil and sodium and high in protein, is important in the frozen-fish industry of the West Coast, reaching a tonnage about half that of the total salmon. With these processed fishes, only about 25% of the total weight of the fish is packaged, the remainder being used for oils, feeds, and fertilizer. The variety of **tuna fish** known as **skipjack,** *Katsuwonus pelamis,* is the most important commercial fish of the Pacific. It is migratory, ranging from California to Japan and the Philippines. Known as **aku** in Hawaii, it abounds in that area, but is also caught in warm areas of the Atlantic. The **albacore tuna** likewise ranges over the Pacific and Indian Oceans and into the Atlantic.

The usual types of fish processed for marketing as **smoked fish** are mackerel, mullet, sturgeon, catfish, and flounder. The **sturgeon** of the Caspian Sea attains a length of 30 ft and a weight of 4,000 lb. It is valued for meat, liver vitamins, isinglass, oil, skins, and **caviar,** the latter being the **roe,** or eggs, also obtained from shad and some other large fish. In the processing of frozen fish, an average of only 33% of the whole fish is shipped as edible packaged fish, but the amount of fillets taken from cleaned fish may be as high as 55% for pollock and 70% for large, 8-lb, steelhead trout. **Industrial fish,** for the production of oil, animal feeds, and fertilizer, consists usually of mixed small fish, but in some areas there is no sorting, and fish inedible to humans may be included.

The **fish scales** which are removed from processed edible fish are high in edible proteins, and are also used in animal feeds. Scales from the pollock contain 70% protein. **Fish solubles** usually consist of a 50% solids concentration of the residue liquor, known as **stickwater,** from processing plants and canneries. In addition to protein, it is rich in vitamins B, G, and B_{12}. It is mixed with alfalfa leaf meal for animal feed. **Fishskins** have a close texture and are impervious, but sharkskin is the only fishskin of commercial importance.

Fish meal is produced from whole fish or from the residue of processed food fish. Whole fish is ground, cooked below 212°F to avoid loss of protein, and the oil solvent extracted. About 2% oil is retained in the meal, but for the manufacture of fish flour this residue oil is removed by alcohol extraction. Prior to the extraction of the oil, which may be up to 16%, fish meal contains up to about 23% protein, and up to about 30% minerals, including calcium, phosphorus, iron, and copper. The proteins have all the essential amino acids to supplement cereal foods for poultry raised by commercial methods where the birds lack access to normal feeding. Man, also, is by nature a carnivorous animal requiring first-class proteins not available in vegetable foods. In the American diet the deficiency for nonmeateaters is largely compensated for by the addition of fish and meat proteins to bakery products and prepared foods.

Fish flour is a low-cost source of protein, and is used for enriching flours, baby foods, sauces, and prepared soups, and for adding proteins to breads, cakes, pastries, and other bakery products. It is prepared from fish meal by refining and deodorizing. It is an additive rather than a flour; it does not thicken soups, and in bakery products it does not have the elastic and extensible properties inherent in cereal flours. In the food industries it is called **animal protein concentrate,** and the high-protein grade contains 95% animal protein. It is also high in calcium and phosphorus, and contains thiamin, niacin, and riboflavin. An edible **fish-protein concentrate** may now be made directly from finely ground industrial fish. Oils, fats, fatty acids, and lipid-containing materials are extracted by a solvent such as isopropyl alcohol. About 20% by weight of raw fish is recovered as a dry, odorless, tasteless powder which can be mixed with a variety of foods to upgrade the human diet. Fish flour has negligible contents of carbohydrates, and no more than 0.4% fat, but **Viking egg white,** an odorless gray powder made in Germany from whitefish, is a soluble albumin used as a substitute for egg white in bakery goods.

Fish oils are obtained by boiling the fish and skimming off the oil, or by solvent extraction from the fish meal. The crude oil has a brownish color and an offensive odor, but it is usually decolorized and deodorized. Oil content of fish varies from 0.5 to about 16%, depending on the type of fish, the season, and the area. Fish in cold waters tend to have more oil than those in warm waters. There is only a small difference in the composition of oils from different species. They usually contain 20 to 30% of saturated acids and 70 to 80% unsaturated acids. The average specific gravity is about 0.930. Much of the commercial oil is from the cod, herring, menhaden, sardine, and salmon. **Japan fish oil** consists of a mixture of sardine and herring oils. Fish oil is of the nondrying class, and is used for lubricants, leather dresssings, soaps, and heat-treating oils, but is also used for blown oils or for fractionating for use in paints and in plastics.

FLAX. A fiber obtained from the flax, or linseed, plant, *Linum usitatissimum,* used for making the fabrics known as linens, and for thread, twine, and cordage. It is valued because of its strength and durability. It is finer than cotton, and very soft, and the fibers are usually about 20 in. long. Flax consists of the **bast fibers,** or those in the layer underneath the outer bark, which are of fine texture. The plants are pulled up by the roots, retted, or partly decayed, scraped, and the fibers combed out and bleached in the sun. For the best European flax the preparation is entirely by hand.   The important centers of flax preparation are in Russia, central Europe, Italy, Ireland, France, and Egypt.   Some flax is also grown in the United States.   The plants that are grown for the oil seed yield a poor fiber and are not employed to produce flax.

FLINT.   An opaque variety of chalcedony or nearly pure amorphous quartz which shows no visible structure.   It is deposited from colloidal solution and is an intimate mixture of quartz and opal.   It contains 96 to 99% silica, and may be colored to dull colors by impurities.   Thin plates are translucent.   When heated, it becomes white.   Flint is finely crystalline.   It breaks or chips with a convex, undulating surface.   The hardness is 7, and the specific gravity is 2.6.   It was the prehistoric utility material for tools, and was later used with steel to give sparks on percussion.   **Gun flints** are still made from a type of flint mined at Brandon, England, for special uses.   **Lydian stone,** or **touchstone,** was a cherty flint used for testing gold.   Flint is now chiefly used as an abrasive, and in pottery and glass manufacture.   **Flint paper** for abrasive use contains crushed flint in grades from 20 to 240 mesh, usually coated on one side of 70- or 80-lb paper.   Flint is also used in the form of grinding pebbles.   **Potters' flint,** used for mixing in ceramics to reduce the firing and drying shrinkage and to prevent deformation, is ground flint of about 140 mesh made from white **French pebbles.**   **Bitstone** is a name used in the ceramic industry for calcined flint chips ground to the size of wheat, employed for sprinkling on the bottom of the saggers so that the ware will not stick in firing.   **Hornstone** is a flint with chalcedony inclusions.   It splinters instead of chipping, and is not used for abrasives.

FLUORINE.   An elementary material, symbol F, which at ordinary temperatures is an irritating pale-yellow gas, F_2.   Fluorine gas is obtained by the reduction and electrolysis of fluorspar and cryolite.   It has a density of 1.69 and a boiling point of $-187°C$, and it solidifies at $-223°C$.   It is used in the manufacture of fluorine compounds.   It combines violently with water to form hydrofluoric acid, and it also reacts strongly with silicon and most metals.   **Liquid fluorine,** at temperatures below $-367°F$, is used as an oxidizer for liquid rocket fuels.   In combustion, a pound of fluorine produces a pound of hydrogen fluoride which is highly corrosive.   Fluorine is one of the most useful of the halogens.

The gas **sulfur hexafluoride,** SF_6, resembles nitrogen in its inactivity. It is odorless, colorless, nonflammable, nontoxic, and 5 times as heavy as air.   It is used as a refrigerant, as a dielectric medium in high-voltage equipment, as an insecticide propellant, and as a gaseous diluent.   It remains stable to 800°C.   **Aluminum fluoride,** AlF_3, is a white crystalline solid used in ceramic glazes and for fluxing nonferrous metals.   Other metallic fluorides are marketed for special purposes. **Silver difluoride,** AgF_2, is a blackish powder used as a fluorinating agent; it contains about 26% fluorine. **Chlorofluorine gas,** ClF_3, is a violent fluorinating agent, and is used for the fluorination of some metals otherwise difficult to separate, such as uranium.

Fluorocarbons are compounds of carbon in which fluorine instead of hydrogen is attached to the carbon atoms. They range from gases to solids. When not less than two fluorine atoms are attached to a carbon atom they are very firmly held, and the resulting compounds are stable and resistant to heat and chemicals. Fluorocarbons may be made part hydrocarbon and part fluorocarbon, or may contain chlorine. The fluorocarbons used as plastic resins may contain as much as 65% fluorine and also chlorine, but are very stable. **Liquid fluorocarbons** are used as heat-transfer agents, hydraulic fluids, and fire extinguishers. Benzene-base fluorocarbons are used for solvents, dielectric fluids, lubricants, and for making dyes, germicides, and drugs. Synthetic lubricants of the fluorine type consist of solid particles of a fluorine polymer in a high-molecular-weight fluorocarbon liquid.

FLUORSPAR. Also called **fluorite.** A crystalline or massive granular mineral of the composition CaF_2, used as a flux in the making of steel, for making hydrofluoric acid, in opalescent glass, in ceramic enamels, for making artificial cryolite, as a binder for vitreous abrasive wheels, and in the production of white cement. It is a better flux for steel than limestone, making a fluid slag, and freeing the iron of sulfur and phosphorus. About 5.54 lb of fluorspar is used per ton of basic open-hearth steel.

Fluorspar is mined in Illinois, Kentucky, Nevada, and New Mexico. American ore usually runs 35 to 75% CaF_2, but high-grade ore from Spain and Italy contains up to 98%. The specific gravity is 3.18, hardness 4, and the colors light green, yellow, rose, or brown. When ground, the color is white. The melting point is 1650°F. The usual grades for fluxing are smaller than $\frac{1}{2}$ in. and contain 85% min CaF_2, with 5 max SiO_2. High-grade fluorspar for ceramic frit has 95 to 98% CaF_2, 3 max SiO_2, and 0.12 max Fe_2O_3, and is known as No. 1 ground. **Acid spar** is a grade used in making hydrofluoric acid. It contains over 98% CaF_2 and 1 max SiO_2, and is produced by flotation. It is also used for making refrigerants, plastics, and chemicals, and for aluminum reduction. **Optical fluorspar** is the highest grade but is not common. **Fluoride crystals** for optical lenses are grown artificially from acid-grade fluorspar. Pure **calcium fluoride,** Ca_2F_6, is a colorless crystalline powder used for etching glass, in enamels, and for reducing friction in machine bearings. It is also used for ceramic parts resistant to hydrofluoric acid and most other acids.   **Calcium fluorite** has silicon in the molecule, $CaSiF_6 \cdot 2H_2O$, and is a crystalline powder used for enamels.   The clear rhombic fluoride crystals used for transforming electric energy into light are **lead fluoride,** PbF_2.

FLUX. A substance added to a refractory material to aid in its fusion.   A secondary action of a flux, which may also be a primary reason for its use, is as a reducing agent to deoxidize or decompose impurities and remove them as slags or gases.   In soldering, a flux may serve to remove oxides from the surface to be soldered.   Materials such as charcoal or impure boron carbide used to cover baths of molten metals may also be considered as fluxes.   **Fluxing stone** is a common term for the limestone or dolomite used in the melting of iron.   About 900 lb of limestone are employed for every long ton of pig iron produced in the blast furnace.   If iron ore were reduced without a basic flux, the silica and alumina would unite with the iron oxides to form double silicates of iron and alumina, and there would be a heavy loss of iron.   With the addition of limestone, the silica and alumina, having strong affinity for the lime and magnesia, form compounds that contain very little iron.   These compounds form a liquid slag which floats on the surface of the molten iron and can be removed readily.   The flux also removes sulfur and phosphorus from the iron.   Some iron ores contain sufficient lime carbonate to be almost self-fluxing.   Lime is more effective as a flux than limestone, but is more expensive.   The action of the blast furnace is first to convert the limestone to lime.   Upon being heated to 1525°F limestone breaks down to lime, which then begins fusion with silica to form the slag at about 2600°F.   Limestones for use as flux must be fairly pure, or additional undesirable compounds will be formed.   For brass, bronze, or soft white metals, resins may be used, and the covering flux may be charcoal, salt, or borax.   Cryolite is a flux for aluminum and for glass.

Fluxing alloys for brasses and bronzes are phospor tin, phosphor copper, or silicon copper.   They deoxidize the metals at the same time that alloying elements are added.   For tinning steel, palm oil is used as a flux.   For ordinary soldering, zinc chloride is a common flux.   Tallow, rosin, or olive oil may also be used for soldering.   Acetamide is used for soldering painted metals.   **Solder H-32,** of the Fairmont Chemical Co., is a soft solder with a core of hydrazine.   This flux wets metals well, and vaporizes with the heat of soldering to leave no residue.   For silver solders, borax is a common flux.   For soldering stainless steel, the borax is mixed with boric acid, or pastes are made with zinc chloride and borax.   Borax may also be used as a welding flux.   **White flux** is a mixture of sodium nitrate and nitrite, and is a strong oxidizer used for welding.

Welding fluxes for high-temperature welding are usually coated on the rod and contain a deoxidizer and a slag former.   **Lithium fluoride,** LiF, is a powerful flux with the fluxing action of both lithium and fluorine, and it gives a low-melting liquid slag.   Deoxidizers may be ferromanganese or silicomanganese.   **Slag formers** are titanium dioxide, magnesium carbonate, feldspar, asbestos, or silica.   Soluble silicate is a binder, while cellulose may be used for shielding the arc.   **Manganox,** of the Foote Mineral Co., is a prepared hausmanite with a manganese metal content of 64%, used for coating welding rods.   It is more stable than the ferromanganese often used.   **Murex,** of the Metal & Thermit Corp., is a welding rod coated with a mineral flux and covered with asbestos.   The flux and the asbestos form a slag that falls off the weld.   **Lapix,** of E. F. Houghton & Co., is a mixture of carbon and clay used to cover the top of molten steel after pouring in ingot molds.   It is exothermic and helps to maintain a longer liquid period so that the deoxidized materials rise to the top.

FOIL. Very thin sheet metal used chiefly for wrapping, laminating, packaging, insulation, and electrical applications.   The word comes from the Latin *folium,* meaning leaf.   **Tinfoil** is higher in cost than some other foils, but is valued for wrapping food products because it is not poisonous; it has now been replaced by other foils such as aluminum.   Ordinary tinfoil is made in thicknesses from 0.006 mm (0.00024 in.) to 0.200 mm (0.00787 in.), the former having 16,037 sq in. per lb, and the latter 432 sq in. per lb.   Tinfoil for radio condensers has 14,500 sq in. per lb.   An English modified tinfoil, which has greater strength and is nontoxic in contact with foods, contains 8.5% zinc, 0.15 nickel, and the balance tin. It can be rolled to thinner sheets.

Lead foil, used for wrapping tobacco and other nonedible products, is rolled to the same thickness as tinfoil, but because of its higher specific gravity has less coverage.   The thinnest has 10,358 sq in. per lb, and the thickest 279 sq in. per lb.   Lead foil has a dull luster, but it may be modified with some tin and other elements to give it a brighter color. **Stainless-steel foil** is produced in thicknesses from 0.002 to 0.015 in. for laminating and for pressure-sensing bellows and diaphragms.   Type 302 steel foil, for facing, comes in a thickness of 0.003 in., highly polished, in rolls 24 in. wide.   **Steel foil** is carbon steel coated with tin and produced by the U.S. Steel Corp. in sheets as thin as 0.001 in. with widths to 40 in. It is easily formed and soldered and is used for strong packaging and laminating.

Aluminum foil has high luster, but is not as silvery as tinfoil.   The thin foil usually has a bright side and a matte side because two sheets are rolled at one time.   Aluminum foil also comes with a satin finish, or in colors or embossed designs.   It is made regularly in 34 thicknesses, from

0.006 mm, having 43,300 sq in. per lb, to 0.200 mm, having 1,169 sq in. per lb, but can be made as thin as 60,000 sq in. per lb. The most used thickness is 0.00035 in., with 29,300 sq in. per lb. For electrical use the foil is 99.999% pure aluminum, but foil for rigid containers is usually **aluminum alloy 3003,** with 1 to 1.5% manganese, and most other foil is of **aluminum alloy 1145,** with 99.45% aluminum. The tear resistance of thin aluminum foil is low, and it is often laminated with paper for food packaging. **Trifoil,** of Tri-Point Industries, Inc., is aluminum foil coated on one side with Teflon and on the other with an adhesive. It is used as coatings for tables and conveyors or liners in chemical and food plants. Since polished aluminum reflects 96% of radiant heat waves, this foil is applied to building boards or used in crumpled form in walls for insulation. **Alfol** is a name applied to crumpled aluminum foil for this purpose by the British National Physical Laboratory. Aluminum foil cut in tiny strips has been used for scattering from aircraft to confuse radar detection. A bundle of 6,000 such strips weighs only 6 oz and scatters widely.

Aluminum yarn, for weaving ribbons, draperies, and dress goods, is made from aluminum foil, 0.001 to 0.003 in. thick, by gang-slitting to widths from 0.0125 to 0.125 in. and winding the thread on spools. **Gold foil** is called **gold leaf** and is not normally classed as foil. It is used for architectural coverings and for hot-embossed printing on leather. It is made by hammering in books, and can be made as thin as 0.0000033 in., a gram of gold covering 5,184 sq in. Usually, gold leaf contains 2% silver and copper for hardening.

Metal film, for overlays for plastics and for special surfacing on metals or composites, comes in thicknesses from flexible foils as thin as 0.002 in. to more rigid sheets for blanking and forming casings for intricately shaped parts. Metal films marketed by Composite Sciences, Inc., come in almost any metal or alloy, such as a film of tungsten carbide in a matrix of nickel alloy for wear-resistant overlays. They are made by rolling and sintering 325-mesh powder. The foils may be cemented to the substrate with an epoxy resin, but for operating temperatures above 400°F, brazing or welding is needed. **Metal overlays** give a smoother and more uniform surface than is usually obtained by flame-spray or chemical deposition.

FOODSTUFFS. A great group of materials employed for human consumption, while those employed for feeding animals are called **feeds.** Foodstuffs are derived mainly from vegetable and animal life, but some, like common salt, are produced from mineral sources, and some may be entirely synthesized. Foodstuffs are intended primarily for the maintenance and growth of the body, and technically could embrace drugs which are taken primarily for their physiological effects, and cosmetics that feed the skin and hair. Tobacco, used also for its physiological effect, is classed with foodstuffs in government statistics.

Proteins, carbohydrates, and fats are called the essential foodstuffs, and about 1.5 lb total of these are considered as needed daily for the human system. But these alone are inadequate for metabolism. Almost every element is required directly, or indirectly as catalysts, in the building up and maintenance of the innumerable highly complex chemical compounds in the human body, and the form in which they are taken into the body is of great importance. Iodine, for example, is an essential element in the thyroid gland, with minute amounts also required in every cell of the body, but if taken directly into the system in even small amounts is an intense poison.

Some complex chemical compounds, required for proper health, cannot be synthesized in the human body and must be taken in through the eating of foodstuffs containing them. First-class proteins are essential for full health, but they are not synthesized in the human body and are not available in vegetable products, so that they must be obtained from the eating of meats from animals that synthesize them. About one-third of the protein required daily should come from animal sources. Fish and shellfish can supply the essential amino acids, but abnormally large quantities would be necessary.

So little is yet known of metabolism balance, and metabolism varies so greatly among individuals because of unbalances in their systems, that chance plays a predominant part in the complex and involved application of foodstuffs. Foodstuff consumption varies radically in different countries and among different nations. In Asia, starches, chiefly rice and cassava, supplemented by inadequate amounts of fish and vegetables, form the bulk of the food, and the preferences are often so radicated in ancient customs that any change is difficult. In the United States, the changes are continuous, tending to a widening variety of foodstuffs, and often following cost patterns. The average per capita annual consumption of meats is 172 lb, but the consumption of beef has declined while that of poultry has increased. Largely because of a price differential, consumption of butter has dropped more than one-half, but consumption of margarine has more than equaled the loss. Milk consumption has varied little in 40 years, but the consumption of canned milk has tripled. An increasingly large food-packing and food-processing industry now separates the farm from the consumer, and the bulk of vegetables, fruits, and other products now reaches the consumer in cans or frozen packages, or in ready-to-cook forms.

Concentrated foods are now used in vast quantities for military supplies and for prepared food mixes. They may be spray-dried powders, comminuted **dehydrated vegetables** or fruits, or freeze-dried cooked foods. For example, dehydrated onions with particle size of ¼ in. can be handled in automatic metering equipment for adding to soup mixes or meat dishes, and 1 lb of the dried onions equals 8 lb of fresh onions. For mixes cooking times are balanced by partial pressure cooking or puffing. Celery is cross-cut in fine flakes and dehydrated. Rehydration gives 25 to 1 volume. For use uncooked it requires only immersement in cold water. **Concentrated wine,** used in flavoring foods, is made by evaporating sherry or other wines. One ounce is equal to 8 oz of wine, but it contains no alcohol. **Banana crystals,** for flavoring bakery products and milk-based beverages, is a light-tan crystalline powder made by vacuum dehydration of bananas, the fruit of the tall treelike herbaceous plant, *Musa paradisiaca,* native to southern Asia but now grown in all tropical countries. There are more than 300 varieties of the plant. The powder contains 50% banana solids and 50% corn-syrup solids, while the natural banana contains 25% solids and 75% water. The powder crystals are easily soluble in water, reconstituting to 80% banana solids and 20% corn-syrup solids, giving a true banana flavor and the natural food value. For food manufacturers bananas are also marketed in canned form, either sliced or mashed. A 7-lb No. 10 can contains 400 ¼-in slices equivalent to 18 average bananas, and the fruit retains its color and stability. For efficient high-production processing of bakery, confectionery, and other food products, most types of fruits and flavors are now available in the forms of dry powders, nuggets, pastes, solutions, or cooked or semicooked sections. Advantages are economy in shopping and storing, ease of handling in automatic equipment, and uniformity of quality. For example, the **fruit nuggets** of the Foamat Foods Corp. are in foamed particles 25 to the ounce, easily metered in automatic machines. Nuggets of berries contain no seeds. For dry-mix packaging the flavors may be in capsule. The citrus flavors of Sunkist Growers, Inc., called **Perma-Stabil flavors,** are oil solutions in small water-soluble gum capsules.

Agriculture and livestock raising, including the production of clothing fibers, are rated as the basic industry in all civilized countries, and are supervised and aided when necessary by governments. In the United States, foodstuffs processing is also a basic industry, including scientific research laboratories, and the health aspects are supervised by Federal and local agencies and controlled by laws.

Proper balance of quantity and type of foodstuff is a major consideration of health, and a body that is absorbing proper foods in correct amounts is most resistant to diseases, but functional disorders may prevent proper absorption even when the amount and nature of the foods are correct. Sugars are essential for health, but diabetics cannot tolerate sugar directly from food and must depend upon sugars formed in the system.   Parasites which cause diseases exist in immense numbers in all regions and attack all human life, but they may remain incapable of operation and harmless in a body that is chemically resistant by proper absorption of balanced foods, while inhabitants of some areas are susceptible to some diseases because of lack of certain foodstuffs.   Cholera is epidemic in all parts of the world, but is only endemic in a few places of poor eating habits.   Sea fish contain much iodine, and in fish-eating nations goiter is unknown.

Climatic conditions also affect metabolism.   Rickets is common in northern areas of scanty sunlight unless offsetting foods are taken liberally, while rickets is rare in the tropics even with poor food.   Nutritional diseases are common in areas where the people have only one product as the chief food, as among the rice eaters of Asia.   In some areas the body receives too high a calcium level from the foods and water, and urinary diseases result.   People living in cold climates require large amounts of fats, while the same quantity in warmer climates might cause gall bladder failure from inability to utilize the amount.   Some unsaturated fats are necessary to transport cholesterol from the tissues to the blood, but a high intake of saturated fats in persons leading a sedentary life may cause an excess which induces coronary diseases.

Calorific value is only an imperfect measurement of food value.   In the American diet, about 12% of the calorific value is in the form of proteins, about 40% in fats, and the remainder largely carbohydrates, but the trace percentages of mineral compounds and such chemical compounds as vitamins are of vital importance to proper metabolism and health.   **Therapeutic foods** are mixtures, usually in powder form to be mixed in water, to give a balance of proteins, fats, and carbohydrates for food satisfaction without overeating.   They may be designed for reducing excessive weight, for adding weight, or as a soft diet for invalids or babies, and are usually intended to contain sufficient for a rounded diet. **Metrecal,** of Mead-Johnson & Co., for example, for reducing weight, is a powder containing milk, soya flour, sugar, starch, corn oil, coconut oil, yeast, vitamins, and minerals.   But it is extremely difficult to obtain all the essentials in a synthetic food.   Iron is a common essential, readily absorbed from many natural foods, but as an additive for deficient systems it must be in chemical compounds that yield ferrous iron to the system. **Toleron,** of the Mallinckrodt Chemical Works, used for this purpose, is **ferrous fumarate,** $FeC_4H_2O_4$, an odorless and tasteless reddish powder. Trace quantities of zinc in enzymatic proteins are necessary to catalyze the reaction of carbonic anhydrase to sustain life, and are also needed in the liver and in the eyes.   Other metals, such as cobalt and rubidium, are also necessary, and the highly complex processes are as yet only imperfectly understood.

FORMALDEHYDE. Also called **methylene oxide.** A colorless, poison-ous gas of the composition HCHO, boiling at $-21°C$. It is very soluble in water, and is marketed as a 40% solution by volume, 37% by weight, under the name of **formalin.** The commercial formalin is a clear colorless liquid with a specific gravity of 1.075 to 1.081. When shipped by tank cars it contains 11 to 12% methanol, or 6 to 7% when shipped in drums, as a stabilizer to prevent precipitation of polymerized formaldehyde. The material is obtained by oxidation from methyl alcohol. It is used in making plastics, as a reducing agent, as a disinfectant, and in the produc-tion of other chemicals. **Trioxane** is polymerized formaldehyde, or a ring compound of anhydrous formaldehyde, $(HCHO)_3$. It is marketed as colorless crystals of a pleasant ether-alcohol odor, with a specific gravity of 1.17, melting point of 62°C, and boiling point of 115°C. It is used as a source of dry formaldehyde gas, as a tanning agent, and as a solvent. It ignites at 113°C and burns with a hot, odorless flame, and is used in tablet form to replace solidified alcohol for heating.

Glyoxal, of Union Carbide, is **dialdehyde,** or **ethanedial,** $CHO \cdot CHO$, marketed as a water solution as a substitute for formaldehyde for resin manufacture and as a hardening and preserving agent, and for treating rayon fabrics. It is faster in action and has less volatility and odor than formaldehyde. It is a light-yellow liquid boiling at 50°C. **Paraformal-dehyde,** $(CH_2O)_3$, also called **paraform,** is a white amorphous powder used instead of formaldehyde where a water solution is not desirable. It is used as a catalyst and hardener for the resorcinol and some other synthetic resins, and as an antiseptic. **Formamide,** $H(CO)NH_2$, is a clear, viscous water-soluble liquid with a faint odor of ammonia, boiling at 210°C. It is used as a solvent for metal chlorides and inorganic salts, and for lignin, glucose, or cellulose, and as a softener for glues. **Formol** is a trade name for a solution of formaldehyde in methanol and water, used as an antiseptic. **Formcel,** of the Celanese Corp., is a solution of formaldehyde in either methanol or butanol, to replace formalin where a water-free solution is desired. **Glutar aldehyde,** $O:HC(CH_2)_3 \cdot CH:O$, made from acrolein, has a reaction similar to formaldehyde, and is used as a cross-linking agent in plastics, and for insolubilizing starches, casein, and gelatin.

Hexamine is a white, crystalline powder used chiefly for the manufac-ture of synthetic resins in place of formalin and its sodium hydroxide catalyst. It is formed by the action of formaldehyde and ammonia. It is hexamethylene tetramine, $(CH_2)_6N_4$, melting at 280°C, and is very stable when dry. It is readily soluble in water and in alcohol. It is also known as **formin, ammonio formaldehyde, urotropin, crystogen, aminoform,** and **cystamine.** In pharmacy it is called **methenamine.** In the presence of an acid it yields formaldehyde and is used in medicine as an internal antiseptic. It is also used as an accelerator for rubber.

FORMIC ACID. Also called **methanoic acid** and **hydrogen carboxylic acid.**   Formic acid is the simplest of the organic acids, with the composition HCOOH, and was originally distilled from red ants, receiving its name from the Latin name for ants.   It is made synthetically, or is obtained from the black liquor of sulfite paper mills where it occurs as a sodium salt.   It is a pungent colorless liquid of specific gravity 1.22, boiling point 101°C, and freezing point 8.4°C, soluble in water and in alcohols.   It is an easily oxidized reducing agent, and small amounts will blister the skin and give the stinging sensation of ant or bee bites or nettle stings, all of which are caused by formic acid.   The acid has greater reducing action than acetic acid, and is thus used in textile finishing, especially in the chrome dyeing of wool.   It is also used in leather processing as a dye-bath exhausting agent.   Other uses are as a food preservative, in electroplating, as a germicide, as a fermentation assistant in brewing, and as a coagulant for rubber.   **Methyl formate,** $HCOOCH_3$, is a white volatile liquid boiling at 31.75°C, with a pleasant ester odor, soluble in water.   It hydrolyzes to form methanol and formic acid, and is used as an intermediate, but it is also a good solvent for cellulose esters and for acrylic resins.   **Protan,** of Hercules Inc., is a **sodium formate.**

FUEL BRIQUETTES. Various-shaped briquettes made by compressing powdered coal, usually with an asphalt or starch binder, but sometimes as **smokeless fuel** without a binder.   They are sometimes also made waterproof by coating with pitch or coal tar.   They have the great advantage over raw coal that they do not take up large amounts of water as coal does and thus have uniformity of firing.   Fuel briquettes are made from anthracite screenings usually mixed with bituminous screenings as the bituminous coals require no binders.   The usual forms of the briquettes are pillow-shaped, cubic, cylindrical, ovoid, and rectangular, and the usual size is not over 5 oz.   The term **packaged fuel** is used for cube-shaped briquettes wrapped in paper packages, used for hand firing in domestic furnaces.   **Koal Pak,** of the Johnson Coal Cubing Co., consists of coal cubes wrapped eight to a package.   The **coal briquettes** of the Blaw-Knox Co. are made with anthracite dust and a small amount of Pocahontas-type bituminous coal with an asphalt binder.   The cakes are 3 by 3 by 3 in. wrapped in kraft paper.   **Coal logs,** of the Coal Logs Co., Inc., are briquetted smokeless fuel which consists of high-temperature coke made by carbonizing Utah low-grade coal, yielding 20 to 40 gal of tar as a by-product per ton of coal.   **Charcoal briquettes** for home fuels are charcoal powders pressed with a resin binder.

FUEL OIL. Distillates of petroleum or shale oil used in diesel engines and in oil-burning furnaces. True fuel oils are the heavier hydrocarbons in kerosene, but the light or distillate oils are used largely for heating, and the heavy or residual oils for industrial fuels. In some cases only the light oils, naphtha and gasoline, are distilled from petroleum and the residue is used for fuel oil, but this is wasteful of the lighter oils. Commercial grades of **furnace oil** for household use and **diesel oil** for trucks may be low grades of kerosene. Fuel oil of low specific gravity requires preheating to obtain complete atomization. At 10°Bé the minimum temperature to atomize fuel oil is 300°F, but at 40°Bé a temperature of only 40°F is required. Fuel oils used in oil burners are 28 to 32°Bé, and have a Btu content of 142,000 per gal, completely atomizing at 90°F. **Gas oil,** which receives its name from its use to enrich fuel gas and increase the luminance of the flame, is also used as a fuel in oil engines. It is the fraction of petroleum distilling off after kerosene, or above about 300°C. It is brownish in color and has a specific gravity of about 0.850. Ignition temperatures of crude oils vary from 715 to 800°F in air at atmospheric pressure. **Bunker C oil,** for diesel engines, is a viscous, black fuel oil of specific gravity 1.052 to 0.9659 with a flash point above 150°F. The National Bureau of Standards lists six grades of fuel oils with flash points from 100 to 200°F. For general comparison of oil and coal, with comparable fire and boiler equipment, 4.5 bbl of Bunker C oil equal one net ton of low-ash, highly volatile West Virginia coal.

FUELS. The term normally covers a wide range, since innumerable organic materials can be used as fuel. Coal, oil, or natural gas, or products derived from them, are the basic industrial fuels, but other materials are basic in special situations, such as sawdust in lumbering areas and bagasse in sugarcane areas. **Fuel conversion factors** for industrial fuels are based on the relation to the fuel value of a metric ton of coal having a calorific value of 12,000 Btu per lb. Thus, a ton of lignite is equal to 0.3 ton of coal, a ton of crude oil is equal to 1.4 tons of coal, 1,100 cu ft of natural gas is equal to 1.33 tons of coal, and 1,000 kwhr of hydroelectricity is equal to 0.4 ton of coal.

But modern technical reference to fuels generally applies to **high-energy fuels** for jet engines, rockets, and special-use propellants, and the comparisons of these fuels are in terms of **specific impulse,** which is the thrust in pounds per pound of propellant per second. The molecular weight of the products produced by the reaction of a fuel must be extremely low to give high specific impulses, that is, above 400. Hydrogen gives a high specific-impulse rating, but it has very low density in the liquid state and other unfavorable properties, so that it is usually employed in compounds. The initial impulse of a rocket is proportional to the square root of the combustion temperature of the fuel. **Hydrogen fuels** reacted with pure oxygen produce temperatures above 5000°F, and some fuels may react as high as 9000°F. Aluminum powder or lithium added to hydrogen increases the efficiency. Boron fuels in general release 50% higher Btu per pound than petroleum hydrocarbons. The first Saturn space rocket had kerosene–liquid oxygen in the first stage and liquid hydrogen–oxygen in the following three stages. **Solid rocket fuels,** designed for easier handling, have a binder of polyurethane or other plastic. **Fuel oxidizers,** for supplying oxygen for combustion, may be ammonium, lithium, or potassium perchlorates. In solid fuels, oxidizers make up as much as 80% of the total.

A **monopropellant** high-energy fuel is a chemical compound which, when ignited under pressure, undergoes an exothermic reaction to yield high-temperature gases. Examples are nitromethane, methyl acetylene, ethylene oxide, and hydrogen peroxide. Gasoline oxidized by hydrogen peroxide gives a specific impulse of 248, while pentaboranes under pressure and oxidized with hydrogen peroxide give a specific impulse of 363. **ASTM fuel A,** for jet engines, is isooctane, and **ASTM fuel B** is isooctane and toluene. **Turbine jet fuel,** or **JP fuel,** for commercial aircraft is a special grade of kerosene. American specifications are for a flash point of 125°F, but for military planes the flash point may be 110°F using additions of methane or naphthene. The specific heat of standard commercial turbine jet fuel is 0.47 Btu-lb-F° compared with 3.39 Btu for hydrogen gas fuel. The **napththalenes,** such as **decahydro naphthalene,** have high thermal stability, and they have a high density which gives a high Btu per gallon. **Decalin,** of Du Pont, is this material. **Naphthene,** C_nH_{2n}, is a general term for nonaromatic cyclic hydrocarbons in petroleum.

Hydrazine with liquid oxygen has a specific impulse of 282, and with liquid fluorine as an additive the specific impulse is 316. The rocket fuel **hydyne** is a 60–40 mixture of unsymmetrical dimethyl hydrazine and diethylene triamine. Other liquid fuels may be this dimethyl hydrazine with nitric acid, or with nitrogen tetroxide, or with liquid oxygen. **Alkyl boranes** are used in rockets, but they leave a deposit and they exhaust boric acid in a dense cloud. **Diborane,** B_2H_6, is the simplest compound of boron and hydrogen. It is a gas which burns with high flame speed and high heat. It is used to produce the **boron hydrides** such as **decaborane,** $B_{10}H_{14}$, or $HH(H \cdot BB \cdot H)_5HH$, employed for **boron fuels** and for making boron plastics.

Sodium borohydride, a white crystalline solid of composition $NaBH_4$, made by reacting sodium hydride with methyl borate, is also used to produce the boranes for fuels. **Triethyl borane,** $(C_2H_5)B$, used for jet fuels and as a flame-speed accelerator, is a colorless liquid. It is spontaneously flammable, its vapors igniting with oxygen. Any element or chemical which causes spontaneous ignition of a rocket fuel is called a **hypergolic material.**

Chemical radicals are potential high-energy fuels, as the recombining of them produces high specific impulses. But chemical radicals normally exist only momentarily, and are thus not stable materials and, in general, are not commercial fuels. **Ion propellants** operate on the principle that like charges repel each other, and the fuel is an ion-plasma jet actually formed outside of the engine. The original fuel is a metal such as cesium from which electrons can be stripped by passing the vapor through a hot screen, leaving positive cesium ions, which are formed into a beam and exhausted from the thrust jet to be electronically neutralized in the ionized plasma.

FULLER'S EARTH. A soft, opaque clay with a greasy feel used as a filtering medium in clarifying and bleaching fats, greases, and mineral and vegetable oils. It absorbs the basic colors in the organic compounds. It is also used as a pigment extender and a substitute for talcum powder. It was formerly much used in the textile industry as a fuller for woolen fabrics, cleansing them by absorbing oil and grease. It is a hydrated compound of silica and alumina. It may contain 75% silica, 10 to 19 alumina, 1 to 4 lime, 2 to 4 magnesia, and sometimes ferric oxide. The usual color is greenish white to greenish brown. The rose-colored fuller's earth from Florida is a variation of **montmorillonite,** $(MgCa)O \cdot Al_2O_3 \cdot 4SiO_2$. The Florida fuller's earth marketed by the Floridin Co. under the name of **Floridin** is a grayish-white material graded by sizes from B, which is 16 to 30 mesh, to XXX, which will pass 90% through a 200-mesh screen. **Florex** is this material processed by extrusion to increase the absorption capacity. A typical analysis gives 58.1% silica, 15.43 alumina, 4.95 iron oxide, 2.44 magnesia, with small amounts of CaO, Na_3O, and K_2O. The specific gravity is 2.3. **Florigel** is the hydrated material which forms viscous suspensions in water, and is used to replace bentonite as a filler for soaps, and for clarifying liquids. **Diluex** is finely powdered Florida fuller's earth used as a diluent or carrier for insecticides. **Activated clay,** or **bleaching clay,** for bleaching oils, may be acid-treated fuller's earth, or it may be bauxite or kaolin. **Florite,** of the Floridian Co., is activated bauxite. It is a red, granular, porous material of 20 to 60 mesh.

FULMINATES. Explosives used in percussion caps and detonators because of their sensitivity. They may be called **cap powder** in cartridge caps and detonators when used for detonating or exploding artillery shells. **Mercury fulminate,** $Hg(CNO)_2$, a gray or brown sandy powder, is the basis for many detonating compositions. It is made by the action of nitric acid on mercury and alcohol, and is 10 times more sensitive than picric acid. It may be mixed with potassium chlorite and antimony sulfide for percussion caps. The fulminates may be neutralized with a sodium thiosulfate. The **azides** are a group of explosives containing no oxygen. They are compounds of hydrogen or a metal and a monovalent N_3 radical. **Hydrogen azide,** HN_3, or **azoic acid,** and its sodium salt are soluble in water. **Lead azide,** $Pb(N_3)_2$, is used as a substitute for fulminate detonators. It is much more sensitive than mercury fulminate and in large crystals is subject to spontaneous explosion, but it is precipitated to suppress crystal formation and to form a free-flowing powder less sensitive to handling. **Lead bromate,** $Pb(BrO_3)_2 \cdot H_2O$, is in colorless crystals which will detonate if mixed with lead acetate. For primer caps, a substitute for mercury fulminate is a mixture of lead styphnate, lead triagoacetate, lead nitrate, and lead sulfocyanate. **Lead styphnate,** used as a detonator, is made by the sulfonation and nitration of resorcinol to form **styphnic acid,** or **trinitro resorcinol,** $(NO_2)_3C_6H(OH)_2$. This powder is treated with magnesia and with a lead nitrate solution to form the lead styphnate powder. **Azoimide,** or **iminazoic acid,** $HN \cdot N_2$, is an extremely explosive colorless gas liquefying at $37°C$ which can be used in the form of its salts. **Silver azoimide,** $AgN \cdot N_2$, is highly explosive, and **barium azoimide,** BaN_6, explodes with a green flash. **Cyanuric triazide** is a powerful explosive made by reacting cyanuric chloride with sodium azide. **Lead nitrate,** a white crystalline water-soluble powder of the composition $Pb(NO_3)_2$, is used in match heads and explosive compositions. It is also employed as a mordant in dyeing and printing, and in paints.

FURFURAL. Also known as **furfuraldehyde, furol,** and **pyromucic aldehyde.** A yellowish liquid with an aromatic odor, having a composition $C_4H_3O \cdot CHO$, specific gravity 1.161, boiling point $161.7°C$, and flash point $132°F$. It is soluble in water and in alcohol but not in petroleum hydrocarbons. On exposure it darkens and gradually decomposes. Furfural occurs in different forms in various plant life and is obtained from cornstalks, corncobs, straw, oat husks, peanut shells, bagasse, and rice. A ton of furfural can be obtained from 15 tons of rice hulls. Furfural is used for making synthetic plastics, as a plasticizer in other synthetic resins, as a preservative, in weed killers, and as a selective solvent especially for removing aromatic and sulfur compounds from lubricating oils. It is also used for the making of butadiene, adiponitrile, and other chemicals.

Various derivatives of furfural are also used, and these, known collectively as **furans,** are now made synthetically from formaldehyde and acetylene which react to form butyl nedole. This is hydrogenated to butanediol, then dehydrated to tetrahydro furan. Furan, or **tetrol,** C_4H_4O, used for plastics manufacture, is a colorless liquid boiling at 32°C. **Methyl furan,** or **sylvan,** $C_4H_3O \cdot CH_3$, is a colorless liquid boiling at 62°C. **Tetrahydro furan,** $(CH_2)_4O$, is a water-white liquid boiling at 66°C, having strong solvent powers on resins.   It reacts with carbon monoxide to form adipic acid, and is also an intermediate for the production of other chemicals.   **Furfuryl alcohol,** $C_4H_3O \cdot CH_2OH$, a yellow liquid with a brinelike odor, boiling at 176°C, and flash point at 167°F, is used as a solvent for nitrocellulose and for dyes, and for producing synthetic resins. It is made by hydrogenation of furfural.   **Furfuryl alcohol resins,** made by reacting with an acid catalyst, are liquid materials that are low in cost and highly chemical-resistant.   They are much used for protective coatings, tank linings, and chemical-resistant cements.   They are dark in color.   The **Alkor cement** of the Atlas Mineral Products Co. is a furfuryl alcohol solution which produces coatings resistant to chemicals and to temperatures to 380°F.   **Furacin,** of the Norwich Pharmaceuticals, is a nitro-furfural semicarbazone, a yellow crystalline powder made by nitrating furfural and reacting it with hydrazine hydrate.   It is used as a bacterial treatment for wounds and burns.   **Furoic acid,** or **pyromucic acid,** $C_4H_3O \cdot$ COOH, is a colorless crystalline powder soluble in water.   It is **furan carboxylic acid** used for making pharmaceuticals, flavors, and resins.

Tetrahydro furfuryl alcohol, $(CH_2)_3OCH \cdot CH_2OH$, is the usual starting point for making furfuryl esters, ethers, and straight-chain compounds, and it is also a high-boiling solvent for gums, resins, and dyes.   It is a liquid of specific gravity 1.064, boiling at 177.5°C, and is soluble in water. **Furfural acetone,** $C_4H_3O \cdot CH:CHCOCH_3$, is a reddish-brown liquid boiling at 229°C.   Furfural, when treated with aniline at 150°C, forms an insoluble black **furfural-aniline resin** used in resistant protective coatings and enamels.   **Furfural-acetone resin,** or **furfuracetone,** is a transparent elastic resin made by the reaction of furfural and acetone in the presence of an alkali.   Furfural also polymerizes with phenol to form **furfural-phenol resins** that are self-curing.   They have high heat, chemical, and electrical resistance, and have excellent adhesion to metals and other materials, making them adaptable for chemical and electrical coatings. The resins have high gloss, but a very dark color.   The **Tygon resins** of the U.S. Stoneware Co. are furfural resins used for brush application as protective coatings for such purposes as chemical tank linings.   They cure by self-polymerization, will withstand temperatures to 350°F, and are resistant to acids, alkalies, alcohols, and hydrocarbons.   **Furafil,** of the Quaker Oats Co., is a by-product material containing modified cellulose, lignin, and resins, used as an extender for phenolic plywood glues, as an additive for phenolic molding resins, and as a binder for foundry sand molds.   Under the name of **Fur-Ag,** it is used as a conditioner and anticaking agent in fertilizer mixtures.   The material is a dark-brown, absorbent powder.

Furane plastics have high adhesion and chemical resistance, but they do not have high dielectric strength, and are black or dark in color. They are used for pipe, fittings, and chemical-equipment parts, and for adhesives and coatings. **Eonite** pipe is produced from **Durez 16470,** a furfural alcohol resin of the Hooker Chemical Co. The pipe will resist hot acids and alkalies to 300°F, is strong, and does not sag in long lengths. **Furfural-ketone resin** is used to blend with epoxy laminating resins to reduce cost and improve the properties.

FUSIBLE ALLOYS. Alloys having melting points below the boiling point of water, 100°C. They are used as binding plugs in automatic sprinkler systems, for low-temperature boiler plugs, for soldering pewter and other soft metals, for tube bending, and for casting patterns and many ornamental articles and toys. They are also used for holding optical lenses and other parts for grinding and polishing. They consist generally of mixtures of lead, tin, cadmium, and bismuth. The general rule is that an alloy of two metals has a melting point lower than that of either metal alone. By adding still other low-fusing metals to the alloy a metal can be obtained with almost any desired low melting point. The original **Newton's alloy** contained 50% bismuth, 31.25 lead, and 18.75 tin. **Newton's metal,** used as a solder for pewter, contained 50% bismuth, 25 cadmium, and 25 tin. It melts at 203°F, and will dissolve in boiling water. **Lipowitz alloy,** another early metal, contained 3 parts cadmium, 4 tin, 15 bismuth, and 8 lead. It melts at 158°F, is very ductile, and takes a fine polish. It was employed for casting fine ornaments, but now has many industrial uses. A small amount of indium increases the brilliance and lowers the melting point 1.45°C for each 1% of indium up to a maximum of 18%. **Wood's alloy,** or **Wood's fusible metal,** was patented in 1860 and was the first metal used for automatic sprinkler plugs. It contained 7 to 8 parts bismuth, 4 lead, 2 tin, and 1 to 2 cadmium. It melts at 160°F, and this point was adopted as the operating temperature of sprinkler plugs in the United States; in England it is 155°. The alloy designated as **Wood's metal** by the Cerro Corp. contains 50% bismuth, 25 lead, 12.5 tin, and 12.5 cadmium. It melts at 158°F. An early alloy for tube bending contained 50% bismuth, 16.7 lead, 13.3 tin, and 10 cadmium. It melts at 158°F, and can be easily removed from the tube after bending by dipping in boiling water or by applying steam.

Cerrobend, or **Bendalloy,** of the Cerro Corp., is a fusible alloy for tube bending which melts at 160°F. **Cerrocast** is a **bismuth-tin alloy** with pouring range of 280 to 338°F, and shrinkage of only 0.0001 in. per in., used for making pattern molds. **Cerro-safe,** or **Safalloy,** is a fusible metal used for toy-casting sets as the molten metal will not burn wood or cause fires. Alloys with very low melting points are sometimes used for this reason for pattern and toy casting. A fusible alloy with a melting point at 60°C contains 26.5% lead, 13.5 tin, 50 bismuth, and 10 cadmium. These alloys expand on cooling and make accurate impressions of the molds. **Boiler-plug alloys** have been made under a wide variety of trade names with melting points usually ranging from 212 to 342°F. **D'Arcet's alloy,** melting at 200°F, contained 50% bismuth, 25 tin, and 25 lead. **Lichtenberg's alloy,** melting at 198°F, contained 50% bismuth, 30 lead, and 20 tin. **Guthrie's alloy** had 47.4% bismuth, 19.4 lead, 20 tin, and 13.2 cadmium. **Rose's alloy** contained 35% lead, 35 bismuth, and 30 tin. **Homberg's alloy,** melting at 251°F, contained 3 parts lead, 3 tin, and 3 bismuth. **Malotte's metal,** melting at 203°F, had 46% bismuth, 20 lead, and 34 tin. The variation of these different alloys was largely because of the relative cost of the different alloying metals at various times. Fusible metals have also been used in strip form to test the temperature of steels for heat-treating. The **Temperite alloys** of the Cornish Wire Co. were for this purpose with melting points between 300 and 625°F in steps of 25 deg. The **Tempil pellets** of the Tempil Corp. are alloy pellets made with melting points in steps of 12.5, 50, and 100°F for measuring temperatures from 113 to 2500°F. The **Semalloy metals** of Semi-Alloys cover a wide range of fusible alloys with various melting points. **Semalloy 1010** with a melting point at 117°F can be used where the melting point must be below that of thermoplastics. It contains 45% bismuth, 23 lead, 19 indium, 8 tin, and 5 cadmium. **Semalloy 1280,** for uses where the desired melting is near the boiling point of water, melts at 204°F. It contains 52% bismuth, 32 lead, and 16 tin.

FUSTIC. Known also as **Cuba wood.** The wood of the tree *Chlorophora tinctoria* of tropical America, used for cabinetmaking and as a dyewood. It has a yellow color, is very hard, and has a fine, open grain. The weight is about 41 lb per cu ft. The liquid extract of the wood produces the yellow dyestuff **morin,** $C_{15}H_{11}O_7$, and the red dye **morindone,** $C_{15}H_{11}O_5$. **Fustic extracts** are mordant dyes and give colors from yellow to olive with various mordants. Morin is used also as an indicator to detect aluminum, with which it develops a green fluorescence. **Young fustic,** or **Hungarian yellow wood,** is a yellow dyewood from the *Rhus cotinus.* **Osage orange,** called **bois d'arc,** is the bright orange wood of the bush *Maclura pomifera* growing in the swamplands of Texas and Oklahoma. It has a high tannin content and is used in the textile and leather industries for orange-yellow and gold colors and to blend with greens. As a tanning agent it may be blended with quebracho and chestnut extracts.

GALLIUM. An elementary metal, symbol Ga, originally called **austrium.** It is silvery white, resembling mercury in appearance but having chemical properties more nearly like aluminum. It melts at 85.6 F, and boils at 2912°F, this wide liquid range making it useful for high-temperature thermometers. Like bismuth, the metal expands on freezing, the expansion amounting to about 3.8%. Pure gallium is resistant to mineral acids, and dissolves with difficulty in caustic alkali. It forms many salts at different valencies. The weight is only about half that of mercury, having a specific gravity of 5.9. Commercial gallium has a purity of 99.9%. In the molten state it attacks other metals, and small amounts have been used in tin-lead solders to aid wetting and decrease oxidation, but it is expensive for this purpose. **Gallium-tin alloy** has been used where a low-melting metal was needed. It is also used as an electron carrier in silicon semiconductors, and crystals of **gallium arsenide,** GaAs, are used as semiconductors. Gallium arsenide can be used in rectifiers to operate to 600°F. The material has high electron mobility. This material in single-crystal bars is produced by Monsanto for lasers and modulators. **Gallium selenide,** GaSe, **gallium triiodide,** GaI_3, and other compounds are also used in electronic applications.

Gallium exists in nature in about the same amount as lead, but it is widely dissipated and not found concentrated in any ore. It is found in small amounts associated with zinc ores and is recovered from smelter flue dust. In Germany it is produced as a by-product of copper smelting. It is also a minor constituent in the mineral sphalerite to the extent of 0.01 to 0.1%, and it also occurs in almost all aluminum ores in the ratio of 50 to 100 grams of gallium per ton of aluminum. In the United States it is a by-product of aluminum production. About 1 oz of gallium is obtained commercially per ton of bauxite.

GALLS. Tanning materials obtained from the **nutgalls,** or **gall nuts,** from the oaks of Europe and the Near East and from the sumac of China and Japan. Nutgalls are plant excrescences caused by the punctures of insects. They contain 50 to 70% tannins, and are the richest in tannin of all the leather-tanning materials. The tannin is also valued for inkmaking and in medicine for treating burns. **Green galls,** or **Aleppo galls,** are obtained from the twigs of the **Aleppo oak,** *Quercus infectoria,* a shrub of the Near East. Those of blue color are the best quality, with green second, and the white of inferior grade. **Chinese galls,** from species of *Rhus,* are in the form of irregular roundish nuts which enclose the insect. They show no vegetable structure but have a dense resinous fracture and are very high in tannin.

The product known as **gall** in the pharmaceutical industry is an entirely unrelated material. It is **beef gall,** or **ox bile,** a bitter fluid from the livers of cattle. It is used for steroid production, and also in the textile industry for fixing dyes and in soaps for washing dyed fabrics. **Steroids,** or

hormones, made from ox bile, have a great number of possible combinations that have an influence on the behavior of the human cellular system. They are based on a 4-ringed, 17-carbon cyclo pentamorphen anthrene nucleus, and arranging the side group in different ways gives compounds with distinct physiological properties. **Cortisone,** made by moving the oxygen atom of the steroid nucleus from the 12th to the 11th position, is one of the many steroids. Steroids are now synthesized from the more plentiful cholesterol, from the **stigmastrol** of vegetable oils, and from the **sapogenins** of plants.

GALVANIZED IRON. Iron or steel sheets coated with zinc and used for roofing, sheathing, culverts, and for making articles that require to be rust-resistant without painting. The most common sheets are of low-carbon steel, but the copper-bearing iron and steels are also used to give added corrosion resistance. The common dipped sheets are annealed, pickled, cold-rolled to increase the polish, and then dipped in molten zinc. They have a characteristic spangle which in thick coats is likely to peel and flake off under distortion. Sheets are graded by perfection of coating, gage, and size, as primes, seconds, and gray-coated. Primes are the perfect sheets. **Galvanized sheets** are either plain or corrugated. They come usually in lengths of 6, 7, and 8 ft, and widths of 24, 26, 28, 32, 34, and 36 in. The thickness is by gage sizes, usually from No. 14 to No. 30. The No. 14 sheet carries a 2-oz zinc coating.

In hot-dip galvanizing the molten zinc reacts with the steel to form a zinc-iron alloy which is brittle. Addition of a small amount of aluminum to the zinc retards formation of the brittle alloy, and control of temperature also reduces the formation of the alloy and produces a more ductile coating. Small amounts of magnesium added to the zinc improve greatly the corrosion resistance in marine atmospheres. With an alloy of 97% zinc and 3 magnesium, about 0.05% by weight is added to the coating. **Zinc alloy steel,** of the Inland Steel Co., is **zinc-coated steel** sheet with the coating fused in and alloyed with the steel so that there is no spangle. The sheet can be spun or drawn without cracking the coating. **Gal-Van-Alloy** is the trade name of this company for the galvanized sheet. **Bethcon Jet-coat,** of the Bethlehem Steel Co., is high-temperature hot-dip galvanized steel sheet in which the zinc is chemically combined to leave no free zinc. It has a uniform gray color without spangles. It is easily welded, and is more corrosion-resistant and takes paint better than ordinary galvanized steel.

Zinc-coated steel is now made extensively by continuous electroplating. This **electrogalvanized steel** has a uniform homogeneous deposit of pure zinc tightly bonded to the steel, and has a smooth, shiny surface that does not peel or flake. **Weirzin,** of the Weirton Steel Co., is zinc-electroplated sheet steel.   **Zincgrip,** of the Armco Steel Corp., is zinc-coated sheet steel for deep drawing.   The coating does not flake or peel in the drawing dies. **Galv-Weld,** of Morton L. Clark Enterprises, is a low-melting zinc alloy in stick form for regalvanizing welded joints.   **Coronized steel** refers to steel parts with a zinc-nickel coating.   The steel parts are first nickel-plated, and then coated with zinc and heat-treated at about 700°F to give a smooth, semilustrous, nickel-zinc surface.

Galvanized wire is steel wire coated with zinc for rust resistance either by dipping in molten zinc or by continuous electroplating, and is marketed plain, twisted, or barbed.   **Barbed wire** has double-pointed wire barbs held in the twisted wire.   **Bethanized steel,** of the Bethlehem Steel Co., is wire electrogalvanized and then passed through a die which polishes and hardens the coating.

GAMBIER. Also spelled **gambir.**   A tanning and dyeing material extracted from the leaves and twigs of the shrubs *Uncaria gambier, U. Dacyoneuro,* and other species of India, Malaysia, and the East Indies.   It is similar to catechu, and is also called **white cutch, yellow cutch, cube cutch,** and **tara japonica.**   The cubes of extract are brittle, have a dull-gray color, and a bitter astringent taste.   The material contains **catechin,** $C_{15}H_{14}O_6$, a yellow astringent dye also found in catechu and kino resin.   Catechin is soluble in hot water and in alkaline solutions and is neutral with no acid properties.   Gambier also contains **catechutannic acid,** a reddish tannin. The liquid extract contains 25% tannin, and the cube gambier has 30 to 40%.   Gambier is used in tanning leather and in dyeing to give yellow to brown colors.   It produces the **cutch brown** on cotton fabrics.   It has excellent fastness as a dye and is used in shading logwood and fustic, or as a mordant for fixing basic dyes.   In tanning it gives a soft porous leather, has less astringency than other tannins, and is employed for tanning coat leathers and for blending with other tannins.   Gambier is also used in boiler compounds and in pharmaceuticals.   **Plantation gambier,** or **Singapore cube,** is refined clear gambier in small square cubes, while ordinary gambier may have dark patches or a black color with a fetid odor.   **Gambier bulat** is round gambier, and **gambier papu** is in long black sticks, both used locally for chewing.

GARNET. A general name for a group of minerals varying in color, hardness, toughness, and method of fracture, used for coating abrasive paper and cloth, for bearing pivots in watches, for electronics, and the finer specimens for gemstones.   Garnets are trisilicates of alumina, magnesia, calcia, ferrous oxide, manganese oxide, or chromic oxide.   The general formula is $3R''O \cdot R'''_2O_3 \cdot 3SiO_2$, in which R'' is Ca, Mg, Fe, or Mn, and R''' is Al, Cr, or Fe.   There are thus 12 basic types of garnets, but sodium and titanium may also occur in the crystals, replacing part of the silicon, and there are also color varieties. Asterism in the garnet, because of the isometric crystal, appears as 4-, 8-, or 12-ray stars instead of the 6 rays of the ruby.

Hardness of garnet varies from the Mohs 6 of grossularite to 7.5 of almandite and rhodolite, a hard garnet having a Knoop hardness of 1,350. The specific gravity is 3.4 to 4.3, with a melting point about 1300°C. The color is most often red, but it may be brown, yellow, green, or black. **Spanish garnet** is pale pink. High-iron garnets have the lowest melting points and fuse to a dark glass, while the high-chromium garnets have high melting points. Garnets occur in a wide variety of rocks in many parts of the world. The immense alluvial schist deposits of the Emerald Creek area of Idaho contain about 10% garnet. **Almandite,** $3FeO \cdot Al_2O_3 \cdot 3SiO_2$, forms crystals of a fine deep-red color with a hardness of about 7.5, which fuses to a glassy mass at 1315°C. It is the most common garnet and is produced chiefly in New York state. It is crushed and graded for coating abrasive paper and cloth. The choice crystals are used as gemstones. **Cape ruby,** from South Africa, is a red almandite. **Pyrope** has the composition $3MgO \cdot Al_2O_3 \cdot 3SiO_2$. It has a deep-red color to nearly black, and hardness of 6.5 to 7.5. The nearly transparent or translucent crystals are selected for gemstones. **Rhodolite,** a pale-rose to purple variety of garnet, is a mixture of pyrope and almandite. These two garnets are found in the eastern states. The garnet of North Carolina is a by-product of kyanite mining, the ore containing 10% garnet, 15 kyanite, and 30 mica.

Andradite has the composition $3CaO \cdot Fe_2O_3 \cdot 3SiO_2$, and the colors are yellow, green, or brown to black, with a hardness of 6.5. The orange-yellow variety is called **hessenite;** the yellow-green is **topazolite;** the green is **demantoid;** and the black variety is called **melanite.** The **Uralian emeralds** are choice green crystals of demantoid from the Ural Mountains. **Uvarovite** has the composition $3CaO \cdot Cr_2O_3 \cdot 3SiO_2$, and is emerald green. **Grossularite,** $3CaO \cdot Al_2O_3 \cdot 3SiO_2$, or $Ca_3Al_2(SiO_4)_3$, may be white, yellow, or pale green. **Succinite** is an amber variety; **romanzovite** is brown; and **wiluite** is pale green. **Spessartite,** $3MnO \cdot Al_2O_3 \cdot 3SiO_2$, is brown to red, the yellowish-brown variety being **rothoffite.** The sodium garnet is **lagoriolite,** and a variety of calcium spessartite is called **essonite.**

The best **abrasive garnets** come from almandite, although andradite and rhodolite are also used. Garnet is crushed, ground, and separated and graded in settling tanks and sieves. Hornblende is a common impurity and is difficult to separate, but good-quality abrasive garnet should be free of this softer mineral. **Garnet-coated paper** and cloth are preferred to quartz for the woodworking industries, because garnet is harder and gives sharper cutting edges, but aluminum oxide is often substituted for garnet.

The less expensive quartz is sometimes colored to imitate garnet. The grades of garnet grains used on **garnet paper** and cloth range from No. 5, the coarsest, which is about 15 mesh, to 7/0, the finest, which is about 220 mesh. The paper used as a backing is a kraft of 50 to 70 lb weight, or a manila stock. The usual size is 9 by 11 in. The cloth is usually in two weights, the lightweight being used as a flexible rubbing-down material. Some garnet is made into wheels by the silicate process, but vitrified wheels are not made because of the low melting point of garnet.

Synthetic garnets for electronic applications are usually **rare-earth garnets** with the general structure of grossularite, but with a rare-earth metal substituted for the calcium, and iron substituted for the aluminum and the silicon. **Yttrium garnet** is thus $Y_3Fe_2(FeO_4)_3$. **Yttrium-aluminum garnets** of 3-mm diameter are used for lasers. **Gadolinium garnet** is marketed by Semi-Elements, Inc., for microwave use.

GASKET MATERIALS. Any sheet material used for sealing joints between metal parts to prevent leakage, but gaskets may also be in the form of cordage or molded shapes. The simplest gaskets are waxed paper or thin copper. A usual requirement is that the material will not deteriorate by the action of water, oils, or chemicals. Gasket materials are usually marketed under trade names. **Felseal,** of the Felt Products Mfg. Co., consists of sheets of paper or fiber, 0.010 to 0.125 in. thick, coated with Thiokol to withstand oils and gasoline. **Corbestos,** of the Dana Corp., to resist high heat and pressure, consists of sheet metal coated with graphited asbestos, the sheet metal being punched with small tongues to hold the asbestos. **Chrome lock,** of the Products Research Co., is felt impregnated with zinc chromate to prevent corrosion and electrolysis between dissimilar metal surfaces.

Foamed synthetic rubbers in sheet form, and also plastic impregnants, are widely used for gaskets. Some of the specialty plastics, selected for heat resistance or chemical resistance, are used alone or with fillers, or as binders for fibrous materials. **Haveg 16075,** of the Haveg Industries, Inc., a gasketing sheet to withstand hot oils and superoctane gasolines, is based on **Viton,** of Du Pont, a copolymer of vinylidene fluoride and hexafluoro propylene. It contains about 65% of fluorine, has a tensile strength of 2,000 psi with elongation of 400%, and will withstand operating temperatures to 400°F with intermittent temperatures to 600°F. Another synthetic of this company, used for gaskets of high chemical resistance at temperatures to 350°F, is **Hypalon CSM-60,** a chlorosulfonyl polyethylene, made by reacting polyethylene with sulfur and chlorine. It has a tensile strength of 2,250 psi, elongation of 30%, and Durometer hardness of 60. The square rope-type packing of the Marlo Co., called **Graphlon C,** has a core of braided asbestos fibers impregnated with Teflon over which is a braided jacket of Teflon fiber, with an outer jacket of graphite fabric. It has a low coefficient of friction, is self-lubricating, has high chemical resistance, and withstands service temperatures to 675°F.

GASOLINE. Known in England as **petrol.** A colorless liquid hydrocarbon obtained in the fractional distillation of petroleum. It is used chiefly as a motor fuel, but also as a solvent. Ordinary gasoline consists of the hydrocarbons between C_6H_{14} and $C_{10}H_{22}$, which distill off between the temperatures 69 and 174°C, usually having the light limit at **heptane,** C_7H_{16}, or **octane,** C_8H_{18}. The octane number is the standard of measure of detonation in the engine. **Motor fuel,** or the general name gasoline, before the wide use of high-octane gasolines obtained by catalytic cracking, meant any hydrocarbon mixture that could be used as a fuel in an internal-combustion engine by spark ignition without being sucked in as a liquid and without being so volatile as to cause imperfect combustion and carbon deposition. These included also mixtures of gasoline with alcohol or benzol.

The Federal specifications for motor fuel called for a hydrocarbon of which 90% would evaporate at 180°C, 50% at 125°C, and 10% at 65°C, with a maximum of 0.10% sulfur. **Gasanol,** used in the Philippines, contained only 20% gasoline, with 5 kerosene and 75 ethyl alcohol, while the German **Dynakol** contained 70% gasoline with alcohol and benzol. The **Dynax motor fuel** contained a methanol-benzol blend. In Brazil, alcohol produced from excess sugar is mixed with gasolines, and at times all commercial automotive fuels there contain alcohol. But gasolines containing as much as 15% alcohol require special carburetion. In the United States alcohol is not normally used in gasoline fuels.

The common commercial gasolines in the United States had an upper limit at 225°C, and an average specific gravity of 0.75, with the **aromatic-free gasolines** having a specific gravity of 0.718. **Aviation gasoline** formerly had a boiling range below 150°C, but aviation gasolines are now the high-octane cracked and treated gasolines. Straight-run distillation yields gasoline octane numbers from about 40 to 60, and the yield is 20 to 30% of the petroleum. In the heat-cracking process the heavy hydrocarbons of the petroleum are fragmentated and converted into lighter hydrocarbons of gasoline range. The octane number of the gasoline then ranges from 55 to 70, and the yield is higher. With catalytic cracking the octane number can be brought up to 100 or higher, and the yield proportionately increased. **Cracked gasolines** may be rich in the olefins, C_nH_{2n}, or ethylene series, which have antiknock properties but which polymerize and form resins with high heat. They are stabilized with antioxidants. Filtering straight-run gasoline with bauxite removes sulfur impurities that cause knocking and raises the octane number. The octane number and the antiknock qualities are improved by slight additions of tetraethyl lead, but high-quality gasolines that do not need lead additions are produced by catalytic cracking. **Amoco gasoline,** of the American Oil Co., is such a product.   Small amounts of tricresyl phosphate may also be added to motor gasoline to give more uniform combustion and eliminate knock. **TCP gasoline,** of the Shell Oil Co., contains this material.   All lead compounds are toxic and the exhaust fumes from **leaded gasoline** may remain in the atmosphere for long periods with injury to animals and vegetation.

Alkylated gasoline is made by adding **neohexane,** which is produced by combining isobutane and ethylene, or by adding other alkylates. **Alkylates** are produced by reacting butylenes plus propylenes and amylenes with isobutane and an acid catalyst.   They are clean-burning fuels with high octane rating.   As much as 35% may be added to a premium grade of gasoline to improve the sensitivity and raise the aviation performance number to above 115.

Synthetic gasoline was first produced in Germany by the Bergius process of hydrogenation of powdered lignite at high temperatures and pressures to produce gasoline, an intermediate oil, and a heavy oil.   But gasolines are also produced from the high-volatile bituminous coal.   The low-grade fuel bituminous coals contain a high proportion of **anthraxylon,** or **vitrain,** which is that part of bituminous coal consisting of undisintegrated parts of trees and plants.   This structure of coal has less carbon and can be liquefied more easily to produce gasoline and oils.   A low-grade bituminous, such as Vigo No. 4 vein, with 65% anthraxylon, gives a liquefaction to gasoline and oils of more than 96%, while a Pennsylvania medium-volatile fuel coal gives only 79% liquefaction and requires a greater consumption of hydrogen. **Natural gasoline** consists of the liquid hydrocarbons from C_5 upward, extracted from natural gas and separated from propane and other higher fractions.   It has high vapor pressure, and is used for blending with motor fuels.   However, under controlled production gasolines from the various sources are the same.

Gasoline gel, used in incendiary bombs, is gasoline made into a thick gel with a chemical thickener.   It adheres to the surface where it strikes and will produce a temperature of 3000°F for 10 min. **Kerosene gel,** similarly made, is used to dissolve tight formations and increase the flow in oil wells.   The gel known as **napalm** is sodium palmitate, but may also be an aluminum soap made with an oleic, naphthenic, and coconut, fatty acid mixture.   The same principle is used for making quick-firing gels for commercial power boilers, but diesel oil is used instead of gasoline.   The motor fuel known as **triptane** is **trimethyl butane.**   In automotive engines it is free from knock so that higher compressions may be employed.   In blends with 100-octane gasoline it increases the power output about 25% in aviation engines.

GELATIN. A colorless to yellowish water-soluble tasteless colloidal hemicellulose obtained from bones or from skins and used as a dispersing agent, sizing medium, coating for photographic films, and stabilizer for foodstuffs and pharmaceutical preparations. It is also flavored for use as a food jelly, and is a high-protein, low-calorie foodstuff. While albumin has a weak, continuous molecular structure that is cross-linked and rigidized by heating, gelatin has an ionic or hydrogen bonding in which the molecules are brought together into large aggregates, and it sets to a firmer solid. Gelatin differs from glue only in the purity. **Photographic gelatin** is made from skins. **Lithogel,** of the American Agricultural Chemical Co., used for film and photogelatin engraving, has the composition $C_{102}H_{151}O_{39}N_{31}$. **Vegetable gelatin** is not true gelatin, but is algin from seaweed.

Collagen is the gelatin-bearing protein in bone and skins. The bone is dissolved in hydrochloric acid to separate out the calcium phosphate and washed to remove the acid. The organic residue is called **osseine** and is the product used to produce gelatin and glue. About 25% of the weight of the bone is osseine, and the gelatin yield is about 65% of the osseine. One short ton of green bones, after being degreased and dried, yields about 300 lb of gelatin. When skins are used, they are steeped in a weak acid solution to swell the tissues so that the collagen may be washed out. The gelatin is extracted with hot water, filtered, evaporated, dried, and ground or flaked.

GERMANIUM. A rare elementary metal, symbol Ge. It is a grayish white crystalline metal of great hardness, being 6.25 Mohs. The specific gravity is 5.35, and melting point 958°C. It is resistant to acids and alkalies. The metal is trivalent and will form chain compounds like carbon and silicon. It gives greater hardness and strength to aluminum and magnesium alloys, and as little as 0.35% in tin will double the hardness. It is not used commonly in alloys, however, because of its rarity and great cost. It is used chiefly in the form of its salts to increase the refraction of glass, and as metal in rectifiers and transistors. A **germanium-gold alloy,** with about 12% germanium, having a melting point at 359°C, has been used for soldering jewelry.

Germanium is obtained as a by-product from flue dust of the zinc industry, or it can be obtained by reduction of its oxide from the ores, and is marketed in small irregular lumps. Metal of 99.9+ purity for electronic use is made by passing an ingot slowly through an induction heater so that the more soluble impurities pass along through the molten zones and are cut off at the end of the ingot. **Germanium crystals** are grown in rods up to 1⅜ in. diameter for use in making transistor wafers. High-purity crystals are used for both P and N semiconductors.

The chief ore of the metal is **germanite,** which is a copper ore found in southwest Africa. Germanite contains no less than 20 elements. Together with about 45% copper and 30 sulfur, it contains 6 to 9% germanium and 1 gallium, with various amounts of iron, zinc, lead, arsenic, silica, titanium, tungsten, molybdenum, nickel, cobalt, manganese, cadmium, and carbon. **Renierite,** found in the Congo, is a **germanium sulfide** containing up to 7.8% germanium in the ore. The rare lead-silver ore, **ultrabasite,** found in central Europe, also contains germanium. Many other metal ores, such as lepidolite, sphalerite, and spodumene, contain small amounts of germanium, so that it has an indirect use, especially in ceramics. As much as 1.6% **germanium oxide,** GeO, occurs in some English coals.

GILSONITE. A natural asphalt used for roofing, paving, floor tiles, storage-battery cases; in coatings; and for adding to heavy fuel oils. It is also referred to as **Utah coal resin.** It is a lustrous, black, almost odorless, brittle solid, having a specific gravity of 1.10. Gilsonite is one of the purest asphalts and has high molecular weight. It is soluble in alcohol, turpentine, and mineral spirits. The mineral was named for Samuel Gilson, who discovered it about 1875. The very pure gilsonite called **uintahite** takes its name from the Indian word uintah meaning mountain. The mineral in Utah occurs in vertical veins up to 20 ft wide and 1,400 deep, sometimes 8 miles long. The selects come from the center of the veins, are very pure, have high solubility in naphtha, and have fusing points from 270 to 310°F. But most commercial gilsonite is now melted and regraded. **Elaterite** and **wurtzilite** are similar asphalts found in Utah, used chiefly for acid-resisting paints. **Grahamite,** or **glance pitch,** is another pure asphalt found in large deposits in Oklahoma, and in Mexico, Trinidad, and Argentina. It is used in insulation and molding materials and in paints. **Gilsonite dust,** used for foundry cores, is a by-product of Utah mining. **Manjak** is a variety of grahamite from Cuba, Barbados, and Trinidad, used for insulation and varnishes. It is the blackest of the asphalts, has a higher melting point than gilsonite, but is usually not as pure. **Millimar,** of R. T. Vanderbilt Co., Inc., is processed gilsonite in 20-mesh powder used for rubber compounding. **Gilsulate,** of the American Gilsonite Co., is an insulation grade of gilsonite. **Millex,** of Cary Chemicals, Inc., is a dark-brown gilsonite melting at 250°F, used for blending in synthetic rubbers and vinyl resins to improve processing. **Gilsonite coke** is a high-grade, low-sulfur coke produced by the American Gilsonite Co. from Utah gilsonite, 630 tons of gilsonite yielding 250 tons of coke, 1,300 bbl of gasoline, and 300 bbl of fuel oil. **Insulmastic,** of the Pittsburgh Coke & Chemical Co., is a solution of gilsonite with mica flakes and asbestos fibers, used for protective coatings.

GINGER. The most important spice obtained from roots, and one of the first Oriental spices known in Europe. It is the prepared root of the perennial herb *Zingiber officinale,* grown in India, China, Indonesia, and Jamaica. The roots are pale yellow and contain starch, an essential oil, and a pungent oleoresin, **gingerin.** The first crop is the best; the product from the regrowth is called **rhatoon ginger** and is inferior. Ginger is employed as a spice and condiment, in flavoring beverages and confections, and in medicine as a digestive stimulant and carminative. It has a cooling effect on the body. **Preserved ginger** is made by peeling off the thick scaly skin of the boiled roots and boiling in a sugar solution. **Dried ginger** is prepared by drying the peeled roots in the sun. When the roots have been boiled in lime water before peeling, **black ginger** is produced. **White ginger** is made by bleaching the roots.

Other plants of the ginger family are also used as spices and flavors. **Angelica** is from the perennial herb *Angelica archangelica,* of Syria and Europe. All parts of the plant are aromatic. **Angelica oil,** distilled from the fruit, is used in perfumes, flavors for vermouth and bitters, and in medicine. **Candied angelica** consists of the stems steeped in syrup. It is bright green in color, has an aromatic taste, and is used for decorating confections. **Galangal** is from the roots of the perennial herb *Languas officinarum,* of China. It has an aromatic odor and pungent taste similar to a mixture of ginger and pepper. It is used chiefly as a flavor, but also in medicine. **Turmeric,** highly popular in India and Malaya as an ingredient of curries, is from the rhizomes of the perennial plant *Curcuma longa,* of southeast Asia and Indonesia. When used as a dye it is called **India saffron.** The roots are cleaned and dried in the sun. It is very aromatic, with a pungent bitter taste. **Curry powders** are not turmeric alone, but mixtures of turmeric with pepper, cumin, fenugreek, and other spices. Turmeric is used to flavor and color foodstuffs, and as a dyeing agent for textiles and leather and in wood stains. The natural dye is reddish brown, and gives a yellowish color to textiles and foods. It is also used as a chemical indicator, changing color with acidity or alkalinity. **Zedoary** consists of the dried roots of the perennial plant *C. zedoaria,* grown in India. **Zedoary oil** is a viscid liquid of reddish color with an odor resembling ginger and camphor. It is used in flavoring, in medicine, and in perfumery.

GLASS. An amorphous solid made by fusing silica with a basic oxide. Its characteristic properties are its transparency, its hardness and rigidity at ordinary temperatures, its capacity for plastic working at elevated temperatures, and its resistance to weathering and to most chemicals except hydrofluoric acid. The so-called **organic glasses** of transparent plastics, and the soft, soluble glasses with phosphates replacing the silica, are not glass in the established sense of the term, regardless of their transparency. Glass was made in ancient times by fusing sand and an alkali. The Eygptians were famous glassmakers, and were able to blend in various mineral oxides for color and other effects, but glass was not used extensively for windows until modern times. A simple **soda-lime glass** may be represented by the formula $Na_2O \cdot CaO \cdot 6SiO_2$, which is nearly the type formula of the garnets except for the silicate crystallization, but glass is not a simple chemical compound. The structure is described as an open structure of silicon, with molecules of other oxides occupying the spaces in the loose structure. It does not crystallize like silica alone, and many garnets when melted will cool to an amorphous glass. However, to obtain a chemically homogenous vitreous, or glassy, solution, with a minimum number of molecules in the crystalline state, requires a controlled slow cooling of the glass.

In its simplest form glass is made by melting together silica and soda ash. **Bottle glass** is a simple soda-lime-silica glass, the greenish color being due to iron impurities. The lime acts as a flux, and the calcium silicate produced gives the glass a chemical stability which quartz and fused silica do not have. The brilliance and sparkle in glass for bottles for food and drug containers are obtained by adding a small amount of barium. Small amounts of cerium will absorb ultraviolet light without distorting the passage of visible light. Cerium also acts as a **glass decolorizer** by changing the crystal structure of the iron impurities, energizing it from the normal divalent which is bluish to the trivalent which is colorless. Glass is made in special furnaces by melting selected batches of raw materials to which may be added broken scrap glass called **cullet.** The hardness, transparency, and brilliance of the glass vary with the composition. It is estimated that more than 50,000 formulas have been developed for producing glass, each giving different characteristics.

Metallic oxides may be used to color glass or to give special properties. Feldspar is employed as a source of alumina and to prevent disassociation of the soda ash and silica. Soda ash prevents fogging. **Crown glass** for windows is a hard, white soda-lime glass high in silica, a typical composition being 72% SiO_2, 13 CaO, and 15 Na_2O. It derives its name from the circular crowning method of making the sheets, but it is highly transparent and will take a brilliant polish. **Hard glass,** or **Bohemian glass,** for brilliant glassware, is a potash-lime glass with a high silica content, the potash glasses in general not being as hard as the soda glasses, and having lower melting points. The artistry is largely responsible for the quality of Bohemian glass.

Heat-resistant glass may be borosilicate glass that is heat-treated or leached to remove the alkali. Such glasses withstand high heat and sudden cooling without shattering. The **Duran glass** used in Germany for chemical tubes and pipes contained B_2O_3 and a small amount of alumina, with the smallest possible amount of alkali.   A standard **borosilicate glass** contains 81% SiO_2, 13 BO, 4 Na_2O, and Al_2O_3.   It has a density of 2.23, softening point 825°C, strain point 513°C, and thermal shock point 150°C.   The low thermal expansion coefficient gives it good thermal shock resistance.   Attack by acids is slow, the hydrogen replacing the sodium forming a hydrated layer at the surface.   **Kimax,** of Owens Illinois, Inc., is this glass, and **Pyrex,** of the Corning Glass Co., has about the same formula.   They are useful for chemical equipment and cooking utensils.   The borosilicates are used as ablatives.   The **Vicor glass** of the latter company is a silica glass made from a soft alkaline glass by leaching in hot acid to remove the alkalies, and then heating to 2000°F to close the pores and shrink the glass.   The glass will withstand continuous temperatures to 1600°F without losing its strength or clarity.   It will withstand temperatures to 1800°F, but becomes cloudy and opaque.   The glass has high thermal shock resistance.   **Filter glass** is flat porous glass sheets or disks to replace high-alloy metals for filtering chemicals.   The filter disks of Ace Glass, Inc., come in five porosities, from A, with pore diameters from 145 to 175 microns, to E, with pore diameters of 4 to 8 microns.

Phosphate glass, developed by the American Optical Co., will resist the action of hydrofluoric acid and fluorine chemicals.   It contains no silica, but is composed of P_2O_5 with some alumina and magnesia.   It is transparent and can be worked like ordinary glass, but it is not resistant to water.   **Fluorex glass,** marketed in rods and tubes by the Haverford Glass Co., is a phosphate glass containing 75% P_2O_5 and less than 0.5 silica.   It is decomposed by alkalies.

Industrial glass is a general name usually meaning any glass molded into shapes for product parts.   The lime glasses are the most generally used because of low cost, ease of molding, and adaptability to fired colors.   For electronic applications, lead glasses are used because of high electrical resistivity and good physical properties.   For such uses as light lenses and condenser cases, the borosilicate heat-resistant glasses may be used.   **Glass flake** is produced by cooling rapidly very thin sheets of glass which shatter into fine flakes 0.0003 in. thick.   It is used for reinforcement in plastics to permit higher filler loadings than with glass fiber.   It also gives higher strength and rigidity, and dielectric strengths as high as 3,000 volts per mil in plastics with 65% glass flake filler.   The flake used as a substitute for mica flake in paints and plastics comes in particles 1 to 4 microns thick and $\frac{1}{32}$ in. in diameter.   In paints it produces a tilelike appearance.   **Carboglas 1600** is a coating material of a chemically resistant polyester solution containing glass flake.   When sprayed, a 0.030-in. coating will contain 120 layers of the thin glass flake.

Filmglas, of the Owens-Corning Corp., is glass flake in tiny platelets. The 10- to 18-mesh flake is 2 microns thick. **Powdered glass,** used as a filler in plastics and coatings, is made by grinding broken scrap glass.

Nucleated glass may be glass of almost any composition treated with a **nucleating agent** to transform the glass into a crystalline material. Nucleation is the first stage of crystal growth, and is the formation of a sufficient number of molecules in a supersaturated solution into aggregates until the tendency for growth is greater than the tendency to lose molecules in the solution. It is controlled by heat and pressure so that the crystal grows from the seed. From 2 to 20% of titanium dioxide may be used in glass for this purpose. **Pyroceram,** of the Corning Glass Works, is a hard, strong, opaque-white nucleated glass with a fine nonporous crystalline structure. It has a flexural strength to above 30,000 psi, a density of 2.4 to 2.62, a softening point at 2460°F, and high thermal shock resistance. It is used for molded mechanical and electrical parts, heat-exchanger tubes, and coatings. **Pyroceram balls,** made by the Hartford-Universal Co., are used to replace steel balls in bearings and valves. They have the hardness of hardened tool steel with only one-third the weight, are corrosion-resistant, have a low coefficient of expansion, and will withstand temperatures to 2200°F. **Nucerite,** used by the Pfaudler Co. for lining tanks, pipes, and valves, is nucleated glass. It has about 4 times the abrasion resistance of a hard glass, will withstand sudden temperature differences of 1200°F, and has high impact resistance. It also has high heat-transfer efficiency. **Cer-Vit,** of Owens Illinois Glass Co., consists of tiny ceramic crystals in a vitreous matrix and is used for molded electronic parts. The thermal expansion can be varied from zero to small positive or negative values. **Glass spheres** and **ceramic spheres** are thin-walled hollow balls of glass or oxide ceramics used as fillers and strengthening agents in plastics and lightweight composites. They act as thermal and sound insulators. They are available in many sizes ranging from fine powder to about 1/4 in. diameter. **Corcel 46,** of Interspace Corp., is a glass-sphere powder of 100 to 325 mesh size used as a filler for aerospace insulation composites. In molding resins for mechanical parts the spheres improve the resin flow in molding and increase the modulus of the molded part. Typical is **Well-Sphere,** of Nichols & Co., which is a nylon with glass sphere filler for high-strength electrical and mechanical parts.

Quartz glass, or pure fused quartz, is entirely transparent to ultraviolet rays, but it is not a glass in the strict sense of the term, and fused quartz must have a special long heat treatment to prevent crystallization. **Flint glass** for windows is a highly transparent soda-lime-quartz glass. **Lustra-glas,** of the American Saint Gobain Corp., is a highly transparent flat-drawn quartz glass. **Window glass** is any highly transparent glass for windows. **Thermopane,** of the Libbey-Owens-Ford Glass Co., is a heat- and sound-insulating window glass made with two panes of glass separated by a metal bonded to the edges of the glass, leaving an insulating layer of dehydrated air between the two glass sheets.   The highly refractive flint glass used in the **rhinestones** for cheap jewelry and for the **paste diamonds,** which derive their name from their softness as compared with the diamond, contains lead.   It has an index of refraction of 1.67, but lacks the double refraction and regular molecular arrangement of true gem crystals.   Lead is also used in the **crystal glass** used for cut glassware, and the brilliance from the lead is higher in the potash glasses than the soda.   **English crystal,** which is a potash glass, contains as high as 33% lead oxide.   It has high clarity and brilliancy, but is soft.   Leaded glasses are heavy, a crystal glass having a specific gravity of 6.33 compared with 2.25 for a borate glass.

The boric oxide glasses, or **borax glasses,** are transparent to ultraviolet rays.   The so-called **invisible glass** is a borax glass surface treated with a thin film of sodium fluoride.   It transmits 99.6% of all visible light rays, thus casting back only slight reflection and giving the impression of invisibility.   Ordinary soda and potash glasses will not transmit ultraviolet light.   Glass containing 2 to 4% ceric oxide absorbs ultraviolet rays, and is also used for X-ray shields.   Glass capable of absorbing high-energy X-rays or gamma rays may contain tungsten phosphate, while the glass used to absorb slow neutrons in atomic-energy work contains cadmium borosilicate with fluorides.   The shields for rocket capsule radio antennas are made of 96% silica glass.   It is transparent to radio signals, and will withstand temperatures above 900°F.   **Fluorescent glass** for mercury-vapor discharge tubes contains ceric oxide.   **Kromex glass** of the MacBeth-Evans Glass Co., used for gasoline dispensing pumps, is a glass made to stop the passage of ultraviolet rays.

Conductive glass, used for windshields to prevent icing and for uses where the conductive coating dissipates static charges, is plate glass with a thin coating of stannic oxide produced by spraying glass, at 900 to 1300°F, with a solution of stannic chloride.   Coating thicknesses are 50 to 550 millimicrons, and will carry current densities of 6 watts per sq in. indefinitely.   The coatings are hard and resistant to solvents.   The light transmission is 70 to 88% that of the original glass, and the index of refraction is 2.0, compared with 1.53 for glass.   **Electrapane,** of the Libbey-Owens-Ford Glass Co., and **Nesa,** of the Pittsburgh Plate Glass Co., are conductive glasses.

Transparent mirrors are made by coating plate glass on one side with a thin film of chromium.   The glass is a reflecting mirror when the light behind the glass is less than in front, and is transparent when the light intensity is higher behind the glass.   **Photosensitive glass** is made by mixing submicroscopic metallic particles in the glass.   When ultraviolet light is passed through the negative on the glass, it precipitates these particles out of solution, and since the shadowed areas of the negative permit deeper penetration into the glass than the highlight areas, the picture is in three dimensions and in color.   The photograph is developed by heating the glass to 1000°F.   **Photochromic glass** becomes dark under ultraviolet light and regains full transparency when the rays are removed. In sunlight rearrangement of the oxides forms dark spots that impede the light rays.

Metal salts are used in glass for coloring as well as controlling the characteristics.   Manganese oxide is added to most glass to neutralize iron oxide, but an excess colors the glass violet to black.   **Jena blue glass** gets its color and fluorescence from a mixture of cobalt oxide and ceric oxide. **Ruby glass,** of a rich red color, is produced with selenium and cadmium sulfide, or with copper oxide.   It is also produced with **purple of cassius,** or **gold-tin purple,** a brown powder which is a mixture of the yellow **gold chloride** $AuCl_3$ and the dark-brown tin oxide.   **Copper-ruby glass** has a greenish tinge and is suitable for automobile taillights, but signal lens glass is made with selenium, cadmium sulfide, and arsenious oxide which give a distinct ruby color with heat-treatment.   **Amber glass** is made with controlled mixtures of sulfur and iron oxide that give tints varying from pale yellow to ruby amber.   Amber glass is much used for medicine bottles to prevent entry of harmful light rays.   The **actinic glass** used for skylights and factory windows has a yellow tint that softens and diffuses the light and impedes passage of heat rays.   **Neophane glass** is glass containing neodymium oxide which reduces glare and is used in yellow sunglasses, or small amounts may be used in windshield glass.   **Opticolor glass,** of the Chicago Dial Co., containing neodymium oxide, for television tube filters, transmits 90% blue, green, and red light rays, and only 10% of the less desirable yellow rays.   The pictures are bright with improved color contrasts.   **Opalescent glass,** or **opal glass,** used for light shades, table tops, and cosmetic jars, has structures that cause light falling on them to be scattered, and they thus are white or translucent.   They owe their properties to tiny inclusions with different indexes of refraction, such as fluorides, sulfides, or oxides of metals.   **Alabaster glass** has inclusions of larger dimensions in lower numbers per unit than opal glass, and it shows no colors, whereas opalescent glass appears white by reflected light but shows color images through thin sections.   Opal glass may contain lepidolite, which mineral contains various metals.

Monax glass, of the MacBeth-Evans Glass Co., is a white diffusing glass for lamp shades and architectural glass.   **Glass blocks** for translucent units in factory walls are made from types of opalescent glass.   **Insulex,** of the Owens-Illinois Glass Co., is a translucent glass brick of this kind.   **Cellulated glass,** or **foamed glass,** is **expanded glass** in the form of blocks and sheets used for thermal insulation of walls and roofs.   It is made by heating pulverized glass with a gas-forming chemical at the flow temperature of the glass.   The glass expands and forms hollow cells which may comprise up to 90% of the total volume.   The density is usually about 10 lb per cu ft.   It has a compressive strength of 100 psi, a flexural strength of 75 psi, and will retain rigidity to 800°F.   **Low-melting glass,** for encapsulating electronic components, is made by adding selenium, thallium, arsenic, or sulfur to give various melting points from 260 to 660°F. These glasses can be vaporized and condensed as thin films.   Some are insulators, and some are semiconductors, and all are chemical-resistant.

Polarized glass, for polarizing lenses, is made by the American Optical Co. by adding minute crystals of tourmaline or peridote to the molten glass, and stretching the glass while still plastic to bring the axes of the crystals into parallel alignment.   **Florentine glass** does not refer to a mixture but to an ornamental glass made by casting on an embossed bed, or by rolling with a roll upon which the designs are cut.

GLASS FIBER.   The fine flexible fibers made from glass, used for heat and sound insulation, fireproof textiles, acid-resistant fabrics, retainer mats for storage batteries, panel boards, filters, and electrical insulating tape, cloth, and rope.   It is distinct from mineral wool in that it is a glass made to definite formulation with a uniformity not found in mineral wool. Molten glass strings out easily into threadlike strands, and this **spun glass** was early used for ornamental purposes, but the first long fibers of fairly uniform diameter were made in England by spinning ordinary molten glass on revolving drums.   The original fiber was about 0.001 in. in diameter. It was called **glass silk** and **glass wool,** and the loose blankets for insulating purposes were called **navy wool.**   The term navy wool is still used for the insulating blankets faced on both sides with flameproofed fabric, used for duct and pipe insulation and for soundproofing.

Glass fibers are now made by letting the molten glass drop through tiny orifices and blowing with air or steam to attenuate the fibers.   The usual composition is that of a soda-lime glass, but it may be varied for different purposes.   The glasses low in alkali have high electrical resistance, while those of higher alkali are more acid-resistant.   They have very high tensile strengths, up to about 400,000 psi, but the breaking strength of yarns is expressed in pounds for any given yarn.   The **Fiberglas** fibers of the Owens-Corning Fiberglas Co. are made in standard diameters from 0.0002 to 0.008 in.   **Staple glass fiber** is usually from 0.00028 to 0.00038 in., is very flexible and silky, and can be spun and woven on regular textile machines.   **Fiberglas yarns** are marketed in various sizes and twists, in continuous or staple fiber, and with glass compositions varied to suit chemical or electrical requirements.   **Vitron yarn,** of Glass Fibers, Inc., is a plied low-twist yarn for braided insulation for wire.   **Glass sewing thread** has a high twist.   The minimum breaking strength of the 0.014-in. thread is 12 lb.

Fiberglas cloth and **Fiberglas tape** are made in satin, broken twill, and plain weaves, the satin-weave cloth 0.007 in. thick weighing 7 oz per sq yd.   **Lagging cloth** for high-temperature pipe insulation is 20 oz per sq yd.   **Glass insulating sheet,** for electrical insulation, is a tightly woven fabric impregnated with insulating varnish, usually in thicknesses from 0.005 to 0.012 in.   The 0.005-in. sheet has a tensile strength of 110 per inch of width, and a dielectric strength to 1,200 volts per mil.   **Glass fabric** of the Soule Mill for varnishing is .001 in. thick and weighs 0.81 oz per sq yd.

Glass cloth of plain weave of either continuous fiber or staple fiber is much used for laminated plastics.   The usual thicknesses are from 0.002 to 0.023 in. in weights from 1.43 to 14.7 oz per sq yd.   Cloth woven of monofilament fiber in loose rovings to give better penetration of the impregnating resin is also used.   **Glass mat,** composed of fine fibers felted or intertwined in random orientation, is used to make sheets and boards by impregnation and pressure.   **Glasfloss,** of the Glasfloss Corp., is glass mat in thicknesses down to 0.10 in.   **Fluffed glass fibers** are tough twisted glass fibers.   **Textrafluff felt,** of Pittsburgh Plate Glass Co., is made from these fibers compacted without a binder.   For filters and insulation the felt withstands temperatures to 1000°F.   **Chopped glass,** consisting of glass fiber cut to very short lengths, is used as a filler for molded plastics.   The **Vitro-Strand fiber** of Johns-Manville Fiber Glass, Inc., also used as a filler, is short staple, $\frac{1}{64}$ in. long, made by a special process from any type of glass.   Translucent corrugated building sheet, such as **Alysinite** of the Allied Synthetics Co., is usually made of glass fiber mat with a resin binder.   All of these products, including chopped fiber, mat, and fabric preimpregnated with resin, and the finished sheet and board, are sold under a wide variety of trade names.   **Aerorove 4,** of Glass Fibers Products, Inc., are high-strength glass fibers and yarns for structural composites.   The **Fiberglas PF** is glass fiber bonded with a thermosetting resin and preformed for pipe and other insulation coverings.   **Fiberglas block** is also available to withstand temperatures to 600°F.   **Glass filter cloth** is made in twill and satin weaves in various thicknesses and porosities for chemical filtering.   **Glass belting,** for conveyer belts for handling hot and corrosive materials, is made with various resin impregnations.   Many synthetic resins do not adhere well to glass, and the fiber is sized with vinyl chlorosilane or other chemical.

GLASS SAND. Sands employed in glassmaking.   They are all screened, and usually washed to remove fine grains and organic matter.   The grain standards of the American Ceramic Society specify that all should pass through a No. 20 screen, between 40 and 60% should remain on a No. 40 screen, between 30 and 40% should remain on a No. 60 screen, between 10 and 20% on a No. 100 screen, and not more than 5% should pass through a No. 100 screen. Sand for first-quality optical glass should contain 99.8% SiO_2, a maximum of 0.1 Al_2O_3 and 0.02 Fe_2O_3. Third-quality flint glass may contain only 95% SiO_2 and as high as 4 Al_2O_3. Only in the eighth- and ninth-quality amber glasses is the content of Fe_2O_3 permitted to reach 1%. **Potters' sand** is usually a good grade of glass sand of uniform grain employed for packing to keep the ware apart.

GLUCOSE. A syrupy liquid of the composition $CH_2OH(CHOH)_4CHO$, which is a monosaccharide, or single sugar, occurring naturally in fruits and in animal blood, or made by the hydrolysis of starch. It is also produced as a dry white solid by evaporation of the syrup. Glucose is made readily from cornstarch by heating the starch with dilute hydrochloric acid, which is essentially the same process as occurs in the human body. Commercial glucose is made from cornstarch, potato starch, and other starches, but in Japan it is also produced from wood. Glucose is only 70% as sweet as cane sugar and has a slightly different flavor. It is used in confectionery and other foodstuffs, in tobacco and inks to prevent drying, in tanning, as a reducing agent, and for blending with cane sugar and syrups to prevent crystallization on cooling and because it is usually cheaper than sugar. The name glucose is usually avoided by the manufacturers of edible products, because of prejudices against its substitution for sugar, but in reality it is a simple form of sugar easily digested. It is used in medicine as a blood nutrient and to strengthen heart action, and may be harmful only in great excess. When free from starch, it is called **dextrose.** It is also marketed as **corn syrup,** but corn syrup is not usually pure glucose, as it contains some dextrine and maltose. The **maltose,** or **malt sugar,** in the combination has the empirical formula $C_{12}H_{22}O_{11}$. When hydrolyzed in digestion, it breaks down easily to glucose. It is produced from starch by enzyme action. When purified, it is transparent and free of malt flavor. It is not as sweet as the sucrose of cane sugar, but is used in confectionery and as an extender of cane sugar. **Dry corn syrup** is in colorless glasslike flakes. It is made by instantaneous drying and quick cooling of the syrup. **Sweetose,** of the A. E. Staley Mfg. Co., is a crystal-clear enzyme-converted corn syrup used in confectionery to enhance flavor and increase brightness.

Glucose derived from grapes is called **grape sugar.** The glucose in fruits is called **fruit sugar, levulose,** or **fructose.** This is dextroglucose, and when separated out is in colorless needles which melt at 104°C. It is used for intravenous feeding and is absorbed faster than glucose. It is also used in low-calorie foods, and in honey to prevent crystallization. It is normally expensive, but is made synthetically. It can be made from corn and is superior to corn syrup as a sweetening agent. **Isomerose,** of Clinton Corn Processing Co., is a corn syrup that is treated with an enzyme to convert part of the dextrose into fructose. It contains 14% fructose and has double the sweetness of sucrose. **Corn sugar** is also a solid white powder, being glucose with one molecule of water of crystallization. When the refined liquor is cooled, the corn sugar crystallizes in a mother liquor known as **hydrol,** or **corn-sugar molasses.** This molasses is screened and washed off, and marketed for livestock feed. The crystalline monohydrate sugar is known as **cerelose.** **Methyl glucoside,** made from corn glucose, is a white crystalline powder melting at 164°C. It has the composition $C_7H_{13}O_6$, with four esterifiable hydroxyls, and is used in making tall oil esters and alkyd resins. **Ethyl glucoside,** $C_8H_{16}O_6$, is marketed as a colorless syrup in water solution with 80% solids and a specific gravity of 1.272. It is noncrystallizing, and is used as a humectant and plasticizer in adhesives and sizes.

GLUE. A cementing material usually made from impure gelatin from the clippings of animal hides, sinews, horn and hoof pith, from the skins and heads of fish, or from bones. The term **animal glue** is limited to **hide glue, extracted bone glue,** and **green bone glue.** Fish glue is not usually classed with animal glue, nor is casein glue. The vegetable glues are also misnamed, being classed with the mucilages. Synthetic resin glues are more properly classed with adhesive cements. Animal glues are **hot-work glues** which are applied hot and which bind on cooling. Good grades of glue are semitransparent, free from spots and cloudiness, and are not brittle at ordinary temperatures. **Bone glue** is usually light amber in color; the strong hide and sinew glues are light brown. The stiffening quality of glue depends upon the evaporation of water, and it will not bind in cold weather. Glues made from blood, known as **albumin glues,** and from casein are used for some plywood. However, they do not have the strength of the best grades of animal glue, and are not resistant to mold or fungi. **Marine glue** is a glue insoluble in water, made from solutions of rubber or resins, or both. The strong and water-resistant plywoods are now made with synthetic resin adhesives.

Animal glue has been made since ancient times, and is now employed for cementing wood, paper, and paperboard. It will not withstand dampness, but white lead or other material may sometimes be added to make it partly waterproof. Casein glues and other protein glues are more water-resistant. **Soybean glue** is made from soybean cake and is used for plywood. It is marketed dry. It has greater adhesive power than other vegetable glues, or pastes, and is more water-resistant than other vegetable pastes. Hide glue is used in the manufacture of furniture, abrasive papers, and cloth, gummed paper and tape, matches, and print rollers. The bone glues are used either alone or blended in the manufacture of cartons and paper boxes. Green bone glue is used chiefly for gummed paper and tape for cartons. In making bone glue the bones are crushed, the grease extracted by solvents, and the mineral salts removed by dilute hydrochloric acid. The bones are then cooked to extract the glue. Glues are graded according to the quality of the raw material, the method of extraction, and the blend.

There are 16 grades of hide glue and 15 grades of bone glue. Those with high viscosity are usually the best. Most glue is sold in ground form, but also as flake or pearl. Glues for such uses as holding abrasive grains to paper must have flexibility as well as strength, obtained by adding glycerin. The **animal protein colloid** of Swift & Co. is a highly purified bone glue especially adapted for use as an emulsifier, and for sizing, water paints, stiffening, and adhesives. Hoof and horn-pith glue is the same as bone glue, and is inferior to hide glue. **Fish glue** is made from the jelly separated from fish oil, or from solutions of the skins. The best fish glue is made from Russian isinglass. Fish glues do not form gelatin well and are usually made into **liquid glues** for photo mounting, gummed paper, household use, and for use in paints and sizes. The liquid glues are also made by treating other glues with a weak acid. Pungent odors indicate defective glue. The glues made from decomposed materials are weak. Preservatives such as sulfur dioxide or chlorinated phenol may be used. The melting point is usually about 140°F.

GLYCERIN. A colorless, syrupy liquid with a sweet, burning taste, soluble in water and in ethyl alcohol. It is the simplest trihydroxy alcohol, with the composition $C_3H_5(OH)_3$. It has a specific gravity of 1.26, a boiling point at 220°C, and a freezing point at 17°C. It is also called **glycerol,** and was used as a lotion under the name of **sweet oil** for more than a century after its discovery in 1783.

Glycerin occurs as **glycerides,** or combinations of glycerin with fatty acids, in vegetable and animal oils and fats, and is a by-product in the manufacture of soaps and in the fractionation of fats, and is also made synthetically from propylene. Coconut oil yields about 14% glycerin, palm oil 11%, tallow 10%, soybean oil 10%, and fish oils 9%. It does not evaporate easily and has a strong affinity for water, and is used as a moistening agent in products that require to be kept from drying, such as tobacco, cosmetics, foodstuffs, and inks. As it is nontoxic, it is used as a solvent in pharmaceuticals, as an antiseptic in surgical dressings, as an emollient in throat medicines, and in cosmetics. Since a different type of groups can replace any one or all of the three **hydroxyl groups,** (OH), a large number of derivatives can be formed, and it is thus a valuable intermediate chemical, especially in the making of plastics. It is also used as a plasticizer in resins, and to control flexibility in adhesives and coatings. An important use is in nitroglycerin and dynamite. In water solutions the freezing point is lowered, reaching $-60°F$, the lowest point, at 37% of water, and it is thus valuable as an antifreeze. **Glycerogen,** a German substitute made by the hydrogenation of wood hexose, is not pure glycerin, but contains also glycols and other hexyl alcohols.

GOLD. A soft, yellow metal, known since ancient times as a precious metal on which all material trade values are based. It is so chemically inactive that it is found mostly in the native state. It is found widely distributed in all parts of the world. It is employed chiefly for coinage, ornaments, jewelry, and for gilding. Gold is extracted by crushing the ores and catching the metal with quicksilver. About 25% of the gold produced in the United States is placer gold and about 5% is a by-product of the copper industry. The average gold recovered from ore in western United States is 0.2 oz per ton of ore; that in Alaska is 0.044 oz per ton; and the low-grade carbonaceous ore of Nevada contains about 0.3 oz per ton. **Native gold** is usually alloyed with silver, placer gold being the purest. The natural alloy of gold and silver was known as **electrum,** and under the Egyptian name of **Asem** was thought to be an elementary metal until produced as an alloy by the Romans.

Among most civilized nations gold has always been the standard upon which trade values were set, even when gold itself was not used. For more than 25 centuries, until the extensive use of the precious metals for industrial purposes, gold retained a $15\frac{1}{2}$ or 16 to 1 value with silver, the only other metal meeting the tests for a **coinage metal.** These tests are, that it must have an intrinsic value to the people as a whole, as for ornamentation; that it must be readily workable but highly corrosion-resistant and permanent; that, while reasonably scarce, it must be available in all parts of the world and not a monopoly of any nation or group of nations. Thus, the value of gold (and silver) is regulated by law in all countries, and only gold and silver pieces are true coinage, those of other metals being merely **tokens,** and paper money being merely promissory notes.

Gold is the most malleable of the metals, and can be beaten into extremely thin sheets. A gram of gold can be worked into leaf covering 6 sq ft, and only 0.0000033 in. thick, or into a wire 1.5 miles in length. **Cast gold** has a tensile strength of 20,000 psi. The specific gravity is 19.32, and the melting point $1943°F$. It is not attacked by nitric, hydrochloric, or sulfuric acid, but is dissolved by aqua regia, or by a solution of azoimide, and is attacked by sodium and potassium cyanide plus oxygen. The metal does not corrode in the air, only a transparent oxide film forming on the surface. Its reflectivity of ultraviolet and visual light rays is low, but it has high reflectivity of infrared and red rays, and is thus valued for plating some types of reflectors. For radiation-control coatings for spacecraft **gold flake** is used. Gold of 24-carat purity is used in the form of tiny laminar platelets which overlap to form a film. **Gold flake No. 14,** of the Metz Refining Corp., has particles 10 microns in diameter and 0.5 micron thick. The particles of No. 16 are 30 microns in diameter and 1 micron thick. Gold-plated grid wires in electronic tubes give high conductivity and suppress secondary emission. **Gold-gallium** and **gold-antimony** alloys of the J. M. Ney Co., for electronic uses, come in wire as fine as 0.0005 in. diameter, and in sheet as thin as 0.001 in. The maximum content of antimony in workable gold alloys is 0.7%. A gold-gallium alloy with 2.5% gallium has a resistivity of 90 ohms per cir mil ft, and has a tensile strength of 55,000 psi with elongation of 22%. **Gold powder** and **gold sheet,** for soldering semiconductors, are 99.999% pure. The gold wets silicon easily at a temperature of 700°F. Chemically reduced powder is amorphous and comes in particle size from 1 to 8 microns. **Atomized gold powder** has spherical free-flowing particles from 30 to 400 mesh. The "gold" powder used in some paints and plastics is bronze powder. The gold coating on spacecraft for radiation control must be hard for resistance to meteorite particles. The metallizing powder contains up to 20% platinum or palladium with a glass frit.

Because of its softness, gold is almost always alloyed with other metals, usually copper, silver, or nickel, and graded on a basis of degrees of fineness in 1,000 parts, or on the basis of carat gold value, pure gold being 24 carats. **Green gold,** used in making jewelry, is an alloy of gold, silver, and copper, graded from 14 to 18 carats. The 18-carat green gold contains 18 parts gold and 6 silver, with no copper. The 15-carat grade contains 15 parts gold, 8 silver, and 1 copper. The 14-carat grade contains 14 parts gold, $8\frac{1}{4}$ silver, and $1\frac{3}{4}$ copper. **Coinage gold** in the United States is 90% gold and 10 copper. In England it is 91.66% gold and 8.33 copper, and this alloy is called **standard gold.** In Australia 8.33% silver is used instead of the copper, and the **gold-silver alloy** is called **Australian gold.** **Dental gold** is a term for a wide range of wrought and cast alloys with usually from 65 to 90% gold, 5 to 12 silver, and frequently platinum and sometimes palladium. A very small amount of iridium may also be used for hardening. Colors vary from white to yellow, and such alloys are also used for jewelry and for acid-resistant plates. Gold is easily electroplated on other metals from cyanide solutions in controlled thicknesses from 0.000005 to 0.005 in. **Sodium gold cyanide,** used for gold-plating solutions, is a water-soluble yellow powder of the composition $NaAu(CN)_2$, containing 46% gold. **Gold plate** is thus much used for jewelry, ornaments, and for chemical resistance, but the gold is so soft that thin plates wear off easily.   But small amounts of other metals harden the gold and also give a color range from red and pink gold to lemon yellow.   For plating electrical contacts, alloys with 1 to 6% nickel are used.   The hardness of gold doubles with each 2% increase in nickel content, but the electrical resistance increases.   Hard gold plate is a **gold-indium plate.**   The process of the Indium Corp. of America is to plate the gold and indium successively and then alloy by diffusion at 330°F.   Precipitation hardening takes place, giving a hard, wear-resistant coating.

South Africa is the most important producer of gold.   Other important producers are Canada, the United States, and Australia, but gold is produced in 90 other countries.   The ore of gold known as **calaverite,** found in Colorado, California, and west Australia, is a **gold telluride,** $AuTe_2$, occurring in monoclinic crystals, while the variety known as **krennerite** is Au_8Te_{16}, in orthorhombic crystals.   They are found with the **gold-silver telluride** called **sylvanite,** $(AuAg)Te_2$, a silvery-white granular mineral of specific gravity 9.35, and hardness 2.5, easily fusible.

GRANITE. A coarse-grained, igneous rock having an even texture, and consisting largely of quartz and feldspar with often small amounts of mica and other materials.   There are many varieties.   Granite is very hard, compact, and takes a fine polish, showing the beauty of the crystals.   It is the most important building stone, and is also used as an ornamental stone.   An important use is also for large rolls in pulp and paper mills. **Granite surface plates,** for machine-shop layout work, are made in sizes up to 30 by 72 in. and 10 in. thick, ground and highly polished to close accuracy.   It is extremely durable, and since it does not absorb moisture as limestone and sandstone do, it does not weather or crack as these stones do.   The colors are usually reddish, greenish, or gray.   **Rainbow granite** may have a black or dark-green background with pink, yellowish, and reddish mottling, or it may have a pink or lavender background with dark mottling.   The weight is 170 lb per cu ft, the specific gravity 2.72, and the crushing strength is from 23,000 to 32,000 psi.   The most notable granite quarries are in northern New England.   **Mount Airy granite** from North Carolina is light gray in color, and is a **biotite** containing feldspar, quartz, and mica.   It is somewhat lighter in weight and of lower crushing strength than **Maine granite.**   The hard composite igneous rock **diabase,** called **black granite,** is used by the Bahn Granite Surface Plate Co. for making precision parallels for machine-shop work.   **Unakite** is a granite of Virginia and North Carolina with a mosaic of red, green, and other colors. It is used as an ornamental building stone.   **Balfour pink granite** of North Carolina contains 72% silica, 14.1 alumina, 2 soda, 6 potash, 1.2 iron oxide, 0.12 titanium oxide, 0.20 manganese oxide, and 0.36 lime.   The granite known as **pegmatite,** of which there are vast quantities, contains beryllium in the form of beryl as a minor constituent.

GRAPHITE. Also called **plumbago.** It was formerly known as **black lead,** and when first used for pencils was called **Flanders' stone.** A natural variety of elemental carbon having a grayish-black color and a metallic tinge. It occurs in two forms: foliated and amorphous. **Foliated graphite** is used principally for crucibles and lubricants, and amorphous for lead pencils, foundry facings, electric brush carbons, molded parts, and paint pigments. It is infusible, subliming at 6700°F, but oxidizing above 600°C. It is a good conductor of heat and electricity, is resistant to acids and alkalies, and is readily molded. **Molded graphite** is usually made by mixing calcined petroleum coke with a binder of coal-tar pitch, pressing, baking in an inert atmosphere, and then heating to above 3500°F to promote crystal growth. Molded parts increase in strength with increasing temperature up to about 4500°F. The specific gravity of graphite is 2 to 2.5. The hardness is 1 to 2, sometimes less than 1, and it has a decidedly greasy feel. It is a good lubricant, especially when mixed with grease, but the natural graphite contains silica and other abrasive materials so that the artificial graphite is preferred for lubricants.

Natural graphite comes chiefly from Mexico, India, Ceylon, and Malagasy. In the United States it is found in Alabama. It occurs in veins in rocks, and always contains some impurities. The high-grade lump graphite of Ceylon, often preferred for crucibles, is found in closely foliated masses in underground veins in gneiss interbedded with limestone. Graphite is marketed in grades by purity and fineness. No. 1 flake should contain at least 90% graphitic carbon. Mexican **amorphous graphite** contains 80%. The best Malagasy graphite contains 95% carbon, while the powders may be as low as 75%. **Crystalline graphite** and **flake graphite** are synonymous terms for material of high graphite content as distinguished from amorphous. Some natural graphite, useful for paints, contains as little as 35% graphitic carbon, but high-grade graphite, suitable for crucibles and nuclear reactors, is made from low-grade ores containing only 20% carbon by flotation, purification at high heat, and pressing into blocks. Ultrapure graphite, for nuclear reactors, is graphitized at temperatures to 5400°F to free it of silicon, calcium, aluminum, and manganese, and treated with a Freon gas to eliminate boron and vanadium. In general, **artificial graphite** made at high temperatures in the electric furnace is now preferred for most uses because of its purity.

Graphite is used for crucibles, molded parts to resist high heat or corrosive chemicals, electrodes, and as a pigment and a lubricant. Finely ground impure natural graphite was much used for foundry-mold facing, and was called **molding graphite** or **combination lead,** but colloidal graphite in spraying solutions is now used for this purpose. Extremely fine particles of pure artificial graphite, or **colloidal graphite,** will remain in suspension indefinitely, and are marketed in distilled water, oils, or solvents, under trade names. **Mexacote,** of the U.S. Graphite Co., is colloidal graphite powder to be mixed with water for spraying on sand molds. When a solution of colloidal graphite in alcohol is sprayed on machine bearings, the alcohol evaporates to leave a thin coating of graphite as a lubricant. **Prodag,** of Acheson Industries, Inc., is a solution in water for foundry facings. **Dag dispersion 154,** of the same company, is colloidal graphite in ethyl silicate used to produce black coatings on glass. **Dag 440** is **graphite powder** in a silicone resin for use as a resistance coating for continuous temperatures up to 500°F. A 0.002-in. coating has a volume resistivity of 100 ohms per sq in. **Grafita** and **Grafene,** of the U.S. Graphite Co., are grease and oil solutions of colloidal graphite for producing lubricating films. **Acheson 1127,** of Acheson Colloids, is a **release agent** for spraying on molds in aluminum die-casting machines. It is a water solution of graphite powder. It prevents adherence of the metal to the die and also gives better flow of metal because of reduced friction.

For making **lead pencils,** amorphous graphite is mixed with clay and fired, the amount of clay determining the hardness of the pencil. **Flexicolor pencils,** of Koh-I-Noor, Inc., have a plastic binder to give pliable strength to the pencil. **Poco Graphite,** of the Pure Oil Co., is a graphite powder with maximum particle size of 0.001 in. used for molded parts. The parts have a smooth surface and a tensile strength to 6,000 psi. **Graphite carbon raiser** is a term given to graphite powder used for adding to molten steel to raise the carbon content. Molded **graphite brushes** for motors and generators may have metal powders mixed with the graphite to regulate the conductivity or may be molded from carbon-graphite powder especially heat-treated. **Graphited metals,** used for bearings and bushings, are made by molding metal powders with graphite and sintering, and may contain up to about 45% graphite evenly dispersed in the metal matrix to act as a lubricant. Or powdered oxides of the metals may be used, and these oxides are reduced in the sintering to give greater porosity for oil retention. The **Genelite,** of the General Electric Co., is a porous **graphited bronze** made with oxides of copper, tin, and lead, with graphite powder. It will absorb about 20% by volume of oil. It has a compressive strength of 50,000 psi, and a tensile strength of 8,000 psi. **Durex bronze,** of the General Motors Corp., made by reducing the oxides with graphite under pressure, will take up 29% by volume of oil. Graphited metals, with the matrix of bronze or of babbitt, are marketed in the forms of rods and bushings under a variety of trade names such as **Gramix,** of the U.S. Graphite Co., **Graphex,** of the Wakefield Bearing Corp., and **Ledaloyl,** of the

Johnson Bronze Co. **Iron-bonded graphite,** developed by the Ford Motor Co. for oilless bearings, is made by powder metallurgy with a content of 40 to 90% graphite and the balance iron powder and a calcium-silicon powder. The calcium-silicon overcomes the normal low compatibility of the iron and graphite, resulting in a strong, nonbrittle material.

The **supergraphite,** of the National Carbon Co., used for rocket casings and other heat-resistant parts, is recrystallized molded graphite. It will withstand temperatures to 5500°F. **Pyrolytic graphite,** developed by the General Electric Co., is an oriented graphite. It has high density, with a specific gravity of 2.22, has exceptionally high heat conductivity along the surface, making it very flame-resistant, is impermeable to gases, and will withstand temperatures to 6700°F. It is made by deposition of carbon from a stream of methane on heated graphite, and the growing crystals form with thin planes parallel to the existing surface. The structure consists of close-packed columns of graphite crystals joined to each other by strong bonds along the flat planes, but with weak bonds between layers. This weak and strong electron bonding is characteristic of a semimetal, giving the laminal structure. The material conducts heat and electricity many times faster along the surface than through the material. The flexural strength is 25,000 psi, compared with less than 8,000 for the best conventional graphite. At 5000°F the tensile strength is 40,000 psi. Sheets as thin as 0.001 in. are impervious to liquids or gases. It is used for nozzle inserts and reentry parts for spacecraft. **Boron Pyralloy,** of High Temperature Materials, Inc., for atomic shielding, is this material with an addition of boron.

GRAVEL. A natural material composed of small, usually smooth, rounded stones or **pebbles.** It is distinguished from sand by the size of the grain, which is usually above ¼ in., but gravel may contain large stones up to 3 in. in diameter, and some sand. It will also contain pieces of shale, sandstone, and other rock materials. Gravel is used in making concrete for construction, and as a loose paving material. Commercial gravel is washed to remove the clay and organic matter, and screened. **Pea gravel** is screened gravel between ¼ and ½ in. in diameter. It is used for surfacing with asphalt, or for roofing. Gravel is sold by the cubic yard or by the ton, and is shipped by weight. **Bank-run gravel,** with both large and small material, weighs about 3,000 lb per cu yd.

GREENHEART. The wood of the tree *Octotea rodioei* of Guyana, especially valued for shipbuilding, dock timbers, planking, and lock gates because of its resistance to fungi and termites. It also goes under the name of **Demerara greenheart,** and under its native name of **bibiru.** The tree grows to a height of 120 ft, with diameter of 2 to 3 ft, clear of branches for 50 to 70 ft.   The wood is very strong and hard with good wearing qualities.   The average weight is 62 lb per cu ft with 12% moisture.   The specific gravity, oven-dried, is 0.80.   The heartwood is light olive to nearly black, and the sapwood pale yellow to greenish.

Surinam greenheart is the wood **bethabara,** from the tree *Tecoma leucoxylon* of Surinam and French Guiana.   It is distinguished from greenheart by the yellow deposits in the pores, and is not as resistant as greenheart.   **Manbarklak,** the wood of the tree *Eschweilera corrugata,* of Surinam, is reddish brown in color, weighs 76 lb per cu ft, is equal to greenheart for marine construction, but is scarcer.   **Angelique,** the wood of the tree *Dicorynia paraensis* of the Guianas and lower Amazon, is very resistant to fungi and insect attack, and is used as a substitute for greenheart in marine construction.   It is hard but not as heavy as greenheart, weighing 50 lb per cu ft.   It has an olive-brown color with reddish patches. **African greenheart** is **dahoma,** the wood of the large tree *Piptadena africana* of the west coast of Africa.   It is yellowish brown in color, weighs 50 lb per cut ft, but is not as resistant to marine borers as greenheart.   The wood of a species of tonka bean tree of Panama, known as **almendro,** *Coumarouna panamensis,* is very resistant to marine borers and is used as a substitute for greenheart.   It is yellowish brown in color and is very heavy.   The almondlike seeds of the tree are used as a food.

GRINDING PEBBLES.   Hard and tough rounded small stones, usually of flint, employed in cylindrical mills for grinding ores, minerals, and cement. Pebbles from Greenland, marketed usually through Denmark and known as **Danish pebbles,** are of great hardness and toughness.   Newfoundland also supplies these pebbles.   Quantities of **flint pebbles** also come from Denmark for use in tube mills.   They are smooth, round pebbles formed by the washing of the sea on the chalk cliffs, and come from the islands off the Danish coast.   Danish pebbles are graded in seven sizes, according to French standards from No. 0 which is 30 to 40 mm ($1\frac{1}{2}$ to $1\frac{3}{4}$ in.) to size E which is 100 to 130 mm (4 to 5 in.).   Small pebbles, $\frac{1}{2}$ in. in diameter, are used for polishing iron castings by tumbling.   American grinding pebbles are chiefly from Minnesota, Ohio, Nevada, and from the beaches of California.   **Quartzite pebbles** are produced in Nova Scotia and Saskatchewan.   **Quartz pebbles** from Alabama are 99% silica and low in iron, but they do not wear as well as true flint pebbles.   Granite, rhyolite, and andesite pebbles are also used for grinding.   The **granite pebbles** produced in North Carolina from feldspar or other mineral processing are broken into cubes and wet-milled to remove the edges and corners.   They are graded in sizes from $1\frac{1}{2}$ to 5 in.   Because of greater uniformity of size and hardness, manufactured abrasive materials are now generally preferred to natural pebbles.

The **tumbling abrasives,** for use in tumbling barrels, come in aluminum oxide or silicon carbide preformed balls, cubes, triangles, or cylinders of various sizes to conform to the parts being tumble-polished. Typical are the aluminum oxide balls, $\frac{3}{4}$ to 2 in. diameter, pressed to a uniform density and marketed under the name of **Starrlum** by the American Refractories & Crucible Corp. **Porcelain grinding balls** are made of high-grade resistant porcelain, and are marketed in stock sizes for grinding and polishing. They have the advantage over flint pebbles of greater uniformity. The material is dense, and is 80% heavier and 50% harder than flint.

GRINDSTONES. Sandstones employed for grinding purposes. Grindstones are generally employed for the sharpening of edged tools, and do not compete with the hard emery, aluminum oxide, and silicon carbide abrasive wheels which are run at high speeds for rapid cutting. Grindstones are quarried from the sandstone deposits and made into wheels usually ranging from 1 to about 6 ft in diameter, and up to 16 in. in thickness. They are always operated at low speeds because of their inability to withstand high centrifugal stresses. The grades vary from coarse to fine. Good grindstones have sharp grains, without an excess of cementing material that will cause the stone to glaze in grinding. The texture must also be uniform so that the wheel will wear evenly. The hard silica grains are naturally cemented together by limonite, clay, calcite, quartz, or mixtures. Too much clay causes crumbling, while too much calcite results in disintegration in the atmosphere. An excess of silica results in a stone that is too hard.

GUAIACUM OIL. An essential oil distilled from the wood of the guayacan tree of Paraguay, used in medicine, soaps, and perfumes. It is light gray in color, and is solid at temperatures below 45°C. The odor is that of a combination of tea leaves and roses. It is also called **guaiacwood oil.** The wood yields 5 to 6% of the oil. **Guaiac gum,** also called **guaiacum,** is gum resin of the true lignum vitae trees for use in varnishes, as a chemical indicator, and to prevent rancidity and loss of flavor in preserved and dehydrated foods. It is an effective antioxidant, although its chief use is in medicine as a stimulant and laxative. The resin comes in greenish-brown tears. **Azulene** is a blue dye extracted from guaiacum oil, from eucalyptus oil, and from some balsams. The azulenes derive names from the source, as **guaiazulene,** but they all have the empirical formula $C_{15}H_{18}$, the molecule having two rings and five double bonds. The synthetic material is known as **vetivazulene.** It comes in cobalt-blue crystals melting at 90°C.

GUANIDINE NITRATE. A white granular powder of the composition $(H_2N \cdot CNH \cdot NH_2) \cdot HNO_3$, produced from cyanamide and ammonium nitrate, and employed in making flashless propellants and pharmaceuticals, for coating blueprint paper to speed up development time, and in photographic fixing baths. It melts at 206 to 212°C and is strongly acid. **Guanidine carbonate** is a white nonhygroscopic granular powder of the composition $(H_2N \cdot CNH \cdot NH_2)_2 \cdot H_2CO_3$. It decomposes at 198°C. It is soluble in water, and has an alkaline reaction. Guanidine carbonate is used in the manufacture of pharmaceuticals, as an emulsifier in soaps, and in photographic developing solutions. Other derivatives of guanidine, such as **diphenyl guanidine,** are used as plasticizers and accelerators for rubber.

Guanidine, also called **carbamidene,** is a white crystalline hygroscopic powder of the composition $HN=C(NH_2)_2$, produced from ammonium thiocyanate, chloropicrin, or cyanogen chloride for use in plastics, pharmaceuticals, and other chemicals. It is a strong base and forms salts with acids even as weak as carbonic. It is classified generally with the single-carbon group of chemicals based on **cyanogen,** $N \vdots CC \vdots N$, which itself is a poisonous colorless gas. The chemistry of this vast interrelated group is highly complex, including urea and the amino acids, and the **purines** which are the basic cyclic organic compounds of which **uric acid** is the best known. The purines also include caffeine and **xanthine,** found in plants, and **guanine,** found in guano and in the fish scales used for imitation pearl. **Kelzan,** of the Kelco Co., used as a thickening and stabilizing agent, is synthetic **Xantham gum** made by fermentation of glucose. It is nontoxic and soluble in water. Xantham gum is a polysaccharide of **xanthic acid** occurring in many plants.

GUAVA. The fruit of the tree *Psidium guajava* of the myrtle family to which the clove, allspice, and eucalyptus belong. Because of its content of acids, sugars, pectin, and vitamins, it is valued in the food industries for blending in jellies, preserves, and beverages. The pulp is also used in ice-cream manufacture. Vast quantities of guava are used for hard jellies in Latin America. The fruit has more than 10 times the vitamin C content of the orange and retains it better. It also contains vitamins A and B_1 and 11.6% carbohydrates. The tree is native to America from Mexico to Peru and is also grown extensively in Brazil and the West Indies. It was one of the original Aztecan and Incan fruits, and is still known under the Carib name of **guayaba** in Brazil and Argentina. There are about 150 varieties, and the large seedy fruit has a fragrant aroma and distinctive sweet flavor.

GUAYULE. A perennial plant, *Parthenium argentatum,* of the *Compositae* family, grown in the semiarid regions of northern Mexico and southern California as a source of rubber. The plants are hardy woody shrubs that mature into the highest rubber content in 7 years.   They contain in the dry state up to 22% guayule rubber, in all parts except the leaves.   The plant is uprooted in 3 to 5 years and is crushed and pulverized in mills, and the rubber extracted by flotation.   The guayule rubber contains from 20 to 25% resin so that it is suitable only for blending or for cements unless deresinated.   Natural crude guayule is softer than hevea rubber, owing to the content of natural resins which act as plasticizers.   In the low-sulfur compounds it remains permanently tacky, and is thus valued for use as a coating adhesive for the permanently tacky binding tape known as **Scotch tape.**   When deresinated by extraction of the resin with acetone or other solvent, the rubber is suitable for all the uses of hevea rubber.   The by-product **guayule resin** is used in plastics.   From 400 to 1,000 lb of rubber are produced per acre under cultivation.

GUM.   The wood of the tree *Liquidambar styraciflua,* of the United States and Mexico.   It is also called **red gum** and **sweet gum.**   In England it is known as **California red gum** although the gumwood of California is from a eucalyptus tree.   In Europe, also, the term **satin walnut** is used for the heartwood and **hazel pine** for the sapwood.   Gum has a reddish-brown color, is soft with a fine, close grain, and weighs about 40 lb per cu ft.   It is used for furniture, veneer, inside trim, cooperage, and the making of pulp for book paper.   The timber is cut mostly in the southern states, especially in Louisiana, Mississippi, and Arkansas.   The trees have a height 80 to 100 ft and average $1\frac{1}{2}$ to 3 ft in diameter with a straight clear trunk.   Red gum is from the heartwood of mature trees and is reddish brown.   **Sap gum** comes from the outer portion of logs or from young trees and is white tinged with pink.   Nearly 25% of all the hardwood used in the United States is red gum.   It has an interlocking grain which gives a fine appearance in veneers, but has a tendency to warp.

Gum is graded according to standards of the National Hardwood Lumber Association from firsts through selects to No. 3B common. Local names for red gum are **southern gum, sycamore gum, bilsted,** and **star-leafed gum.**   **Cotton gum,** or **tupelo,** of Louisiana, is from the tree *Nyssa aquatica.*   It is also known as **water tupelo, tupelo gum, swamp gum, sour gum.**   **Black gum,** or **black tupelo,** also of the southern states is *N. sylvatica.*   **Swamp tupelo,** also called **water gum** and **swamp black gum,** is from the tree *N. biflora.*   **Ogeche tupelo** is from the tree *N. ogecha,* and is not common.   It is also called **gopher plum, wild limetree,** and **sour tupelo.**   Black tupelo grows from New Hampshire to central Texas, but water tupelo is found chiefly along the coasts and river valleys of the South.   The shipments of woods are usually mixed.   Tupelo woods from the various species of *Nyssa* are fine-textured but with large pores. The heartwood is brownish gray and the sapwood is grayish white.   They are tough and difficult to split, having an interlocking grain, and find wide use for such articles as mallets, toilet seats, furniture, and bottle cases.

GUM ARABIC. Also called **acacia gum.** The gum exudation of the small tree *Acacia arabica,* and various other species of acacia trees of Africa. **Kordofan gum,** or **hashab gum,** is a variety from the Red Sea area and forms the chief export of the Sudan. It is obtained by tapping the wild tree *A. verek,* and is of high quality. **Sennaar gum** is gum arabic exported from Arabian ports on the Red Sea. **Gum senegal,** from the *A. senegal,* comes from the dry regions of northwest Africa. **Gum talha, talco gum,** or **talh gum,** is a brittle and low grade of gum arabic from the North African acacia, *A. stenocarpa.* Gum arabic is used for adhesives, for thickening inks, in textile coatings, and in drug and cosmetic emulsions. As a binder in pharmaceutical tablets the powder acts as a **disintegrating agent** to make the tablets easily soluble in water. In confectionery glazes it prevents crystallization of the sugar.

To obtain the gum the trees are wounded and the sap allowed to run out, forming in yellowish, transparent lumps. It is also marketed as a white powder of 120 mesh, soluble in water, but insoluble in alcohol. Gum arabic is a mixture of calcium, magnesium, and potassium salts of **arabic acid,** in a complex of the saccharides **arabinose, galactose, rhamnose** or **manno methylose,** and the open-chain **glucuronic acid.** It has a molecular weight of 240,000, and an acid reaction. For drug uses gums are selected, blended, and ground to a powder of uniform characteristics. **Arabasan,** of the Tetroid Co., Inc., is a spray-dried blended gum of this kind. It is a white powder, colorless in solution. **Larch gum,** or **galactan gum,** leached from chips of the western larch, is a copolymer of arabinose and galactose and is very similar to gum arabic. **Stractan,** of Stein Hall and Co., is this material in white powder form. It is used as a stabilizer and binder in coatings, adhesives, pharmaceuticals, and in low-calorie foodstuffs. **Tamarind seed gum** is from the pod beans of the Tamarind tree, *Tamarindus indica,* of India. It is a white to tan, water-soluble powder used as a low-cost alternate for gum arabic. It is a polysaccharide but differs from arabic chemically by containing 12% tartaric acid and 30% sugars. It is used also in medicine and for beverages under the name of tamarind.

Various synthetic water-soluble gums and emulsifiers are now used as replacements for gum arabic in drugs, cosmetics, adhesives, and foodstuffs. The **Bemul** of the Beacon Co. is a glyceryl monostearate, soluble also in alcohol. The water-soluble **Kelzan gum** of the Kelco Co. is made from glucose. The wood of the gum arabic tree is the **satinwood** of the Near East, valued since ancient times for its great durability. It is light in weight, hard, close-grained, and has an orange-brown color that darkens with age.   But the satinwood of Brazil, known also as **setim,** is a yellow-wood from the large tree *Aspidosperma eburneum,* used for inlays.

GUMWOOD. The wood of several species of **eucalyptus** trees native to Australia and Tasmania, but now grown in many parts of the world.   The wood is used in construction and for inferior furniture.   The wood known as gum in southern United States is from the tupelo and species of *Liquidambar.*   The **blue gum** is *Eucalyptus globulus,* which attains a height of 300 ft and is grown on the West Coast of the United States.   The wood has a pale straw color and is hard and tough.   It has a twisted grain, shrinks and warps easily, but is very durable.   The weight is about 50 lb per cu ft, being heavier than southern gum.   **Salmon gum,** from *E. salmonophloria,* has a salmon-red color, is dense and hard, and has a fine, open grain.   It is superior and has a great variety of uses.   The weight is about 60 lb per cu ft.   **Red gum,** from *E. calophylla,* has a yellowish-red color, is strong, tough, and weighs about 45 lb per cu ft.   The grain is fine, but has gum veins intersecting.   Other species of gumwood are marketed under the names of **York gum, blackbutt, tuart,** and **Australian red mahogany.**   **Jarrah,** from the *E. marginata,* and **ironbark,** from the *E. paniculata,* are hardwoods commonly used for flooring and cabinet-work.   They have a reddish color, an interlocking grain, are very hard, and weigh about 55 lb per cu ft.   **Karri,** from *E. diversicolor,* is quite similar to jarrah.   The **wandoo tree,** *E. redunca,* of Western Australia, the wood of which is known as **redunca wood,** has a high percentage of pyrogallol tannin.   The solid extract is called **myrtan,** and it produces a solid, firm sole leather lighter in color than that from chestnut.   The wood of the *E. saligna,* of South Africa, is hard, and has a fine, even, interlocking grain which makes it strong in all directions.   It is used in the United States for small turned articles, saw handles, and paintbrush handles.   It has a reddish tinge.   **Blackbutt** is from the trees *E. pilularis, E. patens,* and some other species native to Australia, but now grown in other countries. It is used as a substitute for oak, but tends to warp and crack.

   Eucalyptus oil, obtained from the dried leaves of the *E. globulus,* is used in pharmaceuticals for nose and throat treatment.   It is the source of **cineole,** also called **eucalyptole.**   From 3 to 4% oil is obtained from the leaves.   It is a pungent yellowish oil.   This type of eucalyptus oil contains **phellandrine** used in Australia as an antiknock agent in gasoline.   **Eucalyptus dives oil,** from the leaves of the Australian tree *E. dives,* contains 92 to 94% **piperitone,** and is used in the manufacture of menthol.   The yield is about 50% **levo menthol** with a melting point of 33 to 35°C.   It lacks the odor of USP menthol of which only 15% can be produced from this oil.   Much eucalyptus oil is produced in Chile.   More than 300 species of eucalyptus trees are known, and each produces a different type of oil.

GUNMETAL. The name for a casting bronze containing 88% copper, 10 tin, and 2 zinc. It was originally used for small cannon but is now used where the golden color and strong noncrystalline structure are desired. It casts and machines well, and is suitable for making steam and hydraulic castings, valves, and gears. It has a tensile strength of 32,000 to 45,000 psi, with elongation 15 to 30%. The specific gravity is 8.7, weight 0.315 lb per cu in., and Brinell hardness 65 to 74. This alloy is the same as the **G bronze** of the U.S. Navy. In England it is called **admiralty gunmetal,** and is specified as **BES No. 383** for sand castings. **Gunmetal ingot,** of H. Kramer & Co., may have the zinc replaced by 2% lead. Such an alloy is easier to machine but has less strength. **Modified gunmetal** contains lead in addition to the zinc. It is used for gears and for bearings. A typical modified gunmetal by William H. Barr, Inc., contains 86% copper, 9.5 tin, 2.5 lead, and 2 zinc. It has a tensile strength up to 40,000 psi, elongation 15 to 25%, Brinell hardness 63 to 72, and weight 0.31 lb per cu in.

GUNPOWDER. Also known as **black powder.** An explosive extensively used for blasting purposes and for fireworks. It was introduced into Europe prior to 1250, and was the only propellant used in guns until 1870. It is now superseded for military uses by high explosives. Black powder deteriorates easily in the air from the absorption of moisture. It is a mechanical mixture of potassium nitrate, charcoal, and sulfur, in the usual proportions of 75, 15, and 10. More saltpeter increases the rate of burning; additional charcoal decreases the rate. A slow-burning powder for fireworks rockets may have only 54% saltpeter and 32 charcoal. Commercial black powder comes in grains of graded sizes and is glazed with graphite. The grain sizes are known as **pebble powder,** large-grain, fine-grain, **sporting powder, mining powder, Spanish spherical powder,** and **cocoa powder.** The potential energy of gunpowder is estimated at 500 ft-tons per lb, but the actual gun efficiency is less than 10% of this. A temperature of about 2100°C is produced by the explosive. Gunpowder is the slowest-acting of all the explosives, and has a heaving, not a shattering effect. Hence, it is effective for blasting and breaking up stone. **Blasting powder** is divided by Du Pont into two grades: A and B. The **A powder** contains saltpeter; the **B powder** contains nitrate of soda. The other ingredients are the usual sulfur and charcoal. B powder is not so strong or water-resistant as A powder, but is cheaper and is extensively used. **Pellet powder** is blasting powder made up in cylindrical cartridges for easier use in mining. **White gunpowder** is a powder in which the saltpeter is replaced by potassium chlorate. It is very sensitive and explodes with violence. It is used only for percussion caps and for fireworks. **Lesmok powder,** used in 22-caliber cartridges, is composed of 15% black powder and 85 nitrocellulose.

GURJUN BALSAM. Also known as **wood oil,** and sometimes called **East Indian copaiba.** An oleoresin obtained from various species of the *Dipterocarpus* tree, about 50 varieties of which grow in India, Burma, Ceylon, and the Malay Peninsula. It is a clear liquid with a greenish fluorescence. The specific gravity is 0.955 to 0.965. It is soluble in benzene. Gurjun balsam is used in lacquers and varnishes that are capable of resisting elevated temperatures. The Burmese trees form two groups yielding products known as kanyin and in. **Kanyin oils** are brown in color, while the **In oils** are whitish and heavier. Gurjun balsam may consist of either or both of these products. Commercial **gurjun oil** is obtained by steam distillation of the balsam, and has a specific gravity of 0.900 to 0.930. It is soluble in alcohol. **Copaiba balsam** is a resin obtained from the **copaifera tree,** a species of *Dipterocarpus,* of South America. **Maracaibo copaiba** and **Pará copaiba** are the principal varieties. They are dark yellow or brown in color, and are soluble in alcohol. The resin is used as a plasticizer, in varnishes, tracing paper, and in pharmacy. The specific gravity is 0.940 to 0.990.

GUTTA PERCHA. A gum obtained by boiling the sap of species of trees of the order *Sapotaceae,* chiefly *Palaquium gutta* and *P. oblongifolia,* native to Borneo, New Guinea, and Malaya. It is grayish white, very pliable, but not elastic like rubber. It is harder and a better insulator than rubber. Gutta percha, like rubber, will vulcanize with sulfur and form a hard material. It is used for mixing with rubber, but its chief use was in the covering of electric cables. It has a greater pliability than rubber for the given hardness required in cable insulation. This property with its greater resistance to water makes it valuable for golf balls and dental fillings. It molds easily at 180°F. It is also employed like balata for impregnating driving belts, and for washers and valve seats, and in adhesives. Gutta percha is often imported as mixtures with inferior guttas from other trees. **Gutta soh,** for example, is a mixture from Singapore often colored ied artificially. **Gutta siak** is a low-grade gutta from Sumatra. It has a reddish color, and is lightly elastic. **Gutta sundik** is from the tree *Payena leerii* of Malaya and Indonesia. It is white in color, and is mixed with gutta percha. Another gutta used to adulterate gutta percha is **gutta hangkang,** from the *Palaquium leiocarpum* of Borneo. It is slightly reddish. **Gutta jangkar** is a low-grade red gutta from Sarawak. **Gutta susu** of Indonesia is a gray-colored material, slightly elastic. With increasing use of synthetic resin insulating materials gutta percha has become of only secondary importance.

GYPSUM. A widely distributed mineral which is a hydrated **calcium sulfate,** $CaSO_4 \cdot 2H_2O$, used for making building plaster, wallboard, tiles, as an absorbent for chemicals, as a paint pigment and extender, and for coating papers. Natural gypsum of California, containing 15 to 20% sulfur, is used for producing ammonium sulfate for fertilizer. Gypsum is also used to make sulfuric acid by heating to 2000°F in an air-limited furnace. The resultant calcium sulfide is reacted to yield lime and sulfuric acid. Raw gypsum is also used to mix with portland cement to retard the set. Compact massive types of the mineral are used as building stones. The color is naturally white, but it may be colored by impurities to gray, brown, or red. The specific gravity is 2.28 to 2.33, and the hardness 1.5 to 2. It dehydrates when heated to about 190°C, forming the hemihydrate $2CaSO_4 \cdot H_2O$, which is the basis of most gypsum plasters. It is called **calcined gypsum,** or when used for making ornaments or casts is called **plaster of paris.** When mixed with water, it again forms the hydrated sulfate that will solidify and set firmly owing to interlocking crystallization. Theoretically, 18% of water is needed for mixing, but actually more is necessary. Insufficient water causes cracking. Water solutions of synthetic resins are mixed with gypsum for casting strong waterproof articles. **Palestic,** of the Palestic Corp., is gypsum mixed with a urea-formaldehyde resin and a catalyst. It expands slightly on hardening, and thus gives a good impression of the mold. The tensile strength of the molded material is 1,100 psi, and the compressive strength is 12,000 psi.

Calcium sulfate without any water of crystallization is used for paper filler under the name of **pearl filler,** but is not as white as the hydrated calcium sulfate called **crown filler.** The paint pigment known as **satin spar** is a fibrous, silky variety of gypsum, and is distinct from the pigment called **satin white,** made by precipitation of aluminum sulfate with lime. **Terra alba** is an old name for ground gypsum as a paint filler. The anhydrous calcium sulfate in powder and granular forms will absorb 12 to 14% of its weight of water, and is used as a drying agent for gases and chemicals. It can then be regenerated for reuse by heating. **Drierite,** of the W. A. Hammond Drierite Co., is this material. The mineral mined at Billingham, England, as **anhydrite,** is **anhydrous calcium sulfate.** It is used for producing sulfur, sulfur dioxide, and ammonium sulfate. The **Hydrocal** of the U.S. Gypsum Co., used as a filler for paints and plastics, is $CaSO_4 \cdot \frac{1}{2}H_2O$. Much calcined gypsum, or plaster of paris, is used as **gypsum plaster** for wall finish. For such use it may be mixed in lime water or glue water, and with sand. Because of its solubility in water it cannot be used for outside work. **Neat plaster,** for walls, is the plaster without sand. When the term **plaster** alone is used, it generally refers to gypsum plasters, but the **calcium plaster** made from spent fuller's earth has greater workability and better water resistance than gypsum plaster.

Plaster board, or **gypsum wallboard,** consists of sheets or slabs of gypsum mixed with up to 15% of fibers, employed as a fire-resistant material for walls, ceilings, or partitions, but most of the **wallboard** used in dwelling houses is gypsum board faced on both sides and edged with paper. It usually comes ½ in. thick, 4 by 8 ft, weighing 2 lb per sq ft. **Macoustic,** of the National Gypsum Co., is a lightweight gypsum acoustical plaster. **Grain board** is a fireproof gypsum board with an imitation wood-grain surface used for walls. The hard-finish plasters for **flooring plaster** may contain alum or other materials. **Scott's cement** is a plaster made by grinding lime with calcined gypsum. It sets rapidly. **Mack's cement** is a hard cement made of dehydrated gypsum to which is added a small percentage of calcined sodium sulfate and potassium sulfate. It sets quickly and has good adhesion. It is used for walls, and for floors when mixed with sand.

Patterns, models, and molds of plaster of paris have their strength raised and are made water-resistant by impregnating the dried and hardened plaster with a synthetic resin, particularly the furane resins which cure at low temperatures without pressure. The ordinary casting plaster of 100 parts solids and 60 parts water, called **hydrocal,** is slightly acid, and must be treated with an acid-catalyzing resin, while the low-expansion plaster of 100 parts solids and 45 water, called **hydrostone,** is alkaline and is treated with alkaline-catalyzed resin. Impregnation of plaster-of-paris castings with resin raises the compressive strength from 2,000 up to 9,000 psi, and the flexural strength from 700 to 3,500 psi. Special liquid resins are marketed for this purpose. The **Plaspreg** of Furane Plastics, Inc., is a furane solution to which a catalyst is added before use.

A crystalline variety of gypsum, known as **selenite,** occurs in transparent crystals and usually splits in thin laminations. A fine-grained, marble-like variety, called **alabaster,** is employed in ornamental building work, and for lamps, vases, and novelties. Much alabaster is produced in Colorado. **Travertine,** which resembles alabaster but is grained like wood, is a water-deposited calcium carbonate. The **Italian travertine** is notable as a decorative building stone, but is also found in Georgia, Montana, and California. It is an ancient building material, and the great Coliseum at Rome was built of this stone.

HAFNIUM. An elementary metal, symbol Hf. It occurs in nature in about the same amount as copper, but is sparsely disseminated and is costly to extract. All zirconium minerals contain some hafnium, but the two metals are so similar chemically that separation is difficult. All zirconium chemicals and alloys may contain some hafnium, and hafnium metal usually contains about 2% zirconium.   The melting point is higher than that of zirconium, about 4000°F, and heat-resistant parts for special purposes have been made by compacting hafnium powder to a density of 98%. The metal has a close-packed hexagonal structure.   The electrical conductivity is about 6% that of copper.

Hafnium oxide, or **hafnia,** HfO_2, is a better refractory ceramic than zirconia, but is costly.   The inversion of the crystal from the monoclinic to the tetragonal occurs at 3100°F with an expansion of only 3.4%, compared with 2000°F and an expansion of 7.5% in zirconia.   **Hafnium carbide,** HfC, produced by reacting hafnium oxide and carbon at high temperature, is obtained as a loosely coherent mass of blue-black crystals. The crystals have a hardness of 2910 Vickers, and a melting point of 4160°C.   It is thus one of the most refractory materials known.   **Heat-resistant ceramics** are made from **hafnium titanate** by pressing and sintering the powder.   The material has the general composition $x(TiO_2) \cdot n(HfO_2)$, with varying values of x and n.   Parts made with 18% titania and 82% hafnia have a density of 0.26 lb per cu in., a melting point at about 4000°F, a low coefficient of thermal expansion, good shock resistance, and a rupture strength above 10,000 psi at 2000°F.

HAIR. The fibrous covering of the skins of various animals, used for making coarse fabrics and for stuffing purposes.   It is distinguished from wool in having no epidermal scales.   It cannot be spun readily, although certain hairs, such as camel hair, are noted for great softness and can be made into fine fabrics.   **Horsehair** is from the manes and tails, and is used as a brush fiber and for making haircloth.   It is largely imported from China and Argentina, cleaned and sorted.   The imported hair from live animals is more resilient than domestic hair from dead animals. **Brush hair** is usually cut to 3 to $5\frac{1}{2}$ in. long, but tail hair for making **curled hair** for weaving comes in lengths up to 30 in.   **Cattle hair** is taken from slaughtered animals in packing plants.   The body hair is used as a binder in plaster and cements, for hair felt, and for stuffing. The tail hair is used for upholstery, filter cloth, and stuffing.   The **ear hair** is used for brushes.   It has a strong body and a fine tapered point suitable for poster brushes.   In the brush industry it is known as **ox hair. Camox** is a mixture of squirrel hair and ox hair to combine the fineness of squirrel hair with the springiness of ox hair for one-stroke brushes and flowing brushes.

Artificial horsehair, or **monofil,** was a single-filament cellulose-acetate fiber, used for braids, laces, hair nets, rugs, and pile fabrics.   **Crinex** is a German artificial horsehair made of cuproammonium filament and used as a brush fiber.   **Haircloth** is a stiff, wiry fabric with a cotton or linen warp and a filling of horsehair.   It is elastic and firm, and is used as a stiffening and interlining material.   The colors are black, gray, and white.   The fabric is difficult to weave and disintegrates easily, as the hairs cannot be made into a single strand and must be woven separately.   **Press cloth,** used for filtering oils, was made from human hair, which has high tensile strength, resiliency, and resistance to heat.   The hair came from China, but filter fabrics are now made from synthetic fibers.   **Rabbit hair** from Europe and Australia is used for making felt hats and is referred to as **rabbit fur,** although it does not felt like wool.   The white rabbit hair known as **Angora wool** is from the Angora rabbit of France and Belgium, called **Belgian hare.**   The hairs are clipped or plucked four times a year when they are up to 3 in. long.   They are soft and lustrous, dye easily to delicate shades, and are used for soft wearing apparel.   Because of its fluffiness and hairy characteristics, the wool is difficult to spin, and is usually employed in mixtures.

HEAT INSULATORS.   Materials having high resistance to heat rays, or low heat conductivity, used as protective insulation against either hot or cold influences.   The materials are also called **thermal insulators.**   Insulators for extremely high external temperatures, as on aerospace vehicles, are of ablative materials.   Efficiency of heat insulators is measured relatively by the Btu per hr per sq ft per deg F per ft, known as the **k factor.**   The thermal conductivity of air and gases is low, and the efficiency of some insulators, especially fibrous ones, is partly due to the air spaces.   On the other hand, the thermal conductivity of a porous insulator may be increased if water is absorbed into the spaces.

A wide variety of materials are used as thermal insulators in the forms of powder or granules for loose fill, blanket batts of fibrous materials for wall insulation, and in sheets or blocks.   Although metals are generally high heat conductors, the polished white metals may reflect as much as 95% of the heat waves, and make good **reflective insulators.**   But for this purpose the bright surface must be exposed to air space.   Aluminum has a high k factor, up to 130, but crumpled aluminum foil is an efficient thermal insulator as a fill in walls.   Wool and hair, either loose or as felt, with a k factor of 0.021, are among the best of the insulators, but organic materials are usable only for low temperatures, and they are now largely replaced by mineral wool or ceramic fibers.   Mineral wool has a low k factor, 0.0225.   The **Tipersul,** of Du Pont, is a **potassium titanate fiber** used loose or in batts, blocks, or sheet.   Its melting point is 2500°F, and it will withstand continuous temperatures to 2200°F.   Another ceramic fiber, called **Fibrox,** for the same purpose, is a **silicon oxycarbide,** SiCO, in light fluffy fibers.

Magnesia or asbestos, or combinations of the two, is much used for insulation of hot pipelines, while organic fibrous materials are used for cold lines.   **High-heat insulators,** for furnaces and boilers, are usually made of refractory ceramics such as chromite.   For intermediate temperatures, expanded glass, such as the **Foamglas** of the Pittsburgh-Corning Corp., may be used.   Foamed glass blocks will withstand heats to 1000°F, and the blocks have a crushing strength of 150 psi.   Some rigid materials of good structural strength serve as structural parts as well as insulators. **Roofinsul,** of Johns-Manville, used for roof decks, is a lightweight board compressed from wood fibers.   **Ludlite board,** of the Allegheny Ludlum Steel Co., for paneling, is thin stainless steel backed with a magnesia-asbestos composition.   Insulators in sheets, shapes, and other forms are sold under a great variety of trade names.   **Dry-Zero,** of the Dry-Zero Co., for refrigerator insulation, consists of kapok batts encased in fiberboard.   The French cold-storage insulation known as **Isotela** consists of pads of matted coir.   The **balsam wool,** of the Wood Conversion Co., is wood fibers chemically treated to prevent moisture absorption.

HEAT-RESISTANT ALLOYS. Almost all of the high alloys are heat-resistant, and the highly alloyed tool steels and stainless steels are very heat-resistant, but the term generally means the nickel-chromium-iron alloys resistant to scaling and to corrosive atmospheres at temperatures of 1500°F or above.   They usually contain 5 to 80% nickel, 13 to 25% chromium, and the balance iron, but some of the alloys for electric resistance wire may contain little or no iron.

Castings of the nickel-chromium-iron alloys have a more rigid grain structure than the wrought alloys, and are used for such items as heat-treating boxes and furnace parts.   The alloys are generally marketed on the basis of the maximum service temperature rather than on the content. An alloy of 67% nickel, 16 chromium, 12 iron, and 1 manganese has a tensile strength of 64,000 psi, which drops to 30,000 psi at about 1500°F, but will resist oxidation for long periods at 1800°F.   The alloys are sold under trade names such as **Hoskins alloys** of the Hoskins Mfg. Co., **Fahrite** of the Ohio Steel Foundry Co., **Cromax** and **Veriloy** of the Driver-Harris Co., **Accoloy** of the Alloy Engineering & Casting Co., the **Q-Alloys** of the General Alloys Co., **Amsco alloy** of the Amsco Div., Abex Corp.   Grades of these alloys may be modified with manganese, aluminum, silicon, titanium, and other elements to increase heat resistance, lower the coefficient of expansion, add creep resistance, and increase strength, or to increase resistance to hot corrosive chemicals.   **Nimonic 80,** of the Mond Nickel Co., Ltd., is an 80–20 alloy modified with aluminum.   It has good creep resistance at 750°C.   Another grade of **Nimonic alloy** for jet turbine blades has 75% nickel, 21 chromium, 2.5 titanium, 0.7 iron, 0.6 aluminum, and 0.05 carbon.   It has a tensile strength of 17,200 psi at 1500°F.

Nichroloy, of the Walker Metal Products, Ltd., contains 23% nickel, 20 chromium, 1 manganese, 1 vanadium, and 0.50 aluminum, and is for temperatures to 2000°F. **Alloy K,** of the C. O. Jeliff Mfg. Co., for resistance to high temperatures in sulfur atmospheres, contains no nickel. It has 22% chromium, 4.5 aluminum, and the balance iron.

Heat-resistant alloys for structural uses are generally complex alloys. Many of them are called stainless steels, although their compositions are much more complex than ordinary nickel-chromium stainless steels. Westinghouse Electric Corp. produces these alloys in many grades. **Alloy 545** contains 26% nickel, 13.5 chromium, 3 titanium, 1.75 molybdenum, 1.5 manganese, 0.20 boron, with small amounts of aluminum, copper, and silicon. It was designed for jet-engine turbine disks to resist high centrifugal forces above 1200°F. This alloy has a tensile strength of 162,000 psi, and at 1200°F it is 120,000 psi with a Brinell hardness of 300. **Alloy K42B** is a nickel-chromium-cobalt alloy with high strength and creep resistance at 1350°F. **Discaloy,** for turbine blades, is an austenitic alloy containing 26% nickel, 13.5 chromium, 3.2 molybdenum, 1.6 titanium, 0.8 silicon, 0.7 manganese, 0.03 carbon, and the balance iron. At a temperature of 1200°F the tensile strength is 100,000 psi. **Refract-alloy 80** has 20% each of nickel, chromium, and cobalt, 10 molybdenum, 5 tungsten, and 15 iron. **Alloy S-816,** for turbine buckets, has 20% nickel, 20 chromium, 43 cobalt, 4 molybdenum, 4 tungsten, 4 columbium, and 5 iron. **Waspaloy** has 55% nickel, 20 chromium, 13 cobalt, 4 molybdenum, 3 iron, and some titanium and aluminum. **Kromarc 55** is an austenitic steel that is easily welded and will retain high strength to 1200°F. It has 20% nickel, 16 chromium, with manganese, molybdenum, and a small amount of silicon. **Kromarc 58,** for high-strength welded structures, has a similar composition but with additions of vanadium, zirconium, and boron. It will retain a tensile strength of 80,000 psi at 1200°F. **Crucible CG-27,** of the Crucible Steel Co., contains 38% nickel, 13 chromium, 5.75 molybdenum, 2.5 titanium, 1.6 aluminum, 0.7 columbium, 0.01 boron, 0.05 carbon, and the balance iron. The yield strength is 135,000 psi, with elongation of 20%, and at 1200°F it retains a strength of 80,000 psi.

The **Udimet 500** of Special Metals is a vacuum-cast nickel-base alloy containing 18% chromium, 18 cobalt, 4 molybdenum, 3 aluminum, 3 titanium, 2 iron, 0.2 silicon, 0.2 manganese, 0.08 boron, and the balance nickel. The tensile strength is 110,000 psi, and at 1700°F the strength is 25,000 psi. **Alloy RA303** of Rolled Alloys, Inc., is resistant to oxidation at temperatures to 2100°F, though the normal tensile strength of 105,000 psi drops to 10,000 psi at 1950°F. It contains 45% nickel, 26 chromium, 3 tungsten, 3 cobalt, 3 molybdenum, 2 manganese, 1.25 silicon, 0.50 copper, and 0.08 max carbon. **Haynes alloy 25,** of the

Union Carbide Corp., has exceptional rolling and deep-drawing qualities and retains high strength to 1800°F. It has 50% cobalt with the balance chromium, nickel, and tungsten. Metals & Controls Corp. produces this alloy in thin gage down to a thickness of 0.001 in., and the cold-rolled sheet has a tensile strength of 320,000 psi, elongation 2%, and Rockwell hardness C55. **Haynes alloy 56,** for service temperatures to 1900°F, has 13% nickel, 21 chromium, 11.5 cobalt, 4.5 molybdenum, 1.5 tungsten, 1.5 manganese, 1 silicon, 0.75 columbium, 0.30 carbon, and 0.10 nitrogen, with the balance iron. The tensile strength is 129,500 psi. At a temperature of 1600°F the strength is 43,700 psi with elongation of 42%, and at 2000°F it still retains a strength of 15,200 psi. **Haynes alloy 150** is a cobalt-base alloy with no tungsten but 20% each of chromium and iron. It has a melting point of 2600°F and is used for cast and wrought parts. **Hastelloy N** of the same company was designed for resistance to molten fluoride salts, and it also has good oxidation resistance to 1800°F. It contains 16.5% molybdenum, 7 chromium, 5 iron, 0.8 manganese, 0.5 silicon, 0.01 boron, 0.5 aluminum and titanium, 0.06 carbon, and the balance nickel. The tensile strength of the wrought metal is 115,000 psi with elongation of 50%, and that of the castings is 87,000 psi with elongation of 22%. At 1700°F the strength is 34,000 psi.

The **Supertherm alloy** of the Electro-Alloys Div., Abex Corp., designed for furnace conveyor castings to withstand temperatures above 1800°F for long periods, has 35% nickel and 26 chromium, with cobalt, tungsten, and iron. **Allegheny alloy D-979,** of the Allegheny Ludlum Steel Corp., for wrought parts and forgings to give good strength and creep resistance at service temperatures to 1600°F, contains 43.5% nickel, 14.3 chromium, 3.7 tungsten, 3.8 molybdenum, 2.9 titanium, 1 aluminum, 0.46 silicon, 0.25 manganese, 0.01 boron, 0.07 carbon, and the balance iron. Another structural alloy of this company, **Allegheny alloy AF-71,** for service temperatures to 1500°F, contains none of the scarcer metals nickel and cobalt. It has 12.6% chromium, 18.4 manganese, 3 molybdenum, 0.24 silicon, 0.18 boron, 0.80 vanadium, 0.19 carbon, and the balance iron. **Pandex alloy,** of the Latrobe Steel Co., for jet turbine blades and fuel nozzles at operating temperatures to 1300°F, contains 26% nickel, 15 chromium, 2 titanium, 1.5 manganese, 1.25 molybdenum, 0.30 vanadium, 0.75 silicon, 0.20 aluminum, and 0.05 carbon. For the temperature range around 1200°F for jet-engine and gas turbine parts, the chromium-type, nonnickel steels are modified to give better forging, welding, and machining qualities. **Carpenter steel H-46,** of Carpenter Technology, has 12% chromium, 0.65 manganese, 0.40 silicon, 0.45 nickel, 0.65 molybdenum, 0.30 vanadium, 0.40 columbium, 0.08 nitrogen, and 0.18 carbon. At 1000°F it retains a strength of 100,000 psi. **Linco steel** and **Hychrom 5616,** of the Latrobe Steel Co., are intended to give higher strength and corrosion resistance at about 1200°F than the Type 400 stainless steels.   The first has 11.5% chromium, 2.75 molybdenum, 1.1 manganese, 0.35 nickel, 0.35 silicon, 0.25 vanadium, and 0.30 carbon, while the second, for higher strength, has 13% chromium, 3 tungsten, 2 nickel, 0.35 manganese, 0.35 silicon, and 0.18 carbon.

For high strength and corrosion resistance at service temperatures above 2000°F the iron-based alloys are generally not suitable.   The **vanadium-columbium alloys** developed by Union Carbide, containing 20 to 50% columbium, have a tensile strength above 100,000 psi at 700°C, 70,000 psi at 1000°C, and 40,000 psi at 1200°C (2192°F).   The **heat-resistant tubing** of the Uniform Tubes, Inc., for temperatures to 2100°F, is of Nichrome V alloy.   However, steels of moderate alloy content can be made scale-resistant and corrosion-resistant at high temperatures by surface-coating with tungsten or other refractory metal.   **Chromized steel** is steel surface-alloyed with chromium by diffusion from a chromium salt at high temperature.   The reaction of the salt produces an alloyed surface containing about 40% chromium.   **Plasmaplate** was a name given by the Linde Div. to protective coatings of tungsten or molybdenum, deposited by a plasma torch which gives a concentrated heat to 30,000°F, but the refractory metals can now be deposited at lower temperatures by decomposition of chemical compounds.   **Molybdenum pentachloride,** $MoCl_5$, is a crystalline powder which deposits an adherent coating of molybdenum metal when heated to about 900°C.

HEAT-TRANSFER AGENTS. Liquids or gases used as intermediate agents for the transport of heat or cold between the heat source and the process, or for dissipating heat by radiation.   Water, steam, and air are the most common heat-transfer agents, but the term is usually applied only to special materials.   Air can be used over the entire range of industrially important temperatures, but it is a poor heat-transfer medium.   Water can be used only between its freezing and boiling points, unless high pressures are employed to keep the water liquid.   A liquid agent should have a wide liquid range, be noncorrosive and nontoxic, and have low vapor pressure to minimize operational loss.

Gallium, with a freezing point at 85.6 and boiling point at 3600°F, offers an exceptionally wide liquid range, but it is too costly for ordinary use, and the liquid metal also attacks other metals.   Mercury is used for heat transfer, but is costly and toxic, and at 1200°F it exerts a vapor pressure of 500 psi.   **Anisol** is a methyl phenyl ether of the composition $C_6H_5OCH_3$.   It freezes at −37°C and boils at 154°C, has low vapor pressure, and is used for heat transfer, although its chief use is as a solvent for plastics and for recrystallization processes.   **Aroclor 1248,** of Monsanto, can be used for temperatures up to 550°F and, like anisol, is easily pumped at room temperature.   It is a chlorinated biphenyl and is noncombustible.

Brine solutions of sodium or calcium chlorides are used for heat transfer for temperatures down to −6°F, but are corrosive to metals.   Molten sodium and potassium salts are used for temperatures from 600 to 1400°C, but are corrosive to metals.   The **sodium-potassium salt,** NaK, called **Nack,** is also highly corrosive.   The salt known as **Hitec,** which is a 50–50 mixture of sodium nitrite and potassium nitrate, melts at 282°F, remains liquid at high temperatures, and has no appreciable vapor pressure at 1200°F.   **Tetraryl silicate** remains liquid between −40 and 700°F, but is costly for most uses.

HEAVY ALLOY. A name applied to **tungsten-nickel alloy** produced by pressing and sintering the metallic powders.   It is used for screens for X-ray tubes and radioactivity units, for contact surfaces for circuit breakers, and for balances for high-speed machinery.   The original composition was 90% tungsten and 10 nickel, but a proportion of copper is used to give a lower sintering temperature and to give better binding as the copper wets the tungsten.   Too large a proportion of copper makes the product porous.   In general, the alloys weigh nearly 50% more than lead, permitting space saving in counterweights and balances, and they are more efficient as gamma-ray absorbers than lead.   They are highly heat-resistant, retain a tensile strength of about 20,000 psi at 2000°F, have an electrical conductivity about 15% that of copper, and can be machined and brazed with silver solder.

An alloy of 90% tungsten, 7.5 nickel, and 2.5 copper has a tensile strength of 135,000 psi, compressive strength 400,000 psi, elongation 15%, Rockwell hardness C30, and weight 0.61 lb per cu in.   **Kenertium,** of Kennemetal, Inc., has this compostion.   **Hevimet,** of the General Electric Co., and **Mallory 1000,** of P. R. Mallory, Inc., are similar metals. **Mallory 3000** is in the form of rolled sheet for radiation shielding.   The tensile strength of the sheet is 195,000 psi, with a Rockwell hardness of A63.   **Fansteel 77 metal,** of Fansteel, Inc., contains 89% tungsten, 7 nickel, and 4 copper.   The density is 16.7, tensile strength 85,000 psi, elongation 17%, and Brinell hardness to 280.   The coefficient of expansion is low, 0.0000065 in. per in. per deg C.   **Heavy metal powder,** of the Astro Alloys Corp., for making parts by powder metallurgy, is prealloyed with the tungsten in a matrix of copper-nickel to prevent settling out of the heavy tungsten.

HELIUM. A colorless, odorless, elementary gas, He, with a specific gravity of 0.1368, liquefying at −268.9°C, freezing at −272.2°C.   It has a valency of zero and forms no electron-bonded compounds.   It has the highest ionization potential of any element.   The lifting power of helium is only 92% that of hydrogen, but it is preferred for balloons because it is inert and nonflammable, and is used in weather-station balloons.   It is also used instead of air to inflate large tires for aircraft to save weight.   Because of its low density, also, it is used for diluting oxygen in the treatment of respiratory diseases.   Its heat conductivity is about 6 times that of air, and it is used as a shielding gas in welding, and in vacuum tubes and electric lamps.   Because of its inertness helium can also be used to hold free chemical radicals which, when released, give high energy and thrust for missile propulsion.   When an electric current is passed through helium it gives a pinkish-violet light, and is thus used in advertising signs.   Helium can be obtained from atmospheric nitrogen, but comes chiefly from natural gas, the gas of Texas yielding 0.94%, with some gases yielding as much as 2%.   It also occurs in the mineral **cleveite.**   Helium is transported as a liquid in trucks and tube trailers.   Helium marketed by Matheson Gas Products Co. for use in semiconductor production and where noncontaminating atmospheres are needed is 99.9999% pure.

HEMLOCK. The wood of the coniferous tree *Tsuga mertensiana,* of northeastern United States.   This species is also called **mountain hemlock,** and is now scarce.   **Eastern hemlock,** *T. canadensis,* was formerly a tree common from eastern Canada to northern Alabama.   In the southern area it is called **spruce pine,** and in the northern area **hemlock spruce.**   The wood is coarse with an uneven texture, splintering easily.   The trees are up to 80 ft in height and up to 3 ft in diameter.   It is used for paper pulp, boxes and crates, and inferior lumber.   **Western hemlock,** *T. heterophylla,* is a wood produced in abundance from Alaska to northern California.   It is known also as **West Coast hemlock, hemlock spruce, Prince Albert fir, gray fir, Alaskan pine,** and **western hemlock fir.**   Trees 100 years old are about 20 in. in diameter and 140 ft high.   The stand of the tree is estimated at more than 140 billion bd ft in the United States, of which 85 billion is in Washington and Oregon.   The wood is light in color, with a pinkish tinge, light in weight, moderately soft, and straight-grained.   It is nonresinous and is free from resin ducts, but black knots are frequent.   The select grades of the lumber are free from knots and suitable for natural and paint finishes.   The wood is used for general construction, boxes, woodenware, and pulpwood.   The lumber often comes mixed with Douglas fir.   It is easy to work but does not plane smooth like pine.   It has frequent dark streaks from heart rot, common in old trees.   **Hemlock-bark extract** is obtained from the bark of the eastern hemlock, and is an important tanning material.   **Western hemlock bark** is not in general use for tanning, but the bark contains 22% tannin. The extract is used with resorcinol-formaldehyde or other resins as **cold-setting adhesives** for plywood.   They are strong and water-resistant.

Adhesive HT-120, of Raynier, Inc., is hemlock-bark extract modified with a phenol resin.

HEMP. A fiber from the stalk of the plant *Cannabis sativa,* valued chiefly for cordage, sacking, packings, and as a fiber for plastic filler. In normal times it is grown principally in southern Russia, central Europe, the Mediterranean countries, and Asia, but during the Second World War was extensively cultivated in the United States. The fiber, which is obtained by retting, is longer than that of the flax plant, up to 75 in., but is coarser and not suitable for fine fabrics, although the finest and whitest fibers are sorted out in Europe and used in linen fabrics. It is also more difficult to separate the fiber and to bleach. It is stronger, more glossy, and more durable than cotton, and has been used for toweling and coarse fabrics to replace the heavy linen fabrics. It is high in alpha cellulose, containing about 78%. **Hemp rope** was once the chief marine cordage, but it has been replaced largely by rope of abaca which is lighter and more water-resistant. Hemp contains a toxic alkaloid, and in India the stalks are chewed for the narcotic effect. The drug known in medicine as **cannabis,** is called **marijuana** when smoked in cigarettes. Cannabis is an exhilarator and painkiller, and is used in medicine as a depressive antidote, but in excess the drug causes hallucinations. The plant's resin, which in a fully ripe cultivated plant covers the flowers and top leaves, contains the active ingredients. The least potent grade is **bhang,** derived from the tops of uncultivated plants. **Ganja** is the product of select, cultivated plants. The most potent and highest-grade version of the drug, called **charas,** is made from the resin alone and is the only grade which may properly be referred to as **hashish. Synthetic cannabis,** or **synhexyl,** is a pyrahexyl more powerful in action than the natural material. **Hempseed oil,** used in paints and varnishes, is made by pressing the seed of the hemp plant. It has a specific gravity of 0.926, iodine value of 148. **Oakum,** used for seam calking, is made from old hemp ropes pulled into loose fiber and treated with tar, usually blended with some new tow. Some grades may have sunn or jute fibers. It comes in balls or in rope form. **Marine oakum** is made entirely from new tow fibers.

HERRING OIL. A fish oil obtained by extraction from several species of fish of the herring family, *Clupeidae.* The **sardine** is the smaller fish of this family. The **Norwegian herring,** *Clupea harengus,* or **sea herring,** is the sardine of Maine, eastern Canada, and the North Sea. The herring is an abundant fish, but it is objectionable as a food because of the quantity of sharp bones. In the very small sardines the bones are soft and edible when cooked. In Norway the oil is produced by boiling the whole fish, pressing, and separating the oil from the water centrifugally. A process used in the United States is to grind the whole fish into liquid form, remove the oil, and condense the remaining solution until it is 50% solids, which is marketed as homogenized condensed fish for use as poultry feed.

In California and western Canada the sardine is a much larger fish, the **pilchard,** *Sardinia coerulea,* usually about 8 in. long.   The pilchard, or **California sardine,** constituted about 25% of the entire fish catch of the United States by weight, but since 1948 the number of sardines in California waters has decreased greatly.   The oil yield is about 30 gal per ton of fish, but much of the sardine oil is a by-product of the canning industry.   The oil content of herring is 10 to 15% of the total weight of the fish, being low in the 1-year-old fish and reaching a peak in the third year.   The fish builds up its oil in the summer.   In winter the herring tends to stay close to the bottom, or at great depths, and uses up much of its oil.   Commercially, the yield of herring oil is from 3 to 5 gal per 250-lb bbl of raw fish.   Much of the fish oil of South Africa is from the pilchard, *C. sagax.*   In France, Spain, and Portugal the **European pilchard,** *C. pilchardus,* and the *C. sardinus* are used.   The oil from the latter has a high iodine value.   In Norway, the **sprat,** *C. sprattus,* is also used.   The **Japanese herring** is the *C. pallasi.* **Herring oil,** or **sardine oil,** is employed as a quenching oil in heat-treating, either alone or mixed with other oils, in soaps, printing inks, lubricants, and for finishing leather.   It is also fractionated to use in blends for paint oils. Herring oil contains 25% of **clupanodonic acid,** $C_{21}H_{35}COOH$, 20% **arachidonic acid,** $C_{19}H_{31}COOH$, 18% **palmitoleic acid,** $C_{15}H_{29}COOH$, 13 linoleic, 9 oleic, 8 palmitic, and 7 myristic.   The specific gravity is 0.920 to 0.933, iodine value 123 to 142, and saponification value 179 to 194.   It can be made clear and odorless by hydrogenation.   Sardine oil contains some stearic acid, higher percentages of palmitic and linoleic acids, and less of the other acids.   **Pilchard oil** is quite similar, but has less oleic acid.   Both of these oils contain about 15% of **tetracosapolyenoic acid,** a 24-carbon acid, also occurring in herring oil.

HICKORY. The wood of the **shagbark hickory** tree, *Carya ovata,* and other species of the walnut order.   It is prized as a wood for ax, pick, and other tool handles, and for such items as wheel spokes or golf clubs where resiliency and shock absorption are necessary.   The color of the thick sapwood is white, and the heartwood is reddish brown.   It has a fine, even, and straight grain, and is tough and elastic, having 30% greater strength than white oak and twice the shock resistance, although not as durable.   The weight is 45 to 52 lb per cu ft.   The chief producing states are Arkansas, Louisiana, Mississippi, Tennessee, and Kentucky, but the trees grow from New Hampshire to Texas.   A mature shagbark tree 200 to 300 years old averages 100 ft high and over 2 ft in diameter.   For handle manufacture the white wood and the red wood are considered equal in physical properties, and both possess the smooth feel required for handles.   The average specific gravity when kiln-dried is 0.79, compressive strength perpendicular to the grain 3,100 psi, and shearing strength parallel to the grain 1,440 psi.   There are more than 30 species of hickory, including the pecan trees.   Besides the *C. ovata* three other species are important for the commercial wood: the **shellbark hickory,** *C. laciniosa,* also called **kingnut;** the **pignut hickory,** *C. glabra,* also called **black hickory** and **bitternut;** and the **mockernut hickory,** *C. alba,* also called **ballnut, hognut,** and **white hickory.**   The kernels of the nuts of all species are edible, although some are bitter and astringent.   The pecan hickories include the **pecan,** *C. illinoensis,* the **water hickory,** *C. aquatica,* and **nutmeg hickory,** *C. myristicaeformis.*   The pecan trees are cultivated widely in the southern states for the nuts.   **Pecan nuts** are widely used in confectionery and bakery products, but they become off-taste rapidly unless sprayed with an antioxidant.

HIGH BRASS. Sometimes called **common brass,** and formerly known as **market brass.** The most common of all the commercial wrought brasses. The usual mill standard is 65% copper and 35 zinc, and grades containing from 66 to 70% copper are referred to as **deep-drawing brass.** High brass is marketed in sheets, rolls, and strips, and is used largely for drawing, forming, and spinning.   In the hard tempers it is used for parts made by blanking, forming, and bending.   It is a cold-working material and is not suitable for hot working.   The 65–35 brass marketed by the American Brass Co. under the name of **yellow brass** has a tensile strength of 45,000 psi and elongation 60% when soft, and a strength of 76,000 psi and elongation 5% when hard-rolled.   The weight is 0.306 lb per cu in., melting point 930°C, and coefficient of expansion 0.0000106.   Bar stock of high brass, for turned parts, called **high-brass bar,** invariably contains some lead, up to about 3%, as the unleaded brass is tough and the turned chips do not break easily.   The most commonly used **die-casting brass** is a modified 60–40 yellow brass.   The nominal composition is 57% copper, 1.5 lead, 0.25 tin, with sometimes small amounts of iron, silicon, or manganese, and the balance zinc.   This is **ASTM alloy Z30A.**   The tensile strength is 45,000 psi, elongation 10%, and melting point about 1575°F.   It is more difficult to cast than aluminum alloys.

The alloy listed in Federal specifications as **commercial brass** for wrought shapes actually covers the brasses from muntz metal to high brass, and is leaded.   It contains 60 to 65% copper, with lead permissible up to 3.75%.   The government specifications for commercial brass for castings are equally broad.   **Butt brass,** for hinges, has 64% copper, 35 zinc, and 1 lead.   The term **etching brass** refers to the temper rather than to the composition.   It is a high-brass sheet in quarter-hard or half-hard temper used for name plates and dials.   **Bobierre's metal** is an old name for 63–37 high brass.   This alloy is called in England **basis brass,** and **BES No. 265.   Bristol brass** and **Prince's metal** are old names for high brass.   **Spring brass** is usually a high brass with 66 to 72% copper rolled 8 numbers hard but may be modified with tin or other elements and called **spring bronze.**   The tensile strength, hard-rolled, is about 68,000 psi, and elongation 11%; spring wire may be 100,000 psi.   SAE specifications require that a spring wire be capable of bending 180 deg around a wire of its own diameter without cracking.   **Pin metal,** for common pins, has 62% copper and 38 zinc, and is not annealed from the working. **Shim stock** is usually a soft high brass in thicknesses of 0.001 and 0.002 in. for shims and gaskets.

HIGH-LEAD BRONZE.   Bronze alloys containing high percentages of lead to give a soft matrix metal for bearing use, as distinct from bronzes containing small amounts of lead to make them free-machining.   The first high-lead bronze was invented in England in 1870 under the name of **Dick's bronze,** and was used on British railways.   In 1892 C. B. Dudley in the United States produced **ExB metal** containing 77% copper, 15 lead, and 8 tin.   It is still used as a car bearing metal and called **car brass.** A common type of **leaded bronze** used for bearings is the 80–10–10 mixture, and this alloy is also known as **ordnance bronze.**   It has a Brinell hardness of 58, a tensile strength of 30,000 psi, and when deoxidized with phosphorus has a dense structure.   Lead does not alloy well with copper unless a catalyzer is present, the copper absorbing only about 3.5% lead. It also tends to sweat out at a temperature of 327°C.   High-lead bronze is now deoxidized with phosphorus, or contains small amounts of nickel, arsenic, or some other element to aid in holding up the lead.

The alloys containing tin are true bronzes, and are not as difficult to cast as the copper-lead alloys.   Some lead bronzes also contain antimony, which gives them a crystalline structure useful for bearings.   They are easy to cast.   **Retz alloy** and **Reith alloy** contained about 75% copper, 10 each of tin and lead, and 5 antimony.   **Cyprus bronze** contained 65% copper, 30 lead, and 5 tin.   **Allen red metal** is a copper-lead alloy with 50% lead and a small amount of sulfur to hold the lead in solution. **Allen's metal** was an early alloy containing 40% lead, 55 copper, and 5 tin.   Part of the lead was put in in the form of galena ore or lead sulfide. **Johnson bronze No. 25,** used for high-speed bearings, contains 75% copper, 19 lead, 5 tin, and 1 nickel.   High-lead bronzes are resistant to acids and, when used for casting chemical machine parts, are called **anti-**

acid bronze. The name **lead bronze** is used in England for an alloy of 75% copper, 1 to 2 tin, and the balance lead.

A bronze for motor bearings, **Johnson alloy 29,** of the Johnson Bronze Co., is **SAE alloy 67,** containing 78% copper, 15 lead, and 7 tin. **Lubrico,** of the Buckeye Brass Mfg. Co., contains 75% copper, 20 lead, and 5 tin. **Sabeco metal,** of the Fredericksen Co., has 21% lead and 9 tin. **Sumet bronze,** of the Sumet Corp., is the trade name of a group of bearing bronzes in grades from the softest with 28% lead and Brinell hardness 30 to 33, to the hardest with 17.5% lead and hardness of 58 to 62 Brinell. **Arctic bronze,** of the National Bearing Metals Corp., is the name of leaded bearing bronzes chill-cast in metal molds to give fine grain structure. **Bearium,** of the Bearium Metals Corp., refers to a group of high-lead bronzes containing 17.5 to 28% lead and about 10 tin. The softest grade, with a hardness of 35 Brinell, has a compressive limit of 7,800 psi. **Durbar bronze,** of the Buffalo Die Casting Corp., has 24% lead and 4 tin. **Durbar hard bronze** has 10% tin and 20 lead. **Monarch metal,** of the Monarch Alloy Co., is a high-lead bearing bronze in various compositions. It is melted in sealed crucibles and water-cooled in pouring, resulting in a fine dispersion of the lead. **Tri-Alloy,** of the Ford Motor Co., is a high-lead alloy for crankshaft bearings for heavy loads and high speeds. It contains 35 to 40% lead, 4.5 to 5 silver, and the balance copper. The alloy is cast on strip steel and formed into bearings. **Copper-lead alloys** are now made also by sintering together copper powder and copperplated lead powder. They can thus be made in any proportion of lead.

HIGH-SPEED STEEL. A general name for high-alloy steels which retain their hardness at very high temperatures and are used for metal-cutting tools. They are now divided into three general classes. The tungsten steels form the oldest class and are an outgrowth of the older mushet steels. **Mushet steel,** or **air-hardening steel,** was invented in England in 1868. It contained 5 to 8% tungsten, 2.5 manganese, 1.5 silicon, and very high carbon. From 1893 to 1898 F. W. Taylor experimented with cutting tools made with a substitution of chromium for the high manganese and with less carbon, and the **Taylor-White steel** marketed in 1900 contained 8% tungsten, 1.8 chromium, 1.15 carbon, 0.18 manganese, and 0.25 silicon. In 1900 the Bethlehem Steel Co. brought out the tungsten-chromium-vanadium steel now known as 18–4–1. Because of its balance of red-hardness, toughness, and cutting edge, this formula, and the English preference for a harder 14–4–2 steel, still remains the basic standard for tungsten high-speed steel, although most modern steels are now modified. **Star-Zenith,** of Carpenter Technology, is an 18–4–1 steel with the alloying elements in slight excess of standards. **ML steel,**

of the Allegheny Ludlum Steel Co., has the vanadium increased to 1.85% and an addition of 0.50 molybdenum.   It gives a keener edge.

The property of red-hardness is the ability of the steel to retain the hard carbides at the high cutting temperatures up to about 1750°F. Tungsten adds red-hardness to steel; chromium gives deep-hardening and strength; vanadium adds hardness, refines the grain, and improves the cutting edge.   Molybdenum has a much more pronounced effect than tungsten on red-hardness, but alone it tends to make the steel more brittle and also subject to decarbonization.   Cobalt gives red-hardness, but the steels are more brittle and difficult to forge.   **Molybdenum high-speed steel** and **cobalt high-speed steel** are thus really modifications of the basic formula rather than separate types.   The cobalt steels were first called **super-high-speed steels.**

The first molybdenum high-speed steel was **Mo SH steel** of the Sanderson Steel Co., marketed in 1898 and called **self-hardening steel.**   Later, research by the Army Ordnance Department to substitute molybdenum for the imported metal tungsten resulted in the **Watertown Arsenal steel** containing 9.5% molybdenum, 4 chromium, 1.25 to 2 tungsten, 0.90 to 1.5 vanadium, up to 0.40 manganese and 0.50 silicon, and 0.80 carbon. **Motung steel** contained about 8% molybdenum, 1.5 tungsten, 4 chromium, 1.25 vanadium, up to 0.50 each of manganese and silicon, and up to 0.85 carbon.   **Van Lom steel,** of Vasco, had up to 10% molybdenum, about 4 chromium and 4 vanadium, and up to 1.2 carbon.   The early molybdenum steels required careful heat-treatment to prevent decarburization, and later steels contained less molybdenum and more tungsten.   **Bethlehem 66 steel,** of the Bethlehem Steel Co., had about 5.5% tungsten, 5 molybdenum, 4 chromium, 1.5 vanadium, and 0.80 carbon.   **Unicut steel,** of the Universal-Cyclops Steel Corp., had 6.25 tungsten, 6.25 molybdenum, 4 chromium, 2.4 vanadium, and 1 carbon.   **Twin Mo steel,** of H. Boker & Co., Inc., is a 6–6–2 tungsten-molybdenum steel.   **Speed Star steel,** of the Carpenter Steel Co., contains 5.5% tungsten, 4.25 molybdenum, 4 chromium, 15 vanadium, and 0.80 carbon.   It is a general-purpose tool steel with a fine grain and surface hardness of Rockwell C65. **Star-Mo M-2 steel,** of Firth Sterling, is typical of the steels designed to combine the desirable tool qualities of both the tungsten and the molybdenum steels.   It contains 6.40% tungsten, 5 molybdenum, 4 chromium, 2 vanadium, and 0.83 carbon.   It weighs 6% less than the 18–4–1 types of steel, is easily machined at the annealed hardness of less than 240 Brinell, and is hardened to about Rockwell C65.   The high-speed steels are sometimes modified for use as casting alloys for such uses as jet engine parts.   **Haynes alloy 589,** of Union Carbide, for high-heat abrasion resistance in moving parts, contains 17% chromium, 16 molybdenum, 2 vanadium, with up to 4% carbon, 1.5 silicon, and maximum 0.5 manganese.

The cobalt high-speed steels are the "super" steels for high production, but they are balanced in composition for particular service and usually require a specified heat-treatment. Those with high tungsten and cobalt have high red-hardness and can be run at higher speeds and feeds. Those with high molybdenum have a lower red-hardness and a narrower heat-treating range. **Circle C steel,** of Firth Sterling, has 18.5% tungsten, 4.5 chromium, 2 vanadium, 1 molybdenum, 9 cobalt, and 0.77 carbon, while **Super Hi-Mo steel** of this company has 1.8 tungsten, 8.5 molybdenum, 4 chromium, 5 cobalt, 1.2 vanadium, and 0.80 carbon. **Congo steel,** of the Braeburn Steel Corp., for cutting hard materials, has 12% cobalt, 4 tungsten, 5 molybdenum, 4 chromium, 1.4 vanadium, and 0.78 carbon.

Rex AAA steel, of the Crucible Steel Co., is an 18–4–1 steel modified with 5% cobalt and 0.50 molybdenum. **Red Cut Cobalt steel** of Vasco, **Co-Co steel** of the Colonial Steel Co., and **Maxite steel** of the Columbia Tool Steel Co. were also 18–4–1 steels modified with cobalt and molybdenum. **Vasco Supreme steel** of Vasco has 5% vanadium instead of the usual 1%, with 5% cobalt, 4.75 chromium, 12.5 tungsten, 0.25 manganese, and 1.5 carbon, and has good wear life at cutting speeds double those for standard 18–4–1 steel. **XDH steel,** of Firth Sterling, is an 18–4–1 steel with low carbon, 0.55%, to give greater shock resistance for dies and punches.

General-purpose **cutting steels** are usually tungsten-molybdenum steels. **Crusader XL steel,** of the Latrobe Steel Co., which hardens to Rockwell C66 and gives good red-hardness and wear resistance, contains 6% tungsten, 6 molybdenum, 4.1 chromium, 3.2 vanadium, and 1.20 carbon, while **Electrite Corsair XL** is a variation of this steel with added sulfur to make it easier machining for form tools. **Electric Star steel,** of this company, for machining abrasive castings, contains 5.5% tungsten, 4.5 molybdenum, 4.5 chromium, 4 vanadium, 0.25 silicon, 0.25 manganese, and 1.28 carbon. **STM steel,** of the Simonds Saw & Steel Div., for saws, knives, and chisels, has up to 9.5% molybdenum, 1.5 tungsten, 3.75 chromium, 2 vanadium, and from 3 to 8 cobalt, with 0.80 to 1 carbon. **Amotun steel,** of the Atlantic Steel Co., for dies and taps, is quite similar with 6% cobalt. **Rex M2S,** of Crucible Steel, is a grade of M2 high-speed cutting steel with 1% carbon to give a Rockwell hardness of C65 with only a slight decrease in impact strength.

For high wear resistance when cutting at red heats, some of the steels have higher percentages of tungsten and cobalt. **Imperial Major steel,** of A. Milne & Co., has 13% cobalt and 22 tungsten. **Gray Cut Cobalt steel,** of Vasco, has 20.5% tungsten, 12.25 cobalt, 4.25 chromium, 1.3 vanadium, 0.60 molybdenum, and 0.80 carbon. The high-speed steels are sold under a great variety of trade names in rods, bars, flats, and tool shapes.   Among these are **Supremus steel** and **Jessco steel** of the Jessop Steel Co., **Milvan steel** of A. Milne & Co., **Rex, Champion,** and **Peerless** of the Crucible Steel Co., **Blue Chip, Van Chip,** and **Circle M** of Firth Sterling, **Clarite steel** of the Columbia Tool Steel Co., and **Panther steel** and **DBL steel** of the Allegheny Ludlum Steel Co.

HOLLY. The wood of the tree *Ilex aquifolium,* and several other species of *Ilex,* or holly tree, native to Europe, and the tree *I. opaca,* of south-eastern United States.   It is valued as a wood for inlaying because of its white color, its fine, close grain, and its ease of staining to imitate ebony. It is hard, and the weight is 47 lb per cu ft.   It is also used for scientific and musical instruments, model boats, and sporting goods.

HORN. The excrescent growth, or horns, from the heads of certain animals, notably beef cattle.   Horn is used for making handles and various articles.   The quality depends largely upon the size and age of the animal from which it comes, the No. 1 grade being the large steer horns, and the No. 2 those below 40 lb per hundred.   Horns occur on the head in pairs and are hollow, growing on a core of pithy bone.   The horns are split by saws, soaked to make them flexible, and then flattened under pressure. **Horn meal,** made from the bone refuse, is sold largely as fertilizer.   **Horn pith,** extracted by boiling the horns, is used for glue and for gelatin.

HOT-DIE STEELS. A general name for alloy steels that will resist shock and retain their hardness when operating in forging machines at high temperature.   When used in hot-heading machines, they are also called **hot-work steels.**   These are two general types, one being chromium steel with 3 to 10% or more of chromium, and the other tungsten steel with 8 to 10% tungsten, but they are usually modified with other elements and often do not differ greatly from the general-purpose high-speed steels.

The plain chromium steels are oil-hardening.   They develop a high hardness and are deep-hardening with high impact value, and are used for dies for compressive action, as for header machines.   The tungsten steels are air-hardening, have high impact value and superior service life at high heats, but, unless modified, are not hard enough for cutting dies.   Both types of steel now usually have additions of vanadium, molybdenum, nickel, and other elements to give added physical qualities.   The commonly used 3 to 5% chromium complex steels are air-hardening and have the alloy content adjusted to give a balance of hardness, toughness, and resistance to heat checking.   **LPD die steel,** of the Latrobe Steel Co., for forging and extrusion dies, has 5% chromium, 1.6 molybdenum, 1.3 tungsten, 1 silicon, 0.30 vanadium, 0.30 manganese, and 0.35 carbon.

VDC die steel, for die-casting dies, has 5.25% chromium, 1.2 molybdenum, 1 vanadium, 1 silicon, 0.40 manganese, and 0.40 carbon. Both of these steels harden to Rockwell C55.

A tough and wear-resistant air-hardening steel for swaging and forming dies and for knives is **Airque V,** of the Braeburn Alloy Steel Div. It has 5.25% chromium, 1.15 molybdenum, 1 vanadium, 0.50 manganese, 0.30 silicon, and 1.25 carbon. It hardens to Rockwell C65. **HWD 3 steel,** of Firth Sterling, for forging dies and aluminum die-casting dies, has a quite similar composition but with only 0.40 carbon. It hardens to Rockwell C52, but can be nitrided for greater surface hardness. **Potomac M steel,** of the Allegheny Ludlum Steel Corp., is also similar and may be either air- or oil-hardened. **Hot-work steel B-47** of the same company, for extrusion and forging dies and hot-punch tools, is more complex. It has 4.25% each of chromium, tungsten, and cobalt, 2.25 vanadium, 0.40 molybdenum, 0.35 manganese, 0.25 silicon, and 0.40 carbon. It retains a tensile strength of 178,000 psi at 800°F. **Crescent steel** and **La Belle steel,** of the Crucible Steel Co., and **C.Y.W. steel,** of Firth Sterling, are 3.5 to 3.9% chromium steels modified to require only easy heat-treatment to give a good balance of physical properties.

The tungsten steels are generally suited for more severe service, but are more costly. **Mohawk steel,** of the Allegheny Ludlum Steel Co., has 14% tungsten, 3.5 chromium, 0.70 vanadium, and 0.50 carbon, while **Atlas steel** has 10% tungsten, 3.5 chromium, 0.45 vanadium, and 0.35 carbon. **Peerless A steel,** of the Crucible Steel Co., has 9% tungsten, 3.25 chromium, and 0.25 vanadium. **Vasco Marvel steel,** of Vasco, contains 9.25% tungsten, 3.5 chromium, 0.40 vanadium, and 0.35 carbon, while **Vasco Extrude Die steel,** for hot-extrusion dies, has 15.5% tungsten, 3 molybdenum, 4 chromium, and 2 nickel. High-speed steels are also used for bearings and other parts where hardness and high strength at high temperatures are needed. **Vasco Matrix II-CUM,** for bearings and gears, contains 20% total tungsten, vanadium, molybdenum, chromium, cobalt, and 0.55% carbon. It is hardened at 2000°F and tempered at 1000°F. The tensile strength is above 400,000 psi at a hardness of Rockwell C64. **Excelo steel,** of the Carpenter Steel Co., for hot shears, has 2.5% tungsten, 1.5 chromium, 0.35 vanadium, and 0.55 carbon, but **T-K steel,** for swaging dies, has 9% tungsten, 3.5 chromium, 0.40 vanadium, and 0.35 carbon, and for higher heat resistance **D.Y.O. steel** has 14.5% tungsten, 4 chromium, and 0.50 vanadium. **Hot-work 8 steel,** of the Bethlehem Steel Co., is molybdenum steel with 8.5% molybdenum and 1.5 vanadium. It is tough, shock-resistant, abrasion-resistant, and resists heat checking. General-purpose, easily heat-treated steels with low tungsten and chromium and some vanadium are not highly heat-resistant, but are suitable for die-casting dies and, because of their resistance to shock, are also used for upsetting dies.   **Tungo steel,** of the Colonial Steel Co., and **Par-Exc steel,** of Vasco, are examples of these.

Die block steel refers to hot-work steels furnished in finished blocks for forging and die-casting dies, heat-treated to a temper permitting machining but not requiring further heat treatment.   **Hardtem steel** and **C55 steel,** of the Heppenstall Co., are such steels.   They eliminate the possibility of warpage in the heat treating of the finished die.   For general-purpose use in plants not equipped with extensive heat-treating facilities, low-alloyed tungsten-chromium steels are produced that have a good balance of hardness, toughness, and heat resistance for both hot forging and heading and for cold work.   **JS steel,** of Firth Sterling, has 2.5% tungsten, 1.4 chromium, 0.25 vanadium, 0.30 manganese, and 0.50 carbon.   It can be oil-hardened over a wide temperature range.   When tempered at 800°F, it has a hardness of Rockwell C49, but can be readily pack-hardened to give a surface hardness of Rockwell C65.   Where high hardness and compressive strength are needed, high-chromium, air-hardening steels modified with small percentages of other elements are also used as general-purpose hot-work steels.   **Olympic FM die steel,** of the Latrobe Steel Co., is such a steel.   It contains 12% chromium, 0.90 vanadium, 0.75 molybdenum, 0.50 manganese, 0.30 silicon, 1.5 carbon, plus sulfides to make it readily machinable.

HYDROCHLORIC ACID.   Also called **muriatic acid,** and originally called **spirits of salt.**   An inorganic acid used for pickling and cleaning metal parts, production of glues and gelatin from bones, manufacture of chlorine, pharmaceuticals, dyes, pyrotechnics, and for tanning, etching, reclaiming rubber, and treating oils and fats.   It is a water solution of **hydrogen chloride,** HCl, and is a colorless or yellowish fuming liquid, with pungent, poisonous fumes.   The specific gravity of the gas is 1.269, the solidifying point −112°C, and boiling point −83°C.   It is made by the action of sulfuric acid on sodium chloride, or common salt.   The commercial acid is usually 20°Bé equaling 31.45% HCl gas, and has a specific gravity of 1.16.   Other grades are 18 and 22°Bé.   **Fuming hydrochloric acid** has a specific gravity of 1.194, and contains about 37% hydrogen chloride gas. Hydrochloric acid is shipped in glass carboys.   Anhydrous hydrogen chloride gas is also marketed in steel cylinders under a pressure of 1,000 psi for use as a catalyst.   The boiling point is 85.03°C.   The acid known as **aqua regia,** used for dissolving or testing gold and platinum, is a mixture of 3 parts hydrochloric acid and 1 nitric acid.   It is a yellow liquid with suffocating fumes.

HYDROCYANIC ACID.   Also called **prussic acid, formonitrile,** and **hydrogen cyanide.**   A colorless, highly poisonous gas of the composition

HCN. The specific gravity is 0.697, the liquefying point is 26°C, and it is soluble in water and in alcohol. It is usually marketed in water solutions of 2 to 10%. It is used for the production of acrylonitrile and adiponitrile and for making sodium cyanide. It is also employed as a disinfectant and fumigant, as a military poison gas, and in mining and metallurgy in the cyanide process. It is so poisonous that death may result within a few seconds after it is taken into the body. It was used as a poison by the Egyptians and Romans, who obtained it by crushing and moistening peach kernels. It is produced synthetically from natural gas. The French war gas known as **vincennite** was hydrocyanic acid mixed with stannic chloride. **Manganite** was a mixture with arsenic trichloride. **HCN discoids,** of the American Cyanamid Co., are cellulose disks impregnated with 98% hydrocyanic acid, used for fumigating closed warehouses.

HYDROFLUORIC ACID. A water solution of **hydrogen fluoride,** HF. It is a colorless, fuming liquid, highly corrosive and caustic. It dissolves most metals except gold and platinum, and also glass, stoneware, and organic material. The choking fumes are highly injurious. It is widely used in the chemical industry, for etching glass, and for cleaning metals. In cleaning iron castings it dissolves the sand from the castings. The specific gravity of the gas is 0.713, and liquefying point −19°C. Hydrofluoric acid is made by treating calcium fluoride or fluorspar with sulfuric acid. It is marketed in solution strengths of 30, 52, 60, and 80%. The anhydrous material, HF, is used as an alkylation catalyst. **Hydrobromic acid,** HBr, is a strong acid which reacts with organic bases to form bromides that are generally more reactive than chlorides. The technical 48% grade has a specific gravity of 1.488.

HYDROGEN. A colorless, odorless, tasteless elementary gas. With an atomic weight of 1.008, it is the lightest known material. The specific gravity is 0.0695, and its density ratio in relation to air is 1:14.38. It is liquefied by cooling under pressure, and its boiling point at atmospheric pressure is −252.7°C. Its light weight makes it useful for filling balloons, but, because of its inflammable nature, it is normally used only for signal balloons, for which use the hydrogen is produced easily and quickly from hydrides. Hydrogen produces high heat, and is used for welding and cutting torches. For this purpose it is used in atomic form rather than the usual H_2 molecular form. Its high thrust value makes it an important rocket fuel. It is also used for the hydrogenation of oil and coal, for the production of ammonia and many other chemicals, and for **water gas,** a fuel mixture of hydrogen and carbon monoxide made by passing steam through hot coke.

Hydrogen is so easily obtained in quantity by the dissociation of water and as a by-product in the production of alkalies by the electrolysis of brine solutions that it appears as a super-abundant material, but its occurrence in nature is much less than many of the other elements. It occurs in the atmosphere to the extent of only about 0.01%, and in the earth's crust to the extent of about 0.2%, or about half that of the metal titanium. However, it constitutes about one-ninth of all water, from which it is easily obtained by high heat or by electrolysis.

Hydrogen has three isotopes. **Hydrogen 2,** called **deuterium,** occurs naturally in ordinary **hydrogen 1** to the extent of one part in about 5,000. Deuterium has one proton and one neutron in the nucleus, with one orbital electron revolving around. A gamma ray will split off the neutron, leaving the single electron revolving around a single proton. The physicist's name for hydrogen 1 is **protium.** Deuterium is also called **double-weight hydrogen. Deuterium oxide** is known as **heavy water.** The formula is H_2O, but with the double-weight hydrogen the molecular weight is 20 instead of the 18 for ordinary water.

Heavy water is used for shielding in atomic reactors as it is more effective than graphite in slowing down fast neutrons. It is also made with oxygen 17 and oxygen 18. Chemicals for special purposes are also made with hydrogen 2. The **deuterated benzene** of Ciba, Ltd., is made with deuterium, and the formula is expressed as C_6D_6. **Hydrogen 3** is **triple-weight hydrogen,** and is called **tritium.** It has two neutrons and one proton in the nucleus, and is radioactive. It is a beta emitter with little harmful secondary ray emission which makes it useful in self-luminous phosphors. It is a solid at very low temperatures. **Liquid hydrogen** for rocket-fuel use is made from ordinary hydrogen. It is required to be within 0.00001% of absolute purity. This material has a boiling point at $-423°F$, and the weight is 0.6 lb per gal. With a chamber pressure of 300 psi, the specific impulse is 375. The **Hydripills** of Metal Hydrides, Inc., used for producing small quantities of hydrogen, are tablets of a mixture of sodium borohydride and **cobalt chloride,** $CoCl_2$. When water is added the chloride reacts to produce hydrogen from both the borohydride and the water. **Gelled hydrogen** for rocket fuel is liquid hydrogen thickened with silica powder.

HYDROGENATED OILS. Vegetable or fish oils that have been hardened or solidified by the action of hydrogen in the presence of a catalyst. Partial hydrogenation also clarifies and makes odorless some oils. The solidifying process is carried on to any desired extent, and these oils have a variety of uses. For mechanical uses they are employed in cutting oils, and in place of palm oil in tinplate manufacture. By hydrogenation the fatty acids, such as oleic acid, are converted into stearic acid. Peanut oil, coconut oil, and cottonseed oil can thus be made to have the appearance, taste, and odor of lard, or they can be made like tallow. **Lard compound,** previous to the passage of the Food and Drugs Act of 1906, was cottonseed oil mixed with oleostearin from beef tallow. It was later sold under trade names, but has now been replaced by hydrogenated oils under the general name of **shortenings,** and under trade names such as **Crisco.** Hydrogenated oils have lower iodine values and higher melting points than the original oils.

INDIGO. Once the most important of all vegetable dyestuffs and valued for the beauty and permanence of its color. Commercial blue indigo is obtained from the plants *Indigofera tinctoria,* and several other species, of India and Java, and the plant *Isatis tinctoria,* of Europe, by steeping the freshly cut plants in water, and after decomposition of the glucoside **indican,** $C_{14}H_{17}O_6N$, the liquid is run into beating vats where the indigo separates out in flakes which are pressed into cakes. About 4 oz of indigo are produced from 100 lb of plants. **Indigo red,** or **indirubin,** $C_{16}H_{10}$-N_2O_2, is a crimson dyestuff obtained in the proportion of 1 to 5% in the manufacture of indigo. **Indigo white** is obtained by reducing agents and an alkali. Another product obtained in the manufacture of synthetic indigo is **indole,** a white crystalline solid with a melting point of 52°C. In concentrations it has a powerful disagreeable odor, but in extreme dilution has a pleasant floral odor and is used in many perfumes. It occurs naturally in oils of jasmine, neroli, orange blossom, and others, and is made synthetically as **benzopyrrole.** **Skatole** is made by adding a methyl group to the No. 3 position of the indole ring. It is a solid melting at 95°C, and is found as a decay product of albumin in animal excrement. It has an overpowering fecal odor, and the synthetic material is used as a fixative in fine perfumery. **Oxindole,** or **hydroxy indole,** is a lactam of aminophenyl acetic acid, easily made synthetically, and is the basis for the production of a wide variety of chemicals.

INDIUM. A silvery-white metal with a bluish cast, whiter than tin. It has a specific gravity of 7.31, tensile strength of 15,000 psi, and elongation 22%. It is very ductile and does not work-harden, as its recrystallization point is below normal room temperature, and it softens during rolling. The metal is not easily oxidized, but above its melting point, 155°C, it oxidizes and burns with a violet flame.

Indium was first found in zinc blende, but is now obtained as a by-product from a variety of ores. Because of its bright color, light reflectance, and corrosion resistance, it is valued as a plating metal, especially for reflectors. It is softer than lead, but a hard surface is obtained by heating the plated part to diffuse the indium into the base metal. It has high adhesion to other metals. When added to chromium plating baths it reduces brittleness of the chromium.

In spite of its softness small amounts of indium will harden copper, tin, or lead alloys and increase the strength. About 1% in lead will double the hardness of the lead. In solders and fusible alloys it improves wetting and lowers the melting point. In lead-base alloys a small amount of indium helps to retain oil film, and increases the resistance to corrosion from the oil acids. Small amounts may be used in gold and silver dental alloys to increase the hardness, strength, and smoothness. Small amounts are also used in silver-lead and silver-copper aircraft-engine bearing alloys. **Lead-indium alloys** are highly resistant to corrosion, and are used for chemical-processing equipment parts. **Gold-indium alloys** have high fluidity, a smooth lustrous color, and good bonding strength. An alloy of 77.5% gold and 22.5 indium, with a working temperature at about 500°C, is used for brazing metal objects with glass inserts. **Silver-indium alloys** have high hardness and a fine silvery color. A silver-indium alloy of the Westinghouse Electric Corp., used for nuclear control rods, contains 80% silver, 15 indium, and 5 cadmium. The melting point is 1375°F, tensile strength 42,000 psi, and elongation 67%, and it retains a strength of 17,600 psi at 600°F. It is stable to irradiation, and is corrosion-resistant in high-pressure water up to 680°F. The thermal expansion is about six times that of steel.

Indium sulfate, used for plating, has three forms. The normal sulfate is $In_2(SO_4)_3 \cdot 9H_2O$; the acid salt is $In_2(SO_4)_3 \cdot H_2SO_4 \cdot 7H_2O$; and the basic salt is $In_2O(SO_4)_2 \cdot 6H_2O$. **Indium oxide** is an amorphous yellow powder of the composition In_2O_3, and specific gravity 7.179, used to give a beautiful yellow color to glass. The color may be varied from light canary to dark tangerine-orange. **Indium monoxide,** InO, is black, and is not stable.

INDUSTRIAL JEWELS. Hard stones, usually ruby and sapphire, used for bearings and impulse pins in instruments and for recording needles. **Ring jewels** are divided into large and small. The large rings are about 0.050 in. in diameter and 0.012 in. in thickness with holes above 0.006 in. in diameter. Ring jewels are used as pivot bearings in instruments, timepieces, and dial indicators. From 2 to 14 are used in a watch. **Vee jewels** are used in electrical instruments and in compasses. **Cup jewels** are used for electric meters and compasses. **End stones** are flat undrilled stones with polished faces to serve as end bearings. **Pallet stones** are rectangular impulse stones for watch escapements. **Jewel pins** are cylindrical impulse stones for the escapement of a timepiece. In making **bearing jewels** the synthetic sapphire boules are split in half, secured to wooden blocks, and then sawed to square blanks.   These are then rounded on centerless grinding machines, and flat-ground to thickness by means of copper wheels with diamond powder.   **Quartz bearings** are made from fused quartz rods.   A notch is ground in the end of the rod, then polished and cut off, repeating the process for each bearing.   Quartz has a hardness of only 7 Mohs, while the synthetic ruby and sapphire have a hardness of 8.8, but quartz has the advantage of low thermal expansion.

The making of industrial jewels was formerly a relatively small special-ized industry, and a national stockpile of cut jewels was maintained for wartime emergencies.   But the process of slicing and shaping hard crystals for semiconductors and other electronic uses is essentially the same, and stones of any required composition and cut to any desired shapes are now regularly manufactured.

INGOT IRON. Nearly chemically pure iron made by the basic open-hearth process and highly refined, remaining in the furnace 1 to 4 hr longer than the ordinary time, and maintained at a temperature of 2900 to 3100°F. In England, it is referred to as **mild steel,** but in the United States the line between iron and steel is placed arbitrarily at about 0.15% content of carbon.   Ingot iron has as low as 0.02% carbon.   It is obtainable regu-larly in grades 99.8 to 99.9% pure iron.   Ingot iron is cast into ingots and then rolled into plates or shapes and bars.   It it used for construction work where a ductile, rust-resistant metal is required, especially for tanks, boil-ers, enameled ware, and for galvanized culvert sheets.   The tensile strength, hot-rolled, is 48,000 psi, elongation 30%, and Brinell hardness 82 to 100. Dead soft, the tensile strength is 38,500 psi, elongation 45%, and Brinell hardness 67.   **Armco ingot iron,** of Armco Steel Corp., is 99.94% pure, with the carbon 0.013 and the manganese 0.017%.   It is used as a rust-resistant construction material, for electromagnetic cores, and as a raw material in making special steels.   The specific gravity is 7.858, and melting point 1530°C.   **Enamelite** is a sheet iron especially suited for vitreous enameling, produced by the Sharon Steel Co.   Ingot iron may also be obtained in grades containing 0.25 to 0.30% copper, which in-creases the corrosion resistance.   Iron of very low carbon content may also be used for molds and dies which are to be hobbed.   The iron is quite plastic under the hob and is then hardened by carburizing.   **Plastiron,** of Henry Disston & Sons, Inc., is such an iron.

INK. Colored liquids or pastes used for writing, drawing, marking, and printing.   Black writing inks usually contain gallotannate of iron which is obtained by adding an infusion of nutgalls to a solution of ferrous sulfate. Good **writing ink** is a clear, filterable solution, not a suspension.   It must flow easily from the pen without clogging, give a smooth, varnishlike coating, and it must adhere to inner fibers of the paper without penetrating through the paper. It must have an intense color that does not bleach out. Ink is essentially a pigment in a liquefying and adhesive medium, but the iron-gallotannate writing inks develop their full color by chemical action and become insoluble in the outer fibers of the paper. For the proper development of the black color in gallotannate inks a high percentage of iron is needed, and this requires a liberal use of acid which will tend to injure the paper. It is thus usually the practice to reduce the amount of iron and bring up the color with dyes or pigments. Gums or adhesive materials may also be added.

Carbon inks are composed of lampblack or carbon black in solutions of gums or glutenous materials. **India ink** is a heavy-bodied drawing ink. The original India ink, or **Chinese ink,** was made with a jet-black carbon pigment produced by burning tung oil with insufficient air. The pigment was imported into Europe in compressed sticks known as **indicum.** India ink was originally only black ink, but the name is now used also for colored heavy drawing inks made with various mineral pigments. **Marking inks** are usually solutions of dyes that are fast to laundering, but they may also be made with silver salts which develop full color and stability by application of heat. **Fountain-pen ink** is not a special-composition ink, but is a writing ink free of sediment and tendency to gum. It usually contains tannic, gallic, and hydrochloric acids with a pH above 2 to avoid corrosion. **Permanent inks** contain dissolved iron, not over 1% to avoid sludge. **Ballpoint ink** is usually a paste and is a true solution with 40 to 50% dye concentration. It must be stable to air, noncorrosive, and a good lubricant. An **encaustic ink** is a special writing ink that will penetrate the fibers of the paper and set chemically to make erasure difficult, but an **indelible ink** for textiles is a marking ink. **Invisible-writing inks,** or **sympathetic inks,** are inks that remain invisible until the writing is brought out by the application of heat or with another chemical which develops the color. They are made with sal ammoniac or salts of metals. **Magnetic ink** for use on bank checks to permit mechanical processing contains 50 to 70% of a magnetic powder smaller than 5 microns particle size. The powder may be hydrogen-reduced iron, carbonyl iron, or electrolytic iron.

Printing inks are in general made with carbon black, lampblack, or other pigment suspended in an oil vehicle, with a resin, solvent, adhesive, and drier. But there are innumerable modifications of printing inks to meet different conditions of printing and varieties of surfaces. The oil or chemical vehicles are innumerable, and the pigments, resin strengtheners and gloss formers, adhesives, tackifiers, and driers vary greatly to suit the nature and surface coating of the base material. Oils may dry by oxidation, polymerization, absorption, or solvent evaporation, and resins may be used to add gloss, strength, hardness, color fastness, or to increase the speed of drying.   It is estimated that there are about 8,000 variables in an ink, and thus printing ink is a prescription product for any given job.   They are not normally purchased on composition specification, but on ability to meet the requirements of the printing.   **Aremco-Mark 530,** of Aremco Products, Inc., is a black **ceramic ink** that withstands temperatures to 2000°F. These inks are ceramic solutions that must be heat-cured.   **Flexographic ink** and **rotogravure ink** may be made with cellulose-acetate-propionate ester resin which is soluble in alcohol and in other resins.   When used with urea it cross-links to form a permanent thermoset film.

INSECTICIDES. Chemicals, either natural or synthetic, used to kill or control insects, particularly agricultural pests, also referred to as **pesticides.** Of about 800,000 known species of insects, half feed directly on plants, retarding growth of the plant and causing low yields and inferior crops. The production of insecticides is now one of the important branches of the chemical industry, and increasing quantities are used, but the specification and use of insecticides require much skill because of the cumulative toxic effect in the earth and in animal or plant life.   Indiscriminate use may destroy honey bees and other useful insects, produce sterility of soils by killing worms and anaerobic life, and poison the waters of lakes and streams. DDT, for example, is highly valuable for the control of malaria and other insect-borne diseases, but its uncontrolled use as an insecticide has been disastrous to wildlife.

Insecticides are generally classed as **stomach poisons** and **contact poisons.** Stomach poisons include **calcium arsenate,** a white powder of the composition $Ca_3(AsO_4)_2$, which constitutes about half of all insecticides used, and also paris green, lead arsenate, and white arsenic.   An **antimetabolite** is not a direct poison, but acts on the insect to stop the desire for food so that the insect dies from starvation.   Dimethyl triazino acetamilide, used against corn-ear worms, is such a chemical.   Contact poisons include rotenone dust, sulfur dust, and nicotine sulfate solution.

A **larvicide** is a chemical, such as chloropicrin, used to destroy fungi and nematodes in soils, and insect eggs and organisms in warehouses. Chemicals used against fungi and bacteria are called **fungicides** and **bactericides,** and those used to control plant diseases caused by viruses are called **viricides.**   None of these are properly classed as insecticides, but are often used with them.   **Herbicides** are used to kill weeds, usually by overstimulating cell growth.   **Amino triazole,** used as a weed killer, may cause cancer in animal life.   Most of the pest-control chemicals are cumulative toxic poisons.   **Benzene hexachloride** destroys bone marrow, and all of the chlorinated hydrocarbons affect the liver.   **Deodorants** may have an insect-kill action, but are usually chemicals such as chlorophyll which combine with impurities in the air to eliminate unpleasant odors.

Insecticides may be solids or liquids, and the solids may be applied as a fine powder, usually in dilution in a dusting powder, or the powder may be suspended in a liquid carrier. Usually, the proportion of poison mixed with a mineral powder is no more than 5%. The mineral carrier, or **dusting powder,** for this purpose should be gritless and inert to the insecticide. Ordinary **dusting clay** is a light, fluffy, air-floated kaolin, or it may be finely ground soft limestone. **Sodium fluorosilicate,** Na_2SiF_6, comes as a fine white powder for this purpose. Calcium sulfate is also used as a carrier but has itself a poisoning effect. One of the oldest of solid insecticides still used either dry or in liquid sprays is **Bordeaux mixture,** made by reacting copper sulfate with lime, giving a product with an excess of hydrated lime. Liquid carriers for insecticides may be kerosene or other petroleum hydrocarbons, or they may be liquid chemicals that have toxic properties, but they must be chosen to avoid deleterious effects, such as the yellowing of papers and organic materials in warehouses or archives, or the injuring of plants from active chlorine in some chemicals.

Some materials, such as citronella oil, used as mosquito repellents in households, have little or no value as insecticides for the eradication of mosquitoes in important applications such as at military sites or mining and lumbering camps. The **aerosol bomb** employed during the Second World War contained 3% DDT, 2 to 20 pyrethrum concentrate, 5 cyclohexanone, 5 mineral oil, and the balance a carrier gas. **Dimethyl phthalate,** a liquid of the composition $C_6H_4(CO_2CH_3)_2$, is a mosquito repellent having an effect lasting $1\frac{1}{2}$ hr in the open air. Thiourea is used to kill mosquito larvae in water and is harmless to fish.

The insecticide called **DDT** is dichloro diphenyl trichloroethane, $C_6H_3\text{-}Cl_2(C_6H_4 \cdot CH_2CCl_3)$, used effectively during the Second World War against flies, mosquitoes, body lice, and agricultural pests. It has no noxious odor, but it is cumulative and in concentration is toxic to man and to other warm-blooded animals. Oil paint containing 0.5 to 5% DDT kills flies on walls painted with it. **Deenate,** of Du Pont, is DDT combined with a carrier for use as an agricultural insecticide. **Monoxychlor,** of the same company, is a trichloroethane analog of DDT, more effective than DDT and less toxic to warm-blooded animals. **Methoxychlor,** called **Marlate** by Du Pont, is a methoxyphenyl trichloroethane and has higher killing power than DDT. **Chlordane** is a liquid of the composition $C_{10}H_6Cl_8$. It is a powerful insecticide. **Lindane,** of Hooker Chemical Co., is a chlorinated hydrocarbon in the form of pellets. It releases chlorine gradually, and is toxic to humans when used continuously.

Sabadilla is used in cotton sprays. It is also known as **cevadilla,** or **Indian barley,** and consists of the dried ripe poisonous seeds of the plant *Veratrum sabadilla* of the lily family growing in Central America, of which there are about 20 known species in Central and South America. The seeds contain **veratric acid** from which is derived **veratraldehyde,** or **vetraldehyde,** a crystalline solid of the composition $(CH_3O)_2C_6H_3 \cdot CHO$, which gives the heliotrope flavor to the vanilla of Samoa and to some synthetic vanilla from coniferin. The alkaloid poison is extracted with a hydrocarbon solvent, and when the extract is used as an insecticide in combination with a synthetic, it gives greatly increased toxicity. The powdered seeds are also used as an agricultural insecticide dust which has greater staying power than pyrethrum. The cresols in various forms are also used as insecticides. **Dinitro orthocresol,** a yellow crystalline material melting at 83.5°C, is used in fruit-tree sprays. **Thanite,** of Hercules, Inc., is isobornyl thiocyano acetate, an amber liquid with a camphorlike odor. It has 5 times the toxicity of pyrethrum, and is used in insecticides and cattle sprays. Sodium antimony lacto phenate, known as **salp,** is an effective insecticide against chewing insects. Some insecticides are sprayed on the ground or on the foliage to be absorbed into the plant, poisoning the insect that feeds on the plant. **Systox** of the Pittsburgh Agricultural Chemical Co., is a diethyl ethyl mercapto ethyl thiophosphate for this purpose.

CPR dust base, of U.S. Chemicals, Inc., used as a general agricultural insecticide, contains rotenone, pyrethrin, and piperonyl cyclononene. The **Pyrenones** of this company are mixtures of pyrethrum with piperonyl cyclononene or piperonyl butoxide. **Pyrenone Aerosol** has 5% pyrethrin and 40 piperonyl butoxide. **Santobane,** of the Monsanto Chemical Co., is formulated DDT. **Gix** is a German variant of DDT. It is difluoro diphenyl trichloroethane, and is more effective but more expensive. The German insecticide **Bladen** is **hexaethyl tetraphosphate.** A more powerful improvement on this material is **tetraethyl pyrophosphate,** $(C_2H_5)_4P_2O_7$, produced as **Nifos-T** by the Monsanto Chemical Co. It is soluble in aromatic solvents, but loses its activity in water. **Strobane,** of the B. F. Goodrich Chemical Co., is a chlorinated terpene with about the same toxicity as pyrethrin. It is a heavy liquid. **Acrylon,** of the American Cyanamid Co., is a 50–50 mixture of acrylonitrile and carbon tetrachloride. **Pencal,** of the Pennsylvania Salt Mfg. Co., is a neutral calcium arsenate for combination with DDT or other insecticides.

Insecticide 666, of the Imperial Chemical Industries, is **hexachlorocyclohexane,** $C_6H_6Cl_6$, with four isomers, and is made by passing chlorine into benzol with ultraviolet light as a catalyst. The gamma isomer, called **gammexane,** which has a melting point of 112.5°C, is separated out as it is the most active poison. It is soluble in naphtha, benzene, and in alcohol. It is 100 times more toxic against roaches than DDT, but nearly parallels that chemical for other uses. Both kill insects and larvae, but do not have the quick kill of pyrethrum. The fungicide known as **Dowicide 7,** of the Dow Chemical Co., is **pentachloro phenol,** $C_6(OH)Cl_5$, an odorless brownish flaky powder soluble in most organic solvents.   It is insoluble in water and is an effective fungicide and preservative for wood-work and textile fibers such as jute.   **Dowicil 100,** used as a preservative in paper coatings and adhesives, contains no phenol or mercury.   It is a quaternary ammonium which releases formaldehyde slowly with low toxicity.   **Santophen 20,** of Monsanto, is this chemical in an oil solution for use as a wood preservative.   **Dowicide G** is the sodium salt, $C_6(ONa)Cl_5$, soluble in water, used as a fungicide and preservative in insulation board and water-soluble paints.   A solution of **thioacetamide,** CH_3CSNH_2, is used to spray oranges in storage to kill the fungi that cause blue and green molds.   **Fermate,** of Du Pont, is **ferric diethyl dithiocarbamate,** a fine black powder used as a fruit fungicide.

Wood preservatives are not usually classed as insecticides though their chief purpose is to kill insects and fungi.   The most widely used **wood preservative** is coal-tar creosote or its derivatives.   **Sodium fluoride,** or **fluorol,** NaF, is a water-soluble white powder used as a wood preservative as well as an insecticide and vermin poison, although this material is better known as an industrial chemical.   Single crystals of it are used for windows for ultraviolet and infrared equipment as it transmits these rays.   When wood is treated with an alkaline water solution of acrylonitrile ethylates the cellulose fibers are cyanoethylated and the wood becomes resistant to the attack of enzymes and fungi.   Wood treated with pyradine and acetic anhydride is given dimensional stability as well as resistance to insect and fungi attack.   The termite-resistant and decay-resistant wood called **Cellon wood** by the Koppers Co. has been pressure-treated with liquefied penta-chloro phenol.   The wood contains about 0.3 lb of crystalline pentachloro phenol per cubic foot uniformly distributed through the fibers, and is highly resistant to insect and fungi attack.   The color, weight, strength, and working qualities of the wood are not changed.

A **fumigant** is a liquid, powder, or gas which kills insects, worms, or burrowing animals by toxic fumes.   For general use a fumigant should not be injurious to grains or stored foodstuffs.   **Repellents** are fumigants used for driving out insects but do not kill.   However, some repellents contain naphthalene, rotenone, or other materials having toxic properties, and these are insecticides rather than fumigants.   **Methyl bromide,** or **bromomethane,** CH_3Br, a gas with a liquefying point at $4.6°C$, is an effective fumigant not injurious to grains.   **Dowfume BR10,** of the Dow Chemical Co., is a methyl bromide with chlorinated hydrocarbons, used in pressure cylinders for fumigating warehouses.   Methyl bromide is also used for fumigating clothing warehouses and does not shrink or wrinkle woolen fabrics.   **Carboxide,** of the Carbide & Carbon Chemicals Corp., is a mixture of carbon dioxide and ethylene oxide used as a fumigant. It does not injure grains or foodstuffs.   **Dihydroacetic acid** is used on dried fruits in storage to prevent decomposition.   It acts in the nature of a fungicide.

INSULATORS. Any materials that retard the flow of electricity, used to prevent the passage or escape of electric current from conductors.   No materials are absolute nonconductors; those rating lowest on the scale of conductivity are therefore the best insulators.   An important requirement of a good insulator is that it not absorb moisture which would lower its resistivity.   Glass and porcelain are the most common line insulators because of low cost.   Pure silica glass has an average dielectric strength of 500 volts per mil, and glass-bonded mica about 450 volts per mil, while ordinary porcelain may be as low as 200 volts per mil, and steatite about 240 volts per mil.   Slate, steatite, and stone slabs are still used for panelboards, but there is now a great variety of insulating boards made by compressing glass fibers, quartz, or minerals with binders, or standard laminated plastics of good dielectric strength may be used.   **Vulcoid,** of the Budd Co., and **Vulcabeston,** of Johns-Manville, are typical.   For slots and separators, natural mica is still valued because of its heat resistance, but, because of the irregular quality of natural mica and the difficulty of handling the small pieces, it has been largely replaced by synthetic mica paper, polyester sheet, or impregnated papers or fabrics.   The impregnated fish paper of the Spaulding Fibre Co., called **Armite,** comes in thicknesses down to 0.004 in., and has a dielectric strength of 500 volts per mil.

Synthetic rubbers and plastics have now replaced natural rubber for wire insulation, but some aluminum conductors are insulated only with an anodized coating of aluminum oxide.   Wires to be coated with an organic insulator may first be treated with hydrogen fluoride, giving a coating of copper fluoride on copper wire and aluminum fluoride on aluminum wire. The thin film of fluoride has high dielectric strength and heat resistance. The AIEE classification for wire insulation is by heat resistance, from **Class O insulation,** for temperatures to 195°F, to **Class C insulation,** for temperatures above 355°F.

Insulating oils are mineral oils of high dielectric strength and high flash point employed in circuit breakers, switches, transformers, and other electric apparatus.   An oil with a flash point of 285°F and fire point of 310°F is considered safe.   A clean, well-refined oil will have high dielectric strength, but the presence of as low as 0.01% water will reduce the dielectric strength drastically.   The insulating oils, therefore, cannot be stored for long periods because of the danger of absorbing moisture.   Impurities such as acids or alkalies also detract from the strength of the oil. Since insulating oils are used for cooling as well as for insulating, the viscosity should be low enough for free circulation, and they should not gum.   **Askarel** is an ASTM designation for **insulating fluids** which give out only nonflammable gases if decomposed by an electric arc.   They are usually chlorinated aromatic hydrocarbons such as trichloro benzene, but fluorinated hydrocarbons are also used.   They have high dielectric strength, and a dielectric constant below 2.   **Insulating gases** are used to replace air in closed areas to insulate high-voltage equipment.   Sulfur hexafluoride for this purpose, with a density of 0.755, has a dielectric strength 2.35 times that of air.   The insulating oil, fluids, and gases are generally referred to as **dielectrics,** although this term embraces any insulator.

Insulation porcelain, or **electrical porcelain,** is not usually an ordinary porcelain except for common line insulators.   For such uses as spark plugs they may be molded silica, and for electronic insulation they may be molded steatite or specially compounded ceramics, more properly called **ceramic insulators.**   Insulation porcelains compounded with varying percentages of zirconia and beryllia have a crystalline structure, and have good dielectric and mechanical strengths at temperatures as high as 2000°F. These porcelains may have some magnesia, but are free of silica.   However, **zircon porcelain** is made from zirconium silicate, and the molded and fired ceramic is equal to high-grade steatite for high-frequency insulation.   **Vitrolain,** of the Star Porcelain Co., is an electrical porcelain of high strength and density with porosity of only 0.25%.   **Thyrite,** of the General Electric Co., is a porcelain that possesses the property of being an insulator at low potentials and a conductor at high potentials.   It is used for lightning arrestors.   The German **Hartporzellan,** or **hard porcelains,** are specially compounded ceramics having good resistance to thermal shock. The material called **Nolex** by the Naval Ordnance Laboratory is made by hot-molding finely powdered synthetic fluorine mica.   The molded parts are practically pure mica.   They can be machined, have high dimensional precision because they need no further heat treatment, and have high dielectric strength.   Beryllia is a valued insulator for encapsulation coatings on heat-generating electronic devices as it has both high electrical resistivity and high heat conductivity.

IODINE.   A purplish-black, crystalline, poisonous elementary solid, chemical symbol I, best known for its use as a strong antiseptic in medicine, but also used in many chemical compounds and war gases.   In tablet form it is used for sterilizing drinking water, and has less odor and taste than chlorine for this purpose.   It is also used in cattle feeds.   Although poisonous in quantity, iodine is essential to proper cell growth in the human body, and is found in every cell in a normal body, with larger concentration in the thyroid gland.

The Chilean production of iodine is as a by-product of the nitrate industry.   In Scotland, Norway, and Japan it is produced by burning seaweed and treating the ashes.   A ton of seaweed produces about a pound of iodine. It is also produced from salt brines and from seawater, and in California from the waste waters of oil wells, the brine containing 65 parts of iodine per million. The lump iodine from this source is 99.9% pure. As much as 1,000 tons of iodine is present in a cubic mile of seawater. The specific gravity of iodine is 4.98, melting point 114.2°C, and boiling point 184°C. It is insoluble in water, but is soluble in alcohol, ether, and alkaline solutions. **Tincture of iodine,** a 7% alcohol solution of iodine in a 5% solution of potassium iodide, is used in medicine as a caustic anti-septic. As an antiseptic iodine has the disadvantage that it burns and stains the skin. **Vodine,** of the Lanteen Laboratories, Inc., is a 2% oil-and-water emulsion of iodine containing also lecithin. It does not burn, and the faint stain washes off easily. An **iodophor** is a chemical containing iodine which is released on contact with organic material. **I-O-Dynamic,** of Field Bros., Inc., is a detergent containing iodine. **PVP iodine,** of the General Aniline & Film Corp., is iodine combined with polyvinyl pyrrolidine to give a product that retains the germ-killing properties of iodine without the toxic and burning effects. **Wescodyne,** of the West Disinfecting Co., is another nonburning and nonstaining iodine. **Clearodine,** of the U.S. Peroxide Corp., is a water-soluble iodine in powder form for disinfectant purposes. In water solution it releases a colorless **hypoiodous acid**, IHO. It has a higher bacteriological effect than ordinary iodine and does not stain or irritate. **Iodine cyanide,** ICN, an extremely poisonous colorless crystalline material soluble in water, is used as a preservative for furs and museum specimens. Alfa Inorganics produces the acid as **iodic acid** HIO_3, and a stable **iodine pentoxide** I_2O_5 is also marketed. The iodine atom is very regular with a valence of 7, but having three spheron pairs in opposite polarity which can be broken to give valences as 1, 3, 5, and 7. A wide range of compounds are made for electronic and chemical uses.

IRIDIUM. A grayish-white metal of extreme hardness, symbol Ir. It is insoluble in all acids and in aqua regia. The melting point is 2443°C and the specific gravity is 22.65. The annealed metal has a hardness of 172 Brinell. Iridium is found in the nickel-copper ores of Canada, pyroxinite deposits of South Africa, and platinum ores of Russia and Alaska. It occurs naturally with the metal osmium as an alloy, known as **osmiridium,** 30 to 60% osmium, used chiefly for making fountain-pen points and in-strument pivots. Iridium is employed as a hardener for platinum, the jewelry alloys usually containing 10%. With 35% iridium the tensile strength of platinum is increased to 140,000 psi. **Iridium-rhodium alloys** are used for high-temperature thermocouples. Electrodeposition is dif-ficult, but coatings have been obtained with a fused sodium cyanide electrolyte or with an iridium salt and organic compound in solution and, after application, volatilizing the vehicle and reducing the compound to the metal. Iridium-clad molybdenum or tungsten is produced by swaging an iridium tube onto the base metal and drawing at 600°C. Iridium plating is used on molybdenum to protect against oxidation at very high temperatures. Above 600°C iridium tarnishes and above 1000°C it forms a volatile oxide. It gives a bright ductile plate with a Vickers hardness of 170. It is also used as a catalyst. It is resistant to most molten metals except copper, aluminum, zinc, and magnesium. **Iridium wire** is used in spark plugs as it resists attack of leaded aviation fuels. **Iridium-tungsten alloys** are used for springs operating at temperatures to 800°C. Iridium intermetallic compounds such as Cb_3Ir_2, Ti_3Ir, and $ZrIr_2$ are superconductors. Iridium is multivalent with most of its compounds formed in its trivalent state, as $IrCl_3$. The metal is sold by the troy ounce, a cubic inch of the metal weighing 11.82 troy oz.

IRON. The most common of the commercial metals, although not as plentiful as aluminum. It has been in use since the most remote times, but it does not occur native except in the form of meteorites, and early tools of Egypt were apparently made from nickel irons from this source. The common iron ores are magnetic pyrites, magnetite, hematite, and carbonates of iron. To obtain the iron the ores are fused to drive off the oxygen, sulfur, and impurities. The melting is done in a blast furnace directly in contact with the fuel and with limestone as a flux. The latter combines with the quartz and clay, forming a slag which is readily removed. The resulting product is crude pig iron which requires subsequent remelting and refining to obtain commercially pure iron. A short ton of ore, with about 1,000 lb of coke and 600 lb of limestone, produces an average of 1,120 lb of pig iron. Sintered iron and steel are also produced without blast-furnace reduction by compressing purified iron oxide in rollers, heating to 2200°F, and hot-strip rolling. The final cold-rolled product is similar to conventional iron and steel.

Iron is a grayish metal, which until recently was never used pure. It melts at 1525°C and boils at 2450°C. Even very small additions of carbon reduce the melting point. It has a specific gravity of 7.85. All commercial irons except ingot iron and electrolytic iron contain perceptible quantities of carbon, which affect its properties. Iron containing more than 0.15% chemically combined carbon is termed steel. When the carbon is increased to above about 0.40%, the metal will harden when cooled suddenly from a red heat. Iron, when pure, is very ductile, but a small amount of sulfur, as little as 0.03%, will make it **hot-short,** or brittle at red heat. As little as 0.25% of phosphorus will make iron **cold-short,** or brittle when cold. Iron forms carbonates, chlorides, oxides, sulfides, and other compounds. It oxidizes easily and is also attacked by many acids.

Electrolytic iron is a chemically pure iron produced by the deposition of iron in a manner similar to electroplating. Bars of cast iron are used as anodes and dissolved in an electrolyte of ferrous chloride. The current precipitates almost pure iron on the cathodes which are hollow steel cylinders. The deposited iron tube is removed by hydraulic pressure or by splitting, and then annealed and rolled into plates. The iron is 99.9% pure, and is used for magnetic cores and where ductility and purity are needed. Highly refined nearly pure iron is marketed by the Westinghouse Electric Corp. under the name of **Puron** in rod form for use for spectroscopic and magnetic standards. It contains 99.95% iron, with only 0.005 carbon, 0.003 sulfur, and less than 0.001 phosphorus. By high-temperature hydrogen annealing, the carbon can be reduced to 0.001%, bringing the purity to 99.99%. **Iron whiskers** are single-crystal pure iron fibers, 0.00004 in. in diameter, for electronic uses. The tensile strength is as high as 500,000 psi.

Iron powder, as originally produced in Sweden, is made by reducing iron ore by the action of carbon monoxide at a temperature below the melting point of the iron and below the reduction point of the other metallic oxides in the ore. In the United States it is made by the reduction of iron oxide mill scale, or by electrolysis of steel borings and turnings in an electrolyte of ferric chloride. Iron powder is used for molded parts made by sintering. Soft **electrolytic iron powder** for making sintered molded parts has 99% min iron, 0.04 max carbon, a hydrogen loss of 0.9 max, and 0.1 max of other impurities. Up to 40% passes through a 325-mesh screen. The apparent density is 2.5, and the final density of the molded part is 7.2 to 7.7. **Magnetic iron powder,** used for electrical cores of high permeability, is made by reducing iron oxide with hydrogen. For this purpose it must be free of carbon and sulfur. A 10- to 40-micron powder with an apparent density of 2.75 will compress to a density of 6.85 at 150,000 psi. **Carbonyl iron powder,** used for magnetic cores for high-frequency equipment and for medical application of iron, is metallic iron of extreme purity and in microscopic spherical particles. It is made by the reaction of carbon monoxide on iron ore to give liquid **iron carbonyl,** $Fe(CO)_5$, which is vaporized and deposited as a powder. Iron powders made by the carbonyl process are marketed by Antara Chemicals in other types for powder metallurgy. These include powders with a steellike concentric shell structure of the particles which measure 3 to 8 microns. The high-purity, silica-free iron powder, produced by the Powdered Iron Corp. for electronic cores, is made by electrolytic deposition in a mercury cathode. The fine dendritic particles are recovered by distillation of the cathode.

HVA iron powder, produced electrolytically in Germany for making strong, high-density parts by powder metallurgy, contains a maximum of 0.02% silicon, 0.05 carbon, 0.06 manganese, 0.01 phosphorus, and 0.01

sulfur.   The standard powder has up to 35% of the grains under 0.06 mm, up to 30% from 0.10 to 0.06 mm, and a maximum of 5% over 0.20 mm.   The sponge grade, for making porous parts, has a greater percentage of smaller particles, with up to 50% under 0.06 mm.   Parts made with electrolytic iron powder to a density of 7.5 have a tensile strength of about 40,000 psi with elongation of 30%.

Reduced iron, used for special chemical purposes, is a fine gray amorphous powder made by reducing crushed iron ore by heating with hydrogen.   **Nu-Iron,** of the U.S. Steel Corp., is iron powder made by reducing Fe_2O_3 with hydrogen at 1300°F to FeO, and then at 1100°F to iron to prevent sintering of the particles.   **H-iron,** of the Bethlehem Steel Co., is a **hydrogen-reduced iron.**   Iron powder made by this process is usually pyrophoric, and is made nonpyrophoric by heating in a nonoxidizing atmosphere.   **Ferrocene,** of the Ethyl Corp., used as a combustion-control additive in fuels, and in lubricants and plastics for heat stabilization and radiation resistance, is a **dicyclo pentadienyl iron,** $(C_5H_5)_2Fe$.   It is a double-ring compound with the iron atom between parallel planes and symmetrically bound to the five carbon atoms of each ring.   It is an orange-yellow powder melting at 173°C, but resisting pyrolysis to 470°C. **Iron 55** is a very pure radioactive iron produced in minute quantities by cyclotronic bombardment of manganese and used in medicine for increasing the red blood pigment, **hemoglobin,** in the human system.   **Busheled iron** is an inferior grade of iron or steel made by heating bundles of scrap iron or steel in a furnace and then forging and rolling into bars.   It is not uniform in composition or in the welding together, and is used only in isolated places or in wartime.

IRON ORES. Iron-bearing minerals from which iron can be extracted on a commercial scale.   The chief iron ores in order of importance are hematite, magnetite, limonite, and siderite.   More than 90% of the iron ores mined in the United States are **red hematites,** Fe_2O_3, containing theoretically 70% iron, but usually not over 60%.   The districts include the Lake Superior region and northern Alabama.   It is also the ore from the Furness district in England and parts of Spain and Germany.   The color is various shades of reddish brown, and the structure is usually earthy. The variety known as **kidney ore** is columnar with a fibrous appearance; **specular hematite** has a brilliant luster and foliated structure.   The specific gravity is 4.8 to 5.3.   **Brown hematites** contain from 35 to 55% iron.   Ores containing more than 50% iron are considered high grade. Lake Superior ores are now averaging only 52% Fe, with 8 silica.   This region also has large reserves of **taconite,** a ferroginous chert which is an alteration product from **greenalite,** or ferrous silicate.   Taconite eventually leaches and becomes a hematite by the loss of silica, but the Mesaba taconite is a very hard gray-green sedimentary chert in the form of a compact silica rock with 20 to 35% iron. It cannot be used directly in a blast furnace but is crushed to powder, concentrated to 65% iron, and pelletized for use. **Rubio iron ore** of Spain is classed both as limonite and brown hematite. It is a **hydrated ferric oxide,** $Fe_2O_3 \cdot H_2O$, brown-streaked with a silica gangue. It contains 77.4% ferric oxide, 9.2 silica, 1.76 alumina, and 1.1 manganese oxide.

The **hematite ores** are preferred for the Bessemer process because of their freedom from phosphorus and sulfur. **Natural iron** is the percentage of iron in the ore before drying; **dry iron** is the percentage of iron in the ore after drying at 212°F. Low-grade hematite and limonite ores can be concentrated by passing the ground ore through a reducing gas at high temperature, which causes a part of the iron in each particle to become magnetic and thus capable of being separated. Low-grade ores of 30% iron are also ground to a fine powder and separated from the gangue by flotation, concentrated to 60% iron, and pelleted with a bentonite binder. **Self-fluxing iron ore** is concentrated iron ore combined with limestone and pelleted.

Magnetite, or **magnetic iron ore,** is found in northern New York, in New Jersey, and in Pennsylvania. It has the composition $FeO \cdot Fe_2O_3$, containing theoretically 72.4% iron but usually only about 62%. Magnetite may also contain some nickel or titanium. The specific gravity is 5.18, the melting point is 1540°C, the color is iron black with a metallic luster, and the material is strongly magnetic. The natural magnet known as **lodestone** is magnetite.

Siderite and carbonate ores are used in Great Britain, Germany, and Russia, much of which is not considered commercial in the United States, but the **dogger iron ore** of Germany contains as high as 35% iron. **Siderite** is the chief iron ore in Great Britain. It is found in Staffordshire, Yorkshire, and Wales, and in the United States in Pennsylvania and Ohio. It is an **iron carbonate,** $FeCO_3$, containing theoretically 48.2% iron. It usually occurs granular or compact and earthy. Its specific gravity is 4.5 to 5, and the hardness is 3.5 to 4. The color is light to dark brown, with a vitreous luster. It often is impure, with a mixture of clay materials or forming stratified bodies with coal formations. It is also known as **carbonate ore, ironstone,** and as **spathic iron ore.** Impure forms mixed with clay and sands are called **clay ironstones,** or **black band.** The ironstone and black-band ores are the important ores of England and Scotland, but there is only a slight usage of carbonate ore in the United States. The **minette ore** of Luxembourg and Germany averages about 26% iron, 22 CaO, 11 silica, and 2 $CaOSiO_2$, with 0.54 phosphorus and 0.06 vanadium. The ore mined in Norway and Sweden is very pure, and it is the ore used for the **dannemora iron** made with charcoal as a fuel.

Limonite, also called **brown hematite, brown ore, bog iron ore,** and **shot ore** when in the form of loose rounded particles, was the common iron ore of early New England. It is a mineral of secondary origin formed by the water solution of other iron minerals. Its composition is $2Fe_2O_3 \cdot 3H_2O$, containing theoretically 59.8% iron, but usually 30 to 55%. It occurs earthy or in stalactitic forms of a dark-brown color. The specific gravity is 3.6 to 4. Limonite is found in Alabama, Tennessee, and Virginia, and is also an English and German ore. **Goethite** is a minor ore of iron of the composition $Fe_2O_3 \cdot H_2O$, found in the Lake Superior hematite deposits and in England. It is yellowish brown in color with a specific gravity of 4.3. It is also called **turgite.** The largest known deposits of high-grade iron ores are in Brazil and extending into Venezuela. The ore in southwestern Brazil is with deposits of manganese. The hematite of Minas Gerais contains 57 to 71% iron. Large deposits of high-grade iron ores are also found in the Labrador-Quebec region of Canada, in India, and in the South Africa–Rhodesia area. The nearest approach to a native iron is the iron-nickel mineral **awaruite,** $FeNi_2$, found in gravel in New Zealand and Alaska, and **josephinite,** $FeNi_3$, found in serpentine in Oregon.

IRON PYRITE. A mineral sometimes mined for the zinc, gold, or copper associated with it, but chiefly used for producing sulfur, sulfuric acid, and copperas. It is an **iron disulfide,** FeS_2, containing 53.4% sulfur. It often occurs in crystals, also massive or granular. It is brittle, with a hardness of 6 to 6.5 and specific gravity 4.95 to 5.1. The color is brass yellow, and it is called **fool's gold** because of the common error made in detection. In the Italian method of roasting pyrites, the oxygen combines with the sulfur to form sulfur dioxide, and also with the iron. In a yield of 100,000 tons of concentrated sulfuric acid there is obtained a by-product of 50,000 tons of 65% iron ore. **Pyrite** is found in rocks of all ages associated with different minerals. The pyrites mined in Missouri, known as **marcasite,** also used for gemstones, have the formula FeS, and the gem specimens have a yellow color with a greenish tinge. **Sulfur pyrites,** found in great quantity in Shasta County, Calif., are roasted to produce sulfuric acid and the residue is used for making cement and ferric sulfate. The distillation of 370 tons of pyrite of Ontario yields 62 tons of sulfur and 252 tons of iron oxide sinter, the latter being used in steel mills. In Japan pyrite is chlorinated, producing sulfur, copper, gold, silver, and zinc, and the residue of sintered pellets of Fe_2O_3 is used in blast furnaces.

IRON SHOT. An abrasive material made by running molten iron into water. It is employed in tumbling barrels and also in the cutting and grinding of stones.   The round sizes between No. 30 and No. 20 are used for the shot peening of mechanical parts to increase fatigue resistance.   **Peening shot** is marketed by SAE numbers from 6 to 157, the size numbers being the diameter in thousandths of an inch.   Grit numbers in shot for grinding are from No. 10 to No. 200; the No. 10 is 0.0787 in., and the No. 200 is 0.0029 in. in diameter.   **Steel grit** is made by forcing molten iron through a steam jet so that the metal forms into small and irregular pieces of chilled iron.   The regular globules are screened and graded into **steel shot** in sizes from No. 6 to No. 35, and the irregular pieces and large globules are crushed into steel grit in sizes from No. 8 to No. 80.   It is preferred to sand for sandblasting some materials. **Steelblast,** of the Steelblast Abrasives Co., is this material for tumbling and sandblasting.

Tru-Steel shot,** of the American Wheelabrator & Equipment Corp., is steel shot which has been heat-treated to give toughness to prevent breakdown into fragments.   **Cutwire shot,** of the Precision Shot Co., is made by cutting SAE 1065 steel wire into short pieces.   **Pellets shot,** of Pellets, Inc., is steel wire of a hardness of Rockwell 50 cut to lengths equal to the diameter of the wire, ranging from 0.028 to 0.41 in.   **Kut-Steel** is a similar abrasive of the Steelblast Abrasives Co.   **Permabrasive,** of the National Metal Abrasive Co., is a treated **malleable iron shot** to give a soft resilient body with a hard exterior.   All of these materials for metal cleaning are termed **blasting shot.**

ISINGLASS. A gelatin made from the dried swimming bladders, or **fish sounds,** of sturgeon and other fishes.   **Russian isinglass** from the sturgeon is the most valued grade, and is one of the best of the water-soluble adhesives.   It is used in glues and cements, and in printing inks.   It is also used for clarifying wines and other liquids.   It is prepared by softening the bladder in water and cutting it into long strips.   These dry to a dull-gray, horny, or stringy material.   Isinglass is also known as **ichthyocolla.   Ichthyol** is an entirely different material.   It is a reddish-black syrupy liquid with a peculiar odor and burning taste, distilled from an asphaltic shale found in the Austrian Tyrol.   It is used as an antiseptic astringent.   The name isinglass was also used for mica when employed as a transparent material for stove doors.

IVORY. The material that composes the tusks and teeth of the elephant. It is employed mostly for ornamental parts, art objects, and piano keys, although the latter are now usually a plastic which does not yellow.   The color is the characteristic ivory white, which yellows with age.   The specific gravity is 1.87.   The best grades are from the heavy tusks weighing more than 55 lb, sometimes 6 ft long.   The ivory from animals long dead is a gray color and inferior. The softer ivory from elephants living in the highlands is more valuable than the hard and more brittle of the low marshes. The west coasts of Africa, India, and southern Asia are the chief sources of ivory. The tusks of the hippopotamus, walrus, and other animals, as well as the fossil mammoth of Siberia, also furnish ivory, although of inferior grades. **Odontolite** is ivory from fossil mammoths of Russia. Ivory can be sawed readily, and is made into thin veneers for ornamental uses. It takes a fine polish. Artificial ivory is usually celluloid or synthetic resins.

Vegetable ivory, used for buttons and small articles, is from the **ivory nut,** called **tagua nut** in Colombia and Ecuador, and **jarina** in Brazil. The ivory nut is the seed of the low-spreading palm tree, *Phytelephas macrocarpa,* which grows in tropical America. The nuts are about 2 in. in diameter, growing in clusters and encased in shells. They have a fine white color and an even texture. They can be worked easily and they harden on exposure to the air. They take dyes readily and show fine polished colors. A similar nut called the **dom nut** is used in Eritrea for making buttons and novelties.

JAPAN WAX. Sometimes called **sumac wax** and **Japan tallow.** A vegetable fat used for extending beeswax, and in candles and polishes. It occurs between the kernel and the outer skin of the berries of plants of the genus *Rhus,* which grow in Japan and in California. The fat, which is misnamed wax, is extracted by steaming and pressing the berries, and then refining. The crude wax is a coarse greenish solid, but the bleached wax is in cream-colored cakes which darken to yellow. Japan wax melts at 51°C. The specific gravity is about 0.975. It contains chiefly palmitic acid in the form of glyceryl palmitate with also stearic and oleic acids, and a characteristic acid, **japonic acid,** which is also found in catechu. The saponification value is 220. It is sometimes adulterated with common tallow. **Lac** is the gum exudation of the wood of the same sumac plants, notably *R. vernicifera,* of Japan and Korea. It is used as a drying oil in clear lacquers and baking enamels. Lac is distinct from shellac of the lac insect.

JEWELRY ALLOYS. An indefinite term which refers to the casting alloys used for novelties to be plated and to the copper and other nonferrous sheet and strip alloys for stamped and turned articles. The base-metal jewelry industry, as distinct from the precious-metal industry, produces costume jewelry, trinkets, souvenirs, premium and trade goods, clothing accessories known as notions, and low-cost religious goods such as medals and statuettes. The soft white alloys of this type are not now as important as they were before the advent of plastics, and articles now produced in metals are likely to be made from standard brasses, nickel brasses, and cupronickels, but laminated and composite sheet metals are much used to eliminate plating.   When the base metals are clad or plated with gold they are called **gold-filled metal** if the gold alloy is 10-carat or above and the amount used is at least 5% of the total weight.   When the coating is less than 5% it is called **rolled-gold plate.**   Formerly, a great variety of trade names were used for jewelry alloys.   **Argentine metal** was a silvery alloy for casting statuettes and small ornaments.   It contained 85.5% tin and 14.5 antimony, and produced silvery-white, hard, and clean-cut castings.   An alloy known as **Alger metal** contained 90% tin and 10 antimony.   A harder but more expensive white alloy known as **Warnes metal** contained 10 parts tin, 7 nickel, 7 bismuth, and 3 cobalt.   **Fahlum metal,** used for stage jewelry, contained 40% tin and 60 lead.   When faceted, it makes highly reflective brilliants.   **Rosein** was a white metal for jewelry and ornamental articles containing 40% nickel, 30 aluminum, 20 tin, and 10 silver.   When polished it has a high white luster without plating. **Mock silver** was an aluminum alloy containing about 5% silver and 5 copper.   **Argental** was a rich low brass whitened and strengthened with about 5% cobalt.   **Kuromi,** a Japanese white jewelry alloy, is copper whitened with tin and cobalt.   **Argent français,** or **French silver,** is cupronickel containing considerable silver.   **Platinoid** was a nickel-silver-tungsten alloy with the small amount of tungsten added to the melt in the form of phosphor tungsten.   **Proplatinum,** another substitute for platinum, was a nickel-silver-bismuth alloy.   **Nuremberg gold,** with a nontarnishing golden color, contained 90% copper, 7.5 aluminum, and 2.5 gold.

JOJOBA WAX.   Also called **jojoba oil,** pronounced ho-hó-bah.   A liquid wax obtained by pressing or solvent extraction from the seed beans of the evergreen shrub *Simmondsia californica* growing in the semiarid region of southwest United States and northern Mexico.   The beans contain 50% oil which has high-molecular-weight acids and alcohols and no glycerin and is a true wax.   It is used as a substitute for sperm oil in lubricants, in leather dressing, and also in cosmetics.   **Jojoba alcohol,** extracted from the bean, is a complex alcohol used as an antioxidant to prevent deterioration of fats.

JUJUBE.   The oval fruit of the small spiny tree *Ziziphus jujuba* of the buckthorn family growing in dry alkaline soils.   It is native to northern China, but is also grown in the Mediterranean countries and in the southwestern United States.   It is also known as the **Chinese date,** or **tsao.**   The fruit has high food value, being higher in sugars than the fig, 65 to 75%, and higher in protein than most fruits, 2.7 to 6%, but is very acid, containing up to 2% acid.   Some varieties develop butyric acid in ripening.

Jujube is used for flavoring, and in confections, preserves, and sweet pickles.

JUNIPER. The wood of the juniper tree *Juniperus virginiana* growing in the eastern United States from Maine to Florida. It is also called **red cedar, red juniper,** and **savin.** The heartwood has a bright to dull-red color, and the thin sapwood is nearly white. The wood is light in weight, soft, weak, and brittle, but is durable. It is used for chests, cabinets, and closet lining because of its reputed value for repelling moths. It was formerly employed on a large scale for lead-pencil wood, and was known as **pencil cedar,** but it is now scarce and other woods are used for this purpose, notably **incense cedar,** *Libocedrus decurrens,* of California and Oregon, a close-grained brown wood with a spicy resinous odor. **Rocky Mountain juniper** is from a medium-sized tree of the Mountain states, *J. scopulorum,* valued for fence posts and lumber. **African pencil cedar** is from the tree *J. procera,* of eastern Africa. It is harder and heavier and less fragrant than incense cedar. There are more than 40 species of juniper. The fruit or **juniper berries** of the common varieties are used in flavoring gin. **Cade oil** is a thick brownish essential oil, of specific gravity 0.950 to 1.055, distilled from the wood of the **European juniper,** and used in antiseptic soaps. It is also called **juniper tar oil.** The juniper oil known as **savin oil** is distilled from the leaves and tops of the **juniper bush,** *J. sabina,* of North America and Europe. It is used in medicine as a diuretic and vermifuge, and also in perfumes. **Cedarwood oil,** used in perfumes and soaps, is distilled from the sawdust and waste of the eastern red cedar. The red heartwood contains 1 to 3% oil.

JUTE. A fiber employed for making burlap, sacks, cordage, ropes, and upholstery fabrics. It is obtained from several plants, of which *Corchorus capsularis* of India is the most widely cultivated, growing in a hot, steaming climate. This fiber in Brazil is called **juta indiana,** or **Indian jute.** Most of the commercial jute comes from Bengal. The plant grows in tall slender stalks like hemp, and the fiber is obtained by retting and cleaning. The fiber is long, soft, and lustrous, but is not as strong as hemp. It also loses its strength when damp, but is widely used because of its low cost and because of the ease with which it can be spun. Its chemical composition is intermediate between hemp and kapok. It contains 60% alpha cellulose, 15 pentosan, 13 lignin, and 4.5% of **uronic anhydride** which is also a constituent of kapok. The crude fiber may be as long as 14 ft, but the commercial fibers are from 4 to 8 ft. The butts, or short ends of the stalks, and the rough fibers are used for paper stock. **Jute paper,** used for cement bags, is a strong paper made of these fibers usually mixed with old rope and old burlap in the pulping. It is tan in color.   **Jute fiber** is also used for machine packings.   The **Rel-Kol** of the Reliance Packing Co. is jute fiber treated with synthetic rubber and braided into square sections.

Brazilian jute is fiber from plants of the mallow family, *Hibiscus kitaibelifolius,* or *H. ferox,* cultivated in the state of São Paulo, Brazil.   It is also called **juta paulista.**   The fiber is long, strong, resilient, and durable. It is used for making burlap for coffee bags.   The fiber known as **paco-paco** is from the *H. cannabinus,* of Bahia and Minas Gerais.   It is used for cordage, burlap, and calking.   In Indonesia it is called **Java jute.**   In India it is called **Bimlipatam jute** and **Deccan hemp,** and is mixed with *Corchorus* fibers as jute and in burlap.   As a substitute for hemp it is known as **sunee,** or **brown Indian hemp.**   The species known as **amani-urana** is from the *H. furcellatus* of the Paraguay River Valley.   The fibers are very soft and silky and are made into sacks and bags.   The species *H. sabdariffa,* known as **vinagreira,** is used as a substitute for jute.   In the East Indies it is called **roselle fiber** and has characteristics similar to India jute, but is lighter in color.   In El Salvador it is called **kenaf fiber** and is used for coffee bags.   **Brazilian hemp** is from the *H. radiatus,* and is stronger than true hemp.   It is cultivated in Bahia.   **Aramina fiber** is from the very long stalks of a plant *Urena lobata,* of the mallow family, of Brazil.   In the north of Brazil it is known as **carrapicho.**   The fiber is used for cordage, twine, and burlap fabrics.   In Cuba this fiber is known as **white malva** and **bowstring hemp.**   **Cuba jute** is from the *Sida rhombifolia.*   Both Cuba jute and aramina fiber belong to the mallow family, *Malvaceae,* and in Cuba and Venezuela are also known as **malva fiber.** The *U. lobata* is also grown in the Congo where it is known as **Congo jute.**

Pitá fiber, used in Colombia and Central America for coffee bags, is from a plant of the pineapple genus, *Ananas magdalenae.*   The fiber is a light cream color, lustrous, very long, and finer and more flexible than most hard fibers, so that it is useful for ropes, twines, and fabrics although most of the fibers of this botanical class are brush fibers.   It has excellent resistance to salt water.   The word pitá means yellow or reddish in the Indian language, and this name is also used for grades of yucca and other fibers.   **Tucum fiber** is from the leaves of the oil palm *Astrocaryum tucuma* of Brazil.   The fibers are long, flexible, water-resistant, and durable.   They are used for ropes, hammocks, and marine cordage, but are not classed as burlap fiber.   Another fiber of great length and noted for resistance to insect attack is **curana,** from the stalks of the plant *Bromelia sagenaria* of northeast Brazil.   There are two chief grades: the white and the roxo or purple.

KAOLIN. Also called **China clay.** A pure form of hydrated **aluminum-silicate clay.**   There are three distinct minerals, **kaolinite, nicrite,**

and **dickite,** all having similar composition.   The formula for kaolin is usually given as $Al_2O_3 \cdot 2SiO_2 \cdot 2H_2O$, but is also expressed as $Al_2Si_2O_5$-$(OH)_4$.   It occurs in claylike masses of specific gravity 2.6, and of a dull luster.   Kaolin is used for making **porcelain** for **chinaware,** and **chemical porcelain** for valves, tubes, and fittings, as a refractory for bricks and furnace linings, for electric insulators, as a pigment and filler in paints, as a filler in plastics, and as an abrasive powder.

In firebricks kaolin resists spalling.   Its melting point is 3200°F, but this lowers with impurities.   The color of all varieties is white, but inferior grades burn to a yellow or brownish color, and it should be free of iron.   Porcelain made from kaolin is fired at about 2300°F, but the upper service limit of the products is only about 500°F since it has a low heat-transfer rate and low thermal shock resistance.   Porcelain parts have a specific gravity of 2.4 to 2.9, a hardness of 7.5 Mohs, and a compressive strength from 60,000 to 90,000 psi.

When kaolin is employed as an inert colloidal pigment in paints it is called **Chinese white.**   The powder is hydrophobic and cannot be wet by water, but it has good compatibility in oils and many organic solvents. As an extender in plastics and rubbers it reduces absorption of moisture and increases dielectric strength.   Kaolin is a decomposition product of granite and feldspar, and its usual impurities are quartz, feldspar, and mica, which can be washed out.   The **aluminum silicate RER-45,** of the Georgia Kaolin Co., is purified kaolin ground to a fineness of 0.2- to 4.5-micron particle size.   It is used in paints, coatings, and plastics.   The **modified kaolin** of the Minerals & Chemical Corp., for rubber and plastics, has the composition $(Al_2O_3)_3(SiO_2)_2$ and the particles are in thin flat plates averaging 0.55 micron.

The **Cornwall kaolin** of England and the **Limoges kaolin** of France are the best known.   English China clays contain little or no iron oxide, and the yellow clays contain only organic materials that can be bleached out. The best grade of English clay is used for coating and filling paper. **Cornish clay,** known as **China stone,** is used for the best grades of porcelain glazes.   Cheaper grades of kaolin, called **mica clay,** are used for earthenware glazes, and as an absorbent in oil purifying.   The clay of Kentucky and Tennessee, known as **ball clay,** occurs in massive beds of great purity. It has high plasticity and good bonding strength, and is light in color when fired.   It is used for high-grade porcelain and for wall tiles.   Impure varieties of kaolin, called **kaolonic earth,** are used for refractories.   **Kaolin fiber** of extreme fineness, with average diameter of 3 microns, is made from kaolin containing about 46% alumina, 51 silica, and 3 iron and titanium oxides.   It will withstand continuous temperatures to 2000°F. **Kaowool,** of the Babcock & Wilcox Co., is kaolin fiber in the form of insulating blankets of ¼ to 3 in. thickness.   **Kaowool paper** is made from the fibers compressed to thicknesses up to 0.08 in. with or without a binder. It will withstand temperatures to 2000°F and is used for filters, separators, and gaskets.   The fibers may also be compressed into **kaowool blocks** of 4 in. thickness.

Halloysite has about the same composition as kaolinite but contains more alumina and water.   It occurs with kaolinite.   In association with alunite in Arkansas it is called **newtonite.**   Some varieties, such as **glossecollite,** are waxlike, and with an electron microscope the grains appear as tubular structures.   A variety of halloysite is marketed in France as a fine gray powder for use as a filler in rubber latex compounds.   **Indianaite,** or **allophane,** is an impure halloysite.   It is a white, waxy clay found in Indiana, and is used for pottery.   The Indiana halloysite used for refractories is called **malinite.   Bone clay** is a pure kaolin from feldspar and granite.   It makes a strong porcelain.   But **bone china** is a name given to high-grade English pottery made with China clay and 25% calcined bone.   **Flesh clay** is formed from feldspar and quartz.   It gives resilience to the porcelain.   Clays can be mixed to give desired characteristics.

Micronized clay is pure kaolin ground to a fineness of 400 to 800 mesh, used as a filler in rubber.   **Dixie clay,** of the R. T. Vanderbilt Co., is ground kaolin of 300 mesh, used as a stiffening or reinforcing agent in rubber and adhesives.   **Osmose kaolin** is kaolin deposited by electro-osmosis from an alkaline solution to eliminate iron and other impurities and raise the alumina ratio.   As a fine powder it is used for making electrical insulators and synthetic mica, and for cosmetics.   **Osmo,** of E. Fougera & Co., is a finely ground kaolin for cosmetics.   **Alumina flake,** of the Aluminum Flake Co., is a white, flaky kaolinic clay from Missouri, ground for use in paints, adhesives, and rubber.   The **tile kaolin** of the Georgia Kaolin Co. is selectively mined and water-washed to obtain low iron and titania content.   It has high plasticity and fires white with good translucency.   The mean particle size is about 1.2 microns with 65% below 2 microns.   The pH is 4 to 6.5.   **Quickcast kaolin** of the same company is a coarse powder of iron-free Georgia kaolin with 200-mesh particle size.   It is used for mixing with other clays to increase the casting and drying times and to improve whiteness in tile and ceramic products.

KAPOK. A silky fiber obtained from the seed pods of the silk-cotton trees of the genera *Ceiba, Bombax, Chorisia,* and *Ochroma,* now grown in most tropical countries.   It is employed for insulation and fine padding work.   It is extremely light and resilient.   The chemical constituents are the same as those of jute, but the proportions are different.   Kapok is low in alpha cellulose, 43%, and high in pentosans, 24%, lignin, 15%, and uronic anhydride, 6.6%.   Most of the commercial kapok normally comes from Java and is from the *Ceiba pentandra.*   The tree was brought originally from Brazil where it was known as **samaúma**.   It grows to a height up to 100 ft, with diameters to 10 ft, making the picking of the kapok pods difficult.   The fibers are long, white, and silky, similar in appearance to cotton, but are too brittle for spinning.   It is also known as **Java cotton** and **Illiani silk.**   A silky cotton somewhat similar but inferior to kapok is **madar,** from the shrub *Calotropis gigantea* of India and the East Indies.   Another species, **akund,** is from the *C. procera.* Both fibers are sometimes mixed with kapok, but are less resilient.   They are known in the East Indies as **vegetable silk.**   **Red silk cotton,** known as **simal,** is from the large tree *Bombax ceiba* or *B. malabaricum,* of India. The fiber is reddish.   **Shilo fiber** is from the tree *B. ellipticum.*   **White silk cotton** is from the tree *Cochlospermum gossypium* of India.   It is quite similar to kapok.   The kapok of Ecuador is from various species of the tree *Chorisia.*   The fiber from the balsa trees, of the genus *Ochroma* of Central America, Colombia, and Ecuador, is dark in color. **Mexican kapok** is from the *Bombax palmeri* and from the *Ceiba schottii* and *C. acuminata,* the fibers from the two latter being more buoyant than the Java fiber.   The kapok from the Lower Amazon region is from the *C. samaúma,* and the **pochote fiber** of El Salvador is from the *C. aesculifolia.*   The **balsa fiber** of Central America is from the tree *O. velutina.* **Paina kapok** is from a ceiba tree of Brazil.   **Kapok oil** is a semidrying oil obtained from the seeds of the kapok tree.   It is used in margarine and for soaps.

A substitute for kapok for sound and heat insulation, and as stuffing for life jackets, cushions, furniture, and toys, is **typha,** or **cattail fiber.**   It is the fluffy fiber from the cylindrical flowers of the *Typha latifolia* which grows in swamps throughout the temperate climates of North America. As an insulating material the fiber has about 90% the efficiency of wool. **Milkweed floss,** used also as a substitute for kapok, is the bluish-white silky fiber from the seed pods of the common milkweed, *Asclepias syrica,* of the eastern United States.   It is not grown commercially.

KARAKUL. The curly lustrous fur pelts of newly born lambs of the karakul sheep originally of Afghanistan and Siberia, but now grown extensively in southwest Africa for the fur.   The wool of the older sheep is clipped for carpet wool, but the fur pelts of the young animals are highly valued for coats and garment trim.   The best qualities are those with small curl and medium curl to the fur.   The fur skins are also graded by color, the gray and flora being most valued and the brown the least valued. **Persian lambskin** is a name for pelts of small tight curl.

KAURI GUM. A fossil gum dug from the ground in New Zealand and New Caledonia, used in varnishes and enamels to increase the body and increase the elasticity and hardness.   It is also used in adhesives, and the lower grades of chips are used in linoleum.   It was first known as **New Zealand gum,** and first spelled cowrie, although **cowrie** is the name of a genus of mollusk shells found in the Indian Ocean and formerly used as money in China.   Kauri is a product of kauri tree exudations buried for long periods, but it also comes from the conifer tree *Agathis australis.* There is little extraction of the gum from the present kauri forests, whose wood is employed for lumber, but some **bush gum** is obtained by collecting the deposits in the forks of branches.   **Range gum** is found in clay deposits, and some is transparent.   **Swamp gum** is brown in color and varies from hard to friable.   The fossil gum has a specific gravity of 1.05, a melting point of 182 to 232°C, and is soluble in turpentine, benzol, and alcohol. The **kauri tree** grows to a height of 100 ft and great diameters, and yields a yellowish-brown, straight-grained wood free from knots much prized as a useful softwood.   It weighs 36 lb per cu ft.   Mottled and figured **kauri pine** is used as a cabinet wood.

KERMES. A brilliant red natural dyestuff similar in color to cochineal, having a beautiful tone and being very fast.   It is one of the most ancient dyes, but is now largely replaced by synthetic dyestuffs.   Kermes is an insect found on the **kermes oak** tree, *Quercus coccifera,* of southern Europe and North Africa.   The body of the animal is full of a red juice, and the coloring matter, **kermesic acid,** $C_{18}H_{12}O_9$, is separated out in brick-red crystals.   It has only about one-tenth the coloring power of cochineal.   **Garouille** is the root bark of the kermes oak.   It contains 18 to 32% tannin, and is used for making sole leather.   The color is darker than oak tannin.

KEROSENE. Originally the name of illuminating oil distilled from coal, and also called **coal oil.**   It is now a light, oily liquid obtained in the fractional distillation of petroleum.   It distills off after the gasoline, and between the limits of temperatures of 174 and 288°C.   It is a hydrocarbon of the composition $C_{10}H_{22}$ to $C_{16}H_{34}$, with a specific gravity between 0.747 and 0.775.   Commercial kerosene may be as high a distillate as 325°C, with a corresponding higher specific gravity up to 0.850, but in states where it is distinguished from gasoline in the tax laws it is more sharply defined. In Pennsylvania, kerosene is defined as having a flash point above 114°F, with not over 10% distillable at 175°C and not over 45% at 200°C. Kerosene is employed for illuminating and heating purposes, and as a fuel in internal-combustion engines, and for turbine jet fuels.   The heaviest distillate known as **range oil** is sufficiently volatile to burn freely in the wick of a heating range, but not so volatile as to be explosive.   It is nearly free from odor and smoke.   **Deodorized kerosene,** used in insect sprays, is a kerosene highly refined by treatment with activated earth or activated carbon.   **Fialasol,** of Fred Fiala, Inc., is a **nitrated kerosene** used as a solvent for the scouring of wool.   It is less flammable and has a slower rate of evaporation than kerosene, and it is odorless.

KHAYA. A class of woods from trees of the genus *Khaya,* growing chiefly in tropical West Africa and known commercially as **African mahogany.** The woods closely resemble mahogany, but they are more strongly figured than mahogany, are slightly lighter in weight, softer, and have greater shrinkage.   The pores are larger, and the wood coarser. The wood is used for furniture and store fixtures, musical instruments, and paneling.   It is not as suitable for patterns as mahogany.   African mahoganies are marketed under the names of the shipping ports, as the shipments from the various ports usually differ in proportion to the different species cut in the region.   The chief wood of the genus, from which the native name Khaya derives, is known commercially as **dry zone mahogany,** *K. senegalensis.*   It is also known as **kail** and **oganwo.**   It grows from Gambia to Angola on the west coast and eastward to Uganda.   The heartwood is dark reddish brown, and the thick sapwood is grayish to pinkish red.   The most favored commercial wood is that of the **red khaya,** or **red mahogany,** *K. ivorensis,* known locally as **dukuma** and **dubini.**   This wood is highly figured, with interlocking grain, and when quartered shows a ribbon figure with alternate light and dark stripes.   It comes chiefly from the Ivory Coast, Ghana, and Nigeria.   **Sassandra mahogany** is chiefly this species.   **Duala mahogany** is chiefly **white mahogany,** *K. anthoteca,* known also as **diala, krala,** and **mangona.**   The wood is lighter in color but tinged with red.   **Big-leaf mahogany,** *K. grandifolia,* has a reddish-brown color. Much African mahogany is cut into veneer, and the standard thickness for the face veneer is $\frac{1}{28}$ in.

Gaboon mahogany and **Port Lopez mahogany** are chiefly **okume wood,** from the tree *Aucoumea klaineana* of the Guinea coast.   The tree belongs to the family *Meliaceae* to which khaya belongs, and the wood resembles African mahogany but is lighter in weight and softer.   It is light pinkish brown in color.   It is shipped chiefly to Europe where it is used for furniture, chests, boxes, and boats.   **Cola mahogany,** from the Ivory Coast and Ghana, is **niangon,** *Tarrietia utilis.*   The heartwood is light reddish brown, and the wood shows a herringbone figure on the quartered surface.   It is heavier than khaya, and the pores are larger and more numerous.   **Cherry mahogany,** or **makore,** is a plentiful wood on the Ivory Coast, Ghana, and in Nigeria.   It is from the tree *Minusops heckelii.*   The wood is dark reddish brown without figure.   It is heavier than khaya and is finer in texture.

KID. A name for leather made from the skins of young goats, but commercial **kidskin** leather is now from both young and old animals, and the term **goatskin** is not liked in the American trade.   It is thin and has a fine, close-grained texture, with tiny groups of pores, and the leather is soft and pliable but strong and nonscuffing.   Kid is usually chrome-tanned and dyed to many colors.   It has a natural lustrous surface which is heightened by glazing or polishing.   The leather is sorted by grain or size of pores, weights, and sizes into 10 grades.   India, Argentina, Brazil, South Africa, and northwest Africa are large producers of goatskins. About 70% of the goat and kid leather of the world is tanned in the United States although this country produces less than 1% of the skins. Kidskin is used for shoes, gloves, pocketbooks, jerkins, and for pads and linings.   The term **Vici kid,** used in the shoe industry, was the name originally given to chrome-tanned leather.   The best kidskins come from arid regions, and these are used for the fine French kid leather.   In the glove trade the term **chevreau** is used to designate young goats that have never browsed, while **chevrette** refers to the small skins of older kids that have eaten grass.   **Capeskin** is goatskin from South Africa.   **Glazed kid** is made by pressing a seasoning agent into the leather and then ironing the dry leather with a glass cylinder.

KIESELGUHR.   A variety of tripoli, or **infusorial earth,** obtained in Germany, and employed chiefly as an absorbing material.   It is also used as an abrasive, as a heat insulator, for making imitation meerschaum, and as an absorbing material for nitroglycerin in making dynamite.   Kieselguhr is very absorbent and will hold 75% of its own weight of sulfuric acid. It is insoluble in water.   Desirable characteristics as an insulator are closed cells and very high porosity, giving low density and low thermal conductivity.   It is also used as a catalyst carrier in chemical processing. Kieselguhr from Oberhole, Germany, has 88% silica, 0.1 alumina, 8.4 water, and the remainder organic matter.   **Randanite,** found at Clermont-Ferrand, France, is similar to kieselguhr but has a gray color.   **Moler earth,** from the Jutland Peninsula of Denmark, is similar to kieselguhr and is made into insulation bricks.   **Nonpareil insulating brick,** of the Armstrong Cork & Insulating Co., is made of pulverized kieselguhr mixed with ground cork, molded into brick form, and dried.   The cork is burned out, leaving small air pockets to increase the insulating effect.   The bricks will withstand temperatures up to 1000°C; the heat transmission is lower than for natural kieselguhr.

KINO RESIN.   Also known as **gum kino.**   The red exudation of the tree *Pterocarpus marsupium,* of India and Ceylon, and of *P. erinaceus,* of West Africa, formerly much used for colored varnishes and lacquers and used in throat medicines.   **Bengal kino,** or **butea gum,** from the tree *Butea frondosa,* is now limited to medicinal use, as is also the **Australian red kino**

from species of eucalyptus. Kino belongs to the group of red resins known as **dragon's blood** when used in spirit varnishes for musical instruments and furniture, but now replaced by synthetic colors. The dragon's blood resins from the East Indies are from the ripe fruit of various species of the tree *Daemonorops*. The resin is separated out by boiling and is shipped in small oval drops or long cylindrical sticks. It is used in fine lacquers and varnishes. The dark-red dye known as **red sandalwood** is the boiled-down juice of another kino tree *P. santelinus* of India. Still another *Pterocarpus* tree of southern India produces the wood **padouk** valued for furniture, cabinetwood, and veneer. The heartwood is red with black stripes. It is hard and takes a high polish.

KYANITE. A natural **aluminum silicate,** $Al_2O_3 \cdot SiO_2$, used as a refractory especially for linings of glass furnaces and furnaces for nonferrous metals. Molded or cast ceramic parts have a nearly zero thermal expansion up to 2300°F. It is a common mineral but occurs disseminated with other minerals and is found in commercial quantities and grades in only a few places. Most of the world production has been in eastern India, but high-grade kyanite is now obtained from Kenya. It is also mined in North Carolina, Georgia, Virginia, and California. The related minerals sillimanite and dumortierite are mined in western United States. The specific gravity is 3.56 to 3.67, and the hardness is 6 to 7 Mohs. Kyanite of 97 to 98% purity is obtained by flotation, but gravity concentrates rarely exceed 90%. Low-grade kyanite ore from California, containing 35% kyanite and much quartz, is used for ceramics. Kyanite is usually marketed ground to finenesses from 35 to 325 mesh. Low-grade kyanite is used in glassmaking as a source of alumina to increase strength and chemical and heat resistance. Aluminum silicate minerals are widely distributed in nature combined in complex forms, and the aluminum silicate extracted from them is called synthetic. **Kyanite powder,** produced from Florida beach sands, has round single-crystal grains of kyanite and sillimanite in nearly equal proportions. The beach sands are screened and graded and marketed as granules of various sizes for compacting and sintering into refractory ceramic parts. The smooth rounded grains give bonding properties superior to those of crushed kyanite. **Cerox ceramic,** of the Babcock & Wilcox Co., is a synthetic aluminum silicate in molded shapes for electronic and furnace parts. It is marketed in grades containing 50 to 90% alumina. **Cerox 200,** with a melting point at 3290°F, contains 64.3% alumina, 32.4 silica, 2.1 titania, and 1 iron oxide. It is a hard, white, nonporous ceramic which is spall- and wear-resistant.

The mineral known as **staurolite** is a vitreous, translucent, red-brown complex aluminum silicate, $Fe_2Al_9O_7(SiO_4)_4OH$. The orthorhombic crystals occur quite commonly as twins crossing at nearly 90° in cruciform shape and are cut as gemstones. **Zoisite** is a complex calcium aluminum silicate occurring worldwide, usually in the mineral **saussurite** which is altered feldspar. A variety of zoisite named **tanzanite** is a dark-blue gemstone found in Tanzania. **Tourmaline** is a boron aluminum silicate of wide occurrence and usually black or green in color. But pink crystals of gem quality are found on Madagascar, yellow in Ceylon, and dark green in Brazil. A colorless variety found in Malagasy is called **achroite.** The fine red tourmaline, **rubellite,** is scarce. Tourmalines from the pegmatite veins of New England, Pennsylvania, and California are found in all colors. Tourmaline, from Brazil, has good piezoelectric properties, and can be used for frequency control and pressure transducers, but is more expensive than quartz crystal. It is used in submarines to measure depth. Tourmaline is also a **pyroelectric.** When heated, an electric charge is produced, with the crystal becoming positive and negative at opposite ends, the poles reversing themselves on cooling.

LACQUER. Originally the name of an **Oriental finish** made with lac. The original **Chinese lacquer** was made with the juice of the lac plant, *Rhus vernicifera,* mixed with oils. The juice is milky but it darkens with age, and the lacquer is a glossy black. Later, the name referred to transparent coatings made with shellac, and to glossy pigmented spirit varnishes. Still later, it referred to quick-drying finishes made with nitrocellulose or cellulose acetate. The word lacquer has now come to mean glossy, quick-drying enamels that are not baked on.

The true lacquers were made with copals and other natural resins, a pigment, a softener or plasticizer, and one or more volatile solvents, with the time of drying controlled by the evaporation of the solvents. Too rapid drying may cause the cloudiness called blushing, because of the absorption of moisture from the cooling caused by the rapid evaporation. Various resins impart different characteristics. Dammar gives high gloss and hardness. Kauri gives hardness and wear resistance. The softeners are usually the amyl, ethyl, and butyl phthalates. The usual solvents are anhydrous alcohol, ethyl acetate, benzol, and toluo. But modern lacquers may contain nitrocellulose or cellulose esters, or they may be made with acrylic, melamine, or other synthetic resins.

For industrial work, lacquers are usually sprayed, and the feature is quick drying. **Brushing lacquers** are also quick-drying, but with a longer drying period to prevent streaks and lumps in the application. Lacquers are harder and tougher than enamels, but not as elastic, and they are more expensive. They are usually not as solvent-resistant nor as weather-resistant, and are generally not suited for exterior work. A good lacquer requires no buffing, and retains the original gloss well. The word lacquer is also used to describe a highly transparent varnish used to produce a thin protective film on polished or plated metals to preserve their luster. Lacquers are sold under a variety of trade names.   Some early cellulose lacquers were marketed as **Duco, Agateen, Zapon, Brevolite,** and **Zeloctite,** but solutions of methyl acrylate or other crystal-clear resins may now be used.   **Bronzing liquids** are the clear lacquer-base mediums marketed ready for incorporation of bronze or aluminum powders.   **Cable lacquers** are clear, black, or colored lacquers prepared from synthetic resins, and are characterized by high dielectric strength, resistance to oils and heat, and by their ability to give tough, flexible coatings.   **Chromate-protein films** may be used instead of clear lacquers for the protection of metal parts.   The parts are dipped in a solution of casein, albumin, or gelatin, and, after drying, dipped in a weak chromic acid solution.   The thin, yellowish film is hard and adherent and will withstand temperatures to 300°F.

LAMPBLACK.   A soot formed by the smudge process of burning oil, coal tar, resin, or other carbonaceous substances in an insufficient supply of air, the soot being allowed to settle on the walls or floors of the collecting chambers.   Lampblack is practically pure carbon, but inferior grades may contain unburnt oil.   It is chemically the same as carbon black made from gas but, since it may contain as high as 2.5% oil, it is not generally used in rubber.   The particle size is large, 65 to 100 microns, and the pH is low, 3 to 3.5.   However, some **amorphous carbon,** made from crude oil by spraying the oil and air into a closed retort at 3000°F to obtain partial combustion, is equal to carbon black for many uses.   Lampblack is used in making paints, lead pencils, metal polishes, electric brush carbons, crayons, and carbon papers.   It is grayish black in color, and is flaky and granular.   The color is not as intensely black as carbon black.   One pound occupies from 200 to 230 cu in.   For use as a pigment for japan the powder should pass through a 325-mesh screen.   **Lampblack oil** is a coal-tar product marketed for making lampblack.

LANCEWOOD.   The wood of the tree *Guatteria virgata,* of tropical America.   It is used as a substitute for boxwood, and for fine work where a uniform, tough, durable wood is needed.   The wood is yellowish in color and has a fine, close, smooth grain.   The weight is 52 to 63 lb per cu ft.   It is very hard and elastic.   **Yaya** is a name given in the Honduras trade to lancewood.   **Degami lancewood,** or **degami wood,** is a yellowish wood with a fine, dense grain, from the *Calycophyllum candidissimum* of the West Indies.   **Burma lancewood,** used in India for implements, is a strong, straight-grained, heavy wood from the large tree *Homalium tomentosum.*   It has a light-brown color and weighs 60 lb per cu ft.

LARCH.   The wood of the coniferous tree *Larix occidentalis,* of the northwestern United States and southwestern Canada.   It is also called **western larch, western tamarack, mountain larch, Montana larch,** and **hackmatack.** The wood is heavier than most softwoods, having a specific gravity of 0.48 and weight of 36 lb per cu ft.   It is fine-textured and straight-grained. In strength and hardness it ranks high among the softwoods, but shrinks and swells more than most softwoods.   The heartwood is reddish brown and the narrow sapwood is yellowish.   It finishes well, but splits easily. Butt logs contain galactan gum, which darkens the color.   Larch is used for bridge timbers, flooring, paneling, and general construction.   The trees reach a diameter of 5 ft, and a height up to 200 ft.   Shipments of western larch and Douglas fir mixed are known commercially as **larch fir.** Larch is also the name given to the **tamarack** tree of New England, *L. larincina.*   **European larch,** *L. europea,* is an important wood in Russia and some other countries.

LARD. The soft white fat from hogs.   It is used chiefly as a shortening in bakery and food products, and as a cooking grease.   The inedible grades are used for the production of lard oil and soaps, and for splitting into fatty acids and glycerin.   The types of edible lard for use in the United States are defined in regulations of the Department of Agriculture. **Steam-rendered lard** is made by applying steam directly to the fats in a closed container.   Open-kettle rendered lard is made by applying steam to the outside of the kettle.   The **neutral lard** used for making margarine is produced by applying hot water in place of steam.   **Rendered pork fat** is an edible material that does not meet the specifications for lard.   Average production of edible lard is about 24 lb per animal.

Leaf lard is from around the kidneys and intestines and is the best edible grade.   **White grease** is an inedible lard from the kidneys and the back. **Yellow grease** is the residue from the parts of the hog remaining after the parts yielding white grease are separated.   USP grade of lard is called **adeps** in pharmacy.   It is purified internal fat of the abdomen, and is a soft unctuous solid of bland taste.   It is used in **benzoated lard** for ointments.   **Modified lard,** of Armour & Co., is a **plastic lard** which is plastic at lower temperatures and also retains its body at higher temperatures than ordinary hydrogenized shortenings.   It is made by treating with sodium methylate which re-forms the esters in random orientation to give the soft plastic texture.

Lard oil is an oil expressed from lard by subjecting it to hydraulic pressure.   Prime or first-grade lard oils are nearly colorless, or greenish, and have little odor.   The commercial oils vary from the clear sweet oil to the acid and offensive-smelling brown oils.   The oils contain oleic, stearic, and palmitic acids.   They are used in cutting and in lubricating oils, sometimes in illuminating oils.   They may be adulterated with cottonseed oil or blown oils.   The flash point of pure lard oil is 480°F, saponification value 192, and specific gravity 0.915.   **Mineral lard oil** is a mixture of refined mineral oil with lard oil, the fatty content being 25 to 30%.   The flash point is about 300°F.   **Petrofac,** of the Sun Oil Co., is a lard-oil substitute made entirely from petroleum.   **Lardine** is an old name for blown cottonseed oil used in lubricants.

LATEX. The milklike juice of the rubber tree, now much used instead of the cured crude rubber for many rubber applications such as adhesives, rubber compounds, and rubber powder.   The properties of latex vary with the type of tree, age of tree, method of tapping, and climate.   Latex from young trees is less stable than from older trees.   Intensive tapping of the trees results in less rubber content, which may vary from 20 to 50%.   For shipping, a preservative and anticoagulant is added to the latex, usually ammonia or sodium sulfate.   Concentrated 60% latex is a stable liquid of creamlike consistency.   **Heveatex** is the trade name of latex of various grades of the Heveatex Corp.   **Latex foam** is a cellular sponge rubber made by whipping air into latex, pouring into molds, and vulcanizing.   **Air-cell,** of the B. F. Goodrich Co., is a latex foam made from natural rubber latex.   **Artificial latex** is a water dispersion of reclaimed rubber.   **Dispersite** was a trade name of Dispersions Process, Inc., for water dispersions of crude or reclaimed rubbers, produced by swelling and dissolving the rubber in an organic solvent, treating with an organic acid or with ammonia, and emulsifying.   It resembles latex, but is softer and more tacky, and is used for adhesives.   **Lotol** and **Revertex** are brands of latex.   The Revertex process consists in the concentration of latex by evaporation in the presence of protective colloids.   Latex foams are now usually made by incorporating a chemical which releases a gas to form the cells.

The term latex now also refers to water dispersions of synthetic rubbers and of rubberlike plastics.   **Neoprene latex** is a water dispersion of Neoprene rubber, and has the dispersed particles smaller than those of natural latex, giving better penetration in coating paper and textiles.   **Teflon TE-9500,** of Du Pont, is a water dispersion of fluorocarbon resin containing 6.5 lb of microfine resin powder per gallon.   It comes clear or in enamel-green color, and by heating the sprayed film to 600°F an impervious fused coating is obtained.   **Naugatex J-8174,** of the U.S. Rubber Co., is a butadiene-styrene latex with 68% solids for producing foamed rubber, and **Nitrex 2614** is a nitrile rubber latex.   **Nubun,** of the Firestone Tire & Rubber Co., is **Buna S latex.**   **Adiprene L,** of Du Pont, is a urethane rubber suspension, and **Nelco 70-A,** of the Allied Chemical Corp., for use in paints and spar varnishes, is a 70% solids suspension of urethane resin in mineral spirits.   **Pliolite 5352,** of the Goodyear Tire &

Rubber Co., for producing foams, is a synthetic-natural isoprene rubber latex.   **Latex water paints** are now usually made with synthetic rubber or plastic dispersions.

LAUAN. The wood of trees of several genera of the Philippines, Malaya, and Sarawak, known in the American market as **Philippine mahogany.** The woods resemble mahogany in general appearance, weight, and strength, but the shrinkage and swelling with changes in moisture are greater than in the true mahoganies.   The lauan woods are used for furniture and cabinet woods, paneling, and for boatbuilding.   The lauans belong chiefly to the genus *Shorea,* and the various species have local or common names.   The so-called dark-red Philippine mahogany is **tangile,** *S. polysperma,* and **red lauan,** *S. negrosensis.*   Tangile is also called **Bataan mahogany,** and has the closest resemblance to true mahogany of all the species.   The thick sapwood is light red and the heartwood dark brownish red.   It has greater tendency to warp than mahogany.   Red lauan has larger pores, but is favored for boat construction because of the large sizes available.   **Tiaong,** from the *S. teysmanniana,* resembles tangile but is lighter and softer.   **Almon,** from the tree *S. eximia,* is harder and stronger than red lauan or tangile, but is coarser in texture and less lustrous.

White lauan is from a different genus of the same family and is *Pentacme contorta.*   It has about the same mechanical properties as tangile, but is gray with a pinkish tint.   **Mindanao lauan,** *P. mindanensis,* is quite similar but is lighter and softer.   **Mayapis,** from the tree *Shorea palosapis,* is coarser in texture than tangile and is subject to warping and checking like red lauan.   It is intermediate in color, and the light-colored wood is marketed as white lauan, while the dark wood is sold as red lauan.   **Yellow lauan** is from the trees **kalunti,** *S. kalunti,* **manggasinoro,** *S. philippensis,* and **malaanonang,** *S. polita.*   Yellow lauan is yellowish in color and has lower strength and greater warpage than other lauans.   **Bagtikan,** from the tree *Parashorea malaanonan,* is reddish gray in color, not lustrous, but is heavier and stronger than the other lauans.   Sometimes mixed with Philippine mahogany is the wood known as **lumbayan,** from an entirely different family of trees.   It is from the tree *Tarrietia javanica.*   The thick sapwood is light gray in color and the heartwood reddish.   The weight and strength are about equal to tangile but the pores are larger.   When marketed separately, it is a more valuable wood than the lauans for furniture manufacture.   The reddish woods from Sarawak, Sumatra, and Malaya known as **meranti,** or **morenti,** are *Shorea* species of the lauan types.   In the East Indies morenti is used for barrels, casks, and tanks for palm oil.   Similar woods from North Borneo are called **seraya,** or known as **Borneo cedar** or **Borneo mahogany.**   The *Shorea* trees yield Borneo tallow and dammar.   **Merawan** is a wood from various species of trees of the genus *Hopea* of Malaya. It is valued for furniture and interior work. Much of the so-called mahogany normally shipped from the Philippines is **Apitong,** the wood of the tree *Dipterocarpus grandiflorus* also grown in Borneo and Malaya. The wood weighs 44 lb per cu ft.

LAVA. A name given to ceramic material used for molding gas-burner tips, electrical insulating parts, nozzles, and handles. It may be calcined talc, steatite, or other material. As produced by the American Lava Corp., it is molded from magnesium oxide, and it is hardened by heat treatment after shaping and cutting. It is baked at 2000°F. The compressive strength is from 20,000 to 30,000 psi. It will resist moisture and has high dielectric strength. Rods as small as 0.020 in. in diameter can be made. **Alsimag** is the trade name of lava produced by this company from ground talc and sodium silicate, but **Alsimag 602** is phosphate-bonded steatite talc, used for thyratron tubes and as a substitute for mica in receiving tube spacers. **Porcelava** is a similar ceramic produced by Burgess & Co., for electric heating appliances. **Isolantite,** of the Isolantite Co. of America, Inc., is a steatite ceramic molded with a binder and then vitrified. It can be machined or threaded before firing and, by allowing for the contraction, parts can be made with great accuracy. The specific gravity of the vitrified material is 2.5, hardness 8 to 9 Mohs, and crushing strength 80,000 to 120,000 psi, and the dielectric strength of $\frac{1}{8}$-in. thickness is 40,500 volts. **Lavalloy,** of the Lava Crucible Co., is a high-strength ceramic made from a mixture of mullite and alumina. **Lavolain,** of the Star Porcelain Co., is a strong, dense, heat-resistant ceramic for electric insulation.

LEAD. A soft, heavy, bluish-gray metal, symbol Pb, obtained chiefly from the mineral galena. It surface-oxidizes easily, but is then very resistant to corrosion. It is soluble in nitric acid but not in sulfuric or hydrochloric, and is one of the most stable of the metals. Its crystal structure is cubic face-centered. It is very malleable, but it becomes hard and brittle on repeated melting because of the formation of oxides. The specific gravity of the cast metal is 11.34, and that of the rolled is 11.37. The melting point is 621°F, and boiling point 2777°F. The tensile strength is low, that of the rolled metal being about 3,600 psi with elongation of 52% at normal temperatures, but at low temperatures the strength is greatly increased. At −40°F it is about 13,000 psi, with elongation of 30%. The coefficient of expansion is 0.0000183, and the thermal conductivity is 8.2% that of silver. The electrical conductivity is only 7.8% that of copper. It is used for bullets and for shielding. When used in storage batteries the metal is largely returned as scrap after a period and is remelted and marketed as **secondary lead,** as is also that from pipes and cable coverings.   Secondary-lead production in the United States is large, and the recovered metal has the same uses as new metal.   Lead alloys easily with tin and zinc, and forms many commercial alloys, including solders and bearing metals.   Although the amount of lead going into chemicals other than white lead, red lead, and tetraethyl lead is relatively small, there are about 200 lead chemicals that have a wide variety of industrial uses.   Lead and its compounds are poisonous, and are not used in contact with the skin or near foodstuffs.   **Tetraethyl lead,** also called **ethyl lead,** is a liquid of the composition $Pb(C_2H_5)_4$, used in a blend with halogens as an additive in gasoline to increase octane number and resistance to knock.   The compound is so volatile that it distributes widely in the atmosphere from exhaust fumes and the lead is not recovered.   It is highly toxic and gasolines containing it are dyed for identification.   Various other compounds, such as cyclo pentadiene manganese carbonyl, can be used as antiknock agents.   **Methyl lead,** $(CH_3)_4Pb$, a liquid boiling at $110°C$, is more effective then tetraethyl lead in some respects, and is used in mixtures.

Commercial lead is sold in pigs weighing 100 lb.   Seven grades of pig lead are marketed.   **Corroding lead,** 99.94% pure, is for making white lead.   **Chemical lead,** 99.90% pure, with some silver and copper, is the **undesilverized lead** from Missouri ores.   Soft undesilverized lead is 99.93% pure and is used for storage batteries, sheet, and for pipes and cable coverings.   Chemical lead has a hardness of 80 Rockwell B compared with 60 for the purer corroding lead.   **Desilverized lead** is produced from the silver-lead ores of the Rocky Mountain states and is at least 99.85% pure.   **Common lead A** is desilverized and is 99.85% pure, while **common lead B** is 99.73% pure.   **Acid lead** is made by adding copper to fully refined lead, and **copper lead** is produced in the same way.   These two grades are 99.90 and 99.85% pure.   The percentages given for the seven grades of lead are ASTM minimums.   **Work lead** is the pig lead from the blast furnaces before the silver is extracted.   About 60% of the world production of lead is in the United States, Australia, Mexico, Germany, and Canada, though the ores are widely distributed and many other countries produce lead.

Lead wool is lead in a shredded form used for calking.   The strands are 0.005 to 0.015 in. in diameter, and come in ropes $5/8$ to $3/4$ in. in diameter.   **Blue lead** is a term meaning all lead products such as pipe and shot that have not been changed chemically in manufacture.   Blue lead is also a name for a basic sulfate, a by-product of the smelting of lead ores obtained by collecting and filtering the smoke from the furnace.   It is a mixture of the products of the partial combustion of the ore and coal.   It consists of lead sulfate, lead sulfide, lead sulfite, lead oxide, zinc oxide, and carbon.   It is used in base-coat paints for steel.

Sheet lead is produced by cold-rolling, and is designated by weight. A sheet of lead $\frac{1}{64}$ in. thick weighs approximately 1 lb per sq ft, and is called a 1-lb sheet. Thus, 4-lb sheet lead is $\frac{1}{16}$ in. thick, and 8-lb sheet is $\frac{1}{8}$ in. thick. As a sound barrier in building construction an 0.008-in. thickness of lead is equal to $\frac{3}{4}$ in. of fir plywood for sound absorption.

Lead has a high capacity for the capture of neutrons and gamma rays and is used for **radiation shielding** in the form of sheet lead or as metal powder in ceramic mortars and blocks, paints, and in plastic composite structures. **DS Lead,** of Sherrit Gordon Mines, Ltd., is a **dispersion-strengthened lead** containing up to 1.5% lead monoxide evenly distributed through the structure. The oxide combines chemically with the lead, doubling the strength and stiffness of the metal, but increasing its brittleness. It is used for chemical piping and fittings. A **neoprene-lead fabric** of Raybestos-Manhattan, Inc., is a neoprene fabric impregnated with lead powder. It has a radiation shielding capacity one third that of solid lead sheet. It comes in thicknesses of $\frac{1}{32}$ to $\frac{1}{4}$ in., and its flexibility makes it suitable for protective clothing and curtains. **Shielding cements** for X-ray and nuclear installation shielding are **metallic mortars** containing a high percentage of lead powder with ceramic oxides as binders and other elements for selective shielding. They are mixed with water to form plasters or for casting into sections and blocks. The formulation varies with the intended use for capture, attenuation, or dissipation of neutrons, gamma rays, and other radiation. **Shielding paints** are blended in the same manner. **Chemtree 82,** of the Chemtree Corp., is a lead powder with an organic binder soluble in water for application as a paint or molded into brick. The cured material is 95% lead with linear attenuation about 60% that of lead. **Chemtree 1-6-18** designed for neutron beam attenuation has 78% lead and a high hydrogen content together with the neutron-capturing isotopes lithium-6 and boron-10.

Battery-plate lead for the grid plates of storage batteries contains 7 to 12% antimony, 0.25 tin, and small amounts of arsenic and copper. **Silvium alloy,** for positive-plate grids, contains silver. **Lead-coated copper,** used for roofing and for acid-resistant tanks, is 16-oz copper sheet, coated on both sides with lead, made with either a rough or smooth finish. **Leadtex,** of Revere Copper & Brass, Inc., is a lead-coated sheet copper. **Roofloy,** of this company, is a strong, stiff, creep-resistant sheet lead used for flashings and gutters. It contains 99.7% lead, 0.20 tin, 0.015 calcium, and 0.012 magnesium. **Tea lead,** used for wrapping tea, is lead with 2% tin. **Tinsel lead** contains 1.5% antimony and up to 4% tin. **Shot lead** is lead hardened with 2 to 6% antimony and a small amount of arsenic. Shot up to 0.23 in. in diameter is made by pouring from the top of a tower through a pan perforated with holes smaller than the diameter desired. In falling, the lead assumes a spherical shape and drops into water to avoid flattening.   **Frangible bullets,** which shatter on striking a target surface and are used for aerial gunner practice, are made of lead powder and synthetic resin powder pressed into shape.

LEAD ALKALI METALS. Lead hardened with small amounts of alkali metals used chiefly as bearing metals.   Alloys of this type are also called **tempered lead** and **alkali lead.**   The original alkali lead, known as **Bahn-metall,** was made under a German patent.   It contains 0.73% calcium, 0.04 lithium, 0.55 sodium, and the balance lead, and is made by electrolysis of the fused alkali salts, using a molten lead cathode.   **Calcium-lead alloy** is made in the same manner, and contains up to 1% calcium.   The calcium forms a chemical compound, Pb_3Ca, with part of the lead, and the crystals of this compound are throughout the lead matrix.   The Brinell hardness is 35, and the compressive strength 25,000 psi, being thus superior in strength to the high-tin-bearing metals.   But the metal is difficult to melt without oxidation, and is easily corroded.   The melting point is 370°C, and it retains its bearing strength at more elevated temperatures than bab-bitts.   **Calcium lead,** with about 0.04% calcium, is used as cable sheathing to replace antimonial lead, giving greater fatigue resistance.   It is also used for grids in storage batteries, and has a lower rate of self-discharge than antimonial lead.   The small amount of lithium in Bahnmetall is intended to prevent the corrosion set up by the calcium.   It also increases the compressive strength to about 30,000 psi.   **Mathesius metal,** another German alloy, contains calcium and strontium to form Pb_3Sr crystals.   **Frary metal,** of the National Lead Co., is a lead-calcium-barium alloy containing about 1.5% of the alkali metals.   These alloys give low friction loss at low temperatures, but they have higher coefficients of friction than the lead-tin alloys at temperatures above 65°C.   A European lead-calcium-barium alloy known as **Ferry metal** contained 0.25% mercury to decrease the coefficient of friction.   Another bearing alloy, **Noheet metal,** contained some antimony and tin in addition to the alkali metals.   **B metal,** a German alloy, contains 0.73% calcium, 0.66 sodium, 0.05 lithium, and 0.03 potassium.

LEAD ORES. The chief ore of the metal lead is **galena,** a lead sulfide, PbS, containing theoretically 86.6% lead.   The ore, however, contains many other minerals and usually carries only 4 to 11% lead.   It is concentrated by gravity methods to contain 40 to 80% galena.   Galena has a bright metallic luster, streaked gray, a specific gravity of about 7.5, and hardness of 2.75.   It frequently contains silver and sometimes cadmium, bismuth, and copper.   The lead is obtained from the concentrated ore by roasting to remove the sulfur, and smelting.   The **ingot lead** from the blast furnace contains silver, copper, zinc, and other impurities.   It is refined and desilverized.   Southern Missouri is the chief source of galena in the United States.

The abundant lead ores **cerussite** and **anglesite** are secondary minerals formed by the oxidation of galena.   Cerussite is a lead carbonate, $PbCO_3$, found in crystals or in granular crystalline aggregate or massive.   Its color is white to gray, transparent to opaque.   The hardness is 3 to 3.5, and the specific gravity 6.55.   Anglesite is found usually in the oxidized portions of lead veins associated with galena and other minerals.   It is a common mineral occurring in many localities.   Anglesite is a **lead sulfate** of the composition $PbSO_4$, containing 68% lead.   It occurs in crystals, massive or granular.   Its hardness is 2.75 and specific gravity 6.12 to 6.39.   The color may be white or pale shades of yellow or blue, or it may be colorless.

Basic lead sulfate, $PbSO_4 \cdot PbO$, called **lanarkite,** is in white crystals with a specific gravity of 6.92.   It is formed by the action of heat and air on galena.   It is used as a paint pigment combined with zinc oxide.   **Alamosite** is **lead metasilicate,** $PbSiO_3$, and is in white crystals.   It can be produced by fusing litharge and silica, and is used in glazing ceramics and in fireproofing textiles.   **Barysilite** is **lead orthodisilicate,** $Pb_2Si_2O_7$, a white solid of specific gravity 6.6.   Other rarer minerals are **clausthalite,** which is **lead selenide,** $PbSe$, occurring in lead-gray cubical crystals of specific gravity 8.1, **attoite,** which is **lead telluride,** $PbTe$, occurring in tin-white cubical crystals of specific gravity 8.16, and **lead tungstate,** $PbWO_4$, called **lead wolframite,** and occurring as **raspite** in monoclinic crystals, or as **stolzite** in colorless tetragonal crystals.   The material is manufactured as a yellow powder of specific gravity 8.235, and used as a paint pigment.

Vanadinite is a minor ore of lead and a source of vanadium.   It is a mineral of secondary origin found in the upper oxidized parts of lead veins.   It is found in Arizona, New Mexico, Mexico, and Spain.   It has the composition $9PbO \cdot 3V_2O_5 \cdot PbCl_2$, with sometimes phosphorus and arsenic replacing part of the vanadium.   It occurs in reddish crystals and globular forms and as incrustations.   The specific gravity is 7, and hardness 3.

LEAD PIGMENTS. Chemical compounds of lead used in paints to give color.   They are to be distinguished from the lead compounds such as lead oleate, used as driers for paints.   **White lead** is the common name for **basic lead carbonate,** the oldest and most important lead paint pigment, and also used in putty and in ceramics.   It is a white, amorphous, poisonous powder of the composition $2PbCO_3 \cdot Pb(OH)_2$.   It is insoluble in water, and decomposes on heating.   The specific gravity is 6.7.   It is made from metallic lead, and is marketed dry, or mixed with linseed oil and turpentine in paste form.   **Lead carbonate,** $PbCO_3$, is used as a pigment in the same way as the basic compound, but it discolors more easily. Basic lead sulfate, called **sublimed white lead,** makes a fine white pigment. Commercial sublimed white lead contains 75% lead sulfate, 20 lead oxide, and 5 zinc oxide.   Commerical white lead may be mixed with lithopone, magnesium oxide, antimony oxide, witherite, or other materials.

The basic **silicate white lead,** $3PbO \cdot 2SiO_2 \cdot H_2O$, is made by fusing silica sand with litharge and hydrating by ball-milling with water.   It has corrosion-inhibiting properties, and is used in metal-protective paints for underwater service.   It is also used in ceramics and as a stabilizer in vinyl plastics.   **Basic lead silicate** is made from silica and litharge with sulfuric acid as a catalyst.   The material has a core of silica with a surface coating of basic lead silicate, giving a pigment of lower weight per unit of volume but retaining the activity of the silicate white lead.   **Chrome yellow,** or **Leipzig yellow,** is **lead chromate** of the composition $PbCrO_4$, and comes in yellow, poisonous crystals.   The specific gravity is 6.123.   It is insoluble in water and decomposes at 600°C.   **Basic lead chromate,** $2PbO \cdot CrO_3$, is red in color and is used for anticorrosive base coats for steel.   **American vermilion,** also called **Chinese scarlet** and **chrome red,** is basic lead chromate made from white lead.   **Orange mineral** is the red oxide, Pb_3O_4. **Cassel yellow,** or **Montpelier yellow,** is oxychloride of lead.   Mixtures of white lead and heavy spar are known as **Venetian white.**   **Dutch white** is composed of three parts of sulfate and one part of carbonate.   **Lead thiosulfate,** PbS_2O_3, is a white insoluble powder, used chiefly in matches.   All of the lead compounds are poisonous by skin absorption or when taken internally.   **Lead sulfide,** PbS, is used as a feeler in missiles as it is very sensitive to heat rays.

Litharge is the yellow **lead monoxide,** PbO, also called **massicot.**   It is a yellow powder used as a pigment and also in the manufacture of glass, and for the fluxing of earthenware.   An important use is as a filler in rubber.   With glycerin, litharge is used as a plumbers' cement.   The specific gravity is 9.375.   Litharge is produced by heating lead in a reverberatory furnace and then grinding the lumps.   For storage-battery use the black oxide, or suboxide of lead, is now largely substituted.   **Lead dioxide,** or **lead peroxide,** PbO_2, comes as a brown crystalline powder, and is used in making matches, dyes, and pyrotechnics, as a mordant, and as an oxidizing agent.   The natural mineral is called **plattnerite.**   Litharge, or **lead oxide,** converts to Pb_3O_4 at 800°F.

LEADED HIGH BRASS.   An alloy containing approximately 65% copper, from $\frac{1}{2}$ to $3\frac{1}{2}$ lead, and the remainder zinc.   It is one of the standard grades of brass, and is also called **free-cutting brass,** or **high-speed brass.** It is easier to machine than high brass but is less ductile.   It is used especially for cupped, drawn, or formed parts on which a clean thread must be cut.   The lead is present in finely dispersed particles, and the property of free cutting is gained at the expense of its drawing capacity, but the material is mostly employed in the form of rods for screw-machine work or in sheets for blanking.   The free-cutting brass rod of the Bridgeport Brass Co. contains 61.5% copper, 35.5 zinc, and 3 lead.   All impurities, including iron, are below 0.25%, since as little as 0.50% iron will harden brass 20 points Rockwell.   The free-cutting brass of the Chase Brass & Copper Co. has the same amount of copper, but has 3.5% lead.   A brass of this class will have a tensile strength of 57,000 psi, elongation 25%, and Brinell hardness up to 110.   **Ledrite brass** is the name of the Bridgeport Brass Co. for leaded brass containing 60 to 63% copper and 2.5 to 3.75 lead.   The alloy known as **architectural bronze,** used for extruded moldings and for forgings, contains 57% copper, 40 zinc, 0.25 tin, and 2.75 lead.   The free-machining alloy known as **arsenical bronze** is a leaded high brass modified with other elements.   A typical analysis is copper, 56.5%; zinc, 39; lead, 0.70; nickel, 2; iron, 1.20; and arsenic, 0.60.   The tensile strength is 65,000 to 87,000 psi, elongation 11 to 40%. It is both wear- and corrosion-resistant.

LEADED STEEL.   A free-machining steel containing about 0.25% lead. Lead does not alloy with iron but when a stream of finely divided lead is shot at the stream of molten steel to the ingot mold the lead is distributed in the steel in tiny particles and strings.   The lead gives free machining without imparting to the steel the unfavorable characteristics given by sulfur or phosphorus.   There is little weakening of the physical properties of the steel.   In cutting, the lead acts as a lubricant, reducing friction of the cutting tool, and aiding in producing a smooth finish.   **Ledloy,** of the Inland Steel Co., contains 0.15 to 0.30% lead in the regular SAE grades of steel.   **La-Led steel** of the LaSalle Steel Co. is a low-carbon leaded free-machining bessemer screw steel marketed in cold-finished rounds.   **Super La-Led steel** contains 0.25% lead with up to 0.50 sulfur.   **Rycut 40 steel,** of Joseph T. Ryerson & Son, Inc., is a chrome-molybdenum AISI steel 4140 containing 0.15 to 0.35% lead.   It can be machined 50% faster than unleaded steel of the same composition.   The tensile strength is 129,000 to 200,000 psi with elongation of 12 to 21%, depending on the tempering.   **Ledloy 170,** of the same company, is leaded cold-drawn seamless tubing.   It is a 1015 analysis steel with 0.15 to 0.35% of lead added.

LEATHER.   The skin or hides of animals, cured by the chemical action of tannins.   Leather is used for belting, gaskets, shoes, jackets, handbags, linings, coverings, and a variety of other products.   The action of tannins precipitates the protein of the hide, changes its colloidal structure, and makes it more pliable and capable of resisting decay.   The process of tanning hides consists essentially in soaking then in solutions of the tanning material after they have been unhaired in caustic lime.   This soaking may be for weeks or months, after which the hides are washed, oiled, and rolled.   Rapid tanning in strong solutions gives inferior leathers.

The quality of leather depends upon the type of animal, its physical condition, the care used in taking off the hide, the method of preserving the hide before tanning, and the care used in tanning.   Leather is made from many kinds of skins, including sheep, goat, deer, alligator, seal, and shark, although the bulk of commercial leather is made from **cattle hides.** Commercially, the term **hides** refers to the skins of full-grown beef cattle. **Kip skins** and **calfskins** are the names given to the hides of the younger animals.   Calfskins, from animals that have not eaten grass, produce a softer leather than cattle hides.   Hides of other animals besides the beef cattle, *Bos taurus,* are usually designated with the name of the animal, as **horsehide.**   The hides of smaller animals are designated as **skins,** either tanned or untanned, as **pigskin.**   Quantities of wild pigskins, known as **capivara skins,** are imported from Colombia.   Cattle hides are shipped in immense quantities from India, Argentina, Uruguay, and other pastoral countries.   Animals raised in the open have hides that produce tough, close-grained leather; breeded cattle raised for meat produce the weakest leather.   But in general, packing-house hides, well skinned and packed in brine, make the best leather if properly tanned.

Buffalo hides are from the domesticated **water buffalo** of southern Asia and the Philippines.   They are heavy, with a coarse grain, and are used to make a heavy, rough leather for buffing wheels and heavy boots, and also for **rawhide** mallets and gears.   Rawhide is a treated but untanned form of leather.

Belting leather is usually made from salted hides free from cuts and scratches, and is either oak- or chrome-tanned.   It is then stuffed with oils or tallows.   Belting leather weighs about 0.035 lb per cu in. and has an ultimate strength of about 3,800 psi.   Belting is now sold by the thickness instead of the weight because the leather is easily weighted by the addition of heavy impregnations.   But because of the use of direct drives and of the use of fabric belts impregnated with resins or rubbers, leather has lost its former importance for power transmission.   **Lace leather,** for splicing machinery belting, was originally **porpoise leather** tanned with alum and impregnated with cod oil, making a tough, pliable, and strong leather, but it is now a semitanned, oil-treated cowhide or calfskin.   Lacing for fastening sporting goods is now usually made of plastics, such as the **Cotalace** of Freydberg Bros.-Strauss, Inc.   **Helvetia leather,** for light belts and lacings, was weak-tanned with gambier and oil-impregnated.   **Belt dressings** are compounds of waxes and oils to maintain flexibility, and rosin or chemicals to improve grip.

Leather was once used widely for packings and gaskets but, because it is dissolved by mineral oils and becomes brittle at high temperatures, it has now been largely replaced for such uses by compounded materials. **Fibrated leather,** of the Armstrong Cork Co., for gaskets and packing, is shredded leather impregnated with a protein binder. It is resilient, resistant to oils, and will withstand temperatures to 300°F. It comes in sheets.

The **wax calf leather,** once popular for men's shoe uppers, was a leather heavily stuffed with grease and wax. It sheds water and is wear-resistant, but oily leathers are no longer desired in shoes. **Patent leather** is an old name for glossy burnished black leather for shoes and handbags. It cracks easily, and plastic finishes are now usually employed. **Helios leather,** of the Wilmington Enameling Co., has a base coat of linseed-oil gel on a chrome-tanned leather, and a finish coat of urethane plastic, giving 20 times more flex life than patent leather. **Ostrich leather,** once valued for handbags, is marked with tiny rosettes where the quills are extracted. It is now imitated in embossed calfskin. **Kangaroo leather** is a strong, supple, and durable leather made from the skins of the Australian kangaroo, used chiefly for shoe uppers and gloves. The skins measure from 2 to 12 sq ft in area, and the small ones are known as **wallaby.** The fibers have an interwoven structure, and the leather does not scuff easily. It takes a brilliant polish. It is rated as the strongest shoe leather per unit of weight. **Cordovan** is a tough, smooth, close-grained leather made from the hind quarters of horsehides. It takes a beautiful polish and is used for boots and fancy articles.

Leather dust consists of the light, fluffy fibers blown from the buffing and sueding wheels in tanneries. It is used as a covering material for **artificial suede** and **sueded fabrics,** and as a filler in adhesives and calking compounds. In Europe it is extensively collected and separated by grade and color, but the American material generally lacks uniformity as it is a mixture of many varieties of leather with different tannages and colors. **Leather flour** is ground and graded leather, uniform in color and in mesh, used as a filler and for sueded fabrics.

Pulped scrap leather is made into stiff board or flexible sheets, and may be called **leather board, fiber leather, synthetic leather,** or **artificial leather,** or may be marketed under trade names such as **Herkolite,** of the Herkimer Fiber Co., or **Reletha,** of the Prospect Mills, Inc. The leather fibers may be mixed with jute or other fibers. The German artificial leathers known as **Fagelan, Fabinette,** and **Nifarine** were made entirely of natural and synthetic textile fibers with various resin and rubber binders. Leather board and sheet is used for luggage, shoe heels, shoe linings, gaskets, and clutch

linings.   **Cotton-leather,** of the Southern Friction Materials Co., is made
from two to six plies of cotton fabric impregnated with a thermosetting
resin, calendered and surface-ground to resemble leather.   It is flexible
and resistant to oil and water, and is used for shoe soles, buffing wheels,
and machinery mountings.   But for many of the former large uses of
leather, including luggage and some types of shoes, leather has been replaced by impregnated laminated fabrics or fibers sheeted with a binder.

LECITHIN. A light-brown, soft, salvelike material of bland taste and
odor obtained from soybeans by solvent and steam extraction.   It is also
obtained from cottonseed, and occurs in small amounts in animal and plant
cells.   Lecithin is a glyceride of complicated chemical structure containing an amine, phosphoric acid, and choline.   It bleaches to a faint gold
color, is insoluble in water but soluble in oils and in alcohol.   At about
150°F it melts to an oil that will disperse readily in chocolate and other
foods as an antioxidant to prevent spoilage, as a stabilizer and emulsifier,
and as a dietetic.   It is also employed in casein paints to regulate viscosity,
in printing inks to impart flow, as a softener and wetting agent in some
other products, and as a curing accelerator in synthetic rubbers.   The
choline, $CH_2OHCH_2N(CH_3)_3OH$, is used in medicine as a heart stimulant.
Emultex R, of the A. E. Staley Mfg. Co., is a lecithin concentrate produced
from soybeans.   It is used as a stabilizer in water-based paints to prevent
pigment migration and settling in storage.   **Sta-Sol Plus,** of the same
company, is a concentrated grade of soybean lecithin containing 68%
active ingredients.   It is a low-moisture emulsifier for coatings and paints.

LEMONGRASS OIL. A pale-reddish essential oil distilled from various
species of *Cymbopogon* grass of the East Indies, Malaya, and tropical
America.   It contains about 75% **citral,** $C_9H_{15}CHO$, which is an aldehyde of several essential oils.   The chief constituents are **citronellal,**
$C_{10}H_{18}O$, and geraniol.   It also contains some **ionone,** $C_{13}H_{20}O$, a terpene
used as a base for violet perfumes.   The oil has a powerful lemonlike
odor.   The plant is a tall, rapid-growing grass.   Three tons of the East
Indian grass yield 24 bottles of oil, each bottle being 25 oz by volume.
Florida lemongrass yields 6.3 lb of oil per ton of grass.   The residue
lemongrass pulp in Florida is dehydrated and mixed with cane molasses
for cattle feed.   The oil is soluble in 70% alcohol.   It is used as a
stabilizer and perfume in soaps and in cosmetics.   The two chief grades
are **East Indian lemongrass,** from *C. flexuosus,* and **West Indian lemongrass,**
from *C. citratus.*   The latter contains less citral and is less soluble, but
partly owing to a difference in the method of distillation.   **Citronella oil**
is a yellow oil with a pleasant odor, distilled from the grass *C. nardus* of
Ceylon, Java, and India.   **Java citronella** is called **serah grass.**   It con-

tains high percentages of geraniol and citronellal.   It is used as a stabilizer and perfume in soaps, as an insect repellent, and for the production of **synthetic menthol** and of geraniol.

Java citronella oil is highest in citronellal, which yields about 20% levo menthol or about 12% USP menthol.   Ceylon oil is highest in geraniol, being sold on the basis of 85%, and is used in soaps and insecticides.   The rose perfume **rhodinol** is obtained from **Réunion geranium oil,** or **geranium Bourbon.**   It is an isomer of **citronellol,** the alcohol of citronellal, and can be made synthetically by isomerizing citronellol with ultraviolet light. **Palmarosa oil,** called **Turkish geranium oil** because the original shipments were through Turkey, is from the **motia grass,** *C. martini,* of India and Java.   It contains 75 to 90% geraniol.   Another variety of *C. martini,* known as **sofia grass,** sofia meaning mediocre, yields the product called **ginger grass oil,** inferior to palmarosa, and containing less geraniol.

LICORICE. The sweet roots of a group of plants of the order *Fabraeceae.* The common licorice of the Near East and Spain is *Glycyrrhiza glabra,* and of Italy, *G. echinata.*   Certain other species, all native to the Mediterranean countries, are also employed.   The roots are crushed and boiled in water, and the juice strained and evaporated.   Finely ground root is added to aid in hardening, but starch or other adulterant may be added.   In medicine it is known as **glycyrrhiza,** and it has an estrogenic, or female-hormone, action.   The dark-colored extracted juice of the roots contains a glucoside, which will not ferment.   The **glycyrrhizin** of MacAndrews & Forbes Co. is an ammoniated form of the tri-terpenoid glycoside.   It is a sweetening agent used in foodstuffs to reduce the amount of sugar and also to intensify flavor.   Licorice also contains a saponin, or froth-producing substance.   In fire extinguishers it is sold under trade names.   An insulating building board made with a proportion of the residue fibers after extraction of the juice is produced by the National Gypsum Co.   It is resistant to insect attack.   Licorice is employed in confectionery, medicines, and tobacco, as a flavoring, and in beverages as a frothing agent, but the saponins, in excess, are toxic.

LIGNIN. A colorless to brown crystalline product recovered from paper-pulp sulfite liquor, and used in furfural plastics, as an extender of phenol in phenolic plastics, as a corrosion inhibitor, in adhesives and coatings, as a natural binder for compressed-wood products, and for the production of synthetic vanilla when it contains coniferin.   It is also used as a fertilizer, providing humus and organic material and some sulfur to the soil.   For this use it may be mixed with phosphates.   Lignin is coprecipitated with natural and synthetic rubbers to produce stronger and lighter-weight products.   When lignin is incorporated into nitrile rubber by coprecipitation the rubber has higher tensile and tear strengths and greater elongation than with an equal loading of carbon black.   **Indulin,** of the West Virginia Pulp & Paper Co., is a pine wood lignin used as an extender for rubber latex to improve coating strength, and in phenolic resins to decrease cost. It is also used as a sequestering agent.   About 100,000 tons of lignin occurs in the liquor from 1,000,000 tons of sulfate-process paper pulp.

The melting point of lignin is 250 to 275°C.   It is a complex material, $C_{41}H_{32}O_6$, with four hydroxyl and four methoxyl groups, pine lignin containing 15% **methoxyl.**   The contained **lignoceric acid** is a C_{24} fatty acid melting at 84.7°C.   Lignin occurs in the waste liquor as a sodium compound, and is precipitated by acidifying.   For making laminates the lignin from soda-process aspen is preferred to spruce kraft lignin because of lower melting point and better flow.   The lignin known as **tomlinite** is obtained from kraft pulp liquor by treating with CO_2, separating the black liquor, and acidifying with sulfuric acid to yield the water-insoluble brown powder.   **Lignin binder,** for surfacing roads, is waste liquor from sulfite mills containing about 5% lignin.   **Lignosol,** of Lignosol Chemicals, Ltd., is a concentrated lignin liquor or powder.   **Spruce extract** is the liquor from sulfite spruce pulping used for mixing with quebracho for tanning leather, or in combination with syntans.   The tanning agent in the liquor is **lignosulfonic acid.**   **Alkali lignin** is produced by acidulation of the black liquor from the soda process.   It is used as the organic expander in the negative plates of storage batteries, as an emulsifier for asphalt to reduce cold flow, and as a binder in paperboard products.   It may also be hydrogenated to produce methane, methanol, and tar acids.

Lignosulfonates produced from the waste liquor of sulfate pulping of soft wood are used to reduce the viscosity of slurries and oil-well muds, as foam stabilizers, as extenders in glues, cements, and synthetic resins, and as a partial replacement for quebracho in tanning leather.   **Orzan A,** of the Crown Zellerbach Corp, is **ammonium lignosulfonate,** while **Orzan S** is **sodium lignosulfonate.**   **Toranil,** of the Lake States Yeast Corp., is **calcium lignosulfonate.**   It comes as a tan powder or as a brown viscous solution.   These lignosulfonates have the wood sugars and the sulfur dioxide removed, and will polymerize with heat.

LIGNITE.   Also called **brown coal.**   A variety of organic mineral of more recent age than coal, occurring in rocks of tertiary age, and intermediate in composition between wood and coal.   It is widely distributed over Europe, and found in many other parts of the world.   Freshly cut lignite often contains a large quantity of water, up to 40%, and is sometimes also high in ash.   When dried it breaks up into fine lumps and powder.   Dry lignite contains 75% carbon, 10 to 30 oxygen, and 5 to 7 hydrogen.   It kindles easily but burns with a low calorific power and a smoky flame.   In retort gas production lignite loses its gas in half the time required for gas removal from bituminous coal, with a temperature of $1270°F$, compared with $1655°F$ for bituminous.   California and Arkansas lignites are processed to extract montan wax, **sap brown dye,** and **Van Dyke brown** pigment.   The color of lignite varies from brown to black, and the lower grades of brown lignite show the woody structure.   The **pitch coal** is brownish black, breaks with a pitchlike fracture, and shows no woody structure.   Lignite is briquetted by crushing and pressing with a binder under heat.   Belgian **lignite briquettes** have a binder of 8% asphalt, with 2 flour to assist binding.   The reserves of lignite in the United States are estimated at 1,000 billion tons, and form a future fuel for use in powdered form, or for distillation of oils and coal-tar products.   Texas lignite is carbonized at $950°F$ to produce a solid fuel known as **char** which has a Btu value of 10,600 per lb.   From 7,000 tons of lignite the yields is 3,200 tons of char and 2,300 lb of by-product tar.   **Lignite tar** is a mixture of hydrocarbons with nitrogen, oxygen, and sulfur complexes.   The tar distillate contains 74% neutral oil, 23 tar acids, 3 tar bases, and 0.9 sulfur.   The neutral oils are cracked for motor fuels.   Other fractions are used for producing phenol, pyridine, and epoxy resins.   **Jet** is a hard, compact, black lignite found in Colorado, Utah, and in Yorkshire, England.   The Utah jet occurs in the form of flattened-out trees, with the entire tree metamorphosed into jet.   It was formerly much used for making buttons and ornamental articles, but is now largely replaced by plastics, and the less brittle black onyx is substituted for jewelry.

LIGNUM VITAE. The wood of the **guayacum** trees, *Guaiacum offinale* and *G. sanctum,* of tropical America, but the commercial shipments of lignum vitae are likely to contain also other species.   The wood of the **guayacan** tree of Brazil and Paraguay is also called by this name.   The best quality of the true lignum vitae comes in logs up to 18 ft long and up to 3 ft in diameter, and originates mostly from Cuba, Haiti, Yucatan, Dominican Republic, and the west coast of Mexico and Central America, but species of the trees grow as far south as Paraguay.   It is very hard, heavy, and tough.   The color is brown to greenish black.   The grain is very finely twisted, and the wood has a greasy feel, containing 3% of natural resin.   The specific gravity is 1.14, with a weight of 80 lb per cu ft and a crushing strength of 10,500 psi.   The wood is used in places where extreme hardness is needed, such as for pulley blocks.   It is also used for rollers, mallet heads, handles, novelties, bearings, and furniture.   In machine bearings it withstands pressures up to 4,000 psi, and is used for propeller-shaft bearings in steamships.   **Palo santo,** *Bulnesia sarmenti,* known as guayacan, of Argentina and Paraguay, and also **vera,** *B. arborea,* of Colombia and Venezuela, are closely related to lignum vitae and were formerly classified as *Guaiacum.* The latter is called **Maracaibo lignum vitae,** and the former is known as **Paraguayan lignum vitae.** The trees are larger than true lignum vitae, but the wood is not as hard. **Philippine lignum vitae** is a hard, heavy wood with interwoven grain, from the tree *Xanthestemon verdugonianus* of the Philippines. **Yellow guayacan,** deriving its name from the yellow flowers, is from the *Tecoma guayacan,* an important timber tree of Panama and Central America. The wood is very hard and strong, but neither this wood nor the Philippine wood has the self-lubricating bearing properties of the oily true lignum vitae. **Ibera vera,** of Argentina and Paraguay, is also called guayacan locally. It is from the tree *Caesalpinia melanocarpa,* and resembles lignum vitae in hardness, strength, and durability, but is lacking in the oily gum resin. It is a valuable ornamental construction wood.

Artificial lignum vitae, or **compressed wood,** or **densified wood,** sold under trade names, is ash or a softwood impregnated with liquid resin and compressed hydraulically to about the specific gravity of lignum vitae. It is used for bearings, or as a substitute for very hard woods. The material developed by the U.S. Forest Products Laboratory under the name **Staypak** is made by compressing veneered softwood containing no resin except that used to bond the veneers. It has a smooth satiny finish, a specific gravity of 1.3 to 1.4, and about double the tensile and flexural strengths of birch. The color is darker than the original wood because of the flow of lignin. **Hiden,** of the Parkwood Corp., is a synthetic hardwood of about the same density and hardness as lignum vitae. It is made of birch veneers impregnated with phenolic resin and compressed to 30% of the original thickness and cured. The boards are used for tabletops, cutlery handles, sheet-metal forming dies, and textile picker sticks.

LIME. A **calcium oxide,** CaO, chemically known as **calcia,** occurring abundantly in nature, chiefly in combination with carbon dioxide as calcium carbonate, in limestone, marble, chalk, coral, and shells. Lime is employed in mortars, cements, as a flux in iron melting, in many chemical processes, as an absorbent, and for liming acid soils. It is obtained by heating limestone in a furnace or kiln to about 1000°F to burn out the carbonic acid gas. The residue is called **quicklime** or **caustic lime.** Pure quicklime is white and amorphous or crystalline. The specific gravity is 3.2 and melting point 4660°F. **Chemical lime,** used in the chemical industries and for water softening, is a high-calcium lime with minimum impurities. A typical analysis is 97.9% CaO, 0.43 silica, 0.45 iron and aluminum oxides, and 0.52 magnesium oxide. The **Kemidol quicklime** marketed by the U.S. Gypsum Co. for glass manufacture is a free-flowing fine powdered lime made from Ohio dolomite. When dolomite quicklime is hydrated, no more than 2 or 3% of the magnesium oxide is converted to the hydroxide, and the lime has a high neutralizing value, useful for neutralization of chemical solutions.   **Oyster shells** have about the same calcium carbonate content as the best grade of high-calcium limestone, with low impurities, and they are used for making quicklime.

Commercial limes for building purposes contain about 94% calcium oxide, some calcium carbonate, and less than 0.50% magnesia.   Water causes the lime to slake with much heat, leaving a white powder, $CaO \cdot H_2O$.   High-calcium limes slake rapidly and expand greatly on slaking and are the strongest.   Limes with much magnesia slake slowly, but magnesia produces the slip that makes easier working.   The so-called **lean limes** contain considerable silica, alumina, and iron oxide, and are slow-slaking and difficult to work.   Lime is marketed in lumps or ground to 20 mesh, and as mill run.   **Hydrated lime** is made by grinding quicklime, slaking the powder with water, and sifting to a fine powder.   It is easier to handle and is a more reliable product than ordinary lime.   High-grade hydrated lime will have a fineness so that 98% will pass through a 100-mesh sieve and will contain not over 2% magnesia.   Some grades contain less than 0.50% magnesia, and 98% pass through a 200-mesh sieve. The pure hydrated lime for the chemical industry has 98.2% $Ca(OH)_2$, or 74.4% CaO, and is a fine air-float powder.   This is **calcium hydroxide,** or **lime hydrate,** and is also used in paints, for dehairing hides, and in medicine.   **Hydraulic lime** that will set under water is a hydrated lime with more than 10% silica.   The **Grappier cement** of France and Belgium is made from limestones that contain 20 to 22% silica and 2 alumina.   **Lime mortar,** made of a mixture of hydrated lime, sand, and water, will have a compressive strength up to 400 psi.   **Soda lime,** used for freeing air of carbon monoxide, as a chemical purifying agent, and in gas masks, is a mixture of hydrated lime with sodium hydroxide.

LIME OIL. An essential oil expressed from the rind of the **lime,** the fruit of the small tree *Citrus aurantifolia,* native to India but now grown in many tropical and subtropical countries.   The fruit is smaller than the lemon, and is greenish yellow in color.   Montserrat in the West Indies, Italy, and Florida are the chief commercial centers.   **Lime juice,** from the pulp of the fruit, is used in flavoring and to give freshness to perfumes, in beverages, and was early used to prevent scurvy, but contains only about 25% as much vitamin C as orange juice.

Of more commercial importance is **lemon oil,** a bright-yellow oil of pleasant odor expressed from the rind of the lemon, the fruit of the tree *C. limonia,* grown commercially in the Mediterranean countries, California, Florida, and the West Indies.   About 1,000 lemons are required to produce 1 lb of oil.   The oil is high in citral with also limonene, terpineol, and citronellal. It is used in flavors, soap, and perfumery. Synthetic lemon oil, used in confectionery and beverages, contains no terpenes. It has a much stronger flavor than the natural oil. **Citropol,** of Dragoco, Inc., is a synthetic lemon oil. **Lemon juice** is from the pulp. It contains 5% citric acid. It is used in beverages and as a bleaching agent. **Lemon juice powder,** prepared by spray-drying from a solution that encases each particle, is a free-flowing, nonhygroscopic powder having long storage life. It is used for foodstuff flavoring.

Citric acid produced from lemons, limes, and pineapples is a colorless, odorless crystalline powder of the composition $(CO_2HCH_2)_2C(OH)COOH$, specific gravity 1.542, and melting point 153°C. It is used in medicine, flavoring extracts, and in soft drinks, but is toxic in excess. It is also used in inks, etching, and as a resist in textile dyeing and printing. It is a good antioxidant and stabilizer for tallow and other fats and greases, but is poorly soluble in fats. **Tenox R,** of Eastman Chemical Products, Inc., a soluble antioxidant, consists of 20% citric acid with 60% propylene glycol and 20% butylated hydroxy anisol. Citric acid is also used as a preservative in frozen fruits to prevent discoloration in storage. Its salt, **sodium citrate,** is a water-soluble crystalline powder used in soft drinks to give a nippy saline taste, and is also used in plating baths. Citric acid is also produced by the fermentation of blackstrap molasses.

LIMESTONE. A general name for a great variety of calcite rocks. Immense quantities of limestone are used as flux in the melting of iron, for the manufacture of lime, and as a building stone. In a broad sense limestone includes dolomite, marble, chalk, or any mineral consisting largely of $CaCO_3$. When the proportion reaches 45% and is in the double carbonate, $CaCO_3 \cdot MgCO_3$, it is called **dolomite.** On calcination, limestone yields lime, CaO. **Portland stone,** of England, consists of fossils cemented together with lime, and the **coquina rock** of Florida is made up entirely of shells, mostly the tiny **coquina shell,** *Donax variabilis.*

The **Indiana limestone,** valued for building, is a noncrystalline massive rock with aggregate, filler, and matrix of 98% calcium carbonate in gray and buff colors. It is an **oolite** with small round grains resembling fish roe. The weight is 135 to 150 lb per cu ft, with compressive strength from 4,000 to 7,000 psi. The mill blocks are from 8 to 12 ft in length, and are 3 ft 6 in., or 4 ft 4 in., square. **Bangor limestone,** from Alabama, is also an important building stone. It is an oolite with 97% $CaCO_3$. **Dolomitic limestone** from Minnesota is also used for building. **Kasota stone** from Minnesota is a recrystallized variety resembling marble and coming in yellow and pink. It contains 49% $CaCO_3$ and 39% $MgCO_3$ with silica. Its crushing strength is more than double that of Indiana limestone. It is used largely for interior work. **Mankato stone** contains slightly higher $CaCO_3$ with about 4.5% alumina in addition to silica. It weighs 155 lb per cu ft, and has a compressive strength of 13,500 psi. Desirable buff and yellow coloring in limestones comes from small amounts of iron oxides, but iron sulfides produce weather staining, and are not desired in building stone. **Sohnhofen stone,** or **lithographic stone,** produced at Sohnhofen, Germany, is a limestone with an exceptionally homogeneous fine grain, very low in impurities, and with a Mohs hardness of 3. It occurs in layers 2 to 6 in. thick, with partings of gray clay. Limestone is widely distributed, and a very large proportion of all crushed and broken stone used for construction purposes in the United States is limestone. **Agricultural limestone,** known as **agstone,** used for liming soils, is stone of high calcium carbonate content ground to a fineness of 200 to 325 mesh. A grade for chemical use is specified with a minimum of 97.5% $CaCO_3$, and maximums of 0.30 silica, 0.20 alumina, and 0.07 iron.

LINEN. A general name for the yarns spun from the fiber of the variety of flax plant cultivated for its fiber, or for the cloth woven from the yarn. **Linen yarns** and fabrics have been made from the earliest times, and the ancient Egyptian linen fabrics were of exceeding fineness containing 540 warp threads per inch, not equaled in Europe until the twentieth century. Ireland, Belgium, and France are the principal producers of linen. Linen yarns are used for the best grades of cordage, and linen fabrics are employed industrially wherever a fine, even, and strong cloth is required. **Linen fabrics** are sold under a wide variety of trade names. They are graded chiefly according to the fineness of the yarns and the class of weave and may contain some fine hemp fibers. **Lisle** was formerly a fine, hard linen thread, made at Lille, France, but is now a fine, smooth yarn made of long-staple cotton spun tightly in a moist condition. **Tow yarns** are the coarsest linen yarns, used for making **crash,** a coarse, plain-woven fabric used for towels or covers. **Chintz** is a plain-woven linen fabric in brightly colored designs. It is also made in cotton as **cotton chintz.** The name is from the Hindu word meaning color. **Damask** is a jacquard reversible woven linen fabric for table linen. It is now also made in cotton, silk, or rayon.

LINOLEUM. A general name for floor-covering material consisting of a mixture of ground cork or wood flour, rosin or other gum, blown linseed oil, pigments, with sometimes a filler such as lithopone, on a fabric backing of burlap or canvas, rolled under pressure to give a hard, glossy surface. It is pigmented or dyed in plain colors, or printed with designs. The cork is usually in about 50-mesh particles. Linoleum was patented in 1863 and displaced a more expensive floor covering known as **Kamptuli-**

con, which was made of rubber, cork, rosin, and oil.   Because of its low cost, linoleum still has a wide usage, but it is not durable and has a tendency to crack, and it has been largely replaced by sheeting compounded with synthetic resins marketed under trade names and by tile.   **Battleship linoleum,** a very heavy grade in plain colors or mosaics, is described in Federal specifications as made with oxidized linseed oil, fossil or other resins or oxidized rosin, and an oleoresinous binder, mixed with ground cork, wood flour, and pigments, processed on a burlap back.   Because of its resiliency, battleship linoleum is still valued for high-grade flooring, and is coated with an adherent, wear-resistant lacquer based on cellulose ester and alkyd resins.

LINSEED OIL. This oil is the most common of the drying oils, and is widely used for paints and varnishes, and for linoleum, printing inks, and soaps.   It is obtained by pressure from the seeds of the flax plant, *Linum usitatissimum,* which is cultivated for oil purposes.   It is sometimes referred to as **flaxseed,** though this name properly belongs only to the seed of the flax plant for producing flax fiber.   The varieties producing linen fiber do not yield much seed.   The seed contains up to 40% oil, and Argentine seed averages 38.5%, but the usual conversion factor is 34%. The linseed plant can stand high temperatures and drought, but is sensitive to cold, while the flax fiber plant needs a cool and humid climate.   In normal times 80% of the world's linseed is grown in the Mesopotamia region of Argentina and Uruguay, and much of the remainder in northern India and southern Russia, while the flax plant is grown in northern Europe and the Baltic region.   When prices are high, much linseed is grown in the United States and Canada.   The commercial oil is hot-pressed and has a bitter taste, but a cold-pressed oil is used in Russia for food purposes.   The residue **linseed cake** is used for cattle feed and fertilizer. The oil imported from Holland under the name of **Haarlem oil** is linseed oil mixed with sulfur and turpentine.   It is used in the southern states as a diuretic medicine.   Linseed oil contains about 48% linoleic and 34 linolenic acids.   The specific gravity is 0.925 to 0.935.   It is a yellowish oily liquid with a peculiar odor and a bland taste.   It is soluble in turpentine, ether, and benzene.   It dries with a distinct gloss and makes a hard film.

The best **Baltic oil** is used as a standard in measuring the drying power of other oils.   Genuine linseed oil has an iodine value of at least 170, and the best approaches 190.   The linseed grown in cooler climates from the same type of plant generally yields oil of higher iodine value than that grown in warm climates.   Baltic oil has an iodine value of 190 to 200, though this high value is from the type of plant as well as from the climate, the European plant being the flax plant yielding less seed.   Oils from seeds grown in different areas vary widely in the acid content. North Dakota oil contains 26 to 33% linolenic acid, while the **Punjab oil** of India has as high as 54% of this acid. The **puntis oil** used in Pakistan to extend linseed oil is a fish oil from the puntis, *Barbus stigma,* caught off the Indian coast.

.For varnish use, linseed oil may be used as **boiled linseed oil,** prepared by heating to not over 600°F in a closed container, or by heating with oxidizing driers such as the salts of lead or manganese. When prepared with driers, it is called **bung oil.** **Stand oil,** also known as **lithographic oil,** is linseed oil heated for several hours without blowing, at a temperature of 550 to 650°F. It has the consistency of honey and is used in oil enamel paints. Blown oils and boiled oils are not greasy like the original oil. **Linoxyn** is a trade name for blown linseed oil. The purity and adulteration of linseed oil for paint and varnish use are controlled by state laws. The law of the state of Ohio, which is typical, defines boiled linseed oil as prepared from pure, raw linseed oil heated to a temperature of 225°F, and incorporating no more than 4% by weight of drier, and with specific gravity at 60°F of not less than 0.935 and not greater than 0.945. **Esskol** and **Solinox,** of Textron, Inc., are hydrogen-treated linseed oils used as substitutes for tung oil and castor oil. **Keltrol L,** of this company, is **styrenated linseed oil** made by reacting linseed oil with styrene. It is used for paints, in which it dries rapidly to a hard, tough, and alkali-resistant film. The heavy-bodied linseed oils of ADM Chemicals are oxidized oils with specific gravities of 0.980 to 0.990, and iodine numbers from 210 to 230. **Linopol,** of the Sherwin-Williams Co., is a polymerized linseed oil in water emulsion for use in latex paints.

LINTERS. The short cotton fibers that adhere to the seed after ginning. **Cotton linters** removed from the cottonseed are from 0.04 to 0.6 in. long. The first cuts, or longer fibers, are used for upholstery and for mattresses, and amount to 20 to 75 lb per ton of seed. The second-cut short fibers vary from 125 to 180 lb per ton of seed, and are called **hull fiber.** The No. 1 grade of long linters is spinnable, and can be used for mixing with cotton for yarns. This grade is also used for making absorbent cotton. The short hull fiber is cleaned and processed to produce **chemical cotton,** which is a pure grade of alpha cellulose used for making rayon, nitrocellulose, and plastics. Chemical cotton is marketed as loose pulp in bales, and as sheet pulp with the sheet stacked in bales of 200 or 400 lb, or with the continuous sheet in rolls. Formerly, cotton linters were considered as the only source of pure cellulose for making nitrocellulose explosives, but pure alpha cellulose from wood is now used for this purpose.

LITHIUM. The lightest of all metals, with a specific gravity of 0.534. It is abundant, and is found in more than 40 minerals, but is obtained chiefly from lepidolite and spodumene and from salt brines. The brine of Searles Lake contains a ton of Li_2O in every 8,750 tons of brine. The dried crude concentrate from the flotation cells contains about 20% Li_2O. It may be extracted by solar evaporation from the brines of underground lakes in Nevada and other locations. It occurs also in seawater in lesser concentrations. North Carolina has immense reserves of lithium ores.

Lithium melts at 186°C and boils at 1370°C. It is unstable chemically and burns in the air with a dazzling white flame when heated to just above its melting point. The metal is silvery white but tarnishes quickly in the air, and a **lithium nitride,** Li_3N, is formed. The metal is kept submerged in kerosene. Lithium resembles sodium, barium, and potassium, but has a wider reactive power than the other alkali metals. It combines easily with oxygen, nitrogen, and sulfur, to form low-melting-point compounds which pass off as gases, and is thus useful as a deoxidizer and degasifier of metals. In glass the small ionic radius of lithium permits a lithium ion coupled with an aluminum ion to displace two magnesium ions in the spinel structure. **Lithium cobaltite,** $LiCoO_2$, and **lithium zirconate,** Li_2ZrO_3, are also used in ceramics. **Lithium carbonate,** Li_2CO_3, is a powerful fluxing agent for ceramics, and is used in low-melting ceramic enamels for coating aluminum. It is used in medicine to treat mental depression.

Lithium metal, 99.4% pure, is produced by the reduction of **lithium chloride,** LiCl. The salts of lithium burn with a crimson flame, and lithium chloride is used in pyrotechnics. It is also used for dehumidifying air for industrial drying and for air conditioning, as it absorbs water rapidly. It is also employed in welding fluxes for aluminum. Lithium is also used in storage batteries. The anode is lithium, the cathode is a **lithium-tellurium alloy,** and the electrolyte is a molten bath of lithium salts at 800°F. **Lithium ribbon,** of Foote Mineral Co., for high-energy battery use, is 99.96% pure metal in continuous strip form, 0.02 in. thick. It comes on spools packed dry under argon. An anhydrous form of **lithium hexafluoro arsenate** powder is used as the anode in dry batteries.

Because of the low weight, lithium compounds give the highest content of hydrogen, oxygen, or chlorine. **Lithium perchloride,** $LiClO_4$, is a stable solid used as a source of oxygen in rockets and flares, with lithium chloride as a residue. One cubic foot yields 91 lb of oxygen. On a volume basis it has 29% more oxygen at normal temperature than liquid oxygen at its boiling point. **Lithium hydride,** LiH, a white or gray powder of specific gravity 0.82 and melting point 680°C, is used for the production of hydrogen for signal balloons and floats. A 1-lb can of hydride when immersed in water will liberate 45 cu ft of hydrogen gas. It is more stable to heat than sodium hydride, and it provides molecular hydrogen, not atomic hydrogen. **Lithium aluminum hydride,** or **lithium alanate,** $LiAlH_4$, is used in the chemical industry for one-step reduction of esters without heat.

Lithium metal is very sensitive to light, and is used also in light-sensitive cells. **Lithium 7,** which comprises 94% of natural lithium, has low neutron absorption. The other isomer, **lithium 6,** has high neutron absorption, and is used in nuclear reactors.

LITHIUM ALLOYS. Lithium is soluble in most commercial metals only to a slight extent. Although the metal alone is unstable, the small atom and the high electronegativity permit incorporation in many alloys as a beneficial element. It is a powerful deoxidizer and desulfurizer of steel, but no lithium is left in the **lithium-treated steel.** In stainless steels it increases fluidity to produce dense castings. Cast iron treated with lithium has a fine grain structure and increased density with high impact value. Not more than 0.01% remains in the casting when treated with lithium-copper. In magnesium alloys the tensile strength is increased greatly by the addition of 0.05% lithium. The solid solubility of lithium in lead is not over 0.09%, but lithium refines the grain structure of the lead, increasing the strength, and it hardens the lead by the formation of a compound, Pb_3Li_2. **Lithium-treated lead** is called **alkali lead,** and is used for machine bearings.

Since lithium is only about 30% the weight of magnesium, **superlight alloys,** such as magnesium-lithium LA 141A, can be made that are as light as plastic. These alloys are not stable under heat and high stress conditions, but with additions of 10 to 20% of other elements such as aluminum and zinc, **lithium-magnesium alloys** can be heat-treated to tensile strengths of 65,000 psi. The lithium alters the normal hexagonal structure of the magnesium, giving the alloy greater ductility. It has good damping properties, and is resistant to the penetration of high-velocity radiation, making it suitable for containers and shields.

Lithium-copper master alloys consist of a group of foundry alloys containing usually 90, 95, or 98% copper with the balance lithium, used for deoxidizing and degasifying nonferrous alloys. Lithium combines easily in the molten bath with oxygen, hydrogen, nitrogen, sulfur, and the halides. The compounds formed are stable, of a nonmetallic nature, of low melting points, and volatilize easily so as to pass off as vapors at the pouring temperature of the metals. **Lithium copper** is a high-conductivity, high-density copper containing a minute quantity of residual lithium, 0.005 to 0.008%, made by treating copper with a 50–50 lithium-calcium master alloy. The conductivity of lithium copper is 101.5% IACS. The tensile strength is 31,500 to 36,500 psi, with elongation 60 to 72%. The wrought metal is tougher than phosphorized copper, and has exceptional deep-drawing properties. The cast metal has a density of 8.92. Lithium is an excellent desulfurizer for nickel alloys. From 1 to 7% calcium may also be included in lithium-copper master alloys. **Lithium-calcium alloys** usually contain 30 to 50% lithium, with the balance calcium.   They are silvery white in color, with a metallic luster, and are hard and brittle. The melting range is 230 to 260°C.   They must be kept in tight containers under kerosene.   The alloys are used for treating steel, cast iron, or nickel where no residual copper is to be left.   **Copper-manganese-lithium** contains 60 to 70% copper, 27 to 30 manganese, 0.5 to 5 lithium, and sometimes 5 to 7 calcium.   **Copper-silicon-lithium** contains 80 to 84% copper, 10 to 11 silicon, 2.5 to 10 lithium, and sometimes 2.5 calcium.

LITHIUM ORES. One of the chief ores is **lepidolite** which also carries more rubidium than any other known mineral, containing from a trace to 3% **rubidium oxide,** Rb_2O.   It may also have as much as 0.77% **cesium oxide.**   It is a **lithia mica,** $LiF \cdot KF \cdot Al_2O_3 \cdot 3SiO_2$, occurring in small plates together with muscovite.   It is the most widespread of the lithium minerals, being found in various parts of the United States, Canada, northern Rhodesia, South Africa, India, China, Japan, Russia, and Germany.   The hardness is 2.5 to 4, and specific gravity 2.8.   It has a pearly luster, and color pink and lilac to grayish white.   It is insoluble in acids.   Lepidolite is employed as a source of lithium compounds, and of the metals rubidium and cesium.   It is also used in making opal and white glasses.   **Glassmaker's lepidolite** contains 4% Li_2O; West African lepidolite usually contains 3.75%.   **Amblygonite,** plentiful in Sweden, has the formula $Al_2O_3 \cdot 2LiF \cdot P_2O_5 \cdot Li_2O$, and contains 4.24 to 5.26% lithium.   The amblygonite from South Dakota is sold on the basis of 8 to 9% Li_2O, and the ore from southern Rhodesia contains 9% Li_2O, 48% P_2O_5, and 34% Al_2O_3.   Other lithium ores are **lithiophilite,** $Li_2O \cdot 2MnO \cdot P_2O_5$, containing 4.6 to 5% lithium; **cryolithionite,** $3LiF \cdot 3NaF \cdot 2AlF_3$, with 5.35% lithium; **petalite,** $Li_2O \cdot Al_2O_3 \cdot 8SiO_2$, with 1.4 to 2.26% lithium; and **manandonite,** $7Al_2O_3 \cdot 2LiO \cdot 2B_2O_3 \cdot 6SiO_2$, with 2.13% lithium.

LITHOPONE. Also known under various trade names: **Ponolith, Sunolith, Beckton white, Zincolith, Sterling white,** and others.   A white pigment consisting of barium sulfate and zinc sulfide.   A standard lithopone is 66% barium sulfate and 34 zinc sulfide.   High-strength lithopones contain about 50% zinc sulfide, which latter is one of the whitest pigments. **Titanated lithopone** contains a percentage of titanium dioxide.   **Tidolith** is a titanated lithopone of the United Color & Pigment Co. having 85% lithopone and 15 titanium oxide.   **Cadmolith** is the trade name of the Glidden Co. for cadmium red and cadmium yellow lithopones used as pigments for plastics, as they are chemical-resistant and nonbleeding. Commercial lithopone is a fine white powder used in the manufacture of paints, inks, oilcloth, linoleum, and rubber goods.   For paints the powder should pass through a 325-mesh screen.   The ground paste should contain

76 to 80% pigment and 20 to 24 linseed oil. As a paint pigment, lithopone has good hiding power and is lower in cost than other whites, but is not as durable for outside use as white lead or zinc white. It is the most used white pigment for interior work. **Albalith** is a 70–30 lithopone of the New Jersey Zinc Co., also used in rubber goods, inks, and paper.

LOCUST. The wood of the locust tree, *Robinia pseudoacacia,* also known as **acacia, false acacia, black locust,** and **red locust.** The tree is native to North America, but is also grown in Europe. The wood is strong and durable, with a weight of 43 to 52 lb per cu ft. Its hardness is about the same as ash, and the strength, flexibility, and shock resistance are greater than oak. The grain is coarse, but the surface is lustrous and satiny. Locust is used for furniture, wheel spokes, posts, crossties, and in construction. **Honey locust** is a lighter and weaker wood from the tree *Gleditsia triacanothos.* The name locust is also applied to the wood of the tree *Hymensea courbaril* of tropical America. This wood has a brownish color, with an open grain, and takes a beautiful polish. The wood of the **Australian locust,** *Acacia melanoxylon,* known as **Australian blackwood** and **Tasmanian blackwood,** and employed for cabinetwork, is reddish brown to black in color and beautifully grained. It is similar in durability and appearance to rosewood, but lighter in weight. Various species of true acacia trees furnish the tannins catechu and wattle. The **silver wattle** of New Zealand, *A. prominens,* used for ax handles and fruit cases, is hard and tough. The black locust has clusters of very fragrant white flowers, and it is now widely grown as a shade tree and for shelterbelts in the eastern area of the United States.

LOCUST BEAN GUM. Also called **locust bean flour,** and **carob flour.** A tasteless and odorless white powder obtained by milling the bean kernels of the locust trees of tropical America, Africa, and the Mediterranean countries, notably *Cerafonia siliqua* of Cyprus, Syria, and Spain. The **carob bean,** or pod, contains 6 to 10 hard seeds, which are the **locust beans,** the bean in the pod averaging 9% of the weight. In Gambia the locust bean is called **netto.** When dissolved in water and boiled, it produces an adhesive, transparent jelly, which dries into a colorless, strong elastic film. It contains galactose and mannose in a complex polymer, and is a polysaccharide or complex sugar. It is used for coating textiles and also as a thickener and binder in glues, pastes, and latex, in leather finishes, and in sizings for yarn and paper. The flour dissolves in cold water and swells in warm water. It is edible and is also used in jellies and in bakery products. The dried pods are used also in flavoring dog biscuit and tobacco. In the Near East they are eaten like candy, and are also used as cattle and horse feed. The pods also yield **tragasol** gum, which is used as a textile size and in leather tanning.   The production of carob beans in Spain is large, and fully 90% of the crop is used locally for livestock feed.

The **algaroba tree,** *Prosopis chilensis,* growing in semiarid regions of Mexico, Central and South America, called also **mesquite,** and in Hawaii called **keawe,** furnishes an important stock feed from the pods and beans, which are similar to the locust.   An acre of mesquite produces four times as much food for beef cattle as an acre of corn.   The wood of the mesquite also contains up to 1% pyrogallol tannin valuable for tanning leather. **Guar gum,** used as a replacement for carob bean gum and gum arabic in foods and pharmaceuticals, is a water-soluble, odorless, and tasteless white powder obtained from the endosperm of the seed of the guar plant, *Cyamopsis tetragonoloba,* grown in Pakistan as cattle feed and cultivated in Texas and Arizona.   The gum is a polysaccharide with a straight chain of mannose units having one galactose group on every other mannose unit. There is a 3:1 ratio of mannose to galactose compared with a 4:1 ratio in locust bean gum.   It also contains about 6% protein, about the same as in locust bean gum.   **Guar flour** is a nearly white guar gum.   Its high swelling properties in cold water make it suitable as a disintegrating agent in medical tablets.   It has more than 6 times the thickening power of starch, and is used for upgrading starches.   **Jaguar gum,** of Stein, Hall & Co., is guar gum.   **Jaguar 315,** of this company, and **Guartec** of General Mills, Inc., are derivatives of guar gum that gel in either acid or alkaline solutions, and will form stiff gels with as much as 99% water content. They are polymers of mannose and galactose.

LOGWOOD. An extract obtained from the wood of the tree *Haematoxylon campechianum,* of tropical America, used as a black dye or as a darkening agent in browns and grays.   The wood yields 15% extract. The coloring matter, **hematine,** $C_{16}H_{12}O_6$, forms brownish-red crystals and is produced only in the aged wood or by oxidation of the white extract of fresh wood.   **Logwood extract,** or hematine, is marketed in crystals, solid extract, or water extract.

LOOFA SPONGE. A yellowish, porous, skeletal, fibrous body obtained by retting the fruit or seed pods of the tropical edible cucumber, *Luffa cylindrica* and *L. acutangula,* obtained in India, Japan, and the Caribbean countries.   It is also called **vegetable sponge,** although it is harder and coarser than a sponge.   The paper-thin skin is easily removed when the pod dries.   The skinned sponge is washed to remove the slimy interior, and when redried the seeds are shaken out.   The seeds are used to produce a food oil similar to olive oil but colorless and tasteless.   The sponges vary in size from 8 to 24 in. long.   The plants grow rapidly, giving four annual crops in Brazil, and a hill of 3 seeds can produce 30 sponges. Loofa sponges are used chiefly for filters in feed tanks of ships. A stiff curly fiber used for making hats is obtained from the product by further retting.

LOW-ALLOY STEELS. Any steel that has small amounts of alloying elements below the normal amounts in standard alloy steels may be termed low-alloy, but the name has come to refer to steels with balanced proportions of alloying elements designed to give high strength while conserving chromium, nickel, and other strategic elements. A number of such steels classified during the Second World War by the Iron & Steel Institute were designated as **national emergency steels.** They were primarily intended as a conservation measure to use alloy scrap directly in the mix, and the alloying elements were not uniform. But the advantages of these low-alloy steels for a wide range of use were so apparent that they were then made under controlled conditions to uniform specifications. Plain carbon steel hardens only near the surface, leaving the core soft and weak, but with the small amounts of alloying elements the hardening and strengthening effect is carried deeper and distortion in heat-treating is reduced. Chromium and manganese are important in these steels. Both form hard carbides, and both are soluble in ferrite. Manganese is an austenite-forming element, and austenite is easily cold-worked. But with considerable manganese in steels where chromium is present, martensite and manganese carbide may be formed, and for structural steels that are to be welded without further heat treatment, 0.25% or more silicon is added. Nickel may also be added to balance chromium and add strength. Molybdenum increases impact strength. Small amounts of copper refine the grain, add corrosion resistance, and give better fatigue resistance, but large amounts make the steel hot-short.

The **N-A-X 9100 steels,** of the Great Lakes Steel Corp., are in grades with carbon from 0.08 to 0.70, including shallow-hardening and deep-hardening steels. **N-A-X 9115 steel** has 0.15 carbon, 0.60 chromium, 0.15 molybdenum, 0.10 zirconium, 0.75 silicon, and 0.75 manganese. The hot-rolled plate has a tensile strength of 76,000 psi with elongation of 25%. **N-A-X Finegrain steel** is a general-purpose malleable steel for cold stamping and drawing. It contains 0.70 manganese, 0.75 silicon, 0.05 zirconium, 0.026 each of sulfur and phosphorus, and 0.12 carbon. The minimum tensile strength is 70,000 psi, elongation 22%, and Brinell hardness about 150. **Armco 6 steel,** of the Armco Steel Corp., is another cold-work low-alloy steel containing columbium.

The strength and hardness of the low-alloy steels can be raised by heat treatment. **Carpenter 872 steel,** of the Carpenter Steel Co., which is similar to **NE steel 8715,** contains 0.10% carbon, 0.80 manganese, 0.50

chromium, .50 nickel, and 0.22 molybdenum. When heat-treated it has a tensile strength up to 130,000 psi with elongation of 18%. With 0.45% carbon, **Carpenter 874 steel,** it has a tensile strength to 225,000 psi when heat-treated. The **high-tensile steels** are generally higher-alloyed than the regular low-alloy steels. **SAE steel X4340,** for crankshafts and connecting rods, has up to 2% nickel, 0.90 chromium, and 0.30 molybdenum. The tensile strength of the heat-treated steel is 230,000 psi with elongation of 12%. **Airsteel X200,** of the U.S. Steel Corp., is a high-tensile steel with a tensile strength of 300,000 psi and elongation of 9%, and it retains good strength at a temperature of 1200°F. It contains 2% chromium, 1.6 silicon, 0.90 manganese, 0.50 molybdenum, 0.05 vanadium, and 0.45 carbon. **Strux steel,** of this company, has a tensile strength of 280,000 psi, with a yield strength 90% of the tensile strength. It has 0.90% manganese, 0.90 chromium, 0.75 nickel, 0.70 silicon, 0.50 molybdenum, 0.01 vanadium, 0.0005 boron, and 0.45 carbon.

The low-alloy steel called **Otiscoloy,** of the Jones & Laughlin Steel Corp., contains also 0.30% copper. It has about 3 times the corrosion resistance of a plain copper-bearing steel, and with 1.25% manganese it is abrasion-resistant. **Mayari R steel,** of the Bethlehem Steel Co., has up to 0.70% copper, with up to 1% manganese, 1 chromium, 0.75 nickel, and 0.50 silicon. **Dynalloy,** of the Alan Wood Steel Co., contains also 0.60% copper, and **Hi-Steel,** of the Inland Steel Co., has up to 1.3% copper and up to 0.27 aluminum. The **NE steel 8630,** used for aircraft tubing, is typical of the regular low-alloy steels. It has up to 0.60% chromium, 0.70 nickel, 0.25 molybdenum, and has a tensile strength of 90,000 psi with elongation of 35%. A **bolt steel** used in the automotive industry has an average of 0.37% carbon, 0.90 manganese, 0.55 nickel, 0.50 chromium, and 0.20 molybdenum. **Stroloy 5-C,** of Babcock and Wilcox, for structural tubing is a similar alloy with boron. **Aldecor,** of the Republic Steel Corp., is a low-alloy steel with 0.50% copper. **Kaisaloy,** of the Kaiser Steel Co., is the name of a series of low-alloy steels. The grade called **Kaisaloy 1** contains 0.63% manganese, 0.48 silicon, 0.27 nickel, 0.27 copper, 0.18 chromium, 0.08 vanadium, 0.06 molybdenum, 0.008 titanium, and 0.11 carbon.

LOW-EXPANSION ALLOYS. Alloys, usually of nickel and iron, which have a very low coefficient of expansion at ordinary temperatures, used chiefly for instrument parts and for lead wires to be sealed in glass or other material. The **coefficient of expansion** of a metal is not a quality of the metal but merely a comparative measure of volume change with heat-energy application. This increase in volume is caused by change in shape of the molecule and distance apart of the atoms. Chemically uncombined iron, tungsten, and nickel normally have no molecular shape changes in the solid stage. For low-expansion alloys, elements that cause molecular changes in the solid are avoided. The alloy first developed in France under the name of **Invar** has an expansion so low for measuring purposes, under ordinary conditions, that it is generally taken as zero. This is about 0.0000004 per deg C, but above 120°C the coefficient rises. Invar is used for the measuring guides of accurate instruments and for parts for watches. The typical composition as produced by International Nickel Co., Inc., is 36% nickel, 0.35 manganese, and the balance iron with carbon and other elements kept to a minimum. The tensile strength of the annealed alloy is 71,400 psi with elongation of 41%. It may be used for parts and piping where strength is required at low temperatures. Such an alloy is also very resistant to corrosion. **Nivar** is a similar alloy. **Nivarox,** a Swiss alloy for watch and clock springs of exceptional accuracy, has 37% nickel, 8 chromium, 54 iron, 0.85 manganese, 0.90 beryllium, 1 titanium, 0.20 silicon, and 0.10 carbon. Another Swiss alloy noted for corrosion resistance as well as high fatigue resistance is **Contracid.** It has 60% nickel, 15 chromium, 7 molybdenum, 15 iron, 2 manganese, 0.5 silicon, and 0.5 to 0.75 beryllium. **Nicol,** of the National-Standard Co., for instrument springs, contains 40% cobalt, 20 chromium, 15 nickel, 7 molybdenum, 2 manganese, 0.04 beryllium, 0.15 carbon, and the balance iron. When heat-treated it has a tensile strength of 368,000 psi, and a Vickers hardness of 700. It has an electrical resistance of 600 ohms per cir mil ft, retains its elasticity to 600°F, and is highly corrosion-resistant.

Elinvar, used for chronometer balances and springs for gages and instruments, has low thermal expansion and almost invariable modulus of elasticity. Elinvar for hair springs for watches contains 33 to 35% nickel, 53 to 61 iron, 4 to 5 chromium, 1 to 3 tungsten, 0.5 to 2 manganese, 0.5 to 2 silicon, and 0.5 to 2 carbon. **Elinvar Extra,** of the Hamilton Watch Co., contains 42% nickel, 5.5 chromium, 2.5 titanium, about 0.5 each of manganese, aluminum, and silicon, 0.06 max carbon, and the balance iron. It is nonmagnetic, corrosion-resistant, and has low thermal expansion. **Elgiloy,** of Elgiloy Co., originally a **watch spring alloy,** is superior to carbon and stainless steel for coil and flat springs, and is marketed in wire, rod, and strip for many applications requiring a combination of high fatigue strength, heat-corrosion resistance, dimensional stability, and nonmagnetic characteristics. The alloy contains 40% cobalt, 20 chromium, 15.5 nickel, 7 molybdenum, 2 manganese, 0.15 carbon, 0.04 beryllium, and the balance iron. The tensile strength is 368,000 psi, modulus of elasticity 29,500,000, and Rockwell C hardness 58. The physical properties depend upon cold work and heat treatment at 900°F, and service temperatures are thus below this point. **Platinite,** a French alloy with a coefficient of expansion about the same as that of glass, contains 46% nickel and 54 iron. It is used in light bulbs. **Dilver** and **Adr** are also French low-expansion, nickel-iron alloys. **Super-Invar** is a Japanese product containing 5% cobalt to replace an equal amount of nickel. It has a nearly zero coefficient of expansion at ordinary temperatures. **Nilvar,** of the Driver-Harris Co., used for instrument parts, measuring tapes, and connections through glass, is in various grades with about the same coefficient of expansion as glass or with the zero expansion of Invar. **Fernico,** of the General Electric Co., is an alloy used for sealing vacuum tubes.

Low-expansion alloy 42, of Carpenter Technology, is an Invar with 42% nickel and 0.10 carbon, used for temperatures above 400°F. It has an electrical resistance of 430 ohms per cir mil ft. The hot-rolled material has a tensile strength of 82,000 psi, and elongation 30%. It can be hardened by cold work. **Sylvania 4 alloy,** of Sylvania Electric Products, Inc., is in the form of wire with the same expansion as glass. It has 42% nickel, 5.65 chromium, with small amounts of manganese, silicon, carbon, and aluminum, and the balance iron. The wire is fired at 2300°F in a hydrogen atmosphere to give a coating of Cr_2O_3 which seals it to the glass. **Sealmet HC-4,** of the Allegheny Ludlum Steel Co., is similar.

The **sealing alloy** of the Wilbur B. Driver Co., called **Niron 52,** contains 52% nickel and the balance iron. **Rodar,** of this company, for sealing hard, heat-resistant glass, has 29% nickel, 17 cobalt, 0.3 manganese, and the balance iron. **Niromet 46,** used with vitreous enamels, has 46% nickel and 54 iron. The electrical resistivity is 275 ohms. **Dumet,** of the Westinghouse Electric Corp., is a composite metal for lead-in wires for electric lamps and electronic tubes. It is made of a nickel-steel core with a thin coating of brass and an outer shell of copper tubing. This composite rod is then drawn into wire of diameters 0.010 to 0.040 in. The radial expansion is 0.000009 per deg C, which is close to that of soft glass. The tensile strength is up to 79,000 psi, with elongation 18 to 26%. **Kovar,** of the Stupakoff Ceramic & Mfg Co., is an alloy of 29% nickel, 17 cobalt, 0.3 manganese, and the balance iron, having an expansion the same as that of heat-resistant glass for all temperatures up to the softening point of the glass. It is used for making gastight window assemblies, instrument and radio-tube sealing, and for metal attachments to glass. When the metal is heated to a red heat and applied to the glass, the metal oxide formed dissolves in the glass and gives a gastight seal.

LUBRICATING GREASE. Usually a compound of a mineral oil with a soap, employed for lubricating machinery where the speed is slow or where it would be difficult to retain a free-flowing oil. The soap is one that is made from animal or vegetable oils high in stearic, oleic, and palmitic acids.   The lime soaps give water resistance, or a mineral soap may be added for this purpose.   Aluminum stearate gives high film strength to the grease.   All of these greases are more properly designated as **mineral lubricating grease.**   Originally, **grease** for lubricating purposes was hog fat or the inedible grades of lard, varying in color from white to brown. Some of these greases were stiffened with fillers of rosin, wax, or talc which were not good lubricants.   The stiffness of such a grease should be obtained with a mineral soap.   ASTM specifications for heavy journal bearing grease require 45% soap content.   About 2% calcium benzoate increases the melting point.   Mineral lubricating grease may contain from 80 to 90% mineral oil and the remainder a lime soap.   Federal specifications prescribe 85% mineral oil.   Chemicals may be added to improve the physical properties of grease.   **Oronite GA-10,** of the Oronite Chemical Co., for example, is a sodium salt of terephthalic acid used as a gelling agent in high-temperature greases.   It adds water resistance and stabilizes against emulsion.   **Ortholeum 300,** marketed as a brown flaky powder by Du Pont, is a mixture of complex amines, and small amounts added to a grease will give high heat stability.   **Braycote 617,** of the Bray Oil Co., is a synthetic grease for rockets subject to both heat and cold.   It is a mixture of perfluoro trialkyl amines gelled with tetra fluoro ethylene.   It comes as a translucent lardlike semisolid with a boiling point at 230°C. The lubricating grease known as **trough grease,** used in food plants for greasing trays, tables, and conveyors, contains no mineral oil, and is edible.

Lime greases do not emulsify as readily as those made with a soda base, and are thus more suitable for use where water may be present.   **Hard grease** flows at a temperature of about 90°C; medium grease flows at 75 to 80°C.   Paraffin wax, sometimes added, is an adulterant and not a lubricant.   **Graphite grease** contains 2 to 10% amorphous graphite, and is used for bearings, especially in damp places.   Federal specifications call for 2 to 3% graphite.   For large ball and roller bearings a low-lime grease is used, sometimes mixed with a small percentage of graphite. **Cylinder grease** is made of about 85% mineral oil or mineral grease and 15% tallow.   Compounded greases are also marketed containing animal and vegetable oils, or are made with blown oils and compounded with mineral oils.   The fatty acids in vegetable and animal oils, however, are likely to corrode metals.   Tannin holds graphite in solution; in the gear grease sold under the name **Gredag** by the Acheson Colloids Co. a graphite-tannin mixture is used.   **Metaline,** of the R. W. Rhoades Metaline Co., Inc., is a compound of powdered antifriction metal, oxide, and gums, which is packed in holes in the bearings to form self-lubricating bearings. **Lead-Lube grease,** of Knapp Mills, Inc., has finely powdered lead metal suspended in the grease for heavy-duty lubrication.

Sett greases are mixtures of the calcium soaps of rosin acids with various grades of mineral oils.   They are low-cost semisolid greases used for lubricating heavy gears or for greasing skidways.   Clay fillers may be added to improve the film strength, or copper or lead powders may be incorporated for heavy load conditions.   **Solidified oil** is also a name given to grease made from lubricating oil with a soda soap and tallow, used for heavy bearings.   **Cup grease** is made with soda soap and light lubricating oils.   Greases made with potash and soda soaps tend to form soap fibers when water is present.   A metallic soap that contains no fibers is called a **neat soap,** and gives a smooth grease.   Greases made with lithium stearate have good water and high temperature resistance, and have a buttery texture.   **Alrania grease** of the Shell Oil Co. is a grease of this type.   Fatty acids used for grease making may be hardened by hydrogenation to remove polyunsaturated acids.   The greases have greater resistance to heat discoloration, and do not gum or become rancid. **Lubrex 45,** of W. C. Hardesty, Inc., is a hardened fatty acid of this type. **Slushing oil,** for use in protecting machine parts from corrosion in shipping or storage, is usually a low-melting grease preferably compounded with a waxy fat such as lanolin.   **Paralan,** of the American Lanolin Corp., is such a slushing oil having a lanolin base.

LUBRICATING OILS. Oils used for lubricating the bearing parts of machinery.   They are usually the heavy distillates following kerosene in the fractional distillation of petroleum, between the temperatures 253 and 317°F.   They are separated into grades, light, medium, and heavy, depending upon the molecular weight.   They are also classed as pale, when yellow to reddish, and dark, when brownish black in color.   The flash points range from 300 to 600°F, and the specific gravities usually from 0.860 to 0.940.   **Neutral oils** are light oils obtained by distillation without cracking, and they will not emulsify in contact with water as do the paraffin oils.   They are thus desirable for crankcase lubrication and in circulating systems.   Lubricating oils may be bleached with acid, and they may be mixed with vegetable or animal oils.   The ideal of lubrication is to obtain a full fluid film with little clearance between the moving surfaces so that the shaft rotates on a film of oil.   Hydrodynamic lubrication with pressure gives this condition.   Only a boundary lubrication with contact merely on the bottom is obtained when the clearance is too great, the oil viscosity too low, the load too heavy, or the speed is too slow, so that the film does not support the shaft.

Animal oils are more greasy than mineral oils, but they are acid. Vegetable oils are greasy and have more oiliness, but they oxidize easily and are also acid.   They are likely to gum in use unless an antioxidant is used.   Vegetable and animal oils add the property of adhesion to the lubricating oil, but in no case should any element be added to an oil that will cause emulsification. Federal specifications for marine engine oil call for 15 to 20% blown refined rapeseed or peanut oil. This lubricating oil has a flash point of 350°F. **Steam cylinder oil** has 5 to 10% fatty acid vegetable oils, and the flash point is 450°F. **Absorbed oil** is a name of a combination oil of E. F. Houghton & Co. which acts as both film and lubricant. **Amlo** is a trade name of a mineral oil refined wax-free, used for low-temperature lubrication. The silicones are now much used to replace lubricating oils for very high and very low temperature conditions, but in general the lubricating value is not high.

Antioxidants used in oils to reduce oxidation and minimize sludging and acid formation are usually tin compounds such as tin dioxide, tin tetraphenyl, and tin ricinoleate. Tin dust alone has also an inhibitory action. Detergents are compounded in lubricating oils for internal-combusion engines in order to prevent and break down carbon and sludge deposits. High percentages of animal or vegetable oils may be added to lubricating oils for use on textile machinery. They are called **stainless oils** for this purpose, since such oils wash out of the textile more easily than mineral oils. They also give lower coefficients of friction. The high lubricating qualities of the vegetable oils without the disadvantage of gumming can be obtained with mineral oils by the addition of an **oiliness agent** such as the **cetyl piperidine ricinoleate.** The **EP lubricants** (extreme pressure) for heavy-duty gear lubrication are made with a high-quality oil compounded with a lead sulfonated soap.

For extreme high pressure and high temperatures where oils and greases oxidize, **molybdenum disulfide,** MoS_2, is used alone or mixed with oils or silicones. It is a fine black powder, available in particle sizes as small as 0.75 micron, which adheres strongly to metal surfaces, gives a low coefficient of friction, and will permit operation up to 750°F, but it has an acid reaction and is corrosive to metals. Molybdenum disulfide resembles graphite but is twice as dense. The sulfur attaches itself with a weaker electron bond on one side than the other, forming laminal plates or scales in the molecular structure which tend to split off and give the sliding or lubrication action. Molybdenum disulfide may be used as a filler in nylon gears and bearings to reduce friction. It also increases the flexural strength of the plastic. **Molysulfide,** of the Climax Molybdenum Co., is this material. **Tungsten disulfide** is also used as a lubricant in the same way as molybdenum disulfide. The electron bond of sulfur to tungsten is stronger than that to molybdenum, and it is thus more stable at high temperatures. The tungsten disulfide of Sylvania Electric Products, Inc., is a crystalline, gray-black powder with particle size from 1 to 2 microns. **Molykote,** of the Alpha Corp., and **Liqui-Moly,** of the Lockrey Co., are molybdenum disulfide lubricants. **Dry-film lubricants** are usually graphite or molybdenum sulfide in a resin or volatile solution.

They are sprayed on the bearing surface, and the evaporation of the solvent leaves an adherent thin film on the bearing. **Selenium disulfide,** SeS_2, will retain its lubricating qualities at temperatures to 2000°F and is useful for lubrication under vacuum because of its low emission of gas. Other materials used as **dry lubricants** are **tantalum disulfide,** TaS_2, **tantalum diselenide,** $TaSe_2$, **titanium ditelluride,** $TiTe_2$, and **zirconium diselenide,** $ZrSe_2$.

Hydraulic fluids for the operation of presses must lubricate as well as carry the pressure, and they are mostly mineral oils, but chemicals are used where high temperatures are encountered such as in die-casting machines. **Lindol HF-X,** of the Celanese Corp. of America, is a flame-resistant hydraulic fluid with a tricresyl phosphate base. **Skydrol,** of the Monsanto Chemical Co., for aircraft hydraulic systems, is an oily ester produced from petroleum gas. The ignition point is 1050°F, and it will operate at temperatures as low as −40°F. The **Fluorolube oils** of the Hooker Chemical Corp. are polymers of trifluoro vinyl chloride fractionated to provide grades from a colorless low-viscosity oil to an opaque heavy grease. They have high lubricating values, are resistant to acids and alkalies, and have an operating range from 300°C down to very low subzero temperatures. **Hydraulic fluid QF-6-7009,** of the Dow Chemical Corp., for closed systems operating from −25 to +550°F, is a diphenyl didodecyl silane. **Refrigeration oils,** for lubricating refrigerating machinery, are mineral oils refined to remove all moisture and wax. **Ansul oil,** of the Ansul Chemical Co., is an oil of this class which will remain stable at temperatures as low as −70°F.

The nature of the bearing metals often has an effect upon the action of the lubricating oil. In highly alloyed metals some elements act as catalyzers to oxidize the oil, or the acids or moisture in the oils may act to break down the metal. In lead-bearing metals free magnesium causes disintegration of the lead in contact with moisture. The alkali-lead metals also tend to dissolve in contact with animal or fish oils. Normally, however, none of the white bearing metals are attacked by the animal and vegetable oils used for lubrication unless there are perceptible amounts of a freely oxidizing element present. Graphite adds to the effectiveness of a lubricating oil and can be held in suspension with a tannin. **Graphite lubricants** are used where continuous lubrication is difficult, for running in, for springs, or for bearings where heavy films are desired. The **Dag Lubricants** and **Dag Dispersants** of Acheson Colloids Co. comprise a large group of lubricants, lubricant coatings, and mold partings consisting of graphite or molybdenum sulfide in oils, resins, or solvents, usually applied by spray application. **Glydag** is a solution of 10% graphite in glycerin, **Castordag** is graphite in castor oil, **Glydag B** is graphite in butylene glycol, and **Dag Dispersion 223** is molybdenum disulfide in an epoxy resin. **Neolube,** of Huron Industries, is graphite in alcohol. With these, the carrier liquid evaporates, leaving a film of graphite on the bearing.

LUMINOUS PIGMENTS. Pigments used in paints to make surfaces visible in the dark and in coatings for electronic purposes. They are used for signs, watch and instrument hands, airfield markings, and signals. They are of two general classes. The so-called permanent ones are the **radioactive paints** which give off light without activation, and the **phosphorescent paints,** or **fluorescent paints,** which require activation from an outside source of light. The radioactive paints contain a radioactive element that emits alpha and beta rays which strike the phosphors and produce visible light. Radium, sometimes used for paints for watch hands, gives a greenish-blue light, but it emits dangerous gamma rays. Also, the intense alpha rays of radium destroy the phosphors quickly, reducing the light. Strontium 90 gives a yellow-green light and has a long half-life of 25 years, but it emits both beta and gamma rays and is dangerous. **Tritium paints,** with a tritium isotope and a phosphor in the resin-solvent paint base, have a half-life of 12.5 years and require no shielding. The self-luminous phosphors for clock and instrument dials contain tritium which gives off beta rays with only low secondary emission so that the glass or plastic covering is sufficient shielding. Other materials used are **krypton 85,** with a half-life of 10.27 years, **promethium 147,** with a half-life of 2.36 years, and **thallium 204,** with a half-life of 2.7 years.

Fluorescent paints depend upon the ability of the chemical to absorb energy from light and to emit it again in the form of photons of light. This variety usually has a base of calcium, strontium, or barium sulfide with traces of other metal salts to improve luminosity, and the vehicle contains a moistureproof gum or oil. Temporary luminous paints may be visible for long periods after the activating light is withdrawn. A paint activated by 5 min of exposure to sunlight may absorb sufficient energy for 24 hr of luminosity. **Luminous wall paints** used for operating rooms to eliminate shadows are made by mixing small amounts of zinc or cadmium sulfide into ordinary paints. After being activated with ultraviolet rays, they will give off light for an hour and a half.

Phosphorescent paints are lower in cost than radioactive paints, and may be obtained in various colors. In general, the yellow and orange phosphorescent pigments are combinations of zinc and cadmium sulfides, the green is zinc sulfide, and the violet and blue pigments are combinations of calcium and strontium sulfides. They are marketed in powder form to be stirred into the paint or ink vehicle since mixing by grinding lowers the phosphorescence. The natural minerals are not used, as the pigments must be of a high degree of purity, as little as a millionth part of iron, cobalt, or nickel killing the luminosity of zinc sulfide. These phosphorescent pigments are called **phosphors,** but technically they are incomplete phosphors, and copper, silver, or manganese is coprecipitated with the sulfide as activators or to change the color of the emitted light. The metals that are used as activators are called **phosphorogens,** and their atoms diffuse into the lattice of the sulfide. For fluorescent screens the phosphors must have a rapid rate of extinguishment so that there will be no time lag in the appearance of the events. For television, electron microscope, and radar screens the phosphors must cease to glow $\frac{1}{50}$ sec after withdrawal of excitation. They must also be of very minute particle size so as not to give a blurred image. For a white television screen, mixtures of blue zinc sulfide with silver and yellow zinc-beryllium silicates are used. For technicolor television the screen is completely covered with a mixture of various colored phosphors, especially rare-earth metal combinations. For scintillation counters for gamma-ray-detection phosphors the pulses should be of longer duration, and for this purpose crystals of cadmium or cadmium tungstate are used. Phosphors are used in **postage stamp inks** for automatic separation of mail. Under ultraviolet rays the airmail stamps glow green and the regular-mail stamps glow orange-red. The red phosphor is a manganese-activated calcium silicate, and the green phosphor is zinc silicate. As produced by Sylvania, they are fine powders of 2-micron particle size.

Fluorescent fabrics for signal flags and luminescent clothing are impregnated with fluorescent chemicals which can be activated by an ultraviolet light that is not seen with the eye. Some fluorescent paints contain a small amount of luminous pigment to increase the vividness of the color by absorbing the ultraviolet light and emitting it as visible color. **Fluorescein,** made from phthalic anhydride and resorcinol, has the property of fluorescence in a solvent. Since cellulose acetate will keep it in a permanently solvent state, acetate rayon is used as the carrier fabric. Signal panels are distinguishable from a plane at great heights even through a haze, and at night they give a brilliant glow when activated with ultraviolet rays. Fluorescent paints for signs may have a white undercoat to reflect back the light passing through the semitransparent pigment. In passing through the color pigments the shorter violet and blue wavelengths are changed to orange, red, and yellow hues, and the reflected visible light is greater than the original light. **Uranine,** the sodium salt of fluorescein, is used by fliers to mark spots in the ocean. One pound of uranine will cover an acre of water to a brilliant yellowish green easily seen from the air. One part of uranine is detectable in 16 million parts of water. The **luminous plastic** marketed by the U.S. Radium Corp. for aircraft markings is coated on the inside with radioactive material to give visibility in the dark. The **fluorescent plastic** of the Rohm & Haas Co. is acrylic sheet containing a fluorescent dye. Lettering or designs cut from the sheet will glow brightly in the dark after exposure to light. It is used for direction signs and decorative panels. **Spot-Lite Glo,** of Conrad Precision Industries, is a **phosphorescent frit** for incorporating into ceramics for luminous signs. It contains a zinc sulfide that is stable at high heats and has a long afterglow.

    Whitening agents, optical whiteners, or **brightening agents,** used to increase the whiteness of paper and textiles, are fluorescent materials that convert some of the ultraviolet of sunlight into visible light. The materials are colorless, but the additional light supplied is blue, and it neutralizes yellow discolorations and enhances the whiteness. They were first developed in Germany and called **blankophors.** **Ultrasan,** the first of the German blankophors, was a 1,3,5-trizine derivative. The **M.D.A.C.** of the Carlisle Chemical Works, Inc., is a methyl diethyl amino coumarin of the empirical formula $C_{14}H_{17}O_2N$. It comes in tan-colored granules melting at 70°C, soluble in water and in acid solutions. It gives a bright-blue fluorescence in daylight and adds whiteness to fabrics and makes colors more vivid. As little as 0.001% added to soaps, detergents, or starches is effective for wool and synthetic fibers, but it is not suitable for cotton. It is also used to overcome yellow casts in varnishes and plastics, and in oils and waxes. **Solium,** of Lever Bros., used in detergents, is a whitener of this type. The **DAS triazines,** triazinyl diaminostilbene disulfonic acid, used with naphthyl triazole, is effective for cotton and rayon. Luminous materials also occur in nature as organic compounds. The luminous material of the firefly, **luciferin,** is a water-soluble protein.

LUTES. Adhesive substances, usually of earthy composition, deriving the name from the Latin, *lutum,* meaning mud. A clay cement was used by the Romans for cementing iron posts into stone. Although they often contain a high percentage of silica sand or clays, the active ingredient is usually sulfur. They may also contain other reactive ingredients such as lead monoxide or magnesium compounds. **Plumber's lutes** are used for pipe joints and seams and for coating pipes to withstand high temperatures. Plaster of Paris mixed with a weak glue will withstand a dull-red heat. **Fat lute** is pipe clay mixed with linseed oil. **Spence's metal** is the name of an old lute for pipe joining. It was made by introducing iron disulfide, zinc blende, and galena into melted sulfur. It melts at 320°F and expands on cooling. It makes a good cast joint which is resistant to water, acids, and alkalies. It is not a metal, but is a mixture of sulfur with metallic oxides. **Sulfur cements,** or lutes, usually have fillers of silica or carbon to improve the strength. They are poured at about 235°F. They form a class of acidproof cements used for ceramic pipe connections.

Modern lutes for very high heat resistance do not contain elemental sulfur. Industrial lutes are used for sealing in wires and connections in electrical apparatus, and are compounded to give good bonding to ceramics and metals. A lute cement for adhering knife blades to handles is composed of magnesium acid sulfates, calcined magnesia, with fine silica sand or powder. The term **sealant** generally refers to a wide range of mineral-filled plastics formulated with a high proportion of filler for application by troweling or air gun.

MADDER. Formerly the most important dyestuff with the exception of indigo. It is now largely replaced by the synthetic mauve dye alizarin. It was grown on a large scale in France and the Near East and was known by its Arabic name **alizari** and by the name **Turkey red.** Madder is the ground root of the plant *Rubia tinctorum,* which has been stored for a time to develop the coloring matter, the orange-red **alizarin,** $C_{14}H_{18}O_4$, which is a dihydroxy anthraquinone, a powder melting at 289°C. It occurs in madder root as the glucoside, **ruberythric acid,** $C_{26}H_{28}O_{14}$, but is now made synthetically from anthracene. Its alkaline solution is used with mordants to give **madder lakes.** With aluminum and tin it gives **madder red,** with calcium it gives blue, and with iron it gives violet black. **Purpurin,** $C_{14}H_{18}O_5$, is also obtained from madder, but is now made synthetically. Madder gives fast colors.

MAGNESIA. A fine white powder of **magnesium oxide,** MgO, obtained by calcining magnesite or dolomite and refining chemically. It is used in pharmaceuticals, in cosmetics, in rubbers as a scorch-resistant filler, in soaps, and in ceramics. It requires 6.5 tons of dolomite to yield 1 ton of pure magnesia powder. Particle size of the powder is 0.5 micron. For chemical uses it is 99.7% min purity with no more than 0.06% iron oxide and 0.08 calcium oxide, and the magnesia for electronic parts has a maximum of 0.03% iron oxide and 0.0025% boron. This powder is converted from magnesium hydroxide. **Maglite,** of Whittaker, Clark & Daniels, Inc., used for rubbers, is produced from seawater. **Magox magnesia,** of Basic Chemicals, is 98% pure MgO extracted from seawater. It comes in particle sizes to 325 mesh in high- and low-activity grades for rubber, textile, and chemical uses. A very pure magnesia is also produced by reducing magnesium nitrate.

Magnesia for molding into crucibles and refractory parts is usually electrically fused and crushed from the large cubic crystals. The crystals have ductility and can be bent. The particle size and shape are easily controlled in the crushing to fit the needs of the molded article. Pressed and sintered parts have a melting point at about 5070°F, and can be employed to 2300°C in oxidizing atmospheres or to 1700°C in reducing

atmospheres.   The material is inert to molten steels and to basic slags.
Magnafrax 0340, of the Carborundum Co., is magnesia in the form of
plates, tubes, bars, and disks.   The material has a density of 3.3, and a
thermal conductivity twice that of alumina.   Its vitreous structure gives
it about the same characteristics as a single crystal for electronic purposes.
Magnorite, of the Norton Co., is fused magnesia in granular crystals
with a melting point of 2800°C, used for making ceramic parts and for
sheathing electrical heating elements.   **K-Grain magnesia,** of Kaiser Aluminum and Chemical Corp., is 98% magnesia, containing no more than
0.4% silica.   The **magnesia ceramic,** of the Corning Glass Co., is 99.8%
purity.   The cast, pressed, or extruded parts when high-fired have a fine-
grained dense structure with practically no shrinkage and a flexural strength
of 15,500 psi.

MAGNESITE. A white to bluish-gray mineral used in the manufacture
of bricks for basic refractory furnace linings and as an ore of magnesium.
The ground, burned magnesite is a light powder, is shaped into bricks at
high pressure, and baked in kilns.   Magnesite is a magnesium carbonate,
$MgCO_3$, with some iron carbonate and ferric oxide.   Magnesite releases
carbon dioxide on heating, and forms magnesia, MgO.   When heated
further it forms a crystalline structure known as **periclase,** which has a
melting point of 5070°F and specific gravity of 3.58.   The mineral periclase occurs in nature but is rare.   A crystalline form is called **breun-
nerite.**   The fused magnesia made in the arc furnace is actually synthetic
periclase.   The synthetic material is in transparent crystals up to 2 in.,
which are crushed to powder for thermal insulation and for making refractory parts.   Magnesite in compact earthy form or granular masses
has a vitreous luster, and the color may be white, gray, yellow, or brown.
The hardness is 3.5 to 4.5, and the specific gravity about 3.1.   The American production of crude magnesite is in Nevada, Washington, and California.

The product known as **dead-burned magnesite** is in the form of dense
particles used for refractories.   It is produced by calcining magnesite at
a temperature of 1450 to 1500°C.   **Caustic magnesite** is a product resulting from calcination at 700 to 1200°C which leaves from 2 to 7%
carbon dioxide in the material and gives sufficient cementing properties for use as a refractory cement.   Beluchistan magnesite has 95 to
98% $MgCO_3$, with 0.5 to 1% iron oxide.   Manchurian dead-burned
magnesite has 90.9% magnesia with 4 silica, and some iron oxide and
alumina.

Magnesite for use in producing magnesium metal should have at least
40% MgO, with not over 4.5% CaO and 2 FeO.   **Brucite,** a natural
hydrated magnesium oxide found in Ontario, contains a higher percent-

age of magnesia than ordinary magnesite and is used for furnace linings. Austrian magnesite has from 4 to 9% iron oxide, which gives it the property of fritting together more readily.   Magnesite is a valued refractory material for crucibles, furnace brick and linings, and high-temperature electrical insulation because of its basic character, chemical resistance, high softening point, and high electrical resistance.   Its chief disadvantage is its low resistance to heat shock.   Magnesite brick and refractory products are marketed under a variety of trade names such as **Ritex** of the General Refractories Co., and **Ramix** of Basic Dolomite, Inc. It is also used as a covering for hot piping.   The German artficial stone called **Kunststein** is magnesite.

MAGNESIUM. A silvery-white metal, symbol Mg, which is the lightest metal that is stable under ordinary conditions and produced in quantity. It is the sixth most abundant element, and is only 64% the weight of aluminum and 23% the weight of iron.   By volume, 1 lb of magnesium produces 5 times as much rolled metal as 1 lb of copper.   It was originally called **magnium** by Sir Humphry Davy.   The specific gravity is 1.74, melting point 651°C, and boiling point 1120°C.   It has a tensile strength when cast of 14,000 psi.   The rolled metal has a tensile strength of 25,000 psi, and elongation 4%.   The strength is somewhat higher in the forged metal.   Magnesium has a close-packed hexagonal structure that makes it difficult to roll cold, and its narrow plastic range requires close control in forging.   Repeated reheating causes grain growth.   It is thus usually hot-worked, and at 600°F it can be deep-drawn better than other common metals.   It is the easiest to machine of the metals.   Its heat conductivity is half that of aluminum, and it has high damping capacity.   Electrolytic magnesium is usually 99.8% pure, and the metal made by the ferrosilicon-hydrogen reduction process may be 99.95% pure.

Magnesium is immune to alkalies, it is resistant to seawater, and its sound-damping characteristics make it valuable for diaphragms, resonators, and shielding.   Because of its flammability at high temperatures, it cannot be used safely for parts subject to temperatures above 450°F.   The metal is produced regularly in sheet.   **Thinstrip magnesium,** of the Burgess Battery Co., is commercially pure magnesium sheet in thicknesses from 0.005 to 0.010 in. for die forming and for paneling.   **Magnesium sheet** can be drawn in dies without folding or wrinkling.   For better corrosion resistance the metal may be given a thin coating of zinc by dipping in a pyrophosphate-zinc solution.   Electroplating the metal is done by first depositing a thin zinc plate followed by a copper flash coating as a base for the nickel or other plate.   **Anodized magnesium** is produced by immersing in a solution of ammonium fluoride and applying a current of 120 volts. The fluoride film has a thickness of only 0.0001 in., but it removes cathodic impurities from the surface of the magnesium, giving greater corrosion resistance and better adhesion of paints.

Magnesium is valued chiefly for parts where light weight is needed, but it is not ordinarily used alone. It is a major constituent in many light aluminum alloys, and superlight alloys can be made by alloying magnesium with lithium. Even very small amounts of other elements improve the physical properties of magnesium. **Dow alloy K1X1-F,** of the Dow Chemical Co., contains 0.6% zirconium. It has a fine grain structure with improved ductility, with an elongation of 20% and tensile strength of 25,000 psi when cast. The castability is also improved. **MSR alloy,** of Magnesium Elektron, Inc., another casting alloy, contains 2.5% silver, 0.7 zirconium, and 2% rare-earth metals. The tensile strength is above 36,000 psi, with a yield strength of 15,000 psi at 500°F. **Photoengraving plates** made of commercially pure magnesium, or of slightly alloyed metal, are easier to etch than zinc, lighter in weight, and resistant to wear. As a facing and shielding material in building construction, the light weight of magnesium gives high coverage, 1 lb of 0.005-in. sheet covering 22.2 sq ft.

Magnesium die castings are light weight and easy to cast, and as the metal does not adhere to the die, complicated coring and small-diameter holes can be had with little taper. They are also easy to machine. The alloys are more rigid than aluminum, but dimensional stability is limited to relatively low temperatures since the metal is subject to permanent growth above about 200°F. The most used diecasting alloys contain about 9% aluminum, 0.6 zinc, and 0.2 manganese. This is **ASTM alloy AZ91, SAE alloy 501,** or **Alcoa alloy AM230.** It has a melting point of 1120°F, a specific gravity of 1.81, a tensile strength of 33,000 psi, elongation 3%, and Rockwell hardness E75.

The pure metal ignites easily, and even when alloyed with other metals the fine chips must be guarded against fire. In alloying, it cannot be mixed directly into molten metals because of flashing, but is used in the form of master alloys. The metal is not very fluid just above its melting point, and casting is done at temperatures considerably above the melting point so that there is danger of burning and formation of oxides. A small amount of beryllium added to magnesium alloys reduces the tendency of the molten metal to oxidize and burn. The solubility of beryllium in magnesium is only about 0.05%. As little as 0.001% lithium also reduces fire risk in melting and working the metal. Molten magnesium decomposes water so that greensand molds cannot be used, as explosive hydrogen gas is liberated. For the same reason water sprays cannot be used to extinguish magnesium fires. The affinity of magnesium for oxygen, however, makes the metal a good deoxidizer in the casting of other metals.

Magnesium is produced commercially by the electrolysis of a fused chloride or fluoride obtained either from brine or from a mineral ore, or it can be vaporized from some ores.   Much of the magnesium produced in the United States is from brine wells of Michigan, which brine contains 3% $MgCl_2$, and from seawater.   From seawater the magnesium hydroxide is precipitated, filtered, and treated with hydrochloric acid to obtain a solution of magnesium chloride from which the metal is obtained by electrolysis. The magnesium ion content of seawater is 1,270 parts per million.   One cubic mile of seawater contains up to 12 million pounds of magnesium.   In production, 1 lb of magnesium is obtained from 100 gallons of seawater. Magnesium is also obtained from dolomite by extracting the oxide by reacting the burned dolomite with crushed ferrosilicon in a sealed retort and filtering the vapor in a hydrogen atmosphere.   The dolomite of Ohio averages 20% magnesium oxide, and the metal is obtained 99.98% pure in a solid, dense, crystalline mass which is then melted with a flux and poured into ingots.   Magnesium metal and ferrosilicon are produced from the olivine of Washington state.   In Russia, magnesium is produced from the mineral carnallite.   In Germany it is produced from dolomite, carnallite, magnesite, and the end lyes of the potash industry.   The metal can also be produced from serpentine, olivine, and other siliceous ores by heating the powdered ore in a vacuum retort and driving off the metal as a vapor which is condensed.

Magnesium powder, for pyrotechnic and chemical uses, is made by reducing metallic magnesium into particles in the shape of curly shavings to give maximum surface per unit of weight.   It is produced in four grades: Cutting powder, Standard powder, Special specification, and Fireworks powder.   **Cutting powder** is finely cut shavings in a matted condition, made from magnesium of 99.8% purity.   **Standard powder** is loose powder in fineness from 10 to 200 mesh.   **Fireworks powder** is 100 mesh. The speed of ignition increases rapidly with decreasing particle size.   A 200-mesh powder is used for **flashlight powder,** and a 30- to 80-mesh for more slowly burning flares.   For flares, magnesium gives a brilliant light of high actinic value.   **Incendiary powder,** for small-arms incendiary ammunition, is magnesium powder mixed with barium peroxide.   **Ophorite** is an English name for magnesium powder and potassium perchlorate used as an igniter for incendiaries.   The material known as **goop,** used in fire bombs, is a rubbery mixture containing magnesium powder coated with asphalt, gasoline, and chemicals.

A wide variety of **magnesium chemicals** is used for applications where the magnesium may be the desirable element or as the chemical carrier for another element.   **Magnesium nitrate,** a colorless crystalline powder of the composition $Mg(NO_3)_2 \cdot 6H_2O$, is made from magnesite and used in dry colors and pyrotechnics, and to produce magnesia.   **Magnesium methoxide,** $Mg(OCH_3)_2$, is a white powder used for drying alcohol to produce absolute alcohol, and also for producing stable alcohol gels for use as solid alcohol fuels. The gels are made by adding water to an alcohol solution of the magnesium methoxide. **Magnesium fluoride,** MgF_2, or **sellaite,** is a pale-violet, crystalline powder that melts at 1396°C. It has a very low refractive index and is used on lenses and instrument windows to eliminate reflection. To apply the coating, the fluoride is dissolved in **dimethyl formamide,** $(CH_3)_2NCHO$, and mixed with an essential oil to wet the glass surface. The applied coating is fired at 500°C to leave a coating of pure magnesium fluoride about one-quarter light wavelength thick.

MAGNESIUM ALLOYS. Although magnesium is plentiful in nature, and is the lightest in weight of the structural metals, the use of magnesium alloys has been limited to applications where only moderate temperatures and low stresses are encountered. Alloying has been based largely on the conventional methods for iron and aluminum, but the molecular structure of the metal is very different, and requires selective alloying based on chemical combinations.

Present magnesium alloys, employing additions of aluminum, manganese, silicon, and silver, have a wide range of use in applications where temperatures do not exceed 300°F and dynamic stresses are light. The alloys have good sound-damping qualities, have a high strength-weight factor, have high stiffness, and are resistant to alkalies. They are used for housings for machinery, hand tools, and office equipment, and for such items as ladders, loading ramps, marine hardware, and nonstressed lightweight structural parts.

Standard ASTM magnesium alloys are designated by letter symbols indicating the chief alloying elements with following numbers showing approximate percentage of the contained elements. Aluminum is represented as A, manganese as M, silicon as S, zirconium as K, thorium as H, silver as Q, and rare earths as E. Thus, **magnesium alloy AZ92A** contains about 9% aluminum and 2 zinc. The terminating letters signify physical treatments such as annealed or aged.

In general, the magnesium alloys have a strength-weight factor more than 10 times that of steel, and are easily machined. The AZ92A casting alloy has a tensile strength of 14,000 psi with elongation of 2%. In wrought form this alloy has a tensile strength of 50,000 psi with elongation of 8%.

Wrought alloys usually contain aluminum and manganese; forgings contain aluminum, manganese, and zinc; and die-casting alloys contain aluminum, manganese, and silicon. Aluminum up to 8% refines the grain, increasing hardness, strength, and rigidity, but with higher percentages the alloys become brittle unless modified with other elements. Small amounts of manganese give added corrosion resistance and higher strength. Silicon combines with the magnesium to give a dispersion of the compound Mg:Si:Mg, increasing the strength and heat resistance. The rare-earth metals are usually added as oxides, giving increased stability by a dispersion of high-energy particles.

Zinc, zirconium, lithium, and beryllium form their unit molecules in platelets similarly to magnesium, and the alloys form distinctive classes. **Magnesium alloy ZK60A** has a specific gravity of 1.83, melting point of 1175°F, tensile strength of 50,000 psi, and elongation of about 8%. **Magnesium alloy HK31A** has a tensile strength of 31,000 psi, but retains a tensile strength of 23,000 psi at 500°F.

The **magnesium-lithium alloys** may contain up to 15% lithium and are called lithium alloys. The attractive feature is the light weight, and they were originally developed for aerospace and military uses such as housings, vehicle protective armor, and ammunition containers. **Lithium alloy L14,** produced at Frankford Arsenal, containing 14% lithium and the balance magnesium, has a tensile strength of 14,500 psi with 30% elongation. When modified with 1% aluminum, 1 zinc, and 0.5 silicon, the die-cast metal has a tensile strength of 36,000 psi with elongation of 1%.

The **lithium alloy LA141A** marketed by Brooks & Perkins, Inc., has 14% lithium and 1 aluminum. It has a density of 0.045 lb per cu in., a melting point at 1075°F, a tensile strength of 19,000 psi, and elongation of 10%. In general, the use of lithium alloys is limited to service temperatures below 300°F, and they are very plastic at elevated temperatures unless stabilized with high-energy molecular combinations.

Magnesium alloys may be marketed under company designations or trade names, but they generally follow the standard compositions with slight variations. **Magnesium alloy AM240,** of the Aluminum Co. of America, for permanent-mold castings, has up to 12% aluminum and 0.10 manganese. It has a tensile strength of 20,000 psi with elongation of 2%. **Revere alloy M,** for extruded bars, has up to 2% manganese, while **Revere alloy JS-1,** for sheet and plate, contains 5% aluminum, 1 zinc, and 0.25 manganese. This alloy has a tensile strength of 40,000 psi with elongation of 15%. **Eclipsalloy 56,** of Bendix, has about 9% aluminum, 2 zinc, 0.30 silicon, 0.10 manganese, 0.05 copper, and 0.01 nickel. The tensile strength is about 34,000 psi, elongation 6%, and Brinell hardness 60. **Dowmetal AZ91C** was a casting metal of the Dow Chemical Co. with a similar composition but with less zinc. **Dowmetal F,** for extruded rod, has 4% aluminum and 0.30 manganese. It has a tensile strength of 42,000 psi. One of the earliest aircraft structural magnesium alloys was called **Electron.** The British Air Ministry specification for this alloy was for 1.3 to 1.7% manganese and the balance magnesium, with a tensile strength of 45,000 psi. **Dowmetal M** is this alloy. The German **Elektron** contained 10% aluminum, 4 zinc, and up to 2.5 manganese. **Dowmetal H** of Dow Chemical and **Mazlo alloy AM26S** of Aluminum Co. of America are of this type. **ASTM alloy AZ80X,** for forgings, is a modification of the **C metal** used in England for die castings. C metal contains up to 9% aluminum, up to 1.5 manganese, with slight additions of silicon, copper, and nickel. The tensile strength is about 40,000 psi with elongation of 12%. The English **Electron ZZ** contained up to 5% zinc, up to 1 zirconium, and up to 4 cadmium, and **Electron ZT** and **Electron ZR** contained zirconium and cerium metals for increased strength at elevated temperatures.

Magnesium-nickel is a master alloy of magnesium and nickel used for adding nickel to magnesium alloys and for deoxidizing nickel and nickel alloys. A magnesium-nickel marketed by Alloys & Products, Inc., contains about 50% of each metal, is silvery white in color, and is furnished in round bar form. **Magnesium-monel** contains 50% magnesium and 50 monel metal. Alloys of magnesium with nickel, monel, zinc, copper, or aluminum, used for deoxidizing nonferrous metals, are called **stabilizer alloys.**

MAGNESIUM CARBONATE. A white, insoluble powder of the composition $MgCO_3$, containing also water of crystallization. The specific gravity is 3.10. It is made by calcining dolomite with coke, slaking with water, saturating with carbonic acid gas, and crystallizing out the magnesium carbonate. It is employed as an insulating covering for steam pipes and furnaces, for making oxychloride cement, in boiler compounds, and as a filler for rubber and paper. **Montax,** of the R. T. Vanderbilt Co., used as a filler, is a mixture of hydrated magnesium carbonate and silica powder. Magnesium carbonate is a good heat insulator because of the great number of microscopic dead-air cells in the material. The insulating material known as 85% magnesia has a density of 12 lb per cu ft, a thermal conductivity of 0.35 Btu in. per hr at 100°F, and a conductivity of 0.46 Btu at 400°F. As an insulating pipe covering it is usually mixed with asbestos fibers to give structural strength. Federal specifications for magnesia call for the hydrated magnesium carbonate, $4MgCO_3 \cdot Mg(OH)_2 \cdot 5H_2O$, combined with 10% asbestos fibers, for use in heat-insulating blocks. The hydrated carbonate is a fine white powder called **magnesia alba levis,** slightly soluble in water, and used in medicine.

MAGNESIUM SULFATE. A colorless to white, bitter-tasting material occurring in sparkling needle-shaped crystals of the composition $MgSO_4 \cdot 7H_2O$. The natural mineral is called **epsomite,** from Epsom Spa, Surrey, England. In medicine it is called **epsom salt.** It is used in leather tanning, as a mordant in dyeing and printing textiles, as a filler for cotton cloth, for sizing paper, in water-resistant and fireproof magnesia cements, and as a laxative.   It can also be obtained in the anhydrous form, $MgSO_4$, as a white powder.   The specific gravity of the hydrous material is 1.678, and of the anhydrous 2.65.   It occurs naturally as deposits from spring waters, and is also made by treating magnesite with sulfuric acid.   In Germany it is produced from the mineral **kieserite,** $MgSO_4 \cdot H_2O$, which is abundant in the Strassfurt district, and is used as a source of sulfuric acid and magnesium.   The magnesium sulfate from the waters at Seidlitz, Bohemia, was called **Seidlitz salt,** but **Seidlitz powder** is now a combination of rochelle salt and sodium bicarbonate.   **Synthetic kieserite** is made from the olivine of North Carolina.   The mineral **langbeinite,** found in the potash-deposits at Carlsbad, N.M., is a potassium-magnesium-sulfate containing 22% potassium oxide and 18 magnesia and is used in the production of potassium sulfate and magnesium metal.   **Sulpomag** is langbeinite with the halite and clay washed out.   When the magnesium of epsomite is replaced by zinc the mineral is called **goslarite,** and when replaced by nickel it is called **morenosite,** a green mineral occurring in nickel mines.

MAGNET ALLOYS. Alloys employed for making **permanent magnets,** that is, magnets that retain their magnetism after they are removed from the magnetic field, as distinct from **electromagnets,** which are of soft iron and are magnetized only while in the magnetic field.   Magnet steels were originally good grades of crucible tungsten steel, sometimes containing chromium and manganese.   **Tungsten magnet steels** contain 5 to 6% tungsten and about 0.65 carbon.   They can be hot-forged, and machined when annealed.   They are hardened in water and then tempered in hot oil.   With increased carbon the coercive force increases, but the maximum induction and the residual magnetism decrease.   The coercive force of a 6% tungsten steel is about 75 oersteds.   Molybdenum may be used instead of tungsten, but is employed usually only with other elements.   The cobalt-chromium steels with some molybdenum have very high tensile strengths. **Comol,** of the General Electric Co., has 17% molybdenum, 12 cobalt, and 71 iron.   It can be cast to shape or hot-forged, and has a coercive force of 245 oersteds.   **Indalloy** and **Remalloy** have similar compositions.   They have a hardness of Rockwell C25, can be machined and then precipitation-hardened to C60.   The maximum energy product is 1,100,000 gauss-oersteds.

Chromium magnet steels are less expensive, and contain up to 5% chromium, usually 3, and about 1 carbon.   A standard grade contains 2.25 to 4% chromium, 0.45 manganese, and 0.95 carbon.   The magnetic properties are similar to those of the tungsten steels, and they have the same difficulty in hardening because of breakage when the carbon is high.

Tuncro, of the Allegheny Ludlum Steel Co., is a tungsten-chromium magnet steel, and **Armat** is a magnet steel of the Jessop Steel Co.   **Cobalt magnet steels** contain from 18 to 60% cobalt, part of which may be replaced by the less expensive chromium, or some tungsten may be used. Some cobalt magnet steels contain 1.5 to 3% chromium, 3 to 5 tungsten, 0.50 to 0.80 carbon, with high cobalt.   A Japanese alloy, **KS magnet steel,** contained 30 to 40% cobalt, 5 to 9 tungsten, 1.5 to 3 chromium, and 0.4 to 0.8 carbon.   The coercive force of this alloy is about 3 times that of a 5% magnet steel.   **Alfer magnet alloys,** first developed in Japan to save cobalt, were **iron-aluminum alloys.**   **MK alloy** had 25% nickel, 12 aluminum, and the balance iron, close to the formula Fe_2NiAl.   It is age-hardening, and has a coercive force of 520 oersteds and maximum energy product of 1,350,000 gauss-oersteds.   **Oerstit 400,** used by the Germans during the Second World War because it gave high coercive force in proportion to weight, contained 22% cobalt, 16 nickel, 8 aluminum, 4 copper, and the balance iron.   **Cunico,** of the Indiana Steel Products Co., is a nickel-cobalt-copper alloy that can be cast, rolled, and machined.   It is not magnetically directional like the tungsten magnets, and thus gives flexibility in design.   The weight is 0.300 lb per cu in., the electrical conductivity is 7.1% that of copper, and it has good coercive force.   **Cunico I** contains 50% copper, 21 nickel, and 29 cobalt.   **Cunico II,** with 60% copper, 20 nickel, and 20 iron, is more malleable.   This alloy, heat-treated at 1100°F, is used in wire form for permanent magnets for miniature apparatus.   It has a coercive force of 500 oersteds.   **Hipernom,** of Westinghouse Electric Corp., is a high-permeability nickel-molybdenum magnet alloy containing 79% nickel, 4 molybdenum, and the balance iron.   It has a Curie temperature of 860°F and is used for relays, amplifiers, and transformers.

In the **Alnico alloys** of the General Electric Co., a precipitation hardening occurs with AlNi crystals dissolved in the metal and aligned in the direction of magnetization to give greater coercive force.   This type of magnet is usually magnetized after setting in place.   **Alnico I** contains 63% iron, 20 nickel, 12 aluminum, and 5 cobalt.   The alloy is cast to shape, is hard and brittle, and cannot be machined.   The coercive force is 400 oersteds.   **Alnico II,** a cast alloy with 17% nickel, 12.5 cobalt, 10 aluminum, 6 copper, and the balance iron, has a coercive force of 560 oersteds.   The cast alloys have higher magnetic properties, but the sintered alloys are fine-grained and stronger.   **Alnico IV** contains 12% aluminum, 28 nickel, 5 cobalt, and the balance iron.   It has a coercive force of 700 oersteds, or 10 times that of a plain tungsten magnet steel. **Alnico VIII,** of the Crucible Steel Co., has 35% cobalt, 34 iron, 15 nickel, 7 aluminum, 5 titanium, and 4 copper.   The coercive force is 1,450 oersteds.   It has a hardness of Rockwell C59.   The magnets are cast to shape and finished by grinding.   **Hyflux Alnico IX,** of the same coercive force, has an energy product of 9,500,000 gauss-oersteds.   The magnets of this material made by Indiana General Corp. are cylinders, rectangles, and prisms, usually magnetized and oriented in place.   The **Alnicus magnets,** of the U.S. Magnet & Alloy Corp., are alnico-type alloys with the grain structure oriented by directional solidification in the casting which increases the maximum energy output.   **Ticonal, Alcomax,** and **Hycomax** are alnico-type magnet alloys produced in Europe.   Various other alloys of high coercive force have been developed for special purposes.   **Silmanal,** with 86.75% silver, 8.8 manganese, and 4.45 aluminum, has a coercive force of 6,300 oersteds, but a low flux density.   **Platinax,** with 76.7% platinum and 23.3 cobalt, has a coercive force of 2,700.   **Bismanol,** developed by the Naval Ordnance Laboratory, is a **bismuth-manganese alloy** with 20.8% manganese.   It has a coercive force of 3,600 oersteds, but oxidizes easily.   **Cobalt-platinum,** as an intermetal rather than an alloy, has a coercive force above 4,300 oersteds and a residual induction of 6,450 gausses.   It contains 76.8% by weight of platinum and is expensive, but is used for tiny magnets for electric wristwatches and instruments. **Placovar,** of the Hamilton Watch Co., is a similar alloy that retains 90% of its magnetization flux up to 650°F.   It is used for miniature relays and focusing magnets.   **Ultramag,** of the Mallory Metallurgical Co., is a **platinum-cobalt** magnet material with a coercive force of 4,800 oersteds. The curie temperature is about 500°C, and it has only slight loss of magnetism at 350°C, whereas cobalt-chromium magnets lose their magnetism above 150°C.   The material is easily machined.   **Alloy 1751,** of Engelhard Industries, is a cobalt-platinum intermetal with a coercive force of 4,300 oersteds, or of 6,800 oersteds in single-crystal form.   The metal is not brittle and can be worked easily.   It is used for the motor and index magnets of electric watches.

The **ceramic magnets,** also called **ferromagnetic ceramics** and **ferrites,** were originally made of an iron oxide, Fe_2O_3, with one or more divalent oxides such as NiO, MgO, or ZnO.   The mixture is calcined, ground to a fine powder, pressed to shape, and sintered.   The term ferromagnetic now refers to qualities rather than to iron content.   In iron the net magnetic field appears to be proportionate only to the number of free, or uncombined, electrons, while in the ceramics and intermetals the molecular structures can be varied to make the electrons more readily available.   But the subject of **magnetism** is as yet not fully understood, and a comparison of magnets is usually made by plotting a chart of the orientation lag, known as the **hysteresis loop,** and by measuring the **coercive force** of the magnetic material designated in units of field intensity called **oersteds.** **Electromagnetism** of a material body, or mass, and the force of **gravity** are interrelated and derive from the same source; the **specific gravity** of any material on or near the surface of the earth is thus a measure of the coercive force of the earth as a huge magnet.

Ceramic and intermetal types of magnets have a square hysteresis loop and high resistance to demagnetization, and are valued for magnets for computing machines where a high remanence is desired. A ferrite with a square loop for switching in high-speed computers contains 40% Fe_2O_3, 40 MnO, and 20 CdO. Some intermetallic compounds, such as **zirconium-zinc,** $ZrZn_2$, which are not magnetic at ordinary temperatures, become ferromagnetic with properties similar to ferrites at very low temperatures, and are useful in computers in connection with subzero superconductors. Some compounds, however, are the reverse of this, being magnetic at ordinary temperatures and nonmagnetic below their transition temperature point. This transition temperature, or **Curie point,** can be arranged by the compounding to vary from subzero temperatures to above 212°F. **Chromium-manganese-antimonide,** $Cr_xMn_{2x}Sb$, is such a material. Chromium-manganese alone is ferromagnetic, but the antimonide has a transition point varying with the value of x.

Vectolite is a lightweight magnet of the Indiana Steel Products Co. made by molding and sintering ferric and ferrous oxides and cobalt oxide. The weight is 0.114 lb per cu in. It has high coercive force, and has such high electrical resistance that it may be considered as a nonconductor. It is very brittle, and is finished by grinding. **Magnadur,** of the Ferrox Corp., was made from barium carbonate and ferric oxide, and has the formula $BaO(Fe_2O_3)_6$. **Indox,** of the Indiana Steel Products Co., and **Ferroxdure,** of the Phillips Research Laboratories, are similar. This type of magnet has a coercive force to 1,600 oersteds, with initial force to 2,600, high electrical resistivity, high resistance to demagnetization, and light weight, with specific gravity from 4.5 to 4.9. **Ferrimag,** of the Crucible Steel Co., and **Cromag,** of Henry L. Crowley & Co., Inc., are ceramic magnets. Strontium carbonate is superior to barium carbonate for magnets but is more costly. **Lodex magnets,** of General Electric Co., are extremely fine particles of iron-cobalt in lead powder made into any desired shape by powder metallurgy.

Ceramic magnets shrink in sintering, but by allowance for the shrinkage, shapes can be made to close accuracy. They are too hard to machine. In general, they have only one direction of magnetization, and thus do not have to be magnetized in place. Machinable ceramic magnets are made by bonding the ceramic powders with plastics, but the magnetic properties are reduced in proportion to the amount of bond. **Flexible magnets** are made with magnetic powder bonded to tape or impregnated in plastic or rubber in sheets, strip, or forms. **Magnetic tape** for recorders may be made by coating a strong, durable plastic tape, such as a polyester, with a

magnetic ferrite powder.   For high-duty service, such as for spacecraft, the tape may be of stainless steel.   For recording heads the ferrite crystals must be hard and wear-resistant.   **Ferrocube,** of Ferrox Corp., is manganese zinc.   The tiny crystals are compacted with a ceramic bond for pole pieces for recorders.   **Plastiform,** of the Leyman Corp., is a barium ferrite bonded with rubber in sheets and strips.   **Magnyl,** of the Applied Magnetic Corp., is vinyl resin tape with the fine magnetic powder only on one side.   It is used for door seals and display devices.

   Rare-earth magnets used for computers and signaling devices are usually of very small size, but with coercive forces up to ten times that of ordinary magnets.   They are of several types.   **Rare–earth–cobalt magnets** are made by compacting and extruding the powders with a binder of plastic or soft metal into small precision shapes.   They have high permanency.   **Samarium-cobalt** and **cesium-cobalt mangets** are cast from vacuum melts and, as made by Bell Laboratories, are chemical compounds, $SmCo_5$ and $CeCo_5$. These magnets have intrinsic coercive forces up to 28,000 oersteds.   The **magneto-optic magnets** produced by IBM for memory systems in computers are made in thin wafers, often no more than a spot in size.   These are ferromagnetic ceramics of **europium-chalcogenides.**   Spot-size magnets of europium oxide only 4 microns in diameter perform reading and writing operations efficiently.   Films of this ceramic less than a wavelength in thickness are used as memory storage mediums.

MAGNET WIRE. Insulated wire for the winding of electromagnets and for coils for transformers and other electrical applications.   Since compactness is usually a prime consideration, high-conductivity copper is used in the wire, but where weight saving is important, aluminum wire may be used and has the advantage that an extremely thin anodized coating of oxide serves as the insulation either alone or with a thin varnish coating. Square or rectangular wires may be used, but ordinary magnet wire is round copper wire covered with cotton and an enamel, in OD sizes from No. 40, AWG (0.0071 in.), to No. 8 (0.1380 in.).   **Vitrotex,** of the Anaconda Wire & Cable Co., is a magnet wire coated with a resin enamel and covered with alkali-free glass fiber.   It will withstand temperatures to 130°C, and the glass fibers dissipate heat rapidly.   **Silotex,** of this company, has a silicon resin and glass-fiber insulation and will withstand temperatures to 300°C.   Various types of synthetic resins are used as insulation to give high dielectric strength, heat and abrasion resistance, and flexibility to withstand bending of the wire without cracking.   Heat resistance is usually designated by the AIEE class standards.   **Formvar magnet wire** has a coating of vinyl acetal resin with dielectric strength of 1,000 volts per mil. The General Electric wire coating called **Alkanex** is a modified glycerol terephthalate polyester resin for operating temperatures to 155°C. **Bondar coating,** of Westinghouse, is an epoxy-modified polyester amide for temperatures to 155°C. **Carthane 8063,** of the Carwin Co., is a liquid urethane resin for flexible and abrasion-resistant coating on magnet wire.

MAHOGANY. A name applied to a variety of woods. All of the true mahogany, however, comes from trees of the family *Meliaceae,* but of various genera and species. The tropical cedars, Spanish cedar and Paraguayan cedar, belong to this family. Mahogany, of the tree *Swietenia mahogani* and other species of *Swietenia,* is obtained from Mexico to as far south as northern Argentina. The Central American has the best reputation and is frequently referred to under the Spanish name **caoba.** The mahogany from Cuba and Santo Domingo has a close grain and beautiful color and is valued for furniture. The so-called **Horseflesh mahogany** from Cuba is from the **sabicu tree.** **Baywood** is an English name originally applied to a superior, straight-grained mahogany from the shores of the Bay of Honduras. **Colombian mahogany** is the wood of the tree *Cariniana pyriformis* of northern South America. It resembles mahogany but is heavier and harder.

The wood of the mahogany tree is obtainable in large logs. It has a reddish color of various shades. The grain is often figured, and it has a high luster when polished. It seasons well, does not warp easily, and is prized for furniture and cabinetwork and for small patterns in foundry work. The weight varies from 32 to 42 lb per cu ft, and the hardness and closeness also vary. The beautiful curled-grain woods are from selected forks of the trees. The mahogany formerly used for airplane propellers, and used also for small boats and boat trim, is either African *Khaya* or American *Swietenia,* with average specific gravity kiln-dried of 0.50. The compressive strength is up to 1,760 psi perpendicular to the grain, and the shearing strength 860 psi parallel to the grain.

Australian red mahogany is from the tree *Eucalyptus resinifera* of Australia. It is hard, durable, of a dark-red color, with a coarse, open grain. **Crabwood,** used as a substitute for mahogany, is the wood of the **carapa tree,** *Carapa guianensis,* of Brazil and the Guianas. It has a deep-reddish-brown color with a coarse grain and weighs 40 lb per cu ft. This tree produces the seed nuts from which **carapa fat** is pressed, used for soap, candles, and as an edible fat. **Oleo vermelho,** from the tree *Myrospermum erythoxylum* of Brazil, is a fine-grained reddish cabinet wood similar to mahogany. The specific gravity is 0.954. It has an agreeable odor. **Cameroon mahogany** is from the tree *Bassia toxisperma* of West Africa. The kernels of the nuts of the tree yield about 60% of a yellowish-white semisolid oil known as **djave butter,** or **adjab butter,** used in Europe for soapmaking. It is used locally for food by steaming off the traces of hydrocyanic acid.

MALLEABLE IRON. A high-tensile-strength white cast iron produced by a long heat treatment of white chilled castings. Iron for malleable iron is usually melted in the reverberatory furnace, which gives it greater strength and ductility than iron melted in the cupola in contact with the fuel. The iron contains 1 to 1.5% silicon and is cooled rapidly to produce white iron. The castings seldom exceed 10 lb in weight. After casting, the parts are packed in annealing pots and subjected to an increasing temperature to about 1650°F, for a period of 48 to 60 hr. They are then cooled slowly with temperature decreasing 8 to 10°F per hr to below 1275°F. The resulting iron has the carbon in regular tiny particles instead of flakes as in gray cast iron. The ordinary American malleable iron called **blackheart iron** has a white shell and a dark core, the outside being completely decarbonized. It is tough and more ductile than the coarse-grained **whiteheart iron** made at higher annealing temperatures.

The iron for malleable iron must have enough silicon to promote graphitization of the iron carbide at sustained high temperature, and sufficient manganese to offset the stabilizing effect of sulfur. The carbon then separates out into nodules of free **temper carbon** embedded in ferrite. Standard malleable iron contains 2.3 to 2.7% of carbon and 0.8 to 1.5 silicon. It is very fluid and will produce thin and intricate castings with a tensile strength of 50,000 psi and elongation of 10%. Slight additions of copper accelerate the annealing of blackheart iron. An iron known as **quick malleable iron,** used for automotive engine castings, has 2.2% carbon, 1.5 silicon, 0.30 to 0.60 manganese, and 0.75 to 1 copper. The copper also increases the tensile strength. For ease of machining, malleable iron normally should have 2.60% or more of carbon, although less carbon is desirable for strength and ductility. An average composition is carbon, 2%; silicon, 0.60 to 1.10; manganese, under 0.30; phosphorus, under 0.20; and sulfur, 0.06 to 0.15, with 1% copper for corrosion resistance. Malleable iron is used for castings for implements, pipe fittings, building hardware, and small machine parts requiring strength. The tensile strength is a minimum of 50,000 psi, and the Brinell hardness 115, with elongation 18%, but higher strengths may be obtained with small controlled additions of alloying elements. Chromium gives a stabilizing effect, and increased amounts of manganese may be used, with also a small amount of molybdenum. But the white irons made with considerable contents of silicon, manganese, nickel, plus heat treatment, are classed as **austenitic cast iron** and not as malleable iron.

The material known as **pearlitic malleable iron** is malleable iron made by controlled heat treatment which develops a matrix of pearlite with temper carbon nodules and from 0.3 to 0.9% combined carbon distributed in the matrix.   It has tensile strengths from 65,000 psi with 10% elongation up to 100,000 psi with 2% elongation.   The weight averages about 8% less than for forged steel.   It machines more easily than steel, gives a fine finish, has good wear resistance and fatigue resistance, and has better damping than steel.   It is used to replace steel forgings for such parts as universal-joint yokes, gears, and small crankshafts.   The hardness is Brinell 200 to 260.

The so-called **certified malleable irons** are made to ASTM specifications. Other general names, such as **shockproof iron,** are used to designate irons with controlled upper levels of silicon and manganese, with elongation to 5%, increased strength, and hardness to 200 Brinell.   Malleable irons are also sold under many trade names, such as **Belmalloy** and **Flecto metal.**

The **Promal,** of the Link-Belt Co., and **Supermal,** of the Jeffrey Mfg. Co., used for such parts as chain links, are specially processed to give high fatigue resistance with hardness to 170 Brinell.   The **Z metal,** of the Ferrous Metals Corp., is a pearlitic malleable iron with tensile strength of 70,000 psi, hardness 180 Brinell, and elongation to 18%.   The **Cu-Z metal** contains about 1% copper, and other grades contain copper and molybdenum to add corrosion resistance, refine the grain, and increase the density, giving high strength and ductility.

MANGANESE. A metallic element, symbol Mn, found in the minerals manganite and pyrolusite, and with most iron ores and traces in most rocks.   Manganese has a silvery-white color with purplish shades.   **Distilled manganese,** with no iron, and with carbon and silicon not over 0.006% total, has a fine silvery-gray luster very resistant to corrosion.   It is brittle but hard enough to scratch glass.   The specific gravity is 7.42, melting point 1245°C, and weight 0.268 lb per cu in.   It decomposes water slowly.   It is not used alone as a construction metal.   The electrical resistivity is 100 times that of copper or 3 times that of 18–8 stainless steel. It also has a damping capacity 25 times that of steel, and can be used to reduce the resonance of other metals.

Manganese is used in the steel industry as a deoxidizer and as a hardener, and nearly all steel now contains some manganese.   For this purpose it is used largely in the form of ferromanganese.   More than 80% of the manganese charged into an open-hearth furnace for making ordinary steel goes off in the slag.   American practice is to use manganese almost exclusively for deoxidizing steel, an average of 14 lb metallic manganese being used per ton of steel produced in the United States.   But alkalies have been used in Germany for deoxidizing steel, and lithium is also an effective deoxidizer for steel.   Manganese is also added to steel in considerable amounts for the production of wear-resistant alloy steels.   **Manga-**

nese metal, for adding manganese to nonferrous alloys, is marketed in crushed form containing 95 to 98% manganese, 2 to 3 max iron, 1 max silicon, and 0.25 max carbon, but for the controlled addition of manganese to nonferrous metals and to high-grade steels, high purity, 99.9% plus, electrolytic manganese metal is now used.   Manganese metal has very high sound-absorbing properties, and **copper-manganese alloys** with high percentages of manganese are used as **sound-damping alloys** for thrust collars for jackhammers and other power tools.

Electrolytic manganese can be produced from low-grade ores by electrochemical methods, 99.9% pure metal.   The material produced by the Electro Manganese Corp. from high-grade ores is designated as **electromanganese.**   It comes in chips about $\frac{1}{16}$ in. thick in sizes larger than 1 in. square.   It is 99.97% min pure metal, with 0.03% max sulfur and iron. **Manganese powder** is powdered metal of high purity, of 150 to 325 mesh, employed for pyrotechnic and metallurgical uses.   **Manganese tablets,** for use in steelmaking, are made by pressing electrolytically reduced powder in an inert atmosphere and then coating the tablets with ammonium chloride to prevent oxidation.   **Manganese carbonyl,** used for vapor deposition of manganese coatings, is a yellow crystalline solid of the composition $Mn_2(CO)_{10}$, melting at 154°F and soluble in common organic solvents.

MANGANESE ALLOY. A series of nonferrous alloys containing manganese, copper, and nickel.   They can be forged readily and machined, and then age-hardened at 500 to 1000°F to a hardness of 400 to 500 Brinell with tensile strengths of 200,000 psi and high wear resistance. **Chace alloy 720,** of the W. M. Chace Co., contains 60% copper, 20 manganese, and 20 nickel.   It is soft and ductile, but can be hardened to 400 Vickers.   The tensile strength of the forged metal varies from 98,000 to 220,000 psi depending upon the hardness.   The specific gravity is 8.25. It is used for high-strength, corrosion-resistant parts and for springs. **Wyndaloy 720,** of the Wyndale Mfg. Co., is this metal in forgings.   These alloys are also noted for their high electrical resistivity, the 20% manganese alloy having a resistivity of 300 to 500 ohms per cir mil ft, and a conductivity of only 2 to 3.5% IACS.   It is thus used for resistor wire and strip.

The alloys have a high coefficient of thermal expansion, and the **high-expansion alloy** with 72% manganese, 18 copper, and 10 nickel has the highest expansion of any of the common strong alloys.   A high-manganese alloy, used for rheostat resistors and electrically heated expansion elements, is **Chace alloy 772.**   It contains 72% manganese, 18 copper, and 10 nickel.   It can be machined, drawn, and stamped.   The cold-rolled metal has a hardness of 220 Vickers and a tensile strength of 115,000 psi, with elongation 6.5%.   It is nonmagnetic, has a heat conductivity of only 12%

that of steel, and a vibration damping constant 25 times that of steel. The electrical resistivity is 1,050 ohms per cir mil ft. Manganese alloy **resistor wire** is produced by the Driver-Harris Co.

MANGANESE-ALUMINUM. A **hardener alloy** employed for making additions of manganese to aluminum alloys. Manganese lowers the thermal conductivity of aluminum but increases the strength and increases the contraction. Manganese up to 1.5% is used in aluminum alloys when strength and stiffness are required. A manganese-aluminum marketed by the Niagara Falls Smelting & Refining Corp. contains 25% manganese and 75 aluminum. **Manganese-boron** is another alloy used for deoxidizing and hardening bronzes. It contains 20 to 25% boron, with small amounts of iron, silicon, and aluminum. For deoxidizing and hardening brasses, nickel bronze, and cupronickel, **manganese copper,** or **copper manganese,** may be used. The alloys used contain 25 to 30% manganese and the balance copper. The best grades of manganese copper are made from metallic manganese and are free from iron. For nickel bronzes and nickel alloys the manganese copper must be free of both iron and carbon, but grades containing up to 5% iron can be used for manganese bronze. Grades made from ferromanganese contain iron. Manganese copper is usually marketed in slabs with notched sections, or as shot. It has a lower melting point than metallic manganese and is thus more easily dissolved in the brass or bronze. The 30% alloy melts at about 1600°F.

MANGANESE BRONZE. A brass containing iron and manganese which, because of its hardness and crystalline structure, is called a bronze. It casts more easily than aluminum bronze and is used for propeller blades, valve stems, engine frames, and machinery parts requiring high strength and resistance to seawater. Manganese is a deoxidizer in the alloys, but in excess, usually up to 3.5%, it hardens and strengthens the alloy, increases the solubility of the iron in the brass, and acts to stabilize the aluminum when this metal is used. Manganese has nearly the whitening power of nickel in copper alloys. **Turbadium bronze** was an old name used by the British Admiralty for manganese bronze containing 50% copper, 44 zinc, 1 iron, 1.75 manganese, 2 nickel, and 0.5 tin, used for casting propellers and marine parts. The original **Turbiston's bronze** contained 55% copper, 41 zinc, 1 aluminum, 2 nickel, and 1 iron. ASTM and Federal specifications for manganese bronze call for 55 to 60% copper, 38 to 42 zinc, up to 3.5 manganese, up to 1.5 tin, 1.5 aluminum, and up to 2 iron. This alloy has a minimum tensile strength of 65,000 psi and elongation 30% as cast; the wrought metal has a strength of 72,000 psi.

The manganese bronze marketed as **Amcoloy 666** by Ampco Metals, Inc., in extruded round rods for gears, cams, shafts, and bushings, contains

2.5% manganese, 1 aluminum, 0.7 silicon, 0.40 max lead, 57 to 60 copper, and the balance zinc.   The tensile strength is 80,000 to 88,000 psi, with elongation 12 to 18%, and hardness Rockwell B87 to B91.   Even very small amounts of lead decrease the strength of manganese bronze and lower the ductility.   Phosphor copper is sometimes added to make the metal easier-pouring.   The most popular manganese bronze in the automotive and aviation industries for castings contains little manganese.   It has 57% copper, 40.5 zinc, 1 aluminum, 1 iron, and 0.5 manganese.   It is tough and wear-resistant, and has a tensile strength of 65,000 psi min. Manganese bronze has high shrinkage, $\frac{3}{16}$ in. per ft, and large fillets are necessary between changes in section thickness.   **Manganese-tin alloy,** used in England as a substitute for nickel silver, is a white alloy containing 16% manganese, 8 tin, and the balance copper.   The tensile strength is 57,000 psi, with elongation of 48%, but when cold-worked the strength is increased to 103,000 psi with elongation of 2%.

A **super manganese bronze,** used for aircraft engine parts, contains 69% copper, 20 zinc, 2 manganese, 2.5 iron, and 6.5 aluminum.   It has a tensile strength of 110,000 psi and Brinell hardness 225 when heat-treated.   A **manganese-aluminum brass,** under the name of **Hy-Ten-Sl,** marketed by the American Manganese Bronze Co., contains 66% copper, 19 zinc, 10 aluminum, and 5 manganese.   The castings have a tensile strength up to 105,000 psi, elongation 15%, and Brinell hardness 175. It is also made in wrought forms.   The alloys known as **manganese casting brass** are usually muntz metal containing a small amount of manganese. The original **manganese brass,** patented in 1876 under the name of **Parsons' alloy,** contained 56% copper, 41.5 zinc, 1.2 iron, 0.7 tin, 0.1 manganese, and 0.46 aluminum.   An alloy used by one automotive company has 58% copper, 40 zinc, and 2 of a master alloy consisting of tin, iron, manganese, and aluminum.   The lead content is not permitted to exceed 0.15%. The tensile strength is 70,000 psi and elongation 20%.   It is used as a substitute for malleable iron or drop-forged steel.   **Lumen manganese brass,** of the Lumen Bearing Co., is a 60–40 brass with 3% of the copper replaced with 1% iron and some manganese, tin, and aluminum.

MANGANESE ORES.   Manganese is a widely dispersed metal, occurring in many ores and in many parts of the world, but normally less than 10% of the manganese used in the United States is produced domestically, as most of the American ores are low-grade.   The ores are used largely for producing ferromanganese, but some low-grade ores are reduced electo-lytically to the metal, and the oxide ores are used directly in dry batteries, glassmaking, and in the chemical industry.   **Pyrolusite** is the most important manganese ore.   It is a **manganese dioxide,** MnO_2, with a black color and a metallic luster.   The specific gravity is 4.75 and hardness 2 to 2.5.

It is mined in various parts of Europe, Australia, Brazil, Argentina, Ghana, Cuba, India, Canada, and the United States.   It is valued for glass manufacture, and when used as a decolorizer for glass, pyrolusite has been called **glassmakers' soap.**

Some of the high-grade Montana and Ghana ores are used for batteries. **Battery-grade manganese** must be free of lead, copper, iron, and other impurities which are electronegative to zinc, and which would decrease the potential and the life of the dry cell.   Battery manganese must also have the oxygen readily available, and should be poorly crystallized and consist of the gamma oxide known as **cryptomelane,** or a black pseudo-amorphous powder.   Pyrolusite normally has an orthorhombic crystal structure, but also occurs pseudoamorphic, or as **psilomelane,** a colloidal form of the oxide, and it is this material which is separated as the battery grade.   But the natural material is an alteration product in the ore veins, and is irregular in quality.   High-grade battery manganese of uniform purity is manufactured from low-grade ores by leaching the crushed ore with sulfuric acid and precipitating the heavy metal sulfides with barium sulfide, aerating to oxidize the iron and sulfur, and electrolyzing the solution to obtain MnO_2 on the graphite anodes.   For use as a dry-cell depolarizer, it is ground so that 65% passes a 100-mesh screen.   Synthetic manganese dioxide made by electrolysis of the sulfate or by chemical reduction of the carbonate shows an irregularly shaped amorphous structure under a microscope.   It is more reactive and more uniform than the natural material, and gives a longer battery life with a smaller quantity. High-grade battery manganese is also made by reacting manganese sulfate with sodium chlorate at 200°F in the presence of sulfuric acid, and the synthetic manganese oxides are now preferred for battery use.

The ore known as **bog manganese,** also called **wad,** is an impure mixture of MnO_2 and MnO, together with other oxides.   It is a soft, friable mineral of black or brown color and is an impure psilomelane.   The wad ore of Arkansas, used for making manganese sulfate, contains 15 to 50% manganese.   **Manganblend,** or **alabandite,** is a natural **manganese sulfide,** MnS, and is an iron-black mineral with a specific gravity of 4 and a Mohs hardness of 3.5 to 4.   This material in ground form is marketed by the Foote Mineral Co. for making amber glass.   It is stable and produces a clear amber color without muddiness.

Rhodochrosite, found in several parts of the United States and in central Europe, is a **manganese carbonate,** $MnCO_3$, with usually some iron replacing part of the manganese.   It has a rose-red to dark-brown color, with a vitreous luster, specific gravity 3.5, and hardness 3.5 to 4.5.   It usually has a massive cleavable structure.   **Manganite,** found with other manganese minerals and with iron, is an iron-black mineral of the composition $Mn_2O_3 \cdot H_2O$, containing theoretically 62.4% manganese.   It is found in

Germany, England, and in the Lake Superior region of the United States. **Hausmanite,** found in Washington state, is another hydrated oxide, $Mn_3O_4 \cdot 2H_2O$, containing theoretically 62.26% manganese. It is used for coating welding rods.   **Bementite,** from the same area, is a hydrated silicate, $8MnO \cdot 7SiO_2 \cdot 5H_2O$, containing 40.8% manganese. The high silica makes it difficult to use.   **Rhodonite,** $MnO \cdot SiO_2$, found in Colorado, contains 35% manganese so tightly bound chemically that it is difficult to separate by ordinary methods.   It is vaporized with a high-intensity arc, and the simple oxides, MnO_2 and SiO_2, then condense.

In general, an ore for ferromanganese should contain at least 35% manganese.   Much of the American ore contains only 5 to 10% manganese. Arkansas ores are low-grade, with as little as 18% manganese, and high-grade with more than 70%.   The low grades of Montana ore are concentrated by a nodulizing process up to 58% manganese.   Manganese is also extracted from low-grade ores by a chemical process of leaching the pulverized ore with acid, treating with calcium chloride to remove calcium sulfate, and then with limestone, and filtering off the iron oxide.   In Germany, low-grade ore is made into ferromanganese by first smelting to spiegeleisen and then treating part in an acid and part in a basic converter before mixing.   The three grades of ore designated by the Metals Reserve Co. are: High grade, with 48% min manganese and 7 max iron; Low grade A, with 44% min manganese and 10 max iron; and Low grade B, with 40% min manganese and no maximum on iron.   Chemical-grade manganese ore should have 80 to 90% MnO_2, equivalent to 51% min manganese, and not more than 2% iron.   Indian ore is classed as First grade when it has 50% min manganese, Second grade with 48 to 50%, and Third grade with 45 to 48%.   The battery-grade ore from Papua averages 86% manganese dioxide.   The ore of the Congo averages 50% manganese and 4.5 min iron.   By the Nossen process ores with as low as 11% Mn are converted to either metallurgical or battery-grade manganese dioxide.   The process consists in leaching with nitric acid, evaporating the filtered manganese nitrate, and then decomposing in heated drums to form MnO_2, HNO, and some NO_2.

MANGANESE STEEL. All commercial steels contain some manganese which has been introduced in the process of deoxidizing and desulfurizing with ferromanganese, but the name was originally applied only to steels containing from 10 to 15% manganese.   Steels with from 1.0 to 1.5% manganese are known as **carbon-manganese steel, pearlitic manganese steel,** or **intermediate manganese steel.   Medium manganese steels,** with manganese from 2 to 9%, are brittle and are not ordinarily used, but steels with 2% or more of manganese modified with small amounts of molybdenum and chromium form an important class of high-strength, air-hardening, nondeforming tool steels.   Typical of this class is **Lo-Air die steel** which contains 2% manganese, 1.35 molybdenum, 1 chromium, 0.30 silicon, and 0.70 carbon.   It hardens to Rockwell C58, with a tensile strength of 300,000 psi and elongation of 1%.   The original **Hadfield manganese steel** made in 1883 contained 10 to 14.5% manganese and 1 carbon.

Manganese increases the hardness and tensile strength of steel.   In the absence of carbon, manganese up to 1.5% has only slight influence on iron; as the carbon content increases, the effect intensifies.   Air-hardening becomes apparent in a 0.20 carbon steel with 1.5% manganese, and in a 0.35 carbon steel with 1.4% manganese.   The manganese steels used for dipper teeth, tractor shoes, and wear-resistant castings contain 10 to 14% manganese, 1 to 1.4 carbon, and 0.30 to 1 silicon.   The tensile strength is up to 125,000 psi, elongation 45 to 55%, weight 0.286 lb per cu in., and Brinell hardness, when heat-treated, of 185 to 200.   Cold working hardens this steel, and dipper teeth in service will work-harden to a hardness up to 550 Brinell.

High-manganese steels are not commercially machinable with ordinary tools, but can be cut and drilled with tungsten carbide and super-high-speed tools.   The austenitic steels, with about 12% manganese, are exceedingly abrasion-resistant and harden under the action of tools.   They are nonmagnetic.   The coefficient of expansion is about twice that of ordinary steel.   Various trade names are used to designate the high-manganese steels.   **Rol-man steel,** marketed by the Manganese Steel Forge Co., contains 11 to 14% manganese and 1 to 1.4 carbon, and has a tensile strength of 160,000 psi and elongation up to 50%.   **Amsco steel,** of the American Manganese Steel Co., contains 12 to 13% manganese and 1.2 carbon. The tensile strength is 125,000 psi, and it will work-harden to 500 Brinell. **Tisco steel,** of the Taylor-Wharton Iron & Steel Co., has up to 15% manganese, and is used for rails and crossovers where high resistance to abrasion is needed.   **Timang,** of this company, is a high-manganese steel made in the form of wire for rock screens.   A German stainless type of steel, made without nickel, has 12% manganese.   It is called **Roneusil steel.**   **High-manganese steels** are brittle when cast and must be heat-treated.   For castings of thin sections or irregular shapes where the drastic water quenching might cause distortion, nickel up to 5% may be added. The **manganese-nickel steels** have approximately the same characteristics as the straight manganese steels.   Nickel is also used in high-manganese steel wire, and the hard-drawn wire has strengths up to 300,000 psi. **Manganal** is a hot-rolled plate steel of high strength and wear resistance marketed by Joseph T. Ryerson & Son, Inc.   It contains 11 to 13% manganese, 2.5 to 3.5 nickel, and 0.60 to 0.90 carbon.   The tensile strength is 150,000 psi.   Pearlitic **nickel-manganese steel** contains only 1.25% manganese with 1.25 nickel.   It has high yield point and ductility.

A **manganese-aluminum steel,** developed by the Ford Motor Company, has 30% manganese, 9 aluminum, 1 silicon, and 1 carbon. Its tensile strength is 120,000 psi with elongation of 18%, but it work-hardens rapidly, and when cold-rolled and heat-aged the tensile strength is 300,000 psi with a yield strength of 290,000 psi. This alloy forms a special type of stainless steel, with high resistance to oxidation and sulfur gases to 1400°F.

Structural steels with 0.50% carbon and from 1 to 2 manganese have tensile strength above 90,000 psi. **Martinel steel,** or **Martin elastic limit steel,** of Alfred Holt & Co., was an early English steel of this type. **D-steel,** developed by the British Admiralty for warship construction, contains 1.1 to 1.4% manganese, 0.33 carbon, and 0.12 silicon. The tensile strength is 96,000 psi and elongation 17%. N.Y. Central rails have 1.30 to 1.60% manganese and 0.65 carbon. **Man-Ten steel,** of the U.S. Steel Corp., is a medium-carbon, medium-manganese structural steel, with corrosion resistance twice that of carbon steel. The tensile strength of the steel is 75,000 psi, with elongation of 20%. Steels containing 1.30 to 1.90% manganese replace more expensive alloy steels for automotive parts. Most mills now list these steels as special alloy machinery steels; those containing about 0.10% sulfur are designated as **manganese screw stock.**

The **SAE steel X1330** and **X1340** are of this type. **E.Z. Cut steel** plate, of Joseph T. Ryerson & Son, Inc., is a free-machining steel for molds, gears, and machine parts. It has 0.14 to 0.21% carbon, 1.15 to 1.4 manganese, and 0.17 to 0.23 sulfur. The tensile strength is 65,000 psi and elongation 30%, but when carbonized and water-quenched the tensile strength is 100,000 psi. **Max-El No. 4 steel,** of the Crucible Steel Co., is a pearlitic manganese steel with a small amount of chromium and 0.75% carbon, used for spring collets and called **collet steel.** Slight amounts of chromium will increase the strength and hardness of the intermediate manganese steels. The **tank car steel** M-128, of Lukens Steel Co., is a **manganese-vanadium steel** with 0.25% carbon, up to 1.5 manganese, and 0.02 or more vanadium. It has a minimum tensile strength of 81,000 psi with elongation of 18%. This type of steel with up to 1.75 manganese is used for forgings.

MANGROVE. An extract from the bark of the mangrove tree, *Rhizophora mangle,* of Venezuela and Colombia, the **red mangrove,** *R. racemosa,* of Nigeria, the **East African mangrove,** *R. mucronata,* and other species of Africa, the East Indies, southern Asia, and tropical America, used for tanning leather. In Java it is called **baku bark.** The East African bark contains 22 to 38% tannin, and the Nigerian bark contains 15 to 29%, usually at the low level. The South American barks range in tanning content from

5 to 45%.   In the **Brazilian mangrove,** the leaves contain 24%.   The solid extract marketed in blocks contains 62 to 63% solids and 53 to 54 tannin.   The liquid extract contains 25 to 35% tannin.   Red mangrove contains a red coloring matter which is objectionable in tanning, but can be decolorized with albumin.   **White mangrove** produces a pale pinkish-brown leather, fairly soft and of firm texture.   Mangrove from East Africa is called **mangrove cutch,** and is sometimes erroneously referred to as wattle.   The bark is sold in fibrous form and in pieces.

MANILA HEMP. A fiber obtained from the leaf stalks of the **abaca** plant, *Musa textilis,* a tree of the banana family growing in the Philippines, the East Indies, and Central America.   It is employed for rope and cordage and is the strongest of the vegetable fibers.   The fibers are also very long, from 4 to 8 ft, and do not stiffen when wet.   It is thus valued for marine cordage.   The best grades are light in weight, soft and lustrous, and white in color.   The finest fibers, called **lupis fibers,** are used in the East for weaving into cloth.   The plant grows to a height of 20 to 30 ft, with huge leaves characteristic of the banana.   Each successive layer of leaves toward the stalk yields fibers that are lighter in color, higher in strength, and of finer texture than those outside.   There are 15 grades.

MAPLE. The wood of maple trees native to the United States and Canada which include 13 species in the United States.   Of these the **sugar maple,** *Acer saccharum,* is the most plentiful and the most important.   Other names for this tree and wood are **hard maple** and **rock maple.**   The wood is tough and hard, close-grained, and does not splinter easily.   The heart-wood is light reddish brown, and the wide sapwood is white.   The wood has an average specific gravity when kiln-dried of 0.67, compressive strength perpendicular to the grain of 2,170 psi, and shearing strength parallel to the grain of 1,520 psi.   **Black maple,** *A. nigrum,* is similar to sugar maple and is marketed with it.   The **broadleaved maple,** also known as **bigleaf maple** and **Oregon maple,** is *A. macrophyllum,* and is the only species native to the western states.   **Silver maple,** *A. saccharinum,* grows most extensively in the middle states.   It is also called **soft maple, white maple, river maple,** and **swamp maple.**   **Box elder,** *A. negundo,* grows over the northern states east of the Rocky Mountains.   The **red maple** is *A. rubrum,* and the **vine maple** is *A. circinnatum.*   The wood of the maples may be white or yellowish to brownish, and is close-grained and hard.   It often has a curly, twisted grain.   The weight is about 40 lb per cu ft.   The wood of the soft maples is not as heavy or as strong as that of the sugar maple.   Maple is used for furniture, cabinetwork, flooring, rollers, measuring rules, forming dies, shoe heels and lasts, and where a hard, fine-grained wood is needed.   **Rose maple,** used in Australia for cabinetwork and paneling, is not a maple but is from the tree *Cryptocarya ethyroxylon*.   The pinkish-brown wood has a wavy grain, weighs 45 lb per cu ft, is hard, and has a fragrant odor.

Maple sugar, used in confectionery, and in sweetening agents as **maple syrup,** is the boiled-down sap of the sugar maple tree, harvested by tapping the tree in the early spring.   The sugar contains the calcium salt of succinic acid.   The ratio of sap to sugar is 40:1, and an average production is 2 lb per tree, or 20 qt of sap from a 15-in. tree.   Maple sugar is produced chiefly in Vermont, New Hamphire, New York, and Canada. **Maple flavor** is made artificially by the reaction of an alpha amino acid with a reducing saccharide.

MARBLE.   A compact crystalline limestone used for ornamental building, for large slabs for electric-power panels, and for ornaments and statuary. In the broad sense, marble includes any limestone that can be polished, including **breccia,** onyx, and others.   Pure limestone would naturally be white, but marble is usually streaked and variegated in many colors. **Carrara marble,** from Italy, is a famous white marble, being of delicate texture, very white and hard.   In the United States the marbles of Vermont are noted and occur in white, gray, light green, dark green, red, black, and mottled.   A typical white **Vermont marble** slightly mottled with gray is 99% pure carbonates with only slight amounts of manganese and aluminum oxides and organic matter.   But about 60% of American marble is quarried in Tennessee and Georgia.   It is highly crystalline, and is colored white, gray, bluish, or pink.   The 56-ton block in the tomb of the unknown soldier at Arlington, Va., is **yule marble** from Colorado. **Alabama marble** is a pure, low-porosity material of good statuary grade, mostly white.   Much of the **Tennessee marble** is marked with stylolites of zigzag colored bands, and is used for floor tile.   The Victoria pink and Cumberland pink marbles of Tennessee have low porosity and high compressive strength, about 17,000 psi.   The marbles of southern Uruguay are famous for great variety of beautiful colors, and they occur in immense blocks.

Marble has a specific gravity of about 2.72 and weighs about 170 lb per cu ft, with compressive strengths from 8,000 to above 15,000 psi.   It will ordinarily withstand heat up to 1200°F without injury.   **Translucent marble** is selected and processed marble, semitransparent to light.   **Statuary marble** is always selected by experts who have had long experience in cutting.   It must be of a single shade, and be free of hard or soft spots, iron inclusions, and other defects.   **Marble chips** are irregular small graded pieces of marble marketed for making artificial stone.   It is a byproduct of marble quarrying.   **Marble flour,** or **marble dust,** is finely ground chips used as a filler or abrasive in hand soaps and for casting.

Marbelite is an **artificial marble** used for casting statues and small ornamental articles.   It is made by heating potassium alum in water and adding about 10% heavy spar, and then casting in rubber molds.   Marble dust may be added.   **Exsilite,** of the Thermo American Fused Quartz Co., is a synthetic onyx marble in slabs as large as 2 by 3 ft, and up to 3 in. thick. It is made by fusion of pure silica with mineral colors incorporated at high temperatures.

MASTIC. The gum exudation of the tree *Pistacia lentiscus,* called **Chios mastic,** and from the *P. cabulica,* called **Bombay mastic,** both small evergreens native to the Mediterranean countries.   In ancient times the resin was highly valued for artists' paints and coating lacquers, adhesives, and for incense, dental cements, and as a chewing gum from which use it derives its name.   Because of high cost, its use is now largely limited to fine art paints and lacquers and as an astringent in medicine.

Mastic is obtained by making an incision in the tree, a tree yielding 6 to 11 lb annually.   There are two general grades, the purer resin adhering to the tree, and the resin collecting on the ground.   It is easily soluble in turpentine but is more expensive than many other natural resins, and is used for high-grade pale varnishes for art work.   The name mastic is also erroneously applied to asphalt when used in calking or adhesive compounds.

MAURITIUS HEMP. The fiber obtained from the fleshy leaves of the plant *Furcraea gigantea,* of Mauritius, Nigeria, and Ghana, used for rope and cordage.   The product from West Africa is often erroneously termed sisal.   The plant belongs to the lily family.   Similar fibers are obtained from other species, notably *F. foetida,* of Brazil.   The *F. gigantea* is also grown in Brazil under the name of **piteira.**   Each plant yields about 40 leaves annually, from 10 12 ft in length, each leaf giving 35 grams of fiber.   The plant *F. cabuya* produced the ancient cordage fiber of the Mayas.   The term **cabuya,** which means cordage, is applied to the fibers of the several species growing through Central America, the West Indies, and northern South America to Ecuador.   The fibers of the *F. cabuya* of Costa Rica are up to 100 in. long.   The leaves yield up to 3.5% of their green weight in dry fiber, which is coarser than henequen but is used for coffee-bag fabric.   The fibers of the cabuya of Ecuador, *F. andina,* are not as long.   They are used extensively for burlap for bagging.   **Fique fiber,** of Colombia, used for rope and for coffee bags, is from the leaves of the *F. macrophylla.*   The leaves are longer than those of henequen, and the fiber is finer and more lustrous.

MEERSCHAUM. A soft, white or gray, claylike mineral of the composition $3SiO_2 \cdot 2MgO \cdot 2H_2O$, used for making pipes and cigar holders, but also employed for making various other articles, as it can be cut easily when wet and will withstand heat.   When fresh, the mineral absorbs grease and makes a lather; its German name means seafoam.   It is used as a filler in soaps in Germany.   The hardness is about 2 and the specific gravity 1.28.   Most of the commercial meerschaum comes from Asia Minor; the mines at Eskisehir have been worked for 20 centuries.   A little is produced in New Mexico and some in Spain.   **Artificial meerschaum** is made from meerschaum shavings, kieselguhr, and from silicates of aluminum, calcium, and magnesium.

MELAMINE RESIN. A synthetic resin of the alkyd type made by reacting melamine with formaldehyde.   The resin is thermosetting, colorless, odorless, and resistant to organic solvents.   It is more resistant to alkalies and acids than urea resins, has better heat and color stability, and is harder. The melamine resins have the general uses of molding plastics, and also are valued for dishes for hot foods or acid juices as they will not soften or warp when washed in hot water.   **Melamine,** a trimer of cyanamide, has the composition $(N:C \cdot NH_2)_3$.

It may be made by reacting urea with ammonia at elevated temperatures and pressure.   It has a specific gravity of 1.56 and melting point 354°C. Melamine alone imparts to other resins a high gloss and color retention. The melamine resins have good adhesiveness but are too hard for use alone in coatings and varnishes.   They are combined with alcohol-modified urea-formaldehyde resins to give coating materials of good color, gloss, flexibility, and chemical resistance.   **Uformite MU-56,** of the Resinous Products & Chemical Co., is a urea-modified melamine-formaldehyde resin used for coatings and varnishes.   **Melmac 1077,** of the American Cyanamid Co., is a melamine-formaldehyde molding resin with cellulose filler.   It has a tensile strength of 7,500 psi, and dielectric strength 325 volts per mil.   **Melmac 592** has a mineral filler.   It has a dielectric strength of 400 volts per mil and will withstand temperatures to 300°F.   **Melurac 300** is a melamine-urea-formaldehyde resin with a lignin extender used as an adhesive for water-resistant plywood.   **Melmac 483** is a phenol-modified melamine-formaldehyde resin solution used for laminating fibrous materials.   **Melmac 404** is a highly translucent melamine-formaldehyde resin for molding high-gloss buttons.   **Lanoset** is a methylol-melamine made by alkylating a melamine-formaldehyde resin with methyl alcohol.   It is used for shrinkproofing woolen fabrics.   **Resimene 812,** of Monsanto, is a colorless melamine-formaldehyde resin powder that can be dissolved in water or ethyl alcohol, for impregnating paper or fabrics, or for laminating.

MENHADEN OIL. An oil obtained by steaming or boiling the fish *Brevoortia tyrannus,* caught along the Atlantic Coast of the United States.   It

was first called **porgy oil,** the Maine name for the fish.   In Connecticut it
is called **whitefish.**   In the South it is known as **fatback** and **mossbunker.**
The fish, when fully grown, are 12 to 15 in. long, weighing about a
pound.   They yield up to 15% oil, although fish from warm southern
waters yield less oil.   In May the fish migrate north to the New England
coast, and they return south to below the Carolinas in November.   An
annual catch of 1.5 billion fish yields 10.2 million gal of oil and 103,000
tons of meal.   Menhaden is not a desirable food fish because of its oily
nature.   The oil contains 27% oleic acid, 20 arachidonic, 16 clupanodonic,
17 palmitoleic, 7 myristic, and 1 stearic acid.   It has an iodine number of
140 to 180, and a specific gravity of 0.927 to 0.933.   It is used for dressing leather, mixing in cutting oils, and for making paint oils.   It is also
hydroxylated with acetic acid and used for making polyisocyanate and
alkyd resins.   Menhaden oil polymerizes easily, and the drying power is
good, but it does not give an elastic film as do the vegetable oils.   Its
strong odor is due to the clupanodonic acid ester.   The residue **fish meal**
is sold for poultry feed and fertilizer.   The meal is not as rich in vitamins
A and D as that from some other fish, but as much as 15% can be used in
poultry feed without producing a fishy taste in the eggs.

MERCURY.   Also called **quicksilver.**   A metallic element, symbol Hg.   It
is the only metal that is a liquid at ordinary temperatures.   Mercury has a
silvery-white color and a high luster.   Its specific gravity is 13.596.   The
solidifying point is $-40°F$, and its boiling point is 622°F.   It does not
oxidize at ordinary temperatures, but when heated to near its boiling point
it absorbs oxygen and is converted into a red crystalline powder, **mercuric
oxide,** HgO, used as a pigment in marine paints.   Mercury is derived
chiefly from the mineral cinnabar.   Spain, Italy, Russia, Mexico, and
western United States are the chief producers.   The metal is marketed in
steel flasks holding 75 lb.   European flasks hold 76 lb.   It is used for
separating gold and silver from their ores, for coating mirrors, as an expansive metal in thermometers, in mercury-vapor lamps, in tanning, in
batteries, for the frozen-mercury molding process, mercury-vapor motors,
as a circulating medium in atomic reactors, in amalgams, and in its compounds for fungicides, pharmaceuticals, paint pigments, and explosives.
The black **mercurous oxide,** Hg_2O, is used in skin ointments.   **Mercuric
chloride,** or **corrosive sublimate,** $HgCl_2$, is an extremely poisonous, white
crystalline powder soluble in water and in alcohol, used as a wood preservative, as an insecticide and rat poison, in tanning, as a mordant, and
as a caustic antiseptic in medicine.   **Vermilion red,** one of the oldest paint
pigments, is red **mercury sulfide,** HgS, made directly by heating mercury
and sulfur.   It is a brilliant water-insoluble red powder of specific gravity
8.1.   Because of its expense, it is often mixed with other red pigments.

Mercurochrome, $C_{20}H_8O_6Na_2Br_2Hg$, is a green crystalline powder which gives a deep-red solution in water, and is used as an antiseptic. Mercury forms a vast number of compounds, all of which are poisonous and some of which are explosive. **Mercury 203** is radioactive.

METALLIC SOAP. A term used to designate compounds of the fatty acids of vegetable and animal oils with metals other than sodium or potassium. They are not definite chemical compounds like the alkali soaps, but may contain complex mixtures of free fatty acid, combined fatty acid, and free metallic oxides or hydroxides. The name distinguishes the water-insoluble soaps from the soluble soaps made with potash or soda. Metallic soaps are made by heating a fatty acid in the presence of a metallic oxide or carbonate, and are used in lacquers, leather and textiles, paints, inks, ceramics, and grease. They have the properties of being driers, thickening agents, and flattening agents. They are characterized by ability to gel in solvents and oils, and by their catalytic action in speeding the oxidation of vegetable oils.

When made with fatty acids having high iodine values, the metallic soaps are liquid, such as the oleates and linoleates, but the resinates and tungstates are unstable powders. The stearates are fine, very stable powders. The fatty acid determines the physical properties, but the metal determines the chemical properties. Aluminum stearate is the most widely used metallic soap for colloid products. **Aluminum soaps** are used in polishing compounds, in printing inks and paints, for waterproofing textiles, and for thickening lubricating oils. The resinates, linoleates, and naphthanates are used as driers, the lead, cobalt, and manganese being the most common. Soaps of copper, arsenic, and mercury are used in **antifouling marine paints.** **Calcium rosinate** is an insoluble soap of the composition $Ca(C_{44}H_{62}O_4)_2$ produced by boiling rosin with lime water, and filtering. It is also called **calcium abiotate,** and is a yellow powder of high molecular weight, 1349.06, used as a paint drier and for waterproofing. **Calcium linoleate** is a white amorphous powder of the composition $Ca(C_{18}H_{31}O_2)_2$ used in paints and in waterproofing. It is insoluble in water but soluble in alcohol. **Calcium stearate,** $Ca(C_{18}H_{35}O_2)_2$, is a white fluffy powder of 250 mesh. It is used as a flatting agent in paints, for waterproofing cements and stucco, as a lubricant for rubber and plastic molds, as a softening agent in lead pencils, and in drawing compounds for steel-wire drawing. The calcium stearate of the Mallinckrodt Chemical Works, used in food and pharmaceutical emulsions, is an air-float powder of 325 mesh.

Barium stearate, $Ba(C_{18}H_{35}O_2)_2$, is a waxy nontacky white powder with molecular weight 703 and melting point 140 to 150°C. It is used as a dry lubricant for molding plastics, greaseless bearings, wax compounding, and wire drawing. **Chemactant PFC-5,** of Chemactant, Inc., is **barium lanolate,** a soft waxy soap, 25% barium and 75 lanolin acids, used as an additive for paints and coatings to improve adhesion and pigment dispersion. **Strontium stearate,** $Sr(C_{18}H_{35}O_2)_3$, is a white powder with molecular weight 654 and melting point 130 to 140°C. It is partly soluble and gels in benzol, mineral spirits, and hydrocarbons. It is used in grease and wax compounding and in crimson flares and signals. **Chromium stearate** is a dark-green powder of the composition $Cr(C_{18}H_{35}O_2)_3$ which melts at 95 to 100°C. It is used in ceramics, plastics, and in plastic waxes and greases, and as a catalyst. **Manganese stearate** is a pink powder of the composition $Mn(C_{18}H_{35}O_2)_2$, with a melting point 100 to 110°C. It is used in wax and grease compounding. **Cerium stearate,** $Ce(C_{18}H_{35}O_2)_2$, is a very inert, waxy white powder melting at 100 to 110°C, used as a catalyst and in waterproofing compounds. **Nickel stearate** is a green powder, $Ni(C_{18}H_{35}O_2)_2$, with a melting point 150 to 160°C, soluble in aromatic hydrocarbons, and forming gels with petroleum oils. It is used in lubricants, waterproofing compounds, leather finishes, and as a flux in nickel welding.

Dibasic **lead stearate,** $2PbOPb(C_{18}H_{35}O_2)_2$, is a soft white powder of specific gravity 2.02, insoluble in water or mineral spirits. It is used in greases, cutting oils, and as a heat and light stabilizer in vinyl plastics. **Lithium stearate** is a white, odorless powder melting at 217°C. It is used in machinery greases and as an oil-soluble emulsifying and dispersing agent in cosmetics. The **lithium soap greases** are very adhesive to the bearings and are heat-resistant. The **Stanolith greases** of the Standard Oil Co. of Indiana are lithium soap greases containing an oxidation inhibitor. **Uni-Temp grease** of the Texas Co. is a lithium soap grease made with a synthetic hydrocarbon instead of an oil. It has uniform lubricating qualities between −100 and +300°C.

METHANE. Also known as **marsh gas,** in coal mines as **firedamp,** and chemically as **methyl hydride.** A colorless, odorless gas, CH_4, employed for carbonizing steel, in the manufacture of formaldehyde, and as a starting point for many chemical compounds. The molecule has no free electrons and is the only stable **carbon hydride,** though it reacts easily on the No. 1 and No. 2 electrons of the carbon to form the hexagonal molecule called the **benzene ring.** It may thus be considered as the simplest of the vast group of **hydrocarbons** derived from petroleum, coal, and natural gas. Methane occurs naturally from the decomposition of plant and animal life, and is also one of the chief constituents of illuminating gas. It is made synthetically by the direct union of carbon or carbon monoxide with hydrogen. It is also produced by the action of water on **aluminum carbide,** a gray, massive substance of the composition Al_4C_3.

Methane has a specific gravity of 0.560 and, since it is much lighter than air, it is easily diffused in it.   In air the gas is highly explosive, although the gas alone is not explosive.   It liquefies at $-258.6°F$.   **Pintsch gas,** once used widely for car lighting, contained up to 60% methane and was made by spraying petroleum oil into a hot retort.   This type of gas, under the name of **oil gas,** or **carbohydrogen,** and containing as high as 85% hydrogen, gives a low-temperature flame used for flame-cutting torches. **Nitromethane** is nitrated methane.   It is a liquid explosive more powerful than TNT.   Methane is also the chief constituent of **natural gas** from oil fields.   Natural gas contains usually at least 75% methane, although some Pennsylvania gas contains 98.8%, and some gas from Kentucky as low as 23%.   A typical pipeline gas containing gas from several fields and freed of carbon dioxide, hydrogen sulfide, and water vapor has 78% methane, 13 ethane, 6 propane, 1.7 butane, 0.6 pentane, and some higher gases.   **Reformed gas,** used for copper refining, contains 86% methane, and is free of H_2S and from the higher homologs of CH_4.   Natural gas has an energy value of 1,035 Btu per cu ft, almost double that of manufactured gas from coal, but **synthetic gas,** or oil gas, made from crude oil, can be had with an energy value equivalent to that of natural gas.   **Sour gas** is natural gas with more than one grain of H_2S per 100 cu ft.   This hydrogen sulfide is removed to eliminate the odor before being piped. The propane, butane, and heavier hydrocarbons may also be removed for the production of chemicals.   Much of the American production of natural gas is in Texas and Louisiana, but there are large reserves in California and other areas and throughout the Canadian plains area.

METHYL ALCOHOL. Commonly known as **wood alcohol,** and called **methanol** when made synthetically.   A colorless, poisonous liquid of the composition CH_3OH, obtained from the distillation of hardwoods.   It is used as a solvent in lacquers, varnishes, and shellac.   On oxidation it yields formaldehyde, and is used in making the latter product for synthetic molding materials.   The specific gravity of methyl alcohol is 0.795, the solidifying point is $-98°C$, and the boiling point is $65°C$.   It is now produced largely from synthesis gas.

MICA. Known originally as **Muscovy glass.**   A group of minerals with monoclinic crystals which break off easily into thin, tough scales, varying from colorless to black.   **Muscovite** is the common variety of mica, and is called **potash mica,** or **potash silicate,** $H_2KAl_3(SiO_4)_3$.   It has superior dielectric properties, and is valued for radio capacitors.   **Phlogopite** is **magnesium mica,** $H_2KMgSi(SiO_4)_3$, and is distinguished from muscovite by its decomposition in sulfuric acid.   It is also called **amber mica.**   It is superior to muscovite in heat resistance, but is softer and has a brownish-yellow color. It comes from India, Canada, Malagasy, and Tanzania, while the chief producers of muscovite are India, Brazil, and Argentina. The peculiar crystal structure of phlogopite, and the almost infinite number of chemical combinations in which it can be produced, has made it an attractive mica for synthetic production which is generally replacing the natural product. The crystal structure is a repetition of four-layer units, and the layers are in conic thicknesses of indefinite extent. It consists of extremely thin sheets of strongly bonded silica tetrahedra with a weak ionic bond joining the sheets.

The **chromium mica** known as **fuchsite** comes only in small emerald-green flakes. The rare greenish **vanadium mica** known as **roscoelite** is usually in fine scales, and where there are considerable amounts, as in the sandstones of Colorado, Utah, and Arizona, it is most valuable as a source of vanadium, as it contains 1.5 to 3.5% vanadium. **Margarite** is a yellow or purple **calcium mica,** $CaO(SiO_2)_2 \cdot (Al_2O_3) \cdot H_2O$, and is a transition product. The chief uses of mica are as an electrical insulator, a heat insulator, and a filler in plastics and insulating materials.

The value of sheet mica depends greatly upon the absence of staining, especially from iron inclusions which decrease the electric insulating value. Most stains are black from the magnetite or other iron oxide. Reddish stains are usually red iron oxide. The brown-colored micas containing much iron are valueless as electric insulators. While selected high-grade mica is an excellent insulating material, natural mica is, in general, unsuited for economic high-production use because of the difficulty of handling the small irregular pieces and the great wastage of time and material in the selection of uncontaminated pieces. India has been the largest producer of the highest grades of phlogopite, and about 80% of this production comes from Bihar, but less than 1% of Bihar trimmed block mica is suitable for such uses as condenser film. Argentine mica runs 80% stained, 15 semiclear, and only 5 clear.

The specific gravity of mica is 2.7 to 3.1, and the hardness from 2 to 3. Dielectric strength is not an accurate measurement of the electrical quality of mica, and it is measured by the **Q value,** or reciprocal of the **power factor,** the power factor being the measure of the loss of electrical energy in a capacitor in which mica is the dielectric. High-quality capacitor mica should have a minimum Q value of 2,500, or a power factor of 0.04% at a frequency of 1 mc. **Ruby mica** is the finest grade of **Indian mica** for electrical capacitor use. **Madras mica** is greenish, and is not high-quality electric mica. Indian mica is graded as No. 5, first-quality and second-quality bookform; No. 6, loose with powder; extra loose, first-quality and second-quality; special loose, second-quality; and No. 6A loose, third-quality. **Argentine mica** has eight size grades from No. 6 in sheets of 1 to 3 sq in. to AA, or Special, in sheets of 48 sq in. or more.

Mica is marketed as cut or uncut block, sheet, splittings, and ground. **Block mica** is a deceptive term, since the pieces are not blocks. While Indian mica has been mined sometimes in books as large as 15 ft, and in sheets as large as 24 by 30 in., the commercial block mica is usually no more than 0.030 in. thick, and American importers designate block mica as pieces not less than 0.007 in. thick with a minimum usable area of 1 sq in. **Mica splittings** have a maximum thickness of 0.0012 in. and a minimum usable area of 3/4 in. About 85% of the mica imported into the United States is in thin splittings. **Film mica** is split from the best qualities of block mica to thicknesses from 0.0012 to 0.004 in. Importers recognize 11 quality grades of block mica from the densely stained to the clear, all by visual inspection. Splittings, which are usually only 1 or 2 in. in diameter, can be cemented together for use, but it is a costly operation. The original **micanite** made in India consisted of small pieces cemented together with shellac. **Built-up mica** is made by bonding the pieces with a synthetic resin and compressing at high temperature to give uniform thickness. Small pieces and the scrap from manufacture are made into mica powder for use as a filler in plastics and paints, or the powder is chemically cleaned and magnetically separated for making reconstituted sheet.

Because of the difficulty and cost of handling, natural mica sheet has now become almost obsolete for most uses. Sheets and strips made from mica flake can be handled in automatic machines, and are of a uniform quality not found in natural mica. **Reconstituted mica** without a binder is made by sheeting mica flakes by papermaking methods and submitting the sheet to high pressure and temperature to unite the flakes by recrystallization. Natural mica powder processed to give high purity may be used, but synthetic mica flake is preferred because of the ability to select a composition to suit the requirements for dielectric strength and heat resistance. In general, also, the absence of hydroxyl ions in synthetic mica gives higher heat resistance.

Mica sheet with a ceramic binder has been called **ceramoplastic insulation.** The **Synthamica 202,** of the Mycalex Corp., is made with a heat-resistant grade of synthetic mica flake with a glass bond. It comes in continuous strips 3 in. wide in thicknesses from 0.002 to 0.007 in. The dielectric strength is 1,000 volts per mil, operating temperature to 1800°F, and tensile strength 10,000 psi. **Mykroy sheet,** of Electronic Mechanics, Inc., is glass-bonded mica in heavier sheets for panels and structural parts of electronic equipment. **Mica paper** and **mica mat** are usually made with an organic binder to give flexibility. One of the earliest mica papers, called **Watsonite,** was ground natural mica, dehydrated by heating, and sheeted with a resin binder. Many of the mica papers have superior dielectric strength, but the heat resistance is limited to that of the binder.   **Crystal M,** of the Minnesota Mining & Mfg. Co., is a thin, flexible mica paper with a melting point at about 1900°F.   The thermal conductivity is from 0.30 to 1.5 Btu, and it is used for fire-resistant thermal insulation.   Mica paper made with about 90% mica flake and 10% epoxy resin has a dielectric strength of 1,300 volts per mil, power factor of 0.012, and flexural strength of 40,000 psi.   **Isomica,** of the Mica Insulator Co., is mica paper with an epoxy binder.   **Transformer-grade mica,** for Class H insulation, may be made with a silicone binder.   **Flexi-Mica,** of the Spruce Pine Mica Co., is mica bonded with a silicone resin.   The 0.002-in. sheet has a dielectric strength of 800 volts per mil and a tensile strength of 10,000 psi.

The first **synthetic mica** as made by Siemens & Halske was produced by melting a mixture of 11.6% aluminum oxide, 32.6 magnesium oxide, 30.7 kieselguhr, and 25.1 K_2SiF_6.   The crucible of melted material was enclosed in a silicon carbide crucible with the space filled with fused alumina sand, and brought to a temperature of 1500°C.   After cooling slowly the material is removed by breaking the inner crucible.   The solidified mass splits into thin clear sheets equal to high-grade natural mica.   The synthetic mica developed by the Bureau of Mines is a **fluorine-phlogopite mica** produced by calcinating a mixture of quartz, bauxite, and magnesite to drive off the carbon dioxide, adding potassium fluorosilicate, and melting at 1400°C.   As the furnace cools, the mica crystals grow from a seed at the bottom of the crucible.   The mica has the composition $K_4Mg_{12}Al_3O_{40}F_8$, and is similar to a natural mica in which the hydroxyl radical has been replaced by fluorine.   **Fluorine mica** has superior heat resistance and dielectric strength, but it is harder and not as flexible as natural phlogopite mica.   The number of combinations that can be produced in the fluorine type of phlogopite mica alone is very large.   Potassium can be replaced by sodium, rubidium, calcium, cesium, strontium, barium, thallium, or lead.   Magnesium can be replaced by iron, cobalt, nickel, manganese, titanium, copper, or zinc.   Aluminum can be replaced by iron, manganese, vanadium, boron, or beryllium.   **Boron phlogopite** as made synthetically is soft and flexible, with a melting point at 1150°C. Almost any desired combination of characteristics of heat resistance, electric resistivity, and chemical resistance can be obtained within wide ranges in synthetic micas by varying the composition.   However, sheet mica made synthetically embraces the same costly procedures of splitting and handworking of the relatively small sheets as for natural mica, so that synthetic mica is normally made as flake for reconstituting into sheet and strip of uniform purity and thickness.

Plastics are often heavily filled with mica powder and marketed under trade names such as **Micabond** and **Lamicoid** in the form of sheet, tubes, and molded parts, but they are distinct from the **mica ceramics** molded with an inorganic binder and having generally higher physical properties. One of the first of these, called **Mycalex,** produced by the Mycalex Corp. and the General Electric Co., was composed of ground mica and lead borate heated together to the softening point of the borate, 675°C, and compressed while plastic. Part of the mica combines to form a lead borosilicate. Such a molding has good strength, water resistance, resistance to arcing, and a low coefficient of expansion. **Supramica 620BB,** of the Mycalex Corp., has a lead borate binder. The molded parts have a specific gravity of 3.8, a flexural strength of 12,000 psi, hardness of Rockwell M110, and an operating temperature to 1200°F. Mica ceramics are made in various grades. Molded parts made with **boron mica** have a power factor below 0.07, and those of **barium mica** have power factors as low as 0.03. The traverse strengths of the mica ceramics are as high as 10,000 psi at 400°C.

The first wartime German **mica substitute,** called **Glushartgewebe,** was made by impregnating a very fine high-alkali glass-fiber fabric with an alcohol solution of osmose kaolin and a synthetic resin and compressing at high temperature. The General Electric **Terratex** was made from bentonite and asbestos fiber impregnated with ethyl silicate. Other substitute micas made from bentonite were **Alsifilm** and **Diaplex,** in thin, transparent hard sheets. **Tissuglas,** of the Amflex Products Dept., American Machine & Foundry Co., is made of extremely fine glass fibers matted on a papermaking machine into sheets 0.0006 to 0.012 in. thick, in continuous rolls up to 38 in. wide. It withstands temperatures to 1200°F and has higher dielectric strength than natural mica. **Fiberfilm,** of the same company, for such uses as capacitors and transformers, comes in thicknesses from 0.0008 to 0.0017 in., and has a dielectric strength of 4,000 volts per mil and an operating temperature to 250°C. It is made with fine glass fiber bonded with tetrafluoro ethylene resin. It is stiffer and stronger than ordinary plastic film. **Glass paper** developed by the Naval Research Laboratory is made from borosilicate glass flake bonded with alkyd, phenolic, or silicone resin. Where temperatures are not high, various plastic films are used for slot insulation. **Anilite,** of the National Vulcanized Fibre Co., is a phenolic impregnate in sheets as thin as 0.004 in. **Kynor,** of Pennwalt Corp., is vinylidene fluoride in thin sheet. The dielectric strength is 1,280 volts per mil, and heat distortion temperature 340°F.

MICA POWDER. Mica in very small flakes used as a filler in plastics, in paints, in roofing and asphalt shingles, and for making glass-bonded mica. When produced by grinding the small scrap pieces from mica workings, it is known as **ground mica.** The ground mica from Canada is phlogopite. It comes in 20, 60, 120, and 150 mesh. Mica in paints helps to bond the film and prevent cracking, acting similarly to aluminum leaf.   Mica powder for plastic filler and paints is produced directly from mica schists by froth flotation.   The powder recovered averages more than 50% of sizes smaller than 200 mesh and 20% between 150 and 200 mesh.   The recovered mica equals in every way the powder made by grinding mica scrap.   **Sericite mica,** or **damourite,** from North Carolina kaolin workings, and in pockets in the fireclay deposits of Adelaide Co., Australia, is a type of potash mica related to muscovite but softer. It occurs as a finely divided powder with a talclike feel.   Mixed with aluminum powder it produces a finish paint superior to aluminum alone. It has some activating properties, and is a substitute for zinc oxide in rubber.   It is also used as a filler in plastics, and replaces graphite as a foundry core and mold wash.   The recovery from North Carolina clay is 10% of the gross weight of the clay.   **Water-ground mica** is ground to a fineness of 90% through a 325-mesh screen 9% on a 325-mesh.   It is for paint and rubber use.   The mica powder **Micalith G,** of the General Mining Assoc., is sericite mica from Pennsylvania washings with 0.5% graphite embedded in the mica crystals.   The graphite improves the wetting and dispersion in paints.   **Micronized mica** is a powder of a fineness of 400 to 1,000 mesh, used as a filler.   **Mica flake,** used in the manufacture of shingles and roofing, is washed from pegmatite deposits, but the mica flake used for molding into mica ceramic electrical insulators is ground phlogopite scrap, or from various compositions of synthetic mica.

MILK.   The secretion of the mammary glands of mammal animals.   Commercial milk in the United States is almost entirely from the cow.   Besides its use as a food for direct consumption and in bakery products, it is employed for making cheese, butter, casein, ice cream, lactic acid, and lactose chemicals.   The production of cow's milk in the United States from registered dairy animals averages about 6,100 lb per cow, but the output from cows under the Dairy Herd Improvement Assoc. is 8,000 lb per year per animal.   The composition of milk is 87.34% water, 3.75 butterfat, 3 caseinogen, 0.4 lactalbumin, and 0.75 mineral salts.   It also contains vitamins A, B, and C.   The vitamin A content is low during the winter months when the animals do not feed on green grasses.   The ultraviolet rays of sunlight may destroy the fat-digesting enzyme and the vitamins B and C in milk unless milk is protected in opaque bottles or in cartons.

Much of the American production of milk is used in foodstuffs manufacture in the form of **dried milk,** or **milk powder,** which is made largely from **skim milk,** that is, milk from which the fatty **cream** has been separated.   One gallon of milk yields 1.2 lb of dried milk.   **Powdered milk** produced by spray drying in an air stream has 90% of its particles larger than 75 microns and will disperse more easily than a powder of fine particles.   Milk powders processed above 180°F may have a cooked taste, but powders with no off taste are produced by evaporation at 95°F and a quick dry at 160°F.   **Milk proteins** may be separated from milk and used for enriching foodstuffs.   **Crest 6S,** of the Crest Foods Co., is a milk protein powder containing 60% soluble protein and 26% lactose, with calcium and phosphorus.   It also improves the whiteness and water-holding ability of milk powders.   **Condensed milk,** formerly used widely where refrigeration was not available, is now used in confectionery to replace cream.   It is very sweet, and contains 8.5% milk fats, 19.5 milk protein solids, 42 sugar, and 30 water.

While milk has many useful applications in cookery and commercial baking, it is essentially a natural baby food to build up the original low-calcium soft bones and to provide calcium for bones and teeth.   Too much milk in the diet of adults may give an excess of calcium in the arteries and also cause cirrhosis or fatty growth of the liver.   It may also cause an excess of lactic acid.   The **Savortex** milk powder of the Western Dairy Products, Inc., for use in sausage and other comminuted meat products, has sodium substituted for a part of the calcium by ion-exchange methods.   It is less greasy, and gives a smoother texture to the meats.

Pasteurized milk is milk that has been heated to kill disease organisms. Sterilization at 285°F for a few seconds leaves better flavor and color than heating at low temperature for long periods.   **Homogenized milk** is milk that has been treated by sonic vibration to break up the fat globules and distribute them evenly in the liquid.   In natural milk the fat and proteins are in colloidal solution.   Under the U.S. Food and Drugs Act milk must contain not less than 3% milk fat and 8.5 solids not fat.   In most countries the handling of milk is regulated by laws, as it is easily contaminated.

Cow's milk for direct consumption and for industrial use is produced on a large scale in the United States, Canada, Europe, Argentina, New Zealand, and Australia.   **Kumyss** is sweetened cow's milk fermented with yeast, used as a nutrient.   **Soy milk** is a water solution of soybean solubles combined with sugar, calcium phosphate, irradiated sesame oil, and vitamins.   It has the approximate composition of cow's milk and is chemically almost indistinguishable from it.   It is used in foodstuffs, but is not permitted to be marketed under the name of milk.   **Sesa-Lac,** of John Kraft Sesame Corp., is a **milk substitute** used by food processors in bakery products, creamed desserts, and beverages.   It is made by crushing hulled sesame seed, homogenizing, and spray drying into a cream-colored powder.   It has good nutritional value and has a pleasant sweet flavor. Another **imitation milk** is made from sodium caseinate, coconut oil, or other vegetable oils.

Lactic acid derives its name from the fact that it was originally obtained from milk. It has a wide industrial use and is now produced synthetically from sulfite pulp liquor, or by fermentation of carbohydrates. **Lactic acid** is a liquid of the composition $CH_3CHOHCOOH$, but a carbon may attach to four different groups, and the acid can thus exist in four forms. The dextrorotary isomer which occurs in milk is optically active. This form, called **sarcolactic acid,** is also produced naturally in the human muscles and joints by exercise to give the normal feeling of tiredness and induce sleep, but large amounts of lactic acid taken into the body are injurious. The dextrorotary acid made by the fermentation of sucrose is used in beverages and foodstuffs to minimize undesirable odors, and in animal feeds to improve the efficiency of protein utilization. **Polylactic resins,** made by the heat reaction of lactic acid with castor oil or other fatty oil, are soft, elastic resins used to produce tough, water-resistant coatings. Many useful chemicals are made from lactic acid. **Lactonitrile,** $HO(CH_3)CHCN$, is a colorless liquid of specific gravity 0.9834, which has the reactions of an alcohol and those of a nitrile.

MILLET. The very small seeds of a number of grasses. It is one of the most ancient of food grains, and is an important grain in Asia, being used as a food by a third of the population of the world. Nearly 40 million acres are cultivated to this grain in India alone. The plant is drought-resistant, but will not withstand frost. The seeds are high in phosphate, protein, minerals, and oil. In the United States millet seed is used as a birdseed, and the plant is grown for pasturage and silage. **German millet,** also known as **foxtail millet** and as **Hungarian grass,** is from the grass *Setaria italica.* The seed contains phosphates and many minerals and vitamins A and E. It is an important food in Europe and Asia, but in North America is a forage crop. **White millet,** or **proso millet,** from the grass *Panicum miliaceum* is one of the richest grains in food value, but is employed in the United States only as a birdseed. It is much used in Russia as a food. The millet from the plant *Sorghum vulgare* is a staple food in India. **Sanwa millet,** from the *Echinochloa frumentacea,* is an important food in Japan. The plant will produce as many as eight forage crops per year.

MILLSTONE. Any stone employed for grinding paint, cement, grain, or minerals. Millstones are made from sandstone, basalt, granite, or quartz conglomerate. **Burrstone** is a millstone made from chalcedony silica of cellular texture, usually yellowish in color. The stone is also used as a building stone. **Esopus stone** is a conglomerate of this type from Ulster County, New York. The most noted burrstones for grinding grains are the European stones cut in wedge-shaped blocks 6 in. long, $3\frac{1}{2}$ to 4 in.

wide, and 2 to 2½ in. thick bound together with iron hoops. The French stones are chalcedony quartz, creamy white, with a cellular structure, the cavities formerly occupied by fossil shells. German burrstones are basaltic lava. Millstones vary greatly in sharpness of grain and size of grain, and thus synthetic stones of even texture are often preferred. **Chaser stones** are very large stones run on edge in mills for grinding minerals.

Pulpstones are blocks of sandstone cut into wheels and used for grinding, chiefly for the grinding of wood pulp in paper manufacture. The American pulpstones are produced in Ohio and West Virginia. The sandstones for pulpstones must be uniform in texture, have sharp grains, have medium hardness, and be composed of even quartz grains of which 85% will be retained on a 150-mesh screen, and 90% on a 200-mesh screen. The cementing material may be siliceous, calcareous, or argillaceous, but must be firm enough to hold the stone together when working under pressure, and soft enough to wear faster than the quartz grains and prevent glazing. The standard diameter of pulpstones is 54 in. and width of face 27 in. The stones are aged or seasoned from 1 to 2 years before use. Aging is quickened by heating the stones to about 180°F in a closed room and cooling slowly. Large pulpstones for paper mills are now made of silicon carbide or aluminum oxide in fitted sections.

MINERAL WOOL. A fibrous material employed as a heat insulator in walls or as a sound insulator. It was first obtained as a natural product from volcanic craters in Hawaii and was known as **Pele's hair.** It is made by mixing stone with molten slag from blast furnaces and blowing steam through it. Slags from copper and lead furnaces are also used. **Slag wool** is made from slag without the rock. A lead slag containing 30 to 50% calcium and magnesium oxides makes a mineral wool that will withstand temperatures to 1500°F when made into blocks or boards. Mineral wool usually consists of a mass of fine, pliant, vitreous fibers, which are incombustible and a nonconductor of heat. **Rock wool** is made by blowing molten rock in the same manner, and is more uniform than common mineral wool, with physical qualities depending, however, on the class of rock used. The rock wool marketed by Johns-Manville under the name of **Banrock** is made from high-silica limestone and is used for insulating oven walls for temperatures up to 1000°F. **Zerofil** is a nonsweating, low-temperature insulating material of the same company consisting of rock wool coated with asphalt. The rock wool of the Philip Carey Co., known as **Rocktex,** has a heat conductivity of 0.22 Btu per hr per sq ft per deg F difference in temperature. **Rock cork** is a name for a low-temperature insulating material made of rock wool molded in sheet form with a waterproof binder, used for walls in cold-storage rooms. **Mineral-wool board,** of the Armstrong Cork Co., is a moisture-resistant board in thicknesses of 1, 1½, 2, 3, and 4 in. for cold-storage insulation. The thermal conductivity is 0.31 to 0.33 at 90°F. **Mono-Block,** of the Baldwin-Hill Co., is rock wool made into standard blocks and slabs by a felting process. It is used for both cold and heat insulation to temperatures up to 1600°F. The weight is 18 lb per cu ft. The heat conductivity at 200°F is 0.325 Btu.

Granulated mineral wool is the fiber milled into pellets of about ½ in. diameter. The pellets can be poured into a space for insulation, giving a density of 4 to 6 lb per cu ft, or they may be pressed into insulating blocks. **Supertemp block,** of the Eagle Picher Lead Co., is such a block compressed with a mineral binder and having tiny dead-air pockets. The thermal conductivity is 0.50 Btu, and the service temperature is 1700°F. The block insulation of the Harbison-Walker Refractories Co., for backing up firebrick, is mineral wool compressed with a mineral binder to a density of 21 lb per cu ft. The service temperature is 1900°F. **Rock-wool quilt** consists of felted fibers stitched between layers of kraft paper for wall insulation.

Selected mineral, to give various characteristics, may be used to make rock wools. **Wollastonite,** found in California and New York, is melted to produce a rock wool. It is also ground to a white acicular powder of 30 to 350 mesh for use as a filler in molded plastics. The grains are minute fibers. **Fibrous silica,** used for high-temperature insulation in jet aircraft, is produced from silica minerals in the same manner as rock wool and then extracting the nonsilica content of the fiber. **Refrasil,** of the H. I. Thompson Co., is this material. The fibers have a diameter of 0.00023 in., fuse at 3100°F, and will withstand continuous temperatures to 2000°F. It is produced as fibers, batts, cloth, and cordage. **Silica fiber** in diameters as small as 0.00003 in. comes in random matted form or in rovings. **Irish Refrasil** is 98% silica and has a green color. It is used for ablative protective coatings. It resists temperatures to 2800°F. **Ceramic fiber** differs from mineral wool in that it is made of special composition. **Aluminum-silicate fiber** is made by melting alumina and silica and passing the molten material through a stream of high-pressure air which produces a fluffy mass of extremely fine fibers up to 3 in. long. The melting point of the fiber is about 3000°F, but the maximum usable temperature is about 2300°F as the fibers devitrify at higher temperatures. The fibers are used for thin insulating paper, panel board, filler for plastics, chemical-resistant rope, or woven into fabrics. Aluminum-silicate fabrics of 15 to 75 oz per yd are used for filters, gaskets, belting, insulation, and protective clothing. **Fiberfrax,** of the Carborundum Co., is an aluminum-silicate fiber. **Dyna-Flex,** of Johns-Manville, is a **ceramic felt** made from aluminum silicate chromia fibers.   It will withstand continuous temperatures to 2700°F.

MOHAIR. The long, lustrous fleece of the **Angora goat,** *Capra angorensis,* important as a textile fiber because of its luster, length, strength, and spinning qualities.   **Mohair fabrics** are used for upholstery material for hard service, and valued for summer wearing apparel, linings, and plushes.   Army **necktie cloth,** notable for durability and noncreasing, has a cotton warp and a mohair filling.   Mohair commonly contains shorter fibers, coarse and difficult to dye.   These are known as **kemp** and sometimes comprise 18% of the fiber.   They are removed by combing. Mohair has a natural curl but no crimp, and does not felt as wool does. The **mohair fiber** used for fine paint brushes is usually from the kid and is of white color with a silklike luster and a slippery feel, and the scales are not sharply defined as in wool.   The staple length is 5 to 8 in., but the Turkish fiber is up to 10 in. long.   American production is mostly in Texas.   The average weight of the clip is 5.3 lb per animal.   South Africa produces much mohair.

MOLD STEEL. A term that generally refers to the steels used for making molds for plastics.   Mold steel should have a uniform texture that will machine readily with die-sinking tools.   It must have no microscopic porosity, and must be capable of polishing to a mirrorlike surface.   When annealed, it should be soft enough to take the deep imprint of a hob, and when hardened it must be able to withstand high pressure without sinking and have sufficient tensile strength to prevent breakage of the small mold sections.   It should not warp under ordinary heat-treating processes.   For most plastic molding a case-hardening, low-carbon, low-alloy steel is used, but it must be of tool-steel quality and not of structural-steel grade.   For hot sinking a typical analysis is 0.10% carbon, 0.50 manganese, 0.60 chromium, and 1.25 nickel.   Such a steel has an annealed hardness of 120 Brinell, but will give a hardened case of Rockwell C62 and core of C21, with a tensile strength up to 120,000 psi.   For molds that are machined and not hobbed a higher carbon content is used which increases the strength of the steel.

For severe pressures or resistance to abrasion high-carbon manganese steels with 1.60% manganese may be used, and for high hydraulic pressures alloy steels may be employed.   When electrolytic methods of die sinking are used, the machining ability of the steel is not important, and it can be selected for its use characteristics.   The **Cascade die steel,** of the Latrobe Steel Co., has 4.1% nickel, 1.2 aluminum, 0.20 vanadium, 0.25 chromium, 0.30 manganese, 0.30 silicon, and 0.20 carbon.   Precipitation hardening gives this steel uniform hardness, and it polishes to a fine finish.

A carburizing steel for plastic molds is **SAE steel 3312,** containing 3.5% nickel and 1.2 chromium. **Carpenter 158 steel** has 3.5% nickel, 1.5 chromium, 0.40 manganese, and 0.10 carbon. It gives a surface hardness of Rockwell C62 with a core strength of 165,000 psi. **Samson Extra,** of this company, is a deep-hobbing steel of good machinability and high core strength. It contains 0.10% carbon, 0.30 manganese, 0.20 silicon, and 2.30 chromium. When water-quenched to a hardness of Rockwell C65, it has a tensile strength of 120,000 psi. **Hoballoy,** of the Crucible Steel Co., is a steel of this type with 0.10% carbon. **Plastalloy,** of Henry Disston & Sons, Inc., is a low-carbon, low-alloy, fine-grained steel for molds to be hobbed. **Speed-Cut steel,** of the Vanadium Alloys Steel Co., used for die-casting molds, will air-harden slightly. It contains 1.12% chromium, 0.85 manganese, 0.50 molybdenum, 0.30 silicon, 0.40 carbon, and is free of sulfur and phosphorus. When machined at the heat-treated condition up to 325 Brinell, it requires no further heat treatment, but can be annealed to 170 Brinell for hobbing.

MOLYBDENUM. A silvery-white metal, symbol Mo, occurring chiefly in the mineral molybdenite but also obtained as a by-product from copper ores. About 90% of all molybdenum is produced in the United States, the remainder coming from Chile, Mexico, Peru, and Norway. The metal has a specific gravity of 10.2 and a melting point of 4750°F. It is ductile, softer than tungsten, and is readily worked or drawn into very fine wire. It cannot be hardened by heat treatment, but only by working. The rolled metal has a tensile strength up to 260,000 psi with Brinell hardness 160 to 185. Above a temperature of 1400°F the metal forms an oxide that evaporates as it is formed, but the resistance to corrosion is high, and molybdenum heating elements can be used to 3000°F. The electrical conductivity is 34% that of copper. The thermal expansion is low, and the heat conductivity is twice that of iron. While unalloyed molybdenum in the soft state has a tensile strength of 97,000 psi with elongation of 42%, small amounts of other elements will harden and strengthen it greatly. **Molybdenum-titanium alloy,** with only 0.5% titanium, has a tensile strength of 132,000 psi, and at 1600°F retains a strength of 88,000 psi. This alloy and one modified with an addition of 0.8 zirconium are used for tubing which will retain its shape to near its melting point.

Molybdenum, 99.95% pure, is used for support members in radio and light bulbs, heating elements for electric furnaces, arc-resistant electrical contacts, and high-temperature structural parts for jet engines and missiles. Sheet is available as thin as 0.001 in., and wire as fine as 0.004 in. **Molybdenum ribbon** which retains its flexibility after high temperatures is produced by National Research Corp. As thin as 0.0016 in., it can be bent or twisted into small knots.   **Molybdenum foil,** of the Sylvania Electric Products, Inc., comes in a thickness of 0.001 in. in coiled strips to 150 in length.   **Molybdenum sheet,** of the General Electric Co., in thicknesses to 0.375 in., can be deep-drawn and can be bent double without cracking.   Molybdenum is used as a flame-resistant and corrosion-resistant coating for other metals, and may be arc-deposited.   **Spraybond,** of the Metallizing Engineering Co., is molybdenum wire for this purpose.   But protective coatings of molybdenum can be deposited by vapor deposition of **molybdenum pentachloride** reduced with hydrogen chloride.   The pentachloride melts at 194°C and boils at 268°C, but a temperature of 850°C is used for deposition.

Molybdenum carbonyl, $MoCO_6$, may also be used for this purpose.   Various molybdenum compounds are used for pigments, catalysts, and in chemical manufacture.   **Sodium molybdate** in the anhydrous form, Na_2MoO_4, is used as a dry powder in fertilizers, and the sulfides and selenides of molybdenum are used in lubricants.

Most of the molybdenum used is employed in alloys or in alloy steels. For the latter purpose it is used in the form of **ferromolybdenum,** which is made directly from the ore by reduction with carbon, lime, and silicon, and adding iron.   A standard grade of ferromolybdenum contains 50 to 60% molybdenum with up to 2.5% carbon, and is marketed on the basis of the contained molybdenum.   **Calcium molybdate,** $CaMoO_4$, is also used for adding molybdenum to steels.   It contains about 60.7% MoO_3, with the balance lime.   The specific gravity is 4.35.   **Molyte,** of the Molybdenum Corp., is calcium molybdate with a flux.   It is heavier and will sink in the molten steel.   Also, briquettes of **molybdic oxide,** containing 70 to 75% molybdenum trioxide and 12% carbon, are used for alloying steel.   **Molybdenum-chromium,** produced by the Shieldalloy Corp., for making nonferrous alloys, contains 68 to 72% molybdenum, 28 to 32 chromium, with 0.50 max iron.   **Climelt,** of the Climax Molybdenum Co., is a **molybdenum-tungsten alloy** for making high-temperature structural parts.   It has a melting point at 5100°F.   It contains 70% molybdenum and 30 tungsten.   The tensile strength is 121,000 psi with elongation of 26%, and it retains a strength of 65,000 psi at 1800°F.

MOLYBDENUM CAST IRON. Cast iron containing small amounts of molybdenum added to the iron as ferromolybdenum or as calcium molybdate.   Molybdenum in iron is not a carbide former or a graphitizer.   It goes into direct solid solution and refines the matrix, increasing the strength, toughness, and wear resistance.   Usually the manganese is increased when molybdenum is added, and the irons are more uniform in structure than plain cast iron.   A plain molybdenum cast iron with 0.65% molybdenum has a tensile strength of 44,000 psi and Brinell hardness 223, which can be raised by heat treatment to above 60,000 psi with a hardness above 300 Brinell.   Greater hardness can be obtained in the iron with the addition of small amounts of chromium.   A chrome-molybdenum cast iron with 0.50% chromium, 0.50 molybdenum, and 1.25 manganese added to the cupola, resulting in an iron of 3.1% total carbon, 0.30 molybdenum, 0.33 chromium, and 0.75 manganese, has a tensile strength of 48,000 psi, Brinell hardness 240, and an increase of about 40% in transverse strength over the plain iron.   Raising the amount of molybdenum increases the hardness, but the machinability is kept by the addition of nickel or copper.   **Nickel-molybdenum cast irons** have hardnesses as high as 300 Brinell without massive carbides that interfere with machining. An iron with 0.80% each of molybdenum and nickel, without chromium, has a tensile strength of 50,000 psi and a hardness of 270 Brinell.   It has great uniformity, and can be cast in combined thin and heavy sections.

MOLYBDENUM ORES.   Molybdenite is the chief ore of the metal molybdenum.   It is a molybdenum disulfide, MoS_2, containing 60% molybdenum, occurring in granite, gneiss, and granular limestone.   **Molybdenite** resembles graphite in appearance, with a lead-gray color, metallic luster, and greasy feel.   The hardness is 1, and specific gravity 4.75.   It is infusible.   The American production of molybdenite is from Colorado, New Mexico, and Nevada, but about half of the molybdenum is a by-product of copper mining.   **Wulfenite,** another important ore, is a **lead molybdate,** $PbMoO_4$, and occurs in lead veins with other ores of lead. It is found in Utah, Nevada, Arizona, and New Mexico.   Wulfenite occurs in crystals and also massive granular.   The specific gravity is 6.7 and hardness 3.   Its color is yellow, orange, gray, red, or white.   **Molybdite,** another ore, is a hydrous ferric molybdate of the composition $Fe_2O_3 \cdot 3MoO_3 \cdot 7H_2O$.   It occurs either crystalline massive or as an earthy powder.   It is yellowish, with a specific gravity of 4.5 and a hardness of about 1.5.   Molybdenum ores are converted into ferromolybdenum or into calcium molybdate for use in adding molybdenum to steel.   **Molybdenum trioxide,** MoO_3, the most important molybdenum compound for chemical manufacture, is made by heating molybdenite in air.   It is a white crystalline powder which melts at 795°C.   It is an electrical insulator, but becomes a conductor when molten.

MOLYBDENUM STEEL.   Next to carbon, molybdenum is the most effective hardening element for steel.   It also has the property like tungsten of giving steel the quality of red-hardness, requiring a smaller amount for the same effect.   It is also used in hot-work steels, and to replace part of the tungsten in high-speed steels.   It is added to heat-resistant irons and steels to make them resistant to deformation at high temperatures and to creep at moderate temperatures.   It increases the corrosion resistance of stainless steels at high temperatures.   Molybdenum in small amounts also increases the elastic limit of steel, reduces the grain size, strengthens the crystalline structure, and gives deep-hardening.   It goes into solid solution, but when other elements are present it may form carbides and harden the steel, giving greater wear resistance.   It also widens the heat-treating range in tool steels.   As it decreases the temper brittleness of aluminum steels, small amounts are added to nitriding steels.

Plain **carbon-molybdenum steels** are easier to machine than other steels of equal hardness.   **Molybdenum structural steels** usually have from 0.20 to 0.75% molybdenum.   **SAE steels 4130** and **4140** contain about 1% chromium and 0.20 molybdenum, and are high-strength forging steels for such uses as connecting rods.   **Allenoy,** used by the Allen Mfg. Co. for hollow-head screws, is **SAE 4150 steel.**   SAE steels 4615 to 4650 have no chromium but contain about 1.75% nickel and 0.25 molybdenum. **SAE 4615** is used for molds and dies to be hobbed.   It is easily worked. The alloying elements increase the rate of carbon pickup in carburizing, and the steel has a core hardness of 280 Brinell after hardening.   **SAE 4650 nickel-molybdenum steel** is used for forming dies and, when hardened and drawn to a hardness of 435 Brinell, has a tensile strength of 215,000 psi.   **Hyten M steel,** of Wheelock, Lovejoy & Co., and **Durodi steel,** of A. Finkl & Sons, are high-strength nickel-chromium-molybdenum steels.   Up to 3% molybdenum is used in stainless steels for cast parts for hot-oil and chemical equipment.   **Lebanon 22-XM steel** has 19.5% chromium, 9 nickel, and 3 molybdenum.   **Welmet,** of the Welland Electric Steel Foundry, is a similar steel.

The old **Damascus steel** and **Toledo steel** were molybdenum steels, the molybdenum being in the original ore.   **Damascene steel** is a name referring to the wavy marks made on blades by forging and was not necessarily a molybdenum steel.   But the original **Wootz steel,** or **Indian steel,** of this type, contained small percentages of aluminum incorporated in some unknown manner.   Wootz steel was made in the crucible, although the crucible method was not used in Europe until 1740.

MONEL METAL. A natural alloy produced directly from Canadian bessemer matte obtained by reduction of the nickel ore, but now usually made by alloying.   It was first introduced as a natural alloy in 1905 by the International Nickel Co.   The average composition is nickel, 67%; copper, 28; iron, manganese, silicon, and other elements, 5.   The alloy may be cast, rolled, or forged, and can be annealed after cold working.   It is resistant to corrosion and to the action of many acids, and will retain its bright nickel-white surface under ordinary conditions.   The melting point is about 2460°F and weight 0.318 lb per cu in.   The tensile strength is

65,000 psi with elongation up to 50%, depending on the treatment.   Cast metal may have tensile strengths to 100,000 psi.   The alloys are used for chemical and marine parts where corrosion resistance and white color are important.   The synthetic alloys are widely known by letter symbols, but International Nickel Co. now uses numbers for regular grades.   **Monel alloy 400,** the cold-roll-hardening alloy, is similar to K monel.   **Mond metal** was an early monel with 4% manganese.

S Monel is an alloy of monel metal with 3.75% silicon.   It is used for valves and for castings subject to wear and corrosion.   It has a hardness of 275 to 390 Brinell when heat-treated.   **K Monel** is a modification of monel metal that will age-harden.   The nominal composition is 66% nickel, 29 copper, 2.75 aluminum, 0.9 iron, 0.50 silicon, 0.75 manganese, 0.50 titanium, and 0.15 carbon.   The soft alloy, with a hardness of 145 Brinell, will have a hardness above 300 Brinell when heat-treated, and a tensile strength up to 160,000 psi.   It will retain its hardness up to 700°F and is suitable for high-pressure steam valves.   **R Monel** contains 67% nickel, 30 copper, and 0.35 sulfur.   The cold-drawn rods have a tensile strength of 90,000 psi, elongation 25%, and Brinell hardness 180.   **H Monel** is a sand-casting alloy containing 63% nickel, 31 copper, 3 silicon, 2 iron, and 0.75 manganese.   The tensile strength is 100,000 psi, elongation 15%, and Brinell hardness 210.   **Z Monel** contains 98% nickel, and is really a high-strength nickel.   **Ebonized nickel** is monel metal in commercial forms with a lustrous ebony finish obtained by an oxidizing process.

MORDANT. A substance used in dyeing for fixing the color.   A mordant must have an affinity for the material being dyed and be chemically reactive, that is, the molecule must have free electrons that combine with the dyestuff.   The vegetable fibers, such as cotton and linen, frequently require mordants.   Basic aniline dyes require a mordant for cotton or rayon, and the water-soluble acid dyes need a mordant for vegetable fibers.   The mordant may be applied first, usually in a hot solution, or simultaneously with the dye.   **Mordant dyes** are dyes chemically able to accept and hold a metal atom, the metal being added in the mordant.   The metal atom is held to the oxygen atoms and to one of the nitrogen atoms in each chromophoric group of the dye.

Besides fixing the color, mordants sometimes also increase the brilliancy of the dye, particularly when chelation occurs.   Common mordants are alum and sodium bichromate, but salts of aluminum and other metals are used.   **Sodium stannate,** used both as a mordant and for fireproofing textiles, is a gray-white water-soluble powder of the composition $Na_2SnO_3 \cdot 3H_2O$ made by treating tin oxide with caustic soda.   **Chromium acetate,** used as a mordant for chrome colors, and to produce khaki shades with iron solutions, is a grayish-green powder of the composition $Cr(C_2H_3O_2)_2 \cdot$

H_2O.   It is soluble in water.   In gilding, the term mordant is used to mean a viscous or sticky substance employed to make the gold leaf adhere, but such a material does not have the chemical action of a mordant.

MOTHER OF PEARL.   The hard, brilliant-colored internal layer of the **pearl oyster shell** and of certain other marine shellfish.   It is employed for knife handles, buttons, inlay work, and other articles.   Large oysters of the Indian Ocean, especially off Ceylon and in the Persian Gulf, furnish much of the mother of pearl.   Other producers are Australia and the lands bordering the Coral Sea.   The large Hawaiian pearl oyster is *Pinctada galtsoff*.   The iridescent appearance is due to the structure of the nacre coating, and the shells are also called **nacre.**   Mother of pearl is brittle but can be worked with steel saws and drills using a weak acid lubricant. The shells are thick and heavy, and disks cut from them are split for buttons.   A beautiful pink nacre occurs on the inner surface of the **conch shell,** *Strombus gigas,* a sea snail which grows in great abundance off the Caicos Islands near Haiti.   There are about 56 species, and they grow up to 12 in. long and 8 in wide.   The shells were formerly much used for making cameos.   **Mussel shell,** from fresh-water mussels of the Mississippi River, are also called **pearl shell,** but they do not have the iridescence of mother of pearl.   There is a large production in Iowa, used for buttons. The waste shell from the manufacture is crushed and marketed for poultry feed.   **Pearl essence,** used for making **imitation pearls** and in plastics and lacquers, is a motley-silver compound extracted from the scales of fish, notably the sardine, herring, and alewife.   Only a few types of fish have iridescent scales.   The chief constituent is guanine, a chemical related to caffeine.   One ton of scale is produced from 100 tons of Pacific herring, and this yields 1 lb of essence.   **Nacromer,** of the Mearl Corp., is pearl essence.   It gives high luminosity and iridescence to lacquers.   **Synthetic pearl essence** may be ground nacreous shells in a liquid vehicle, or it may be produced chemically.   Compounds of basic lead carbonate and lead monohydrogen phosphate have multiple reflectivity and give an optical effect resembling that of mother of pearl.   **H-scale,** of the Celanese Corp., and **Ko-Pearl,** of the Ultra Ray Pearl Essence Corp., are synthetic pearl essences.

MUCILAGE.   A sticky paste obtained from linseed and other seeds by precipitation from a hot infusion, and used as a light adhesive for paper and as a thickening agent.   It contains arabinose, glucose, and galactose, and is easily soluble in water.   Mucilage as a general name also includes **water-soluble gums** from various parts of many plants and has the same uses.   It is the stored reserve food of plants.   There are two types: the cell-content mucilage which acts as a disorganization product of some of the carbohydrates, and membrane mucilage which acts as a thickening agent to the cell wall.   Membrane mucilage occurs in the acacias, algae (seaweeds), linum (flax plants), ulmus (elms), and astragalus.   When it is collected in the form of exudations from the trees, it is called a gum. **Cherry gum,** from the *Prunus cerasus,* is this type of water-soluble gum, as is also **medlar gum,** from a small tree *Mespilus germanica,* of the same family as the cherry, grown in Europe and the Near East.

MULLITE. A mineral found originally in the Isle of Mull and employed as a refractory material for firebrick and furnace linings.   The natural material occurs as fused argillaceous sediment inclusions in the mineral **buchite,** but it is rare and is produced artificially.   It can be made by decomposing sillimanite or kyanite.   **Artificial mullite,** or **synthetic mullite,** made by a prolonged fusing in the electric furnace of a mixture of silica sand or diasphoric clay and bauxite, has the composition $3Al_2O_3 \cdot 2SiO_2$. It is valued as a refractory because it does not soften below its high melting point, 3290°F, and its interlocked grain will withstand continuous temperature changes without spalling.   The bricks are resistant to flame and to molten ash, have a low, uniform coefficient of thermal expansion, and a heat conductivity only slightly above that of fireclays.   Normally, mullite has very fine crystals which change form and become enlarged after prolonged heating, making the product porous and permeable.   For stable high-temperature refractories the mullite is prefused to produce larger crystals.   At very high temperatures mullite tends to decompose to form corundum and alkali-silicate minerals of lower heat resistance.   Mullite is also made by burning silica clay and alumina at a very high temperature, and is used for making spark plugs, chemical crucibles, and extruding dies.   For spark-plug cores it is fired at a temperature of 1450°C and aged before use.   The tensile strength is above 9,000 psi, or double that of porcelain, and it has high dielectric strength.   The hardness is 6 to 7 Mohs.

Sillimanite, as well as **andalusite** found in California, has the composition $Al_2O_3 \cdot SiO_2$, with the same melting point and a specific gravity of 3.20. **Diaspore andalusite** from Mono County, Calif., is used for spark plugs. **Andalusite crystals** of fine brilliance and of brick-red to yellow-green colors, found in Brazil, are used as gemstones.   Sillimanite is decomposed to mullite and silica when heated above 1550°C.   **Dumortierite,** produced in Nevada, has the composition $8Al_2O_3 \cdot B_2O_3 \cdot 6SiO_2 \cdot H_2O$.   Deep-blue crystals of this mineral from the Colorado River resemble lapis lazuli and are cut as gemstones.   A high-grade electric porcelain material marketed by Champion Sillimanite, Inc., under the name of **Champion sillimanite,** is a mixture of andalusite and dumortierite.   **Shamra** is the trade name of a mullite refractory produced by the Mullite Refractories Co.   **Mullfrax** is a mullite refractory of the Carborundum Co.   **Tervex,** of Du Pont, is **foamed mullite** with a uniformly latticed honeycomb structure for light-weight, heat-resistant structural parts.

MUNTZ METAL. A yellow brass containing 60% copper and 40 zinc, invented in 1832 by George F. Muntz.   In England it is called **yellow metal.**   It is also known as **malleable brass,** and is now a standard product of the brass mills.   Muntz metal has a tensile strength, when annealed, of 52,000 psi, elongation 50%, and Rockwell B hardness 30.   When hard-rolled, the strength is 85,000 psi.   The weight is 0.3015 lb per cu in.   It is used for sheathing, marine fittings, bolts, and parts exposed to corrosion. Wrought muntz metal is frequently modified with small amounts of tin to give greater hardness and corrosion resistance, and is then called **naval brass** or **naval bronze.**   The usual composition is 60% copper, 39.25 zinc, and 0.75 tin.   The **Roman bronze** of Revere Copper & Brass, Inc., has this composition, and the naval brass of the same company has 60% copper, 39 zinc, 0.75 tin, with 0.2 lead to make it easy-machining.   Roman bronze has a tensile strength, annealed, of 60,000 psi, and elongation 45%.   When hard-drawn, the strength is 82,000 psi, and elongation 20%.   The leaded naval brass is slightly lower in strength.

Federal specifications for **naval brass rod** call for 0.5 to 1.5% tin and 0.20 lead.   **Chamet bronze,** of the Chase Brass & Copper Co., has this composition.   The naval brass marketed by the American Brass Co. under the name of **Tobin bronze** contains 59 to 60% copper, 0.5 to 1 tin, and the balance zinc.   In rod form it has a fine-grained structure.   The tensile strength of the soft rod is 52,000 psi, and of the hard-drawn bar 67,000 psi.   The electrical conductivity is 25% that of copper.   **A forging bronze** used for corrosion-resistant marine parts, fittings, and hardware has 58.5% copper, 39.2 zinc, 1 tin, and 1 iron.   It forges easily, and produces parts with a tensile strength from 60,000 to 75,000 psi.   Bronzes with con-siderable amounts of tin are difficult to hot-work because of tin sweat, and because low-melting impurities such as lead and bismuth segregate in the grain boundaries.

Forging brass is usually muntz metal containing up to 1.75% lead, with frequently some iron.   With the copper content below 56% the brass is brittle; with copper above 63% the wear on dies is high.   **Brass forgings** made in smooth dies are tough and compact and need no polishing, being simply pickled in a nitric acid bath to bring out the color.   Forging brass in England is called **hot-stamping brass.**   The British standard, **BES 218,** calls for 58% copper, 40.5 zinc, and 1.5 lead.   The 60–40 brass modified with lead is called **extruding brass. Relleum brass,** of the Mueller Brass Co., for forgings, has 59% copper, 34 zinc, and 2 lead.

Muntz metal is also modified with small amounts of iron and manganese.

Delta metal, first marketed by Alexander Dick in 1883, was a 60–40 brass modified with iron, manganese, and a small amount of lead. An earlier brass known as **Aich's metal** had 60% copper, 38.2 zinc, and 1.8 iron. Somewhat similar casting brasses were called **Gedge's metal** and **Sterro metal,** and a forging alloy was called **Mach's metal.** Iron above 0.35% forms a separate iron-rich constituent which is stable and gives hardness and high strength to the alloys. The addition of manganese helps to absorb the iron and also hardens the alloy. These alloys were also called **high-strength brass,** and were employed for such uses as hydraulic cylinders and marine forgings, but are now largely replaced by manganese bronze or aluminum bronze. **Durana metal** was a forging brass with 1.5% iron and 1.5 aluminum.

MUSIC WIRE. A high-grade, uniform steel originally intended for strings for musical instruments, but now employed for the manufacture of spiral springs. It is the highest grade of spring wire and is made of acid open-hearth steel or electric steel, free from slag or dirt, and low in sulfur and phosphorus. For springs it is usually **SAE steel 1085** reduced about 80% in 8 or 10 drawing passes, but piano wire may have as many as 40 draws from a No. 7 rod. The tensile strength of spring wire, when hard-drawn, is from 225,000 to 400,000 psi, but it should be tough enough to bend 180° flat upon itself without cracking, or wind into a close helix with inside diameter 1 to $1\frac{1}{2}$ times the diameter of the wire. The wire 0.187 in. in diameter has an ultimate strength of 230,000 psi; 0.015 wire has a strength of 400,000 psi. The wire is usually marketed in gage sizes according to the Washburn & Moen and the music-wire gages. Wire below 0.034 in. in diameter (No. 15 gage) is furnished on reels. Larger sizes are in coils. Wire for springs is from No. 00, which is 0.0085 in. in diameter, to No. 36, which is 0.102 in. The smallest size of music wire, 0.003 in. in diameter, has 38,026 ft per lb. **Piano wire,** intended for piano strings but much used for springs, is a cold-drawn, high-quality wire formerly only drawn from Swedish billets or rods but now made from American steels. Piano wire ranges in diameter from 0.03 to 0.065 in. The tensile strength is from 350,000 to 400,000 psi. **Supertensile steel wire,** of the American Steel & Wire Co., for A strings of guitars, is a high-carbon steel made by long cold working and heat treatment. It has a tensile strength of 460,000 psi, permitting a vibrational load of 37.7 lb on a 0.010-in. wire. **Tire cord wire,** of this company, used for automobile tire plies and extra-thin conveyor belts, has a tensile strength of 350,000 psi. The 0.0059-in. wire is stranded into a $\frac{1}{32}$-in. yarn and coated with rubber to make the ply. **High-tensile wire,** of the National-Standard Co., in diameters of 0.005 in. and finer, used as reinforcement in high-strength plastics, contains 0.90% carbon and has a tensile strength of 575,000 psi. **Stitching wire,** for wire-stitching machines, is not as hard-drawn, and has a tensile strength of about 290,000 psi.

While the modulus of elasticity of music wire is 30 million psi compared with no more than 28 million for highly alloyed steels, the plain carbon steels cannot be used for springs operating at elevated temperatures, and the general-purpose stainless steels, such as Type 302, are limited to operation at about 500°F. **Alloy NS-A286,** of the National-Standard Co., a precipitation-hardening austenitic alloy used for springs for jet engines and gas turbines, contains about 25% nickel, 15 chromium, 2 titanium, 1.5 manganese, 1.25 molybdenum, 0.75 silicon, 0.3 vanadium, 0.08 max carbon, and not over 0.01 boron. The tensile strength of the wire with 30% reduction is 198,000 psi at 1350°F. **Alloy NS-355,** for highly stressed springs in jet engines, has a nominal composition of 15.65% chromium, 4.38 nickel, 2.68 molybdenum, 1 manganese, 0.32 silicon, 0.12 copper, 0.124 nitrogen, and 0.142 carbon. The 0.004-in. wire has a tensile strength of 500,000 psi. The modulus of elasticity is 29.3 million psi at normal temperatures and 24.6 million at 800°F.

MUSTARD. A pungent yellowish powder produced from the seeds of the **black mustard,** *Brassica nigra,* and the **white mustard,** *B. alba,* an annual plant of the turnip family grown in most temperate-climate countries. The ground seeds are treated with water, and the enzyme action yields a complex sulfur compound with a sharp taste and pungent action. It is used as a condiment, and in medicine as a counterirritant and emetic. It is one of the most ancient of the condiments and has a stimulating effect on the salivary glands. The product from the black mustard is more pungent than that from the white, and ground mustard may be a mixture of the two to give the desired pungency. **Mustard oil** is a volatile oil obtained from the seeds. It is a powerful vesicant and has a pungent aromatic odor. Also called **horseradish essence,** it is used in medicine and in flavors. Mustard seed which yields on expression the fixed **mustard-seed oil** used extensively in India as a food oil and in lubricants is *B. juncea.* It is closely related to rape oil, containing about 50% erucic acid. Another variety of *Brassica* of India yields **jamba oil,** which contains 46% erucic acid and is a substitute for rape oil for lubricants. Synthetic mustard oil is **allyl isothiocyanate.** It is a nasal irritant and lacrimator and small quantities are added to solvent glues as a sniffing deterrent.

MYROBALAN EXTRACT. A liquid or solid extract made from the dried, unripe fruit of several species of *Terminalia,* especially *T. chebala* of India and China.   The *Phyllanthus emblica* of India also yields the fruit.   The dried fruit, which resembles a plum, contains 30 to 40% tannin in the pulp.   The fruit is graded and marketed as **myrobalans** chiefly on the basis of color, the lighter the color the higher the grade.   The best grades of fruit are oval, pointed, and solid in structure.   Inferior grades are round and spongy.   The **bimlies** from Madras are rated best.   Liquid myrobalan extract contains 25 to 30% tannin, and solid extract contains about 53%.   It is used in tanning light leathers, and gives a quick tan.   The natural acidity of myrobalan plumps the leather, but when used alone on heavy hides it makes a porous leather.   It is used with other tannins.

NAPHTHA.   A light, colorless to straw-colored liquid which distills off from petroleum between 70 and 90°C.   The specific gravity is from 0.631 to 0.660, or slightly higher, ranging from C_6H_{14} to C_7H_{18}.   The lightest of the distillates used as solvents for fats, rubber, and resins approaches petroleum ether; the heaviest distillates approach benzine and gasoline, and are used for fuel.   **Benzine** is a light distillate ranging from C_8H_{18} to C_9H_{20}, with specific gravity from 0.635 to 0.660, and boiling-point limits from 120 to 150°C.   **Petroleum ether,** or **petroleum spirits,** ranges from C_5H_{12} to C_6H_{14} and is distilled off between 40 and 60°C.   Benzine is used as a solvent, as a cleaner, and in lighters.   **Varnoline** and **white spirit** are old names for petroleum ether used as a general-purpose solvent, especially for varnishes.

The name naphtha is also applied to heavier distillates from petroleum and to various grades of light oils obtained in the distillation of coal tar. They are widely used because of their low volatility and safety in handling. These include **solvent naphtha,** having a specific gravity of 0.862 to 0.872, with a boiling point below 160°C, and **heavy naphtha,** a dark liquid of specific gravity between 0.925 and 0.950, and boiling point between 160 and 220°C.   **High-flash naphtha** for solvent purposes is a petroleum fraction with a specific gravity within the range of the gasolines and a boiling point from 150 to 200°C.   Various trade names are given to the light petroleum distillates used as solvents and in paints and varnishes, such as **Naphtholite.**   **Solvesso,** of Humble Corporation, is a hydrogenated distillate in various grades with specific gravities from 0.797 to 0.937.   **Stoddard solvent** is a standardized fraction of petroleum, or naphtha, used in dry cleaning or as a solvent.   It is water-white in color, has a flash point above 100°F, and consists of the distillation fraction not over 410°F with 50% below 350°F.   **HiSolve VM,** of the Pennsylvania Industrial Chemical Corp., is a petroleum naphtha with an initial distillation point at 100°C, and an end distillation at 135C.   It is used as a thinner in paints, as an ink solvent, and in paint removers.   **HiFlash naphtha,** of the same company, is a coal-tar solvent for rubber, for dry cleaning, and for varnish thinning.   The distillation range is 145 to 185°C, and the specific gravity is 0.860.

NAPHTHALENE. Also called **tar camphor.**   A white solid of the composition $C_{10}H_8$, which is one of the heavy distillates from coal tar, and may also be obtained from natural gas.   Crude naphthalene has a melting point of 70 to 78.5°C.   The pure crystalline flakes melt at 79.4°C and boil at 218°C, but vaporize slowly at room temperature.   Naphthalene burns with a smoky flame, is soluble in benzene and in hot alcohol, but not in water.   Refined naphthalene comes in balls, flakes, and pellets, largely for use as an insect repellent, but most of the material is sold in technical grades for use in making dyestuffs, synthetic resins, coatings, tanning agents, and celluloid.   **Naphthalene crystals** are very transparent to fluorescent radiation, and light produced in thick layers can escape and reach a photo surface.   Low pulses can be obtained from the absorption of beta and gamma rays in naphthalene.   It is thus used in photomultiplier tubes as a gamma-ray detector.

The **Halowax** and **Halowax oil** of the Koppers Co. consist of refined fractionated chloronated naphthalene ranging from low-viscosity oils through waxlike solids to hard resinlike solids.   The melting range is 40 to 180°C.   They are chemically stable, resistant to acids and alkalies, have high dielectric strength, are nonflammable, and are used as solvents, for waterproofing and fireproofing fabrics, and for electric-cable coatings.   **Monoamyl naphthalene,** used to give plasticity to synthetic resins at low temperatures, is an amber liquid, $C_{10}H_7C_5H_{11}$, specific gravity 0.96, and boiling point 279°C.   On hydrogenation, naphthalene yields the solvents tetralin and decalin.   **Tetralin,** $C_{10}H_{12}$, of Du Pont, has a specific gravity of 0.975 and boiling point 206°C.   It is a clear liquid that is a good solvent for fats, oils, and resins.   It will burn with a bright flame and can also be used as a fuel.   The flash point is 78°C.   **Decalin,** $C_{10}H_{18}$, is a liquid with specific gravity of 0.884 and boiling point 190°C.

NEATSFOOT OIL. A pale-yellow, inedible oil obtained by boiling the feet and shin bones of cattle in water, skimming the oil from the surface, and filtering.   It was formerly highly valued for leather dressing and as a lubricating oil.   For high-grade, cold-test lubricating oil for fine instruments the stearin is pressed out.   The oil contains 67% of oleic acid, 17 palmitic, 9 palmitoleic, 3 stearic, 1 myristic, 1 myristoleic, and 2 arachidonic and clupanodonic.   The specific gravity is 0.916, iodine value 70, and saponification value 197.

NICKEL. A silvery-white metal with a yellowish cast first isolated in 1751, but used in alloy with copper since ancient times.   Nickel has a specific gravity of 8.84, melts at 2646°F, and is magnetic up to 680°F.   It is marketed in grains or powder, in electrolytic sheets, blocks, shot, and in malleable forms. The metal is resistant to corrosion and to most acids except nitric. The electrical conductivity is 16% that of copper. The tensile strength of hard-rolled sheet is 115,000 psi, elongation 5%, and Rockwell B hardness 100. The tensile strength when annealed is 70,000 psi, elongation 45%, and hardness 60. Commercially pure wrought nickel contains some cobalt which alters its physical properties. The nominal composition of Canadian nickel is 99.4% nickel including cobalt, 0.2 manganese, 0.1 copper, 0.1 carbon, 0.15 iron, and 0.05 silicon. The most commonly used commercial nickel is 99% pure, and is called **A nickel.** The very pure nickel used for sintered plates in nickel-cadmium batteries is produced by vaporizing nickel carbonyl and depositing the nickel as a powder. High-purity thin nickel strip, 99.9% pure, produced by Metals for Electronics, Inc., is rolled by a continuous process from metal powder. Commercially pure nickel resists the corrosive action of caustic soda and other alkalies even at temperatures of 600°F. It forms a thin coating of black oxide which halts further corrosion. **Nickel 200,** of International Nickel, will corrode no more than 0.0001 in. per year from a 50% concentration of caustic soda.

Nickel is difficult to cast when pure as it absorbs oxygen and also dissolves carbon and sulfur. **Z nickel,** of the International Nickel Co., is a 98% nickel with alloying elements. The tensile strength, hot-rolled, is 105,000 psi, with 15 to 35% elongation. When cold-drawn, the tensile strength is 120,000 to 175,000 psi, elongation 15 to 25%, and Brinell hardness 220 to 340. The electrical conductivity is 12% that of copper. **D nickel** contains 95.2% nickel and 4.5 manganese. In the annealed state it has a tensile strength of 75,000 psi, elongation 40%, and Brinell hardness 140. **Duranickel,** of this company, used for springs, bellows, valve disks, and instrument parts, is an alloy containing 93.7% nickel, 4.4 aluminum, 0.5 silicon, 0.35 iron, 0.30 manganese, 0.17 carbon, and 0.05 copper. The hot-rolled metal has a tensile strength of 105,000 psi with elongation of 40%. When age-hardened, the tensile strength is 177,000 psi with elongation of 16%, Brinell hardness of 375, and electrical resistivity of about 270. For springs it has high fatigue resistance and is not affected by heat to 550°F. A modification of the alloy having higher electrical conductivity is called **Permanickel.** Nickel has its greatest use in alloys, particularly in alloy steels, cupronickel, nickel brasses, and German silver. It is also used to make white gold, 15% nickel changing the color of gold to white. Nickel steels have high strength and resistance. Nickel is also used in coinage alloys and in commercial heat-resistant and corrosion-resistant alloys.

Nearly 80% of the world's nickel production comes from Ontario, Canada, and much of the remainder from the garnierite ores of New Caledonia. The standard ASTM grades of virgin nickel are **Electrolytic,** containing 99.5% nickel; **X shot,** containing 98.9; **A shot,** with 97.75; and **Ingot,** with 98.5. But electrolytic nickel is available 99.95% pure, including not over 0.04 cobalt. **Nickel shot,** for adding nickel to iron in the ladle, is a master alloy of nickel and iron containing 50% nickel. **Sponge nickel** is a porous form of nickel made by leaching with caustic soda an alloy of 50% nickel and 50 aluminum. The friable alloy is ground to 140 mesh before dissolving out the aluminum. **Raney nickel,** of the Raney Catalyst Co., is sponge nickel used as a hydrogenation catalyst. Dry **reduced nickel,** used as a catalyst for the hydrogenation of vegetable oils, is made by precipitating nickel hydroxide or nickel carbonate onto kieselguhr and reducing with hydrogen at high temperature. One lb of nickel is required to hydrogenate about 3,500 lb of oils, and the contaminated spent nickel is not recovered.

The **nickel powders** of Sherritt-Gordon Mines, Ltd., are 99.9% pure, graded in particle sizes from 1 micron to 50 mesh. E grade is used for vacuum tubes and semiconductor devices. **Nickel briquettes** of this company are pillow-shaped, compacted S grade powder for alloying. The nickel used for the **nickel-cadmium battery** is **nickel hydroxide** $NiO(OH)$. With cadmium as the negative plate and potassium hydroxide as the electrolyte it gives 1.35 volts per cell.

NICKEL ALLOYS. Any alloy containing nickel as the base metal, or as the chief alloying element. Nickel goes into solution in copper in all proportions and continually raises the melting point of copper alloys. In brasses and bronzes, nickel is used for the color effect and for toughening and strengthening the alloys. Nickel is employed in both ferrous and nonferrous alloys to produce heat-resistant and acid-resistant metals. Nickel-manganese alloys are used for electric-resistance wire. **Cold-resistant alloys** for use at subzero temperatures where ordinary steel would be brittle may be steels with a high proportion of nickel. **AMF alloy,** for liquid-air valves, was an early French alloy containing about 55% nickel, 3 manganese, 0.4 carbon, and the balance iron. The high-strength structural steels for cold resistance, now called **cryogenic steels,** contain about 9% nickel. **ASTM steel A-353,** for liquid-oxygen tanks at temperatures to −320°F, contains 9% nickel, 0.85 manganese, 0.25 silicon, and 0.13 carbon. It has a tensile strength of 95,000 psi with elongation of 20%.

A corrosion-resistant nickel-base alloy of the Waukesha Foundry Co., for use as a bearing metal against stainless-steel shafts, and called **Waukesha metal,** contains about 80% nickel, 8 tin, 6 zinc, 4 lead, and 2 manganese. The tensile strength is 92,000 psi, with elongation of 9%, and Brinell hardness to 200. A group of **acid-resistant alloys** produced by the Burgess-Parr Co. under the names of **Illium** and **Parr metal** are complex alloys.

Illium G contains 56% nickel, 22.5 chromium, 6.4 molybdenum, 6.5 iron, 6.5 copper, 1.25 manganese, 0.65 silicon, and 0.20 carbon. The density is 0.31 lb, the melting point is about 2400°F, and tensile strength of the cast metal is 68,000 psi with elongation of 7.5% and Brinell hardness 170. **Illium R** contains 64% nickel, 22 chromium, 5 molybdenum, 6 iron, 2.5 copper, 0.3 manganese, 0.15 silicon, and 0.05 carbon. This is a wrought alloy, and the tensile strength, annealed, is 113,000 psi with elongation of 54%. The cold-worked metal with 20% reduction and a hardness of Brinell 280 has a tensile strength of 142,000 psi with elongation of 23%.

A group of alloys marketed by the Union Carbide Corp. under the name of **Hastelloy** in cast and wrought forms have high strength and resistance to chemicals at elevated temperatures. **Hastelloy A** contains 60% nickel, 20 molybdenum, and 20 iron. It has a specific gravity of 8.8, tensile strength, annealed, of about 115,000 psi, and Brinell hardness 97. It casts easily and resists most acids except nitric. **Hastelloy B** has 28% molybdenum, 1 max chromium, 5.5 iron, 1 max manganese, 1 silicon, 0.12 carbon, and the balance nickel. The tensile strength, cast, is 80,000 psi with elongation of 8%. This alloy is resistant to molten chloride salts. **Hastelloy C** is resistant to nitric acid and to free chlorine. The nominal composition is 17% molybdenum, 16.5 chromium, 6 iron, 4 tungsten, 1 each of manganese and silicon, 0.15 max carbon, and the balance nickel. The tensile strength of the wrought metal is 130,000 psi, with elongation of 45%, and that of the castings is 80,000 psi with elongation of 8%. **Hastelloy D** contains about 4% copper, 9 silicon, 1 manganese, 1 max each of chromium and iron, and 0.12 max carbon, with the balance nickel. It is resistant to hot sulfuric acid as it becomes coated with a resistant sulfate film. The tensile strength is 38,000 psi. **Hastelloy X** is a high-temperature alloy to replace cobalt alloys. The nominal composition is 45% nickel, 22 chromium, 9 molybdenum, 0.15 carbon, and the balance iron. It comes in sheets, rods, and wire, and the annealed metal can be formed. At room temperature the tensile strength is 71,000 psi, and at 1200°F it is 52,000 psi with elongation of 16%. It has high oxidation resistance, and has been used for ceramic pressure molds at 2200°F. **Hastelloy R-235** is a wrought alloy with a tensile strength of 167,000 psi and elongation of 43% that retains a strength of 90,000 psi at 1500°F. Its strength is derived from the formation of Ni_3Al and $Ni_3(AlTi)$ compounds. It contains 15.5% chromium, 5.5 molybdenum, 10 iron, 2.5 cobalt, 1 silicon, 1 manganese, 2 aluminum, 2.5 titanium, and 0.16 carbon, with the balance nickel.

An age-hardening strip metal, **Ni-Span C alloy,** developed by the International Nickel Co., contains 5.5% chromium, 2.5 titanium, 0.03 carbon, and the balance nickel. The cold-worked metal has a tensile strength of

200,000 psi, elongation 7%, and Brinell hardness 395.   **Inconel W,** of this company, used for springs at temperatures to 1000°F, has 70% nickel, 5 to 9 iron, 0.4 to 1 aluminum, 2 to 2.75 titanium, 17 chromium, 1 manganese, 0.70 silicon, 0.50 copper, 0.08 carbon, and 0.01 sulfur. The annealed metal has a tensile strength up to 160,000 psi with elongation 15 to 35%, while the spring-hard metal has a tensile strength up to 275,000 psi with elongation 2 to 5%.

A series of **paramagnetic alloys,** called **Nitinol,** developed by the Naval Ordnance Laboratory, are intermetallic compounds of nickel and titanium rather than **nickel-titanium alloys.**   The compound TiNi contains theoretically 54.5% nickel, but the alloys may contain Ti_2Ni and $TiNi_3$ with about 50 to 60% nickel.   The TiNi and nickel-rich alloys are paramagnetic, with a permeability value of 1.002, compared with the unity value of a vacuum.   A 54.5% nickel alloy has a tensile strength of 110,000 psi with elongation of about 15%, and hardness of Rockwell C35.   The alloys close to the TiNi composition are ductile and can be cold-rolled. The nickel-rich alloys are hot-rolled.   They can be hardened by heat treatment to give hardnesses to Rockwell C68 and tensile strengths to 140,000 psi.   This class of alloy can also be modified with small amounts of silicon or aluminum, forming complex intermetallic compounds that can be solution-treated.

The alloy known as **nickel-aluminum,** containing about 20% nickel, is a master alloy for adding nickel to aluminum alloys or for making aluminum bronzes.   **Nickel-aluminum bronze,** used for dies, molds, cast propellers, and valve seats, is usually an 8 to 10% aluminum bronze with an addition of nickel to give increased strength, corrosion resistance, and heat resistance to about 750°F.   But **nickel-aluminum alloys** are used for coil springs.   **Duranickel,** with 93.7% nickel and 4.4 aluminum, is age-hardening, and the cold-drawn wire has a tensile strength of 225,000 psi and is corrosion-resistant to 650°F.   **Tin-nickel alloy,** with 65% tin and 35 nickel, is used only for electroplating.   It deposits the chemical compound SnNi, giving a bright-silvery-white, corrosion-resistant plate.

Nickel alloy powders are used for flame-sprayed coatings for hard surfacing and corrosion resistance.   **Metco 14E,** of Metco, Inc., is an alloy powder containing 14% chromium, 3.5 silicon, 2.75 boron, 4 iron, 0.60 carbon, with the balance nickel.   The alloy is self-fluxing and gives an extremely hard coating.   **Colmonoy 72,** of Wall Colmonoy Corp., is a similar alloy powder but with the addition of a high percentage of tungsten. Coatings have a melting point of 1950°F and retain hardness and wear resistance at high temperatures.

NICKEL BRASS.   The alloys that come naturally into this designation are more usually termed nickel silver or are known under a wide variety of trade names. **Nickel-silicon brass** contains very small percentages of silicon, usually about 0.60%, which forms a **nickel silicide,** Ni_2Si, increasing the strength and giving heat-treating properties. Rolled nickel-silicon brass, containing 30% zinc, 2.5 nickel, and 0.65 silicon, has a tensile strength of 114,000 psi. **Imitation silver,** for hardware and fittings, was a nickel brass containing 57% copper, 25 zinc, 15 nickel, and 3 cobalt. The bluish color of the cobalt neutralizes the yellow cast of the nickel and produces a silver-white alloy. **Silvel** was a nickel brass containing 67.5% copper, 26 zinc, and 6.5 nickel, with sometimes a little cobalt. Nickel brass is an alloy used where white color and corrosion resistance are desired.

Seymourite** was an alloy of 64% copper, 18 nickel, and 18 zinc, produced by the Seymour Mfg. Co.   It had a white color and was corrosion-resistant. **Nickeline,** used by the Yale & Towne Mfg. Co. for hardware, had 58 to 60% copper, 16.5 nickel, 2 tin, and the remainder zinc.   It had high strength, a white color, and cast well. **Nickelene** is an old name applied to nickel brass of various compositions, but an alloy patented in 1912 under this name had 55% copper, 12.5 nickel, 20.5 zinc, 10 lead, and 2 tin.   Most of these alloys have good casting qualities, but they do not machine easily unless they contain some lead.   Up to 2% lead does not affect the color and does not decrease the strength greatly. **Tuc Tur,** of the Tuc Tur Metal Corp., was a nickel brass containing 15% nickel and 22 zinc. **Sterlite,** of the Sterlite Foundry & Mfg. Co., contains 25% nickel and 20 zinc, with small amounts of iron, manganese, silicon, and carbon.   A series of corrosion-resistant nickel brasses is marketed by the American Brass Co. under the name of Ambrac. **Ambrac 850** contains 75% copper, 20 nickel, and 5 zinc.   The tensile strength is 50,000 psi soft, and 110,000 hard-drawn.   Other alloys contain more nickel.

NICKEL BRONZE. A name given to bronzes containing nickel, which usually replaces part of the tin, producing a tough, fine-grained, and corrosion-resistant metal. A common nickel bronze containing 88% copper, 5 tin, 5 nickel, and 2 zinc has a tensile strength of 48,000 psi, elongation 42%, and Brinell hardness 86 as cast. When heat-treated or age-hardened, the tensile strength is 87,000 psi, elongation 10%, and Brinell hardness 196.   Small amounts of lead take away the age-hardening quality of the alloy, and also lower the ductility.   But small amounts of nickel added to bearing bronzes increase the resistance to compression and shock without impairing the plasticity.   A bearing bronze of this nature, U.S. Navy 46B22, for heavy loads at high speeds, contains 15 to 20% lead, 73 to 80 copper, 5 to 10 tin, and 1 nickel.   In the **leaded nickel-copper** of American Brass, which contains 1% nickel, 1 lead, 0.2 phosphorus, with the balance copper, a nickel phosphide is dispersed in the alloy by heat treatment, giving a machinability of 80% that of a free-cutting brass.   The tensile strength is 85,000 psi, elongation 5%, and electrical conductivity 55% that of copper.

For decorative bronze parts, nickel is used to give a white color.   In the hardware industry the old name **Chinese bronze** was used for these white alloys.   At least 10% nickel is needed to give a white color.   This amount also gives corrosion resistance to the alloy.   When more than 15% nickel is used, the bronzes are difficult to machine unless some lead is added.   Hardware and plumbing fixtures of these alloys do not require plating.   **Eclipse bronze** is a white bronze of Sargent & Co.   **M-M-M alloy,** of Manning, Maxwell & Moore, Inc., used for pressure valves for superheated steam, contains 60 to 65% nickel, 24 to 27 copper, 9 to 11 tin, and small amounts of iron, silicon, and manganese.   **Mercoloy,** of the Merco Nordstrom Valve Co., is a white valve bronze containing 60% copper, 25 nickel, 10 zinc, 1 tin, 2 lead, and 2 iron.   It has a tensile strength of 44,000 psi, with elongation 20%.

Ni-Vee bronzes of International Nickel are copper-base alloys containing 5% nickel and 5 tin.   Lead and zinc may be added for economy, machinability, and to give bearing qualities.   The amount of lead or zinc is shown by the number designation.   **Ni-Vee Z2** contains 88% copper, 5 nickel, 5 tin, and 2 zinc.   It has a tensile strength of 50,000 psi, and Brinell hardness of 85.   It is used for gears, cams, and construction castings.   **Ni-Vee L10** contains 80% copper, 5 nickel, 5 tin, and 10 lead.   The tensile strength is 35,000 psi, elongation 10%, and Brinell hardness 80.   It is used for bearings and for acid-resistant castings.   **Ni-Vee L5Z5** has a tensile strength of 40,000 psi, elongation 20%, and Brinell hardness 80.   It is used for valves and pump castings.   A wide variety of copper-base alloys containing 10 to 40% nickel, and generally classed as nickel bronzes, are marketed under trade names such as **Aterite** and **Alcumet,** and used for hardware, plumbing fixtures, and where a white color and good corrosion resistance are required.   Some of these may also contain iron, aluminum, or manganese for added strength and hardness.   **Nickel-silicon bronze** of American Brass, called **Cunisil 837,** contains 1.9% nickel, 0.60 silicon, and the balance copper.   It is corrosion-resistant and has a tensile strength of 90,000 psi, and the rod has a machinability rating 40% that of free-cutting brass.   **Nironze 635,** of Bridgeport Brass, has a similar composition.   These alloys, used for bolts, screws, and marine hardware, can be precipitation-hardened to Rockwell B95, with a yield strength of 90,000 psi and elongation of 12%.   The electrical conductivity is 30% that of copper.

NICKEL CAST IRON.   A high-strength alloy cast iron containing nickel. Nickel, like silicon, assists the graphite formation and the carbide decomposition, and therefore reduces chill and acts to eliminate hard carbide spots, chilled edges, and mottled areas.   About 1% nickel is equivalent to $\frac{1}{2}$% silicon, but the effect of nickel is progressive, and does not make the iron brittle as it does silicon.   Nickel in amounts from 0.5 to 10% will also progressively harden cast iron.   A gray cast iron which will have a Brinell hardness of 174 is raised to 350 by the addition of 9% nickel. Since the nickel promotes the formation of the graphite in fine crystals, the iron has a high resistance to wear.   Tensile strengths up to 65,000 psi are obtained in these irons.   Nickel obstructs the passage of electric currents in iron, and iron with 5% nickel is used for resistance grids.   High-nickel iron is also nonmagnetic.

Most nickel irons contain small amounts of chromium to increase the chilling power and refine the grain.   It also increases the strength and hardness.   **Ni-Tensyl iron** is the trade name of International Nickel for a nickel cast iron made by adding to the melt a graphitizer of nickel-silicon to cause partial decomposition of the combined carbon.   With 1.75% nickel this iron has high strength and a hardness of 320 Brinell.   The silicon content is about 1.40% and the chromium about 0.35%.   An iron of this type used for heavy-duty drawing dies is **Paralloy** of the Youngstown Foundry & Machine Co.   As cast, it has a hardness up to 300 Brinell, and a tensile strength up to 50,000 psi.   When heat-treated, the hardness is up to 550 Brinell with tensile strength to 40,000 psi.   **Ryanite,** of the Allyne-Ryan Foundry Co., for dies, is a similar iron.   **Lectrocast,** of the Detroit Gray Iron Foundry, used for automobile body dies, has 2.75% nickel and 0.70 chromium.   **Tensloy,** of the Ensign Foundry Co., and **Novite,** of the Novo Engine Co., have about 1.5% nickel and 0.50 chromium.   **Mitchalloy A,** of the Robert Mitchell Co., Ltd., has 2.5% nickel and 0.90 chromium.   **Cariron, Bryiron,** and **Diamite** are nickel-chromium irons, but alloy irons now usually conform to ACI specifications.

High-nickel-chromium irons are used for pump and compressor parts handling hot liquids and may contain up to 30% nickel and 5 chromium. **Pyrocast** is a high-test nickel-chromium cast iron of the Pacific Foundry Co.   **Niresist,** developed by International Nickel, is an alloy cast iron containing monel metal with also chromium and manganese.   A typical analysis range is nickel, 12 to 15%; copper, 5 to 7; chromium, 1.25 to 4; manganese, 1 to 1.5; silicon, 1 to 2; and total carbon, 2.75 to 3.1.   The tensile strength is 20,000 to 35,000 psi, with a Brinell hardness 130 to 170.   It can be chilled to a hardness of 350 to 400.   It has a low coefficient of expansion, 0.0000100 per deg F, or about the same as the aluminum-silicon alloys used for pistons.   **Nogroth metal** is such an iron. **Nicrosilal,** developed by the British Cast Iron Research Assoc., contains 5% silicon, 17 nickel, and 3 chromium.   It has high-heat distortion resistance, and is used for heat-resistant castings.

Vanadium in nickel irons adds strength and wear resistance.   **Vanick** is the name of a **nickel-vanadium cast iron** of the Malleable Iron Fittings Co.   Nickel cast irons and **nickel-chromium cast irons** are marketed under many trade names, such as **Frankite,** of the Frank Foundries Corp., **Alco Ni-Iron,** of the American Locomotive Co., **Elfur iron,** of the Cramp Brass & Iron Foundry, **Tylerite,** of the W. S. Tyler Co., **Domite,** of the Dominion Wheel & Foundry Co., and **Maxtensile,** of the Farrel-Birmingham Co.   The nickel-chromium cast irons may also contain molybdenum for greater hardness and wear resistance.   **Ni-Chillite,** of the Mackintosh-Hemphill Co., is a nickel-chromium-molybdenum chilled cast iron for heavy rolls.   **Mocasco iron,** of the Motor Casting Co., is a wear-resistant iron capable of being cast into thin sections without chill.   **Mocasco 30,** for cylinders, has 1 to 1.35% nickel, 0.25 to 0.30 chromium, and 0.75 molybdenum.   **Strenes metal** is the name of the Advance Foundry Co. for a nickel-chromium-molybdenum cast iron for heavy dies.   **Durite** is a wear-resistant iron of the Birdsboro Steel Foundry & Machine Co.   **Iron-ite,** of the Kinite Corp., is a chromium-nickel-vanadium cast iron used for cams, gears, and wear-resistant parts. **Low-expansion iron,** for dies, gages, and machine parts held to close tolerances, is nickel cast iron. **Minovar,** of the International Nickel Co., is such an iron with only one-third the expansion of ordinary cast iron.

NICKEL-CHROMIUM ALLOYS. A group of alloys of nickel and chromium employed as heat-resistant metals, for resistance wires, and as corrosion-resistant metals for chemical machinery.   An alloy of 80% nickel and 20 chromium will withstand temperatures up to 2100°F.   **Chromel A,** of the Hoskins Mfg. Co., has this composition.   The resistivity is 650 ohms per cir mil ft, tensile strength 120,000 psi, and melting point 1420°C. **Chromel C,** with 60% nickel, 16 chromium, and 24 iron, has an electrical resistivity 10% higher than Chromel A at high temperatures, but its oxidation resistance is limited to 1700°F.   It is used for electrical-appliance heating wire.   **Chromel D** contains 35% nickel, 18.5 chromium, and the balance iron.   Its resistivity at room temperature is 600 ohms per cir mil ft, but its hot resistivity is greater than that of Chromel A.   It is for temperatures not over 1200°F.

For general-purpose castings for use at temperatures to 1800°F the **HT alloy** of the Alloy Casting Institute has 35% nickel, 15 chromium, and 1.5 columbium.   For lower temperatures, from 1600 to 1800°F, the **HK alloy** has 20% nickel, 25 chromium, and 0.40 max carbon.   **Misco metal,** of the Michigan-Standard Alloy Casting Co., contains 35% nickel and 10 chromium, with the balance iron.   **Misco C** contains 29% chromium, 9 nickel, 0.55 manganese, 0.60 silicon, and 0.25 carbon.   **Miscrome** is resistant to nitric acid.   It contains 28% chromium with no nickel.

Centricast alloys, of the same company, are these corrosion-resistant alloys centrifugally cast for pipes. A group of alloys for heat-resistant parts is marketed by the Electro-Alloys Div., American Brake Shoe Co., under the name **Thermalloy.**   **Thermalloy 72,** for temperatures to 2000°F, has 12 to 14% chromium and 58 to 63 nickel. **Thermalloy 40** is a general-use machinable alloy to resist temperatures from 1200 to 1500°F. It contains about 26% chromium and 12 nickel. **Chemalloy F32M,** of the same company, is primarily for parts to resist chemical action. It has 26 to 29% chromium, 3 to 6 nickel, and 1 to 1.5 molybdenum. It has high strength at elevated temperatures, is resistant to sulfur atmospheres, and is used for parts for refineries and pulp mills.

A group of heat-resistant and acid-resistant nickel-chromium alloys is sold by the Michigan-Standard Alloy Casting Co. as Standard alloy. **Standard alloy HR-3,** a cast alloy for heat-treating equipment, contains 37% nickel, 17 chromium, 1.5 silicon, 1.2 manganese, and 0.50 carbon. At room temperature it has a tensile strength of 68,000 psi with elongation of 10%, and at 1800°F the tensile strength is 12,000 psi with elongation of 26%. It has a Brinell hardness of 187. It is austenitic, and is not affected by heat treatment. It resists air oxidation to 2000°F, and is resistant to tempering salts and carburizers. A lower-cost metal for general heat resistance to 2100°F is **Standard alloy HR-6,** which is **AISI alloy Type 309** containing 25% chromium and 12 nickel with 1 manganese, 1.25 silicon, and 0.40 carbon. Another group is marketed by the Cooper Alloy Foundry Co. under the names of **Sweetaloy** and **Cooper alloys.** **Cooper alloy S-16** has 14 to 20% chromium and 65 nickel; **Cooper alloy S-21A** is this combination with 3% molybdenum and 1.5 silicon. **Cooper alloy V2B** has high resistance to acids, high strength and wear resistance, and welds easily. It contains about 19.25% chromium, 10 nickel, 3 silicon, 3.25 molybdenum, 2 copper, 0.60 manganese, 0.15 beryllium, and 0.07 max carbon. The hardness as cast is 302 Brinell, but it can be quench-annealed for machining. The tensile strength is 150,000 psi, with elongation of 3%. **Cimet,** of the Driver-Harris Co., used for mine pump parts, has 26% chromium, 10 nickel, and the balance iron. **Gridnic alloys,** of this company, are nickel-chromium alloys used for radio grids. **Nirex,** of the same company, has 80% nickel, 14 chromium, and 6 iron. In annealed sheet form it has a tensile strength of 90,000 psi with elongation 50%. **Chromel No. 502** has 36% nickel, 20 chromium, and the balance iron. It is used for furnace fixtures, either rolled or cast. **Inconel,** developed by the International Nickel Co., used for dairy and food equipment, contains 79.5% nickel, 13 chromium, 6.5 iron, 0.08 carbon, and slight amounts of copper, manganese, and silicon. The tensile strength of the hot-rolled plate is 100,000 to 140,000 psi with elongation 20 to 40%, and Brinell hardness 160 to 240. Heat-treating boxes of this alloy give furnace serv-ice life of 12,000 hr at 2000°F. **Inconel X,** a wrought alloy for gas turbine blades, contains 70 to 73% nickel, 15 chromium, 2.5 titanium, 0.70 to 1.20 columbium, 0.40 to 1 aluminum, 5 to 9 iron, 0.30 to 1 man-ganese, 0.5 max silicon, 0.20 max copper, and 0.08 max carbon. It has a tensile strength of 160,000 psi, retains 90% of its strength at 900°F, and 80% up to 1100°F. The specific gravity is 8.3, and the melting range is 2540 to 2600°F. It can be age-hardened to 400 Brinell, but loses its hardness at 1500°F. **Incoloy T,** of this company, has high corrosion resistance to above 1600°F, but loses three-quarters of its strength at that temperature. It contains about 32% nickel with cobalt, 20 chromium, 1.5 manganese, 1 silicon, 1.25 titanium, with maximums of 0.50 copper and 0.10 carbon. The tensile strength is above 80,000 psi. **Inconel 718** for use at subzero temperatures has up to 55% nickel with contained cobalt, up to 21% chromium, 5 columbium plus tantalum, 3 molybdenum, and 1 each of cobalt and titanium.

Nickel-chromium-iron alloys, with silicon and other elements forming complex alloys, are employed for acid-resistant and corrosion-resistant castings and wrought metals for high temperatures. **Durimet,** of the Duriron Co., Inc., is marketed in various grades normally containing 19.5 to 23% nickel, 18 to 22 chromium, 2.75 to 3.75 silicon, 0.50 to 0.75 manganese, 1 to 1.5 molybdenum, and 0.25 to 0.45 copper. **Durimet 20** contains 29% nickel, 20 chromium, 1.75 molybdenum, 3.5 copper, 1 sili-con, and 0.07 max carbon. The heat-treated castings have a tensile strength of 65,000 to 75,000 psi, elongation 35 to 50%, and Brinell hardness 120 to 150. It is especially resistant to sulfuric and mixed acids. This alloy is produced as **Esco 20** by the Electric Steel Foundry Co., **Isocast 20** by Empire Steel Castings, Inc., **Aloyco 20** by the Alloy Steel Products Co., **Fahrite C-20** by the Ohio Steel Foundry Co., **Misco 20** by the Michi-gan Steel Castings Co., and **Utilloy 20** by the Utility Electric Steel Foundry. **Carpenter stainless 20** is this alloy in wrought forms with slightly less copper and more molybdenum. The tensile strength of the wrought bar is 85,000 psi, elongation 35 to 50%, and hardness 150 to 180 Brinell. **Carpenter stainless 20Cb-3** contains 34% nickel, up to 1% columbium plus tantalum, and is for high resistance to hot acids. **Durimet FA-20,** of the Cooper Alloy Foundry Co., has 20% chromium, 29 nickel, 4 copper, 3.5 molybdenum, 1 silicon, 1 manganese, with the carbon kept below 0.07 to prevent intergranular corrosion. The tensile strength is 75,000 psi, elongation 40%, and Brinell hardness 150. It is resistant to sulfuric acid and to strong, hot alkalies and chlorates. **Donegal alloy DC-50,** of the Donegal Mfg. Corp., used for pump parts, has corrosion resistance about equal to an 18–8 steel. It contains 16.5% chromium, 4 nickel, 4 copper, and 0.05 carbon. When hardened, it has a tensile strength of 135,000 to 210,000 psi, with elongation of 6 to 15%, and hardness of 375 to 440 Brinell.

Chemalloy N4, of the Electro-Alloys Div., used as a stain-resistant metal for food equipment, contains 30% nickel, 5 chromium, 5 silicon, and the balance iron. It will resist oxidation to 1400°F. **Pyromet 860,** of Carpenter Technology, used for turbine blades and aircraft engine parts, contains 43% nickel, 14 chromium, 6 molybdenum, 4 cobalt, 3 titanium, 1 aluminum, 0.1 carbon, and the balance iron. The tensile strength is up to 180,000 psi, and it retains good strength up to about 1400°F. **Rezistal,** of the Crucible Steel Co., is marketed in many grades resistant to heat, acids, and corrosion. They include stainless steels and special-composition nickel-chromium alloys. They are also produced in supersoft sheet form, 0.012 to 0.018 in. thickness, for flashings, gutters, and expansion joints in building construction. They provide high strength and durability but may be cut with ordinary tools. **Rezistal 2600,** formerly known as **Atha's 2600 alloy,** contains 22% nickel, 8 chromium, 1.75 silicon, 1 copper, 0.70 manganese, and 0.25 carbon. It is nonmagnetic, resistant to acids, and is easily machinable. **RA 330 alloy,** of Rolled Alloys, Inc., contains 35% nickel, 19 chromium, 1.25 silicon, 2 manganese, 0.50 copper, and 0.06 carbon. It is austenitic, and has a tensile strength of 85,000 psi with elongation of 40%. At 1200°F the tensile strength is 59,000 psi, and at 1800°F it is 10,500 psi. Castings are now generally standardized under specifications of the Alloy Casting Institute and, although foundries vary the compositions, the accent is most often on quality control methods to meet service requirements.

NICKEL-CHROMIUM STEEL. Steel containing both nickel and chromium, usually in a ratio of 2 to 3 parts nickel to 1 chromium. The 2:1 ratio gives great toughness, and the nickel and chromium are intended to balance each other in physical effects. The steels are especially suited for large sections which require heat-treatment, because of the deep and uniform hardening power. Hardness and toughness are the characteristic properties of these steels. Nickel-chromium steel containing 1 to 1.5% nickel, 0.45 to 0.75 chromium, and 0.38 to 0.80 manganese is used throughout the carbon ranges for case-hardened parts and for forgings where high tensile strength and great hardness are required.

Low nickel-chromium steels, but with more carbon, from 0.60 to 0.80%, are used for drop-forging dies and other tools. **R.D.S. steel,** of Carpenter Technology, is an oil-hardening, tough tool steel containing 1.75% nickel, 1 chromium, 0.50 manganese, and 0.75 carbon. An industrial steel of this company, **Carpenter steel 5-317,** contains the same amounts of nickel and chromium, but 0.50 carbon and less manganese. It is oil-hardening, and is used for gears, shafts, and shock-resisting parts.   The tensile strength is up to 295,000 psi.   **Samson steel,** of this company, used for machinery parts for severe service, contains 1.25% nickel, 0.60 chromium, 0.50 manganese, and various amounts of carbon.   The 0.40 carbon steel, when heat-treated, has a tensile strength of 240,000 psi and Brinell hardness 440. **Beaver steel,** of the Colonial Steel Co., used for water-quenched forging-die blocks, contains 1.5% nickel, 0.75 chromium, 0.60 manganese, and 0.55 carbon.   **Colona steel,** of the same company, used for oil-quenched forging dies, has the same nickel and chromium content, but somewhat more manganese and carbon.   **Nikro-Trimmer steel,** of the same company, used for hot trimming dies, has higher carbon, 0.85%, but only small amounts of nickel and chromium, 0.30 to 0.55%, of each.   **Simplex steel,** of the Crucible Steel Co., used for forgings, has 1.25% nickel and 0.60 chromium.   In the low-carbon, case-hardening grades, for gears, it has a tensile strength of 90,000 psi.   **SAE steel 3330,** containing 3.5% nickel and 1.5 chromium, when oil-tempered has a tensile strength of 205,000 psi and elongation 13%.   **Quality steel** is the trade name of Quality Steels, Ltd., for nickel-chromium steels in various grades.

Nickel-chromium steels may have temper brittleness, or low impact resistance, when improperly cooled after heat-treatment.   A small amount of molybdenum is sometimes added to prevent this brittleness.   **Encem steel,** of W. T. Flather, Ltd., is a molybdenum steel of this type.   **Miraculoy,** of the Sivyer Steel Castings Co., contains 1.25% nickel, 0.65 chromium, 0.40 molybdenum, and 1.55 manganese.   The tensile strength is 115,000 psi with elongation 18% and Brinell hardness 275.   **Miscoloy No. 60,** of the Michigan Steel Casting Co., is another steel of this type. A nickel-chromium **coin steel,** used by the Italian government for coins, was a stainless type containing 22% chromium, 12 nickel, and some molybdenum.

Low-carbon nickel-chromium steels are water-hardening, but those with appreciable amounts of alloying elements require oil quenching.   Air-hardening steels contain up to 4.5% nickel and 1.6 chromium, but are brittle unless tempered in oil to strengths below 200,000 psi.   The alloy known as **Krupp analysis steel** contains 4% nickel and 1.5 chromium. The steel under the name of **Millaloy,** used by Doelger & Kirsten, Inc., for heavy shear blades, is of this analysis with 0.40% carbon.   Blades hardened to 530 Brinell have an ultimate strength of 312,000 psi and elongation 11%.   **Nikrome** is a nickel-chromium steel of Joseph T. Ryerson & Son, Inc.   **Nikrome M** contains 2.25% nickel, 1 chromium, and 0.45 molybdenum, with 0.40 carbon.   It is characterized by high strength and uniform hardening, and can be machined up to 450 Brinell.   **H.T.M. steel,** of this company, is a 2% nickel steel with chromium and molybdenum.   **Nykrom** is a steel of W. T. Flather, Ltd.   **Ohioloy** is a nickel-chromium steel of the Ohio Steel Foundry Co.   All of the nickel-chromium steels require special heat treatment to bring out their best qualities.   The nickel-chromium steels used for high strength at elevated temperatures in rockets and aircraft are variations of the stainless-type alloys.   **Unitemp 212,** of the Universal-Cyclops Steel Co., which has a tensile strength of 187,000 psi, and will retain a strength of 108,000 psi at 1400°F with high corrosion resistance, contains 25% nickel, 16 chromium, 4 titanium, 0.08 boron, 0.50 columbium, 0.50 aluminum, 0.05 zirconium, 0.50 manganese, 0.50 silicon, and 0.15 carbon.

NICKEL-COBALT ALLOYS. A group of alloys containing 20 to 30% cobalt and 70 to 80 nickel.   Nickel has a yellowish cast and cobalt a blue cast; alloys of the two metals are almost pure silver in luster and resemble silver.   They are expensive, because of the high cost of cobalt, but the two metals are codeposited in an electroplating bath to form an alloy deposit on iron, steel, or nonferrous metals.   The alloy is harder than either nickel or cobalt alone, and is also more corrosion-resistant.   Another type of nickel-cobalt complex alloy is **Konal,** developed by the Westinghouse Electric Corp., as a heat-resistant and acid-resistant alloy.   It contains 73% nickel, 17.5 cobalt, 6.5 iron, 2.5 titanium, and 0.2 manganese.   At a temperature of 600°C this alloy has a tensile strength of 66,000 psi.   At ordinary temperatures the strength is 100,000 psi.   It was developed for radio-tube filaments.   **Alloy C** of M & T Chemicals is a 50–50 alloy of nickel and cobalt used for plating.

NICKEL COPPER. An alloy of nickel and copper employed for adding nickel to nonferrous alloys.   A 50–50 nickel copper has a melting point of 2330°F and dissolves readily.   **Nickel-copper shot** of this composition is marketed for ladle additions to iron and steel.   The copper-nickel master alloy designated in Federal specifications contains 60% nickel, 33 copper, 3.5 manganese, and may contain up to 3.5 iron.   It is used for alloying high-strength bronzes.   **Copper-nickel alloy** is also used for special purposes.   A grade of **Thermalloy,** of the Electro Alloys Co., used as a temperature-sensitive magnetic metal for magnetic shunts in watt-hour meters, has 66.5% nickel, 30 copper, and 2 iron.   The permeability falls off with increase in temperature and compensates for errors due to temperature changes.

NICKEL-MOLYBDENUM IRON. A group of alloys used for high acid resistance.   They may contain up to 40% molybdenum, which takes the place of the chromium used in the more common corrosion-resistant alloys. The most usual alloy in this class contains about 20% iron, 20 molybdenum, 60 nickel, and small amounts of carbon.   This alloy is very resistant to hydrochloric and sulfuric acids, but for high general acid resistance the iron content should be below 10%.   Iron adds hardness and stiffness to the alloys, but decreases the acid resistance.   Manganese improves the workability, but more than 3% decreases the acid resistance.   The alloys cast easily, and the 20–20–60 alloy is readily machinable.   It can be hot-rolled into sheet, or cold-rolled.   The melting point is 1300°C, and the weight is 0.315 lb per cu in.   The tensile strength, forged, is 118,000 psi and Brinell hardness 207.   This alloy is resistant to all acids except nitric. **Chemalloy H1,** of the Electro-Alloys Div., for severe acid resistance such as for valve and pump parts, contains 21% molybdenum, 21 iron, and the balance nickel.

NICKEL-MOLYBDENUM STEEL.   An alloy steel which is most used in compositions of 1.5% nickel and 0.15 to 0.25 molybdenum, with varying percentages of carbon up to 0.50%.   These steels are characterized by remarkably uniform properties, are readily forged and heat-treated. Molybdenum produces toughness in the steels, and in the case-hardened steel gives a tough core.   Roller bearings are made of this class of steel. A steel used by the Ingersoll Steel & Disc Co. for hand-shovel blades contains an average of 0.45% carbon, 0.50 manganese, 1.35 nickel, and 0.40 molybdenum.   When hot-rolled and heat-treated, it has a tensile strength of 240,000 psi and elongation 6%.   **Superalloy steel,** of the same company, is **SAE steel 3160.**   A 5% nickel steel with 0.30% carbon and 0.60 molybdenum has a tensile strength of 175,000 to 230,000 psi, with elongation 12 to 22%, depending upon the heat-treatment.   Molybdenum is more frequently added to the steels containing also chromium, the molybdenum giving air-hardening properties, reducing distortion, and making the steels more resistant to oxidation.

NICKEL ORES.   Nickel occurs in minerals as sulfides, silicates, and arsenides, the most common being **pyrrhotite,** or **magnetic pyrites,** a sulfide of iron of the formula $Fe_{1-x}S$, where x is between 0 and 0.2   When x is zero the mineral is called **troilite.**   Pyrrhotite has nickel associated with the iron sulfide.   The ore of Copper Cliff, Ontario, is calcined to remove the sulfur, and the nickel is removed, leaving a fine magnetite which is pelletized and fired to give an iron concentrate of 68% iron.   The chief sulfide ore deposit at Sudbury, Ontario, contains sulfides of iron, nickel, and copper, and small amounts of other elements, and some of the matte after removal of the iron and sulfur is used as monel metal without separating the natural alloy.   The extensive ore deposits at Lynn Lake, Manitoba, yield an ore averaging 1.74% nickel and 0.75 copper.   The **garnierite,** or **noumeite,** of New Caledonia is a nickel silicate containing also iron and magnesium.   It is amorphous and earthy, of an apple-green color, with a specific gravity of 2.2 to 2.8, and hardness of 3 to 4. The ore contains about 5% nickel, and is smelted with gypsum to a matte of sulfides of nickel and iron, the sulfur coming from the gypsum. This is then bessemerized, and the matte crushed, roasted to oxide, and reduced to nickel. The material exported from New Caledonia under the name of **fonte** is a directly smelted cast iron containing about 30% nickel.

A minor ore of nickel called **millerite,** occurring in Europe and in Wisconsin, is a **nickel sulfide,** NiS, containing theoretically 64.7% nickel. It is found usually in radiating groups of slender crystals with a specific gravity of 5.6, hardness 3.5, and of a pale-yellow color and metallic luster. **Niccolite,** NiAs, is a minor ore containing theoretically 43.9% nickel, usually with iron, cobalt, and sulfur. It is found in Canada, Germany, and Sweden. The mineral occurs massive, with a specific gravity of 7.5, hardness 5 to 5.5, and a pale-copper color. Nickel is also produced as a by-product from copper ores.

NICKEL SILVER. A name applied in the machine industries to an alloy of copper, nickel, and zinc, which is practically identical with alloys known in the silverware trade as German silver. **Packfong,** meaning **white copper,** is an old name for these alloys. The very early nickel silvers contained some silver and were used for silverware. **Wessell's silver** contained about 2%, and **Ruolz silver** about 20%. **Baudoin alloy,** a French metal, contained 72% copper, 16 nickel, 1.8 cobalt, 2.5 silver, and the balance zinc, but the white jewelry alloys called **Paris metal** and **Lutecine** contained about 2% tin instead of the silver. The English nickel silver known as **Alpaca,** used as a base metal for silver-plated tableware, had about 65% copper, 20 zinc, 13 nickel, and 2 silver. Such an alloy takes a fine polish, has a silvery-white color, and is resistant to corrosion.

Nickel silver is made in regular grades of 5 to 30% nickel, with up to 70% copper, and the balance zinc. Nickel whitens brass and makes it harder and more resistant to corrosion, but the alloys are more difficult to cast because of shrinkage and absorption of gases. They are also subject to fire cracking and are more difficult to roll and draw than brass. The most common nickel silver is the 18% nickel alloy with 55 to 65% copper, and the balance zinc. The higher-copper grades are used for parts where there is much fabricating. As a spring material, with 55% copper, this alloy has a tensile strength of 110,000 psi, and Brinell hardness 160, when cold-rolled. Telephone-equipment springs normally contain 55% copper, 18 nickel, and 27 zinc. **Copper alloy 766** is a nickel silver widely used for electrical contacts, connectors, and current-carrying springs. It contains 56.5% copper, 12 nickel, and 31.5 zinc. It has a tensile strength up to 120,000 psi and does not need plating to resist corrosion even in marine atmospheres. Contacts made with this material by Elco Corp. have a resistance of 0.007 ohm and electrical conductivity of 7.6% IACS.   **Scovill nickel silver** for soft-temper extrusions has 13% nickel, 43 copper, and 44 zinc.   It contains alpha grains in an amorphous beta matrix.   **Benedict metal,** of the American Brass Co., originally had 12.5% nickel, with 2 parts copper to 1 zinc, but the alloy used for hardware and plumbing fixtures contains about 57% copper, 2 tin, 9 lead, 20 zinc, and 12 nickel.   The cast metal has a strength of 35,000 psi with elongation of 15%.   The white alloy known as **dairy bronze,** used for casting dairy equipment and soda-fountain parts, has 63% copper, 4 tin, 5 lead, 8 zinc, and 20 nickel.   The higher-nickel alloys have a more permanent white finish for parts subject to corrosion.   **Ambrac 854,** of the American Brass Co., is a wrought metal with 65% copper, 30 nickel, and 5 zinc.   **Pope's Island white metal,** of this company, used for jewelry, had 67% copper, 19.75 nickel, and 13.25 zinc.   **Victor metal** is an alloy of 50% copper, 35 zinc, and 15 nickel, used for cast fittings.   It is a white metal with a yellow shade.   It casts easily and machines well.

For threaded parts and for casting metals, the nickel silvers usually contain some lead for easier machining.   Federal specifications for casting metals call for 65% copper, 20 nickel, 4 tin, 5 lead, and 6 zinc.   **Leaded nickel silver,** for making keys, has 46.5% copper, 10 nickel, 40.75 zinc, and 2.75 lead.   The extruded metal has a tensile strength of 80,000 psi, elongation of 33%, and Rockwell hardness B82.   **White nickel brass,** for cast parts for trim, is a standard 18% nickel alloy with or without lead.   **Silveroid,** an English alloy for this use, is a cupronickel without zinc.   An English alloy for tableware, under the name of **Newloy,** contains 35% nickel, 64 copper, and 1 tin.   The **stainless nickel** used for silverware by Viners, Ltd., has 30% nickel, 60 copper, and 10 zinc, and is deoxidized with manganese copper, using borax as a top flux.

NICKEL STEEL. Steel containing nickel as the predominating alloying element.   The first nickel steel produced in the United States was made in 1890 by adding 3% nickel in a bessemer converter.   The first nickel-steel armor plate, with 3.5% nickel, was known as **Harveyized steel.**   Small amounts of nickel steel, however, had been used since ancient times, coming from **meteoric iron.**   The nickel iron of meteorites, known in mineralogy as **taenite,** contains about 26% nickel.

Nickel added to carbon steel increases the ultimate strength, elastic limit, hardness, and toughness.   It narrows the hardening range but lowers the critical range of steel, reducing danger of warpage and cracking, and balances the intensive deep-hardening effect of chromium.   The nickel steels are also of finer structure than ordinary steels, and the nickel retards grain growth.   When the percentage of nickel is high, the steel is very resistant to corrosion.   Above 20% nickel the steel becomes a single-phase austenitic structure.   The steel is nonmagnetic above 29% nickel, and the maximum value of permeability is at about 78% nickel.   The lowest expansion value of the steel is at 36% nickel.   The percentage of nickel employed usually varies from 1.5 to 5%, with up to 0.80% manganese.   The bulk of nickel steels contain 2 and 3½% nickel.   They are used for armor plate, structural shapes, rails, heavy-duty machine parts, gears, automobile parts, and ordnance.

The standard ASTM **structural nickel steel** used for building construction is an open-hearth steel containing 3.25% nickel, 0.45 carbon, and 0.70 manganese.   This steel has a tensile strength from 85,000 to 100,000 psi and a minimum elongation 18%.   An automobile steel used by one of the larger companies contains 0.10 to 0.20% carbon, 3.25 to 3.75 nickel, 0.30 to 0.60 manganese, and 0.15 to 0.30 silicon.   When heat-treated, it has a tensile strength up to 80,000 psi and an elongation 25 to 35%.   Forgings for locomotive crankpins containing 2.5% nickel, 0.27 carbon, and 0.88 manganese have a tensile strength of 83,000 psi, elongation 30%, and reduction of area 62%.   A **nickel-vanadium steel,** used for high-strength cast parts, contains 1.5% nickel, 1 manganese, 0.28 carbon, and 0.10 vanadium.   The tensile strength is 90,000 psi and elongation 25%.   **Univan steel,** of the Union Steel Casting Co., for high-strength locomotive castings, is a nickel-vanadium steel of this type.   **Unionaloy steel,** of this company, is an abrasion-resistant steel.

The Federal specifications for 3½% nickel carbon steel call for 3.25 to 3.75% nickel, and 0.25 to 0.30 carbon.   This steel has a tensile strength of 85,000 psi and elongation 18%.   A hot-rolled 3½% nickel medium-carbon steel, **SAE steel 2330,** when oil-quenched develops a strength up to 220,000 psi, and Brinell hardness from 223 to 424, depending upon the drawing temperature.   Standard 3½ and 5% nickel steels are regular products of the steel mills, though they are often sold under trade names. Steels with more than 3.5% nickel are too expensive for ordinary structural use.   Steels with more than 5% nickel are difficult to forge, but the very high content nickel steels are used when corrosion-resistant properties are required.   **Nicloy,** of the Babcock & Wilcox Tube Co., used for tubing to resist the corrosive action of paper-mill liquors and oil-well brines, contains 9% nickel, 0.10 chromium, 0.05 molybdenum, 0.35 copper, 0.45 manganese, 0.20 silicon, and 0.09 max carbon.   The heat-treated steel has a tensile strength of 110,000 psi, with elongation 35%.   The **cryogenic steels,** or **low-temperature steels,** for such uses as liquid-oxygen vessels, are usually high-nickel steels.   **Lukens Nine Nickel,** for temperatures down to −320°F, contains 9% nickel, 0.80 manganese, 0.30 silicon, and not over 0.13 carbon.   It has a minimum tensile strength of 90,000 psi with elongation of 22%.

NICKEL SULFATE. The most widely used salt for nickel-plating baths, and known in the plating industry as **single nickel salt.** It is easily produced by the reaction of sulfuric acid on nickel, and comes in pea-green water-soluble crystalline pellets of the composition $NiSO_4 \cdot 7H_2O$, of a specific gravity of 1.98, melting at about 100°C. **Double nickel salt** is **nickel ammonium sulfate,** $NiSO_4 \cdot (NH_4)_2 \cdot SO_4 \cdot 6H_2O$, used especially for plating on zinc. To produce a harder and whiter finish in nickel plating, **cobaltous sulfamate,** a water-soluble powder of the composition $Co(NH_2SO_3)_2 \cdot 3H_2O$, is used with the nickel sulfate. **Nickel plate** has a normal hardness of Brinell 90 to 140, but by controlled processes file-hard plates can be obtained from sulfate baths. **Micrograin nickel,** of Metachemical Processes, Ltd., with a grain diameter of 0.00002 in., is such a hard plate.

Other nickel salts are also used for nickel plating. **Nickel chloride,** $NiCl_2 \cdot 6H_2O$, is a green crystalline salt which, when used with boric acid, gives a fine-grained, smooth, hard, strong plate. It requires less power, and the bath is easy to control. **Nickel carbonate,** $2NiCO_3 \cdot 3Ni(OH)_2 \cdot 4H_2O$, comes in green crystals not soluble in water, but soluble in acids and in solutions of ammonium salts. **Nickel carbonyl,** $Ni(CO)_4$, used for nickel plating by gas decomposition, is a yellow volatile liquid. It is volatilized in a closed vessel with hydrogen as the carrier, and the nickel is deposited at about 350°F. It will adhere to glass and wood as well as to metals. The material is a strong reducing agent, and is explosive when mixed with oxygen. **Nickel nitrate,** $(NiNO_3)_2 \cdot 6H_2O$, used in electric batteries, comes in thin flat flakes.

NITRIC ACID. Also called **aqua fortis** and **azotic acid.** A colorless to reddish fuming liquid of the composition HNO_3, having a wide variety of uses for pickling metals, etching, and in the manufacture of nitrocellulose, plastics, dyestuffs, and explosives. It has a specific gravity of 1.502 (95% acid) and a boiling point of 86°C, and it is soluble in water. Its fumes have a suffocating action, and it is highly corrosive and caustic. **Fuming nitric acid** is any water solution containing more than 86% acid and having a specific gravity above 1.480. Nitric acid is made by the action of sulfuric acid on sodium nitrate, or purified Chilean saltpeter, and condensation of the fumes. It is also made from ammonia by catalytic oxidation, or from the nitric oxide produced from air. The acid is sold in various grades, depending on the amount of water. The strengths of the commercial grades are 38, 40, and 42°Bé containing 67.2% acid. C.P., or reagent grade, is 43°Bé, with 70.3% acid, very low in iron, arsenic, or other impurities. It is usually shipped in glass carboys. **Anhydrous nitric acid** is a yellow fuming liquid containing the unstable anhydride, **nitrogen pentox-**

ide, N_2O_5. It is violently reactive and is a powerful nitriding agent. The dark-red fuming liquid known as **nitrogen tetroxide,** N_2O_4, is really a concentrated water solution of nitric acid, as this oxide is an unstable polymer of NO_2. It is used as an oxidizer for rocket fuels, as it contains 70% oxygen. **Mixed acid,** or **nitrating acid,** is a mixture of nitric and sulfuric acids used chiefly in making nitrocellulose and nitrostarch. Standard mixed acid contains 36% nitric and 61 sulfuric, but other grades are also used.

NITROCELLULOSE. A compound made by treating cellulose with nitric acid, using sulfuric acid as a catalyst. Since cotton is almost pure cellulose, it was originally the raw material used, but alpha cellulose made from wood is now employed. The cellulose molecule will unite with from 1 to 6 molecules of nitric acid. **Trinitrocellulose,** $C_{12}H_{17}O_7(NO_3)_3$, contains 9.13% nitrogen, and is the product used for plastics, lacquers, adhesives, and celluloid. It is classified as cellulose nitrate. The higher nitrates, or **pyrocellulose,** are employed for making explosives. It was originally called **guncotton,** and the original United States government name for the explosive was **Indurite,** from the Indian Head Naval Powder Factory. It was called **cordite** in England. The nitrated cellulose is mixed with alcohol and ether, kneaded into a dough, and squeezed through orifices into long multitubular strings which are cut into short cylindrical grains. Solid grains become smaller as they burn, so that there would be high initial pressure and then a decreasing pressure of gases. When the multitubular grains burn, the surface becomes greater and thus there is increasing pressure. **FNH powder,** or **flashless powder,** is nitrocellulose which is nonhygroscopic and which contains a partially inert coolant, such as potassium sulfate, to reduce the muzzle flash of the gun. **Ballistite** is a rapid-burning, double-base powder used in shotgun shells and as a propellant in rockets. It is composed of 60% nitrocellulose and 40% nitroglycerin, made into square flakes 0.005 in. thick or extruded in cruciform blocks.

NITROGEN. An element, symbol N, which at ordinary temperatures is an odorless and colorless gas. The atmosphere contains 78% nitrogen in the free state. It is nonpoisonous and does not support combustion. Nitrogen is often called an inert gas, and is used for some inert atmospheres for metal treating and in light bulbs to prevent arcing, but it is not chemically inert. It is a necessary element in animal and plant life, and is a constituent of many useful compounds. Lightning forms small amounts of nitric oxide from the air which is converted into nitric acid and nitrates, and bacteria continuously convert atmospheric nitrogen into nitrates. Nitrogen combines with many metals to form hard nitrides useful as wear-resistant and heat-resistant materials. Small amounts of nitrogen in steels inhibit grain growth at high temperatures, and also increase the strength of some steels.   It is also used to produce a hard surface on steels.   Nitrogen has five isotopes, and **nitrogen 15** is produced in enrichments to 95% for use as a tracer.

Most of the industrial use of nitrogen is through the medium of nitric acid, obtained from natural nitrates or from the atmosphere.   Fixation of nitrogen is a term applied to any process whereby nitrogen from the air is transferred into nitrogen compounds, or **fixed nitrogen,** such as nitric acid or ammonia.   The first step is by passing air through an electric arc to produce **nitric oxide,** NO, a heavy, colorless gas, which oxidizes easily to form **nitrogen dioxide,** NO_2, a brown-colored gas of a disagreeable odor. This oxide reacts with water to form nitric acid.   Or, atmospheric nitrogen can be converted to the oxide by irradiation of the compressed heated air with uranium oxide.   **Calcium cyanamide,** $CaCN_2$, made by reacting atmospheric nitrogen with calcium carbide, is used as a fertilizer and as a chemical raw material.   The chemical radical **cyanamid,** or **hydrogen cyanamide,** $H_2N \cdot C\!:\!N$, is marketed as a stable, colorless 50% aqueous concentrate.   The nitrogen-containing gas **Drycolene,** of the General Electric Co., used for furnace atmospheres for sintering metals, contains 78% N_2, 20 CO, and 2 H_2.   It is produced by burning hydrocarbon gases and air, removing the moisture, and passing through incandescent charcoal to convert the CO_2 and residual moisture to CO and H_2.   Nitrogen liquefies at about $-195°C$, and solidifies at about $-210°C$.   Nitrogen gas occupies 696 times as much space as the **liquid nitrogen** used in surgery.

NITROGLYCERIN. A heavy, oily liquid known chemically as **glyceryl trinitrate** and having the empirical formula $C_3H_5(NO_3)_3$.   It is made by the action of nitric acid on glycerin in the presence of sulfuric acid.   It is highly explosive, detonating upon concussion.   Liquid nitroglycerin when exploded forms carbonic acid, CO_2, water vapor, nitrogen, and oxygen; 1 lb is converted into 156.7 cu ft of gas.   The temperature of explosion is about 6280°F.   For use as a commercial explosive it is mixed with absorbents, usually kieselguhr or wood flour, under the name of **dynamite.** Cartridges of high density explode with a greater shattering effect than those of low density.   By varying the density and also the mixture of the nitroglycerin with ammonium nitrate, which gives a heaving action, a great diversity in properties can be obtained.

Dynamites are rated on the percentage, by weight, of the nitroglycerin that they contain.   A 25% dynamite has 25% by weight of nitroglycerin, and has a rate of detonation of 11,800 ft per sec.   The regular grades contain from 25 to 60%.   **Ditching dynamite** is the 50% grade.   It has a rate of detonation of 17,400 ft per sec, and will detonate sympathetically from charge to charge along a ditch line.   **Extra dynamite** has half of the nitroglycerin replaced by ammonium nitrate. It is not so quick and shattering, and not as water-resistant, but is lower in cost. It is used for quarrying, for stump and boulder blasting, and for highway work. A 50% extra dynamite has a detonation rate of 10,800 ft per sec. **Hercomite** and **Hercotol** are extra dynamites of Hercules, Inc., while **Durox** is an ammonium dynamite of Du Pont, and **Agritol,** a low-velocity dynamite, also of Du Pont is a low-density ammonium dynamite for stump blasting.

Gelatin dynamite is made by dissolving a special grade of nitrocotton in nitroglycerin. It has less fumes, is more water-resistant, and its plasticity makes it more adaptable for loading solidly in holes for underground work. It is marketed as straight gelatin or as **ammonium gelatin,** called **gelatin extra.** The gelatin dynamites come in grades from 20 to 90%. All have a detonation rate of 8,500 ft per sec, but modified high-pressure gelatin has rates to 19,700 ft per sec. These, however, produce large amounts of fumes and are not for use in mines or confined spaces. **Blasting gelatin,** called **oil-well explosive,** is a 100% dense and waterproof gelatin with the appearance of crude rubber, and having a detonation rate of 8,500 ft per sec. **Gelamite** and **Hercogel** are gelatin **blasting dynamites** of Hercules, Inc., although the **Bituminite,** of this company, is a slow permissible ammonium nitrate dynamite for coal mines. **Gelobel** is a gelatin dynamite, and **Monobel** is an ammonium dynamite marketed by Du Pont for mine blasting. The **Gelodyn explosive** of the Atlas Powder Co. is a combination of ammonium gelatin dynamite that is plastic, gives a shattering effect, and does not produce excessive fumes. It is used for construction blasting. **Amocol,** of this company, is a blasting explosive composed of grained ammonium nitrate mixed with ground coal. The double-base solid propellant for rockets, known as **ballistite,** is nitroglycerin-nitrocellulose. With potassium perchlorate as an oxidizer it gives a specific impulse of 180 to 195. It leaves plumes of white smoke. Dynamite is also sometimes used for explosive metal forming as it releases energy at a constant rate regardless of confinement, and produces pressures to 2,000,000 psi. For bonding **metal laminates** a thin sheet, or film, of the explosive is placed on top of the composite, and the progressive burning of the explosive across the film produces an explosive force downward and in vectors that produces a microscopic wave, or ripple, in the alloyed bond that strengthens the bond but is not visible on the laminated sheet.

NONDEFORMING STEEL. Also called **nonshrinking steel.** A group of alloy steels which have the characteristic that they do not easily deform, or go out of shape, when heat-treated. This property makes them suitable for making dies, gages, or tools that must be accurate. The usual nondeforming steel contains from 1 to 1.75% manganese, with or without chromium or other alloying elements. The carbon content is the same as tool steels of the same grade. The phosphorus, sulfur, and silicon impurities are kept as low as possible. The steels are oil-hardening, and do not have the tough core of ordinary tool steels. They have low resistance to shock and are thus not suited for bending or forming dies, except when they have additional alloying elements. But, except for such uses as blanking dies and reamers, the characteristic of nondeformation is not a leading specification in the procurement of a tool steel, and many alloyed tool steels are hardenable at relatively low temperatures and are nondeforming. The principle involved in the nondeforming quality is to obtain a steel so balanced in ingredients that there will be no serious phase changes, i.e., change in shape of the molecules, during the heating and cooling cycle. Structural steels for such uses as casement windows and doors must be nondeforming to assure close fit, and for this purpose many low-alloy steels are considered nondeforming.

Hi Wear 64 steel, of Carpenter Technology, a wear-resistant steel for feed rolls, molds for compacting powdered metals, and for blanking and forming dies for abrasive materials, contains 4% tungsten, 2 manganese, 1 molybdenum, 0.90 chromium, 0.25 silicon, and 1.50 carbon. When air-hardened from 1550°F and tempered at 350°F, a 1-in. piece will return to within 0.0005 in. of its original length, and it does not deform. The nondeforming steel marketed by the Cyclops Steel Co., under the name of **Wando,** contains 1.05% manganese, 0.50 chromium, 0.50 tungsten, and 0.95 carbon. It is employed for making intricate dies, taps, and other tools. **Mansil die steel,** of Henry Disston & Sons, Inc., is an oil-hardening steel containing 1.15% manganese, 0.90 carbon, 0.50 tungsten, and 0.50 chromium. It is deep-hardening, and is used for blanking dies, broaches, reamers, and gages. **Mangano,** of the Latrobe Electric Steel Co., contains about 1.60% manganese, 0.20 chromium, and 0.95 carbon. **Stentor,** of Carpenter Steel, is a nondeforming tool steel containing 1.6% manganese, 0.25 silicon, and 0.90 carbon. It hardens at a low temperature range, 1400 to 1440°F, which aids in avoiding warpage. **Vega steel,** of the same company, is an air-hardening nondeforming steel that hardens uniformly at low temperatures even in large sections. It contains 2% manganese, 1.35 molybdenum, 1 chromium, 0.30 silicon, and 0.70 carbon. It hardens to Rockwell C61 from a temperature of 1550°F. **A-H steel,** of the Bethlehem Steel Co., also has high manganese, 2%, with 1.5 chromium, 1 molybdenum, and 1 carbon. It machines easily when annealed, and air-hardens to Rockwell C62. **Exl-Die steel,** of the Columbia Tool Steel Co., and **Saratoga steel,** of the Allegheny Ludlum Steel Co., have about 1.15% manganese, 0.50 chromium, 0.50 tungsten, and 0.90 carbon. **Amcoh steel,** of A. Milne & Co., called **hollow-die steel,** for ring dies and drawing dies, also has tungsten. It contains 1.25% manganese, 0.50 chromium, 0.50 tungsten, 0.95 carbon, and is oil-hardening. **Hargus steel,**

of the Ziv Steel & Wire Co., for blanking dies, reamers, and gages, has 1% manganese, 0.35 nickel, and 1 carbon. A hollow-die steel of the Timken Roller Bearing Co., called **Graph-Mo steel,** has 1% manganese, 1.29 silicon, 0.25 molybdenum, and 1.45 carbon. The high carbon with silicon gives free graphite to aid machining when annealed, and provides hard carbides for wear resistance when hardened. **Truform steel,** of the Jessop Steel Co., is a high-manganese, oil-hardening steel for cutters and dies. **Deward steel,** of the Allegheny Ludlum Steel Co., contains 1.55% manganese, 0.90 carbon, and 0.30 molybdenum. **Paragon steel,** of the Crucible Steel Co., has about this amount of manganese with 0.50 to 0.75% chromium and 0.25 vanadium. **Kiski steel,** of Braeburn, is similar.

Many of the high-chromium, wear-resistant steels are designated as nondeforming. **Airvan steel,** of Firth Sterling, Inc., used for heavy-duty blanking and forming dies, contains 5.25% chromium, 1.15 molybdenum, 0.25 vanadium, and 1 carbon. When hardened by air cooling, it has a hardness of Rockwell C64 with a compressive strength of 570,000 psi, and when tempered at about 950°F to remove strains, the hardness is Rockwell C59 with added toughness. **Chromovan steel,** of this company, is a nondeforming, wear-resistant steel for coining dies and thread-rolling dies. It has 12.5% chromium, 1.6 carbon, 0.80 molybdenum, and 1 vanadium. **A-H5 steel,** of Bethlehem Steel, is a die steel that has high resistance to distortion and is also wear-resistant and shock-resistant. It contains 1% carbon, 5.25 chromium, 1.1 molybdenum, 0.25 vanadium, and 0.60 manganese. It anneals to 212 Brinell and air-hardens to Rockwell C62. **Carpenter No. 484 steel** is an air-hardening steel for dies and tools. It has 5% chromium, 1 molybdenum, 0.20 vanadium, 0.70 manganese, 0.20 silicon, and 0.95 carbon. **Carpenter No. 883** is a tougher tool steel for forging dies and bulldozer dies. It has 5% chromium, 135 molybdenum, 0.45 vanadium, 1.10 silicon, 0.35 manganese, and 0.40 carbon. **Airtem steel,** of the Lehigh Steel Co., used for blanking and forming dies, has 5.25% chromium, 1.25 molybdenum, 1 silicon, 0.50 manganese, 0.30 vanadium, and 1.30 carbon. It is also shock-resistant. **Air-kool steel,** of the Crucible Steel Co. of America, used for blanking and trimming dies and gages, has 5.25% chromium, 1.15 molybdenum, 0.50 vanadium, and 0.95 carbon. **Sagamore steel,** of Allegheny Ludlum, has 5% chromium, 1 molybdenum, 0.25 vanadium, and 1 carbon. **Ontario steel,** of the same company, is a steel for greater resistance to abrasion. It contains 12% chromium, 0.80 molybdenum, 0.25 vanadium, and 1.5 carbon.

NONMAGNETIC STEEL. Steel and iron alloys used where it is important that no magnetic circuits be set up or magnetic effects be induced. Manganese steel containing 14% manganese is nonmagnetic and casts readily but is not machinable. Nickel steel containing high nickel is also nonmagnetic. Many mills regularly produce nonmagnetic steels containing from 20 to 30% nickel. Manganese-nickel steels and manganese-nickel-chromium steels are nonmagnetic and may be arranged to combine desirable features of the nickel and manganese steels. A nonmagnetic steel of the Jessop Steel Co. has 10.5 to 12.5% manganese, 7 to 8 nickel, and 0.25 to 0.40 carbon. The electrical resistance is 70 microhms per cu cm compared with 5 to 7 for brass. It has low magnetic permeability and low eddy-current loss, can be machined readily, and work-hardens only slightly. The tensile strength is 80,000 to 110,000 psi, elongation 25 to 50%, and specific gravity 8.02. It is austenitic and cannot be hardened. The 18–8 austenitic chromium-nickel steels are also nonmagnetic. The nonmagnetic alloy used for watch gears and escapement wheels is not a steel but is a **cupronickel-manganese** containing 60% copper, 20 nickel, and 20 manganese. It is very hard, but can be machined with diamond tools.

NONSHATTERING GLASS. Also referred to as **shatterproof glass, laminated glass,** or **safety glass,** and when used in armored cars it is known as **bulletproof glass.** A material composed of two sheets of plate glass with a sheet of transparent resinoid between, the whole molded together under heat and pressure. When subjected to a severe blow, it will crack without shattering. The first of these was a German product marketed under the name af **Kinonglas,** which consisted of two clear glass plates with a cellulose nitrate sheet between, and was first used for protective shields against chips from machines. Nonshattering glass is now largely used for automobile and car windows. The original cellulose nitrate interlining sheets had the disadvantage that they were not stable to light and became cloudy. Cellulose acetate was later substituted. It is opaque to actinic rays and prevents sunstroke but has the disadvantage of opening in cold weather, permitting moisture to enter between the layers. The acrylic resins are notable for their stability in this use; in some cases they are used alone without the plate glass, especially for aircraft windows. Polyvinyl acetal resins, as interlinings for safety glass, are weather-resistant and will not discolor. Polyvinyl butyral is much used as an interlayer, but in airplane glass at temperatures above 150°F it tends to bubble and ripple. Silicone resins used for this purpose will withstand heats to 350°F, and they are not brittle at subzero temperatures. **Silastic Type K,** of the Dow Chemical Co., is such a silicone resin used as an interlayer. **Flexseal,** of the Pittsburgh Plate Glass Co., is a laminated plate glass with a vinyl resin interplate with an extension for sealing into the window frame. It will withstand pressure of 20 psi, with a $1/8$-in. plastic interplate, and is used for aircraft windows. **Duplate** is the trade name of the Duplate Corp. for a nonshattering glass. Standard bulletproof glass is from $1\frac{1}{2}$ in., 3 ply, to 6 in., 5 or more ply.

NONWOVEN FABRIC. Cloth made by sheeting random fibers by a process similar to papermaking, but with more careful randomization of the fibers.   There are two general types, one in which heat-sensitive synthetic fibers are bonded to each other by application of heat and pressure, and the other in which a plastic bonding agent is used.   All types of textile fibers or blends are used, but synthetic fibers are usually used and are sometimes blended with cotton.   Some upholstery and industrial fabrics are made of cotton fibers and then coated on one side with a vinyl resin.   For draperies and special uses, the nonwoven fabrics may be had in very great widths. The fabrics come in any color, in printed designs, or embossed.   Their advantages over woven fabrics are light weight, smooth surface, and absence of raveling.   They may be had with high stiffness for interlining, with porosity for filtering, or with high absorbency for toweling.   **Pellon,** of the Pellon Corp., is such a fabric for interlinings made with 75% nylon and a mixture of cotton and rayon.   It is bonded with a synthetic rubber. **Miracloth,** of the Visking Corp., is a lint-free, nonwoven cotton fabric for wiping cloths.   **Viskon,** of the same company, is a name for a general line of nonwoven fabrics.   **Masslin** is the trade name of the Chicopee Mills for nonwoven fabrics, and **Webril** is the designation of the Kendall Mills for a variety of nonwoven fabrics.   **Plastavon,** of the Avondale Mills, is the name of a line of nonwoven fabrics made with a web of cotton fibers running in one direction and bonded with a plastic film.   The **Troyfelt fabrics** of the Troy Blanket Mills are made with Orlon, Dacron, or other synthetic fibers matted without a binder.

NUTMEG. The brown, round, wrinkled seed of the plumlike fruit of the evergreen tree *Myristica fragrans,* native to the Moluccas but now grown extensively also in Grenada.   The bright-red aril covering of the seed is called **mace.**   The trees average about 20 lb of kernels per year, but a large tree may bear as many as 10,000 nutmegs annually.   The average yield in Grenada is taken as 1,500 lb of green nutmegs per acre per year, giving 720 lb of dry sound nutmegs and 150 lb of mace per acre. The nutmeg tree grows best on tropical islands at a height of 500 to 1,500 ft above sea level.   It begins to bear at 6 years, and will bear for a century.   The ripe fruit splits, and the seeds fall to the ground.   Nutmeg is a delicately flavored spice for foodstuffs, but in large amounts is highly toxic.   Mace has a finer but weaker flavor and is used as a savory, but the **oleoresin mace** of Fritzsche Bros., Inc., a dark-brown liquid produced from mace, gives a lasting spicy nutmeg flavor, and is used as a substitute for nutmeg oil.   **Nutmeg butter** is a solid yellow fat obtained from the rejected nutmegs of the spice trade.   To obtain the fat the kernels are roasted and ground before extraction.   The nutmeg contains about 40% of the fat.   It is used chiefly in ointments.   **Nutmeg oil** is an essential oil extracted from the nutmeg and used in medicine, in flavoring tobacco, and in dentrifices.   It is also called **myristica oil** and is high in **myristicin,** a yellow poisonous oil of the composition $C_3H_5 \cdot C_6H_2(O_2CH_2)OCH_3$.   It is now synthesized from pine oil.

NUX VOMICA. The seeds of the ripe fruit of the deciduous tree *Strychnos nux vomica* of India, Ceylon, and Australia, used as the source of the alkaloids strychnine and brucine.   The powdered seed may also be used.   The fruits contain three to five hard grayish seeds which yield 1 to 1.25% strychnine alkaloid and about the same amount of brucine.   **Strychnine** is an odorless, crystalline, intensely bitter powder of the composition $C_{21}H_{22}N_2O_2$ with a very complex multiring molecular structure.   It is a spinal stimulant and in quantity is a violent convulsive poison.   It is used in proprietary and prescription medicines of the tonic class, and also in rat poisons.   For medicinal use it is used mostly in the form of **strychnine sulfate** which is easily soluble in water.   **Brucine** is a bitter crystalline alkaloid of the composition $C_{23}H_{26}N_2O_4$ with similar characteristics but much less active.   It is **dimethoxy strychnine.**   It is also used as a denaturant for rapeseed oil and other industrial oils.   The woody vine **woorali,** *S. toxifera,* of the Amazon and Orinoco valleys, from which the arrow poison **curare** was obtained, contains strychnine and **curine,** a benzyl isoquinoline alkaloid.   Curare inactivates the motor nerves without affecting the sensory and central nervous system, and is used in medicine as a local anesthetic.   The synthetic **Mytolon,** of Winthrop-Stearns, is used as a more potent and safer substitute.   It is a complex diethylamino propylamino benzoquinone benzyl chloride in the form of red crystals.

NYLON. A group of polyamide resins which are long-chain polymeric amides in which the amide groups form an integral part of the main polymer chain, and which have the characteristic that when formed into a filament the structural elements are oriented in the direction of the axis. Nylon was originally developed as a textile fiber, and high tensile strengths, above 50,000 psi, are obtainable in the fibers and films.   But this high strength is not obtained in the molded or extruded resins because of the lack of oriented stretching.   When nylon powder that has been precipitated from solution is pressed and sintered, the parts have high crystallinity and very high compressive strength, but they are not as tough as molded nylon.

Nylon may be defined as a class of plastics produced from the polymerization of a dibasic acid and a diamine.   The most common one of the group is that obtained by the reaction of adipic acid with hexamethylene diamine.   Each of these has six carbon atoms, and the product is called **nylon 66.**   The nylon molding and extruding resin of Du Pont, **Elvamide 8042,** formerly **Zytel 42,** has a tensile strength of 12,500 psi with elongation above 100%, a flexural strength of 13,800 psi, hardness of Rockwell R118, a flow temperature of 480°F, and a dielectric strength of 350 volts per mil.

All of the nylons are highly resistant to common solvents and to alkalies, but are attacked by strong mineral acids. Molded parts have light weight, with a specific gravity about 1.14, good shock-absorbing ability, very low coefficient of friction, and high melting point, up to about 482°F. They are much used for such parts as gears, bearings, cams, and linkages. The electrical characteristics are about the same as those of the cellulosic plastics. As a wire insulation, nylon is valued for its toughness and solvent resistance. **Nylon fibers** are strong, tough, and elastic, and have high gloss. The fine fibers are easily spun into yarns for weaving or knitting either alone or in blends with other fibers, and they can be crimped and heat-set. The **Nyloft fiber** of the Firestone Tire & Rubber Co., used for making carpets, is nylon staple fiber, lofted, or wrinkled, to give the carpet a bulky texture resembling wool. **Caprolan tire cord,** made from nylon 6 of high molecular weight, has the yarn drawn to four or five times its original length to orient the polymer and give one-half twist per inch. **Nylon film** is made in thicknesses down to 0.002 in. for heat-sealed wrapping, especially for food products where tight impermeable enclosures are needed. **Nylon sheet,** for gaskets and laminated facings, comes transparent or in colors in thicknesses from 0.005 to 0.060 in. **Nylon monofilament** is used for brushes, surgical sutures, tennis strings, and fishing lines. Filament and fiber, when stretched, have a low specific gravity down to 1.068, and the tensile strength may be well above 50,000 psi.

Nylon fibers made by condensation with oxalic acid esters have high resistance to fatigue when wet. Other grades of nylon are made for specialty purposes, but the standard types are those designated by the carbon numbers. **Nylon 6** is made from **caprolactam,** which has the empirical formula $(CH_2)_5NH \cdot C:O$, with a single 6-carbon ring. Molded parts have a tensile strength of 11,700 psi, elongation 70%, dielectric strength 440 volts per mil, and melting point 420°F. **Nylon foam,** or **cellular nylon,** for lightweight buoys and flotation products, is made from nylon 6. The foam is produced by Du Pont in slabs, rods, and sheets. Densities range from 1 to 8 lb per cu ft. The low densities are flexible, but the high-density material is rigid with a load-carrying capacity about the same as that of balsa wood. **Nylon 9** is made from soybean oil by reacting with ozone. It has better water resistance than other nylons and is used for coatings. **Nylon 11,** originally marketed in France as **Rilsan,** is a polycondensation product of **amino undeconoic acid** which is made by a complex process from the recinoleic acid of castor oil. This type of nylon has superior dimensional stability and is valued for injection moldings. **Nylon 12** is a similar plastic. It is a lauro lactam synthesized from butadiene. It has low water absorption and good strength and stability, and it is used for packaging film, coatings for metals, and moldings. **Nylon 4** is a polypyrrolidine used for textile fibers. The molecular chain has more amide groups than do the chains of other nylons, and its ability to absorb moisture is about the same as that of cotton. Fabrics made from it do not have the hot feel usual with other synthetic fibers and they have better pressability and are free of static. **Alrac Nylon,** of Radiation Research Corp., is nylon 4. Moldings of **nylon 6-6** have a specific gravity of 1.14, tensile strength of 11,500 psi, and elongation. It is used for gears and mechanical parts and its physical properties may be further increased by adding glass fibers or spheres as filler.

Nylon products are marketed under many trade names. **Nylatron G,** of the Polymer Corp., is graphite-impregnated nylon in rods and strip for making gears, bearings, and packings. **Nylasint,** of this company, for bearings, is sintered nylon impregnated with oil. **Flalon,** of Burgess-Berliner Assoc., is a **nylon flannel** of 15-denier crimped fibers carded on both faces. It has the appearance of cotton flannel, but is superior in heat resistance and wear resistance. **Raynile,** of Hewitt-Robbins, Inc., is a rayon-nylon fabric with nylon traverse threads. It is flexible and has about twice the strength of cotton fabric. It is used for conveyor belts. **Fiber-thin,** of the U.S. Rubber Co., is a thin waterproof fabric used to replace heavier tarpaulins for protective coverings. It is woven of nylon and coated with plastic. It weighs 5 oz per sq yd, and has a tensile strength of 175 lb per in. of width. **Facilon,** of Sun Chemical Corp., a caprolan nylon fabric impregnated with vinyl resin, is used for facing wall panels and flexible floor coverings. It comes in colors and embossings.

OAK. The wood of a large variety of oak trees, all of the natural order *Cupuliferae,* genus *Quercus.* European oak, under various names, such as **Austrian oak** and **British oak,** are from two varieties of the tree *Q. robur.* The wood is light brown in color, with a coarse, open grain, firm texture, and weight of about 45 lb per cu ft. **American red oak** is from the tree *Q. rubra* or *Q. falcata.* It is also called **black oak,** although black oak is from the *Q. velutina,* and the **red oak** of the Lake states is *Q. borealis.* The heartwood is reddish brown, and the sapwood whitish. **Southern red oak** of the Gulf Coast, a valued wood for furniture and cabinetwork, is the **shumard oak,** *Q. shumardii,* also known as **Schneck oak** and **Texas oak. Nuttall oak,** *Q. nuttallii,* of the lower Mississippi Valley, is also called red oak. American **white oak** is from the tree *Q. alba* of the eastern states. The heartwood is brown, and the sapwood white. The grain of these species is coarse, but the texture is firm. **Post oak,** of the southern states, is *Q. stellata.* **Chestnut oak,** of the Appalachian range, is *Q. montana,* but this name is also applied to the **chinquapin oak,** *Q.*

muehlenbergii, a large tree which grows profusely over a wide area of the eastern half of the United States, and was early valued for railroad ties and heavy construction timbers. **Overcup oak,** *Q. lyrata,* is an important tree from New Jersey to Texas. **Scarlet oak,** of Pennsylvania, is *Q. coccinea.* **Western white oak,** *Q. garryana,* has a more compact texture and straighter grain. **Spanish oak,** *Q. oblongifolia,* is native to California and New Mexico. The grain is finer and denser. American oaks are widely distributed in the United States and Canada. There are more than 400 varieties of oak on the North American continent. An enormous stand of oak in Costa Rica is made up of immense trees of **copey oak,** *Q. copeyensis,* the trees being up to 8 ft in diameter with clean boles to 80 ft to the first limb. The wood has a hardness between that of white and live oaks, and the bark has a high content of tannin.

Oak is used for flooring, furniture, cask staves, and where a hard, tough wood is needed. For cabinetwork the boards are variously sawed at angles and quarters to obtain grain effects known as **quartered oak. Fumed oak** is not a kind of oak, but a finish produced by the action of ammonia vapor. **Butt oak,** or **pollard oak,** also known as **burrwood,** is the wood of the decapitated **European oak** trees, *Q. pedunculata* and *Q. sessiliflora,* of Great Britain. A pollard tree is one whose head has been cut for ornamentation purposes. The growth in height is permanently arrested and innumerable branches shoot out from the trunk, which produce humps, or burrs, with the grain of the wood running in all directions. **Burr oak** is valued for ornamental work. Burr oak of the northern and central United States is not a pollard oak but is a name for the tree *Q. macrocarpa.* The commercial red and white oaks have an average gravity when kiln-dried of 0.69. The compressive strength perpendicular to the grain is 1,870 psi, with shearing strength parallel to the grain of 1,300 psi.

The woods often called oaks in the Southern Hemisphere are not true oaks. **Australian oaks** are from a variety of trees, and **Chilean oak** is from a species of beech. **Beef oak,** of Australia, is a hard, heavy, brownish wood from the tree *Grevillea striata.* It has an irregular grain. **She oak** is from the Australian tree *Casuarina stricta,* and **swamp oak** is from *C. suberosa.* These woods are lighter in weight than oak. **Silky oak,** used for cabinetwork, is a brownish wood that has a uniform texture and can be quartersawn to show attractive figuring. It is from the tree *Cardwellia sublimis* of Australia.

Oak extract, which is an important tanning material for the best grades of heavy leather, is chiefly from the bark of the **swamp chestnut oak,** *Q. prinus,* but also from the white oak and red oak. The **tanbark oak** of California is the tree *Lithocarpus densiflora.* The extract of the **scarlet oak,** *Q. coccinea,* is dark in color and is known as **quercitron extract.** The bark of the tanbark oak yields 10 to 14% tannin, but the extract contains

25 to 27% tannin.   **Quercetin** is a complex phenyl benzyl pyrone derived from oak bark and from Douglas fir bark.   It is an antioxidant and absorber of ultraviolet rays, and is used in rubber, plastics, and in vegetable oils.   **Valonia** consists of the acorn cups of the oak *Q. aegilops* of Asia Minor and the Balkans.   **Smyrna valonia** contains 32 to 36% tannin which produces a light-colored, lightweight leather with a firm texture and bloom.   When used alone, however, valonia makes a brittle leather, and is thus always used in blends.   Valonia is marketed as cups or as extract, the latter containing about 60% tannin.

OATS. An important grain which is the seed of the tall plant *Avena sativa.* The grain is surrounded by a hull, and grows in many spikelets as a spreading or one-sided panicle inflorescence.   It can be grown farther north than any other grain except rye, and on poor soils.   Although it is one of the most nutritious of grains, most of the oats grown in the United States are used for animal feed.   **Rolled oats** and **oatmeal** are used as cereal foods and for some bakery products, but the grain is not suitable for breadmaking.   **Oat hulls** are used for the production of furfural and other chemicals.   The largest production of oats is in the United States and Russia, but large quantities are produced in Canada, western Europe, and Argentina.   It is the chief grain crop of Scotland.   The yield per acre in the United States is about 30 bu, but it is twice that figure in Great Britain.   Oats are often called by the Spanish name **avena** in international trade.   **Turkish oats,** cultivated in central Europe, are from the species *A. orientalis.*   **Horse gram,** used as a substitute for oats in India, is from the plant *Dolichus bifloris.*   The **gram,** from the *Cicer arientinum,* is an important food grain in India.

OCHRE. A compact form of earth used for paint pigments and as a filler for linoleum.   It is an argillaceous and siliceous material, often containing compounds of barium or calcium, and owing the yellow, brown, or red colors to hydrated iron oxide.   The tints depend chiefly upon the proportions of silica, white clay, and iron oxide.   Ochres are very stable as pigments.   They are prepared by careful selection, washing, and grinding in oil.   They are inert, and are not affected by light, air, or ordinary gases.   They are rarely adulterated, because of their cheapness, but are sometimes mixed with other minerals to alter the colors.   **Chinese yellow** and many other names are applied to the ochres.   **Golden ochre** is ochre mixed with chrome yellow.   **White ochre** is ordinary clay.   A large part of the American ochre is produced in Georgia.   **Sienna** is a brownish-yellow ochre found in Italy and Cyprus.   The material in its natural state is called **raw sienna.**   **Burnt sienna** is the material calcined to a chestnut color.   Indian red and Venetian red are hematite ochres.

Vandyke brown is a deep-brown pigment made originally from lignitic ochre from Cassel, Germany.   It was named after the Dutch painter Van Dyck, and is also called **Cassel brown, Cassel earth,** and **Rubens brown.** It is also obtained from low-grade coals of Oklahoma and California. Imitation Vandyke brown is made from a mixture of lampblack, yellow ochre, and iron oxide.   **Cologne earth** is a Vandyke brown made from American clays which are mixtures of ochre, clay, and bituminous matter, roasted to make the color dark.   **Yellow ochre** and **brown ochre** are limonite, but yellow iron oxide is made in Germany by the aeration of scrap iron in the presence of copperas.   **Umber** is a brown siliceous earth colored naturally with iron oxides and manganese oxide.   It comes chiefly from Italy and Cyprus.   For use as a pigment it is washed with water and finely ground.   It is inert and very stable.   **Cyprus umber** is a rich coffee-brown color and as a pigment has good covering qualities.   It is a modified marl with impregnations of iron and manganese.   **Burnt umber** is redder in color than umber, and is made by calcining the raw umber.   **Caledonian brown** and **Cappagh brown** are varieties of umber found in Great Britain.

OILCLOTH. A fabric of woven cotton, jute, or hemp, heavily coated with turpentine and resin compositions, usually ornamented with printed patterns, and varnished.   It was employed chiefly as a floor covering, but a light, flexible variety having a foundation of muslin is used as a covering material.   This class comes in plain colors or in printed designs.   It was formerly the standard military material for coverings and ground protection, but has been replaced by synthetic fabrics.   **Oilskin** is a cotton or linen fabric impregnated with linseed oil to make it waterproof.   It was used for coverings for cargo and for waterproof coats, but has now been replaced by coated fabrics.   **Oiled silk** is a thin silk fabric impregnated with blown linseed oil which is oxidized and polymerized by heat.   It is waterproof, very pliable, and semitransparent.   It was much used for linings, but has now been replaced by fabrics coated with synthetics.

OILS. A large group of fatty substances which are divided into three general classes: vegetable oils, animal oils, and mineral oils.   The vegetable oils are either fixed or volatile oils.   The fixed oils are present in the plant in combined form, and are largely glycerides of stearic, oleic, palmitic, and other acids, and they vary in consistency from light fluidity to solid fats.   They nearly all boil at 500 to 600°F, decomposing into other compounds.   The volatile, or essential, oils are present in uncombined form and bear distillation without chemical change.   Oils are found in all plants, particularly in the seeds, and in nearly all parts of animal bodies.   Fish oils are thick, with a strong odor.   Vegetable and animal oils are obtained by pressing, extraction, or distillation.   Oils that absorb oxygen easily and become thick are known as drying oils and are valued for varnishes, because on drying they form a hard, elastic, waterproof film. Unsaturation is proportional to the number of double bonds, and in food oils these govern the cholesterol depressant effect of the oil.   Oils and fats are distinguished by consistency only, but waxes are not oils.   Mineral oils are derived from petroleum or shale and are classified separately.   The most prolific sources of vegetable oils are palm kernels and copra.   About 2,500 lb of palm oil is produced per acre annually, and the yield of coconut oil per acre from plantation plantings is 1,200 lb.   This compares with 350 lb of oil per acre from peanuts and 200 lb per acre from soybeans. Under comparable aggressive plantation work, from 10 to 20 times more palm and coconut oil can be produced per acre than peanut or soybean oil. Babassu oil is almost chemically identical with coconut oil, and vast quantities of babassu nuts grow wild in northeast Brazil.

Blown oils are fatty oils that have been oxidized by blowing air through them while hot, thereby thickening the oil.   They are mixed with mineral oils to form special heavy lubricating oils such as marine engine oil, or are employed in cutting oils.   They are also used in paints and varnishes, as the drying power is increased by the oxidation.   The flash point and the iodine value are both lowered by the blowing.   The oils usually blown are rapeseed, cottonseed, linseed, fish, and whale oils.   The **blown fish oils** of the Archer-Daniels-Midland Co., used for paints, enamels, and printing inks, are preoxidized and destearinized, and have specific gravities from 0.980 to 1.025.   **Crystol oils,** of this company, are kettle-boiled fish oils for paints.

OILSTONE. A fine-grained, slaty silica rock used for sharpening edged tools.   The bluish-white and opaque white oilstones of fine grain from Arkansas are called **novaculite,** and received their name because they were originally used for razor sharpening.   They are composed of 99.5% chalcedony silica and are very hard with a fine grain.   Novaculite is a deposit from hot springs.   It is fine-grained and the ordinary grades are employed for the production of silica refractories.   Arkansas oilstones are either hard or soft and have a waxy luster.   They are shipped in large slabs or blocks, or in chips for tumbling barrel finishing.   **Washita oilstone,** from Hot Springs, Ark., is a hard compact white stone of uniform texture.   **Onachita stones** come in larger and sounder pieces but are coarser than the Arkansas.   **Water-of-Ayr stone,** also known as **Scotch hone,** is a fine sandstone used with water instead of with oil.   **Artificial oilstones** are also produced of aluminum oxide.   **India oilstone** was originally blocks of emery, but the name now may refer to aluminum oxide stones.

OITICICA OIL. A drying oil obtained from the kernels of the nuts of the tree *Licania rigida* of northeastern Brazil.   The oil contains about 80%

licanic acid, which, like the **eleostearic acid** of tung oil, gives a greater drying power than is apparent from the iodine value.   The specific gravity is 0.944 to 0.971, saponification value 187 to 193, and iodine number 142 to 155.   The properties as a varnish oil are much like those of tung oil, both producing wrinkled films when applied pure, and both lacking high gloss.   **Cicoil** is a name for a treated oiticica oil with improved qualities. The oiticica nuts are 1 to 2 in. long with the kernel about 60% of the nut, yielding about 60% oil.   The average yield per tree is 350 lb of nuts, but a full-grown tree may yield 10 times that amount.   Another species of the tree, *L. crassifolia,* of Surinam, yields a similar oil.   Mexican oiticica is from the nuts of another species and is called **cacahuanache oil.**   The kernels yield 69% of light-colored heavy oil.

OLEIC ACID.   Also called **red oil, elaine oil, octadecenoic acid,** and **rapic acid,** although the latter is a misnomer based on a former belief that it was the same as the erucic acid of rapeseed.   It occurs in most natural fats and oils in the form of the glyceride, and is obtained in the process of saponi- fication or by distillation.   Much of this acid is obtained from lard and other animal fats, but **Emery 3758-R,** of Emery Industries, is produced from soybean or other vegetable sources.   It is an oily liquid with a specific gravity of 0.890, boiling at 286°C.   Below about 14°C it forms colorless needles.   It is a complex acid of the composition $CH_3(CH_2)_7$-$CH:CH(CH_2)_7COOH$, and if heated to the boiling point of water it reacts with oxygen to form a complex mixture of acids, including a small percentage of acetic and formic acids.   When it is hydrogenated in food fats it converts to stearic acid.   When reacted with potassium hydroxide it is converted into an acetate and a palmitate.   It is also readily converted to pelargonic and other acids for making plastics.   Oleic acid is a basic foodstuff in the form of the glyceride, and the acid has a wide use for mak- ing soaps, as a chemical raw material, and for finishing textiles.   In soluble oils and cutting compounds it forms **sodium oleate,** $C_{17}H_{33}COONa$.   The two commercial grades of oleic acid, yellow and red, are known as distilled red oil and saponified.   They may be sold under trade names. **Ahcolein 810,** of Arnold, Hoffman & Co., Inc., is a clear, distilled red oil used for textile treating.   **Monoenoic acid** is a modified isomer of oleic acid which produces soaps that are nonirritating to the skin.   It is used in cosmetics.   **Hydrofol C-18,** of the Archer-Daniels-Midland Co., is this acid.

OLIVE OIL.   A pale greenish oily liquid extracted from the ripe fruit of the olive tree, *Olea europaea,* a small evergreen grown largely in the Medi- terranean countries but also in California and in Argentina.   The fruits are eaten ripe (purple) and green.   They are rich in oil, and vast quantities are crushed for oil.   The oil contains 69 to 85% oleic acid, 7 to 14 palmitic acid, 4 to 12 linoleic acid, with some stearic, arachidic, and myristic acids.   The specific gravity is 1.912, iodine value 85, and saponification value 190.   The best grades of the oil are used for food chiefly as a salad and cooking oil, and in canning sardines, but some is used in the manufacture of castile soaps.   The industrial oil consists of the **olive oil foots** obtained in the third pressing or in the last extraction with carbon bisulfide, and is used for finishing textiles, degumming silk, and in soaps. **Florence oil** is a grade of Italian olive oil.   In Italy olive oil is also known as **Lucca oil.**   **Synthetic olive oil,** or **olive-infused oil,** is used as a foodstuff.   It is made from highly refined corn oil by infusing the corn oil with about 20% of a paste made of finely ground, partly dehydrated ripe olives ground with a small amount of corn oil.   The olive-infused oil has the flavor of olive oil, and also contains carotene, or vitamin A, contained in the olive pulp.   Other fractionated oils reblended to give high oleic acid content are also used as substitutes for olive oil.   **Olevene,** of Jacques Wolf & Co., is a sulfonated synthetic oil used instead of olive oil for treating textiles.

OLIVINE.   A translucent mineral, usually occurring in granular form, employed as a refractory.   The formula is usually given as $(Mg \cdot Fe)_2 \cdot SiO_4$, but it is a solid solution of **forsterite,** $2MgO \cdot SiO_2$, and **fayalite,** $2FeO \cdot SiO_2$.   The fayalite lowers the refractory quality, but forsterite is not found alone.   The mineral is also called **chrysolite,** and the choice green stones used as gems are called **peridot.**   **Dunite** deposits in Washington and North Carolina carry up to 90% olivine which has only 5 to 15% fayalite.   It is olive green in color, vitreous, with a hardness of 6.5 to 7 and a specific gravity 3.3 to 3.5.   As a refractory it is neutral up to about 1600°C but may then react with silica.   The fayalite fuses out at 2700°F, making the material porous and subject to attack by iron oxide. Although the name olivine indicates a green color, not all is green.   Dunite takes its name from Dun Mountain of New Zealand, dun being the Irish and Scotch word for reddish brown.   The melting point of forsterite is 3470°F.   When used mixed with chrome ore, the low-fusing elements form a black glass which presents a nonporous face.   Some refractory material marketed as forsterite may be olivine blended with magnesite, or may be serpentine treated with magnesite.   **Forsterite firebrick** in the back walls of basic open-hearth steel furnaces gives longer life than silica brick but only two-thirds that of chrome-magnesite brick.   Forsterite refractories are usually made from olivine rock to which MgO is added to adjust the composition to $2MgO \cdot SiO_2$.   **Monticellite,** $CaMgSiO_4$, may also occur with forsterite.   They are also made by synthetic mixtures of MgO and silica.   The thermal expansion of olivine is lower than that of magnesite.   **Olivine sand** is substituted for silica sand as a foundry sand where silica is expensive.   There are large deposits of olivine in the Pacific Northwest.   When olivine is used as a foundry sand, it is noted that the heat-resisting qualities decrease with particle size.   Olivine contains from 27 to 30% magnesium metal, and is also used to produce magnesium by the electrolysis of the chloride.   **Magnesium-phosphate** fertilizer is made by fusing olivine with phosphate rock at 1600°C, tapping off the iron, and spray-cooling and crushing the residue.   It contains 20% citric acid–soluble phosphate, 14 MgO, 29 CaO, and 23 SiO_2, and is useful for acid soils.

ONYX. A variety of chalcedony silica mineral differing from agate only in the straightness of the layers.   The alternate bands of color are usually white and black, or white and red.   Onyx is artificially colored in the same way as agate.   It is used as an ornamental building stone, usually cut into slabs, and for decorative articles.   **Onyx marble** is limestone with impurities arranged in banded layers.   American onyx comes largely from Arizona, California, and Montana.   **Mexican onyx** is banded limestone obtained from stalactites in caves.   These materials are cut into such articles as lamp stands.   **Argentine onyx** is a dark-green or a green-yellow translucent stone of great decorative beauty.   In the United States it is called **Brazilian onyx** and is used for bookends, lamp bases, inkstands, and ornaments.   **Opalized wood** is an onyxlike petrified wood from Idaho.   It is cut into ornaments.

OPACIFIERS. Materials used in ceramic glazes and vitreous enamels primarily to make them nontransparent, but opacifiers may also enhance the luster, control the texture, promote craze resistance, or stabilize the color of the glaze.   An opacifier must have fire resistance so as not to vitrify or decrease the luster.   Tin oxide is a widely used white opacifier, and up to 3% also increases the fusibility of the glaze or enamel.   Titanium oxide adds scratch hardness and high acid resistance to the enamel.   It also increases the flow, making possible thinner coats which minimize chipping. Opacifiers may also serve as the pigment colors.   Thus, cobalt oxide gives a blue color, and platinum oxide gives a gray.   Lead chromate gives an attractive red color on glazes fired at 900°C, but when fired at 1000°C the lead chromate decomposes and a green chromium oxide is formed.   If the glaze is acid, the basic lead chromate is altered and the color tends toward green.   **Lufax 77A,** of the Rohm & Haas Co., is a crystalline zirconia which provides nuclei for the formation of zirconia crystals from the molten enamel, adding gloss and opacity and stabilizing the color on the blue side.   Antimony oxide as an opacifier gives opaque white enamels of great brilliance but is expensive and is poisonous.   The **zirconium opaci-**

fiers have a wide range of use from ordinary dishes to high-heat electrical porcelain and sanitary-ware enamels.   The amount of zirconium oxide used is a minimum of 3%.   The opacifiers may be in prepared form with lead oxide or other materials to give particular characteristics.   **Opax,** of the Titanium Alloy Mfg. Co., is a zirconium oxide with small percentages of silica, sodium oxide, and alumina.   It is used for hard-glaze dinnerware and wall-tile glaze.   **Zircopax** is zirconium silicate, $ZrSiO_4$, with 33.5% silica in the molecule.   It gives color stability and craze resistance.   **Super-pax,** of the same company, is a finely milled zirconium silicate powder with an average particle size less than 5 microns.   In white ceramic glazes very small amounts will give opacity.   The **Ultrox opacifiers** of M & T Chemicals, Inc., are refined zirconium silicates.   **Ultrox 1000W,** for maximum opacity and whiteness, has 65% ZrO_2 and 35 SiO_2 with particle size of 0.5 micron.   Lead oxide is used to lower the melting point of a glaze. Matte effects are obtained by adding barium oxide, magnesia, or other materials to the opacifier.

OPEN-HEARTH STEEL. Steel made by the process of melting pig iron and steel or iron scrap in a lined regenerative furnace, and boiling the mixture with the addition of pure lump iron ore, until the carbon is reduced.   The boiling is continued for a period of 3 to 4 hr.   The process was developed in 1861 by Siemens in England.   The furnaces contain regenerative chambers for the circulation and reversal of the gas and air. The fuels used are natural gas, fuel oil, coke-oven gas, or powdered coal. Both the acid- and basic-lined open-hearth furnaces are used, but most steel made in the United States is basic open hearth.   Ganister is used as a lining in the acid furnaces, and magnesite in the basic.

An advantage of the open-hearth furnace is the ability to handle raw materials that vary greatly and also to employ scrap.   Iron low in silicon requires less heating time.   The duplex process consists in melting the steel in an acid bessemer furnace until the silicon, the manganese, and part of the carbon have been oxidized, and then transferring to a basic open-hearth furnace where the phosphorus and the remainder of the carbon are removed.   Open-hearth steel is of uniform quality, and is produced in practically all types.

OPIUM. The dried juice from the unripe capsules of the **poppy plant,** *Papaver somniferum,* cultivated extensively in China, India, and the Near East, but also growing wild in many countries.   The opium poppy is an annual with white flowers.   After the petals drop off, the capsules are cut and the juice exudes and hardens.   The crude opium is a brownish mass. It contains about 20 alkaloids which are useful in medicine.   Opium alone is a powerful narcotic, but the material is usually processed and the alkaloids are employed separately or in combinations for their particular effects.

Morphine, $C_{17}H_{19}NO_3 \cdot H_2O$, a white powder melting at 253°C, is the most important of the opium alkaloids.   It is a powerful narcotic and pain-killer.   It has a complex five-ring molecular structure which can be synthesized from the three-ring **phenanthrene,** $C_{14}H_{10}$, an isomer of anthracene occurring in coal tar.   **Codeine,** a white powder melting at 247°C, is a methyl ether of morphine, and is a pain-killer less drastic than morphine. It is much used in cough medicines.   **Dionine** is **ethyl morphine,** and is also an important drug.   **Heroin** is **diacetyl morphine.**   It is a powerful narcotic, but its use is prohibited in the United States.   **Colchicine,** $C_{22}H_{25}$-NO_6, is a complex three-ring alkaloid used as a gout remedy.   Its action is to quicken the release of **heparin** from intestinal cells which decomposes fat in the blood and prevents blood clotting.   It is chemically similar to morphine, but has the acetyl amino group in a different position.

Laudanum is an alcohol solution of opium.   **Amidone** is a German synthetic morphine.   It is a diphenyl dimethylamino heptanone, is stronger than morphine as a pain-killer, and, like morphine, is an exhilarant and is habit-forming.   The English drug **Heptalgin** is a similar morphine substitute.   **Poppy-seed oil** is a colorless to reddish-yellow liquid of specific gravity of about 0.925 and iodine number 157 used as a drying oil in artists' varnishes.   The cold-pressed white oil is used locally as an edible oil.   The very dark grades are used in soaps and in paints.   The oil from the seed does not contain opium.

OPTICAL GLASS. A highly refined glass, usually a flint glass of special composition, or made from rock crystal, used for lenses and prisms.   It is cast, rolled, or pressed.   In addition to the regular glassmaking elements, silica and soda, optical glass contains barium, boron, and lead.   The high-refracting glasses contain abundant lead oxide or barium oxide, and the low-refracting glasses contain abundant silica or boron oxide.   A requirement of optical glass is transparency and freedom from color.   Traces of iron make the glass greenish, while manganese causes a purple tinge. First-quality optical glass should contain a minimum of 99.8% SiO_2. Borax is used in purifying and in increasing the strength and brilliance of the glass.   Besides the control of chemical composition, careful melting and cooling are necessary to obtain fine transparency, and then intense polishing.   The pouring temperature is about 1200°C.   The best optical glass has a transparency of 99%, compared witth 85 to 90% for ordinary window glass.   A **borate glass** with lanthanum and tantalum oxides but no silica is used for airplane-camera lenses and for eyepieces for wide-angle field glasses.   It has a high refractive index and a low dispersion. The **telescope mirror glass** of Owens-Illlinois, called **Cer-Vit optical glass,** has near zero expansion and no deflection of light rays.

Beryllium fluoride glass of the American Optical Co. is made by substituting beryllium fluoride for silicon dioxide.   It has a low refractive index with low color dispersion, and light travels faster through it than through ordinary optical glass.   It has the disadvantage that it is hygroscopic.

ORE. A metal-bearing mineral from which a metal or metallic compound can be extracted commercially.   Earths and rocks containing metals that cannot be extracted at a profit are not rated as ores.   Ores are named according to their leading useful metals.   The ores may be oxides, sulfides, halides, or oxygen salts.   A few metals also occur native in veins in the minerals.   Ores are usually crushed and separated and concentrated from the **gangue** with which they are associated, and then shipped as **concentrates** based on a definite metal or metal oxide content.   The metal content to make an ore commercial varies widely with the current price of the metal, and also with the content of other metals present in the ore. Normally, a sulfide copper ore should have 1.5% copper in the unconcentrated ore but, if gold or silver is present, an ore with much less copper is workable, or, if the deposit can be handled by high-production methods, a mineral of very low metal content can be utilized as ore.   Low-grade lead minerals can be worked if silver is recoverable, and low-grade manganese minerals become commercial when prices are high.   Thus, the term ore is only relative, and under different economic conditions, minerals that are not considered ores in one country may be much used as ores in another.

OSMIUM. A platinum-group metal noted for its high hardness, about 400 Brinell.   It also has a high specific gravity, 22.50, and a high melting point, 4890°F.   The boiling point is about 9900°F.   Osmium has a close-packed hexagonal crystal structure, and forms solid-solution alloys with platinum, having more than double the hardening power of iridium in platinum.   However, it is seldom used to replace iridium as a hardener except for fountain-pen tips where the alloy is called **osmiridium.** The name osmium comes from the Greek word meaning odor, and the tetroxide formed is highly poisonous.   Osmium is not affected by the common acids, and is not dissolved by aqua regia.   The metal is sold by the troy ounce, 1 cu in. weighing 11.86 troy oz.

OXALIC ACID. Also known as **ethane diacid.**   A strong organic acid of the composition HO_2CCOOH, which crystallizes as the ortho acid $(Ho)_3$-$CC(OH)_3$.   It reduces iron compounds, and is thus used in writing inks, in stain removers, and in metal polishes.   When it absorbs oxygen it is converted to the volatile carbon dioxide and to water, and it is used as a bleaching agent, as a mordant in dyeing, and in detergents.   Oxalic acid occurs naturally in some vegetables, notably **Swiss chard,** and is useful in carrying off excess calcium in the blood. The acid is produced by heating sodium formate and treating the resulting oxides with sulfuric acid, or it can be obtained by the action of nitric acid on sugar, or strong alkalies on sawdust. It comes in colorless crystals with a specific gravity of 1.653, melting at 101.5°C, and soluble in water and in alcohol. **Oxamide,** $(CONH_2)_2$, is a stable anhydrous derivative with a high melting point, 419°C. It is a white crystalline powder used in flameproofing and in wood treatment. **Potassium ferric oxalate,** $K_3Fe(C_2O_4)_3$, is stable in the dark, but is reduced by the action of light, and is used in photography.

OXYGEN. An abundant element, constituting about 89% of all water, 33% of the earth's crust, and 21% of the atmosphere. It combines readily with most of the other elements, forming their oxides. It is a colorless and odorless gas and can be produced easily by the electrolysis of water, which produces both oxygen and hydrogen, or by chilling air below −300°F, which produces both oxygen and nitrogen. The specific gravity of oxygen is 1.1056. It liquefies at −113°C at 59 atm. **Liquid oxygen** is a pale-blue, transparent, mobile liquid. As a gas, oxygen occupies 862 times as much space as the liquid. Oxygen is one of the most useful of the elements, and is marketed in steel cylinders under pressure, although most of the industrial uses are in the form of its compounds. An important direct use is in welding and metal cutting, for which it should be at least 99.5% pure.

Oxygen is the least refractive of all gases. It is the only gas capable of supporting respiration, but is harmful if inhaled pure for a long time. **Ozone** is an allotropic form of oxygen with three atoms of oxygen, O_3. It is formed in the air by lightning, or during the evaporation of water, particularly of spray in the sea. In minute quantities in the air it is an exhilarant, but pure ozone is an intense poison. It has a peculiar odor, which can be detected with 1 part in 20 million parts of air. Ozone is a powerful oxidizer, capable of breaking down most organic compounds, and bleaching vegetable colors. **Liquid ozone** explodes violently in contact with almost any organic substance. It is bright blue in color, and is not attracted by a magnet, although liquid oxygen is attracted. Ozone absorbs ultraviolet rays, and a normal blanket in the upper ozonosphere at heights of 60,000 to 140,000 ft, with 1 part per 100,000 of air, shields the earth from excess short-wave radiations from the sun. As an oxidizer in the rubber industry, ozone is known as **activated oxygen.** It is used widely as a catalyst in chemical reactions. It is made commercially by bombardment of oxygen with high-speed electrons.

Oxygen for bleaching and oxidizing purposes may be obtained from compounds that readily yield the gas, such as the liquid **hydrogen peroxide,**

H_2O_2, or the granular solid **sodium peroxide,** Na_2O_2.   The C.P. grade of hydrogen peroxide is a colorless liquid with 90% H_2O_2 and 10 water. The specific gravity is 1.39.   It contains 42% active oxygen by weight, and one volume yields 410 volumes of oxygen gas.   Grades for oxidation and bleaching contain 27.5 and 35% H_2O_2.   It is also used as an oxidizer for liquid fuels.   A variety of chemicals is used for providing oxygen for chemical reactions.   These are known as **oxidizers** or **oxidants,** and they may be peroxides or superoxides which are compounds with the oxygen atoms singly linked.   They break down into pure oxygen and a more stable reduced oxide.   Sodium peroxide is used in submarines to absorb carbon dioxide and water vapor and to give off oxygen to restore the air.   To provide oxygen in rockets and missiles, **lithium nitrate,** $LiNO_3$, with 70% available oxygen, and **lithium perchlorate,** $LiClO_4 \cdot 3H_2O$, with 60% available oxygen, are used.   Another rocket fuel oxidizer which is liquid under moderate pressure and is easily stored is **perchloryl fluoride,** ClO_3F, normally boiling at $-52°F$.

Albone, of Du Pont, is hydrogen peroxide, and **Solozone** is sodium peroxide with 20% available oxygen.   **Ingolin** was a German name for hydrogen peroxide used in rockets.   **Liquid air** was used in the first V-2 rockets, with alcohol, potassium permanganate, and hydrogen peroxide. Liquid air is used in the chemical industry, and for cold-treating.   It is atmospheric air liquefied under pressure, and contains more than 20% free oxygen.   The boiling point is $-310°F$, and 1 cu ft makes 792 cu ft of free air.

Tetrabutyl hydroperoxide, an organic peroxide, is a powerful oxidizing agent used as an accelerator in curing rubbers, as a drying agent in oils, paints, and varnishes, and as a combustion aid for diesel fuel oils.   The commercial 60% solution in water has a boiling point of 82°C and specific gravity of 0.859.   **Urea peroxide,** $(CO \cdot NH_2)_2O_2$, is a white crystalline material with 16% by weight of active oxygen, used in bleaching, polymerization, and in oxidation processes.   **Magnesium peroxide,** MgO_2, **calcium peroxide,** CaO_2, and **zinc peroxide,** ZnO_2, are stable white powders insoluble in water, containing, respectively, 14.2 ,13.6, and 7.4% active oxygen.   They are used where the oxidation is required to be at high temperatures.   **Uniperox,** of the Union Oil Co. of California, is a peroxide of the composition $C_7H_{13}OOH$, made from petroleum fractions.   At low temperatures it is stable, but at 110°C the decomposition is exothermic and rapid.   It is used as a diesel fuel additive to raise the cetane number, and also as a polymerization catalyst for synthetic resins.

OZOKERITE.   Also known as **mineral wax,** and as **earth wax.**   A natural paraffin found in Utah and in central Europe, and used as a substitute or extender of beeswax, and in polishes, candles, printing inks, crayons, sealing waxes, phonograph records, and insulation.   Ozokerite is a yellowish to black, greasy solid, melting at 55 to 110°C and having a specific gravity of 0.85 to 0.95.   It is soluble in alcohol, benzol, and naphtha, but not in water.   The wax occurs in rocks, which are crushed, and the wax is melted out.   The wax is then refined by boiling, treating with an alkali, and filtering.   The refined and treated ozokerite is called **ceresin** and is white to yellow in color and odorless.   The melting point is up to 142°F.   It is used for waxed paper, polishes, candles, and compounding.

A similar wax, called **montan wax,** or **lignite wax,** is produced in Germany from lignite.   Montan wax is white to dark brown in color, and has a melting point of 80 to 90°C, usually 83 to 85°C.   The wax is obtained from the powdered lignite by solvent extraction with a mixture of benzene and ethyl alcohol and subsequent removing of the bitumen by oxidation with chromic acid.   The brown coals of Oklahoma and Texas also contain as much as 13% montan wax.   **IG wax S** is extracted and purified montan wax, but **IG wax V** is a synthetic substitute consisting of the octadecyl ether of vinyl alcohol, $C_{17}H_{34}CH_2 \cdot O \cdot CH{:}CHOH$.   Montan wax is valued for leather finishes, polishes, phonograph records, insulation compounds, and as a hard wax in candles.   The mineral waxes are sold in white, waxy cakes, or in flakes.

PAINT. A general name to designate a solution of a pigment in water, oil, or organic solvent, used to cover wood or metal articles either for protection or for appearance.   Paints always contain pigments; the solutions of gums or resins, known as varnishes, are not paints, although their application is usually termed painting.   Enamels and lacquers, in the general sense, are under the classification of paints, but specifically the true paints do not contain gums or resins.   **Stain** is a varnish containing enough pigment or dye to alter the appearance or tone of wood in imitation of another wood, or to equalize the color in wood.   It is usually a dye rather than a paint.   **Enamel paint** is also a pigment in varnish.   The vast bulk of paint is made with about 65% pigment by weight and 35 vehicle.   The best **house paint** for outside work consists of high-grade pigment and linseed oil, with a small percentage of a thinner and drier.   The volatile thinner in paints is for ease of application, the drying oil determines the character of the film, the drier is to speed the drying rate, and the pigment gives color and hiding power.   Part or all of the oil may be replaced by a synthetic resin.

Paints are marketed in many grades, some containing pigments extended with silica, talc, barytes, gypsum, or other material; fish oils, or inferior semidrying oils in place of linseed oil; and mineral oils in place of turpentine.   Metal paints contain basic pigments such as red lead, ground in linseed oil, and should not contain sulfur compounds.   Red lead is a rust inhibitor, and is a good primer paint for iron and steel, though it is now largely replaced by chromate primers. White lead has a plasticizing effect which increases adhesion. It is stable and not subject to flaking. Between some pigments and the vehicle there is a reaction which results in progressive hardening of the film with consequent flaking or chalking, or there may be a development of water-soluble compounds. Linseed oil reacts with some basic pigments, giving chalking and flaking. Fading of a paint is usually from chalking. The composition of paints is based on relative volumes since the weights of pigments vary greatly, although the custom is to specify pounds of dry pigment per gallon of oil.

Bituminous paints are usually coal tar or asphalt in mineral spirits, used for the protection of piping and tanks, and for waterproofing concrete. For line pipe heavy pitch coatings are applied hot, but a bitumen primer is first applied cold. The **Bitumastic primer** of the Koppers Co., Inc., for such purpose, is refined coal-tar pitch in a quick-drying solvent. The bituminous paints have poor solvent resistance, but have high outdoor weathering resistance. **Battery paint** is usually asphalt or gilsonite in a petroleum solvent. It forms a heavy, acid-resistant, and water-resistant coating. Ordinary **aluminum paint** is made with aluminum flake in an oil varnish or in a synthetic lacquer. In lacquers the powder does not leaf, and the paint dries to a hard, metallic surface with a frosted effect. Aluminum paints will reflect 70% of the light rays, and they are used for painting tanks, but where high resistance is needed, especially for industrial atmospheres, the paints have a synthetic resin base. For painting chimneys and ovens, aluminum paints consist of aluminum flake in a silicone resin, and they resist heats to 1000°F. When aluminum is used in asphalt paints for tanks and roofing, the aluminum pigment leaf comes to the surface to form a reflective shield. The so-called **heat-resistant paints** are usually aluminum pigment in a silicone resin. The heat resistance comes more from the reflective power of the aluminum than from the actual melting point of the resin. Sericite mica flake is sometimes mixed with aluminum flake to give a different color tone. The **Opal-Glo paint** of the Sherwin-Williams Co. contains a small amount of opaque aluminum particles to give a three-dimensional opalescent glow without the metallic sheen of a flaked powder. The **Lumiclad paint** of the Asbestos Mfg. Corp., for roofing, is aluminum flake and asbestos powder in an oil-resin vehicle. **Calibrite,** of Clairmont Polychemical Corp., is a borited aluminum powder which retains the silvery color of aluminum in the paint.

Lead powder may be incorporated in paints as a protection against gamma rays. **Leadoid paint** is an English paint of this kind. **Ceramic paints** are refractory oxides or carbides in a soluble silicate vehicle, but they are generally only temporary repair coatings. But the **Pyromark paint** of the Tempil Corp. has the color pigment in a silicone vehicle which is converted by applied heat into an inorganic silica film which will withstand temperatures to 2500°F.   **Intumescent paints,** which bubble and swell to form an insulating barrier to protect the base material from fire damage, may contain borax or a percentage of an intumescent resin.   **Resyn 1066,** of the National Starch & Chemical Corp., is such an additive.   It is a high-solids emulsion of a vinyl resin.   **Masonry paints** may have a silicone resin base for water resistance, but they may also be made with synthetic rubbers and be designated for special purposes such as **traffic paints, road-marking paints,** and **pool paints.**   Road-marking paints were formerly made with Manila copal, but they are now made with synthetics.   **Imron,** of Du Pont, to withstand heavy traffic on industrial building floors, is based on a urethane resin.   It dries quickly without a catalyst, and is resistant to greases and cutting oils.   **Pliolite AC,** of the Goodyear Tire & Rubber Co., used in road-marking and pool paints, is a styrene-acrylate copolmyer resin. It needs no catalyst for curing, and has high adhesion to concrete.   The **Mobilzinc 7 paint** of the Socony Paint Products Co., for use on iron and steel, withstands temperatures to 750°F and severe weathering conditions. It contains zinc silicate up to 82% by weight and bonds chemically with the metal.   **Foliage paints** are made with a base of vinyl-acrylic resin. They are used for coloring Zoyzia grass lawns in winter and for other turfs.   **Vitalon,** of Mallinckrodt Chemical Works, is such a colorant.

The simplest **water paints** consist of gypsum or whiting with some zinc oxide, with water as the vehicle and glue for adhesion.   **Kalsomine** is an old name for wall paint made with whiting and glue and some linseed oil and water colors.   **Whitewash** may be merely quicklime and water, or may be slaked lime, salt, whiting, and glue.   These materials are still used for interior painting of farm buildings where low cost is the prime factor. Modern water paints may be **casein paints,** consisting of pigments and extenders in a casein solution, which are more water-resistant and more durable than glue paints, or they may be **resin-emulsion paints.**   These are usually water emulsions of oil-modified alkyd or other resins which dry to leave tough films of resin.   The **Gelva paint** of the Shawinigan Resins Corp. consists of a pigment in a water solution of a polyvinyl resin.   These paints are grease-resistant and washable.   They are sold under a variety of trade names.   The **SMA resin** of the Texas Butadiene & Chemical Corp., used to give high adhesion and hiding power to water paints, is a white powder which is a copolymer of styrene and maleic anhydride.   Interior gloss paints and enamels are now mostly water paints with a vehicle of a latex water solution of a synthetic resin.   The resin may be an acrylic emulsion, a styrene-acrylic, or water-dispersible polyesters and alkyds, or water-soluble epoxies.   They can be applied to wet surfaces and they cure rapidly to water and chemical resistant films.   The acrylic resin emulsions are valued because of their ability to produce pastel shades and their good flow and leveling properties for one-coat application.   **Rhoplex AC-35,** of Rohm and Haas, is such an emulsion.   **Piezoelectric paints** for transducers are coating materials made from intermetallic resin powders in a solvent.   The **Microducer paints** of Clark Electronics are these materials in many grades.

Paint removers, for removing old paint from surfaces before refinishing, are either strong chemical solvents or strong caustic solutions.   In general, the more effective they are in removing the paint quickly, the more damaging they are likely to be to the wood or other organic material base.   The hiding power of a paint is measured by the quantity which must be applied to a given area of a black and white background to obtain nearly uniform complete hiding.   The hiding power is largely in the pigment, but when some fillers of practically no hiding power alone, such as silica, are ground to microfine particle size, they may increase the hiding power greatly. Paint making is a highly developed art, and the variables are so many and the possibilities for altering the characteristics by slight changes in the combinations are so great that the procurement specifications for paints are usually by usage requirements rather than by composition.

PALLADIUM. A rare metal found in the ores of platinum, symbol Pd. It resembles platinum, but is lighter in weight and has a more beautiful silvery luster.   It is only half as plentiful but is less costly.   The specific gravity is 12.10 and the melting point is 1554°C.   The Brinell hardness of the annealed metal is 40, with a tensile strength of 27,000 psi, and that of the hard-drawn metal with 60% reduction is 100 with a tensile strength of 50,000 psi.   It is highly resistant to corrosion and to attack by acids, but, like gold, it is dissolved in aqua regia.   It alloys readily with gold, and is employed in some white golds.   It alloys in all proportions with platinum, and the alloys are harder than either of the constituents.

Although palladium has low electrical conductivity, 16% that of copper, it is valued for its resistance to oxidation and corrosion.   Palladium-rich alloys are widely used for low-voltage electrical contacts.   **Palladium-silver alloys,** with 30 to 50% silver, for relay contacts, have 3 to 5% the conductivity of copper.   A palladium-silver alloy with 25% silver is used as a catalyst in powder or wire mesh form.   A **palladium-copper alloy** for sliding contacts has 40% copper with a conductivity 5% that of copper.   Many of the palladium salts, such as **sodium palladium chloride,** Na_2PdCl_4, are easily reduced to the metal by hydrogen or carbon monoxide, and are used in coatings and electroplating.   A **palladium-iridium alloy** with 20% iridium has a Brinell hardness of 140, and can be work-hardened to Brinell 260 with a tensile strength of 190,000 psi.   A **palladium-nickel alloy** with 20% nickel has a hardness of Brinell 200, and can be rolled to a hardness of Brinell 360 with a tensile strength of

170,000 psi. **Palladium alloys** are also used for instrument parts and wires, dental plates, and fountain-pen nibs. Palladium is valued for electroplating as it has a fine white color which is resistant to tarnishing even in sulfur atmospheres. **Palladium leaf** is palladium beaten into extremely thin foil and used for ornamental work like gold leaf. Hydrogen forms solid solutions with palladium, forming **palladium sponge** which has been used for gas lighters. **Palladium powder** is made by chemical reduction and has a purity of 99.9% with amorphous particles 0.3 to 3.5 micron in diameter. Atomized powder has spherical particles of 50 to 200 mesh and is free-flowing. The powders are used for coatings and parts for a service temperature to 2300°F. **Palladium flake** has tiny laminar platelets of average diameter of 3 microns and thickness of 0.1 micron. The particles form an overlapping film in coatings.

PALM OIL. An oil obtained from the fleshy covering of the seed nuts of several species of palm trees, chiefly *Elaeis guineensis,* native to tropical Africa, but also grown in Central America. The tree attains a height of about 60 feet, and the nuts occur in large bunches similar to dates. The fruit is of an elongated ellipse shape, about 1½ in. long, enclosing a single kernel. The fleshy part carries about 65% oil, which is a semisolid fat. The iodine value is about 55, and the saponification value 205. West African palm oil has four grades: Edible, with 11% max free fatty acid; Soft, with 18% max; Semihard, with 35% max; and Hard, with more than 35%. The high-grade edible oil is from unfermented fruits. Fresh palm oil has an agreeable odor and a bright-orange color, but the oil often has a rancid stench and is of varying colors. The oil is used as a fluxing dip in the manufacture of tinplate, for soaps, candles, margarine, and for the production of palmitic acid. About 10% by weight of the palm oil is recovered as by-product glycerin in making soaps or in producing the acid.

Palm oil contains 50 to 70% **palmitic acid,** $C_{15}H_{31}COOH$, which in the form of glyceride is an ingredient of many fats. When isolated, it is a white crystalline powder of specific gravity 0.866, and melting point 64°C, soluble in hot water. It is used in soaps, cosmetics, pharmaceuticals, food emulsifiers, and in making plastics. The **Neo-Fat 16,** of the Armour Chemical Co., is 95% pure palmitic acid, with 4% stearic and 1 myristic acids. This is a powder with an acid value of 220 and a saponification value of 221. But the **Greco 55L,** of A. Gross, Inc., which is a white crystalline solid, for cosmetics and soaps, is 50% palmitic acid with the balance stearic acid.

The oil from the kernel of the palm nut, known as **palm kernel oil,** is different in characteristics from palm oil. It contains about 50% lauric acid, 15 myristic acid, 16 oleic acid, and 7 palmitic acid, together with capric and caprylic acids found in coconut oil, while palm oil is very high in palmitic and oleic acids. The specific gravity is 0.873, iodine number 16 to 23, saponification value 244 to 255, and melting point 24 to 30°C. The American species of palm oil is from the dwarf tree *E. melanococca* growing from Mexico to Paraguay and called **noli palm** in Colombia. The pulp of the nuts yields 30% of an oil similar to African palm oil. The tall **Paraguayan palm** *Acrocomia sclerocarpa* has the fruit also in bunches, and the pulp yields 60% of oil similar to palm oil.

PAPAIN. The dried extract, or enzyme, obtained from the fruit and sap of the papaya tree, *Carica papaya*, of tropical America, East Africa, and Asia. It is marketed as a dry, friable powder, and has a complex structure. It is a **proteolytic agent,** which splits proteins, and it also contains a lipase which accelerates the hydrolysis of fatty acid glycerides, and it contains an antibacterial. The latex from the fruit is dried by low heat, since temperatures above 70°C destroy the enzymes. Papain is used in beer and other beverages to remove protein haze, in medicine as a digestive aid and in combination with urea and chlorophyll to promote the healing of wounds, as a meat tenderizer, in degumming silk, and treating textiles.

The **papaya** tree grows to a height of 25 ft without branches, and is crowned with large leaves. The melonlike fruit grows out from the trunk, and has orange-colored flesh. It is eaten raw like a melon, but as it spoils rapidly it is not easily shipped. The papaya is called **pawpaw** in Florida. **Meat tenderizers** marketed by Papaya Industries, Inc., in powder and liquid forms, are papain with or without seasoning spices. They are applied to the meats before or during cooking. Papain is also injected into the beef animals 10 min before slaughtering. The enzyme spreads throughout the circulatory system of the animal, remaining in the meat and tenderizing it during the cooking cycle. It also inhibits discoloration of the meat in aging. **Pro-Ten,** of Swift & Co., is a solution of papain for this purpose. **Augment,** of the Calgon Corp., is a mixture of papain powder and sodium chloride for use in a dip solution for tenderizing meats.

PAPER. The name given to cellulose made into paste form from plant sources and rolled into thin sheets, used as a material for writing, printing, and wrapping. It may be considered as a thin felting of fibers bonded by a water-soluble cellulose formed on the fiber surfaces, to which a coating material such as clay may be added with starch or other sizing material. Most papers are less than 0.006 in. thick, but the dividing line between paper and paperboard is taken as 0.012 in.

The original **Egyptian paper,** known as **papyrus,** was made from the stems of the rush *Cyperus papyrus* growing along the Nile. It was made in sheets, sometimes as long as 130 ft. The Chinese process of papermaking from hempen and linen rags was brought to the Near East when the

Arabs took Samarkand in A.D. 704.   The papers used in Medieval Europe were **charta damascena,** from the Arab factory at Damascus, and **charta bombycina,** from the factory at Bombyce near Antioch, both sold in reams (from the Arabic word razmah).   **Greek parchment,** used in later medieval times, was made from cotton.   **Aztec paper,** called **amatl,** was made from the inner bast fibers of species of wild fig trees, *Ficus.*   The fibers were felted into sheets and beaten with a ribbed mallet.   The thin white sheets used for writing were then polished with a curved stone celt which closed the pores and smoothed the sheets.   Some very large sheets were made for folding into books.   The fibers of the yellow fig tree, *F. petolaris,* were made into a yellow paper used for coloring for decorations.

There are many varieties and grades of paper, depending upon the source of the cellulose and the method of manufacture.   Wood is a lignified form of cellulose, and the wood is chipped and cooked with chemicals to dissolve out the lignin.   The material so treated is known as **chemical wood pulp** to distinguish it from **mechanical wood pulp** used for making wallboard and **newsprint paper,** the latter requiring some chemical pulp to give fiber and strength.   There are four processes for producing chemical pulp: the sulfite, with calcium sulfite; the soda, with sodium carbonate; the sulfate, with sodium sulfate; and the magnesium bisulfite.   Hardwoods are cooked in a soda-ash solution and sulfited.   The bleaching of pulp is done with chlorine dioxide which oxidizes lignin to water-soluble colorless compounds without reducing the strength of the cellulose.

Book paper is usually a mixture of sulfate and soda pulp, the latter process producing a bulky pulp.   **Wrapping paper** is a strong, coarse paper made usually from mixed pulps.   **Kraft paper** is a heavy, brown, sulfate pulp paper of high strength, sized with rosin, used for wrapping or as building paper.   **Manila paper** is a strong wrapping paper originally made from Manila hemp, but the name is now applied to any strong chemical wood pulp or mixed paper of a slightly buff, or Manila, color.   **Clupak paper,** of the West Virginia Pulp & Paper Co., is a tough extensible kraft paper for bags and wrappings, made by compressing the plastic web of paper on a rubber blanket in the papermaking machine.   The paper is soft but strong, and stretches 10% in any direction.   **Absorbent paper,** such as for **blotting paper** and **filter paper,** is made from spongy bulky fibers, such as poplar, or is loosely felted fiber.   The **Kimtowels,** of the Kimberly-Clark Corp., to replace cotton waste for machine cleaning, are made from bulky, specially treated pulp.   The paper can be saturated with oil or solvent for cleaning purposes.   The **Netone filter paper** of the National Filter Media Co. is a 60-lb kraft paper impregnated with Neoprene to give chemical resistance.   This type of paper has 3 to 10 times the strength of cellulose papers, and it is also used for electrical insulation.   But the **Permalex paper** of the Rogers Corp., for electrical insulation, is a kraft paper in which the cellulose fibers have been treated to replace hydroxyl groups with cyano ethyl groups. The paper has high tensile strength, is more heat-resistant, and has higher dielectric strength than ordinary paper. The **X-Crepe paper,** of the Cincinnati Industries, Inc., used as a substitute for burlap for bags, as a barrier paper, and as a reinforcement for laminated plastics, is a heavy, soft-texture kraft paper that is creped and cross-creped to produce a material that is stretchable in varying degrees from 15 to 60%. It has a bursting strength to 260 psi. **Balancing paper,** used with the core material in structural plastic laminates to prevent warping, is heavy kraft paper impregnated with a phenol resin.

Cotton is nearly pure cellulose and makes an excellent paper material. Old cotton rags are thus scoured and used for papermaking. Linen rags are also used and produce a fine grade of **writing paper.** The best quality writing and **printing papers** are 50, 75, or 100% rag papers. **Bond paper** is a hard-finished writing paper made from spruce which has a long fiber. Highly rolled and coated printing papers are called supercalendered papers. They are used for printing fine-screen halftones. In England this paper is called **art paper.** **Tuf-Flex T,** of the Martin Cantine Co., is a tough flexible printing paper impregnated with an acrylic resin and clay coated which takes color printing readily. **Offset paper** for offset printing is given the required porosity without affecting physical properties by coating with an alkali-swellable resin. Fine linen **ledger paper** is made with 100% white rags. Good-quality bond **typewriter paper** may have 80% white rags. These papers are sold by weight per ream, a ream usually consisting of 500 sheets of a specified size in inches. **Watermarked paper** can be made in various ways, but the simplest method is by printing the mark with a solution of castor oil in methyl alcohol. Papers are generally described in terms of basic weight, which is the weight in pounds per 3,000 sq ft. Standard-weight papers are 90 to 105 lb; lightweight papers are 60 to 65 lb.

Drawing paper is a heavy paper, usually white or buff color, employed for making drawings. For mechanical drawings the buff color is preferred as it is easier on the eyes and not so readily soiled. Drawing papers are smooth or rough, the smooth being hot-pressed. Good grades of drawing paper should permit considerable erasure without destroying the appearance. Buff detail paper for pencil use is made slightly rough or grained. High-grade paper for ink work is extra-hard-sized and coated. Drawing paper is marketed in rolls of widths from 30 to 72 in., and in standard sheets varying from cap, 17 by 13 in., to antiquarian, 52 by 31 in. **Tracing cloth** is made from thin, fine cotton or linen fabric, of plain weave, heavily sized and glazed on one side. It is used for making tracings in ink and is quite transparent. It can also be obtained with the glaze on both sides. Tracing cloth is usually marketed in rolls of 24 yd. The sizing of ordinary tracing cloth is easily soluble in water, and will there-fore not withstand wetting, but special grades are made with impervious resin coatings.   Plastic-treated papers are now made that have high strength and better transparency than tracing cloth while retaining the drafting qualities of a fine paper.   **Tracing paper** is usually a good grade of hard transparent tissue paper in sheets and rolls, in white or buff colors. The **Ozatrace paper** of the General Aniline & Film Corp., for tracings and for maps, is a 16-lb, 100% rag-textured vellum paper with a transparent resin added in the pulp.   It takes ink without feathering, and pencil lines may be erased as many as 10 times on the same spot.   **Tracing paper PTM-173,** of the Frederick Post Co., is made of rag paper stock with microscopic pores filled with a synthetic resin, roll-pressed to give an evenly textured surface.   **Vindure paper,** of George Vincent, Inc., is 100% rag paper processed to give transparency, dimensional stability, and water resistance.

Granite paper is made by the addition of colored fibers to the pulp or by adding several shades of dyed pulp to the regular stock.   **Oatmeal paper,** used chiefly for wallpaper, has a flaky finish produced by washing a solution of wood flour over the sheet on the forming wire in the paper ma-chine.   The wood flour may be natural or dyed in colors.   **Cartridge paper** is 50- to 80-lb Manila paper, waxed on one side, originally used for muzzle-loading cartridges, but now employed where a stiff, waterproof material is needed.   **Glassine** is a transparent thin paper used for envelope windows and for sanitary wrapping.   It is made of sulfite pulp subjected to long-continued beating and supercalendered.   **Glassoid** is a more highly fin-ished transparent paper.   **Onionskin paper** is a lightweight highly fin-ished transparent writing paper made transparent by hydration of the pulp in the beaters.   Transparent papers are now often made water-resist-ant and stronger by adding a synthetic resin to the pulp.   **Albanene tracing paper,** of Keuffel & Esser Co., is a thin rag paper treated with a transparent synthetic resin.   It takes ink well, and erases easily.   **Silicone tissue,** for wiping glass, is soft tissue paper treated with silicone resin. **Tissue paper** is a very thin, almost transparent paper.   It may be loosely felted to give absorbent qualities, or it may have a hard, smooth surface for wrapping paper.   **Detergent paper,** for washing windows, is a soft paper impregnated with a detergent.   **Keel,** of the Kee-Lox Mfg. Co., is a paper of this type.

To make paper smooth-surfaced and resistant to the spreading of inks, adhesive sizing materials are used together with inert fillers such as China clay which give body, weight, opacity, and added strength to the paper. The usual coating adhesives are starches and proteins.   The proteins, such as casein, are more uniform than starch, but give a more brittle film. Starch films are not water-resistant unless the treated starches are used.

Waterproof paper was formerly paper treated with a copper-ammonium solution and hot-rolled, or was paper coated with rubber latex to which had been added a creaming agent such as a metallic soap, but various synthetic resins are now incorporated in the sizing or mixed in the pulp. High-styrene butadiene latex gives a flexible and glossy film for printing papers. Acrylic latex also gives a strong, glossy, and flexible coating. Polyvinyl acetate is also used for printing papers. **Scriptite 31,** of the Monsanto Chemical Co., used to give a tough, water-impervious surface to offset papers, is a methylated methylol melamine resin, which forms a molecular link with the protein of the coating. **Wet-strong paper** is usually specially processed paper in which the water resistance is due to the processing and interlocking of the fibers as well as to impregnation with a small amount of melamine, urea-formaldehyde, or other resin. It is used for maps, documents, and wrapping. **Resistall,** of the L. L. Brown Paper Co., is a paper of this type. The **Anti-adhesive paper** of the Central Paper Co., for interleafing sticky materials and for box linings, is a kraft paper treated with a silicone resin. The **Kastek paper** of the Plastic Film Corp., for waterproof wrapping, is 30- to 100-lb paper with a very thin film of polyethylene or vinyl resin bonded to the surface. The **washable wallpaper** of Richard E. Thibaut, Inc., has a 0.00088-in. Lumarith cast film laminated to the paper.

Capacitor paper, used as a dielectric in capacitors, is made from Swedish spruce sulfate pulp, is highly purified, and is nearly transparent. It is extremely thin, 0.00015 to 0.0004 in., but is strong and tough. **Insulating paper,** commonly called **varnished paper,** is a standard material for insulation of electrical equipment. It is usually bond or kraft paper coated on both sides with black or yellow insulating varnish. The thicknesses are 0.002 to 0.020 in., with dielectric strengths of 500 to 2,000 volts per mil. Special insulating varnishes of high dielectric strength are now marketed for this purpose. **Cyanoethylated paper,** used in condensers, is a thin paper treated with acrylonitrile which improves the electrical insulating properties. **Quinorgo,** of Johns-Manville, is a group of asbestos papers containing 80% chrysotile fibers bonded with organic resins. The resins are varied to give differing physical properties. The papers come in thicknesses from 0.003 to 0.015 in. and have high dielectric strength. **Laminating paper,** for making laminated plastics, is a white or brown paper of uniform basis weight and uniform internal structure capable of having a controlled resin pickup. It usually comes in thicknesses from 0.004 to 0.020 in. **Nibro-Cel,** of the Brown Co., is such a paper. **Flameproofed paper** is paper treated with ammonium sulfate and ammonium and sodium phosphates. Paper and nonwoven textile fabrics may be treated with a **fire-retardant agent** such as **FireTard,** of National Starch and Chemical Corp., an emulsion of vinylidene chloride copolymer with an equal amount of antimony trioxide.   **Metallized paper,** of Smith Paper, Inc., used for capacitors, is a lacquer-coated kraft paper with a thin layer of zinc deposited on one side.   **Vaculite,** of the Vaculite Corp., used for packaging and as a barrier paper, is **aluminum-coated paper** produced by vacuum metallizing. It has the appearance of bright aluminum, but has the flexibility and physical properties of paper.

Building paper, used for sheathing houses, is a heavy kraft paper, plain or rosin-sized.   Specially treated building papers are also marketed under trade names.   The **barrier paper** of the Presstite Engineering Co., for lining storage rooms, is kraft paper saturated with gilsonite, asphalt, and wax.   It is odorless and black in color.   **Weatherite,** of Johns-Manville, is a kraft building paper treated with a black waterproofing.   **Copperskin** is an insulating construction material made by facing 1-oz electro-sheet copper on one or two plies of heavy building paper impregnated with bitumen.   **Cop-O-Top,** of the Chase Brass & Copper Co., and **Copperkote,** of the Cheney Co., are similar materials.   **Sisalkraft,** of the Sisalkraft Co., is a waterproof building paper made with sisal fibers.   **Fibreen,** of this company, is a tough, strong, flexible, waterproof paper used for wrapping bundles of steel and other heavy products.   It is made of two layers of kraft paper reinforced with two crossed layers of sisal fibers embedded in asphalt, and the whole combined under heat and pressure.   **Brownskin,** a waterproof sheathing paper of the Angier Corp., is high-strength building paper impregnated with a bituminous compound and crimped to give it stretch and resiliency.   **Burlap-lined paper,** for heavy wrapping, has 4- to 10-oz burlap laminated to heavy kraft paper with asphalt as the binder.   It is waterproof.   **Papier maché** is comminuted paper made into a water paste with an adhesive binder and molded.   It was formerly widely used for toys, dishes, and novelties, but dishes and novelties now made of paper stock are produced directly from the wood pulp and are more uniform and stronger.   Kraft paper impregnated with phenolic resin laminated in blocks and heavy sheet is used for short run tooling.   **Panelyte 750,** of Thiokol Chemical Corp., is this material with a compressive strength of 28,000 psi.

PAPER PLANTS. Cellulose for papermaking is obtained from a wide variety of plant life, made directly into **paper pulp,** or obtained from old rags which were originally made from vegetable fibers.   Animal fibers incorporated into some papers are fillers for special purposes and not papermaking materials.   The papyrus of Egypt was made from a reed, but the **baobab** of India was from the bark of the tree *Adamsonia digitata*. **Rice paper** of China came from the *tetrapanax papyriferum,* but the so-called rice paper used for cigarettes in the United States is made from flax fiber.   **Cigarette paper** is also made from ramie and sunn hemp.   The distinction between cigarette paper and the tissue paper used for wrapping is that it must be free of any substance that would impart a disagreeable flavor to the smoke and it must be opaque and pure white, must burn at the same rate as tobacco, and must be tasteless.

Wood pulp is now the most important papermaking material.   Spruce is the chief wood used for the sulfite process, but hemlock and balsam fir are also used.   Aspen and other hardwoods are used in the soda process, and also southern pine.   White fir is readily pulped by any process, but western red cedar is high in lignin content, about 30%, and reduced with difficulty by the sulfate process to a dark-colored pulp.   It is pulped by the kraft process.   Its fibers are fine and short, yielding a paper of high bursting strength.   Normally, the **pulpwoods** of the West Coast are western hemlock, white fir, and Sitka spruce, leaving the Douglas fir to the lumber mills.   The same species of trees grow in Alaska and British Columbia as in Oregon and Washington, but Douglas fir decreases to the north and hemlock and spruce become more abundant but with smaller trees.   A stand of spruce in Canada at the age of 80 years yields about 18 tons of pulp per acre, while a stand of pine in the southern states at 24 years of age yields about the same amount.   Western hemlock, balsam, and spruce are the chief pulpwoods of Canada.   Pines are used extensively in the United States, especially for kraft paper, paperboard, and book paper.   More than 50% of all pulpwood used in the United States is now from the southern states, and about 10% of this is salvage from lumber mills.   But, in general, special methods are used for pulping pine since conventional sulfite liquor does not free the fibers as the phenolic compounds in the heartwood condense to form insoluble compounds.

The kraft paper made by Rayonier, Inc., and called **Fibrenier,** is sulfate-pulped from a mixture of 50% western hemlock, 25 western red cedar, and 25 Douglas fir.   The fir has a coarse fiber which gives high tear strength; cedar has a long thin fiber which gives a smooth surface; hemlock is abundant and used as a filler.   Poplars are also used for pulpwood, and the Scott Paper Co. uses fast-growing scrub alder.   Newsprint made from hardwoods has a bursting strength 20% higher than that made from softwoods, and the brightness value is higher, but the pulping of hardwoods is usually a more involved chemical process.

In England fine printing papers are made by the soda process from **esparto** grass.   It gives a soft, opaque, light paper, although the cellulose content is less than 50%.   Esparto is the plant *Stipa tenacissima* of the dry regions of North Africa.   In Tunisia it is called **alfa.**   It grows to a height of about 3 ft, with cylindrical stem.   The fine, light fibers, about $1/2$ in. long, are from the leaves.   Some grades of cardboard and some newsprint are made from straw.   **Deluwang paper** of the East Indies is made from the scraped and beaten bark of the **paper mulberry** tree, *Brous-*

sonetia papyrifera. It is an ancient industry in Java, and the paper is used for lamp shades and fancy articles. Under the name of **tapa cloth** the sheets were dyed and used as a muslinlike fabric by the Polynesians. The strips are welded together by overlapping and beating together the wet material. Bagasse is of increasing importance as a papermaking material in the sugar-growing areas of the world.

PARAFFIN. A general name often applied to paraffin wax, but more correctly referring to a great group of hydrocarbons obtained from petroleum. Paraffin compounds begin with methane, CH_4, and are sometimes called the methane group. The compounds in the series have the general formula C_nH_{2n+2}, and include the gases methane and ethane, and the products naphtha, benzine, gasoline, lubricating oils, jellies, and the common paraffin. The name paraffin indicates little affinity for reaction with other substances. In common practice the name is limited to the waxes that follow petroleum jelly in the distillation of petroleum. These waxes melt at from 40 to 60°C, and consist of the hydrocarbons between C_{22} and C_{27}; the refined waxes may range up to 90°C. They burn readily in the air. Paraffin occurs to some extent in some plant products, but its only commercial source is from natural petroleum. **Chlorinated paraffin** is a pale to amber-colored, odorless, soft wax or viscous oil of specific gravity 0.900 to 1.50. It is flame-resistant, and is used in treating paper and textiles. **Chlorowax,** of the Diamond Alkali Co., is a chlorinated paraffin for adhesive, fire-resistant, and water-resistant compounds. It is a cream-colored powder containing 69 to 73% chlorine, and is insoluble in water but soluble in organic solvents. A water-dispersible form of this wax is **Delvet 65,** a white, viscous liquid containing 65% solids. **Clorafin 42,** of Hercules, Inc., is an amber-colored viscous liquid chlorinated paraffin containing 42% chlorine. **Cereclor,** of the Chemical Mfg. Co., Inc., is a similar product. **Clorafin 70** is a yellow solid containing 70% chlorine and softening at 90 to 100°C. The former is used as a plasticizer in resins and for coatings; the latter is for flameproofing and waterproofing textiles.

Paraffin oil is drip oil from the wax presses in the process of extracting paraffin wax from the wax-bearing distillate in the refining of petroleum. The oil is treated, redistilled, and separated into various grades of lubricating oils from light to heavy. They may be treated and bleached with sulfuric acid, and neutralized with alkali. When decolorized with acid and sold as filtered, they are brilliant liquids, but are not suitable in places where they may be in contact with water, since the sulfo compounds present cause emulsification. The specific gravities of paraffin oils are between 21 and 26°Bé. **Triton oil** is a 100% pure paraffin oil produced by the Union Oil Co. of California.

PARAFFIN WAX. The first distillate taken from petroleum after the cracking process is known as wax-bearing, and is put through a filter press and separated from the oils.   The wax collected on the plates is called **slack wax,** and contains 50% wax and 50 oil.   This is chilled to free it from oil.   The yellow wax is filtered to make a white semitranslucent refined wax, which is odorless and tasteless.   For large-scale operations, solvent methods of wax extraction are used.   Paraffin wax is soluble in ether, benzine, and essential oils.   **Match wax** has a melting point of 105 to 112°F; white crude wax, 111 to 113°F; yellow crude, 117 to 119°F; and special white, 124 to 126°F.   The refined waxes are in various melting-point ranges from 115 to 136°F, and are used for coating paper and for blending in coating and impregnating compounds.   They are also used in candles and other products.   The refined paraffin wax used for molded goods and for rubber compounding is a white solid having a melting point of 122°F and a specific gravity 0.903.

Borneo wax has a very high melting point and a hard crystalline structure which makes it valuable for coatings and for high-quality candles. By treatment of the waxes from American petroleums to remove the low-melting constituents, a similar wax is obtained having branched-chain molecules and a fine crystalline structure.   This is known as **microcrystalline wax.   Aristowax,** of the Union Oil Co. of California, is a treated wax of this kind with melting points from 145 to 165°F.   **Petrolite wax,** of the Petrolite Corp., is a microcrystalline wax with melting point at 195°F. **Sunwax,** of the Sun Oil Co., is a microcrystalline wax in two grades, a brown with melting point of 175°F, and a yellow with melting point of 185°F.   **Warcosine wax,** of the Warwick Wax Co., Inc., is a white microcrystalline wax melting at about 153°F, while **Fortex wax** has a melting point at about 195°F.   Microcrystalline wax does not emulsify easily like carnauba wax, but when oxidized with a catalyst it is emulsifiable and the melting point is raised so that is can be used in hard, self-polishing floor waxes.   **Cardis wax** and **Polymekon wax,** of this company, have melting points at 198 and 250°F.   **Petronauba D,** of the Bareco Oil Co., is an oxidized wax with a melting point of 192.2°F, used as a partial replacement for carnauba.   Microcrystalline waxes are also compounded with polyethylene and other materials to increase strength, flexibility, and other properties.   The paraffin waxes are sold under many trade names.   **Arwax,** of the American Resinous Chemicals Corp., may contain butyl rubber or polyethylene.   **Advawax 2575,** of the Advance Solvents & Chemical Corp., for paper coatings, contains polyisobutylene.   **Santowax,** of the Monsanto Chemical Co., is a high-melting microcrystalline wax.   **Wax tailings** is a name for the distillate that comes from petroleum after the wax-bearing distillate is removed.   It contains no wax, but at ordinary temperatures looks like beeswax.   It is very adhesive and is employed in roofings and for waterproof coatings.

Synthetic paraffin wax, called **Ruhr wax,** is made in Germany from low-grade coals and other hydrocarbon sources.   The waxes, with molecular weights of 900 to 1600, are white flakes, water white when melted.   They are odorless, free of sulfur and aromatics, with ash content below 50 ppm.   The melting points are between 105 and 126°C.   They are used as additives in paper coatings and printing inks and for mixing with refined paraffin.

PARCHMENT. Originally, goatskin or sheepskin specially tanned and prepared with a smooth hard finish for writing purposes.   It was used for legal documents, maps, and fancy books, being more durable than the old papers.   The extremely thin high-quality parchment that was used for documents and handmade books was rubbed with pumice and flattened with lead.   Parchment now is usually **vegetable parchment.**   It is made from a base paper of cotton rags or alpha cellulose called **waterleaf** which contains no sizing or filling materials.   The waterleaf is treated with sulfuric acid which converts a part of the cellulose into a gelatinlike amyloid.   When the acid is washed off, the amyloid film hardens on the fibers and in the interstices of the paper.   The strength of the paper is increased, and it will not disintegrate even when fully wet.   The paper now has a wide usage in food packaging as well as for documents as a competitor of the resin-treated wet-strong papers.   The wet strength and grease resistance are varied by differences in acid treatment and subsequent sizing.   **Patapar,** of the Paterson Parchment Paper Co., is a vegetable parchment marketed in many grades.   **Parchment papers** are also waterproofed by dipping in the solution of copper hydroxide and ammonium hydroxide known as **Schweitzer's reagent,** and then hot-rolling.   **Vellum** is a thick grade of writing paper made from high-grade rag pulp pebbled to imitate the original calfskin parchment called vellum.

PASTEBOARD. A class of thick paper used chiefly for making boxes and cartons, and for spacing and lining.   It may be made by pasting together several single sheets, but more usually by macerating old paper and rolling into heavy sheets.   It may also be made of straw, certain grasses, and other low-cellulose paper materials, and is then known as **strawboard.** Colloquially, the term pasteboard applies to any paper-stock board used for making boxes, including the hard and stiff boards made entirely from pulp, and the term pasteboard is not liked in the paper industry.   The bulk of the packaging boards are now pulp boards treated with resin and are called **carton boards.**   **Cardboard** is usually a good quality of chemical pulp or rag pasteboard used for cards, signs, or printed material, or for the best-quality boxes.   **Ivory board,** for art printing and menu cards, is a highly finished cardboard clay-coated on both sides.   **Bristol board** is a high-class white cardboard, supercalendered with China clay, or it may be made by pasting together sheets of heavy ledger paper, but the name is also applied to any high-grade printing or drawing board over 0.06 in. thick.   **Index bristol** is always made solid on a Fourdrinier machine to prevent splitting in use or warping.   The original board made in Bristol, England, was made in this way.   **Jute board,** used for folding boxes, is a regular product of the paper mills, and is a strong solid board made of kraft pulp.   **Chipboard** is a cheap board made from mixed scrap paper, used for boxes and book covers.   When made with a percentage of mechanical wood pulp, it is called **pulpboard.**   A heavy rope-pulp paper or board, usually reddish in color and used for large expansion filing envelopes, is called **paperoid.**

PEANUT OIL. Also known as **groundnut oil.**   A pale-yellow oil with a distinctive nutty taste and odor, obtained from the pressing of the seed kernels of the peanut, a legume of the genus *Arachis,* of which there are many species.   It was native to Brazil, brought to Africa in slave ships and thence to the United States.   It is now grown in many countries.   The Spanish peanut, cultivated in temperate climates, has small seeds, while the common variety, *A. hypogaea,* known in the United States as the **Virginia peanut,** has pods up to $1\frac{1}{2}$ in. long with seeds twice the length of the Spanish varieties.   The **Spanish peanut,** however, is easily grown and gives a high yield per acre.   The **Brazilian peanut,** *A. nambyquarae,* has pods up to 3 in. in length.   Vast quantities of peanuts are roasted and marketed as food nuts or for confections or ground to make edible **peanut butter.**   The best grades of cold-pressed oils are marketed as edible oils, but the oil is also used industrially for soaps, in diesel-engine fuels, and for blending in lubricating and varnish oils.   The **arachidic acid,** $CH_3(CH_2)_{18}COOH$, contained in the oil to the extent of 4%, however, makes a hard soap.   The oil also contains 52 to 62% oleic, 21 to 25 linoleic, besides palmitic, stearic, and lignoceric acids.   The specific gravity is from 0.916 to 0.922, saponification value 189 to 196, and iodine value 83 to 101.   The oil known as **arachis oil,** or as **Katchung oil** when imported from the Orient, is from the peanut *A. hypogaea.*   It is used in lubricating, for varnishes, and for softening leather.   **Peanut meal,** left after extraction of the oil, is sold as stock feed, or that from the final extraction of the inedible oil is used for fertilizer.   **De-oiled peanuts** are marketed as a low-calorie, nonfat food.   Most of the oil is removed by solvent extraction, but the nuts retain the high-protein value, color, and flavor.   The calorific value is reduced about 80%.

PEAT. An earthy mass formed by the rapid accumulation of quick-growing mosses and plants, and valued as a fuel in countries where fuels are expensive.   Large quantities are used for fuel in Finland, Switzerland, Ireland, and some other countries.   In Russia large amounts are used to produce fuel gas and for processing the tar into chemicals.   In the United States it is used for fertilizer, insulation, and packing.   The dried **peat moss** is used for making insulating board.   Peat bogs, or beds, are found mainly in moist districts in temperate climates.   The top layers are only slightly decayed, are brown in color, and of low specific gravity.   But at greater depths peat is nearly black and is very compact.   In the peat of southern New Jersey there are layers of trees as large as 5 ft in diameter, buried for centuries.

The reserves of peat are very large in the states bordering on the Great Lakes, those in the state of Minnesota alone being estimated at 7 billion tons.   Fresh peat often contains as high as 80% moisture and must be dried before use.   Wicklow dried peat contains about 71% volatile matter, 27% being fixed carbon, and 28% coke.   The calorific value of peat is about 5,000 Btu.   It is sometimes semicarbonized and made into fuel briquettes.   **Charred peat** is peat that has been subjected to a temperature to cause partial decomposition.   It is marketed as fertilizer.   Peat is also distilled, yielding mainly gas and a high percentage of tar.   **Peat wax,** extracted from peat in England, is a hard wax with characteristics similar to those of montan wax, and is a substitute for it.

PENTAERYTHRITOL. A tetrahydric alcohol of the composition HOH_2-$C \cdot C(CH_2OH)_3$ produced by the condensation of formaldehyde and acetaldehyde.   It is a white, crystalline solid melting at about 262°C.   The commercial grade is 85 to 90% pure.   It is employed for the production of explosives, plastics, drying oils, and chemicals.   Pentaerythritol will combine with the fatty acids of vegetable oils to form esters that are superior to linseed oil as drying oils.   Combined with the fatty acids of linseed oil, it will give a drying oil that will dry completely in 6 hr compared with 16 hr for a bodied linseed oil, and as a varnish oil it gives higher gloss and greater water resistance.   **Synthetic waxes** are also made by combining pentaerythritol with long-chain, saturated, fatty acids, and these waxes have higher melting points than beeswax or carnauba wax, but do not have the natural gloss of carnauba.   **Pentawax 177,** of the Heyden Chemical Co., is a **pentaerythritol stearate.**   It is a light-brown wax melting at 53°C, used for coating paper, in printing inks, and in cosmetics.   **Pentamull 126** of this company is an ester of pentaerythritol and oleic acid.   It is an amber-colored oil used as an emulsifying agent.   **Pentex** is a technical grade of pentaerythritol containing 85% mono pentaerythritol and the balance higher polymers.   It produces fast-drying and glossy varnishes.   The

Pentalyn resins of Hercules, Inc., which are employed to replace copals in varnishes, are pentaerythritol esters of rosin.   **Pentalyn 802A** is a phenol-modified pentaerythritol rosin ester for gloss printing inks and traffic paints. It is pale in color, and has high resistance to chemicals and wear.

PEPPER. One of the oldest and most important of the spices.   **Black pepper,** the common household spice, is the ground, dried, unripe fruit of the evergreen shrub or vine, *Piper nigrum,* of India and Southeast Asia. There are two grades of Indian pepper, **Alleppey** and **Tellicherry;** the latter is bolder and heavier and the more expensive grade.   The fruits are small, berrylike drupes.   They change in ripening from green to bright red to yellow.   When dry the unripe berries are reddish brown or black.   The vine comes into full production in 3 years and lives for 20 to 30 years.   A vine yields 5 to 10 lb of pepper.   **White pepper,** preferred for the preparation of commercial foods, is from the nearly ripe berries.   It has a yellow to gray color.   Pepper is used as a condiment and stimulates the flow of gastric juices.   White pepper is not as pungent as black pepper.   Commercial pepper is often a blend of the two kinds.   **Pepper oil,** used for flavoring, is a yellowish essential oil of specific gravity 0.873 to 0.916 with a pepperlike odor and flavor but not pungent like pepper.   It is extracted from the common pepper berries.   **Pepperoyal,** of the Griffith Laboratories, is pepper flavor extracted from black pepper and converted to minute soluble globules that disperse easily in foodstuffs.   **Soluble pepper,** of Fritzsche Bros., used for food processing, is a liquid solution of black-pepper oleoresin from which there is no precipitation of piperine crystals during processing or cold storage.   The synthetic **piperidine,** $C_5H_{11}N$, is a colorless liquid with an odor resembling pepper.   It yields crystalline salts, and it occurs in natural pepper in combination with **piperic acid** in the form of the alkaloid **piperine,** $C_{17}H_{19}NO_3$, which is the chief active constituent of pepper.   **Piperazine,** made synthetically, is used in medicine as an anthelmintic and as an intermediate for pharmaceuticals.   It is a six-membered heterocyclic ring compound with two nitrogen atoms in the para position.   **B-Cap,** of the Evans Chemetic Co., is a cinnaylidene acetoyl piperide, a synthetic with a pepperlike flavor used in prepared foods.

Long pepper, esteemed in some countries for preserves and curries, is more aromatic and is sweeter than common pepper.   It is from the tiny fruits of the climbing plant *P. retrofractum* of Malaya and the *P. longum* of India and Indonesia.   **Ashanti pepper,** of western Africa, is from the vine *P. guineense,* also known as **Guinea pepper,** although this name is applied to **grains of paradise,** the pungent peppery seeds of the perennial herb *Aframomum melegueta* of West Africa, which are used for flavoring and in medicine.   The seeds are also called **alligator pepper** and **melegueta pepper,** and are used as pepper in Europe, but the plant is of the ginger family.   **Cubeb** is the dried unripe fruit of the climbing vine *P. cubeba* of India, Indonesia, and the West Indies.   The berries resemble those of black pepper, but have a strong, peculiar odor and a bitter aromatic taste. Cubeb is used in medicine and cigarettes.   **Cubeb oil** is from the berries, which yield 10 to 16% of the pale-green oil with a pepperlike odor.   It is used in perfumery and in soaps.   **Paprika** is the ground dried fruit of the *Capsicum annuum* of Europe and America.   When full, red, ripe pods are used, and the seeds, cores, and stems are removed, a uniform maximum red color is produced.   Yellow pods give low red value.   Paprika is used as a condiment.   **Chili pepper** is from the smaller podlike berries of species of *Capsicum* which grow as small trees or shrubs.   It is a tropical plant. The ground fruits as a condiment are known as **red pepper,** or **cayenne pepper.**   In medicine it is known as **capsicum,** and is used as a carminative and as a source of vitamin P.   It is also used in soft drinks in place of ginger.   The Samoan beverage known as **kava** is made by steeping in water the ground root of a species of pepper plant, *Piper methysticum.*   It has a peppery flavor.   But the Kava of Borden, Inc., is not a pepper but is an instant coffee powder processed to neutralize the coffee acids.

PEPPERMINT. An oil distilled from the perennial herb *Mentha piperita* which grows in the temperate climate of America, Europe, and Asia.   The oil has a pleasant odor and a persistent cooling taste and is valued as a flavor and in soaps, toothpastes, perfumes, and pharmaceuticals.   The oil contains **menthol,** $C_{10}H_{20}O$, which is extracted for use as an antiseptic, in perfumery, and in medicine for colds and as an antispasmodic and anodyne. **Japanese peppermint** is from the *M. arvensis* grown extensively in Japan, Brazil, and the United States.   The oil is less fragrant, and is used for the production of menthol as it has a higher menthol content.   The plant is propagated from roots and grows to a height of 2 to 3 ft.   It is cut when it blooms and partly cured like hay.   The crude oil is obtained by steam distillation; the menthol is obtained by freezing and recrystallization, with a yield of 50% menthol crystals to total crude oil.   The residue oil is called **cornmint oil.**   It retains the peppermint flavor and is used in perfumery and flavoring.   **Spearmint** is from the *M. viridis,* grown largely in Michigan.   The oil is sharper in odor and taste and used chiefly in chewing gums.   **Pennyroyal oil** is distilled from the dried leaves and tops of the small annual plant *Hedeoma pulegioides* or *M. pulegium* which grows in the eastern United States.   The oil is a counterirritant and is used in liniments.   It is also used in insect repellents and for the production of menthol.   The plant yields 0.7% oil, and the oil will yield 65% menthol with a melting point of 33 to 35°C, or 40% of 42°C menthol.   **Horsemint oil** is from the plant *M. canadensis,* used for the production of thymol.   Menthol and menthol substitutes are also synthesized from coal tar.   **Cyclonol,**

of W. J. Bush & Co., Inc., is a derivative of cyclohexanol.   It lacks one H and one CH of the structural formula of menthol, but has the characteristic odor and cooling effect.   **Levomenthol,** produced synthetically by the Glidden Co., is used as a replacement for natural menthol.

PERFUME OILS. Volatile oils obtained by distillation or by solvent extraction from the leaves, flowers, gums, or woods of plant life, although a few are of animal origin.   Perfumes have been used since earliest times, not only for aesthetic value, but also for antiseptic value and for religious purposes.   Simple perfumes usually take their name from the name of the plant, but the most esteemed perfumes are blends, and the blending is considered a high art.   It is done by tones imparted by many ingredients. Some oils with repugnant odors have an attractive fragrance in extreme dilution and a persistence which is valued in blends and for stabilization. Some oils with heavy odors, such as coumarin, are used in dilution to give body.   Since many of the odors come directly from esters, aldehydes, or ketones, they can be made synthetically from coal-tar hydrocarbons and alcohols.   Synthetics are now most used in perfumes, although some natural odors have not yet been duplicated synthetically, and about 30,000 aromatics have been developed.   A perfume may contain 50 components, sometimes as high as 300, and the average perfume manufacturer employs about 3,000 components.   Some of the chemicals are not odors, but give lasting qualities or enhance odor.   Some are used as fixatives or blending agents.   **Hydro quinone dimethyl ether,** $C_8H_{10}O_2$, has an odor of sweet clover but is used as a fixative in other perfumes.

In general, the aldehyde odors are fugitive, and some become acid in the presence of light or oxygen.   Ketones are more stable.   Esters are usually stable, but some are saponified in hot solution and cannot be used for soaps.   Some esters, made from complex high alcohols, are used to give a fresh top note to floral perfumes.   **Linalyl acetate,** produced from citral, is an example.   Acid perfumes neutralize free alkali and cannot be used in soaps.   Phenol odors alter the color of soaps, and the odor may also become disagreeable.

Some odors are never extracted from the flowers, but are compounded. **Crab apple,** for example, which is a peculiarly sweet odor, is compounded of 16 oils, including bois de rose, ylang-ylang, nutmeg oil, jasmine, musk, heliotropin, coumarin, and others.   **Wisteria** is the honeylike odor of the mauve and white flowers of the climbing plant *Wisteria sinensis*.   The oil is never extracted but is compounded from geranium, Peru balsam, benzoin, bois de rose, and synthetics.   Some oils, such as **lavender,** from the flowers of the *Lavandula vera,* have no value when used alone but require skillful blending to develop the pleasant odor.   Apple and peach odors are **allyl cinnamate.**   Synthetic **rose** is the ester of phenyl ethyl alcohol made from benzene and ethylene oxide.   Although the natural rose odor is readily extracted, it is more expensive.

Fixatives are used for the finer perfumes.   They are essential oils that are less volatile and thus delay evaporation.   The animal oils, such as musk and civet, are of this class, and also the balsam oils.   Some evil-smelling distillates from chemical manufacture may also be used as fixatives.   **Musk** is from the male musk deer of Tibet.   It is one of the most expensive materials.   Synthetic musk is as powerful as the natural.   The synthetic musk of Du Pont is called **Astrotone.   Musk ambrette** is made from metacresol.   **Ambrette oil** has a strong musklike odor distilled from the **musk seed,** or **amber seed,** of the plant *Hibiscus abelmoschus* of Ecuador, India, and Egypt.   **Civet** is an odorous yellow fluid from the civet cat of tropical Asia and Ethiopia.   **Civettone** is a liquid with a clean odor and easily soluble in alcohol, distilled from civet.   **Patchouli oil** is one of the best fixatives for heavy perfumes.   It is a powerfully odorous viscous liquid obtained by distilling the fermented leaves of the shrub *pogostemon patchouli* of India, China, and the Philippines.   The odor resembles sandalwood.   **Cassie** is a valuable oil with an odor similar to violet obtained by maceration in oil of the flowers of the shrub *Acacia farnesiana* of the Mediterranean countries and the West Indies.   It is used to scent pomades and powders.   **Versilide,** of Givaudan-Delawana, Inc., is a cyclic ketone synthetic musk that is very stable in soaps and cosmetics and does not discolor.

Attar of rose is one of the most ancient and popular of perfume oils. The name is derived from the Persian atar, and is sometimes incorrectly given as **ottar** but with the same French pronunciation.   The finest attar of rose is from Bulgaria, where it is distilled from the flowers of the **damask rose,** *Rosa damascena.*   The fresh oil is colorless, but turns yellowish green.   About 20,000 lb of flowers are needed to make 1 lb of essence, and it is so valuable that it is usually adulterated with geraniol or synthetic rose.   In France the oil is obtained from the *R. centifolia.*   **Rose water** is the scented water left after distillation, or is made by dissolving attar in water.   The **Otto of baronia** of Australia is a high-grade **rose oil.**

Geranium oil is obtained from the leaves or flowers of the *Pelargonium graveolens* of the Mediterranean countries and other species of geranium. It is used as an adulterant or substitute for rose oils in perfumes and soaps. **Zdravetz oil** is a geranium oil from the *P. macnorhijum* of Cyprus, used in rose bouquet and lavender perfumes.   Many geranium and rose oils are derived from geraniol obtained from citronella and other oils.   A synthetic rose-geranium is **diphenyl methane,** $(C_6H_5)_2CH_2$, a colorless solid melting at about 25°C.   **Benzophenone** is also used for rose-geranium perfumes.   It is a **diphenyl ketone,** $C_6H_5(CO)C_6H_5$, melting at 47°C. This material is also used for making fine chemicals.   **Geraniol,**

from citral, is a colorless liquid with a sweet, delicate rose odor. **Vetiver,** a very sweet-scented oil used in high-grade perfumes and in medicine, is distilled from the roots of the **khuskhus** plant *Vetiveria zizamioides* native to India but produced chiefly in Java, Réunion, and Haiti. **Opopanox,** used in incense and in medicine, is an oleoresin from the roots of the *pastinaca opopanox* of the Orient and British Somaliland. **Frankincense,** used in incense and perfumes, and in medicine under the name of **olibanum,** is a gum resin from the tree *Boswellia carterii* of the Sudan and Somaliland. It comes in hard yellow grains. **Kiounouk,** used as a fixative, is a clear yellowish semiliquid obtained from olibanum. **Mecca balsam,** used in oriental types of perfume, is a greenish oleoresin from the plant *Commiphora opobalsamum* of Arabia. It has the odor of rosemary. **Rosemary** is an oil distilled from the fresh flowering tops of the sweet-smelling evergreen shrub *Rosemarinus officinalis* of the Mediterranean countries. It is used in eau de cologne, soaps, and medicine. **Jasmine oil,** a highly valued perfume material, is from the fragrant flowers of the shrub *Jasminum grandiflorum,* a species of jasmine grown in southern France especially for perfume. The oil is extracted from the fresh flowers by enfleurage. A synthetic **jasmine-rose oil,** which also has a **peach-apricot flavor** and a sweet taste, is **benzyl propionate,** $CH_3CH_2COOCH_2C_6H_5$. It is a liquid boiling at 220°C, and is used in perfumes and as a flavor. **Ylang-ylang,** or **cananga oil,** is a valuable essential oil from the flowers of the tree *Canangium odorata,* cultivated in Indonesia, Malagasy, and the Philippines. No more than 150 lb of flowers are obtained from a tree, but about 400 lb are required to produce 1 lb of oil. It contains linalol and geraniol. Another oil that rivals ylang-ylang in fragrance is **champaca oil,** from the flowers of the large tree *Michelia champaca,* of southern Asia.

Lavender oil, used with rosemary in eau de cologne, and also as **lavender water** in a mixture of the oil in water and alcohol, is obtained from the flowers of the shrub *Lavandula officinalis* of southern Europe. The dried flowers are fragrant and are used in sachets. **Spike lavender** is an inferior oil from the plant *L. latifolia* of France and Spain. It is used in perfumes and sometimes as a food flavor. **Herbandin,** of the UOP Chemical Co., is a synthetic ester made from petroleum and used as a replacement or extender for natural lavender oil. It has a pronounced lavender odor. Espantone is a synthetic ketone with a spike lavender odor. **Bay oil,** or **myrcia oil,** used in the toilet alcohol known as **bay rum,** and also in perfumes, is distilled from the leaves of the bay tree, *Pimenta acris,* of the West Indies, 60 lb of leaves yielding 1 lb of oil, and 1 gal of bay oil being used to 100 gal of rum to make bay rum. It contains eugenol, and has a spicy odor.

Carnation oil is obtained by solvent extraction or by enfleurage from the flowers of the *Dianthus caryophyllus,* of which there are more than

2,000 varieties grown in the Mediterranean countries. The less highly cultivated plants give the richest perfumes. **Violet oil** is derived by solvents or maceration in hot oils from the flowers of the blue and purple varieties of *Viola odorata*. **Synthetic violet** is made from **ionone,** $C_{13}T_{20}O$, derived from lemongrass oil. The ionones are made synthetically by condensation of citral with acetone. They are monoenol and dienol butones. **Velvione,** of Rhodia, Inc., is such an ionone with a powerful violet odor. The true violet odor is **irone,** a complex seven-ring compound. It can be obtained from the iris root and is one of the most odoriferous materials obtained from plants. **Orris** is the dry root of the *Iris florentina,* and the powdered root is used in violet powders and as a flavor. **Oak moss** was one of the perfumes of ancient Egypt. It is obtained from the lichen *Evernia prunastri* and *E. furfuracea* growing on oak and spruce trees of southern Europe. The resinous extract has the odor of musk and lavender. It is used as a fixative in perfumes of the poppy type. **Rue oil,** used for sweet pea perfume, is distilled from the plants *Ruta graveolans* of France and *R. montana* of Algeria.

As with jewelry, the manufacture of perfumes is normally classed as a luxury industry. But the vital test of essentiality comes in wartime, and these aesthetic materials are always considered as essential to the public morale, and hence basic. Even under desperate wartime conditions France never stopped the manufacture of perfumes, and during the life struggle of England in the Second World War, the restrictive regulations placed upon perfume manufacture had to be abandoned quickly because of public pressure. Wartime restrictions placed on the imports of perfume oils into the United States during the Second World War were immediately abandoned.

PERILLA OIL. A light yellow oil obtained from the seeds of the plant *Perilla ocimoides* of China and Japan, and employed in varnishes, core oils, printing ink, and linoleum. It dries to a harder, tougher, and glossier film than linseed oil. The specific gravity is about 0.935, iodine value 200, and saponification value 191. It contains 41 to 46% linolenic acid, 31 to 42 linoleic, and 3 to 10 oleic acid. In Japan it is called **egoma oil.** The raw oil tends to form globules, but this is overcome by boiling or blowing. The blown oil is rapid-drying and is more weather-resistant than linseed oil.

PERMEABILITY ALLOYS. A general name for iron-nickel alloys possessing a magnetic susceptibility much greater than iron. An early alloy determined by experiment was made up theoretically of 78.5% nickel, 21.5 iron, but with other elements approximately as follows: carbon, 0.04%; silicon, 0.03; cobalt, 0.37; copper, 0.10; and manganese, 0.022.

It is produced by the Western Electric Co., sometimes with chromium or molybdenum, under the name of **Permalloy,** and is used in magnetic cores for apparatus that operates on feeble electric currents, and in the loading of submarine cables.   It has very little magnetic hysteresis.

Supermalloy, developed by the Bell Laboratories for transformers, contains 79% nickel, 15 iron, 5 molybdenum, and 0.5 manganese, with total carbon, silicon, and sulfur kept below 0.5%.   It is melted in vacuum, and poured in an inert atmosphere.   It can be rolled to a thinness of 0.00025 in.   The alloy has an initial permeability 500 times that of iron. **Supermendur,** of the Westinghouse Electric Corp., contains 49% iron, 49 cobalt, and 2 vanadium.   It is highly malleable, and has very high permeability with low hysteresis loss at high flux density.   **Transformer cores** made from the alloy give a power output 30% greater than cores made from grain-oriented silicon steel.   It is also used for magnetic modulators and filter chokes.   The **Sendust alloys,** used in Japan during the shortage of nickel and cobalt, contained iron, silicon, and aluminum. They had high permeability.   **Duraperm,** of the Hamilton Watch Co., is a high-flux magnetic alloy containing 84.5% iron, 9.5 silicon, and 6 aluminum.   Special processing gives the alloy good strength and high hardness without the brittleness of the Sendust alloys.   **Mumetal,** of the Telegraph Construction & Maintenance Co., Ltd., has 76% nickel, 6 copper, and 1.5 chromium.   **Permafy** is a French alloy of this type.   It has a lower initial permeability than the plain nickel-iron type, but has a higher resistivity to keep down eddy-current losses.   **Perminvar,** of the Western Electric Co., is an alloy containing 45% nickel and 25 cobalt, intended to give a constant magnetic permeability for variable magnetic fields.   **A-metal** is a nickel-iron alloy containing 44% nickel and a small amount of copper.   It is used in transformers and loudspeakers to give nondistortion characteristics when magnetized.   **Permax** is a French high-permeability alloy of nickel and iron with small additions of manganese and other elements.

Permenorm, first produced in Germany as **Orthonel** and developed at the U.S. Naval Ordnance Laboratory, contains 50% nickel and 50 iron. It is subjected to drastic rolling in one direction followed by a heat treatment to obtain chemical combination of the nickel and iron.   It has a grain orientation which, when subjected to a magnetic field, produces a square hysteresis loop indicating instantaneous magnetization.   It is used as a core material and in magnetic amplifiers.   **Deltamax,** of the Arnold Engineering Co., is this material.

Alfenol, developed by the Naval Ordnance Laboratory, contains no nickel, but has 16% aluminum and 84 iron.   It is brittle and cannot be rolled cold, but can be rolled into thin sheets at a temperature of 575°C. It is lighter than other permeability alloys, and has superior characteristics for transformer cores and tape-recorder heads.   A modification of this alloy, called **Thermenol,** contains 3.3% molybdenum without change in the single-phase solid solution of the binary alloy. The permeability and coercive force are varied by heat treatment. At 18% aluminum the alloy is practically paramagnetic. The annealed alloy with 17.2% aluminum has constant permeability. This alloy has high heat and chemical resistance, and can replace Type 403 stainless steel for jet-engine compressor blades with 15% saving in weight. It is also used for skins for supersonic missiles and for electric-heater elements. The sheet and wire give long life at intermittent temperatures above 2000°F. **Aluminum-iron alloys** with 13 to 17% aluminum are produced in sheet form by the Metals & Controls Corp. for transformers and relays. They have magnetic properties equal to the 50–50 nickel-iron alloys and to the silicon-iron alloys, and they maintain their magnetic characteristics under changes in ambient temperature.

Conpernik, of the Westinghouse Electric Corp., contains equal amounts of nickel and iron with no copper. It is called constant-permeability nickel, and has little permeability variation. It differs from **Hipernik** of the same company only in heat treatment. When heat-treated, Hipernik has higher permeability than silicon transformer steel up to flux density of about 10 kilogausses. Both alloys are used in transformer cores. **Hipernik V** is grain-oriented, giving a square hysteresis loop, with a low degree of coercive force, 0.15 oersted, and a high ratio of residual magnetism to saturation. It comes in thin strip for use in instruments and computer elements. **Hiperco,** of this company, contains 35% cobalt, 64 iron, and 1 chromium. It is ductile and easy to roll to extremely thin strip for instrument parts. The heat-treated metal has high permeability and low hysteresis loss, but in this condition it has low tensile strength and is brittle. **Vicalloy,** developed by the Bell Laboratories, is a high-permeability alloy containing 36 to 62% cobalt, 6 to 16 vanadium, and the balance iron. It is cast and hot-swaged, then drawn into wire or tape as fine as 0.002 in. It retains high permanent magnetism, with coercive forces to 250 oersteds and residual flux of 8,000 gausses, and it retains its magnetism to 600°F.

Iron-nickel permeability alloys are used as loading by wrapping a continuous layer around the full length of the cable. When nickel-copper alloys are used, they are employed as a core for the cable. **Magnetostrictive alloys** are iron-nickel alloys which will resonate when the frequency of the applied current corresponds to the natural frequency of the alloy. They are used in radios to control the frequency of the oscillating circuit. **Magnetostriction** is the stress that occurs in a magnetic material when the induction changes. In transducers it transforms electromagnetic energy into mechanical energy. **Temperature-compensator alloys** are iron-nickel alloys with about 30% nickel. They have the characteristics that they are fully magnetic at −20°F but lose the magnetic permeability in proportion to rise in temperature until at about 130°F they are nonmagnetic. Upon cooling they regain permeability at the same rate. They are used in shunts in electrical instruments to compensate for errors due to temperature changes in the magnets.

PERSIMMON WOOD. The wood of the common persimmon trees *Diospyros virginiana,* of the southeastern United States, and the **black persimmon,** *D. texana* of western Texas. It is used for shuttles, golf-stick heads, and tools, and takes a fine polish. The tree belongs to the ebony family, of which there are listed about 160 species. The persimmon is a small tree not over 50 ft high and 12 in. in diameter. The wood is very hard, strong, and compact, and retains its smoothness under long rubbing. The sapwood is light brown in color, 2 to 5 in. wide, and the heartwood is black but very small, the thickness of a pencil, for example, in a 6-in. tree. The weight is 49 lb per cu ft. The fruit is cultivated for food, and there are only limited quantities of the wood. A fine wood used for fancy articles is **olive wood,** from the olive fruit tree of California. It is yellow with beautifully streaked dark lines.

PETITGRAIN. An essential oil obtained by distillation of the leaves and small twigs of the **bitter orange** tree, *Citrus aurantium,* native to tropical Asia, but now grown in other countries. In Spain, it is known as the **Seville orange.** Paraguay is the chief producer of high-grade petitgrain, which is one of the best fixatives for fine perfumes and is also used in flavoring extracts. One pound of petitgrain is obtained from 100 to 150 lb of leaves. The fruits of the tropical bitter orange are large and of the finest golden appearance, but the pulp is very acid. The juice is used only for blending in orange drinks. It contains a dilactone, **limonin,** which gives it a bitter taste. The rind is used in **marmalade** and **candied orange peel.** An essential oil distilled from the rind is known as **curacao,** and is used in perfumery and in **curaçao liqueur.** The flowers are very fragrant, and from them **neroli oil** is distilled. Neroli is used in perfumery blends and for mixing with synthetic perfumes. **Neroli Portugal** is inferior, and comes from the sweet orange *C. sinensis* by extraction. **Orange oil,** obtained by expression from the ripe rind of the sweet orange, is a less valuable oil. **Bergamot oil** is from the rind of the fruit of the small spiny tree *C. bergamia* of Italy. It has a soft sweet odor, and is used in perfume blends and in soaps. The golden-yellow pear-shaped fruit has an acid inedible pulp.

The **bioflavonoids,** used in cold remedies, are obtained from the white pulp, or **albedo,** of citrous fruits. They are alkaline-soluble crystalline compounds, variations of **chromone,** a **benzpyrone,** and **flavone,** the **phenyl benzpyrone.** The pressed product from the pulp is acidified, crystallized, and dried.   **Citroid,** of the Grove Laboratories, is a product of this kind. About 150 distinct chemicals have been produced from citrous fruits. The bioflavonoids are six-membered, double-ring compounds.   Some are isolated and used directly, as the **naringin** from grapefruit peel, which is an effective substitute for quinine.   Others are synthesized easily.   The chromone and flavone are really the parent substances of many natural vegetable dyes, drugs, and tannins, and are readily convertible to these materials.

PETROLATUM. A jellylike substance obtained in the fractional distillation of petroleum.   Its composition is between $C_{17}H_{36}$ and $C_{21}H_{44}$, and it distills off above 303°C.   It is also called **petroleum jelly.**   It is used for lubricating purposes and for compounding with rubber and resins.   When highly refined for the pharmacy trade, it is used as an ointment.   The specific gravity is from 0.820 to 0.865.   It is insoluble in water but readily soluble in benzine and in turpentine.   For lubricating purposes it should be refined by filtration only and not with acids, and should not be adulterated with paraffin.   The melting point should be between 115 and 130°F.   Petrolatum of Grade O, used as a softener in rubber, is a paleyellow, odorless semisolid of specific gravity 0.84 and melting point 115 to 118°F.   **Sherolatum** is petrolatum jelly of the Sherwood Petroleum Co., Inc., and **Vaseline** is petroleum jelly of the Chesebrough Mfg. Co. But the trade-named petroleum jellies for pharmaceutical uses may be compounded with other materials.

PETROLEUM. A heavy, liquid, inflammable mineral oil stored under the surface of the earth, and originally formed as the by-product of the action of bacteria on marine plants and animals.   It consists chiefly of carbon and hydrogen in the form of hydrocarbons, including most of the liquids of the **paraffin series,** C_5H_{12} to $C_{16}H_{34}$, together with some of the gases, CH_4 to C_4H_{10}, and most of the solids of the series from $C_{17}H_{36}$ to $C_{27}H_{56}$. It also contains hydrocarbons of other series.   While petroleum is used primarily for the production of fuels and lubricating oils, it is one of the most valuable raw materials for a very wide range of chemicals.   The name **petrochemicals** is used in a general sense to mean chemicals derived from petroleum, but it does not mean any particular class of chemicals. Sulfur and helium are by-products from petroleum working.

Petroleums from different localities differ in composition, but tests of oils from all parts of the world give the limits as 83 to 87% carbon, 11 to 14 hydrogen, with sulfur, nitrogen, and oxygen in amounts from traces to 3%.   Mexican and Texan oils are high in sulfur.   The crude oil is split by distillation into naphtha, gasoline, kerosene, lubricating oils, paraffin, and asphalt.   It may also be split by cracking, that is, by subjecting to violent heating in the absence of air.   This process yields a higher proportion of volatile products because of the breaking down of the more complex molecules by the high heat.   Liquefied petroleum gases, including **propane, butane, pentane,** or mixtures, are marketed under pressure in steel cylinders as **bottled gas.**   Propane, $CH_3CH_2CH_3$, is used in cook stoves.   Butane, which has an additional CH_2 group, is used to enrich illuminating and heating gas.   Propane and butane gases have heating values from 2,800 to 3,000 Btu per cu ft.   **Liquid gas** is also used for internal-combustion engines, as a solvent, and for making many chemicals.   **Pyrogen** is the trade name of a gas obtained during the process of recovering gasoline from natural gas.   It is marketed in cylinders for use in flame cutting torches.   **Road oil,** used on dirt roads, is a heavy-residue oil from the refineries.

White mineral oil is petroleum highly refined to color.   Russian and Rumanian oils with high naphthene content were particularly suitable for this refining and the oil was called **Russian oil.**   Pennsylvania paraffin-base oils and Texas asphaltic-base oils are difficult to refine to color. The American white Russian oil is refined from mid-Continent and Gulf Coast oils which contain high naphthenes.   It is used as a laxative, as a carrier of many drugs, in textile spinning, as a plasticizer for synthetic resins, and for sodium dispersions where the alkali metal would normally react with any impurities.   **Klearol** and **Blandol,** of L. Sonneborn Sons, Inc., are viscosity grades of white mineral oil.

Petroleum from Baku was used from ancient times for lighting purposes, and the Bolivian oil was used in the sixteenth century for burning. The first commercial wells in the United States were opened in 1859 at Titusville, Pa.   The chief production of petroleum is in Mexico, the United States, Russia, Rumania, Asia Minor, Peru, and northern South America, but large reserves exist in many other places.   About half the world production of crude petroleum is in the Western Hemisphere, but the largest single field is in the Persian Gulf area.   Only about 1% of the production of crude oil is from the Pennsylvania field, but much of the motor lubricating oil is from this oil.   Many undersea deposits of petroleum are known, but some are at great depth; for example, the water at the Rockall Plateau, northeast of Ireland, is 5,000 ft deep with 10,000 ft of sediment above the oil deposit.

PEWTER.   A very old name for tin-lead alloys used for dishes and ornamental articles, but now referring to the use rather than to the composition of the alloy.   Tin was the original base metal of the alloy, the ancient **Roman pewter** having about 70% tin and 30 lead, although iron and other elements were present as impurities.   Pewter, or **latten ware,** of the sixteenth century contained as high as 90% tin, and a strong and hard

English pewter contained 91% tin and 9 antimony.   This alloy is easily cold-rolled and spun, and can be hardened by long annealing at 225°C and quenching in cold water and tempering at 110°C.   Pewter is now likely to contain lead and antimony, and very much less tin; when the proportion of tin is below about 65%, the alloys are unsuited for vessels to contain food products, because of the separation of the poisonous lead. Antimony is also undesirable in food containers because of its poisonous nature, but when the tin content is low, antimony is needed to make the alloy susceptible to polishing.   Ordinary pewter, with 6% antimony, 1.5 copper, and the balance tin, has a Vickers hardness of 23.   With the addition of 1.5% bismuth, the hardness is 29.   Best pewter, used for high-class articles, contains 100 parts tin, 8 antimony, 2 bismuth, and 2 copper.   Triple has 83 parts tin, 17 antimony, or some lead to replace part of the antimony.   Pewter should have a peculiar bluish-white luster when polished.   It can be spun easily.   Pewters containing much lead are dark in color and must be plated.

Britannia metal is a type of latten ware which also usually contains copper.   The color is silvery white with a bluish tinge, or with a yellowish tinge if the copper is high.   The ordinary composition is quite similar to some babbitts, 89% tin, 7.5 antimony, and 3.5 copper.   It takes a fine polish and does not tarnish easily.   It is easily worked by stamping, rolling, or spinning, or may be cast.   Some zinc may be used in the casting alloys.   English Britannia metal has 94% tin, 5 antimony, and 1 copper.   **Hanover white metal** contains 87% tin, 7.5 antimony, and 5.5 copper.   **Dutch white metal** has 81.5% tin, 8.5 antimony, and 9.5 copper.   **Queen's metal** is a Britannia metal with a small amount of zinc. A typical composition is 88.5% tin, 7 antimony, 3.5 copper, and 1 zinc. The zinc helps to strengthen the alloy.   **Minofor** is another grade containing up to 9% zinc and up to 1 iron.   When zinc is used in these metals, the antimony is lowered because both metals tend to make the alloy brittle.   **Ashberry metal,** for tableware, contains some nickel and aluminum.   **Tutanic metal,** a German utensil alloy, had 88 to 92% tin, up to 3 copper, and 6 to 7.5 lead.   **Ludensheid plate** had 72% tin, 24 antimony, and 4 copper, with a trace of lead to increase fluidity.   **Wagner's alloy** and **Koeller's alloy** were names for utensil alloys, the latter containing some bismuth to improve the casting.

PHENOL.   Also known as **carbolic acid.**   A colorless to white crystalline material of sweet odor, having the composition C_6H_5OH, obtained from the distillation of coal tar and as a by-product of coke ovens.   It is also made by alkylating benzene with propylene to form **cumene,** which is **isopropyl benzene,** $C_6H_5CH(CH_3)_2$, and then oxidizing to cymene hydroperoxide and finally splitting to form phenol and acetone.   Or, it can be made by oxidation of toluene and then a catalytic conversion to phenol. It is also produced by hydrogenation of the lignin from sulfite waste liquor. It is a valuable chemical raw material for the production of plastics, dyes, pharmaceuticals, syntans, and other products.

Phenol melts at about 43°C and boils at 183°C. The pure grades have melting points of 39, 39.5, and 40°C. The technical grades contain 82 to 84% and 90 to 92% phenol. The crystallization point is given as 40.41°C. The specific gravity is 1.066. It dissolves in most organic solvents. By melting the crystals and adding water, liquid phenol is produced, which remains liquid at ordinary temperatures. Phenol has the unusual property of penetration of living tissues and forms a valuable antiseptic. It is also used industrially in cutting oils and compounds and in tanneries. The value of other disinfectants and antiseptics is usually measured by comparison with phenol. The **phenol coefficient** of a disinfectant is the ratio of the dilution required to kill the Hopkins strain of typhoid bacillus in a specified time compared with the dilution of phenol required for the same organism under the same conditions and time. However, phenol is poisonous and gives dangerous burns on the skin, so that as a disinfectant it must be used with caution.

Phenol is a very reactive and versatile compound. In coal tar it occurs with many homologs, and many of the complex chemicals occurring in vegetable life are homologs or complexes of phenol. It can be easily nitrated, sulfonated, or halogenated. The hydroxyl hydrogen is readily replaceable by strong bases to produce **phenolates,** and these are readily convertible to ethers, such as **diphenyl ether,** or **diphenyl oxide,** $(C_6H_5)_2O$, which has a boiling point at 259°C and is used as a heat-transfer medium. Ortho and para compounds are obtained by direct substitution, and these are called **substituted phenols. Thiophenol,** C_6H_5SH, called also **mercapto benzene** and **phenyl mercaptan,** is an evil-smelling liquid boiling at 172°C, used for making dyes and pharmaceuticals. One of the most important applications of phenol is its condensation with formaldehyde to produce synthetic resins, and these resins can be varied greatly by alterations in the phenol. The term **phenols** is a class name for a wide variety of materials, as distinct from the normal phenol.

The Koppers Co. markets **alkylated phenols** for the production of tough and oil-soluble phenol-formaldehyde resins. Tertiary **butyl phenol,** $C_{10}H_{14}O$, comes in flakes melting at 98°C. Tertiary **amyl phenol,** $C_{11}H_{10}O$, is also in flakes melting at 90°C. **Nonyl phenol** is a mixture of monoalkyl phenols with side chains of random-bracketed alkyl radicals on the molecule. It is a liquid of specific gravity 0.94, boiling at 300°C, used for making oil-soluble phenolic resins and lubricating-oil additives. **Phenyl phenol** is used in cosmetics to control odors and prevent bacterial deterioration, and also as a preservative in paper, paints, and leather.

Bisphenol is a hydroxy phenol, $C_{15}H_{16}O$, with high reactivity, used for producing modified phenolic resins and epoxy resins, as an antioxidant for oils, and as a stabilizer for resins.   **Santobrite,** of the Monsanto Chemical Co., is chlorinated phenol, or **sodium pentachloro phenol,** used as a preservative.   **Biolite** is a formulation of Santobrite used for slime and mildew control in laundries and in paper-pulp plants.   Para **nitrophenol,** made by treating phenol with cold dilute nitric acid, is used as a preservative for leather goods to prevent mold growth.   **Lorothiodol,** of the Hilton-Davis Chemical Co., is a sulfurized chlorinated phenol.   It is a more powerful antiseptic than phenol, is odorless and nontoxic, and is used in soaps.   **Pentaphen,** of Sharples Chemicals, Inc., is a para tertiary amyl phenol, $C_5H_{11}C_6H_4OH$, used for making pale-colored, oil-soluble resins by condensation with aldehydes.

A wide range of related materials is produced from **diphenyl,** also called **biphenyl** and **phenyl benzene.**   It has the composition $(C_6H_5)_2$, is a liquid below 71°C, and boils at 255°C.   It is a stable compound and is used as a heat-transfer medium.   But it is made easily by heating benzene to eliminate H_2 and, because of its low cost, is a valuable intermediate chemical.   Like phenol, it can be modified easily to produce innumerable compounds.   **Tetramethyl benzene,** or **durene,** for example, is a 10-carbon aromatic liquid used for making **pyromellitic acid** and its anhydride for the production of polyester resins.   Many other useful acids are also produced.

PHENOL-FORMALDEHYDE RESIN.   A synthetic resin made by the reaction of phenol and formaldehyde, and employed as a molding material for the making of mechanical and electrical parts.   It was the earliest type of hard, thermoset synthetic resin, and its favorable combination of strength, chemical resistance, electrical properties, glossy finish, and non-strategic abundance of low-cost raw materials has continued the resin, with its many modifications and variations, as one of the most widely employed groups of plastics for a variety of products.   The resins are also used for laminating, coatings, and casting resins.

The reaction was known as early as 1872 but was not utilized commercially until much later.   A condensation product of 50 parts phenol and 30 parts 40% formaldehyde made under an English patent of 1905 was called **Resinite,** and was originally offered as a substitute for celluloid. Various modifications were made by other inventors.   **Redmanol** was one of the first of the American products by the Bakelite Corp.   **Juvelite** was made in Germany by condensing the phenol and formaldehyde with the aid of mineral acids, and **Laccain** was made under an English patent by using organic acids as catalysts.   A Russian phenol resin, under the name of **Karbolite,** employed an equal amount of **naphthalene-sulfonic acid,** $C_{10}H_7SO_3H$, with the formaldehyde.

The resins are marketed usually in granular form partly polymerized for molding under heat and pressure, which complete the polymerization, making the product infusible and relatively insoluble.   They may also come as solutions, or compounded with reinforcing fillers and pigments. The tensile strength of a molded part made from a simple phenol-formaldehyde resin may be only about 6,000 psi, with a specific gravity of 1.27 and dielectric strength of about 450 volts per mil.   Reinforcement is needed for higher strength, and with a wood-flour filler the tensile strength may be as high as 10,000 psi.   With a fabric filler the flexural strength may be 15,000 psi, or 18,000 psi with a mineral filler.   The specific gravity is also raised, and the mineral fillers usually increase the dielectric strength.

Proper balance of fillers is important, since too large a quantity may produce brittleness.   Organic fillers absorb the resin and tend to brittleness and reduced flexural strength, although organic fibers and fabrics generally give high impact strength.   Wood flour is the most usual filler for general-service products, but prepared compounds may have mineral powders, mica, asbestos, organic fibers of macerated fabrics, or mixtures of organic and mineral materials.   The **Resinox** resins, of Monsanto, are in grades with fibrous and mineral fillers, and **Moldarta,** of the Westinghouse Electric Corp., is in various grades.   **Bakelite** was the original name for phenol plastics, but trade names now usually cover a range of different plastics, and the types and grades are designated by numbers.

The specific gravity of filled phenol plastics may be as high as 1.70. The natural color is amber, and, as the resin tends to discolor, it is usually pigmented with dark colors.   Normal **phenol resin** cures to single-carbon methylene groups between the phenolic groups, and the molded part tends to be brittle.   Thus, many of the innumerable variations of phenol are now used to produce the resins, and modern phenol resins may also be blended or cross-linked with other resins to give higher mechanical and electrical characteristics.   Furfural is frequently blended with the formaldehyde to give better flow, lower specific gravity, and reduced cost.   The alkylated phenols give higher physical properties.   **Phenol-phosphor resin** is a phenol resin modified with phospho nitrilic chloride.   When cured the resin contains 15% phosphorus, 6 nitrogen, and less than 1 chlorine. The tensile strength is 7,000 psi and it will withstand continuous temperatures to 500°F.   The **Flexiphen 160** resin, of the Koppers Co., has some of the single-carbon methylene linkages replaced by hydrocarbon chains, giving 30% higher flexural strength with 5% lower specific gravity.

Resinox 3700, of the Monsanto Chemical Co., is a mineral-filled phenolic resin of high arc resistance and high dimensional stability for electrical parts.   **Synvar,** of the Synvar Corp., and **Durez,** of the Hooker Chemical Corp., come in a number of grades.

Phenol resins may also be cast and then hardened by heating.   The cast resins usually have a higher percentage of formaldehyde and do not have fillers.   They are poured in syrupy state in lead molds and hardened in a slow oven.   **Crystallin,** of the Crystallin Products Corp., **Phenalin,** of Du Pont, and **Catalin,** of the American Catalin Corp., are cast phenol plastics.   **Ivoricast,** of West Coast Enterprises, is a shock-resistant cast phenolic plastic with wood-flour filler which cures at low heat.   **Prystal** is the name of water-clear Catalin, and **Bois glacé** is **Catalin-coated wood** for desk tops.   **Fiberlon** is a cast phenol plastic of the Fiberloid Corp. **Marblette** is a cast plastic of the Marblette Corp.

PHONOLITE. Also known as **clinkstone.** An aluminum-potassium-silicate mineral used in the production of glass, and in Germany for the production of aluminum.   Phonolite is a variety of feldspar.   It varies greatly in composition, the best of the Eifel Mountains mineral containing 20 to $23\frac{1}{4}$ alumina, 7 to 9 K_2O, 6 to 8 Na_2O, and 50 to 52 silica.   A variety of this mineral, **nepheline,** from the Kola Peninsula, is used in Russia to produce aluminum, with soda and potash as by-products. **Nepheline syanite** from Peterborough Co., Ontario, Canada, is used in the ceramic industry in pottery, porcelain, and tile to increase translucency and reduce warpage and crazing.   From 3 to 5% added to structural clay increases the mechanical strength.   As a substitute for potash feldspar in wall tiles, it increases the fluxing action and lowers the fusing point. **Agalmatolite,** a name derived from the Greek words meaning **image stone,** is the massive form of phonolite from which the Chinese carve figures and bas-reliefs.   It has a soft greasy feel, and varies in color.

PHOSGENE. The common name for **carbonyl chloride,** $COCl_2$, a colorless, poisonous gas made by the action of chlorine on carbon monoxide. It was used as a poison war gas, called **D-stoff** by the Germans and **collongite** by the French.   But it is now used in the manufacture of metal chlorides and anhydrides, pharmaceuticals, perfumes, isocyanate resins, and for blending in synthetic rubbers.   It liquefies at 8.2°C, and solidifies at −118°C.   It is decomposed by water.   When chloroform is exposed to light and air, it decomposes into phosgene.   One part in 10,000 parts of air is a toxic poison.   For chemical warfare it is compressed into a liquid in shells.   **Lacrimite,** also a poison war gas, is thiophosgene mixed with stannic chloride.   **Diphosgene,** $ClCOOC \cdot Cl_3$, called **green cross,**

superpalite, and **perstoff,** is an oily liquid boiling at 128°C. It is an intense lachrymator, has an asphyxiating odor, and is a lung irritant.

PHOSPHOR BRONZE. Originally called **steel bronze** when first produced at the Royal Arsenal in Vienna. It was 92–8 bronze deoxidized with phosphorus and cast in an iron mold. It is now any bronze deoxidized by the addition of phosphorus to the molten metal. It may or may not contain residual phosphorus in the final state. Ordinary bronze frequently contains cuprous oxide formed by the oxidation of the copper during fusion. By the addition of phosphorus, which is a powerful reducing agent, a complete reduction of the oxide takes place, and the resulting bronze has higher strength. Phosphor bronze is not usually a special alloy but is a deoxidized bronze, and all grades of bronze can be converted into it. But when there is residual phosphorus in the metal, the bronze is harder. Phosphor-bronze casting metals for bearings usually contain lead. ASTM Grade B phosphor bronze has 4.0 to 5.5% tin, 2.5 to 4 lead, and 0.03 to 0.25 phosphorus. A foundry alloy known as **standard phosphor bronze** contains about 80% copper, 10 tin, and 10 lead, with about 0.25 phosphorus. When chill-cast, it is fine-grained and has a tensile strength up to 33,000 psi, Brinell hardness 65, and weight 0.325 lb per cu in. One large automotive company lists this metal as **phosphor casting bronze.** The phosphor-bronze ingot metal of this composition marketed by H. Kramer & Co. contains 0.50 to 1% phosphorus, part of which is absorbed in the melting and casting. The residual phosphorus is 0.25%.

Anaconda phosphor bronze, a wrought metal marketed by the American Brass Co., is in grades containing from 5 to 10% tin and 90 to 95 copper. The 90–10 grade for springs has high resistance to fatigue. This is ASTM Grade D wrought phosphor bronze. When soft it has a tensile strength of 65,000 psi with elongation of 65%, and in spring hardness the tensile strength is 125,000 psi with elongation of 4%. **Duraflex** is the name of this company for hard-rolled strip and wire phosphor bronze for springs.

Seymour phosphor bronze, of the Seymour Mfg. Co., used for springs, has 95% copper, 4.75 tin, and 0.25 phosphorus. This is **ASTM spring bronze,** Grade A. The Grade B has 7.75% tin with higher physical properties. For coil and flat springs, these alloys have service temperatures to 225°F. **Carobronze,** of Wrought Bearing Metals, Inc., has 91.2% copper, 8.5 tin, and 0.3 phosphorus. It is produced in hard-drawn tubes and rods to give greater wear resistance and higher impact value than cast bronze for bearings. **Corvic bronze,** of the Chase Brass & Copper Co., has 98.2% copper, 1.5 tin, and 0.30 phosphorus. The tensile strength of the spring material is 95,000 psi, and the electrical conductivity is 42% that of copper. **Telnic bronze** of this company contains 1% nickel, 0.20 phosphorus, 0.5 tellurium, and the balance copper. The phosphor bronze marketed by Revere Copper & Brass, Inc., in sheet, plate, and strip, contains 1.25 to 10% tin with not over 0.05% residual phosphorus. The soft material with hardness to Rockwell B75 has tensile strengths from 40,000 to 73,000 psi, while the hard metal, with Rockwell B hardness from 75 to 104, has tensile strengths from 90,000 to 129,000 psi. **Phosphor bronze rod,** for producing screw-machine parts, contains 88% copper, 4 tin, 4 zinc, and 4 lead. It is free-cutting and has high strength. Hard-drawn phosphor-bronze wire may have a tensile strength exceeding 120,000 psi. **White phosphor bronze,** for bearings, contains 72% lead, 12 antimony, 15 phosphor tin, and 1 copper, and is not a bronze.

PHOSPHOR COPPER. An alloy of phosphorus and copper, used instead of pure phosphorus for deoxidizing brass and bronze alloys, and for adding phosphorus in making phosphor bronze. It comes in 5, 10, and 15% grades and is added directly to the molten metal. It serves as a powerful deoxidizer, and the phosphorus also hardens the bronze. Even slight additions of phosphorus to copper or bronze increase the fatigue strength. Phosphor copper is made by forcing cakes of phosphorus into molten copper and holding under until the reaction ceases. Phosphorus is soluble in copper up to 8.27%, forming Cu_3P, which has a melting point of 707°C. A 10% phosphor copper melts at 850°C, and a 15% at 1022°C. Alloys richer than 15% are unstable. Phosphor copper is marketed in notched slabs or in shot. In Germany **phosphor zinc** was used as a substitute to conserve copper. **Metallophos** is a name for German phosphor zinc containing 20 to 30% phosphorus. The name phosphor copper is also applied to commercial copper deoxidized with phosphorus and retaining up to 0.50% phosphorus. The electrical conductivity is reduced about 30%, but the copper is hardened and strengthened. **Phosphor tin** is a master alloy of tin and phosphorus used for adding to molten bronze in the making of phosphor bronze. It usually contains up to 5% phosphorus and should not contain lead. It has an appearance like antimony, with large glittering crystals, and is marketed in slabs. Federal specifications call for 3.5% phosphorus, with not over 0.50% impurities.

PHOSPHORIC ACID. Also known as **orthophosphoric acid.** A colorless, syrupy liquid of the composition H_3PO_4 used for pickling and rust-proofing metals, for the manufacture of phosphates, pyrotechnics, and fertilizers, as a latex coagulant, as a textile mordant, as an acidulating agent in jellies and beverages, and as a clarifying agent in sugar syrup. The specific gravity is 1.834, melting point 42.35°C, and it is soluble in water. The usual grades are 90, 85, 75%, technical 50%, and dilute 10%. As a cleanser for metals, phosphoric acid produces a light etch on steel, aluminum, or zinc, which aids paint adhesion. **Deoxidine,** of the American Chemical Paint Co., is a phosphoric acid cleanser for metals. **Nielite D,** of Nielco Laboratories, is phosphoric acid with a rust inhibitor, used as a nonfuming pickling acid for steel. **Phosphoric anhydride,** or **phosphorus pentoxide,** P_2O_5, is a white, water-soluble powder used as a dehydrating agent and also as an opalizer for glass. It is also used as a catalyst in asphalt coatings to prevent softening at elevated temperatures and brittleness at low temperatures. **Granusic,** of the J. T. Baker Chemical Co., is this material in granular form for removing water from gas streams.

PHOSPHORUS. A nonmetallic element, symbol P, widely diffused in nature, and found in many rock materials, in ores, in the soil, and in parts of animal organisms. Commercial phosphorus is obtained from phosphate rock by reduction in the electric furnace with carbon, or from bones by burning and treating with sulfuric acid. **Phosphate rock** occurs in the form of land pebbles and as hard rock. It is plentiful in the Bone Valley area of Florida, and also comes from Tennessee, Idaho, and South Carolina. Vast quantities are mined in Morocco and Tunisia. Large deposits are found on many of the Pacific Islands, the Christmas Island resources being estimated at 30 million tons and those on Nauru at 100 million tons. It is a calcium phosphate high in P_2O_5. The mineral **apatite,** widely distributed in the Appalachian range, in Idaho, Brazil, and French Oceania, is also a source of phosphorus, containing up to 20% P_2O_5, with iron oxide and lime. The Egyptian rock contains 62 to 70% tricalcium phosphate. The alumino-calceous phosphate rock of Senegal is treated to obtain a very soluble fertilizer known as **phosphal.** Florida hard phosphate rock contains 80% phosphate of lime. A ton of phosphorus is obtained from 7.25 tons of rock, requiring 30 lb of electrodes and 11,850 kw of electricity. The Tennessee Valley Authority produces about 8 tons of **expanded slag** for each ton of phosphorus produced from the phosphate rock. The slag from the smelter is run onto a forehearth at about 2000°F and treated with water, high-pressure steam, and air. The expanded slag formed is crushed to $3/8$-in. size, bulking 50 lb per cu ft. It is called **TVA slag** and is used for making lightweight concrete blocks. The **superphosphate** used for fertilizers is made by treating phosphate minerals with concentrated sulfuric acid. It is not a simple compound, but may be a mixture of **calcium acid phosphate,** $CaHPO_4$, and calcium sulfate. **Nitrophosphate** for fertilizer is made by acidulating phosphate rock with a mixture of nitric and phosphoric acids, or with nitric acid and then ammoniation and addition of potassium or ammonium sulfate. Natural rock phosphate in finely ground form is also used as a fertilizer for legume crops, but the untreated natural rock is not readily soluble, and is thus not quick-acting as a fertilizer.

Phosphorus is important in foundry work because of its property of combining and greatly modifying the characteristics of metals, and because of its deoxidizing power, especially in nonferrous metals.   It is added to the latter in the form of phosphor copper or phosphor tin.   Small amounts in steel increase the strength and resistance to corrosion and also decrease the tendency of steel sheets to stick together.   But larger amounts promote cold-shortness in the steel.

There are two common forms of phosphorus, yellow and red.   The former, also called **white phosphorus,** P_4, is a light-yellow waxlike solid, phosphorescent in the dark and exceedingly poisonous.   Its specific gravity is 1.83 and it melts at 44°C.   It is used for smoke screens in warfare and for rat poisons and matches.   **Yellow phosphorus** is produced directly from phosphate rock in the electric furnace.   It is cast in cakes of 1 to 3 lb each.   **Red phosphorus** is a reddish-brown amorphous powder, having a specific gravity of 2.20 and a melting point of 725°C.   Red phosphorus is made by holding white phosphorus at its boiling point for several hours in a reaction vessel.   Both forms ignite easily.   **Phosphorus sulfide,** P_4S_3, may be used instead of white phosphorus in making matches.   **Phosphorus pentasulfide,** P_2S_5, is a canary-yellow powder of specific gravity 1.30, or solid of specific gravity 2.0, containing 27.8% phosphorus, used in making oil additives and insecticides.   It is decomposed by water.

Phosphorus is an essential element in the human body, a normal person having more than a pound of it in the system, but it can be taken into the system only in certain compounds.   All of the highly toxic **nerve gases** used in chemical warfare contain phosphorus which combines with and inactivates the choline sterase enzyme of the brain.   This enzyme controls the supply of the hormone which transmits nerve impulses, and when it is inactivated the excess hormone causes paralysis of the nerves and cuts off breathing.   The toxic nerve gas **sarin** is methyl isopropyl fluoro phosphine oxide.   **Organic phosphates** are widely used in the food, textile, and chemical industries.   **Tributyl phosphate,** for example, is a colorless liquid, used as a plasticizer in plastics and as an antifoaming agent in paper coatings and textile sizings.   Flour and other foodstuffs are fortified with **ferric phosphate,** $FePO_4 \cdot 2H_2O$.   **Iron phosphate** is used as an extender in paints.   **Tricalcium phosphate,** $Ca_3(PO_4)_2$, is used as an anticaking agent in salt, sugar, and other food products and to provide a source of phosphorus.   The tricalcium phosphate used in toothpastes as a polishing agent and to reduce the staining of chlorophyll has the formula $(10CaO \cdot H_2O \cdot 3P_2O_5)3H_2O$, and is a fine white powder.   **Dicalcium phosphate,** used in animal feeds, is precipitated from the bones used for making gelatin, but is also made by treating lime with phosphoric acid made from phosphate rock.   **Diammonium phosphate,** $(NH_4)_2HPO_4$, is a mildly alkaline, white crystalline powder used in ammoniated dentifrices, for pH control in bakery products, in making phosphors and to prevent afterglow in matches, and for flameproofing paper.

For manufacturing operations, phosphorus is generally utilized in the form of intermediate chemicals, but the phosphorus marketed by the American Agricultural Chemical Co., for use in doping semiconductors and in electroluminescent coatings, is 99.9999% pure. **Phosphorus trichloride,** PCl_3, is an important chemical for making phosphites. It is a colorless liquid boiling at 76°C. It decomposes in water to form phosphorus and hydrochloric acid. **Phosphorus oxychloride,** $POCl_3$, is a very reactive liquid used as a chlorinating agent and for making organic chemicals. In water it decomposes to form phosphoric and hydrochloric acids. **Phosphorus thiochloride,** $PSCl_3$, is a yellowish liquid containing 18.5% phosphorus and 18.6% sulfur. It is used for making insecticides and oil additives.

PHTHALIC ANHYDRIDE. A white, crystalline material of the composition $C_6H_4(CO)_2O$, with a melting point of 130.8°C, soluble in water and in alcohol. It is made by oxidizing naphthalene, or it is produced from ortho xylene derived from petroleum. It is used in the manufacture of alkyd resins, for the production of dibutyl phthalate and other plasticizers, dyes, and many chemicals. Chlorinated phthalic anhydride is also used as a compounding medium in plastics. It is a white, odorless, nonhygroscopic stable powder containing 50% chlorine. It gives higher temperature resistance and increased stability to plastics. **Niagathal** is a chlorinated phthalic anhydride of the Niagara Alkali Co. **Tetrahydro phthalic anhydride** is a white crystalline powder with a molecular weight of 152.1, melting at 100°C, used to replace phthalic anhydride where a lighter color is desired. It is produced by condensing butadiene with maleic anhydride. In synthetic resin coatings it gives higher adhesion. **Terephthalic acid** may be obtained as a by-product in the production of phthalic anhydride from petroleum. It has a long-chain alkyl group having an amide linkage on one end and a methyl ester on the other. It is used for producing textile fibers. Its sodium salt is used as a gelling agent for high-temperature lubricating greases for uses to 600°F. It forms fine **crystallites** of soft flexible fibers in the grease. **Oronite GA10** is this material. **Isophthalic acid,** made by oxidation of ethyl benzene and ortho xylene, produces alkyd paint resins of greater heat stability than phthalic anhydride. **Maleic anhydride,** $(CHCO)_2O$, is a white crystalline solid used to replace phthalic anhydride in alkyd resins to increase the hardness for baking enamels and to resist yellowing.

PIASSAVA. Also called **Pará grass** and **monkey grass.** A coarse, stiff, and elastic fiber obtained from a species of palm tree, *Leopoldinia piassaba,* of Brazil, used for making brushes and brooms. The plant has long beards of bristlelike fibers, which are combed out and cut off the young plants. These fibers sometimes reach a length of 4 ft. The soft, finer fibers are made into cordage, and the coarser ones are used for brushes. Piassava is very resistant to water. The fiber for brush manufacture is separated into three classes, the heavy fibers being known as **bass,** the medium as **bassine,** and the fine as **palmyra.** The bass is used for heavy floor sweeps. The fiber of the palm *Attalea funifera* which grows in the state of Bahia, Brazil, and is also called piassava, is a harder and stronger material than the piassava of Amazonas. It is used for marine cordage, and is resistant to salt water. A substitute for piassava is **acury,** from the leaves of the palm *A. phalerata* of Matto Grosso. It is used for cordage and brushes, and the coarser fibers are used for brooms.

PICKLING ACIDS. Acids used for pickling, or cleaning castings or metal articles. The common pickling bath for iron and steel is composed of a solution of sulfuric acid and water, 1 part acid to from 5 to 10 parts water being used. This acid attacks the metal and cleans it of the oxides and sand by loosening them. For pickling scale from stainless steels a 25% cold solution of hydrochloric or sulfuric acid is used, or hydrofluoric acid with the addition of anhydrous ferric sulfate is used. Hydrofluoric acid solutions are sometimes used for pickling iron castings. This acid attacks and dissolves away the sand itself. For bright-cleaning brass a mixture of sulfuric acid and nitric acid is used. For a matte finish the mixed acid is used with a small amount of zinc sulfate. Copper and copper alloys can be pickled with sulfuric acid to which anhydrous ferric sulfate is added to speed the action, or sodium bichromate is added to the sulfuric acid to remove red cuprous oxide stains. Brass forgings are pickled in nitric acid to bring out the color. Since all of these acids form salts rapidly by the chemical action with the metal, they must be renewed with frequent additions of fresh acid. The French pickling solution known as **framanol,** used for aluminum, is a mixture of chromium phosphate and triethanol amine. The latter emulsifies the grease and oil, and the aluminum oxide film is dissolved by the phosphoric acid, leaving the metal with a thin film of chromic oxide.

The temperature of most pickling solutions is from 140 to 180°F. An increase of 20°F will double the rate of pickling. **Acid brittleness** after pickling is due to the absorption of hydrogen when the acid acts on iron, and is reduced by shortening the pickling time. **Inhibitors** are chemicals added to reduce the time of pickling by permitting higher temperatures and stronger solutions without hydrogen absorption. **Hibitite,** of Monsanto, is a brown liquid of the composition $C_{27}H_{45}NO_{10}S_2$, used as a metal pickling inhibitor. Addition of a small amount of 2% tincture of iodine to a 5% sulfuric acid solution gives a 95% retardation of acid attack on steel without decreasing the rate of dissolution of the rust.   In plating baths, **fluoboric acid,** HBF_4, has high throwing power and has a cleansing effect by dissolving sand and silicides from iron castings and steel surfaces. It is a colorless liquid with specific gravity of 1.33 and decomposes at 130°C. **Pennsalt FA-42,** of Pennwalt, is this material. It is a 42% solution of fluoboric acid for pickling and for control of acidity of plating baths.

Phosphoric acid is employed in hot solution as a dip bath for steel parts to be finished to a rough or etched surface.   It leaves a basic iron phosphate coating on the steel which is resistant to corrosion and gives a rough base for the finish. **Coslettized steel** is steel rustproofed by dipping in a hot solution of iron phosphate and phosphoric acid. **Parkerized steel** is rust-proofed steel treated in a bath of iron and manganese phosphates. **Bond-erized steel** is steel treated with phosphoric acid and a catalyst to give a rough, tough, rust-resistant base for paints. **Granodized steel** is produced with zinc phosphate.   In general, the coatings left on steel by phosphate treatments are extremely thin, not over 0.0002 in.   The iron-manganese coatings are black, and the iron-zinc-phosphate coatings are gray.

PIG IRON. The iron produced from the first smelting of the ore.   The melt of the blast furnace is run off into rectangular molds, forming, when cold, ingots called pigs. Pig iron contains small percentages of silicon, sulfur, manganese, and phosphorus, besides carbon. It is useful only for resmelting to make cast iron or wrought iron. Pig iron is either sand-cast or machine-cast. When it is sand-cast, it has sand adhering and fused into the surface, giving more slag in the melting. Machine-cast pig iron is cast in steel forms and has a fine-grained chilled structure, with lower melting point. Pig irons are classified as bessemer or nonbessemer, according to whether the phosphorus content is below or above 0.10%.   There are six general grades of pig iron: **low-phosphorus pig iron,** with less than 0.03%, used for making steel for steel castings and for crucible steelmaking; **bessemer pig iron,** with less than 0.10% phosphorus, used for bessemer steel and for acid open-hearth steel; **malleable pig iron,** with less than 0.20%, used for making malleable iron; **foundry pig iron,** with from 0.5 to 1%, for cast iron; **basic pig iron,** with less than 1%, and **low-silicon,** less than 1%, for basic open-hearth steel; and **basic bessemer,** with from 2 to 3%, used for making steel by the basic bessemer process employed in England.

About two-thirds of all pig iron produced in the United States is basic. Since silicon is likely to dissolve the basic furnace lining, it is kept as low as possible, 0.70 to 0.90%, with sulfur not usually over 0.095%. Pig irons are also specified on the content of other elements, especially sulfur. The sulfur may be from 0.04 to 0.10%, but high-sulfur pig iron cannot be used for the best castings. The manganese content is usually from 0.60 to 1%. Most of the iron for steelmaking is now not cast but is carried directly to the steel mill in car ladles. It is called **direct metal.** Elimination of the casting of pigs and of the billet-steel stage reduces the heat requirements from 16 million Btu to 6 million Btu per average ton of steel.

Pig-iron production in the United States is normally about 73% of the production of steel ingots, but may increase to 80% when less scrap is used. Coke consumption is normally about 250 lb per ton of pig iron produced, but is reduced to about 200 lb when a high top-pressure blast furnace is employed. Foundry pig iron is graded by the silicon content, No. 1 having from 2.5 to 3%, and No. 3 from 1.5 to 2% silicon. **Silvery iron** is a name for pig iron of high silicon content because of its silvery fracture. **Puddling iron** is a grade of pig iron used for making wrought or puddled iron in a puddling furnace. A requirement is that the silicon be low, with manganese 0.5 to 1%.

Chateaugay iron is a low-phosphorus pig iron produced from New York state magnetite ore. The original ore as mined contains about 28% iron. The standard analysis of the pig iron is total carbon 4%, silicon 0.75 to 4.0, sulfur 0.03 max, phophorus 0.03 max, manganese 0.10 to 0.15. Chateaugay iron is used for casting rolls, gears, and machine parts. **Norskalloy** is a name for pig iron produced from Norwegian ores containing vanadium and titanium. The standard grade contains from 4 to 4.5% total carbon, 0.5 to 1.5 silicon, 0.20 manganese, 0.20 to 0.25 phosphorus, 0.30 to 0.40 vanadium, and 0.40 to 0.80 titanium. From 15 to 20% Norskalloy pig is added to mixtures where vanadium is required. **Mayari iron** is pig iron made from Cuban ores which contain vanadium and titanium, or is pig iron made to duplicate the Cuban iron. These irons are considered especially suitable for heavy rolls or high-grade castings. Mayari pig, as marketed by the Bethlehem Steel Co., contains 1.60 to 2.50% chromium, 0.80 to 1.25 nickel, 0.25 to 2.25 silicon, 0.10 to 0.20 titanium, 0.05 to 0.08 vanadium, 3.8 to 4.5 total carbon, 0.60 to 2 manganese, under 0.05 sulfur, and under 0.10 phosphorus. **Nikrofer** is a German pig iron from Greek ore that is similar in composition.

PIGMENT. A substance, usually earthy or clayey, which when mixed with oil or other adhesive carrier and a solvent forms a paint. Pigments usually give body as well as color to the paint, and the paint **hiding power** is measured by comparison tests when in the form of a mixed paint. If the hiding power of lithopone is taken as 100, the hiding power of zinc sulfide is 240, and that of titanium dioxide is 400. **Color standards** are distinct from hiding power. Pure magnesium oxide is used as the standard for the measurement of whiteness. The chemical interaction must also be considered in pigments.   For example, zinc oxide increases wear life and mildew resistance in paints, but may tend to react and cause blisters.   The use of pigments is not confined to paints.   In ceramics, their primary choice is by color, but they usually also add other physical properties to the ceramic.   In plastics they add body and strength, as distinct from dyes which do not add body.

A pigment is distinct from a **filler** in that it must retain its opacity when wet.   White powdered quartz, used sometimes as a filler, is not a good pigment as it becomes glassy when wet.   Fillers that retain their opacity are called **extenders,** or **auxiliary pigments,** and the final mixed pigment is called a **reduced color.**   But an extender pigment, such as silica, that does not have good hiding power in itself will increase the hiding power and depth of color of a pigment if the extender is of such fine particle size that it will be dispersed in the voids between the pigment particles.   Extremely fine silica will also cement itself chemically to lead pigments and add wearing qualities.   The **Hi-Sil** of the Pittsburgh Plate Glass Co. is a silica with a particle size of 0.025 micron.   As a pigment for rubber, it adds strength and wear resistance to the rubber.   **Extender RX-2022,** of the Chas. Pfizer & Co., is iron phosphate in the form of white powder for use in paints.   It has low hiding power, with refractive index of 1.7, but is a corrosion inhibitor and is used in undercoats.   **Antimony trioxide** is an opaque yellow powder used in plastics and coatings as a flame-retardant pigment and opacifier.   **Firemaster HHP,** of Michigan Chemical Corp., is this material.   **Thermoguard S,** of M & T Chemicals, is antimony trioxide as a 99.8% pure white powder with average particle size less than 1 micron.

Pigments are mostly of mineral origin, the vegetable pigments such as logwood and the animal pigments such as cochineal being ordinarily classified as dyestuffs.   Bone black, however, is an example of an animal pigment, and vine black is a typical vegetable pigment.   **Vine black,** a fine pigment for inks, was originally made by charring grapevine stems, and was known as **Frankfurt black,** but similar pigments are now made from fruit pits, nut shells, or wood pulp, and are called **vegetable black.** Pigments are also produced by dyeing clays with aniline dyestuffs.   These are called **lakes.**   **Dutch yellow,** for example, is a **yellow lake** made by adsorption of a yellow dye such as quercitron by an inert material such as calcium carbonate.   Various chemicals such as copper acetate and potassium acetate are used as pigments.   **Potassium acetate,** CH_3COOK, is a white powder also used in making crystal glass.   Pigments should be ground fine enough so that all of the powder will pass through a 325-mesh screen.

Natural pigments include ochre, umber, ground shale, hematite, and sienna.   **Sepia** is a dark-brown pigment originally made from the black secretion or inky fluid found in an internal ink sac of the *Sepia* mollusk. It is used in India inks of sepia or dark-brown color. It was formerly employed directly as a writing ink. The red-ochre pigments are the natural red iron oxides of high oxide content. The yellows, or siennas, are the oxides mixed with considerable clay. The browns, or umbers, have manganese present in the clays. **Terre verte,** or **Verona green,** of Cyprus, is a fine blue-green earth valued highly in the Middle Ages as a pigment. In contains 53% silica, 26 ferric oxide, 16 potash, and some magnesia, manganese, and other impurities. **Manganese green,** or **Cassel green,** is **barium manganate,** $BaMNO_4$, a green poisonous powder of specific gravity 4.85, insoluble in water. **Mineral green,** or **Scheele's green,** is **copper arsenite,** $CuHAsO_3$. It is a light-green amorphous powder used in paints and in textile printing. It is also used in medicine. **Orange pigments,** from yellow to brilliant red, with high tinting strength and great fastness, are made with mixtures of **lead chromate,** $PbCrO_4$, lead molybdate, $PbMoO_4$, and **lead sulfate,** $PbSO_4$. Pink to maroon is obtained in ceramic enamels with **calcium stannate,** $CaSnO_3 \cdot 3H_2O$, a white crystalline powder that loses its water at 350°C. **Gloss white,** used as a reduced-color white pigment, and for surface-coating pulp papers and in printing inks, is a coprecipitation product consisting of 75% blanc fixe and 25 aluminum hydrate.

The most important yellow is chrome yellow, but it fades easily. However, the light-fastness and the tinting effect of a pigment depend on the crystal structure as well as on the chemical composition. Normal lead chromate has a monoclinic crystal form, and it gives the strongest and most light-fast of the chrome yellows. Coprecipitated lead chromate and lead sulfate are orthorhombic and greenish in hue, giving primrose and lemon yellows poorer in light-fastness and rust-inhibiting action. **Strontium chromate,** $SrCrO_4$, gives a lemon yellow of good light-fastness. Yellow ochre is inferior as a color but is durable. **Cadmium yellow** is cadmium sulfide and is a brilliant, permanent pigment but expensive. Cadmium selenide produces a bright **cadmium red** which when mixed with the sulfide produces **cadmium orange.** The yellow pigment called **mosaic gold,** or **artificial gold,** is **stannic sulfide,** SnS_2, used in gilding and bronzing paints. **Stannous sulfide,** SnS, used for incorporation in bearings, is a black crystalline material melting at 880°C. Cadmium red and cadmium orange are produced by calcining selenium with cadmium sulfide. These cadmium sulfoselenide pigments give brilliant colors. Cadmium pigments are used in **camouflage paints** to give greater reflection of infrared rays. A building painted with a green containing cadmium has the same reflection as grass or leaves, and is indistinguishable in aerial photographs. An ancient lemon-brown pigment is **bistre.** It was obtained from the collected chimney soot of wood fires, and was much used by the old masters. It is very durable in water colors. The most important green is **chrome green,** which is chrome yellow mixed with Prussian blue; it gives a good color but not permanence.

Ultramarine is the most important blue. It is used in paints and inks and also as **bluing** for whitening paper, textiles, and organic materials by neutralizing the yellow cast. It is an ancient pigment, formerly made by grinding **lapis lazuli,** an azure-blue gemstone which is a sodium silicate sulfide. Ultramarine is now made by calcining a mixture of aluminum silicate and sodium sulfide, and has the empirical formula $Na_7Al_6Si_6O_{24}S_2$. It is a deep-blue, water-soluble powder of 325 mesh, often marketed as a linseed-oil paste. **Egyptian blue,** a chemical-resistant pigment, is a double silicate of calcium and copper, $CaO \cdot CuO \cdot 4SiO_2$. It was used by the ancients, and paintings 1,900 years old still retain the color. It is now made by fusing powdered quartz, chalk, copper oxide, and sodium carbonate. **Cobalt blue** is a good color but is expensive. **Prussian blue,** or **Chinese blue,** is **ferric ferrocyanide,** $Fe_4[Fe(CN)_6]_3$, a blue amorphous powder. It is made by combining iron chloride and potassium ferrocyanide. **Celestial blue** is the light-blue pigment made by extending Prussian blue with barytes. **Milori blue,** used for coloring matches, inks, lacquers, and soaps, is ferric ferrocyanide with gypsum or barium sulfate. **Vermilion pigment** is mercury sulfide, which gives a fine color and is permanent, but it is expensive. High-grade blacks are usually lampblack, bone black, and ivory black, but may be extended with graphite. **Spanish black** is a name used in old texts for the black pigment made by burning cork. It is light and of soft texture. **Mineral black,** or **slate black,** is made by grinding black slate. **Metronite** is a white mineral composed of magnesium and calcium carbonates and magnesium silicate, used as a paint filler and extender. The pigment known as **Plessy's green** is **chromium phosphate,** $CrPO_4$, a bluish-green powder insoluble in water.

The **chemical colors** known as **phthalo cyanines** give high tinting strength and resistance to deterioration by high-temperature baking. They are used for paints, inks, and plastics, and are available as dry colors, in oil- or water-dispersible pastes, and in resin chips for plastics. They are chelated metallic salts of tetrabenzo porphyrazine which is made from phthalamide or ammonium phthalic anhydride in the presence of iron, nickel, or copper salts. **Monastral blue,** Du Pont, is **copper phthalocyanine,** a salt in which the copper is held in a chelate ring complex with four nitrogen atoms. The green is made by chlorination. **Fastolux pigments,** of the Sun Chemical Corp., are phthalo cyanines in fine particle size with a complete range of blue and green colors. The red and bluish-red colors of Du Pont are linear **quinacridones** made from terephthalic acid. The alpha crystal has a bluish-red color, the beta crystal has an intense violet color, and the gamma material has a true red color. The crystal structure can be controlled, and combinations give a range of brilliant, nonbleeding red and violet shades. The **Mercadium colors,** made by Hercules Inc., are compounds of the sulfides of mercury and cadmium to give colors from light orange to dark maroon. All of these pigments give permanence, light and chemical resistance, and a very high tinting strength. The tinting strength of the blue is 15 times that of ultramarine blue, and the green is superior to conventional pigments in brightness and permanence. **Heliogen blue** and **Heliogen green,** of the General Dyestuff Corp., are phthalo cyanine pigments, and **Ramapo blue** and **Ramapo green** are the pigments with a barium resinate extender.

A reactive **fungicidal pigment** used in ship paints and antifouling paints is **cupric oxide hydrated,** a fine dark-brown powder of the composition $4CuO \cdot H_2O$. **Copper quinolinolate** is also used in fungicidal paints. **Cunilate,** of the Scientific Oil Co., is this material. A yellow pigment used in anticorrosive and blister-resistant metal primers is **zinc tetroxy chromate,** $4Zn(OH)_2 \cdot ZnCrO_4$. **Metallic pigments** are most frequently bronze powder or aluminum powder. They are used to increase light reflectivity as well as for appearance. **Stainless-steel flake** for pigment is marketed by Charles Hardy, Inc., as a fine powder in a paste with stearic acid and a solvent. Added to a clear lacquer or varnish it gives a hard silvery coating resistant to corrosive fumes. Aluminum flake gives high heat reflectivity as well as light reflectivity, and is used in silicone-based paints for high heats. Aluminum powder gives iridescent effects when dispersed in vinyl compounds. **Vinylum,** of the Argus Chemical Laboratory, is such a powder in a vinyl copolymer.

PINE. The wood of coniferous trees of the genus *Pinus,* of which there are 37 species in the United States. The **white pine,** or **northern white pine,** *P. strobus,* grows widely in Canada and in the northeastern United States. The trees are 80 to 100 ft high, with trunks 3 to 9 ft in diameter, reaching full size in 80 years. The wood is soft, straight-grained, and free from rosin. The heartwood is light brown, and the sapwood white. It is the chief wood for patternmaking and is also extensively used for cabinetwork and general carpentry. **Cork pine** is a name for the clear, soft, white pieces used for patterns. The white pine is now scarce in New England and red spruce is used in its place. **Yellow pine** is a name for the wood of the **longleaf** or **longstraw pine** tree, *P. palustris,* of the southeastern states, and **shortleaf pine,** *P. echinata,* of the southeast and middle western states, also called **North Carolina pine** and **rosemary pine.** The leaves, called needles or straws, of the longleaf pine are up to 18 in. in length. The longleaf pine tree furnishes the best grades of yellow pine and also is the chief sources of turpentine. It is also called **Georgia pine, southern pine, hard pine,** and **hill pine.**

Slash pine, also known as **Cuban pine** and **swamp pine,** from the tree *P. caribaea,* **Caribbean pine,** growing along the southern coasts of the United States and the Caribbean countries, is a yellow pine. It is one of the most rapidly growing forest trees in the United States and produces one of the heaviest, hardest, and strongest of all the conifers or softwoods. In Central America it is called **ocoté.** Slash pine is next to longleaf pine as a source of turpentine and rosin. As heartwood does not develop until the tree is 20 or more years old, slash pine forms a valuable source of paper pulp. The term **Arkansas pine** in the lumber trade includes mixtures of shortleaf, longleaf, slash, loblolly, and pond pines. **Lodgepole pine,** *P. contorta,* is from a small slow-growing tree of western United States, Canada, and Alaska. It is also called **knotty pine,** scrub pine, and jack pine. The wood is moderately lightweight, yellow to brown in color, with a narrow white sapwood. It is straight-grained with resin ducts, and has large shrinkage. It is used for poles, ties, mine timbers, and rough construction. Also known as **jack pine** is the medium-size tree *P. banksiana* of central Canada, which is used for creosoted telephone poles. **Spruce pine,** or **cedar pine,** is a large tree, *P. glabra,* growing in a narrow area from southern Louisiana to Florida. **Virginia pine,** *P. virginiana,* also called **Jersey pine** and **scrub pine,** is a plentiful tree of the Atlantic states. The wood is soft, very knotty, and not durable. It is used for firewood, but much is used in low-cost houses.

Ponderosa pine, also called **western yellow pine, western white pine,** and **Oregon white pine,** is from the tree *P. ponderosa.* The tree grows to a height of 175 ft and a diameter of 6 ft. It grows throughout the Mountain states from Mexico to Canada, and is also a source of turpentine and rosin. A similar western pine, **Jeffrey pine,** *P. jeffreyi,* contains heptane instead of turpentine in the oleoresin, and is a more economic source of this material than petroleum. The lumber is usually mixed with ponderosa pine and sold as such. It is a moderately soft and lightweight wood with the heartwood light reddish brown, and quite similar to yellow pine. **Loblolly pine,** *P. taeda,* is called North Carolina pine, **Oldfield pine,** and **sap pine.** It grows from Virginia to northern Florida and to Texas; it is adapted to extensive areas and is easily propagated, receiving the name of **field pine.** It is a type of shortleaf pine distinguished by three leaves or straws in each cluster, rough bark, and small prickly burrs. It grows to a diameter of 12 in. in 12 years. **Pitch pine** is the **pond pine,** *P. rigida,* of the southern states, but all yellow pines are called pitch pine in the export trade. **Norway pine,** of the north central states, is *P. resinosa.* The yellow pines are harder and more difficult to work than white pine. They are resinous and more durable. They also take a better polish and show a more figured grain. They are valued for flooring and for general construction. White pine has a specific gravity, kiln-dried, of 0.38, and compressive strength perpendicular to the grain of 780 psi; **western white pine,** *P. monticola,* has a specific gravity of 0.42 and a compressive strength of 750 psi. **Deal** is a European name for the wood of the tree *P. sylvestris,* also known as **Danzig pine, Baltic pine, Scotch fir, Scotch pine,** and **northern pine.** It is popularly called **Scots pine** in England, and is one of the most plentiful of the European conifers, especially in Norway, Sweden, and Finland. It gives a straight pole, up to 70 ft long, valued for telegraph poles.

Paraná pine is a soft, yellowish-white wood with rose veins from the tree *Araucaria brasiliensis* of southern Brazil. In Argentina it competes with American softwoods and is called **Brazilian pine** and **araucarian pine.** The specific gravity is 0.865. The tree is very tall, with branches only at the top, and a notable feature of the wood is the absence of knots. In the United States it is used for telephone-pole crossbars, and to replace birch for such articles as paintbrush handles. Other species of araucarian pine, or **Antarctic pine,** grow in southern Chile and Argentina. **Araucaria oil** is distilled from the wood. It is a viscous reddish oil of roselike odor containing a high percentage of eudeomol and some geraniol. It has a more durable scent than guaiac wood oil for soaps.

The araucarian pines of New Guinea, *A. khinkii* and *A. cunninghamia,* are called **hoop pine.** **New Caledonia pine** is from the tree *A. cooki,* growing to a height of 200 ft with no lower branches. White pine of New Zealand is from the very large tree *Podocarpus dacrydioides,* called also **kahikatea.** The sapwood is white, and the small heartwood is yellow. The wood is straight-grained, inodorous, easily worked, but not durable. It weighs 29 lb per cu ft. It is used for boxes, crates, and packing. Another species, from the tree *P. ferrugineus,* called **miro,** is brownish in color, fine-grained, easily worked, and has high strength. The trees average 65 ft in height and 20 in. in diameter. The New Zealand species known as **black pine,** or **matai,** is from the *P. spicatus.* The wood is yellowish brown, straight-grained, and weighs 38 lb per cu ft. **Red pine,** or **rimu,** is the chief timber of New Zealand, used for furniture, millwork, and kraft pulp. The tree *Dacrydium cupressinum* averages 100 ft in height and 30 in. in diameter. The wood is reddish brown with streaks, straight-grained, easily worked, and weighs 37 lb per cu ft. **Silver pine, pink pine,** and **yellow silver pine** of New Zealand are from several other species of *Dacrydium* obtained only in limited amounts. The name silver is applied to the shiny white woods, and the darker and mottled woods are called pink. They are very durable cypresslike woods. **Mercus pine** is the wood of the tropical pine tree, *P. merkusii,* of the East Indies, India, and the Philippines. It is called **Tinyu pine** in India and **Mindoro pine** in the Philippines. The wood is used in general construction. The tree yields a superior turpentine.

PINE OIL. An oil obtained from the wood of the *Pinus palustris,* or longleaf pine, in the steam extraction of wood turpentine. It is used as a cold solvent for varnish gums and for nitrocellulose lacquers, and as a frothing agent in the flotation of ores. In paints and varnishes it aids dispersion of metallic pigments and improves the flow. It is also used in metal polishes and in liquid and powder scrubbing soaps, as the oil is a powerful solvent of dirt and grease. When free from water, pine oil has a yellowish color, but it is water-white when it contains dissolved water. It has an aromatic characteristic odor, and is distinct from the pine oils distilled from pine leaves and needles and used in medicine. The distillate of the gum of the Jeffrey and Digger pines of California, called **abietine** in medicine, contains 96% heptane and is used as a cleaning agent and insecticide, and as a constituent of standard gasolines for measuring detonation of engines. Pine oil is obtained mainly from old trunks and branches, and is a product formed by hydrolysis. Pine-oil disinfectants are made with steam-distilled pine oil. **Yarmor** is a refined pine oil of Hercules Inc. which is used to increase the detergency of soaps, for dyes, and as a solvent for oils and greases. **Hercosol** is a solvent made from pine oil by the same company. Synthetic pine oil made from gum turpentine by this company has a mild pine odor, a specific gravity of 0.9186, and a flash point of 154°F. It is technically the same as the natural and has the same uses. **Pineroot oil** was produced in Japan on a large scale for the manufacture of fuel oils. The terpenes of the pine oil are converted to aromatic and hydroaromatic compounds by catalytic reaction. The edible **pine kernels** of Europe are the seeds from the large cones of the *P. pinea* of southern Europe and Cyprus. **Pine-needle oil** is distilled from the **Siberian fir** tree, *Abies sibirica,* of northeastern Russia. It is also known as **Siberian pine oil.** It contains a high percentage of **bornyl acetate** and is used in soaps and perfumes.

PLANE WOOD. The wood of the plane tree, *Platanus orientalis,* native to Europe, and *P. occidentalis,* of North America. The latter species is also called **buttonwood** and **buttonball.** It is a yellowish, compact wood with a fine, open grain. The weight is about 40 lb per cu ft. It resembles maple and gives a beautiful grain when quartered. It is employed in cabinetwork.

PLASTIC BRONZE. A name applied by makers of bearing bronzes to copper alloys that are sufficiently plastic to assume the shape of the shaft and make a good bearing by running in. These bronzes have a variety of compositions, but the plasticity is always obtained by the addition of lead, which in turn weakens the bearing. In some cases the lead content is so high, and the tin content so low, that the alloy is not a bronze. These copper-lead alloys are referred to as **red metals.** The plastic bronze ingot marketed by one large foundry for journal bearings contains 65 to 75% copper, 5 to 7 tin, and the balance lead. **Semiplastic bronze** usually contains above 75% copper and not more than 15 lead. **ASTM alloy No. 7** has about 10% lead, 10 tin, 1 zinc, 1 antimony, and 78 copper. The compressive strength is 12,500 psi.

PLATE GLASS. Any glass that has been cast or rolled into a sheet, and then ground and polished. But the good grades of plate glass are, next to optical glass, the most carefully prepared and the most perfect of all the commercial glasses. It generally contains slightly less calcium oxide and slightly more sodium oxide than window glass, and small additions of agents to give special properties may be added, such as agents to absorb ultraviolet or infrared rays, but inclusions that are considered as impurities are kept to a minimum. The largest use of plate glass is for store fronts and office partitions.

While plate glass is now made on a large scale on continuous machines, the principles involved in the manufacture are the same as formerly, namely, pouring on a casting table at a temperature of about 1000°C, smoothing with a roller, annealing, and then setting rigidly on a grinding table and grinding to a polished surface. Normally, the breaking stress of a glass with a ground surface is much less than that of blown or pressed glass, but highly polished plate glass with the surface flaws removed may have double the breaking strength of average pressed glass. The chief advantage of plate glass, however, is that the true parallelism of the ground surfaces eliminates distortion of objects seen through the glass. **Herculite** is a glass of the Pittsburgh Plate Glass Co. which will withstand temperatures up to 650°F without cracking. **Carrara structural glass** of this company is made like plate glass and ground to true plane surfaces. It is made in many colors in thicknesses from $11/_{32}$ to $1\frac{1}{2}$ in., or laminated to give various color effects. It is used for store fronts, counter tops, tiling, and paneling. The weight of the $11/_{32}$ in. is 4.5 lb per sq ft. It does not craze, check, or stain like tile. **Spandrelite,** of this company, is an ornamental structural plate glass made by fusing ceramic color to a plate glass. It is used for cladding buildings.

PLATINUM. A whitish-gray metal, symbol Pt. It is more ductile than silver, gold, or copper, and is heavier than gold. The melting point is 3190°F, and the specific gravity is 21.45. The hardness of the annealed metal is 45 Brinell, with a tensile strength of 17,000 psi; when hard-rolled the Brinell hardness is 97 and tensile strength 34,000 psi. The electrical conductivity is about 16% that of copper. The metal has a face-centered cubic lattice structure, and it is very ductile and malleable. It is resistant to acids and alkalies, but dissolves in aqua regia.   Platinum is widely used in jewelry, but because of its heat resistance and chemical resistance it is also valued for electric contacts and resistance wire, thermocouples, standard weights, and laboratory dishes.   It is generally too soft for use alone, and is almost always alloyed with harder metals of the same group, such as osmium, rhodium, and iridium.   An important use of the metal is in the form of gauze as a catalyst.   **Platinum gauze** is of high purity in standard meshes of 45 to 80 per inch, with wire from 0.0078 to 0.003 in. diameter.   **Dental foil** is of 99.99% purity of maximum softness.   **Platinum foil** for other uses is made in thicknesses down to 0.0002 in.   **Platinum powder** comes in fine submesh particle size.   It is made by chemical reduction and has a minimum purity of 99.9% with amorphous particles 0.3 to 3.5 microns in diameter.   Atomized powder has spherical particles of 50 to 200 mesh, and is 99.9% pure and free-flowing.   **Platinum flake** has the powder particles in tiny laminar platelets which overlap in the coating film.   The particles in **Platinum flake No. 22,** of the Metz Refining Corp., have an average diameter of 3 microns and thickness of 0.1 micron.

Because of the high resistance of the metal to atmospheric corrosion even in sulfur environments, **platinum coatings** are used on springs and other functioning parts of instruments and electronic devices where precise operation is essential.   Electroplating may be done with an electrolyte bath of **platinum dichloride,** $PtCl_2$, or **platinum tetrachloride,** $PtCl_4$.   Hard plates may be produced with an alkaline bath of **platinum diamine nitrite,** $Pt(NH_3)_2(NO_2)_2$.   Coatings are also produced by vapor deposition of platinum compounds; thin coatings, 0.0002 in. or less, are made by painting the surface with a solution of platinum powder in an organic vehicle and then firing to drive off the organic material to leave an adherent coating of platinum metal.

Platinum occurs native in small flat grains or in pebbles usually in alluvial sands, and the native metal generally contains other metals of the platinum group.   The largest nugget ever found came from South America and weighed 2 lb.   The chief sources of the metal are Russia and Colombia, with smaller amounts from Alaska, Canada, and South Africa. Some platinum is obtained from the copper-nickel ores of Canada and South Africa.   There are no commercial ores of the metal, but the rare mineral **sperrylite** is found in Wyoming and in Ontario.   It is a **platinum arsenide,** $PtAs_2$, found in small grains of a tin-white metallic luster.   The only other known natural compound is the rare mineral **cupperite,** which is a **platinum sulfide,** PtS.   The Russian platinum is 99.8 to 99.9% pure, with 0.05 to 0.10% iridium.   Platinum is sold by the troy ounce, 1 cu in. of the metal weighing 11.28 troy oz.

PLATINUM ALLOYS. Platinum-iridium alloys are employed for instruments, magneto contacts, and jewelry.   The alloys are hard and tough and are noncorrosive.   An alloy of 5% iridium and 95 platinum, when hard-worked, has a Brinell hardness of 170; an alloy with 30% iridium has a hardness of 400.   The 5 and 10% alloys are used for jewelry manufacture; the 25 and 30% alloys are employed for making surgical instruments. An alloy of 80% platinum and 20 iridium is used for magneto contact points, and the 90–10 alloy is widely used for electrical contacts in industrial control devices.   The addition of iridium does not alter the color of the platinum.   The 5% alloy dissolves readily in aqua regia; the 30% alloy dissolves slowly.

Platinum-rhodium alloys are used for thermocouples for temperatures above 1100°C.   The standard thermocouple used is platinum versus platinum-10% rhodium.   Other thermocouples for higher operating temperatures use platinum-rhodium alloys in both elements.   The alloys of platinum-rhodium are widely used in the glass industry, particularly as glass fiber extrusion bushings.   Rhodium increases the high temperature strength of platinum without reducing its resistance to oxidation.   **Platinum-rhodium gauze** for use as a catalyst in producing nitric acid from ammonium contains 90% platinum and 10 rhodium.   **Platinum-rhenium alloys** are efficient catalysts for reforming operations on aromatic compounds.   The platinum alloys have lower electrical conductivity than pure platinum,but are generally harder and more wear resistant, and have high melting points.   A platinum-rhenium alloy with 10% rhenium has an electrical conductivity of only 5.5% that of copper compared with 16% for pure platinum.   Its melting point is 1850°C, and the Rockwell T hardness of the cold-rolled metal is 91 compared with 78 for cold-rolled platinum.   **Platinum-ruthenium alloy,** with 10% ruthenium, has a melting point of 1800°C, and an electrical conductivity 4% that of copper.

PLYWOOD. A laminated wood made up of thin sheets of wood glued together with the grains of successive layers set at right angles to give strength in both directions.   Plywood is an outgrowth of the laminated wood known as veneer, which consists of an outside sheet of hardwood glued to a base of lower-cost wood.   The term **veneer** actually refers only to the facing layer of selected wood used for artistic effect, or for economy in the use of expensive woods.   Veneers are generally marketed in strip form in thicknesses of less than 1/8 in. in mahogany, oak, cedar, and other woods.   The usual purpose of plywood now is not aesthetic but is to obtain high strength with low weight.   The term laminated wood generally means heavier laminates for special purposes, and such laminates usually contain a heavy impregnation of bonding resin which gives them more of the characteristics of the resin than of the wood.

Plywood usually comes in 4-by-8-ft panels, and is always built up with an odd number of layers. The cross-ply construction gives strength in both directions, and also gives symmetrical shrinkage stresses. A three-ply softwood panel of equal ply thicknesses may shrink about 0.080 in. in width and 0.100 in. in length, but increasing the thickness of the core ply can equalize the shrinkage, or equalization may be obtained by increasing the number of plies. The odd number of plies gives a symmetry of construction about the core ply. Low-cost plywoods may be bonded with starch pastes, animal glues, or casein, and are not water-resistant, but are useful for boxes and for interior work. Waterproof plywood for paneling and general construction is now bonded with synthetic resins, but when the plies are heavily impregnated with the resin and the whole cured into a solid sheet, the material is known as a hardboard or as a laminated plastic rather than a plywood.

For construction purposes, where plywood is employed because of its unit strength and nonwarping characteristics, the plies may be of a single type of wood without a hardwood face. The Douglas Fir Plywood Association sets up four classes of construction plywood under general trade names. **Plywall** is plywood in wallboard grade; **Plypanel** is plywood in three standard grades for general uses; **Plyscord** is unsanded plywood with defects plugged and patched on one side; **Plyform** is plywood in a grade for use in concrete forms.

The bulk of commercial plywood comes within these classes, the variations being in the type of wood used, the type of bonding adhesive, or the finish. **Etch wood,** for example, is a paneling plywood with the face wire brushed to remove the soft fibers and leave the hard grain for two-tone finish. **Paneling plywoods** with faces of mahogany, walnut, or other expensive wood have cores of lower-cost woods, but the woods of good physical qualities are usually chosen. The tensile strength of a white ash three-ply plywood parallel to the grain of the faces is about 6,200 psi, that of a mahogany plywood is 6,400 psi, and that of a walnut plywood is 8,200 psi. **Stabilite,** of the Georgia-Pacific Corp., is a wood laminate with the veneers impregnated with phenolic resin and bonded together with the grain of the plies parallel. It has the density of hardwood and the workability of cherry wood.

The **K-Veneer** used during the Second World War as a substitute for plywood was a $\frac{3}{16}$-in. fir or hemlock sheet bonded to a heavy kraft paper. The **Welchboard,** of the West Coast Plywood Co., is $\frac{3}{8}$-in. plywood with a smooth grainless surface produced by curing on one side under heat and pressure a mixture of wood pulp and synthetic resin. A great variety of trade-named plywoods are marketed for paneling, but they do not always have the typical characteristics of plywood, and are often **paneling boards** rather than plywoods. Some have metal faces, or they may have special-purpose cores or backings.   **Fybr-Tech,** developed by Technical Plywoods, for aircraft paneling, has a $\frac{1}{64}$-in. walnut veneer on a $\frac{1}{4}$-in. balsa wood core, with a 0.005-in. vulcanized fiber back.   The weight is 0.2 lb per sq ft.   One of the earliest aluminum-faced plywoods was the English **Plymax** of Venesta, Ltd.   The **Plymetl,** of the Haskelite Mfg. Corp., has a core of plywood with facings of aluminum or steels.   **Metal-faced plywoods** are strong and can be riveted.   **Met-L-Wood,** of the Met-L-Wood Corp., has two layers of light wood separated by sheet metal, designed for truck sides.   **Metalite,** developed by the United Aircraft Corp., has thin sheets of strong aluminum alloy bonded to both sides of a balsa wood core, the grain of the wood being perpendicular to the metal faces. **Siding-panel 15,** of Weyerhaeuser Co., has a Douglas fir plywood core and a facing of 0.01 in. embossed aluminum with a vinyl resin finish.   **Flexwood** of U.S. Plywood Corp. consists of very thin sheets of veneer glued under heat and pressure to cotton sheeting, used as an ornamental covering for walls.   **Algonite** is Masonite faced with fancy veneers.   **Protekwood,** of this company, designed for protection against vermin attack, has a sheet of hardwood between two sheets impregnated with asphalt and resin, and bonded with a urea-formaldehyde resin to a total thickness of $\frac{5}{32}$ in. **Parkwood,** of the Parkwood Corp., is a flexible **woven veneer** made with thin strips of mahogany or other fancy wood pressed between sheets of transparent cellulose acetate or other plastic.   **Novoply,** of this company, for panels, furniture, and structural parts, has a core of resin-impregnated wood chips bonded between hardwood veneers.   Sheets are up to $\frac{3}{4}$ in. thick, and have high strength. **Randalite,** of the same company, is birch veneer bonded to a kraft liner.

Laminated woods used for making patterns and mechanical parts are often called plywoods, but the true plywoods come in relatively thin sheets without heavy resin impregnation that would destroy the wood texture of the fibers.   **Compreg,** developed by the Forest Products Laboratory, consists of many layers of $\frac{1}{16}$-in., rotary cut, yellow-birch plies bonded with about 30% resin under a pressure of 600 to 1,500 psi.   The specific gravity is 1.22 to 1.37, and the tensile strength 43,000 to 54,000 psi, depending upon the resin and the molding pressure.   **Impreg,** developed by this laboratory for use in making patterns and models, is produced from $\frac{1}{16}$-in. laminations of mahogany impregnated with a low-molecular-weight phenolic resin and bonded under pressure into a uniform solid of good dimensional stability.   **Flaypreg,** another member of this group of wood products, is hard, strong, dense, and low in cost.   It is made from wood flakes, usually fir or spruce, impregnated with resin, machine-felted, and pressed.   The specific gravity is 1.39, and the water absorption is only 0.44% compared with 1.46 for Compreg.   It is used for making gears, cams, patterns, and table tops.   **Delwood,** of the Gisholt Machine Co., is molded of wood chips, chopped glass fiber, and a binder of polyester resin.   It has the strength of hard maple, and takes nails and screws better than wood.   It is used for shoe lasts, picture frames, and furniture. **Pregwood,** of the Formica Co., is a wood laminate impregnated with a phenolic resin and cured into a hard sheet.   But the **Impreg weldwood,** of the United States Plywood Corp., has the wood plies impregnated only to a short depth before compressing so that it remains a true plywood. It has higher strength and is more resistant than an ordinary resin-bonded plywood.   The **Sprucolite,** of the Sprucolite Corp., for bearings, rolls, gears, and pulleys, is cross-laminated like plywood with thin sheets of western spruce, but is **plywood block** impregnated with resin and subjected to high pressure to make it dense and hard.   Its weight is about 35% that of cast iron.   A similar English laminated wood, called **Hydulignum,** consists of thin birch veneers impregnated with vinyl formal resin and compressed into a dense board with a specific gravity of 1.31 and a tensile strength of 45,000 psi.   Still another type of building board, **Dylite,** of the Koppers Co., has a core of polystyrene plastic jacketed on both sides with plywood or gypsum.

POISON GASES.   Substances employed in chemical warfare for disabling men, and in some cases used industrially as fumigants.   They are all popularly called gases, but many are liquids or solids.   Normally, information on military gases is kept secret, but the tear gases used by police are also poisonous, often causing serious damage to eyes, throat, and lungs. **Anesthetic gases** have so far not been used in chemical warfare, but are used in medicine.   One of the simplest of these, **nitrous oxide,** N_2O, called **laughing gas** and used by dentists, produces a deep sleep.   **Fluorthane,** or **ethyl fluoride,** CH_3CH_2F, is a volatile liquid like ether, but is nonexplosive, and is used to replace ether in surgery.   **Cyclopropane,** $(CH_2)_3$, is a potent anesthetic used in obstetrics.

Poison gases are classified according to their main effect on the human system, but one gas may have several effects.   They are grouped as follows: **lethal gases,** intended to kill, such as phosgene; **lachrymators,** or **tear gases,** which have a powerful irritating effect on the eyes causing temporary blindness and swelling of the eyes with a copious flow of tears; **vesicants,** or skin blisterers, such as lewisite and mustard gas; **sternutatory gases,** which induce sneezing; and **camouflage gases,** which are harmless, but cause soldiers to suffer the inconvenience of wearing gas masks and thus reduce their morale.   Some of the gases have a sour, irritating odor and are also classed as **harassing agents.**   Gases are also sometimes designated as **casualty agents** and further subdivided into persistent and nonpersistent. A **systemic gas** is one that interferes with one phase of the system, such as carbon monoxide, which paralyzes the respiratory function of the blood.

A **labyrinthic gas** is one that affects an organ of the body, such as **dichlor-methyl ether,** which affects the ears.

Effects of persistent gases, such as mustard, remain over the ground for as long as 7 days, but phosgene is quickly decomposed by dampness. **Obscuring agents,** such as white phosphorus, and the **toxic smokes,** such as diphenylaminochloroarsine, are also classed as war gases. Dusts of materials having catalytic properties, but not poisonous themselves, may be used to penetrate gas masks and create poisons, such as carbon monoxide, within the mask. Carbon and oil smokes may be used to choke the filters of gas masks and cause their removal. Absorbents used in gas masks are usually activated charcoal and soda lime. These will absorb or disassociate most of the toxic gases, but will not stop carbon monoxide. A mixture of powdered oxides of copper, manganese, silver, and cobalt, called **Hopcalite,** is used as a catalyst to oxidize carbon monoxide.

Lethal gases are divided into four classes: actual poisons, which kill with little pain, such as hydrocyanic acid; **asphyxiating gases,** which affect the membranes of the lungs, destroying them and allowing blood to fill the air sacs, such as phosgene, diphosgene, and chloropicrin; poisons which destroy the lining of the air passages and block the passages to the lung tissues, such as mustard gas and ethyldichloroarsine; and poisons which affect the nose and throat, causing great pain, headache, and vomiting, such as diphenylchloroarsine. **Mustard gas,** $(CH_2ClCH_2)_2S$, known also as **blister gas, yperite,** and **yellow cross,** is an oily liquid which boils at 210°C and vaporizes easily in the air. It destroys the cornea of the eyes, blisters the skin, affects the lungs, and causes discharge from the nose and vomiting. One part in 14 million parts air is toxic and cannot be detected in dilutions by smell. Another powerful vesicant is **Bromlost,** which is **dibromethyl sulfide,** $(CH_2BrCH_2)_2S$. It is a solid melting at 21°C. **Sulvanite** is **ethylsulfuryl chloride,** $ClSO_3C_2H_5$. It is a colorless liquid boiling at 135°C.

Lewisite, $CHCL:CH \cdot AsCl_2$, is a liquid boiling at 190°C. It is a powerful vesicant causing painful blisters on the skin, pain in the eyes, nose irritation, permanent impairment of eyesight, and arsenic poisoning. It forms a heavy mist and has been called **dew of death. Chloropicrin,** called **aquinite, klop,** and **nitrochloroform,** is **nitrotrichloro methane,** CCl_3NO_2. It is a persistent lachrymatory and lethal poison. It is a colorless liquid boiling at 112°C, with a specific gravity of 1.692. It is used as a soil fumigant to control insects and fungi. **Tonite** is **chloroacetone,** CH_3COCH_2Cl, a clear liquid vaporizing at 119°C. It is a powerful lachrymator and skin blisterer. As it is very reactive, it is also used in the synthesis of pharmaceuticals, dyes, and organic chemicals.

Bromoacetone is a colorless liquid of the composition $CH_2BrCOCH_3$, with a specific gravity of 1.631 and boiling point 126°C. It is thrown in bombs or shells and disseminated as a mist which attacks the eyes. **Bromobenzyl cyanide** is a solid of the composition $BrC_6H_4CH_2CN$, with a melting point of $25°C$; when impure it is a liquid, but it is not purified, as it is easily decomposed. It is very persistent and because of its odor is classed as a harassing agent. It was called **camite** by the French. Another tear gas, **chloroacetophenone**, $C_6H_5COCH_2Cl$, is a white, crystalline solid, specific gravity 1.321, and melting point $59°C$, which, when thrown as a vapor, has a sweet, locustlike odor but produces pains in the eyes and temporary blindness. The tear gas called **Mace,** used for riot control, contains this substance. In contact with the skin it causes severe dermatitis and often permanent damage to the eyes. The French gas **fraissite** is **benzyl iodide,** $C_6H_5CH_2I$, a liquid boiling at $226°C$. The gas **papite** is acrolein with stannic chloride. **Caderite** is **benzyl bromide** with stannic chloride. **Xylyl bromide,** $CH_3C_6H_4CH_2Br$, is a colorless liquid boiling at $216°C$. When disseminated as a mist from explosive bombs, it causes a copious flow of tears. The tear gas known as **CS gas** is **chloro benzol malono nitrile** and is destructive to nasal and lung tissues. Benzyl chloride also has been used as a tear gas.

Martonite, a powerful lachrymator, is a mixture of 20% chloroacetone and 80 bromoacetone. **Bretonite** is **iodoacetone,** CH_3COCH_2I, a brownish liquid boiling at $102°C$, mixed with stannic chloride as a lachrymator. **Manguinite** is **cyanogen chloride,** CNCl, which boils at $13°C$, and is a lachrymator. Mixed with arsenic trichloride to make it more toxic, it was used under the name of **vitrite.** **Campillit** is **cyanogen bromide,** CNBr, a white solid melting at $52°C$ and vaporizing at $61.3°C$. The fumes are highly toxic, paralyzing the nerve centers. **Diphenylchloroarsine,** or **blue cross** $(C_6H_5)_2AsCl$, is a **sneezing gas** which penetrates gas masks, forcing their removal. It affects chiefly the nose and throat, but is used with other more violent gases. **Adamsite** is a greenish granular solid of the composition $(C_6H_4)_2NHAsCl$, which has a pleasant odor but burns the nose and throat. Many of the lachrymators have important industrial uses. **Phenyl isocyanate,** C_6H_5NCO, is a water-white liquid of specific gravity 1.101 and boiling point $162°C$, used for the production of alkyd resins, ureas, urethanes, and other chemicals. **Decontaminants,** used for combatting the effects of poison gases, are neutralizing chemicals. The decontaminant known as STB, or **supertropical bleach,** is a mixture of chlorinated lime and ground quicklime.

POLONIUM. A rare metallic element, symbol Po, belonging to the group of radioactive metals, but emitting only alpha rays. The melting point of the metal is about $1100°C$. It is used in meteorological stations for measuring the electrical potential of the air. **Polonium-plated metal** in strip and rod forms has been employed as a static dissipator in textile coating machines.   The alpha rays ionize the air near the strip, making it a conductor and drawing off static electrical charges.   **Polonium 210** is obtained by irradiating bismuth, 100 lb yielding 1 gram of polonium 210.   It is used as a heat source for emergency auxiliary power such as in spacecraft.   The metal is expensive, but can be produced in quantity from bismuth.

POLYESTER RESINS. A large group of synthetic resins produced by condensation of acids such as maleic, phthalic, or itaconic, with an alcohol or glycol such as allyl alcohol or ethylene glycol, to form an unsaturated polyester which, when polymerized, will give a cross-linked, three-dimensional molecular structure, which in turn will copolymerize with an unsaturated hydrocarbon such as styrene or cyclopentadiene to form a copolymer of complex structure of several monomers linked and cross-linked.   At least one of the acids or alcohols of the first reaction must be unsaturated.   The polyesters made with saturated acids and saturated hydroxy compounds are called **alkyd resins,** and these are largely limited to the production of protective coatings and are not copolymerized.

The resins undergo polymerization during cure without liberation of water, and do not require high pressure for curing.   Through the secondary stage of modification with hydrocarbons a very wide range of characteristics can be obtained.   The most important use of the polyesters is as laminating and impregnating materials, especially for large structures because of the need for only low pressure.   The resins have high strength, good chemical resistance, high adhesion, and capacity to take bright colors.   They are also used, without fillers, as casting resins, for filling and strengthening porous materials such as ceramics and plaster-of-paris articles, and for sealing the pores in metal castings.   Some of the resins have great toughness, and are used to produce textile fibers and thin plastic sheet and film.   Others of the resins are used with fillers to produce molding powders that cure at low pressure of 500 to 900 psi with fast operating cycles.

Polyester laminates are usually made with a high proportion of glass fiber mat or glass fabric, and high-strength reinforced moldings may also contain a high proportion of filler.   A resin slurry may contain as high as 70% calcium carbonate or calcium sulfate, with only about 11% of glass fiber added, giving an impact strength of 24,000 psi in the cured material.   Bars and structural shapes of glass-fiber reinforced polyester resins of high tensile and flexural strengths are made by having the glass fibers parallel in the direction of the extrusion.   The **Glastrusions** of the Hugh C. Marshall Co., in the form of rods and tubes, are made by having the glass-fiber rovings carded under tension, then passing through an impregnating tank, an extruding die, and a heat-curing die.   The rods contain 65% glass fiber and 35 resin. They have a flexural strength of 64,000 psi, and a Rockwell M hardness of 65.

A wide variety of trade names are used for the polyester resins. Physical properties vary with the type of raw materials used and the type of reinforcing agents. A standard glass-fiber filled molding may have a specific gravity from 1.7 to 2.0, a tensile strength of 4,000 to 10,000 psi with elongation of 16 to 20%, a flexural strength to 30,000 psi, a dielectric strength to about 400 volts per mil, and a heat distortion temperature of 350 to 400°F. The moldings have good acid and alkali resistance. But, since an almost unlimited number of fatty-type acids are available from natural fatty oils or by synthesis from petroleum, and the possibilities of variation by combination with alcohols, glycols, and other materials are also unlimited, the polyesters form an ever-expanding great group of plastics.

The **Mylar film,** of Du Pont, is a polyester made by the condensation of terephthalic acid and ethylene glycol. The extremely thin film, 0.00025 to 0.0005 in., used for capacitors and for insulation of motors and transformers, has a high dielectric strength, up to 6,000 volts per mil. It has a tensile strength of 20,000 psi with elongation of 70%. It is highly resistant to chemicals, and has low water absorption. The material is thermoplastic, with a melting point at about 490°F. The textile fiber produced from dimethyl terephthalate and known as **Dacron** has these physical properties, and has exceptionally high flexing endurance. The English textile fibers called **Teron** and **Terylene** are similar materials, and **Melinex** is the English name for the film. **Mylar 50T,** used for magnetic sound-recording tape, has the molecules oriented by stretching to give high strength. The 0.005-in. tape has a breaking strength of 120 oz per $\frac{1}{4}$ in. of width. **Urylon,** a Japanese fiber, has a low specific gravity, 1.07, and a high melting point, 250°C. It is produced from azelaic acid. The polyester film called **Terefilm,** of the Acme Backing Corp., used for insulation and for magnetic tape, is a cyclohexylene dimethylene terephthalate. The dielectric strength of the 0.0005-in. film is 8,000 volts per mil, with tensile strength of 20,000 psi, and heat distortion temperature 340°F. **Electronic tape** may also have a magnetic powder coating on the polyester. But where high temperatures may be encountered, as in spacecraft, the magnetic coating is applied to metal tapes. **Densimag,** of the Whittaker Corp., has the magnetic coating on a nonmagnetic stainless-steel tape, together having a thickness of 0.00105 in. It will operate at temperatures to 600°F.

The **Koplac resins** of the Koppers Co., Inc., are polyesters based on styrene. **Vibrin 135,** of the Naugatuck Chemical Co., is a polyester resin made with triallyl cyanurate and modified with maleic anhydride. Moldings reinforced with glass fiber have a tensile strength of 38,000 psi, and retain a strength of 23,000 psi at 500°F. **Vibrin 136A** has higher strength and very high radar transparency. It is used for radomes and nose cones.

Transparent thermoplastic polyester resins are made by copolymerizing esters of itaconic acid with vinyl chloride, methacrylate, or acrylonitrile. **Itaconic acid,** $CH_2:CCH_2(COOH)_2$, is made from anhydrous glucose. **Pimelic acid,** $HO_2C(CH_2)CO_2H$, made from petroleum as a white crystalline solid, is also used for making polyester and polyamide resins. Another of the many acids used for these resins is **glutaric acid,** HO_2C-$(CH_2)_3CO_2H$, produced from acrylein. **Glutaric anhydride,** $O:HC$-$(CH_2)_3HC:O$, is also used, and its cross-linking ability is employed for insolubilizing starches and proteins to give water resistance to paints and paper coatings. **Het acid,** of Hooker Chemical, is a complex chlorinated phthalic acid produced by hydrolyzing the product of the condensation of maleic anhydride with hexachloro cyclopentadiene made from pentane. This acid is reacted with glycols and maleic anhydride to give a hard polyester resin which is then cross-linked with styrene to give the liquid **Hetron resin** which will cure with heat and a catalyst to an insoluble solid. The resin contains 30% chlorine. It is used for making laminated or reinforced plastics. Another chlorinated polyester resin is **FR resin** of the Interchemical Co. It is flame-resistant, and cures at normal temperatures, and is used for such lay-up lamination work as boat building and tank construction. Some of the polyester-type resins have rubberlike properties, with higher tensile strengths than the rubbers and superior resistance to oxidation. **Vulcollan,** of the Goodyear Tire & Rubber Co., is such a resin with higher wear resistance and chemical resistance than GRS rubber. It is made by reacting adipic acid with ethylene glycol and propylene glycol and then adding diisocyanate to control the solidifying action. It can be processed like rubber, but solidifies more rapidly. **Chemigum SL,** of the same company, is a **polyester rubber.** The polyesters also offer a great variety of possibilities in textile fibers. **Kodel,** of Eastman Chemical Products, Inc., is a white **polyester fiber** that is easily dyed. It is resistant to pilling, which is the tendency of surface fibers to form balls, and it has high dimensional stability and heat resistance. An unlimited number of higher acids for the production of polyester-type resins are easily made from the plentiful natural fatty oils, and from these acids can be made anhydrides of very high membered rings that give products which are stable up to their melting points. For example, the **Empol 1018** of Emery Industries, Inc., used for making polyester and polyamide resins, is a light liquid of specific gravity 0.95, made from unsaturated fatty acids. It contains 83% of a 36-carbon dibasic acid and 17% of a 54-carbon tribasic acid. The acids have high molecular weight with long alkyl chains between the carboxyl groups, giving great flexibility to the resin products. Large numbers of **carboxylic acids** useful for making polyester-type resins are produced from petroleum and coal tar. These include the **toluic acids** which can be made into higher **alkylated acids,** and the **xylic acids.** An example of the latter is **hemellitic acid,** $C_6H_3(CH_3)_2COOH$, which, together with **naphthalic anhydride,** $C_{10}H_6(CO)_2O$, is produced from naphthalene. All of these give special properties to the resins.

An extensive group of polyesters and alkyd resins with good heat stability can be made from **pyromellitic dianhydride,** $C_{10}H_2O_6$, a benzene tetra carboxylic dianhydride. It is marketed by Princeton Chemical Research, Inc., as **PMDA,** a white powder with melting point of 287°C. It reacts with alcohols, benzene, and other hydrocarbons. It is produced from **mellitic acid,** $C_6(COOH)_6$, which has a melting point of 288°C. It occurs in brown coal, peat, and the mineral **mellite,** or **honeystone,** which is hydrous aluminum mellate. **Tetrahydro phthalic anhydride** is easier to combine with styrene than phthalic or maleic anhydride, and gives coating resins that are more flexible and have quicker cure with high gloss.

POLYSTYRENE. A synthetic resin used for molding, in lacquers, and for coatings, formed by the polymerization of monomeric **styrene,** which is a colorless liquid of the composition $C_6H_5CH:CH_2$, specific gravity 0.906, and boiling point 145°C. It is made from ethylene, and is ethylene with one of the hydrogen atoms replaced by a phenyl group. It is also called **phenyl ethylene** and **vinyl benzene.** As it can be made by heating **cinnamic acid,** $C_6H_5CH:CHCO_2H$, an acid found in natural balsams and resins, it is also called **cinnamene.** In the form of **vinyl toluene,** which consists of mixed isomers of methyl styrene, the material is reacted with drying oils to form alkyd resins for paints and coatings.

The polymerized resin is a transparent solid very light in weight with a specific gravity of 1.054 to 1.070. The tensile strength is 3,000 to 8,500 psi, compressive strength 12,000 to 17,000 psi, and dielectric strength 450 to 600 volts per mil. Polystyrene is notable for water resistance and high dimensional stability. It is also tougher and stronger at low temperatures than most other plastics. It is valued as an electrical insulating material, and the films are used for cable wrapping. The films are heat-sealing at above 70°C. The molding plastic is used for cosmetic containers, clock crystals, gage dials, and aircraft panels. For coating purposes plasticizers are added to increase pliability, but are not needed for molding. The plastic has good fluidity and is especially suited for injection molding. When produced from **methyl styrene,** parts have a hardness to Rockwell M83, with tensile strengths to 8,900 psi, and have a stiffness that makes them suitable for such products as cabinets and housings. Dielectric strength is also high, above 800 volts per mil, and the resin is thus used for electronic parts. The heat distortion temperature is 215°F.

Styrene can be polymerized alone, or copolymerized with butadiene, acrylonitrile, and other materials. The low cost, light weight, and good balance of mechanical and electrical properties have made the material one of the most widely used of the synthetic-plastic groups. Its high crystal clarity fades rapidly from light radiation, and oxidation catalyzes the molecular chains, but the effects of radiation and oxidation are easily controlled by the incorporation of antioxidants and ultraviolet-ray absorbing agents. The English **Distrene** was one of the early styrene resins for injection molding, and **Styroflex** was a German styrene tape for cable wrapping. **Styrene resins** for molding are now marketed under a wide variety of trade names, with or without fillers and reinforcing agents. Many of these are copolymer resins, or are modified with plasticizers or cross-linking agents. The styrene-acrylonitrile-butadiene terpolymer resins are generally flexible with elongation to 70%, and can be nailed. They are also light in weight, with specific gravities as low as 1.01. **Kralastic MH,** of the U.S. Rubber Co., for sheets and for injection molding, is such a terpolymer. The tensile strength is about 4,700 psi, dielectric strength 400 volts per mil, specific gravity 1.04, and service temperature range is to 230°F. **Victron,** of this company, is a clear transparent polystyrene. **Lustron,** of Monsanto, is polystyrene in various grades, and **Stymer** is a polystyrene resin for sizing textiles. **Piccotex,** of the Pennsylvania Industrial Chemical Corp., is a styrene copolymer in solid form soluble in mineral spirits for use in paints, coatings, and adhesives. **Styron** and **Styraloy,** of the Dow Chemical Co., are polystyrene molding resins, and **Tyril** of this company, originally called **Styrex,** is a styrene-acrylonitrile copolymer.

Loalin, of the Catalin Corp., is a polystyrene with a specific gravity 1.05 to 1.07. It is crystal clear, and will take light pastel colors. In the clear form it transmits 90% light. It is water-resistant and has a dielectric strength of 500 to 700 volts per mil. It is not affected by alcohol, acids, or alkalies, but is soluble in aromatic hydrocarbons. It is preferably injection-molded. **Exon 860,** of the Firestone Plastics Co., is a soft grade of polystyrene that molds easily into products of high flexibility. The molded material has a tensile strength of 6,000 psi with elongation of 50%, Rockwell hardness of R100, and dielectric strength of 510 volts per mil. **Fibertuff,** of the Koppers Co., marketed in pellets for injection molding, is 60% polystyrene and 40% glass fiber. Molded parts have a specific gravity of 1.33, a tensile strength of 11,000 psi, heat distortion point of 220°F, and high impact resistance.

Isopol, of the Union Bay State Chemical Co., is a high-molecular-weight resin produced from 75% styrene and 25 isoprene. It is a modified polystyrene in which the isoprene acts as an internal plasticizer. The molded and cured resin is a water-white hard solid having the characteristics of polystyrene without the brittleness. It possesses many of the chemical properties of natural rubber, and is soluble in naphtha. When used as picture-frame glass it will fracture without sharp edges. The resin is also used for coatings, and as a stiffener for natural rubber. **NBS resin** of the Mathieson Alkali Works is a dichlorostyrene-styrene copolymer for use with a catalyst as a casting plastic. It has low water absorption and high dielectric strength. **Styrene-butylene resins** are copolymers that mold easily and produce thermoplastic products of low water absorption and good electrical properties. They have strength equal to the vinyls with greater elongation. They are also useful for coatings and for film for packaging. **Cellulite,** of Gilman Bros. Co., is **foamed polystyrene** in blocks and heavy sheets for thermal insulation and for floats. It weighs about 1 lb per cu ft and is rigid. Flexible **styrene foam** is also made into very thin sheets for wrapping frozen foods. It is grease-resistant and a good insulator, and is low in cost. Styrene is now best known for its use in synthetic rubbers, but the difference between resins and rubbers is chiefly in flexibility.

PONTIANAK. A gum from the trees *Dyera costulata* and *D. laxifolia* of Borneo and Malaya. The commercial pontianak is a grayish-white mass like burned lime, and contains 60% water, with only 10 to 25% rubber-like materials. It is a rubber, but has a high content of resin similar to balata and gutta percha, and is classed with the lower guttas. It is used in the friction compounds employed for coating transmission belting, in insulations and varnishes, for mixing with gutta percha, and also to adulterate or replace chicle for chewing gums. It is also called **jelutong. Pontianak copal** is from varieties of *Agathis* trees of Borneo. Its peculiar turpentinelike qualities come from the method of tapping. It is valued for varnishes.

POPLAR. The wood of several species of the tree *Populus.* The **black poplar,** or **English poplar,** *P. nigra,* of Europe, is a large tree with blackish bark. The wood is yellowish white with a fine, open grain. It is soft and easy to work. The weight is about 25 lb per cu ft. It is used for paneling, inlaying, packing cases, carpentry, and paper pulp. **Lombardy poplar** is a hybrid variety of this species. It is a tall, columnar tree that is male only and can be propagated only from rootstocks. It is grown in the United States for shelter belts, but in some countries is grown in fruit districts as a wood for packing boxes. **White poplar,** *P. alba,* is a larger tree native to the United States. The wood is similar to that of the black poplar. **Cottonwood** is another species of poplar. **Gray poplar** is from the tree *P. canescens,* of Europe. The color of the wood is light yellow. It has a tough, close texture somewhat resembling that of maple.

It is used for carpentry and flooring.   The wood of the canary whitewood is called **Virginia poplar,** or simply poplar, but belongs to a different family of trees.   Aspen is also called poplar.

POROUS METALS. Metals with uniformly distributed controlled pore sizes, in the form of sheets, tubes, and shapes, used for filtering liquids and gases at elevated temperatures.   They are made by powder metallurgy, and the pore size and density are controlled by the particle size and the pressure used.   Stainless steel, nickel, bronze, silver, or other metal powders are used, depending on the corrosion requirements of the filter. Pore sizes offered by Purolator Products, Inc., can be as small as 0.2 micron, but the most generally used filters have pores of 4, 8, 12, and 25 microns.   Pores sizes have a uniformity within 10%.   The density range is from 40 to 50% of the theoretical density of the metal.   Standard **filter sheet** is 0.30 to 0.60 in. but thinner sheets are available.   Union Carbide produces sheet as thin as 0.004 in. and with void fractions as high as 90%, for fuel cells and catalytic reactors.   **Porous steel,** of the Micro Metallic Corp., is made from 18–8 stainless steel, with pore openings from 20 microns (0.0008 in.) to 65 microns (0.0025 in.).   The fine-pore sheet has a minimum tensile strength of 10,000 psi, and the coarse has a strength of 7,000 psi.   **Felted metal,** developed by the Armour Research Foundation, is porous sheet made by felting metal fibers, pressing, and sintering. It gives a high strength-to-porosity ratio, and the porosity can be controlled over a wide range.   In this type of porous metal the pores may be from 0.001 to 0.015 in. diameter, and of any metal to suit the filtering conditions. A felted fiber filter of Type 430 stainless steel with 25% porosity has a tensile strength of 25,000 psi.

POTASH. Also called **pearl ash.**   A white alkaline granular powder, which is a **potassium carbonate,** K_2CO_3 or $K_2CO_3 \cdot H_2O$, used in soft soaps, for wool washing, and in glass manufacture.   It is produced from natural deposits in Russia and Germany and also produced from wood and plant ashes.   The American production is largely from potash salts of New Mexico, from the brines of Searles Lake, Calif., and from solar evaporation in Utah.   The material as produced by the Hooker Chemical Co. is a free-flowing white powder of 91 to 94% K_2CO_3, or is the hydrate at 84%, or calcined at 99% purity.   The specific gravity of potash is 2.33 and melting point 909°C.   **Hartsalz,** mined in the Carpathian Mountains and used for producing potash, is a mixture of sodium chloride, potassium chloride, and magnesium sulfate.   It is also a source of magnesium.   The extensive potassium mineral deposits at Strassfurt and Mülhausen contain **sylvite,** KCl; **carnallite,** $KCl \cdot MgCl_2 \cdot 6H_2O$; **kainite,** $K_2SO_4 \cdot MgSO_4 \cdot MgCl_2 \cdot 6H_2O$; and **leonite,** $K_2SO_4 \cdot MgSO_4 \cdot 4H_2O$.   There are at least a billion tons of the potash mineral **Wyomingite** in the deposits near Green River, Wyo. It is a complex mineral containing leucite, phlogopite, diopside, kataphorite, and apatite. It has 11.4% K_2O, with sodium oxide, magnesium oxide, phosphorus pentoxide, and other oxides. The sylvite ore mined at Carlsbad, N.M., contains KCl and NaCl. It is electrically refined to 99.95% KCl, and used to produce caustic potash. Electrolysis of the chloride solution yields caustic potash.

POTASSIUM. An elementary metal, symbol K, and atomic weight 39.1, also known as **kalium.** It is silvery white in color, but oxidizes rapidly in the air and must be kept submerged in ether or kerosene. It has a low melting point, 63.7°C, and a boiling point at 760°C. The specific gravity is 0.819. It is soluble in alcohol and in acids. It decomposes water with great violence. Potassium is obtained by the electrolysis of potassium chloride. Potassium metal is used in combination with sodium as a heat-exchange fluid in atomic reactors and high-temperature processing equipment. A **potassium-sodium alloy** of the Mine Safety Appliance Co. contains 78% potassium and 22 sodium. It has a melting point of −11°C and a boiling point of 784°C and is a silvery mobile liquid. The thermal conductivity at 200°C is 0.06. The cesium-potassium-sodium alloys of this company are called **BZ Alloys. Potassium hydride** is used for the photosensitive deposit on the cathode of some photoelectric cells. It is extremely sensitive and will emit electrons under a flash so weak and so rapid as to be imperceptible to the eye. **Potassium diphosphate,** KH_2PO_4, a colorless, crystalline, or white powder soluble in water, is used as a lubricant for wool fibers to replace olive oil in spinning wool. It has the advantages that it does not become rancid like oil and can be removed without scouring. Potassium, like sodium, has a broad range of use in its compounds, giving strong bonds. Metallurgically it is listed as having a body-centered cubical molecular structure, but the atoms arrange themselves in pairs in the metal as K_2, and the structure is cryptocrystalline.

POTASSIUM CHLORATE. Also known as **chlorate of potash** and **potassium oxymuriate.** A white crystalline powder, or lustrous crystalline substance of the composition $KClO_3$, employed in explosives, chiefly as a source of oxygen. It is also used as an oxidizing agent in the chemical industry, in medicine as a cardiac stimulant, and in toothpaste. It melts at 357°C and decomposes at 400°C with the rapid evolution of oxygen. It is odorless but has a slightly bitter saline taste. The specific gravity is 2.337. It is not hygroscopic, but is soluble in water. It imparts a violet color to the flame in pyrotechnic compositions.

Potassium chloride is a colorless or white crystalline compound of the composition KCl, used for molten salt baths for the heat treatment of steels.

It is also used in fertilizers and in explosives.   The specific gravity is 1.987. A bath composed of 3 parts potassium chloride and 2 barium chloride is used for hardening carbon-steel drills and other tools.   Steel tools heated in this bath and quenched in a 3% sulfuric acid solution have a very bright surface.   A common bath is made up of potassium chloride and common salt and can be used for temperatures up to 900°C.

POTASSIUM CYANIDE. A white amorphous or crystalline solid of the composition KCN, employed for carbonizing steel for case hardening and for electroplating.   The specific gravity is 1.52, and it melts at about 1550°F.   It is soluble in water and is extremely poisonous, giving off the deadly hydrocyanic acid gas.   For cyaniding steel the latter is immersed in a bath of molten cyanide and then quenched in water, or the cyanide is rubbed on the red-hot steel.   For this use, however, sodium cyanide is usually preferred, because of its lower cost and the higher content of CN in the latter.   Commercial potassium cyanide is likely to contain a proportion of sodium cyanide. **Potassium ferrocyanide,** or **yellow prussiate of potash,** can also be used for case-hardening steel.   It has the composition $K_4Fe(CN)_6$ and comes in yellow crystals or powder.   The nitrogen as well as the carbon enters the steel to form the hard case. **Potassium ferricyanide,** or **red prussiate of potash,** is a bright-red granular powder of the composition $K_3Fe(CN)_6$, used in photographic reducing solutions, in etching solutions, in blueprint paper, and in silvering mirrors. **Redsol crystals,** of the American Cyanamid Co., is the name of this chemical for use as a reducer and mild oxidizing agent, or toner, for photography. **Potassium cyanate,** KCNO, is a white crystalline solid used for the production of organic chemicals and drugs.   It melts at 310°C.   The **potassium silver cyanide,** used for silver plating, comes in white, water-soluble crystals of the composition $KAg(CN)_2$. **Sel-Rex,** of the Bart-Messing Corp., is this material.

POTASSIUM NITRATE. Also called **niter** and **saltpeter,** although these usually refer to the native mineral.   A substance of the composition KNO_3, it is used in explosives, for bluing steel, and in fertilizers.   A mixture of potassium nitrate and sodium nitrate is used for steel-tempering baths. The mixture melts at 250°C.   Potassium nitrate is made by the action of potassium chloride on sodium nitrate, or **Chile saltpeter.**   It occurs in colorless, prismatic crystals, or as a crystalline white powder.   It has a sharp saline taste and is soluble in water.   The specific gravity is 2.1 and melting point 337°C.   It is found in nature in limited quantities in the alkali region of western United States.   Potassium nitrate contains a large percentage of oxygen which is readily given up and is well adapted for pyrotechnic compounds.   It gives a beautiful violet flame color in burning.

It is used in flares and in signal rockets. **Potassium nitrite** is a solid of the composition KNO$_2$ used as a rust inhibitor, for the regeneration of heat-transfer salts, and for the manufacture of dyes.

POTATO. The bulbous tubers of the roots of the annual plant *Solanum tuberosum,* native to Peru but now grown in many parts of the world. It is used chiefly as a direct food, but is also employed for making starch and alcohol. The potato was brought to Europe in 1580, and received the name of **Irish potato** when brought to New England in 1719 by Irish immigrants. The plant is hardy and has a short growing cycle, making it adaptable to many climates. The potato constitutes about 40% by weight of all vegetables consumed as food in the United States, but about 90% of the total world crop is normally produced in Europe, mostly in Germany, Russia, and Poland. The tuber contains about 78% water, 18 starch with some sugar, 2 proteins, 1 potash, and only about 0.1 fats. The average water loss in storage is about 11%. There are more than 500 varieties of potato cultivated. The yield per acre in northern Maine, the chief American growing area, is 358 bu, but under subsidy much higher yields were obtained. **Dehydrated potato,** produced as powder, flake, and porous granules, is widely used in restaurants and institutions and is marketed under various trade names for home use, such as **Potato Buds** of General Mills, Inc., which are porous granules, or the many brands of **instant potatoes,** which are fine powder or flake easily reconstituted with hot water or milk.

The **sweet potato** is the root bulb of the trailing perennial vine *Ipomoea batata,* native to tropical America, but now grown extensively in the south of the United States and in warm climates. In South America it is known by the Carib name **batata.** Like the white potato, the sweet potato has a high water content, but is rich in sugars. There are many varieties and two general types: one with a dry mealy yellow flesh and the other with a soft gelatinous flesh higher in sugars. The latter type is called **yam** in the United States, but the true yam is a larger tuber from the climbing plant *Diascorea alata,* grown widely in the West Indies. The sweet potato is used as a direct food, but large amounts are also employed for making preserves, starch, and flour for confectionery. **Alamalt** is cooked and toasted sweet potato ground to a powder for use in confectionery. It adds flavor as well as sugar to the confectionery. **Sweet-potato flake,** used in foodstuffs, is cooked and dehydrated sweet potato in orange-colored flakes with the flavor of candied sweet potato. It is reconstituted with milk or water.

The **taro** is the root tuber of the large leafy plant *Colocasia esculenta,* which constitutes one of the chief foods of southeast Asia and Polynesia. There are more than 300 varieties grown. The tuber is high in starch, has more proteins than the potato, but has an acrid taste until cooked. The pasty starch food known as **poi** in the Pacific Islands is made from taro. In Micronesia the taro is called **jaua,** and the **mwang plant,** *Cyrtosperma chamissonis,* is called taro. This plant is larger, and the rootstock weighs as much as 50 lb, while the taro does not exceed 5 lb. Taro matures in 6 months, while the mwang requires 2 years. The **dasheen** is a variety of taro grown in the south of the United States. The **yautia,** grown in the West Indies, resembles the taro, but is from the large plant *Xanthosma sagittifolium.* It is high in starch and has more food value than the potato.

PRECIOUS METALS. A general term for the expensive metals that are used for coinage, jewelry, and ornaments. The name is limited to gold, silver, and platinum, expense or rarity alone not being the determining factor, but rather the setting of a value by law, with the coin having an intrinsic metal value as distinct from a copper coin which is merely a token with little metal value. The term noble metal is not synonymous, although a metal may be both precious and noble, as platinum. Although platinum was once used in Russia for coinage, only gold and silver fulfill the three requisites for coinage metals. Platinum does not have the necessary wide distribution of source. The **noble metals** are gold, platinum, iridium, rhodium, osmium, and ruthenium. Unalloyed, they are highly resistant to acids and corrosion. Radium and certain other metals are more expensive than platinum but are not classed as precious metals. Because of the expense of the platinum noble metals, they may be alloyed with gold for use in chemical crucibles. **Platino** is an alloy of 89% gold and 11 platinum. **Palau** is the name of an alloy of gold and palladium, and **rhotanium** is a rhodium-gold alloy.

PREFINISHED METALS. Sheet metals that have a polished surface of another metal plated on one side, or have the finish metal bonded and rolled on the base metal. In general, they do not differ from clad metals except that the prime purpose is to obtain a finished stamped or drawn article directly without the operations of polishing and plating. Thus, the base metal is usually a softer and more workable metal than the cladding, and the applied plate must have a ductility that will permit drawing and bending without fracture. One of the earliest groups of metals of this class included the **Brassoid, Nickeloid,** and **Chromaloid** of the American Nickeloid Co., which were brass, nickel, and chromium bonded to zinc sheet. Prefinished metals are now available with almost any metal plated or bonded to almost any other metal, or single metals may be had prefinished or in colors and patterns. They come in bright or matte finishes, and usually have a thin paper coating on the polished side which is easily stripped off before or after forming.   The metals are sold under a variety of trade names and are used for decorative articles, appliances, advertising displays, panels, and mechanical parts.

PRESERVATIVES. Chemicals used to prevent oxidation, fermentation, or other deterioration of foodstuffs.   The antioxidants, inhibitors, and stabilizers used to retard deterioration of industrial chemicals are not usually called preservatives.   The most usual function of a preservative is to kill bacteria, and this may be accomplished by an acid, an alcohol, an aldehyde, or a salt.   A legal requirement under the Food and Drug Act is that a preservative must be nontoxic in the quantities permitted.   Sugar is the most commonly used preservative for fruit products.   Sodium chloride is used for protein foods.   Sodium nitrate is reduced to sodium nitrite in curing meats, and the nitrite has an inhibitory action on bacterial growth, the effect being greatest in acid flesh.   **Potassium sorbate,** $KOCOCH:CH:CHCH_3$, a white water-soluble powder, inhibits the growth of many molds, yeasts, and bacteria which cause food deterioration, and is used in cheese, syrups, pickles, and other prepared foods.

The inhibitory effect of organic acids is due chiefly to the undissociated molecule.   Acetic acid is normally more toxic to bacteria than lactic acid, but when sugar is present the reverse is true, and citric acid then has little toxicity.   The inhibitory action of inorganic acids is due mainly to the pH change which they produce.   The antimicrobe effect of the vanillic acid esters generally increases with increasing molecular weight.   Only small quantities of chemicals are usually needed for preservation.   **Isobutyl vanillate,** an ester of vanillic acid, is effective as a preserving agent in milk and some other foods when only 0.10 to 0.15% is used.   Preservatives are also marketed for external application to foodstuffs in storage, though these are more properly classed as fumigants.   **Barsprout,** of the American Cyanamid Co., is a methyl ester of naphthalene acetic acid in powder form for dusting on potatoes and other root vegetables to keep them from sprouting and to preserve them in storage.

PRIMER. A surfacing material employed in painting or finishing to provide an anchorage or adhesion of the finishing material.   A primer may be colorless, or it may be with color.   In the latter case it is sometimes called an **undercoat.**   A primer is distinct from the filler coat used on woods to fill the pores and thus economize on the more expensive finish.   Primer coats of red lead paint were formerly much used on construction steel to give corrosion resistance, but chromate or phosphate primers are now more common.   **Pigment E,** of the National Lead Co., is a **barium potassium chromate** that gives a pale-yellow coating with good anticorrosion properties for steel, aluminum, and magnesium.   Zinc yellow paints may also be used as primer coats on metal.   Zinc chromate is used as a primer on steel.   It has a tendency to dissolve when moisture penetrates the paint, and this dissolved chromate retards corrosion of the steel.   **Granodine,** of the American Chemical Paint Co., is a zinc phosphate for spray or dip application to iron and steel to give corrosion resistance and to improve paint adhesion.   **Thermoil-Granodine** is a manganese phosphate that forms a dense crystalline coating on steel which acts as a corrosion-resistant base for paint.   **Devcon Z,** of the Devcon Corp., used as a primer paint, is a mixture of 95% zinc powder and 5% epoxy resin binder in a solvent to be brushed or sprayed on.   It gives a gray metallic finish, and the zinc blocks corrosion by galvanic action. In addition to the pigment, various corrosion inhibitors may be used in primer paints.   **Ammonium ferrous phosphate,** $NH_4FePO_4 \cdot H_2O$, has a platelike structure which gives impermeability to the film as well as adding corrosion resistance.   It is greenish in color.   A primer is especially required in the finishing of sheet-metal objects that are likely to receive dents or severe service, but they are not usually necessary for castings or roughened surfaces.   For sheet-metal work, baked enamels were formerly much used for the primers for the lacquer finishes, but synthetic resin primers give good adhesion and are less expensive.

PROPYLENE PLASTICS.   An important group of synthetic plastics employed for molding resins, film, and textile fibers.   They are produced as **polypropylene** by catalytic polymerization of propylene, or may be copolymers with ethylene or other material.   **Propylene** is a **methyl ethylene,** $CH_3CH:CH_2$, produced in the cracking of petroleum, and also used for making isopropyl alcohol and other chemicals.   The boiling point is $-48.2°C$.   It belongs to the class of unsaturated hydrocarbons known as **olefins,** which are designated by the word ending *-ene*.   Thus propylene is known as **propene** as distinct from propane, the corresponding saturated compound of the group of **alkanes** from petroleum and natural gas. These unsaturated hydrocarbons tend to polymerize and form gums, and are thus not used in fuels although they have antiknock properties.

In polypropylene plastics the carbon atoms linked in the molecular chain between the CH_2 units have each a CH_3 and an H attached as side links, with the bulky side groups spiraled regularly around the closely packed chain.   The resulting plastic has a crystalline structure with increased hardness and toughness and a higher melting point.   This type of stereosymmetric plastic has been called **isotactic plastic.**   It can also be produced with butylene or styrene, and the general term for the plastics is **polyolefins.**   Copolymers of propylene are termed **polyallomers.**

Polypropylene is low in weight.   The molded plastic has a density of 0.910, a tensile strength of 5,000 psi, with elongation of 150% and hardness of Rockwell R95. The dielectric strength is 1,500 volts per mil, dielectric constant 2.3, and softening point 150°C. Blown bottles of polypropylene have good clarity and are nontoxic. The melt-flow is superior to that of polyethylene. **Tenite polypropylene,** of Eastman Chemical Products, Inc., for molded parts, film, fibers, pipe, and wire covering, is this material. The **polypropylene film** of the Avisun Corp., called **Olefane,** used for packaging, has a specific gravity of 0.89. It is resistant to moisture, oils, and solvents, is crystal clear, and is flexible. It withstands temperatures to 250°F. The 0.001-in. film has 31,000 ft per lb. **Dynafilm 200,** of U.S. Industrial Chemicals Co., is polypropylene laminated with polyethylene to give easy heat sealing for packaging. The 0.001-in. film has a strength of 3,000 psi and 400% elongation. **Dynafilm 300** has the appearance, feel, and machine-handling properties of a cellophane film. It consists of oriented polypropylene coated on both sides with vinyl acetate. The film comes in thicknesses from 0.0008 to 0.0012 in. and heat seals at 100°F.

Polypropylene fiber was originally produced in Italy under the name of **Merkalon.** Unless modified, it is more brittle at low temperatures and has less light stability than polyethylene, but it has about twice the strength of high-density linear polyethylene. Monofilament fibers of Reeves Bros., Inc., are used for filter fabrics, and have high abrasion resistance and a melting point at 310°F. Multifilament yarns are used for textiles and rope. **Polypropylene rope,** of the Plymouth Cordage Co., produced from the **Prolene** polypropylene fiber of the Industrial Rayon Corp., and used for marine hawsers, will float on water and does not absorb water like Manila rope. It has a permanent elongation, or set, of 20%, compared with 19% for nylon and 11% for Manila rope, but the working elasticity is 16% compared with 25% for nylon and 8% for Manila. The tensile strength of the rope is 59,000 psi. **Gerfil** is the trade name of the G. F. Chemical Co. for fine-denier multifilament polypropylene yarn for weaving and knitting. It dyes easily, and comes in many colors. **Parlon P** is the trade name of Hercules Inc. for a chlorinated polypropylene for use in coatings, paper sizing, and adhesives. It has good heat and light stability, high abrasion resistance, and high chemical resistance.

PROTEIN. A nitrogen organic compound of high molecular weight, from 3,000 to many millions. Proteins are made up of complex combinations of simple amino acids, and they occur in all animal and vegetable matter, but are also made synthetically. They form a necessary constituent of foods and feeds, and are also used for many commercial products, but some proteins are highly poisonous. The poison of the cobra and that of the jellyfish are proteins.

Different types of plant and animal life have different types of proteins.

At least 10 different proteins are known to be essential to human body growth and maintenance, but many others may have subsidiary functions since the amino acids are selective chelating agents, separating copper, iron, and other elements from the common sodium, calcium, and potassium compounds entering the system. The simple proteins are made up entirely of the acids, but the complex or conjugated proteins contain also carbohydrates and special groups, while the cystine of hair and wool also contains sulfur. The constituent amino acids of the protein molecule are linked together with a peptide bond, and the linkage forms the backbone of the molecule, but the arrangement is not similar to the high polymers usually associated with plastics with one type of polymer, or group, repeating itself. The linkage is formed by the loss of carbon dioxide rather than by the loss of water as in plastics.

The simplest proteins are the **protamines** with molecular weights down to about 3,000. They are strongly basic and water-soluble, and contain no sulfur. **Clupeine** in herring, and **salmine** in salmon and trout, are examples. The **histones** which occur in white blood corpuscles contain sulfur and are more complex. The albumins of eggs and milk are soluble in water and coagulate with heat. They also occur in plants, as in the **leucosin** of wheat. **Prolamines** are **vegetable proteins,** as the zein of corn and the **gliadin** of wheat. They are not an adequate human protein food without **animal proteins.**

Biologically, the edible proteins are classified as first-class and second-class, the first being from animal and the second from vegetable origin. Meat and fish proteins are both complete, or first-class proteins, but the digestibility of fish protein is slightly higher than that of beef protein, while oyster protein is high in growth-promoting value. The synthesis of globulin and antibody formation for resistance to disease depends upon the utilization of various amino acids most readily obtained from first-class proteins. The term **protein isolates** used in the food industry refers to proteins from soybean or other sources and containing 85% or more of protein.

Lysine, essential for human nutrition, is found in soy proteins but also made synthetically as a water-soluble white powder, and is added to bakery products to raise the protein value to nearly that of animal protein. **Isoleucine,** a bitter amino acid, occurs in casein. It is an amino **methyl valeric acid** which is fermented by yeast to amyl alcohol. **Sclero proteins,** or **albuminoids,** contain much sulfur, are insoluble in water, resist hydrolysis, and are the most complex of the proteins. They occur in skin, ligaments, horn, wool, and silk. The complex indigestible protein of poultry feathers, used for making brush fibers, is also broken down to produce digestible proteins used in feeds. **Glycine,** or **glycocoll,** is an **amino acetic**

acid, H_2NCH_2COOH, formed by the hydrolysis of complex proteins and also made synthetically. The **methylated glycine,** called **betaine,** occurs in plants and is obtained from sugar-beet molasses.

Hydrolized proteins are used in flavoring foodstuffs. The Japanese condiment **adjinimoto,** made from wheat gluten, is largely **sodium glutamate,** a salt of **glutamic acid,** $C_5H_9O_4$, which also occurs in seeds and beets. **Monosodium glutamate** is sold under trade names such as **Zest** of A. E. Staley Mfg. Co. and **Ac'cent** of Ac'cent International. It is a white crystalline powder derived from soybeans and sugar beats. In small amounts it has no flavor, but intensifies the taste and flavor of foodstuffs. This effect may be greatly increased by adding a chemical compound such as disodium inosinate or disodium guanylate to replace part of the glutamate. **Mertaste,** of Merck and Co., is such a compound which enhances the flavor and acts as a synergist. In large amounts the glutamates have an offensive odor and flavor and are considered toxic. **Insulin,** used in medicine, contains **glutamine,** the half amide of glutamic acid, and also **cystine,** the disulfide of **cysteic acid,** an amino propionic acid essential for nutrition. **Cysteine** is amino mercapto propionic acid. It is used with whey in bakery dough to react with yeast enzymes and give faster rising at lower temperatures. **Royal jelly,** used in face creams, is a protein complex high in vitamin B. It is a secretion of bees to nourish the egg of the queen bee, but has no apparent therapeutic value.

More than half the population of the world suffers from protein deficiency, especially from the lack of first-class proteins. But in the United States vast quantities of first-class proteins are produced from fish meal, meat by-products, and synthetically, and used as additives in foodstuffs manufacturing. **Wheat gluten,** made from flour as a spray-dried powder, contains about 82% protein. It is used as an additive to improve the texture and the shelf life of baked goods. **Soybean protein** is marketed as a highly refined, odorless, and tasteless powder for use in confectionery and other foods to retain freshness and add food value. **Proset-Flake,** of the J. A. Jenks Co., is a soybean protein in flake form to give firmer texture. **Mushroom powder** is used to add proteins to foodstuffs where the flavor is also desirable as in sauces. It is made by sheeting the pulped mushroom, *Agaricus campestris,* on a double-drum drier and then grinding the sheet to a fine powder. **Animal protein factor,** used in animal feeds, and marketed commercially in fish solubles, is an amino-acid combination containing several vitamins. It is used in feeds for single-stomach animals, such as the hog, which cannot synthesize within themselves all of the amino acids necessary for health. It is also used in poultry feeds, as it contains the hatchability factor not adequately supplied by grains. **DL-methionine,** of the Dow Chemical Co., is a synthetic amino acid of the composition $CH_3SCH_2CH_2CH(NH_2)CO_2H$, used in feeds for fattening poultry.   **MPF granules** of General Mills, Inc., are granules of concentrated proteins, vitamins, and minerals for adding to bakery and meat products.   The whey from milk in powder form is added to bread to increase the protein content, and it also refines the texture of bakery products.   In porous granule form it is used as a **flow agent** to add butter, margarine, or oils to bakery products as well as protein.   **Kraflow,** of Kraft Foods, consists of **whey granules** which will absorb eight times their volume of oils.

  Protein plastics are produced by the isolation or precipitation of proteins from animal or vegetable products and hardening or condensing into stable compounds that can be molded into sheets or fiber.   The oldest of the protein plastics is casein plastic which was used to replace bone for toothbrush handles and buttons.   It is still an important molding plastic as it is tough and can be made in pastel shades, but it is more costly than many other molding plastics.   The proteins from soybean meal or other vegetable products are condensed with aldehydes or with various mineral salts or acids to form plastics.   These plastics are distinct from those made from the fatty acids of soybean or other oils.   **Peanut fiber,** under the name of **Ardil,** is made in England by precipitating the protein from peanut meal with an acid at low temperatures so as not to denature the meal.   It is then dissolved in caustic soda and forced through spinnerets into a hardening bath.   The fiber is soft and resilient, moisture-absorbent like wool, moth-resistant, and will dye easily.   It is mixed with wool in weaving fabrics.   **Vicara,** of the Virginia-Carolina Chemical Corp., is a protein fiber produced from the zein of corn.   The fiber is light yellow in color, soft, tough, and strong.   In fabrics it has the warmth of wool, is resistant to mildew, and will withstand temperatures to 310°F.   It can be blended with cotton, wool, or rayons.   Proteins obtained by alkaline extraction from cottonseed are also used to produce woollike fibers. **Azlon** is a general name for protein fibers.   **Chromated protein** finishes to provide a corrosion-resistant undercoat on iron or steel are produced by coating the metal with casein or albumin and then impregnating with a chromate solution which hardens the film.

PUMICE. A porous, frothlike volcanic glass which did not crystallize due to rapid cooling, and frothed with the sudden release of dissolved gases.   Powdered or ground pumice is used as an abrasive for fine polishing, in metal polishes, in scouring compounds and soaps, and in plaster and lightweight concrete and pozzuolanic cement.   In very fine powder it is called **pounce** when used for preparing parchment and tracing cloth. **Pouncing paper** is paper coated with pumice used for pouncing, or polishing, felt hats.   Pumice is grayish white in color, and the fine powder will float on the surface of water.   The natural lump pumice contains 65 to 75% silica, 12 to 15 alumina, and 4 to 5 each of soda and potash. It is produced chiefly in California and New Mexico.   **Pumicite** is a **volcanic ash** similar in composition to pumice, found in large beds in Nebraska, Kansas, and Colorado.   Its chief distinction is that it is fine-grained and has sharp edges suitable for abrasive purposes.   The natural material is dried, pulverized, and screened so that 98.8% will pass a 325-mesh screen.   **Seismotite** is a trade name of the Cudahy Co. for pumice used as an abrasive in scouring compounds.   **Slag pumice,** or **artificial pumice,** is made in Germany by treating molten slag with less water than is required for granulation.   It is used as an aggregate in lightweight concrete and as a heat insulator.   **Obsidian** will change into pumice when melted, but obsidian is a general name for **volcanic glass** and varies in composition.   It is an extrusive igneous rock that gets its glassy nature from its method of cooling, and some obsidian has a composition similar to that of granite.   It is colored black from magnetite, or brown to red from hematite.   Obsidian was used by the ancients for instruments and by the American Indians for arrowheads and knives. Semitransparent smoky-colored obsidian nodules of Arizona ore are called **marekanite,** and are cut for Indian silver jewelry.

Hawaiian obsidian, or **tachylite,** also known as **basalt glass,** is a volcanic glass from Oahu, Hawaii.   It is jet black, takes a fine polish, and is used for making ornamental articles.   The type of obsidian found in Oregon and California, known as **perlite,** is flash-roasted to form a bubblelike expanded material about 15 times original size which is crushed to a white fluffy powder.   Perlite contains about 75% silica.   In California it has been called **calite.**   The powder weighs only 4 to 12 lb per cu ft, and is used in lightweight wallboard, acoustical tile, insulation, and as a light-weight aggregate in concrete.   **Perlalex,** of the Alexander Film Co., is the finely ground powder used for removing smears from drawing paper. **Rhyolite perlite** of California is expanded to ovaloid particles of 590- to 840-micron size containing complete vacuums and weighing only 0.78 lb per cu ft.   This material has about 70% silica, 15 alumina, 2 Fe_2O_3, 1.5 CaO, 2.75 Na_2O, 1 MgO, 4 K_2O, and 4 water.   **Grellex,** of the Great Lakes Carbon Co., is expanded California perlite in fine particle size for use in plastics, adhesives, and insulation.

Other materials besides perlite may be expanded by heat.   **Expanded clay** is made from common brick clays by grinding and screening to 48 to 80 mesh and feeding through a gas burner at a temperature of about 2700°F.   The ferric oxide is changed to ferrous oxide, liberating oxygen and CO_2.   Strong, light bubbles about 0.020 in. in diameter are formed. **Kanamite,** of the Kanium Corp., is this material.   It weighs 17 to 25 lb per cu ft, and is used as an aggregate for lightweight concrete.

PURPLEHEART. The wood of several species of trees, notably *Peltogyne paniculata* of the Guianas. The color of the wood is brown, the heartwood turning purple on exposure. The grain is open and fine. The wood weighs about 53 lb per cu ft, is very hard, strong, and durable. It is used for machine and implement parts, inlays, furniture, and turnery.

PUTTY. A mixture of calcium carbonate with linseed oil, with sometimes white lead added. It is used for cementing window glass in place and also as a filler for patterns. Litharge is often added to putty for steel sash. Another putty for steel contains red lead, calcium carbonate, and linseed oil. The dry pigment for putty, **whiting putty,** according to ASTM specifications, contains 95% calcium carbonate and 5 tinting pigment. **White lead putty** contains 10% or more white lead mixed with the calcium carbonate. Federal specifications call for a minimum of 11% boiled or processed linseed oil with a maximum of 89% pigment as a white lead–whiting putty. **Putty powder** is a mixture of lead and tin oxides, or a mixture of tin oxide and oxalic acid, or it may be merely an impure form of tin oxide. It is used in enameling and for polishing stone and glass, and as a mild abrasive for dental polishes. **Calking putty,** used for setting window and door frames, is made of asbestos fibers, pigments, and drying oils, or with rubber or resins. The older calking compounds used in the building industry for sealing between window and door frames and masonry were made with drying oils and inert fillers, but they had poor adhesion and weathering qualities. **Calking compounds** are now composed of synthetics with usually a polysulfide rubber and a lead peroxide curing agent. They are heavy pastes of 75 to 95% solids. **Koplac 1251–5,** of the Koppers Co., Inc., for automobile body patching and general utility putties, is a low-viscosity polyester resin with 32% styrene. In putty formulations it is used with 50% talc and a catalyst. It hardens rapidly at room temperature.

PYRARGYRITE. An ore of silver, known also as dark **ruby silver.** It is a sulfantimonite of silver, Ag_3SbS_3, containing 22.3% antimony and 59.8 silver. It is found in various parts of Europe, in Mexico, Colorado, Nevada, and New Mexico. It occurs in crystals or massive, and also in grains. Its hardness is 2.5 and specific gravity 5.85. The color is dark red to black, showing ruby red in thin splinters. **Proustite** is another ore of silver occurring in silver veins associated with other metals. It is found in the mines of Peru, Mexico, Chile, and in Nevada and Colorado. It is also called light ruby silver and is a sulfarsenite of silver of the composition Ag_3AsS_3, containing theoretically 65.4% silver. It occurs massive, compact, in disseminated grains. The hardness is 2 to 2.5, specific gravity 5.55, and the color is ruby red with an adamantine luster.

PYRETHRUM. The dried flowers of several species of chrysanthemum, of which the *Chrysanthemum cinerariaefolium* of Yugoslavia and Japan is the best known. It is a slender perennial, about 15 in. high, with daisylike flowers. The powder is used as an insecticide chiefly in sprays. The crude pyrethrum from Kenya contains 1.3% **pyrethrin** as compared with only 0.9% in the Japanese. **Persian powder** is pyrethrum from the species *C. coccineum* of southwestern Asia. **Lethane,** of the Rohm & Haas Co., is a synthetic aliphatic diacyanate used as a substitute for pyrethrum. It is 30 to 40% more powerful than pyrethrum in insect sprays. Pyrethrin contains **pyrethronic acid** and **cyclopentane,** $(CH_2)_5$. The active principles of natural pyrethrum flowers have been designated as pyrethrin and **cinerin,** and the synthetic material marketed by the U.S. Industrial Chemicals, Inc., is a homolog of cinerin. In high concentration, it is more effective than natural pyrethrum. A substitute for pyrethrum for the control of corn worms is **styrene bromide,** or **bromo styrene,** an oily liquid of the composition $C_6H_5CBr:CH_2$. **Ryanodine,** of the composition $C_{25}H_{35}NO_9$, is 3 times more toxic than pyrethrin. It is extracted from the stem wood of the **ryania,** a shrub of Trinidad.

PYROPHORIC ALLOYS. Metals which produce sparks when struck by steel, used chiefly for gas and cigarette lighters. The original pyrophoric alloy, or **sparking metal,** was known as **Auer metal.** It was patented by Auer von Welsbach in 1903, and contained 35% iron and 65 misch metal. The French **kunheim metal** contained 10% magnesium and 1 aluminum instead of iron. A very durable alloy for cigarette lighters is a **zirconium-lead alloy** containing 50% of each metal. Titanium can replace part of the zirconium, and tin can replace part of the lead, but alloys with less than 25% zirconium are not pyrophoric. The 50–50 alloy has a crystalline structure. Some liquids are pyrophoric. **Trimethyl aluminum,** $Al(CH_3)_3$, a colorless liquid made by sodium reduction of methyl aluminum chloride, is used as a pyrophoric fuel.

PYROPHYLLITE. An aluminum silicate mineral found in North Carolina, used as a substitute for talc. It is similar to talc in structure and appearance, but its composition, $Al_2Si_4O_{10}(OH)_2$, is more nearly like kaolin. It is white, gray, or brown, with a pearly or greasy luster, specific gravity 2.8, and hardness 1 to 2. Compact varieties of the mineral are made into slate pencils and crayons. A fine-grained compact rock mined in South Africa, composed of about 90% pyrophyllite, with rutile and other minerals, is called **wonderstone,** and is used for table tops and switchboard panels. It is resistant to weathering, acids, and heat, and it can be planed, sawed, or turned in the lathe. It then becomes harder on exposure. Wonderstone is an ancient indurated clay resembling fireclay in which the colloidal matter has been destroyed by heat, pressure, and age. Unfired refractory bricks are made of dry-pressed pyrophyllite. They have high spalling resistance and do not shrink. **Pyrax,** of the R. T. Vanderbilt Co., is pyrophyllite in fine white powder of 100 mesh, with specific gravity 2.6, used as a filler in rubber. **Silical,** of Herron Bros. & Meyer, is pyrophyllite from Newfoundland in fine powder form as a dusting talc for rubber. The Japanese employ great quantities of pyrophyllite in the making of firebrick, fireclay, and crucibles. The mineral used averages 86.7% pyrophyllite, 12.8 kaolin, and 0.5 diaspore.

QUARTZ. The most common variety of silica. It occurs mostly in grains or in masses of a white or gray color, but often colored by impurities. Pure crystalline quartz is colorless and is called **rock crystal.** Quartz usually crystallizes in hexagonal prisms or pyramids. Many crystals are obtained from nodules, called **geodes,** which are rounded hollow rocks with the crystals grown on the inside surface of the cavity. These rocks range in size from very small to hundreds of pounds. The crystals are not always quartz, but may be grown from minor constituents of the rocks. A geode in limestone usually has a shell of silica and the interior crystals are of quartz or calcite, but some geodes contain crystals of gem quality containing metal coloring constituents. The hard rigid **beta quartz crystals** have a latticelike molecular structure in which each silicon atom is linked to four separate oxygen atoms, each oxygen atom being linked to two different silicon atoms. The formula of quartz crystal, therefore, is $(Si_2O_7)_x$, which is a pattern of the lattice, while the unit crystal of silica is SiO_2 and the silica grains are cryptocrystalline. The grains in sand are often less than 0.04 in., but crystals up to 20 in. have been found. The specific gravity is 2.65. Pure crystals have a dielectric strength of 1,500 volts per mil and a dielectric constant of 3.8, with good corona resistance.

Quartz crystals have the property of generating an electrical force when placed under pressure and, conversely, of changing dimensions when an electric field is applied. This property is termed piezoelectric. A **piezo-electric crystal** is made up of molecules that lack both centers and planes of symmetry. Many materials other than quartz have this property, such as rochelle salt and ammonium dihydrogen phosphate, but most of them are water-soluble or lack hardness. The best quartz crystals are hexagonal prisms with three large and three small cap faces. For electric use the crystals must have no bubbles, cracks, or flaws, and they should be free from twinning, or change in the atomic plane. **Brazilian quartz** crystals are cut into plates of different sizes to initiate and receive various frequencies on multiple-message telephone wires, and to obtain selectivity in radio apparatus. Owing to its peculiar refractive powers, quartz crystal is also employed for the plates in polarization instruments and in lenses. Quartz crystals for radio-frequency control are marketed in three forms: rough-sawed blanks, cut to specified angles; semifinished blanks, machine-lapped to approximate size; and electrically finished blanks, finished by hand and electrically tested. **Synthetic quartz crystals** of large size and high purity and uniformity are grown from seed crystals suspended in an alkaline silica solution at high temperature and pressure. The synthetic crystals are purified by imposing an electric current across the crystal at 500°C, which sweeps out the sodium and lithium impurities by electrolysis. The addition of lithium nitride to the sodium-hydroxide solution used in the hydrothermal growing process increases the Q value of the crystal to the range of natural quartz crystals. These synthetic crystals are used in precision oscillators and highly selective wave filters.

Other materials are also used to replace quartz for electronic use. **Barium titanate** crystals, $BaTiO_3$, are made by die-pressing titanium dioxide and barium carbonate and sintering at high temperature. This crystal belongs to the class of **perovskite** in which the closely packed lattice of barium and oxygen ions has a barium ion in each corner and an oxygen ion in the center of each face of a cube with the titanium ion in the center of the oxygen octahedron. For piezoelectric use the crystals are subjected to a high polarizing current, and they give a quick response to changes in pressure or electric current. They also store electric charges, and are used for capacitors. **Glennite 103,** of the Gulton Mfg. Co., is a **piezoelectric ceramic** molded from barium titanate modified with temperature stabilizers. **Bismuth stannate,** $Bi_2(SnO_3) \cdot 5H_2O$, a crystalline powder that dehydrates at about 140°C, may be used with barium titanate in capacitors to increase stability at high temperatures. **Ceramelex,** of the Erie Resistor Corp., is molded polycrystalline barium titanate. **Ethylene diamine tartrate** crystals may also be used to replace quartz for telephone and sonar work.

Quartz is harder than most minerals, being 7 Mohs, and the crushed material is much used for abrasive purposes. Finely ground quartz is also used as a filler, and powdered quartz is employed as a flux in melting metals. When quartz is fused, it loses its crystalline structure and becomes a silica glass with a specific gravity of 2.2, compressive strength 210,000 psi, tensile strength 4,000 psi, hardness 5, and dielectric strength 410 volts per mil. The chemical formula of this material is sometimes given as SiO_3, but is really SiO_2 repeated in a lattice structure but different from that of quartz crystal. **Fused quartz,** or **quartz glass,** is used for bulbs, optical glass, crucibles, and for tubes and rods in furnaces. Its softening and working temperature is about 3040°F, and it fuses at 3193°F. The translucent material, made from sand, has a specific gravity of 2.7, with much lower strength. It will withstand rapid changes of temperature without breaking.   It can be used continuously at temperatures to 1830°F, and devitrifies at 1920°F, while fused silica of the same chemical content devitrifies at about 1100°F and shatters when cooled suddenly.   Fused quartz made from rock crystal is transparent to visible light, while fused silica is normally translucent or opaque.   **Vitreosil,** of the Thermal Syndicate, Ltd., is fused quartz, containing 99.8% silica.   It comes opaque, translucent, and transparent.   It transmits ultraviolet and short wavelengths, has high electric resistance, and a coefficient of expansion about one-seventeenth that of ordinary glass.   **Quartz tubing** for electronic use comes in round, square, hexagon, and other shapes.   The softening point is 1667°C.   Tubing as small as 0.003 in., produced by the Monsanto Co., is flexible and as strong as steel.

Quartz fiber originally was made by extruding the molten quartz through a stream of high-pressure hot air which produced a fluffy mass of fine fibers of random lengths.   Quartz fibers are now made with many differing compositions and methods of manufacture.   Fibers used for wool or mat have a diameter of 1 to 15 microns.   Those used for continuous filament may be as small as 0.0035 in.   **Astroquartz,** of J. P. Stevens & Co., may be corded as a thread with outside diameters from 0.014 to 0.020 in.   The thread is used for sewing insulation blankets and separation curtains.   **Quartz yarn** made from these filaments is used for weaving into tape and fabric.   **Quartz paper,** or **ceramic paper,** developed by the Naval Ordnance Laboratory and used to replace mica for electrical insulation, is made from quartz fiber by mixing with bentonite and sheeting on a paper-making machine.   It has high dielectric strength, and will withstand temperatures to 3000°F.   **Micro quartz,** of the L. O. F. Glass Fibers Co., is felted fine quartz fibers for insulation.   The felted material has a density of 3 lb per cu ft, and is for service temperatures to 2000°F.

Since quartz crystallizes more slowly than many other minerals, the natural crystals may include other minerals which were crystallized previously.   **Sagenite** is a form of crystalline quartz containing hairlike crystals crossing in a netlike manner.   A variety of fibered quartz with a pale amethyst color which shows deep red by transmitted light, found in Russia and Colorado, is called **onegite.**   **Rutilated quartz** is clear quartz penetrated by rutile crystals.   A smoky dark quartz of this type is the **Venus-hair stone.**   **Aventurine** is a form of quartz crystal containing the inclusion in the form of flakes or spangles.   It comes from the Ural Mountains and from India and is prized for gems.   For costume jewelry it is made synthetically in great quantities under the name of **goldstone** by melting the inclusions into quartz glass.   Amethyst, **topaz,** and many other gemstones are quartz.   The golden-yellow topaz of Mexico and Brazil is a type of quartz called **citrine.**   The yellow variety called **imperial topaz** in Brazil is rare, but yellow-brown stones are common.   **Pink topaz** is also rare, but can be made by heating yellow-brown stones with a risk of breaking.   Inferior-colored amethysts may also be made into yellow or orange-colored citrine by heating.   The **rose quartz** of South Dakota is prized in the beautiful rose color, but in the large deposits the shades may run from milky white through pale pink to deep rose red.   The best stones are used for gems, as are also the translucent pink crystals from Maine.   Other grades are cut into vases, ornaments, and architectural facings.   **Chalcedony** is a cryptocrystalline quartz with a waxy luster deposited in rock veins from colloidal solution, or in concentric rings on rocks.   Its fibers are biaxial instead of the uniaxial of quartz.   The chalcedony of South Dakota known as **beckite** fluoresces under ultraviolet light.   Chalcedony was an ancient gemstone, and was used for intaglios and seals and for figurines and vases.   Some chalcedony from New Mexico and Arizona is stained and cut for costume jewelry.   **Chrysoprase** is a translucent, apple-green variety of cryptocrystalline quartz colored with hydrated nickel silicate found in Silesia.   It is highly valued for mural decorations and as a gemstone.

The so-called **massive topaz** used as a refractory material instead of kyanite is not true topaz or quartz.   The massive topaz mined in North Carolina contains about 50% Al_2O_3 and 40 SiO_2, with iron oxide.   When calcined for refractory use, it has the same composition as kyanite.   The topaz from the wolframite mines of São Paulo, Brazil, used for refractories, has a high alumina content and a high fluorine content.   The purer crystals have a melting point of 1880°C.   The quartz known as **cristobalite,** used as a refractory, differs from ordinary quartz only in the crystal structure. It has a melting point of 3140°F.   **Jasper** is a variety of quartz colored red with iron oxide.   It is cut and polished as an ornamental building stone.   **Egyptian jasper** is brown in color with dark zones.   In ancient times many of the gemstones were silica stones, and the **Athiaenon stone** from Cyprus was jasper of bright colors.   The **jasper iron ore** of Michigan has an iron content of about 33% with less silica than taconite, making it easier to crush, but concentration must be done by flotation which is more expensive than the magnetic separation of taconite.

QUARTZITE. A rock composed of quartz grains cemented together by silica.   It is firm and compact and breaks with uneven, splintery, fractures.   Most of the quartzites used are made up of angular grains of quartz and are white or light in color with a glistening appearance.   It often resembles marble, but is harder and does not effervesce in acid.   Quartzite is employed for making silica brick, abrasives, siliceous linings for tube mills, as a structural stone, and as a broken stone for roads.   It is found as a widely distributed common rock.   **Medina quartzite,** from Pennsylvania, contains 97.8% silica.   The melting point is about 1700°C.

QUASSIA. Also known as **bitterwood.** The wood of the Jamaica quassia tree, *Picroena excelsa,* and of the **Surinam quassia,** *Quassia amara,* of the West Indies and northern South America. The **Jamaica quassia** is a large tree, sometimes called **bitter ash** because the leaves resemble those of the common ash. The wood is yellow, light, dense, and tough. It is odorless, but has an intensely bitter taste. The wood is imported mostly as chips for the production of the extract which is used in medicine as a bitter tonic, and also used in insecticides. It is also used as an ingredient in stock-feed tonics for cattle. In tropical countries the wood is valued for furniture, as it is resistant to insects. The wood of the Surinam quassia is darker in color, heavier, and harder, but has similar properties. **Quassin,** extracted from quassia, is used to denature alcohol.

QUEBRACHO. The wood of the **quebracho colorado,** or **red quebracho** tree, *Aspidospera quebracho,* found only along the west bank of the Paraná and Paraguay Rivers in Argentina and Paraguay. It contains about 24% tannin. The wood is exceedingly hard and has a brownish-red color often spotted and stained almost black. Quebracho is valued as a firewood in Argentina, and is also used for crossties and posts, but is too brittle for structural work. It takes a fine polish and is very durable, carvings of this wood being in perfect condition after 300 years. The weight is 78 lb per cu ft. **Quebracho extract,** from the wood, is a hard, resinous, brownish-black, and extremely bitter solid containing 62% soluble tannins. One metric ton of wood yields about 250 kilos of solid extract. The liquid extract contains 25 and 35% tannin. It is employed in tanning leather and is rapid-acting, but is seldom used alone as it makes a dark leather. It is mixed with alum and salt, or with chestnut extract. Some extract is used in boiler compounds, but one of the larger uses has been for the treatment of oil-well-drilling muds. **Aerosol Q,** of the American Cyanamid Co., is powdered quebracho and an organic colloid for oil-well muds. **White quebracho,** *Schinopois lorentsii,* is a smaller tree than the red quebracho, growing over a wider area of Argentina, Brazil, and Paraguay. It produces a similar tannin. Some **urunday extract** is produced in Argentina for export instead of quebracho. The **urunday wood** is red in color and very hard, but not as brittle as quebracho, and is valued locally for cabinetwork. The tannin from the wood is similar to quebracho extract.

RADIOACTIVE METALS. Metallic elements which emit radiations that are capable of penetrating matter opaque to ordinary light. They give out light and appear luminous, also having an effect on the photographic plate. The metal radium is the most radioactive of all the natural elements, and was much used for luminous paints for the hands of watches and instrument pointers, but, because of the emission of dangerous gamma rays, is now largely replaced for this purpose by radioactive isotopes of other metals.   These isotopes, such as cobalt-60 used as a source of gamma rays and crypton-85 for beta rays, are marketed selectively.   Radioactive metals are used in medicine, for luminous paints, for ionization, for the breaking of particle bonds for powdering minerals, for polymerization and other chemical reactions, and for various electronic applications.

The metals which are naturally radioactive, such as uranium and thorium, all have high atomic weights.   The radiating power is atomic and is unaffected in combinations.   Radium and other radioactive metals are changing substances.   Radium gives out three types of rays; some of the other elements give out only one or two.   The measure of the rate of radioactivity is the **curie,** which is the equivalent of the radioactivity of one gram of radium.

Each radioactive metal has a definite breakdown period, measured in half-life.   **Actinium,** which is **element 89,** has a half-life of 21.7 years. It emits alpha particles to decay to **actinium K,** which is the radioactive isotope of **francium,** and then emits beta particles.   Radioactive metals break down successively into other elements.   By comparison of changing atomic weights, it has been deduced that the metal lead is the ultimate product, and uranium the parent metal under present existing stability conditions.   But heavier metals, now no longer stable under present conditions, have been produced synthetically, notably plutonium.   The heavy **element 103** was first produced in 1961 and named **lawrencium** in honor of the inventor of the cyclotron.   Not all radiation produces radioactive materials, and by controlled radiation useful elements may be introduced into alloys in a manner not possible by metallurgy.   The crystal lattice of an alloy can be expanded, or atoms displaced in the lattice, thus altering the properties of the alloy.   In like manner the molecules of plastics may be cross-linked or otherwise modified by the application of radiation.   For example, ethylene bottles may be irradiated after blowing to give higher strength and stiffness.   Radioactive isotopes are also used widely in chemistry and in medicine, and as sources of electric power.   They are produced regularly by the Atomic Energy Commission and marketed selectively.

RADIUM. A scarce radioactive metal, symbol Ra, scattered in minute quantities throughout almost all classes of rocks, but commercially obtainable only from the uranium ores monazite, carnotite, and uraninite.   It is a breakdown product, and it disintegrates with a half-life of 1,590 years. The metal is white in color, but it tarnishes rapidly in the air.   The melting point is about 700°C.   It was discovered in 1898 by Curie, and the original source was from the pitchblende of the Sudetenland area of

Austria after extraction of thorium oxide, but most of the present supply comes from the carnotite of the Congo and from the pitchblende of western Canada. One gram of radium and 7,800 lb of uranium are obtained from 370 tons of pitchblende. The ratio of radium to uranium in any uranium ore is always about 1:3,000,000. Radium is marketed in the form of bromides or sulfate in tubes and is extremely radioactive in these forms.

In a given interval of time a definite proportion of the atoms breaks up with the expulsion of α, β, and γ rays. When an alpha particle is emitted from radium, the atom from which it is emitted becomes a new substance, the inert gas **radon,** or **element 86,** with a half-life of 3.82 days. During its short life it is a definite elemental gas, but it deposits as three isotopes in solid particles, decaying through polonium to lead. Radium is most widely known for its use in therapeutic medicine. It is also used for making inspections of metal castings in place of X-rays. **Radium-beryllium powder** is marketed for use as a neutron source.

RAMIE. A fiber used for cordage and for various kinds of coarse fabrics, obtained from the plant *Urtica nivea,* of temperate climates, and *U. tenacissima,* of tropical climates. The former plant has leaves white on the underside, and the latter has leaves all green. The name **rhea** is used in India to designate the latter species. It is also grown in China, Egypt, Brazil, and Florida. The plants grow in tall slender stalks like hemp and belong to the nettle family. The bast fibers underneath the bark are used, but are more difficult to separate than hemp fiber owing to the insolubility of the adhesive gums. The fibers are 8 times stronger than cotton, 4 times stronger than flax, and nearly 3 times stronger than hemp. They are fine and white, and are as silky as jute. They are not very flexible and are not in general suitable for weaving, but their high wet strength, absorbent qualities, and resistance to mildew make the fibers suitable for warp yarns in wool and rayon fabrics. The yarn is used also for strong, wear-resistant canvas for such products as fire hose. The fiber is also valued for marine gland packings and for twine. The composition is almost pure cellulose, and the tow and waste are used for making cigarette paper. **China grass** is the hand-cleaned but not degummed fiber. It is stiff and greenish yellow in color. **Grass cloth** is woven fabric made in China from ramie. **Swatow grass cloth,** imported into the United States, is made of ramie fibers in parallel strands, not twisted into yarns.

RAPE OIL. An oil obtained from seeds of the mustard family, *Cruciferae.* The genus *Brassica,* a form of turnip, species of which are referred to as *B. campestris, B. rapa, B. napus,* and *B. hirta,* is grown in India, Pakistan,

Europe, and Canada. **Rapeseed** is one of the principal oil seeds of the world. It is widely used as an edible oil, for making factice, and for mixing with lubricating and cutting oils and for quenching oils. The seeds are very small, an ounce having as many as 40,000 seeds. The seeds contain 40% oil. The edible oil is cold-pressed and refined with caustic soda. The burning and lubricating oils are refined with sulfuric acid. The iodine value is about 100, the specific gravity 0.915, and the flash point 455°F. The oil contains palmitic, oleic, linoleic, and stearic acids and 43 to 50% of the typical acid, **erucic acid,** also called **brassidic acid,** $C_{21}H_{41}COOH$. It has a melting point of 34°C. It occurs also in grape seed oil. **Colza oil** is a rape oil extracted from French seed, used to mix with mineral oils to make cutting oils. The name colza now refers to any refined rape oil. **Chinese colza oil,** from the *B. campestris chinoleifera,* contains the mustard volatile oil. The specific gravity is 0.91, saponification value 174, and iodine number 100.3. From 15 to 20% of blown rapeseed oil is mixed with mineral oil for lubricating marine engines. **Crambe seed oil,** from *Crambe abyssinica,* an Asiatic mustard, contains 55 to 60% erucic acid. The erucic can be broken down to pelargonic acid used as a substitute for dibasic acids such as azelaic and brassylic acids. **Cameline oil,** called also **dodder oil** and **German sesame oil,** has the same uses as rape oil. It is from the plant *Camelina sativa* grown in central Europe. The seeds contain 35% oil which contains oleic and palmitic acids and also erucic acid. The seed itself is high in mineral and protein content and is used in birdseed mixtures.

RARE GASES. A general name applied to the five elements helium, neon, argon, krypton, and xenon. They are rare in that they are highly rarified gases at ordinary temperatures and are found dissipated in minute quantities in the atmosphere and in some substances. All have zero valence and normally make no chemical combinations, but by special catalyzations, except in the case of helium, the outer proton bonding may be broken and compounds produced. For torch shielding in the metallurgical industry these elements are referred to as **inert gases.**

Neon is procured from the air by liquefaction. When it is energized, it emits light and is used for signs and in glow lamps. The specific gravity, compared with air, is 0.674. It liquefies at −248°C. It is colorless, but gives a reddish-orange glow in lamps to which an electric current is applied. Neon is also used in voltage-regulating tubes for radio apparatus, and will respond to low voltages. In television the neon lamp will give fluctuations from full brilliancy to total darkness as many as 100,000 times a second. All colored electric advertising signs are often referred to as neon signs, but the colors other than orange are produced by different gases. **Argon** gives a purple light when an electric current is passed through it.   It occurs free in the asmosphere to the extent of 0.935%.   Its liquefying point is about −187°C.   It is obtained by passing atmospheric nitrogen over red-hot magnesium, forming magnesium nitride and free argon.   It is also obtained by separation from industrial gases.   Argon is employed in incandescent lamps to give increased light and to prevent vaporization of the filament and is used instead of helium for shielding electrodes in arc welding and as an inert blanket for nuclear fuels.

Krypton, which occurs in the air to the extent of 1 part in 1 million, gives a pale-violet light.   It is a heavy gas, with a specific gravity of 2.896. It is used as a filler for fluorescent lamps to decrease filament evaporation and heat loss and to permit higher temperatures in the lamp.   The 3-billion-candlepower aircraft-approach lights first used on the Berlin airlift contained krypton.   **Krypton 85,** obtained from atomic reactions, is a beta-ray emitter with a half-life of 9.4 years.   It is used in luminous paints for activating phosphors and also as a source of radiation.   As marketed by the Tracerlab Co., it comes combined in solid form with a hydro-quinone to give higher concentration of energy and more convenience in use.   American Atomics Corp. markets the isotope in disks of 0.23 and 0.5 in. diameter, encased in acrylic plastic for use with phosphors as luminous sources.   The light is yellow-green.   **Xenon,** another gas occurring in the air to the extent of 1 part in 11 million, gives a sky-blue to green light.   It is the heaviest of the rare gases, with a specific gravity of 4.561 compared with 1 for air.   Its liquefying point is about −108°C. When atomic reactors are operated at high power, xenon tends to build up as a reaction product, poisoning the fuel and reducing the reactivity. **Xenon lamps** for military use give a clear white light known as sunlight plus north-sky light.   This color does not change with the voltage, and thus the lamps require no voltage regulators.   An 800-watt xenon lamp delivers 2,000 lumens, 4 times as much as a 1,000-watt incandescent lamp. The xenon lamp reflects each half cycle, so that shutterless projectors are possible.   Krypton and xenon have lower thermal conductivity and lower electrical resistance than argon.   A helical arc of xenon is used to activate ruby optical masers.   Xenon is a mild anesthetic, the accumulation from air helping to induce natural sleep, but it cannot be used in surgery since the quantity needed produces asphyxiation.

RARE METALS.   A term given to metals that are rare in the sense that they are difficult to extract and are rare and expensive commercially.   They include the elements **masurium, alabamine,** and **virginium** which is called **madavium** in France.   Although radium is a widely distributed metal it is classed as a rare metal.   All of the ultraheavy metallic elements, such as plutonium, which are produced synthetically, are classed as rare metals.

They are called **transuranic metals** because they are above the heavy metal uranium in weight.   They are all radioactive.

The silvery metal **technitium, element 43,** has been produced by bombardment of molybdenum with neutrons.   It is available in the form of **technitium carbonyl,** $Tc_2(CO)_{10}$, which is stable in air and is soluble in most organic solvents but reacts with halogens.   **Element 99,** called **eka-holmium** because it appears to have chemical properties similar to holmium, is produced by bombarding uranium 238 with stripped nitrogen atoms. It decays rapidly to form the lighter **berkelium,** or **element 97.   Neptunium, element 93, californium, element 98,** and **illinium, element 61,** are also made atomically.   The latter also has the names **florentium** and **promethium.**

Plutonium is made from uranium 238 by absorption of neutrons from recycled fuel.   The metal, 99.8% pure, is obtained by reduction of **plutonium fluoride,** PuF_4, or **plutonium chloride,** $PuCl_3$.   It has a melting point of 64°C.   The surface reacts in the air to form the nonadherent **plutonium oxide,** PuO_2, which becomes airborne and is pyrophoric and poisonous.   **Plutonium 238,** and also **239** and **240,** emit chiefly alpha rays. Plutonium 238 has a low radiation level and is used as a heat source for small water-circulating heat exchanges for naval underseas diving suits.

Plutonium 241 emits beta and gamma rays.   Since all the allotropic forms are radioactive, it is a pure nuclear fuel while uranium is only 0.7% directly useful for fission.   It is thus necessary to dilute plutonium for control.   For fuel elements it may be dispersed in stainless steel and pressed into pellets at about 1600°F, or pellets may be made of **plutonium carbide.   Plutonium-iron alloy,** with 9.5% iron, melts at 410°C.   It is encased in a tantalum tube for use as a reactor fuel.   **Plutonium-aluminum** alloy is also used.   These alloys have hard compounds of PuFe and PuAl in the matrix and there is no solubility of the plutonium.   While plutonium 241 has a half-life of only 14 years, the beta emitters plutonium 239 and 240 have half-lives of 24,300 and 16,600 years, respectively.   **Element 102,** called **nobelium,** has a half-life of only 12 min.   Other transuranic metals produced synthetically are **americium, element 95,** and **curium, element 96.**   Curium is used as a heat source in remote applications.   **Curium 244** is obtained as **curium nitrate** in the reprocessing of spent reactor fuel.   It is converted to **curium oxide.**   The by-product americium is used as a component in neutron sources.   The radioactive elements are obtainable only under AEC license.   More than 50 new elements higher than uranium on the atomic scale are made.

RATANY. Also known by the original Inca name of **payta,** and in medicine as **krameria.**   The root of the shrub *Krameria triandria,* which grows in Peru and is used for tanning leather and in medicine as an astringent. The root comes in diameters up to 1 in., and in pieces up to 3 ft in length. It contains about 40% tannin which is extracted by hot water. It gives the leather a deep-brown color, and is usually mixed with other tannins.

RATTAN. The long slender stem of the palm *Calamus rotang* and other species, of Ceylon, Malaya, and Laos. There are more than 40 varieties. The Malay word is rottan, meaning cane. It is tough, flexible, strong, and durable, and is used for canes, umbrella handles, and furniture. When split it is used for car seats, baskets, baby-carriage bodies, furniture, whips, and heavy cordage. Commercial rattans are in pieces 5 to 20 ft long. A substitute for rattan is **jacitará,** from the plant *Desmoncus macro-acanthus,* of Brazil. It is used for seating. Vinylidene chloride plastic is now widely used as a substitute for rattan for seating.

RAYON. A general name for artificial-silk textile fibers or yarns made from cellulose nitrate, cellulose acetate, or cellulose derivatives. The general name was adopted after the Federal Trade Commission had ruled against the use of such terms as **art silk, fiber silk, chardonnet silk,** and **artificial silk.** Some of the products are referred to preferably by the manufacturer's trade name such as Celanese, for cellulose-acetate yarns and fabrics. In general, the name rayon is limited to the viscose, cuprammonium, and acetate fibers, or to fibers having a cellulose base. Other synthetic-fiber groups have their own group names, such as azlon for the protein fibers and nylon for the polymeric amine fibers, in addition to individual trade names. High-tenacity rayons designed for tire-cord use have the general name of **Tyrex.**

Viscose rayon is made by treating the cellulose with caustic soda and then with carbon disulfide to form cellulose xanthate, which is dissolved in a weak caustic solution to form the viscose. With the cuprammonium process the cellulose is digested in an ammonia solution of copper sulfate, and the solution forced through the spinnerets into dilute acid for hardening. Rayons manufactured by the different processes vary both chemically and physically. They are resistant to caustic solutions which would destroy natural silk. They are also mildewproof, durable, and easily cleaned. But they do not have the permeability and soft feel of silk. The **acetate rayons** are more resistant than the viscose or cuprammonium. The lack of permeability of the fibers is partly overcome by having superfine fibers so that the yarns are permeable. The one-denier viscose staple produced by the FMC Corp. by stretching the fiber after it leaves the spinnerets is finer than Egyptian cotton and can thus be made into yarns that are permeable between the fibers. Fabrics made from the superfine yarns have the appearance of sheer silk. **Multicell rayon** of this company, for making nonwoven fabrics and lining and filter papers on regular paper-making machines without the addition of a binder, is a multicellular short-staple fiber cut to uniform $\frac{1}{4}$-in. length. The fibers lock themselves firmly in place with contacting fibers, and the 1.5-denier fiber makes a soft, opaque sheet of paper. The density of the sheets and the strength per unit weight decrease with increase in the fiber denier. **Fiber 40,** of this company, is a type of rayon called **Avril,** made by a special pulping process which decreases the tendency to shrink or felt when the fiber is wet. **Avlin** is a multicellular rayon fiber that gives a tight, firm bulk to fabrics. **Fabray,** of Stearns & Foster, is a thin lightweight porous non-woven fabric of rayon fiber used for throw-away garments.

The objectionable high gloss of synthetic fibers is reduced by pigmentation. **Glos** was an early name for rayon because of this gloss, but the name has now been abandoned. Practically all types of dress fabrics and knitted hosiery and underwear are made from rayons. The material is also used for automotive tire fabrics because of its strength. **Staple fiber** is fiber cut to length for the spinning system to be used. The **Lanese fiber** of the Celanese Corp. of America is 3-, 5.5-, 8-, and 12-denier acetate rayon cut to lengths of $1\frac{1}{8}$ to 2 in. **Seraceta,** of the FMC Corp., is a continuous-filament acetate rayon. **Matesa** is the name of continuous-filament cuprammonium rayon of the American Bemberg Corp.

High-tenacity rayon is produced by stretching the fibers so that the molecular chains run parallel to the filament axis, and a number of small crystalline regions act as anchors for the cellulose chains. **Tire cord** stretched in this way has the tensile strength increased from 27 to 37 lb. **Rayocord,** of Rayonier, Inc., is a high-tenacity rayon for tire cords and reinforcing fabrics for plastics. It is made from sulfite cellulose, is stretched to produce oriented fiber, and has twice the strength of ordinary rayon. **Super Cordura,** of Du Pont, used for tire cords, is high-tensile rayon made from a blend of wood cellulose and cotton linters. The **Nytex tire cord** of the Sieberling Rubber Co. is a combination nylon-rayon cord. The nylon adds strength, and the rayon eliminates the flat-spotting tendency of the nylon.

RED BRASS. The standard wrought metal known as red brass, or **rich low brass,** of the brass mills contains 85% copper and 15 zinc. It is one of the most ductile and malleable of the brasses, and the working stresses can be relieved without softening the metal by heating for a half hour at 275°C. It is also valued for its fine reddish color, ability to take a high polish, and corrosion resistance. It is essentially a drawing and stamping metal and, unless it contains a little lead, will not machine well. The annealed metal has a tensile strength of 35,000 psi, with elongation 40%, while the hard-rolled metal has a strength of 65,000 psi, with elongation 5%, and Rockwell B hardness 75. The melting point is 1875°F, weight 0.316 lb per cu in., coefficient of expansion 0.0000104 per deg F, and electrical conductivity 34.7% that of copper. It is produced regularly in the form of sheets and tubes, and is used for jewelry, nameplates, dials, drawn and stamped hardware and mechanical parts, and corrosion-resistant hot-water pipes. **Plumrite 85,** of the Bridgeport Brass Co., is this alloy in tubes for piping. **Revere alloy 130,** of the Revere Copper & Brass, Inc., is this metal in sheets and tubes. **Redalloy,** of the Chase Brass & Copper Co., contains 85% copper, 14 zinc, and 1 tin. The tensile strength is 42,000 psi and elongation 48%.

The high-copper alloy known in the mills as **commercial bronze** contains 90% copper and 10 zinc. It is widely used for making costume jewelry, weather stripping, stamped hardware, forgings, and screws. It has a bronze color, a weight of 0.318 lb per cu in., and electrical conductivity 43.6% that of copper. The tensile strength, soft, is 38,000 psi, with elongation 40%. The tensile strength of the hard-rolled metal is 60,000 psi and elongation 5%. **Revere alloy 120** is this metal. Federal specifications for gilding metal call for this alloy, and it is also known as government gilding metal. But standard **gilding metal** employed for making cheap jewelry and small-arms ammunition contains 95 to 97% copper. It has a golden-red color, is stronger and harder than copper, but has only about half the electrical conductivity of copper. The English **cap copper,** used for cartridge caps, has 97% copper and 3 zinc. **BES gilding metal** is in three grades, 80, 85, and 90% copper, but the 80–20 alloy has a definite golden-yellow color and is not in the class of red brasses. The 80–20 brass is one of the standard alloys of the brass mills under the name of **low brass.** It was early used for jewelry under the name of **Dutch metal.** It is very ductile and is easily drawn, takes a high polish, and has high strength. It is still much used for cheap jewelry. **Chain bronze,** used for flat-link jack chains, and also for costume jewelry, contains 87 to 89% copper, 0.60 to 1.25 tin, and the balance zinc. The tin increases the hardness, and it has good strength and corrosion resistance.

Many old names used for designating the golden or reddish high-copper brasses, especially for cheap jewelry making, are still in occasional use. **Pinchbeck metal,** originally made by C. Pinchbeck, an English jeweler, contained 88% copper and 12 zinc. This is the same as the **Guinea gold** used for traders' jewelry. **Manila gold,** or **traders' gold,** was about the same with some lead to heighten the color. **Ormolu gold,** a name still used by brass platers, was any composition that would give a golden color. **Rich gold metal** was the 90–10 alloy, and this alloy is still being used for decorative purposes under the name of **copper-rich brass.** **Mannheim gold,** containing 83% copper, 10 zinc, and 7 tin, was a German alloy for cheap jewelry. It is a considerably harder alloy than ordinary red brasses. **Tournay metal** was a French alloy widely used for buttons when brass buttons were in vogue. It was essentially the same as the original **tombac metal** used by the Chinese for buttons, and was the 85–15 alloy containing considerable arsenic to give a brilliant grayish tone to the metal. The alloy is quite brittle. The name tombac is the Malay word tombaga used to designate gold-colored jewelry alloys. **Chrysochalk** is another old name for gilding metal containing enough lead to give a dull gold tone. Japanese low-priced jewelry alloys often contained silver or gold to balance the color and make them resistant to tarnishing. **Shadke** was a high-copper alloy with some gold, and **Shaku-do** contained about 4% gold and 1 silver. The gold color of the red brasses is enhanced by pickling in nitric acid.

RED LEAD. A common lead pigment, also erroneously called minium. It is a **lead tetroxide,** Pb_3O_4, forming a bright-red or orange-red powder of specific gravity 0.096, insoluble in water. As a pigment it has great covering power and brilliancy, but red lead which has not been completely oxidized and contains litharge must be applied immediately after mixing to avoid combination with the oil. It is used as a heavy protective paint for iron and steel. Red lead is also used in storage-battery plates and in lead glass. With linseed oil it is used as a lute in pipe fitting. **Orange mineral** is a pure form of red lead made from white lead and has an orange color. Chemically it is the same as red lead, but it has a different structure, giving it a more brilliant color. Red lead is made from lead metal by drossing and then heating in a furnace. **Fume red lead** is a fine grade made from **fume litharge,** which is made by oxidizing molten lead and passed off as a yellow smoke or fume. Fume red lead is notable for the extreme fineness of its particles, and bulks greater than ordinary red lead. Fume red lead is marketed for pigment as **superfine red lead.**

REDWOOD. Also called **sequoia, California redwood,** and **Humboldt redwood.** The wood of the tree *Sequoia sempervirens,* native to the West Coast of the United States. The wood is light, soft, and spongy but has comparatively high strength and is resistant to decay and insect attack. The trees grow in a narrow coastal strip in California, and are of an immense size, reaching a diameter of 20 ft and a height of 350 ft in 2,000 years. The so-called Big tree, however, is the *S. gigantea* or *S. washingtoniana.* It grows in the mountains at elevations of 5,000 to 8,500 ft, but is not cut for lumber. Planks of redwood can be readily obtained 6 ft in width. The specific gravity is 0.374 to 0.387. It has a tensile strength of from 7,000 to 11,000 psi. The heartwood varies from light-cherry to dark-mahogany color, and the narrow sapwood is almost white. The wood is used in all kinds of common construction. **Redwood bark fiber**

is the shredded fiber of the bark of the redwood. It has excellent felting properties, is water-resistant and fire-resistant, and is an excellent insulator for house walls and refrigerators. It is also used in wool mixtures for blankets and overcoatings. The fiber is short, but has a natural twist that facilitates spinning. The fiber contains a high content of lignin, and makes a good filler for heat-curing plastics. **Palco wool,** of the Pacific Lumber Co., is redwood bark fiber, and **Palco board** is a lightweight insulation board for cold-storage chambers made from the shredded bark fibers. **Palcotan,** of the same company, is a sodium salt of **palcotannic acid,** a weak sulfonated tannic acid, used as a binder in ceramic clays, a stabilizer for asphalt emulsions, and in latex and paste adhesives. **Redwood tannin,** produced by soaking redwood chips in hot water and dissolving out the tannin with ethyl acetate, is used as an oxidation inhibitor in hydrocarbons.

REFRACTORIES. Materials, usually ceramics, employed where resistance to very high temperature is required, as for furnace linings and metal-melting pots. Materials with a melting point above Seger cone 26, or 1580°C, are called refractory, and those with melting points above cone 36, or 1790°C, are called highly refractory. But, in addition to the ability to resist softening and deformation at the operating temperatures, other factors are considered in the choice of a refractory, especially load-bearing capacity and resistance to slag attack and spalling. Heat transfer and electrical resistivity are sometimes also important. Many of the refractories are derived directly from natural minerals, but synthetic materials are much used.

Clay is the oldest and most common of the refractories. The natural refractories are kaolin, chromite, bauxite, zirconia, magnesite, often marketed under trade names. Refractories may be acid, such as silica, or basic, such as magnesite or bauxite, for use in acid- or basic-process steel furnaces. Graphite and chromite are neutral refractories. Magnesia is insoluble in the slag of open-hearth furnaces and is used for linings. Magnesia fuses at 3929°F, chromite at 3722°F, and alumina at 3670°F. The fusing point of the refractory, however, is usually dependent on the binder, as all binders or impurities lower the melting point. **Arco refractory brick,** of the General Refractories Co., with 60 to 80% alumina, will withstand temperatures from 3290 to 3335°F. The melting point of a 99.5% pure alumina is given as 3725°F, and the decomposing point of a 98% pure silicon carbide as 4175°F. **Chrome-magnesite bricks** are made usually with 75% chrome ore and 25 dead-burned magnesite.

The chief artificial refractories are silicon carbide and aluminum oxide. **Refrax,** of the Carborundum Co., is silicon carbide held together by crystallization without a binder. It withstands temperatures to 2240°C, at which point it decomposes. The crushing strength of the brick is 12,500 psi. This type of material can be made only in simple shapes, but is also made into rolls for roller-type furnaces. **Refrax FS** is fused silica bonded with silicon nitride. It is used for formed parts up to 23 in. in diameter for such applications as brazing fixtures, and has dimensional stability and thermal shock resistance to 2250°F. **Silfrax** is in grades with 40 to 78% SiC, and porosities from 9 to 18%. **Monofrax,** of the same company, is a refractory block for lining glass furnaces. It is composed of 98% alpha and beta alumina crystals interlocked in a dense structure weighing 200 lb per cu ft, with only a small amount of bond and impurities. A grade with more open structure weighs 175 lb per cu ft, and the **Monofrax K** contains 80% alumina and the balance chromite crystals saturated with alumina. These materials are resistant to abrasion to temperatures above 3000°F. They have porosities from 20 to 29%. **Aluminite** is furnished by the Philip Carey Co. in blocks for temperatures to 2000°F. **Korundal XD brick,** of the Harbison-Walker Refractories Co., is corundum bonded with mullite. For open-hearth and electric-furnace roofs it will withstand a 25-psi load at a temperature of 3000°F without spalling. The **Lo-Sil brick** of Kaiser Aluminum, for aluminum-melting furnaces, is made with a high alumina content with very low silica to avoid pickup of silicon in the molten aluminum.

The silica brick used in coke ovens has a high coefficient of expansion below about 155°F, so that ovens must be heated gradually over a period of 6 to 8 weeks to prevent cracking of the brick. **Fire sand** is a sand composed of 98% silica and is very refractory. The natural silica refractories used to replace fireclay for high temperatures should contain at least 97% silica and not yield too fine a powder on crushing. In order of merit the materials used are chalcedony, old quartzites, and vein quartz. The refractory known in Europe as **klebsand,** used for steel furnace linings, has 87% SiO_2, 8.6 Al_2O_3, 0.3 TiO_2, and some ferric oxide. **Ganister** is a natural refractory mineral used for furnace linings. In compact form it was used for furnace hearths. It contains about 95% silica, about 1.5 Al_2O_3, and a small amount of lime as a binder. The chief deposits are in the quartzites of Wisconsin, Alabama, and Colorado. An artificial ganister is made with silica and clay. **Ganisand,** of the Quigley Furnace Specialties Co., Inc., is a ganister having a fusing point at 3250°F. **Dinas silica** is an English ganister with about 97% silica, having a melting point of 1680°C. **Silica brick** made from quartzite containing 98% silica has lime added as bond, and the resulting brick usually contains about 96% silica, 2 lime, and 2 alumina and ferric oxide. The bricks are rigid under load, and are resistant to attack by acid slags and to spalling under rapid temperature changes. **Vega silica brick,** of Harbison-Walker Refractories Co., has no more than 0.4% of oxides other than lime, and will withstand temperatures to 3090°F under load.

Foamed silica blocks for lining tanks and for refractory insulation are made from pure fused silica. They have a density of 10 to 15 lb per cu ft with an impermeable closed-cell structure, have a compressive strength of 130 to 210 psi, and will withstand temperatures to 2200°F. **Foamsil,** of the Pittsburgh Corning Corp., is this material.

Pinite, from Nevada, is a secondary mineral derived from the alteration of feldspar and other rocks, and is used for kiln linings in cement plants. It is a hydrous silicate of alumina and potash, and the massive material resembles steatite. It will bond alone like clay and has low shrinkage. At 1125°C, the mineral inverts to mullite. **Agalmatolite** is a massive pinite and can be used in the same way. **Bull-dog** is an old name for a refractory which is a mixture of ferric oxide and silica made by roasting tap cinder with free access of air. **Tap cinder** is a basic silicate of iron.

REFRACTORY CEMENT. A large proportion of the commercial refractory cements used for furnace and oven linings and for fillers are fireclay-silica-ganister mixtures with a refractory range of 2600 to 2800°F. Cheaper varieties may be mixtures of fireclay and crushed brick, fireclay and sodium silicate, or fireclay and silica sand. An important class of refractory cements is made of silicon-carbide grains or silicon carbide–fire sand with clay bonds or synthetic mineral bonds. The temperature range of these cements is 2700 to 3400°F. **Silicon-carbide cements** are acid-resistant and have high thermal and electrical conductivity. For crucible furnaces the silicon-carbide cements are widely used except for molten iron. Alumina and **alumina-silica cements** are very refractory and have high thermal conductivity. Calcined kaolin, diaspore clay, mullite, sillimanite, and combinations of these make cements that are neutral to most slags and to metal attacks. They are electrical insulators. **Chrome-ore cements** are difficult to bond unless mixed with magnesite. **Plastic 695,** of the Basic Refractories, Inc., is a **chrome-magnesite cement** made of treated magnesite and high-grade chrome ore. It sets quickly and forms a hard and dense structure. The melting point is above 3600°F. It is used particularly for hot repairs in open-hearth furnaces. **Magnefer** is the name of a dead-burned dolomite refractory of the same company, while **Basifrit** is a magnesia refractory for resurfacing. **Zircon-magnesite cement** is made with 25% refined zircon sand, 10 milled zircon, 15 fused magnesia, and 50 low-iron dead-burned magnesite bonded with sodium silicate. A wide range of refractory cements of varying compositions and characteristics is sold under trade names, and these are usually selected by their rated temperature resistance. For example, **Hadesite,** of the Eagle-Picher Lead Co., is composed of refractory clay and aggregates, mineral wool, and a binder, and is recommended for temperatures up to 1900°F. **Carbofrax cement,** of the Carborundum Co., is silicon carbide with a small amount of binder in various grades for temperatures from 1600 to 3200°F, depending on the fineness and the bond. **Firefrax cement** of the same company is an aluminum silicate, sometimes used in mixtures with ganister for lining furnaces. It is for temperatures to 3000°F. **Alfrax cement** is fused silica also in various grades for temperatures from 1650 to 3300°F. **Mullfrax cement** has a base of electric furnace mullite, and is for temperatures from 2200 to 3200°F, while **Mullite S cement** is of converted kyanite for ferrous and nonferrous melting furnaces for temperatures to 3150°F. **Ankorite,** of the Harbison-Walker Refractories Co., is a high-alumina hot-setting refractory mortar for laying superduty firebrick. **Thermolith,** of this company, is a chrome-base cold-setting mortar for laying magnesite, chrome, and forsterite brick.

REFRACTORY HARD METALS. True chemical compounds of two or more metals in the form of crystals of very high melting point and high hardness. These materials were originally called **Hartstoffe** in Germany, and they do not include the hard metallic carbides, some of which, with metal binders, have similar uses, nor do they include the hard cermets. The refractory hard metals may be single large crystals, or crystalline powder bonded to itself by recrystallization under heat and pressure. In general, parts made from them do not have binders, or contain only a small percentage of stabilizing binder. The intermetallic compounds, or inter-metals, are marketed regularly as powders of particle size from 150 to 325 mesh for pressing into mechanical parts or for plasma-arc deposition as **refractory coatings,** and the powders are referred to chemically, such as **borides, beryllides,** and **silicides.** The oxides and carbides of the metals are also used for sintering and for coatings, and the oxides are called cermets.

Zirconium boride is a microcrystalline gray powder of the composition ZrB_2. When compressed and sintered to a density of about 5.3, it has a Rockwell A hardness of 90, a melting point of 2980°C, and a tensile strength of 35,000 to 40,000 psi. It is resistant to nitric and hydrochloric acids, and to molten aluminum and silicon, and to oxidation. At 2200°F it has a transverse rupture strength of 55,000 psi. It is used for crucibles and for rocket nozzles.

Chromium boride occurs as very hard crystalline powders in several phases, the CrB orthorhombic crystal melting at 1550°C, the hexagonal crystal Cr_2B melting at 1850°C, and the tetragonal crystal Cr_3B_2 melting at 1960°C. Chromium boride parts produced by powder metallurgy have a specific gravity of 6.20 to 7.31, with a Rockwell A hardness of 77 to 88. They have good resistance to oxidation at high temperatures, are stable to strong acids, and have high heat-shock resistance up to 2400°F. The transverse rupture strength is from 80,000 to 135,000 psi.

Colmonoy, of the Wall Colmonoy Corp., is chromium boride, CrB, used for oil-well drilling. A sintered material, used for gas turbine blades, contains 85% CrB with 15% nickel binder. It has a Rockwell A hardness of 87 and a transverse rupture strength of 123,000 psi.

Molybdenum boride, Mo_2B, has a specific gravity of 9.3, a Knoop hardness of 1,660, and a melting point of about 1660°C. **Tungsten boride,** W_2B, has a specific gravity of 16.7, and a melting point of 2770°C. **Titanium boride,** TiB_2, is light in weight with a specific gravity of 4.5. It has a melting point at about 4700°F. Molded parts made from the powder have a Knoop hardness of 3,300 and a flexural strength of 35,000 psi, and they are resistant to oxidation to 1800°F with a very low oxidation rate above that point to about 2500°F. They are inert to molten aluminum. Intermetal powders of **beryllium-tantalum, beryllium-zirconium,** and **beryllium-columbium** are also marketed, and they are light in weight and have high strength. Sintered parts resist oxidation to 3000°F.

Molybdenum disilicide, $MoSi_2$, has a crystalline structure in tetragonal prisms, and has a Knoop hardness of 1,240. The decomposing point is above 1870°C. It can be produced by sintering molybdenum and silicon powders, or by growing single crystals from an arc melt. The density of the single crystal is 6.24. The tensile strength of the sintered parts is 40,000 psi, and compressive strength 333,000 psi. The resistivity is 29 microhm-cm. It is used in rod form for heating elements in furnaces. The material is brittle, but can be bent to shape at temperatures above 2000°F. **Super Hot Rod,** of the Norton Co., is molybdenum disilicide rod. **Kanthal Super,** of Kanthal Corp., is a similar material. In an inert atmosphere the operating temperature is 1600°C. Furnace gases containing active oxygen raise the operating temperature to about 1700°C, while gases containing active hydrogen lower it to about 1350°C.

Tungsten disilicide, WSi_2, is not as hard and not as resistant to oxidation at high temperatures, but has a higher melting point, 2050°C. **Titanium nitride,** TiN, is a light-brown powder with a cubic lattice crystal structure. Sintered bars are extremely hard and brittle, with a hardness above Mohs 9 and a melting point of 2950°C. It is not attacked by nitric, sulfuric, or hydrochloric acids, and is resistant to oxidation at high temperatures. **Aluminum nitride,** AlN, when molded into shapes and sintered, forms a dense, nonporous structure with a hardness of Mohs 6. It resists the action of molten iron or silicon to 3100°F and molten aluminum to 2600°F, but is attacked by oxygen or carbon dioxide at 1400°F.

Nickel aluminide is a chemical compound of the two metals, and, when molded and sintered into shapes, has good oxidation resistance and heat shock at high temperatures. **Borolite 1505,** of the Borolite Corp., is a nickel aluminide sintered material with a density of 5.9, and a transverse rupture strength of 150,000 psi at 2000°F, which is twice that of cobalt-bonded titanium carbide at the same temperature. The melting point is 3000°F. It resists oxidation at 2000°F. It is used for highly stressed parts in high-temperature equipment. **Metco 405,** of Metco, Inc., is this compound in wire form for welding, flame coating, and hard surfacing. **Metco 404** is aluminum powder coated with nickel. This powder may be mixed with zirconia or alumina which will increase the hardness and heat resistance of the nickel aluminide coating. **Columbium aluminide** is used as a refractory coating as it is highly resistant for long periods at 2600°F. **Tin aluminide** is oxidation resistant to 2000°F, but a liquid phase is formed at about this point.

REFRIGERANTS. Gases, or very-low-boiling-point liquids, used for the heat-absorbent cycle in refrigerating machines. The ideal refrigerant, besides having a low boiling point, should be noncorrosive, nonflammable, and nontoxic. It must be free of water, since as little as 40 parts per million of water may cause freezing in the system. Ammonia is a common refrigerant. Ethyl chloride, methyl ether, carbon dioxide, and various chlorinated and fluorinated hydrocarbons marketed under trade names such as the **Freons** of Du Pont and the **Genetrons** of the Allied Chemical Corp. are also used. **Dichloro difluoro methane,** a nonflammable, colorless, odorless gas of the composition CF_2Cl_2, is one of the Freons. It liquefies at $-21.7°F$. **Freon E3** is a fluorated hydrocarbon which boils at 306°F, and is stable to 570°F. It is pourable at 175°F. It is used for dielectric insulating in electronic equipment. **Trichloro monofluoro methane,** CCl_3F, is used as a refrigerant in industrial systems employing centrifugal compressors, and in indirect expansion-type air-conditioning systems. The boiling point is 74.7°F, and freezing point $-168°F$. The condensing pressure at 86°F is 18.3 psi, and the net refrigerating effect of the liquid is 67.5 Btu per lb. **Genetron 11** is this material. **Genetron 101** has the composition $CH_3 \cdot CClF_2$, with boiling point at $-9.2°C$ and freezing point at $-130.8°C$.

RESINS. An important group of substances obtained as gums from trees, or manufactured synthetically. The common resin of the pine tree is called rosin. The natural resins are soluble in most organic solvents, and are used in varnishes, adhesives, and various compounds. **Oleoresins** are natural resins containing essential oils of the plants. **Gum resins** are natural mixtures of true gums and resins and are not as soluble in alcohol. They include rubber, gutta percha, gamboge, myrrh, and olibanum. Some of the more common natural resins are rosin, dammar, mastic, sandarac, lac, and animi. **Fossil resins,** such as amber and copal, are natural resins from ancient trees, which have been chemically altered by long exposure. The synthetic resins differ chemically from natural resins, and few of the natural resins have physical properties that make them suitable for mechanical parts.

Galbanum, used in medicine, is a gum resin from the perennial herb *Ferula galbaniflua* of western Asia. It comes in yellowish to brownish tears. **Myrrh** is a yellow reddish aromatic gum resin from the *Commiphora malmol* and other species of small trees of India, Arabia, and northeast Africa. There are more than 80 species. The Hebrew word mur means bitter, and the gum has a bitter taste. It consists of a mixture of complex acids and alcohols but mainly the mucilaginous **arabin,** with from 3 to 8% of a volatile oil of the formula $C_{10}H_{14}O$. It is used in incense and perfumes, and in medicine as a tonic. The gum is called **mulmul** and **ogo** in eastern Africa and **herabol** in India. **Sweet myrrh,** or **bisabol myrrh,** is a very ancient perfume and incense. It comes from the tree *C. erythraea* of Arabia. **Herabol myrrh** is from the small tree *C. myrrha* of India and is a brown to black solid. It is used in medicine as a stimulant and antiseptic and in perfumes and incense. **Asafetida** is a gum resin with a foul odor and acrid taste obtained from the roots of the perennial herb *F. assafoetida* and other species. It is used in Asia for flavoring foods, but in the United States is employed in medicines and perfumes.

Creosote bush resin is an amber-colored, soft, sticky resin from the leaves and small twigs of the **greasewood bush,** *Larrea tridentata,* or **creosote bush,** *L. divaricata,* of the desert regions of the Southwest and Mexico. It is used in adhesives, insecticides, core binders, insulating compounds, and pharmaceuticals. When distilled, the resin yields **nordihydro guaiaretic acid,** $(C_6H_3 \cdot Cl \cdot COOH)_2CH_2$, called **NDGA,** formerly used as a preservative but now prohibited by the FDA for use in foods. It is a white crystalline solid melting at 184°C, soluble in fats and slightly soluble in hot water. **Okra gum** is from the pods of the plant *Hibiscus esculentus,* native to Africa but now grown in many countries. It is edible, and is used as a thickening agent in foodstuffs and pharmaceuticals. It has antioxidant properties, and also acts as a stabilizer. As a gelling agent it forms a network molecular structure with branched chains, giving slipperiness valued for foodstuff spreads. It is a tan-colored, water-soluble powder. Okra gum is also used in plating baths as a brightener.

Ammoniac is a gum resin from the stems of the *Dorema ammoniacum,* a desert perennial plant of Persia and India. It forms in hard, brittle, brownish-yellow tears, and has a peculiar fetid odor and an acrid taste. It is used in adhesives, in perfumery, and as a stimulant in medicine. In pharmacy it is called **ammoniacum. Oil ammoniac** is a yellow liquid distilled from the gum. The specific gravity is 0.890, boiling point 275°C, and it is soluble in alcohol and benzol.

RESISTANCE WIRE. The standard alloy for electrical resistance wire for heaters and electrical appliances is nickel-chromium, but nickel-manganese and other alloys are used. For consumer products made in large quantities, cost and the relative scarcity of supply of the alloying elements are important considerations. For high-temperature furnaces, tungsten, molybdenum, and alloys of the more expensive high-melting metals are employed. The much used alloy with 80% nickel and 20 chromium resists scaling and oxidation to 2150°F, but it is subject to an intergranular corrosion known as green rot which may occur in chromium above 1500°F unless modified with other elements. The 80–20 alloy has a resistivity of 650 ohms per cir mil ft. The tensile strength of the annealed wire is 100,000 psi, with elongation of 35%, and the hardness is Rockwell B80. The specific gravity is 8.412. In many appliances high elongation is undesirable because of sag in the wire.

In times of nickel stringency, or for cost reduction, various nickel-chromium-iron alloys are used. An alloy of 60% nickel, 16 chromium, and 24 iron has a resistivity of 675 ohms with oxidation resistance to 1950°F. **Tophet C,** of the Wilber B. Driver Co., is this alloy. The alloy with 30% nickel, 20 chromium, and 50 iron is resistant to 1560°F. The resistivity of the low-nickel, chromium-iron alloys is high, and the heat resistance is ample for some types of appliances, but the strength is lower, with a tendency for the hot wire to sag. **Cromel AA,** of the Hoskins Mfg. Corp., is an 80–20 nickel-chromium alloy for continuous service to 2150°F. It is modified with small amounts of cobalt, manganese, columbium, silicon, and iron, the columbium stabilizing the chromium to prevent green rot. It is also resistant to carbon pickup which tends to make the chromium-iron alloys brittle. The resistance of the wire is 700 ohms per cir mil ft.

The chromium-aluminum-iron alloys have high resistivity and high oxidation resistance, but have a tendency to become brittle. **Hoskins alloy 870** contains 22.5% chromium, 5.5 aluminum, 0.5 silicon, 0.10 carbon, and the balance iron. The resistivity is 875 ohms per cir mil ft. It is used as wire or ribbon in furnaces to 2350°F. The **Kanthal alloys** marketed as wire and ribbon by the Kanthal Corp. have 20 to 25% chromium with some cobalt and aluminum, and the balance iron. **Kanthal A,** with 5% aluminum, will withstand temperatures to 2370°F, has a resistivity of 836 ohms per cir mil ft, and is resistant to sulfuric acid. The tensile strength is 118,000 psi with elongation of 12 to 16%. **Kanthal A-1,** for furnaces, has a resistance of 872 ohms and an operating temperature to 2505°F. The **Nikrothal alloys** of this company are nickel-base modifications of Kanthal. They have higher tensile strength, up to 200,000 psi, to permit rapid winding of tape without breakage. **Nikrothal 6** has 60% nickel, 15 chromium, and 25 iron. **Heating tape,** of the

Rogers Corp., designed for heating rocket batteries, is also used for panel heating and is operable at continuous temperatures up to 250°F. It has three flat wires of copper-nickel alloy encapsulated in Mylar tape 0.008 in. thick and 0.375 in. wide in lengths to 250 ft. The rating is 2 watts per foot, and the dielectric strength is 2,400 volts.

A series of alloys of the Westinghouse Electric Corp., called **Hirox alloys,** contain 6 to 10% aluminum, 3 to 9 chromium, up to 4% manganese, with the balance iron except for small additions of boron and zirconium to reduce the size of the aluminum-iron grains and refine the structure. The alloy with 9% aluminum and 9 chromium has a resistivity of 850 ohms, and a tensile strength of 118,000 psi. At 1300°F the tensile strength is 15,000 psi with elongation of 94%. Wire will give continuous service in air at 2350°F without failure.

Resistance alloys are marketed under a wide variety of trade names, and they are generally specified for specific uses rather than by composition. Controlled resistivity over a temperature range instead of high heat resistance is desired for instrument use, while a definite coefficient of expansion is required for spark-plug wire and other uses where the wire is embedded. In some cases, good heat resistance with selected low resistivity is desired. **Oxalloy 28,** of Sylvania Electric Products, Inc., is copper wire clad with 28% by weight of chromium-iron alloy. It withstands continuous service at 1300°F. The resistivity at 1100°F is 52 ohms per cir mil ft. **Neyoro G,** of the J. M. Ney Co., used for fine resistance wire in potentiometers and electronic applications where high cost is not a factor, has a high gold content with platinum, silver, and copper. The drawn wire has a tensile strength of 185,000 psi and high corrosion resistance.

Copper-manganese alloys have high resistivity, an alloy with 96 to 98% manganese having a resistance of more than 1,000 microhms per cu cm. But when the manganese content is high, they are brittle and difficult to make into wire. Addition of nickel makes them ductile, but lowers the resistivity. A typical alloy contains 35% manganese, 35 nickel, and 30 copper. A resistance alloy developed by the National Bureau of Standards, called **Therlo,** contains 85% copper, 9.5 manganese, and 5.5 aluminum. **Fecraloy,** of the Wilber B. Driver Co., has 15% chromium, 5 aluminum, and the balance iron. It is for temperature to 1400°F. **Sparkaloy,** of the same company, is a **spark-plug wire,** and is a manganese-nickel alloy. The spark-plug wire of the Hoskins Mfg. Co., called **Hoskins alloy 667,** contains 4% manganese, 1 silicon, and the balance nickel. The resistance is 152 ohms per cir mil ft, specific gravity 8.4, and coefficient of expansion 0.0000151 in. per deg C to 500°C. **Manganin,** of the Wilber B. Driver Co., contains 80 to 85% copper, 2 to 5 nickel, and 12 to 15 manganese. It has a tensile strength of 70,000 psi and a resistance of 290 ohms per cir mil ft. It is used for coils and shunt wires in electrical instruments, and also in sheet form for instrument springs.   **Tophet A,** of the same company, is a standard 80–20 nickel-chromium alloy.   The tensile strength is 120,000 psi and resistance 650 ohms per cir mil ft.   **Incoloy,** developed by the International Nickel Co. to replace high-nickel alloys for moderate-temperature resistance wire, contains 34% nickel, 21.5 chromium, and the balance chiefly iron.   The physical properties at normal temperature are about the same as those for inconel.

Calorite, of the General Electric Co., has 65% nickel, 8 manganese, 12 chromium, and 15 iron.   **Excello metal,** of H. Boker & Co., Inc., contains 85% nickel, 14 chromium, and 0.5 each manganese and iron. It is used in electric heaters for temperatures up to 2000°F.   **Alumel,** of the Hoskins Mfg. Co., intended for temperatures up to 1250°C, has 94% nickel, 2.5 manganese, 0.5 iron, and small amounts of other elements. **Calido,** of the Driver-Harris Co., contains 59% nickel, 16 chromium, and 25 iron.   **Nichrome V,** of the same company, is the 80–20 alloy. **Nichrome S** contains 25% nickel, 17 chromium, and 2.5 silicon.   It is marketed in sheet form for temperatures up to 1800°F.   **Comet metal,** of the same company, used for rheostats, contains 30% nickel, 5 chromium, and the balance iron.   It has high strength, up to 160,000 psi, and a resistivity of 570 ohms.   The Driver-Harris resistance alloy known as **Karma** contains 20% chromium, 3 iron, 3 aluminum, 0.30 silicon, 0.15 manganese, 0.06 carbon, and the balance nickel.   Its melting point is 2552°F and its resistivity 800 ohms, and the annealed wire has a tensile strength of 130,000 psi with elongation 25%.   **Hytemco,** of the same company, is an iron-nickel alloy used for low-temperature wire.   The resistance is 120 ohms per cir mil ft.   **Magno** is a 95% nickel, 5 manganese alloy of the same company; **Climax metal** has 74% iron, 25 nickel, and 1 manganese.

RESORCINOL. A colorless crystalline material with the composition $C_6H_4(OH)_2$, melting point 110°C, very soluble in water and in alcohol. It is used in the production of plastics, in the manufacture of fluorescein, in the production of xanthane and azo dyes, particularly the fast **Alsace green,** in medicine as an antiseptic, and in making the explosive lead styphnate.   Resorcinol polymerizes with formaldehyde to form the **resorcinol-formaldehyde plastics** that will cure at room temperature and with only slight pressure.   They are used in strong adhesives for plywood and wood products, and do not deteriorate from acid action as some other plastics do.   **Resorcinol adhesives** remain water-soluble during the working period for 2 to 4 hr and are then insoluble and chemical-resistant.   **Pencolite G-1215,** of the Pennsylvania Coal Products Co., is a resorcinol-formaldehyde adhesive that cures at 75°F and gives a bonding strength of 3,000 psi.   The resorcinol adhesives may be modified with phenol to reduce cost and still retain the low-temperature setting. **Phenac 703,** of the American Cyanamid Co., is a phenol-modified resorcinol resin used as an adhesive for plywoods.   Derivatives of resorcinol are used in medicine as specific bactericides, such as **diverinol** which is propyl resorcinol, and **olivertol** which is amyl resorcinol.

RHENIUM. An elementary metal, symbol Re, present in small quantities in many minerals.   Rhenium has a specific gravity of 21.4, being almost twice as heavy as lead.   The melting point is 5756°F.   It is a hard, silvery-white metal which takes a high polish.   As a plating metal the white color is darker than that of rhodium.   The 99.99% pure metal has a tensile strength of 80,000 psi.   It has good chemical resistance, but is soluble in nitric acid.   The crystal structure is closely packed hexagonal, making it more difficult to work than the cubic-structured tungsten, but the crystal grains are tiny, and small amounts of rhenium added to tungsten give better ductility and improved high-temperature strength to the tungsten for lamp filaments and electronic wire.

Rhenium is obtained from molybdenite, containing 0.0001 to 0.05% of the metal.   But the usual source is from the flue dusts and from the sublimed **rhenium oxide,** Re_2O_7, of stack gases in the smelting of copper and other ores.   It is precipitated from the flue dust of molybdenum-bearing copper ores in the form of **potassium perrhenate,** $KReO_4$, or of **ammonium perrhenate,** NH_4ReO_4.   The Russians also obtain some rhenium from the Ural platinum ores.   The stable **rhenia,** used in alloying, is **rhenium trioxide,** ReO_3, which comes as a red powder.

The metal is obtained as a dense silvery powder which can be compacted, sintered, and cold-rolled with frequent annealing.   It is marketed in the form of rod, strip, foil, and wire.   **Rhenium-tungsten alloys,** with up to about 35% rhenium, are ductile and are used for high heat resistance. The melting point of the alloy, 5650°F, is lower than that of pure tungsten but has higher recrystallization temperature and retains its strength at all temperatures.   Rhenium has a higher electrical resistivity than tungsten, has high arc resistance, and does not become brittle after prolonged heating as tungsten does.   The alloys are used for electronic filaments and small structural parts.   Rhenium metal is used as an undercoat on graphite nozzles under the coating of tungsten to prevent the formation of tungsten carbide and thus give the full heat resistance of the tungsten.   Rhenium or rhenium-tungsten electrical contacts give very long service life.   Rhenium-tungsten versus tungsten thermocouples are good for service to 2800°C. The **tungsten-rhenium alloy** of Englehard Industries, Inc., for thermocouple use, contains 26% rhenium.

RHODIUM. A rare metal, symbol Rh, found in platinum ores such as the nickel-copper ores of Canada and **pyroxinite** of South Africa.   It is very hard and is one of the most infusible of the metals.   The melting point is 3542°F.   It is insoluble in most acids, including aqua regia, but is attacked by chlorine at elevated temperatures and by hot fuming sulfuric acid.   Liquid rhodium dissolves oxygen, and ingots are made by argon-arc melting.   At temperatures above 1200°C rhodium reacts with oxygen to form a **rhodium oxide,** Rh_2O_3.   The specific gravity is 12.44.   Rhodium is used to make the nibs of writing pens, to make resistance windings in high-temperature furnaces, for high-temperature thermocouples, as a catalyst, and for laboratory dishes.   It is the hardest of the platinum-group metals, the annealed metal having a Brinell hardness of 135, and the rolled metal a hardness of 390.   Rhodium is also valued for electroplating jewelry, electrical contacts, appliances, surgical instruments, and reflectors.   For electrodepositing rhodium, an electrolyte of **rhodium sulfate,** $Rh_2(SO_4)_3$, is used.   The coatings are wear-resistant and tarnish-resistant.   The plated metal has a pinkish-white luster of high corrosion resistance and a light reflectivity of 80%.   Decorative finishes are seldom more than 0.0002 in. thick, but plates for electric contacts may be up to 0.005 in.   The electrical resistivity is 4.69, and the Vickers hardness is about 600.   **Rhodium carbonyl** has the general formula, $Rh(CO)$, but with several variations in number of CO groups.   They are used for depositing **rhodium coatings.**

The most important alloys of rhodium are **rhodium-platinum.**   They form solid solutions in any proportion, but alloys of more than 40% rhodium are rare.   Rhodium is not a potent hardener of platinum but increases its high-temperature strength.   It is easily workable and does not tarnish or oxidize at high temperatures.   These alloys are used for thermocouples and in the glass industry.   A **rhodium-iron** alloy with equiatomic proportions of the metal has an ordered crystal structure and changes from antiferromagnetic to ferromagnetic in an electric field. Rhodium is sold by the troy ounce, 1 cu in. weighing 6.56 troy oz.

RICE.   The white seed of the large annual grass *Oryza sativa,* growing to a height of 2 to 4 ft.   It is a tropical plant native to Asia, but grows in hot, moist regions well into the temperate zones and is cultivated in many parts of the world.   Rice fields are flooded after planting to control weeds.   The rice seed grows in an inflorescence composed of a number of fine branches, each terminating in a single grain enclosed in a brown husk. Rice forms the staple food of more than half the population of the world. **Wild rice** was used by the Indians of North America before the first Asiatic rice was brought to South Carolina in 1694.   Rice is high in starch and low in proteins.   It is used as a direct food, also as flour, cereal, in puddings, and for the manufacture of starch and for alcoholic beverages.   **Rice hulls** are used as stock feed, and **rice straw** is used for packing, hats, and other articles.   Rice in the husk before hulling is known by the Hindu name of **paddy.**   **Brown rice** is rice that has been cleaned but not polished. A hundred pounds of paddy yields 62 lb of cleaned rice, while 100 lb of brown rice yields 91.3 lb of polished rice.   Broken grains are sold in the India trade as **coodie** or **khood,** and about 20% of the rice produced from paddy is broken.   **Patna rice** does not refer to the Patna district of India, but to a variety of rice with bold and hard grains especially suited for soups as it holds its shape in boiling.   **Malekized rice,** developed by the General American Transportation Co., is produced by steaming unpolished rice to force the soluble part of the bran and the vitamins into the core of the grain, and then sealing the rice kernel by gelatinization, after which it is polished.   The treated rice holds its shape and does not become gummy when cooked, and the nutritional value is improved.   The beverage known in Japan as **saké** is **rice wine** containing 14% alcohol, made by fermenting rice with the mold **tané koji.**   **Rice bran oil,** used as a salad and cooking oil and in lubricants, is produced from rice bran.   By wet-milling whole rice in a rice oil solution a higher yield of oil and wax is obtained together with a yield of proteins.   It is clear, odorless, and neutral, with a pleasant flavor, and is resistant to oxidation and rancidity. **Rice wax** is produced from rice bran by hot hexane extraction after cold extraction of the oil.   It is a hard, brown, lustrous wax with a melting point of 79°C, used in polishes.   The yield from 100 lb of rice bran, or hulls, is about 15 lb of oil and 0.6 lb of wax.   **Synthetic rice,** used in Japan as a rice extender, is made from wheat flour, potato starch, and powdered rice.

ROSEWOOD. The wood of several species of *Dalbergia* of northern South America, but chiefly from the **jacaranda tree,** *D. nigra.*   It is used for fine cabinetwork, pianos, novelties, and expensive furniture.   It should not be confused with the wood of the tree *Physocalymma floridum,* which also comes from Brazil and is there called **pao rosa** or rosewood. The color of rosewood is dark brown to purple, and it takes a beautiful polish.   It has a characteristic fragrance.   It is very hard and has a coarse, even grain.   The weight is 54 lb per cu ft.   The tree grows to a height of 125 ft.   Another Brazilian wood, **caroba,** from the large tree *Jacaranda copaia,* is also called **jacaranda** and is sometimes confused with rosewood. The tree has purple flowers while the true rosewood has white flowers. Caroba wood is chocolate-colored, and is used for fine furniture and knife handles.   **Indian rosewood** is from the tree *D. sissoo* of India.   It is also called **sissoo,** and is a beautiful, brown hardwood employed for carvings. In Europe it is also used for parquet floors.   **Borneo rosewood,** also known as **ringas,** is the wood of several species of trees of the genus *Melanorrhoea* of Borneo.   The wood has a deep-red color with light and dark streaks. It has a close texture suitable for carving.   **Satinee** is a type of rosewood from the tree *Ferolia guianensis* of the order *Rosaceae,* native to tropical America, particularly the Guianas. The wood is reddish brown, weighs 54 lb per cu ft, is fairly hard, has a fine grain, and takes a lustrous polish. It is used for cabinetwork. **Bois de rose oil,** or **rosewood oil,** is not from rosewood, but is extracted from the heartwood of the tree *Aniba panurensis* of Brazil and the Guianas, though the wood of this tree is also used as a cabinetwood. The oil is also called **Cayenne linaloe,** or **Cayenne oil.** It has a delicate rose odor with a suggestion of orange and mignonette valued in perfumes. It contains a high percentage of **linalol,** a colorless alcohol with a soft, sweet odor, also found in the rose, lilac, lily, lavender, petit-grain, and other plants. It also contains geraniol. **Linaloe oil,** or **Mexican linaloe,** is distilled from the heartwood of the trees *Bursera delpechianum* and *B. aloeoxylon.* It contains less linalol and also terpineol and geraniol. Linalol is closely related to geraniol and nerol. Bois de rose is also made synthetically from geraniol. **Oriental linaloe** is distilled from selected highly perfumed parts of the wood of the large tree *Aquilaria agollocha* of eastern India, Burma, and Java. The odor of the oil is like rose, ambergris, and sandalwood. Like the linaloes of the American continent the oil is a pathological product and comes only from old trees. It is also called **aloe wood oil** and **agar attar,** and is a very ancient perfume. The beautifully figured and fragrant reddish wood of this tree, called **aloes wood, eagle wood,** and **paradise wood,** is used for ornamental articles. True original rosewood oil known as **rhodium oil** was distilled from the wood of the plant *Convolvulus scoparius* of the Canary Islands.

ROSIN. The common resin of several varieties of the pine tree, found widely distributed in North America and Europe. It is obtained by cutting a longitudinal slice in the tree and allowing the exudation to drip into containers. The liquid resin is then distilled to remove the turpentine, and the residue forms what is known as **gum rosin,** or **pine gum. Wood rosin** is obtained by distillation of old pine stumps. It is darker than gum rosin, and is inferior for general use.

Rosin contains seven acids with very similar characteristics, but consists chiefly of **abietic acid,** $C_{19}H_{29}COOH$. Normally, when gum rosin is heated, the natural **pimaric acid** isomerizes to form abietic acid, but in the production of turpentine and rosin from pine sap, the turpentine is removed by steam distillation, and various acids are then extracted. Pimaric acid is closely related to abietic acid. It reacts with maleic anhydride, and the **maleo pimaric acid** is used in printing inks and coatings. Rosin has a specific gravity of about 1.08, a melting point of about 82°C, and it is soluble in alcohol, turpentine, and alkalies. It is used in varnishes, paint driers, soluble oils, paper sizing, and belt dressings; for compounding with rubber and other resins; and for producing many chemicals.

Rosin is generally graded commercially by letters according to color. The darkest grade is B, and the lightest is W. Extra grades are A, nearly black, and WW, water white. Thirteen color grades are designated under the Naval Stores Act. The dark grades of wood rosin are considered inferior. They have high melting point and low acid number and are used for making rosin oil, for battery wax, thermoplastics, dark varnish, and for linoleum manufacture. The ruby-red wood rosin, obtained by extraction from fat pine wood, has high acid number, 155, and low melting point, 175°F. It is used for printing inks, paper size, and adhesives. Rosin is usually marketed in barrels of 280 lb. **Naval stores** is an old name for rosin and turpentine. **Pelletized rosin** consists of free-flowing dustless pellets produced by coating droplets of molten rosin with inert powder. **Colophony** is an old pharmacy name for rosin before distillation of rosin oil. Rosin was referred to by early writers as **Greek pitch,** but the ancient incendiary known as **Greek fire** was tow or pine sawdust impregnated with rosin, pitch, and sulfur. **Burgundy pitch** was originally the resin of the Norway spruce, *Picea abies,* used in medicine, but the name was later applied to a rosin, rubber, and mineral oil compound used for friction tape.

Hardened rosin is a weak resinate made by adding 6 to 8% high-calcium lime to melted rosin. It is used in some varnishes. **Fosfo rosin,** of Newport Industries, Inc., is a **lime-hardened rosin.** It is an FF rosin treated with 4.75% calcium hydrate, which raises the melting point, decreases the free rosin acids, and decreases the tendency to crystallize. It is used in paints, varnishes, and molded products. **Soda-treated rosins,** with about 1% Na_2O, but no free alkali, are used for soap, paper size, and disinfectants. **Rosin size** is alkali-treated rosin in dry powder or emulsion forms for sizing paper. **Dresinite** is such a sodium or potassium salt of rosin. **Cyfor,** of the American Cyanamid Co., is a rosin size fortified with a synthetic resin to give increased water and acid resistance to paper. **Rosin ester,** or **ester gum,** is prepared by heating rosin with glycerin. It is lighter in color than rosin, has a higher softening point, and has a much lower acid number, usually 7 to 9. It is used with tung oil in enamels and varnishes and in adhesives. **Resin V,** of the Advance Solvents & Chemical Corp., is a rosin glycerin ester gum. Rosin esterified with glycerin has lower molecular weight, and is not as stable as rosin esterified with pentaerythritol or other tetrahydric alcohol, but modified rosin ester gums develop hardness quickly in nitrocellulose and are used for such purposes as furniture lacquers. **Cellolyn 102,** of the Hercules Co., is a modified ester gum of this type, and **Lewisol 28** is a maleic alkyd modified rosin ester used for hard, glossy furniture lacquers. **Hydroabietyl alcohol,** used as a plasticizer and tackifier for rubber and for sizing textiles, is a colorless, tacky liquid made by reduction of rosin. The 85% alcohol has a specific gravity of 1.008 and a flash point of 187°C. It is also used for making rosin esters. **Abitol,** of Hercules, is this material. **Abalyn** is a methyl ester of abietic acid, **methyl abietate,** made by treating rosin with methyl alcohol. It is a liquid rosin used as a plasticizer.

Hydrogenated rosin has greater resistance to oxidation than common rosin, has less odor and taste, and has a pale color that is more stable to light. It is used in protective coatings, in paper size, in adhesives, in soaps, and as a tackifier and plasticizer in rubber. Because of its saturated nature it cannot be used for rosin-modified plastics. The average acid number is 162, saponification value 167, and softening point 157°F. **Stabelite resin,** of Hercules, may be glycerol ester or ethylene glycol ester of hydrogenated rosin. **Vinsol resin** is a hard, high-melting, dark resin produced from the distillation of wood, or is the black residue left after rosin is extracted with petroleum solvents. It is soluble in alcohols, has a melting point of 115°C, and is used for insulating varnishes where light color is not essential, and for compounding in thermoplastics. **Hercolyn** is Abalyn hydrogenated to saturate the double bonds with hydrogen. **Flexalyn,** of the same company, is a pale-colored, very tacky, semisolid resin produced by the esterification of rosin acids with diethylene glycol, and has a complex chemical structure. It is used in adhesives to give added tack and strength. The **Pentalyn resins** of Hercules are pentaerythritol esters. The **Pentalyn M** is a phenol-formaldehyde-modified pentaerythritol ester; it has a melting point of 165°C, and when used in linseed oil varnishes gives a tough coating.

Rosin is hardened by polymerization to form a dipolymer of abietic acid. The product is then pale in color, and has a lower acid number and a higher melting point than rosin. **Poly-pale resin,** of Hercules, is a polymerized rosin with melting point of 208 to 217°F, acid number 152 to 156, and saponification value 157 to 160. It can be substituted for natural copals in paints, and in gloss oil it gives water resistance and high viscosity. In the making of metallic resinates it gives higher melting points, higher viscosity, and better solubility than natural rosin. Another modified rosin of this company is **Dymerex resin.** It consists chiefly of dimeric rosin acids, is highly soluble, is resistant to oxidation, and has a high softening point at 282°F. It is used in synthetic resins and protective coatings. **Rosin amine D,** of the same company, is a primary amine made from rosin. It is a yellow viscous liquid that wets glass and siliceous materials. It is soluble in most organic solvents, and emulsifies in water. It is used in cutback asphalts, in road asphalts, in asphalt cements, in ceramic inks, in foundry core binders, and in paper pulp to improve adhesion of resins. **Nuroz** is a polymerized rosin of Newport Industries, Inc., with a melting point of 76°C and acid value 161. It has high resistance to oxidation, and is used in varnishes and soaps.

Rosin oil is an oil produced by the dry distillation of rosin at a temperature of 200 to 360°C There are two qualities of the oil: a light spirit, **pinolin,** which forms from 1 to 5% of the rosin, and a bluish, heavy oil, which forms 80 to 84%. It contains abietic acid and has an acid value of about 28. The commercial oil has a specific gravity of 1.020 with a flash point 160 to 170°C. The refined oil is a yellow liquid with a pleasant odor and is used for blending with turpentine. It is also employed as a plasticizer in rubber, as a tack producer in rubber cements, and in synthetic molding resins. When treated with lime, it may be used to mix with lubricating oils. The light distillate is used sometimes in pharmacy under the name of **oil of amber.** Blended rosin oil is a mixture with mineral oils.

ROUGE. A hydrated iron oxide used for polishing metals and in break-in lubricants for aluminum bronze bearings. It has a hardness of 5.5 to 6.5, and is made by calcining ferrous sulfate and driving off the sulfur. The color is varying shades of red; the darker the color, the harder the rouge. The grains are rounded, unlike the grains of crocus. The pale-red rouge is used for finishing operations; the other grades are used for various polishing of metal surfaces. **Stick rouge** is made of finely crushed powder. Although the word rouge means red, materials of other colors are used for buffing and are called rouge. **Black rouge,** also called **Glassite,** is magnetic iron oxide made by precipitating ferrous sulfate with caustic soda. It is used for buffing but is not popular because it stains the skin. **Green chrome rouge** is **chromium oxide,** CrO, made by the strong heating of chromic hydroxide. It is used for buffing stainless steels. When used as a paint pigment, it is called **Guignet's green.** **Satin rouge** is a name applied to lampblack when used as a polishing medium in the form of brick for polishing silverware. **Crocus** is a name applied to mineral powders of a deep-yellow, brown, or red color made into cakes with grease for polishing. **Polishing crocus** is usually red ferric oxide. **Crocus cloth** is a fabric coated with red iron oxide marketed in sheets and used for polishing metals.

RUBBER. A gum resin exudation of a wide variety of trees and plants, but especially of the tree *Hevea brasiliensis* and several other species of *Hevea* growing in all tropical countries and cultivated on plantations in southern Asia, Indonesia, Ceylon, Congo, and Liberia. The International Rubber Regulation Committee figured costs and allocations on a basis of a rubber yield of 400 lb per acre per year, but yields up to 1,200 lb are not uncommon on estate plantations in Malaya, and 1,000 lb per acre is the average taken for comparison costs with synthetic rubbers, with a requirement of 25,000 tappers and 5,500 other estate workers for

100,000 acres.   To produce the best-yielding trees three species may be grafted together.   One species that is a strong producer of roots is used for the seeding; a second high-yielding species for the latex trunk; and a third species resistant to leaf disease for the foliage.   The *H. rigidifolia,* native to Brazil, is a tree resistant to leaf-spot disease, but yields little rubber.

The gum resin was formerly referred to as **India rubber,** and the name given it by Charles Goodyear was **gum elastic.**   The first highly compounded rubber for insulation, developed in 1867, was called **Kerite.** Brazilian rubber is sometimes called **Pará rubber.**   **Caoutchouc** was an early name for the crude rubber then cured over a fire into a dark, solid mass for shipment.   **Castilla rubber,** or **castilloa,** is from the large tree *Castilla elastica,* and was the original rubber of the Carib and Mayan Indians, but was cultivated only in Mexico and in Panama where it was called **Panama rubber.**   The latex and rubber are identical with **hevea rubber** after purification.   **Euphorbia rubber** is from vines of the genus *Euphorbia,* of which there are 120 species in tropical Africa.   Much **mangabeira rubber** was formerly produced in the Amazon Valley.   It is the latex of the mangabeira tree, which comprises various species of the genus *Hancoria* and yields the edible fruit **mangaba.**   The latex is coagulated with alum or sodium chloride, but the native Indians coagulated it with the latex of the **caxiguba** tree, *Ficus anthelmintica,* giving a better rubber.   The rubber is softer than hevea rubber, but ages better.   The low-grade **Assam rubber** is from a species of **ficus tree,** *F. elastica,* of India and Malaya.   **Ceara rubber** comes from the small, rapid-growing tree, *Manihot glaziovii,* native to the semidesert regions of Brazil but now grown in India and Ceylon.   The rubber is of good grade.

In the United States the largest tonnage of natural rubber has gone into the manufacture of tires and hose, but there are innumerable other applications for molded goods, elastic products, textile coatings, and adhesives. The outstanding characteristic of natural rubber is its elasticity, but natural rubber is softened by oils and is not highly resistant to chemicals, oxidation, and weathering, so that more resistant synthetic rubbers are now used for gasketing, packing, cushioning, and coating, even when a sacrifice in resiliency is necessary.   Thus, except for highly resilient products such as elastic bands, natural rubber has become largely a blending rather than a primary material.

Rubber latex is a colloidal emulsion of the gathered sap, containing about 35% of rubber solids, blended from various sources to give average uniformity.   The latex is coagulated with acid and milled into ribbed sheets called **crepe rubber,** or into sheets exposed to wood smoke to kill bacteria and called **smoked sheet rubber.**   These sheets constitute the commercial **crude rubber,** although much rubber latex is used directly, especially for dipped goods such as gloves, toys, and balloons, for coatings, and for making foam rubber. Rubber has the property of being vulcanized with sulfur and heat, removing the tackiness and making it harder and more elastic in the low-sulfur compounds. All natural rubber except adhesive rubbers is thus vulcanized rubber. Ordinary **soft rubber** contains only 3 to 6% sulfur, but usually also contains softeners, fillers, antioxidants, or other compounding agents, giving varying degrees of elasticity, strength, and other qualities. When as much as 30% sulfur is added the product is called **hard rubber. Vapor-cured rubber** is rubber vulcanized by sulfur chloride fumes and neutralized with magnesium carbonate. It is used for thin goods only. **Acid-cured rubber** is rubber cured in a bath of sulfur chloride in a solvent.

The tensile strength of rubber of low vulcanization is 800 to 1,200 psi of the original cross section. A good soft rubber can be stretched as much as 1,000% without rupture, and will return to close to the original length with little permanent set. The specific gravity is about 1.05, but with fillers may be as high as 1.30. When the term **vulcanized rubber** is now used it generally refers to hard rubber vulcanized to a rigid but resilient solid, used for electrical parts and tool handles. **Ace hard rubber,** of the American Hard Rubber Co., has a specific gravity of 1.27, a tensile strength of 8,700 psi, dielectric strength of 485 volts per mil, distortion temperature 172°F, and water absorption 0.04%. **Vulcanite** and **Ebonite** are old names for hard rubber. **Reclaimed rubber** is produced largely from old tires and factory scrap. It is usually lower in cost than new rubber, but it is easier to process and is employed in large quantities even when the price is higher. It is sold in sheets, slabs, pellets, and powder, but much of the **rubber powder,** or **granulated rubber,** used for adhesives and molding, is not reclaimed rubber but is made by spray-drying latex. **Vultex** is a natural rubber powder in paste form for coatings and adhesives. **Mealorub** is a rubber powder developed by the Indonesian Rubber Research Institute for mixing with asphalt for road surfacing.

Rubber contains **isoprene,** C_5H_8, which is the building unit of balata, gutta percha, and many other rubberlike materials. Natural rubber contains as many as 4,500 isoprene groups and may have a molecular weight as high as 300,000. It is, therefore, a **polyisoprene,** and the vulcanization with sulfur introduces relatively few chemical bonds between the polyisoprene molecules. Rubber is a strong network of molecular chains that are not easily packed together or frozen into crystals by attraction on each other. The elastic property is like that of a gas, the pull on a piece of rubber stretching the molecular chains. The molecular formation of rubber more closely resembles that of the synthetic resins than of the natural resins.

For the rubber used in making automobile tires large percentages of carbon black and zinc oxide are used to reinforce it and give added wearing qualities. Rosin and other resins and gums impart softness to rubber compounds. Carbon black gives wear resistance. Zinc oxide is an accelerator as well as a filler and strengthener. Litharge, lime, and magnesia stiffen rubber and speed up vulcanization. Calcium carbonate increases strength and tear resistance. **Red rubber** is now simply rubber colored red, but was originally rubber vulcanized with antimony pentasulfide which broke down with the heat of vulcanization, yielding sulfur to the rubber and coloring it red with the residual antimony trisulfide. Many trade-named accelerators, fillers, and stiffeners are marketed for rubber compounding. Rubber accelerators may be organic chemicals, usually containing reactive sulfur. **Captax** is such an accelerator, and is **mercapto benzothiazole,** a five-membered ring compound made from aniline, formaldehyde, and sulfur. Chemicals are also added to prevent scorching in fast cures. **Retarder TCM-25,** of Binney & Smith, Inc., consists of 25% trichloro melamine and 75% blanc fixe. **Trimene,** of U.S. Rubber, to aid the cure and add strength, is an aldehyde amine with stearic acid. **Anticrystallizing rubber,** developed by the Natural Rubber Bureau, is made by adding butadiene sulfone which breaks down under heat to release SO_2 gas and modifies the molecular structure. The rubber does not stiffen and lose its elasticity at low temperatures.

The isoprene of rubber is made synthetically by reacting isobutylene with formaldehyde and then dehydrating, or it can be produced from propylene, isopentane, or other materials. The isoprene is then polymerized to produce **isoprene rubber,** called **synthetic-natural rubber** or marketed under trade names. **Natsyn 400,** of the Goodyear Tire & Rubber Co., is a polyisoprene with the formula $[CH_2(CH_3)C:C(H)CH_2]_x$, which, because of its purity and uniformity, is superior in qualities to natural rubber. The **Deuterio rubber** of Goodrich-Gulf has heavy hydrogen, or deuterium, attached to the molecular chains instead of ordinary hydrogen atoms. Deuterium atoms have less attraction for each other than hydrogen atoms, and the rubber is more elastic.

The so-called **synthetic rubbers** are not rubbers, and are generally rubber-like only in the degree of elasticity. In the chemical industry they are called **elastomers.** The flexibility, or ability to recover after stretching, may be in the monomer molecule, as in natural rubber, or in the linkage of the polymer, or both. The C-C, C-O, and C-N linkages produce flexible polymers. Cl, O, and N linkages increase rigidity but improve resistance to chemicals. **Stereo rubbers** are synthetic rubbers chemically balanced for specific purposes. Ethylene and propylene polymerize separately to form definite plastics, but the two together copolymerize to form a rubber-like elastomer. Some other chemicals, such as butadiene or **cyclopenta-**

diene, C_5H_6, polymerize as isoprene does to produce rubberlike products, and the molecular chain may also be capable of side reactions or of attaching carbon or sulfur like polyisoprene. Butadiene is polymerized to form polybutadiene. The **Budene** synthetic rubber of Goodyear is **polybutadiene.** It has a resilience close to that of natural rubber and has higher physical qualities. In a 50–50 blend with styrene-butadiene rubber it gives higher abrasion resistance, better flexing, and better aging resistance than an SBR blend with natural rubber.

The original synthetic rubber was produced in Germany from butane gas by conversion to butadiene and then reacted with styrene to form **butadiene-styrene rubber** which was named **Buna S rubber.** Another type, called **Buna N rubber,** or **nitrile rubber,** was made by reacting butadiene with a nitrile. The original buna-type rubber made in the United States during the Second World War was called **GRS rubber,** meaning **government rubber S.** It contained 76.5% butadiene and 23.5 styrene. It still retains the name, and is also called **SBR rubber,** but because of changes in composition, improved polymerization, and improved methods of processing and compounding, it is a greatly changed rubber with higher physical properties. **GRS hard rubber** has higher strength and hardness than natural hard rubber, but it is not as tough and is subject to chipping, but **Buna N hard rubber** more nearly resembles natural hard rubber and is more chemical-resistant. **Tempron hard rubber** of the American Hard Rubber Co. is made from Buna N rubber. It is rigid to 225°F, has a tensile strength of 8,500 psi, flexural strength of 13,000 psi, elongation 4%, Shore hardness D85, dielectric strength 450 volts per mil, and high moisture and chemical resistance.

Cold rubber is GRS rubber polymerized at 41°F or lower, instead of at the usual 122°F, and with chemicals to accelerate the cold reaction. The rubber is easy to process, has higher elongation, and has increased crack and abrasion resistance. In tires it does not have heat buildup as ordinary GRS rubber does. **Philprene,** of the Phillips Petroleum Co., is a cold rubber with 24% styrene. High-styrene rubbers are light in color and tough. They are used for coatings or for compounding in leather substitutes. **Pliolite S-3,** of Goodyear, for coatings, is a butadiene-styrene copolymer with 85% styrene. It is thermoplastic, and is compatible with natural and synthetic rubbers. **Pliolite latex 190** is a water dispersion of the high-styrene rubber for coating compounds. The **Goodrite resin 50,** of B. F. Goodrich, is also a high-styrene rubber in powder form for compounding with natural or synthetic rubbers to increase hardness and impact strength, improve the workability, and improve electrical properties. **Nitrex,** of the U.S. Rubber Co., is a butadiene-acrylonitrile latex for coating paper and textiles. It is thermoplastic and heat-sealing. The **Kralastic resins** of this company are terpolymers of butadiene, styrene, and acrylonitrile.   They have high impact strength and good chemical resistance.   In the form of pipes and fittings, the material is called **Uscolite.**   The pipes can be used to temperatures up to 170°F.   **Polyco XP24-97,** of the Borden Chemical Co., is an SBR latex made with a metal catalyst which cross-links the molecule to give a hard, tough coating as a baked finish.   **Plioflex 1510,** of Goodyear, is an SBR rubber with a tensile strength of 4,000 psi and elongation of 480%.

Crumb rubber, is any rubber in the form of porous particles that can be dissolved easily without milling, cutting, or pelletizing.   It is used in adhesives and plastics.   **Amerpol 453,** of Goodrich-Gulf Chemicals, Inc., is this form of styrene-butadiene-divinyl-benzene produced by a hot rosin acid soap emulsion process.   The cross-linked terpolymer makes a high viscosity tacky product suitable for pressure-sensitive tapes and for cements.

Oil-extended rubber is a synthetic rubber into which from 25 to 50% of an emulsion of petroleum oil has been incorporated to decrease cost and increase the low-temperature flexibility and the resilience.   **Alfin rubber,** of Goodyear, is a cold rubber in which the polymerization has been carried out in a pentane solvent and the oil added before evaporation of the solvent.   **Rosin-extended rubber** is cold rubber containing up to 50% rosin. The rosin plasticizes the long polymer chains in high-molecular-weight GRS rubber, making a softer, more easily worked rubber of higher strength.   **Diene rubber,** of Firestone, is a butadiene rubber made with a lithium catalyst.   Its polymer structure resembles that of natural rubber. **EPR rubber,** of U.S. Rubber, is an ethylene-propylene copolymer.   Its resilience and rebound characteristics are nearly equal to those of natural rubber, and it has higher chemical and aging properties.   This type of rubber was originally produced in Italy and called **Dutral rubber.**   It is light in weight, with a specific gravity of 0.87.   It is easily cured with peroxides, but is not oil-extendable.   The copolymer with 70% ethylene has a molecular weight of 360,000.   **Royalene,** of the same company, is a terpolymer of ethylene-propylene and a diene.   It has high resistance to ozone and is used for cable coverings.   **Rubber MD-551,** of the Enjay Co., Inc., used for hose, gaskets, and collapsible containers, is a chlorinated butyl rubber made with chlorinated isobutylene polymerized with an olefin. It has a molecular weight of 450,000 and a tensile strength of 2,400 psi with elongation of 300%.   It is impermeable, with good chemical and aging resistance, and higher heat resistance than ordinary rubber.   **Butyl rubber HT** of the same company is a chlorinated butyl rubber used for high-temperature paints.   **Hycar 2202,** of B. F. Goodrich, is a bromated butyl rubber with high heat and ozone resistance, and high adhesive qualities.   For tubeless tires it has high air-holding properties.   **Neoprene RT,** of Du Pont, is produced from chlorinated butadiene and styrene.   It has better cold resistance than regular Neoprene.

Ordinary **butyl rubber** is a copolymer of isobutylene and butadiene, the resulting product containing up to 3% isoprene. It has a low unsaturation, making it more resistant to heat and oxidation than most synthetics, and it retains air pressure in inner tubes better than natural rubber. This rubber was called **Ameripol** by B. F. Goodrich. The German **Oppanol,** developed further as **Vistanex** by Standard Oil, is a polymer of isobutadiene. It is not elastic like rubber, but when compounded with natural rubber gives higher heat and wear resistance and greater resistance to oils and chemicals for such products as insulation, packings, and hose. **S polymer,** of Standard Oil, and **Parasol S,** of the Enjay Co., Inc., are copolymers of isobutylene and styrene. The material is odorless and nontoxic, heat-seals above 45°C, and is used for coating paper for liquid containers.

Chloroprene, a colorless liquid, $CH_2:CHCCl:CH_2$, produced from acetylene or butadiene can be polymerized to form a wide variety of products from soft rubberlike plastics to hard, horny, inelastic, and insoluble polymers. The polymerization can be controlled to yield rubberlike materials with some characteristics superior to natural rubber. **Neoprene,** originally called **Duprene,** of Du Pont, is a **chloroprene rubber** in various grades. It is less elastic than rubber, but is highly chemical-resistant, and is more heat- and light-resistant. The specific gravity is from 1.25 to 1.8, and the tensile strength is from 200 to 4,000 psi, depending on the polymer and the compounding. This material is called **Sovprene** in Russia. **Mustone** is a Japanese chloroprene rubber. Chloroprene rubbers are more costly than the SBR rubbers, but because of their high physical and chemical qualities they have a wide use for hose, tank linings, and molded parts. The German **methyl rubber** is made with methyl chloroprene.

The rubber known as **GRN rubber** is **nitrile rubber,** a copolymer of acrylonitrile and butadiene. **Hycar OR,** of B. F. Goodrich, is a nitrile rubber used for tank linings and for blending with vinyl and phenolic resins to give added toughness and resiliency to molded parts. **Nitrex 2614,** of U.S. Rubber, is a nitrile latex of 40% solids which cures at low temperature with zinc oxide. It gives coatings that are odorless, adherent, with resiliency and chemical resistance. **Royalite,** of the same company, originally called **Versalite,** is an interpolymer of butadiene-acrylonitrile and styrene-acrylonitrile. It is thermoplastic, with tensile strength of 4,800 psi, elongation 30%, and is chemical-resistant. It is made in smooth, grained, or patterned sheets for molding into such articles as luggage and cabinets. **Nysin,** of Goodyear, is a nitrile rubber with a controlled distribution of acrylonitrile to give uniformity.

The **polysulfide rubbers** form an important class of resilient, chemically resistant plastics which are used for molded products, wire covering, and coatings, and can be vulcanized like rubber. The Thiokol rubbers of the Thiokol Chemical Corp., noted for good resistance to oils, gasoline, and solvents, are polysulfides.   **Thiokol A** is made by the reaction of sodium tetrasulfide and ethylene dichloride.   **Thiokol ST** is a general-purpose synthetic gum elastomer which can be blended with other synthetic rubbers for a wide range of uses.   It is made by the reaction of sodium thiosulfide and **formal,** produced from ethylene and formaldehyde.   The gum is a light-brown millable rubber with elongation up to 265%.   With a filler of carbon black the cured rubber may have an elongation of 600%.   **Thiokol 411** is used for spraying on masonry to produce a water-impermeable coating. **Resenit** is a Russian polysulfide, and **Vulcaplas** is a similar English rubber. As with synthetic resins, the number of possible varieties of synthetic rubbers is almost unlimited, and the trade-named products are normally marketed by their use characteristics rather than by chemical composition. A group of polymers with rubberlike properties is produced from trimeric **phospho nitrilic chloride,** $(PCl_2)_3N_3$, which has a ring structure with phosphorus and nitrogen alternating and with two chlorine atoms attached to each phosphorus.   The material polymerizes at about 350°C into rubberlike plastics, or it can be used for the production of copolymers.   **Vulkollon** is a German series of rubbers produced by the reaction of diisocyanates with glycol and other polyoxy compounds.   They have high strength, but have less chemical resistance than buna rubber.   **Adiprene B,** of Du Pont, is a urethane rubber which is resilient at low temperatures.   This type of rubber is usually classed with the plastics.   Some polyacrylates, such as **Hycar PA,** are used for hose, belting, and insulation, and are often referred to as rubbers, although generally considered as plastic resins. Synthetic rubbers may also be compounded with synthetic resins.   **Enrup,** of U.S. Rubber, is a high-styrene-butadiene rubber with a phenolic resin, giving a product with high strength, toughness, and chemical resistance for coatings, insulation, and chemical parts.

Some elastomers with rubberlike properties are made from polyesters of dibasic acids.   **Norepol rubber,** developed by the U.S. Department of Agriculture, is made by the polymerization of linoleic acid from soybean and other oils, while **Agripol** is made from soybean acids polymerized with ethylene glycol.   **Fluoro rubbers** are made from perfluoro butyric acid esters polymerized with acrylic acid or with butadiene.   They have high resistance to oils and solvents.   **Viton B,** of Du Pont, has high resistance to solvents and to hydraulic fluids.   It is a copolymer of perfluoro propylene and vinylidene.   It has a tensile strength of 3,000 psi with elongation of 400% and Shore hardness up to A95.   It retains its properties for long periods at 450°F.   **Magnetic rubbers,** produced in sheets and strips of various magnetic strengths, are made of synthetic rubbers compounded with magnetic metal powders.

RUBIDIUM. A rare metallic element, symbol Rb, atomic weight 85.45, belonging to the group of alkali metals. The chief occurrence of rubidium is in the mineral lepidolite. There is no real rubidium ore, but the element is widely disseminated over the earth in tiny quantities. It is a necessary element in plant and animal life, and is found in tea, coffee, tobacco, and other plants. It is a silvery-white metal, with a specific gravity of 1.53, melting point of 38.5°C, and boiling at 696°C. It takes fire easily in the air, and decomposes water. Of all the alkali metals it is next to cesium in highest chemical activity. It can be obtained by electrolysis, but has few industrial applications owing to its rarity. Its chief use is in electronics. For photoelectric cells it is preferred to cesium, and a very thin film is effective. Like potassium, it has a weak radioactivity by the emission of beta particles, the beta emission being only about one-thousandth that of an equal weight of uranium.

RUBY. A red variety of the mineral corundum which ranks with the best grades of precious stones as a gemstone, while the off-color stones are used for watch and instrument bearings. Most of the best rubies come from Upper Burma, Thailand, and Cambodia, but the center of natural-ruby cutting is near Bombay. Some deep-red rubies are found in East Africa, and they also occur in western North Carolina. The carmine-red, or pigeon's-blood, stones are the most highly prized, and, before the advent of the synthetic ruby, the larger stones were more valuable than the diamond. The pink-to-deep-red colors of the ruby are due to varying percentages of chromic oxide. **Star rubies** contain also a small amount of titania which precipitates along crystallographic planes of the hexagonal crystal, and shows as a movable six-ray star when the gem is cut with the axis normal to the base of the stone. **Spinel ruby** is not corundum but magnesium aluminate and is a spinel, often occurring in the same deposits.

Synthetic rubies are equal in all technical qualities to the natural, and synthetic star rubies surpass the natural stones in perfection and quality. Most of the ruby used for instrument bearings is synthetic corundum colored with chromic oxide, since the instrument makers prefer the red color, but the name ruby is often applied regardless of color. The American practice in bearing manufacture is to start with a cylindrical rod of the diameter of the desired bearing and to slice to the required thickness. The single crystal rods are flame-polished. For industrial uses the name ruby is often applied to the synthetic material even when it is not red in color. Synthetic rubies with 0.05% chromium are also used for **lasers,** or light amplifiers, to produce high-intensity light pulses in a narrow beam for communications. Lasers have a wide range of uses, and various other materials are used for specific purposes. Crystals of **potassium dihydrogen**

phosphate are used to control the direction of narrow beams of light. The crystal is mounted on the face of the cathode ray tube. Platelets of zinc oxide with a phosphor, when activated at 15,000 to 20,000 volts by a pulsated electron stream, give a beam of pure ultraviolet light at 3750 angstroms for use in chemical synthesis.

Rubies are also used in **masers** to detect radio signals for space rockets at great distances. The word maser means microwave application by stimulated emission of radiation. Ruby has the same physical and chemical properties as the sapphire and corundum. But the color inclusions do affect the electronic properties. The **ruby-sapphire crystals** produced by Linde for **optical masers** are grown with a core of ruby and an overlay sheath of sapphire. The ruby core containing 0.05% chromic oxide emits a beam of extremely high frequency, 4.2×10^{14} cycles, for sending messages. The sapphire has a high refractive index, 1.76, and when the sheath is surrounded by a helical xenon arc, the light from the arc excites the chromium atoms in the ruby to emit a concentrated beam of parallel rays from one end.

The cutting of rubies, sapphires, and other hard crystals into tiny shaped bearings was formerly a specialized hand industry, and large stocks of cut stones were kept in the National Stockpile for wartime emergencies. But the slicing and shaping of hard crystals is now widely dispersed on a production basis to meet the needs of the electronic industries, and the equipment is regularly manufactured. For example, the **Accu-Cut wheels** of Aremco Products, for slicing and notching crystals and hard electronic ceramics, are metal disks 0.010 to 0.030 in. thick and 1 to 4 in. in diameter, with diamond grit metallurgically bonded to the periphery.

RUTHENIUM. A hard, silvery-white metal, having a specific gravity of 12.2, a melting point of 2450°C, and a Brinell hardness of 220 in the annealed state. The metal is obtained from the residue of platinum ores by heat reduction of **ruthenium oxide,** RuO_2, in hydrogen. Ruthenium is the most chemically resistant of the platinum metals, and is not dissolved by aqua regia. It is used as a catalyst to combine nitrogen in chemicals. As **ruthenium tetroxide,** RuO_4, it is a powerful catalyst for organic synthesis, oxidizing alcohols to acids, ethers to esters, and amides to imides. Ruthenium has a hexagonal lattice structure. It has a hardening effect on platinum, 5% addition of ruthenium raising the Brinell hardness from 30 to 130, and the electrical resistivity to double that of pure platinum. **Ruthenium-platinum alloys** are used for electrical contacts, electronic wires, chemical equipment, and jewelry. The alloy with 5% ruthenium has a tensile strength, annealed, of 60,000 psi with elongation of 34% and Brinell hardness of 130. The hard metal has a hardness of Brinell 210. The alloy with 10% ruthenium has a tensile strength of 85,000 psi, and a hardness of Brinell 190 in the soft condition and Brinell 280 when hard-drawn.

RYE. The seed of the plant *Secale cereale* used as a food grain, but in the United States and Great Britain it is valued chiefly for the production of whisky and alcohol and for feeding animals.   Only 4% of the world production is in the United States.   The grain looks like wheat, and the stalks of the plant are slender and tough, growing to a height of up to 6 ft. But flour made from the grain produces bread that is dark in color, bitter, and soggy.   When used for flour in the United States, it is mixed with wheat and other flours.   The plant has the advantage that it will grow on poor soil, in arid regions, at high altitudes, and in regions of severe winter. It is thus a grain of poor agricultural countries, and has been called the **grain of poverty.   Rye straw** is the dried and sunbleached stalks of the plant.   It is very tough and resilient, and is the most valued of all the commercial **straw** derived from grains.   It is used for packing, bedding, and for the manufacture of strawboard.

SAGO FLOUR. A starch extracted from the pith of the sago palm, *Metroxylon sagu,* of Indonesia and Malaya, and also from the aren palm. Sago is valued industrially for sizing and filling textiles because, like tapioca, it holds mineral fillers better than other starches.   It gives a tougher and more flexible feel than tapioca, but its tan color limits its use. From 600 to 800 lb of crude sago is obtained from a tree, which is destroyed in the process.   **Pearl sago,** used for food, is the same material made into dough and forced through a sieve.   The aren palm, or **sugar palm,** is the species which yields arenga fiber.   It contains only 20% as much sago as the sago palm, but a juice, called **taewak,** is produced from the cut flower stems and is used to make **palm wine,** or **arak.**   The juice is also boiled down to produce a brown **palm sugar** used for sweetening.

SALMON OIL. A pale-yellow oil obtained as a by-produce in the salmon-canning industry, and employed as a drying oil for finishes and also used in soaps.   There are different classes of the oil, depending upon the type of salmon.   The oil contains an average of 23.5% **arachidonic acid,** $C_{19}H_{31}COOH$, 16.2% clupanodonic, 11.5 linoleic, 17.1 oleic, 15 palmitic, 10.6 **palmitoleic acid,** $C_{15}H_{29}COOH$, 4 myristic, and 2 stearic. The specific gravity is 0.926.   It has a high iodine number, up to 160, but does not form an elastic skin on drying, and is not a good varnish oil untreated.   It is, however, a valuable source of fatty acids for paint-oil blends and for plastics.   The salmon is a valuable food fish and is extensively canned.   There are five commercial species of North Pacific salmon of the genus *Oncorhynchus;* the **steelhead trout,** or **salmon trout,** *Salmo gaird-*

neri, is of the Atlantic.   The **Atlantic salmon,** caught off Newfoundland, is *S. salar.*   The **red salmon,** or **sockeye salmon,** is *O. nerka;* the **pink salmon** is *O. gorbuscha;* and the **Chinook,** or **king salmon,** is *O. tschawytscha.*   The catch is in the rivers on both sides of the Alaska peninsula and in the Columbia River where the fish enter the rivers to spawn. **Australian salmon,** which is the chief fish canned in Australia, is of a different genus, *Arripis trutta.*

SALT. The common name for **sodium chloride,** known in mineralogy as **halite** but chemically a salt; it is any compound derived from an acid by replacing the hydrogen atoms of the acid with the atoms of a metal.   **Common salt,** or sodium chloride, is widely used as a preservative, for flavoring foods, in freezing mixtures, for salt-brine quenching baths, and for the manufacture of soda ash and many chemicals.   Common salt has such a variety of uses that its curve of consumption practically parallels the curve of industrial expansion.   It is a stable compound of the composition NaCl, containing theoretically 60.6% chlorine, but it usually contains impurities such as calcium sulfate and calcium and magnesium chlorides.   The hardness of salt is 2.5, specific gravity 2.1 to 2.6, and melting point 1472°F. It is colorless to white, but when impure may have shades of yellow, red, or blue.   It occurs in crystalline granular masses with cubical cleavage, known as **rock salt,** or **mineral salt.**   Vast deposits of salt are found underground in Louisiana, and a large area of Kansas is underlain with a salt deposit reaching 800 ft in thickness.   The rock salt occurring in immense quantities on the island of Hormoz in the Persian Gulf contains 97.4% NaCl, 1.83 $CaCO_3$, and only very small amounts of magnesium chloride, iron oxide, and silica.   **Bay salt** is an old name for salt extracted from seawater, now known as **solar salt.**   Seawater also contains more than 20% of magnesium chloride and magnesium, calcium, and potassium sulfates, which are extracted to give a purity of at least 99% sodium chloride. A short ton of **seawater** contains about 55 lb of common salt.   But some **sea salt** containing all the original elements is marketed for corrosion tests. The **Sea-Rite salt** of the Lake Products Co. is a synthetic sea salt containing all the elements of natural sea salt except those of less than 0.0004%. From the salt wells of Michigan, magnesium, bromine, and other elements are extracted, and the salt brine is an important source of these elements.

Commercial salt is marketed in many grades, depending chiefly on the size of the grain.   The term **industrial salt** refers rather to the method of packing and shipping than to a grade distinct from **domestic salt,** but most of the industrial salt is rock salt; the bulk of the domestic salt is evaporated salt.   Producers of salt for the food-processing industries usually guarantee a quality 99.95% pure since small amounts of calcium, magnesium, copper, and iron in the salt may give a bitter taste, discolor some foods, or cause oxidation rancidity in foods containing fats.   **Crystal Flake salt,** of Diamond Salt, is 99.5% pure with less than 1.5 parts per million of copper or iron.   **Micronized salt,** of the same company, is 99.9% pure with thin flake particles of super fineness which have a solubility 5 times greater than granulated salt.   **Dendritic salt,** of Morton Salt, is highly purified salt evaporated by a process that produces tiny dendritic crystals instead of the regular cubic form.   It has a faster dissolving rate.   This company produces **Calacid salt,** a formulated salt in tablet form for regulating acidity in canned foods.   It contains 60.9% sodium chloride with citric acid, calcium sulfate dihydrate, and sodium carbonate for effervescence. **Sec 100,** of Diamond Salt, is a noncaking, free-flowing salt for use in automatic food-processing equipment.   It contains 5 ppm of prussiate of soda which blocks the interchemical action of the salt crystals without decreasing solubility, and 0.04% glycerin to increase the free-flowing properties.

Domestic consumption of salt for direct human consumption is large in all countries.   It is required in the blood stream up to about 3.5% and is rapidly exhausted in hot weather.   **Salt tablets,** used in hot weather, or by workers in steel mills, are made with about 70% salt and 30 dextrose. To make domestic salt free-flowing in humid weather, 2% of calcium sulfate may be added.   Salt obtained by simple evaporation of seawater contains salt-resistant bacteria which are capable of developing in salted hides or fish and injuring the material.   Mineral salt is thus preferred for these purposes.   The glasslike salt crystals, called **struvite,** that form in canned fish and some other products in storage, are not common salt, but are crystals of magnesium ammonium phosphite hexahydrate, $Mg(NH_4)PO_4 \cdot 6H_2O$. They are harmless, but objectional in appearance, and common salt is added to inhibit their growth.   In making **salt brines** for steel treating and other industrial purposes, 100 parts of water at ordinary temperature will dissolve 36 parts of common salt, but no more than 15% is ordinarily used because of the corrosive effect.

Sodium hypochlorite, or **sodium oxychlorite,** NaOCl, is a stable, noncorrosive salt used in tanneries.   **Merclor D** is a trade name of Monsanto for this material in water solution.   **Javel water** is a name given in the laundry industry to a water solution of sodium hypochlorite used as a bleach.   Sodium hypochlorite when used as a bleach in the textile industry is called **chemic.   Sodium chlorite,** $NaClO_2$, is a white to yellow crystalline water-soluble powder used as a bleaching agent for textiles and paper pulp.   It is stable up to 150°C.   It yields ClO_2 in the solution, is an oxidizing agent, and attacks the coloring matter without injuring the fibers. It is also used for waterworks purification.   **Textone** is a trade name for sodium chlorite as a bleach for textiles.   **Sodium chlorate,** $NaClO_3$, is used in large quantities as a weed killer and for cotton defoliation, and is also used for paper pulp and textile bleaching. It comes in water-soluble colorless crystals melting at 250°C. It is used as the electrolyte in the chemical machining of metals.

SAND. An accumulation of grains of mineral matter derived from the disintegration of rocks. It is distinguished from gravel only by the size of the grains or particles, but is distinct from clays which contain organic materials. Sands that have been sorted out and separated from the organic material by the action of currents of water or by winds across arid lands are generally quite uniform in the size of grains. Usually commercial sand is obtained from river beds, or from sand dunes originally formed by the action of winds. Much of the earth's surface is sandy, and these sands are usually quartz and other siliceous materials. The most useful commercially are **silica sands,** often above 98% pure. Silica sands for making glass must be free from iron. The sand mined near Hot Springs, Ark., called **amosil,** is 99.5% pure silica, and comes in transparent rounded grains of 3 microns average size. **Beach sands** usually have smooth spherical to ovaloid particles from the abrasive action of waves and tides and are free of organic matter. The white beach sands are largely silica but may also be of zircon, monazite, garnet, and other minerals, and are used for extracting various elements. **Monazite sand** is the chief source of thorium. The **black sands** of Oregon contain chromate, and those of Japan contain magnetite. Kyanite is found in the Florida sands.

Sand is used for making mortar and concrete and for polishing and sandblasting. Sands containing a little clay are used for making molds in foundries. Clear sands are employed for filtering water. Sand is sold by the cubic yard or ton but is always shipped by weight. The weight varies from 2,600 to 3,100 lb per cu yd, depending on the composition and size of grain. Construction sand is not shipped great distances, and the quality of sands used for this purpose varies according to local supply. **Standard sand** is a silica sand used in making concrete and cement tests. The grains are free of organic matter and will pass through a 20-mesh sieve, but will be retained on a 30-mesh. **Engine sand,** or **traction sand,** is a high-silica sand of 20 to 80 mesh washed free of soft bond and fine particles, used to prevent the driving wheels of locomotives or cars from slipping on wet rails.

Molding sand, or **foundry sand,** is any sand employed for making molds for casting metals, but especially refers to sands that are refractory and also have binding qualities. Pure silica is ideal for heat resistance, but must contain enough alumina to make it bind together. Molding sands may contain from 80 to 92% silica, up to about 15% alumina, about 2% iron oxide, and not more than a trace of lime. Some molding sand contains enough clay or loam to bond it when tamped into place. The amount of bond in **Grant sand** and in **Tuscarawa sand** is 17 to 18%. About 33% of these natural sands pass through a No. 100 screen, and 20 through a 150 screen. The finer the grain, the smoother the casting, but fine-grained sand is not suitable for heavy work because of its impermeability to the gases. Sands without natural bond are more refractory and are used for steel molding. Sands for steel casting must be silica sands containing 90% silica, or preferably 98%, and are mixed with 2 to 10% fireclay. For precision casting, finely ground aluminum silicate is used in the silica sand mixes, and it requires less bonding agent. **Calamo,** of the Harbison-Walker Refractories Co., is aluminum silicate for this purpose.

Zircon sand has high heat resistance, and is used for alloy steel casting. **Zircon flour** is finely milled zirconite sand used as a mold wash. **Zirconite sand** for molding is 100 to 200 mesh in its natural state. It is 70% heavier than silica sand, and has a higher heat conductivity that gives more rapid chilling of castings. The zirconite sands have melting points from 3650 to 3850°F. Common molding sands may contain from 5 to 18% of clay materials, and may be mixtures of sand, silt, and clay, but they must have the qualities of refractoriness, cohesiveness, fineness of grain, and permeability. To have refractory quality they must be free of calcium carbonate, iron oxide, and hydrocarbons. **Core sands** also have these qualities, but they are of coarser grain, and always require a bond that will bake solidly but will break down easily at the temperature of pouring. About 25% of a medium molding sand will be retained on a 150-mesh sieve, and about 10% on a 200-mesh sieve. Sand with rounded grains is preferred, and the grains must be very uniform in size to prevent filling. When a molding sand is burned out, it is made suitable for reuse by adding bond, but when fireclay is used as a bond, it adheres to the sand grains and makes it unsuitable for reuse. **Parting sand** is a round-grained sand without bond used on the joints of molds. **Foundry parting** is usually tripoli or bentonite. Cores are made with sand mixed with core oils. **Greensand cores** are unbaked cores made with molding sand.

Sandblast sand is sand employed in a blast of air for cleaning castings, removal of paint, cleaning of metal articles; for giving a dull rough finish to glass or metal goods; or for renovating the walls of stone or brick buildings. Sandblast sand is not closely graded, and the grades vary with different producers. The U.S. Bureau of Mines gives the following usual range: No. 1 sand should pass through a 20-mesh and be retained on a 48-mesh screen; No. 2 should pass through a 10-mesh and be retained on a 28-mesh screen; No. 3 through a 6-mesh and be retained on a 14-mesh; No. 4 through a 4-mesh and be retained on an 8-mesh screen. No. 1 sand is used for light work where a smooth finish is desired; No. 4 sand is employed for rough cast-iron and cast-steel work. Sharp grains cut faster, but rounded grains produce smoother surfaces. The sand is usually employed over and over, screening out the dust. The dust and fine used sand may be blasted wet. This is known as mud blasting and produces a dull finish.

SANDALWOOD. The heartwood of the evergreen tree *Santalum album* and other species of southern Asia. The heartwood is usually equivalent to about one-third of the log. It is sweet-scented and is used for chests, boxes, and small carved work. The chips and sawdust are used for incense and for oil production. **Sandalwood oil** is a yellowish essential oil of specific gravity 0.953 to 0.985, distilled from the wood, which yields 5 to 7% of the oil. It is used in medicine, perfumery, and soaps. West Indian sandalwood oil is called **anyris oil.** **Australian sandalwood** oil is from the tree *S. spicatum.* It has a very strong and lasting sandalwood odor. **Sandela,** of Givaudan-Delawanna, Inc., is a synthetic sandalwood oil. It is a polycyclic alcohol product with the odor and properties of the natural oil.

SANDARAC. Known also as **white gum,** or **Australian pine gum.** A white, brittle resin obtained as an exudation from various species of the coniferous tree *Callitris,* known as **Cyprus pine.** The North African sandarac is from the tree *C. quadrivalis* of the Atlas Mountains, and resembles the resin from the Australian tree *C. arenosa.* The trees in Morocco are tapped from May to June, and two months later the small tears of gum are gathered. Sandarac is used in varnishes and is soluble in turpentine and alcohol. It melts at 135 to 140°C. It gives a hard, white spirit varnish used for coating labels and for paper and leather finishes. Ground sandarac, under the name of **pounce,** was formerly used as a pouncing powder and for smoothing parchment and tracing cloth, but is now replaced by pumice.

SANDPAPER. Originally a heavy paper coated with sand grains on one side, used as an abrasive, especially for finishing wood. Sharp grains obtained by crushing quartz later replaced sand, and the product was called flint paper. But most abrasive papers are now made with aluminum oxide or silicon carbide, although the term sandpapering is still employed in wood polishing. Quartz grains, however, are still much used on papers for the wood industries. For this purpose the quartz grains are in grades from the 20 mesh, known as No. 3½, through No. 3, 2½, 2, 1½, 0, 00, and 000. All of the No. 000 grains pass through a 150-mesh sieve, with 25% retained on a 200-mesh sieve and 80% on a 325-mesh sieve. Good **sandpaper quartz** will contain at least 98.9% silica. The paper used is heavy, tough, and flexible, usually 70- or 80-lb paper, and the grains are bonded with a strong glue. A process is also employed to deposit the grains on end by electrostatic attraction so that the sharp edges of the grains are presented to the work.

SANDSTONE. A consolidated sand rock, consisting of sand grains united with a natural cementing material. The size of the particles and the strength of the cement vary greatly in different natural sandstones. The most common sand in sandstone is quartz, with considerable feldspar, lime, mica, and clayey matter. The cementing material is often fine chalcedony. **Silica sandstones** are hard and durable but difficult to work. **Calcareous sandstone,** in which the grains are cemented by calcium carbonate, is called **freestone** and is easily worked, but it disintegrates by weathering. Freestone is homogeneous and splits almost equally well in both directions. **Chert,** formerly used as an abrasive and, when employed in building and paving, known under local names, as **hearthstone, firestone,** and **malmstone,** is a siliceous stone of sedimentary origin. It has a radiating structure and splintery fracture and is closely allied to flint. In color it is light gray to black or banded. The colors of sandstones are due to impurities, pure siliceous and calcareous stones being white or cream-colored. The yellow to red colors usually come from iron oxides, black from manganese dioxide, and green from glauconite. **Crab Orchard stone** of Tennessee is high in silica with practically no CaO, and is often beautifully variegated with red and brown streaks. It splits in uniform slabs and is used for facing. The compressive strength is high, up to 24,000 psi, and the weight is 165 lb per cu ft. The water absorption is less than 2%.

About half of the commercial sandstone block in the United States comes from Ohio. It weighs 140 lb per cu ft, and has a compressive strength of 10,000 psi, but the average of much other sandstone is 135 lb per cu ft with a compressive strength of 12,000 psi. Sandstones for building purposes are produced under innumerable names, usually referring to the locality. The **bluestone** of New York state is noted for its even grain and high crushing strength, up to 19,000 psi. It contains about 70% silica sand with clay as the binder. **Amherst sandstone** from Ohio contains up to 95% silica with 4% aluminum oxide, and is colored gray and buff with iron oxides. **Flexible sandstone,** which can be bent, comes from North Carolina. It is **itacolumite,** and has symmetrically arranged quartz grains which interlock and rotate against one another in a binder of mica and talc.

Holystone is a block of close-grained sandstone, formerly used for rubbing down the decks of ships and still used for rubbing down furniture and concrete work. **Briar Hill stone** and **Macstone** are trade names for building blocks consisting of lightweight concrete faced with a slab of sandstone. **Kemrock,** of the Kewaunee Mfg. Co., is a sandstone impregnated with a black furfural resin and baked to a hard finish. It is used for table tops and chemical equipment to resist acids and alkalies. The term **reservoir rock** refers to friable porous sandstone that contains oil or gas deposits. The porosity of such sandstone or compacted sand of Pennsylvania is from 15 to 20%, while that of California and the Gulf Coast is 25 to 40%. A sandstone of 20% porosity may contain as much as 75,000 bbl of oil per acre-ft.

SAPELE. The figured woods of various species of trees of tropical Africa which are mixed with khaya and exported from West Africa as **African mahogany.** Sapele woods are harder and heavier than red khaya, but shrink and swell more than khaya with changes in moisture. They are also darker in color with a purplish tinge. **Sapele mahogany,** also called **scented mahogany** and **West African cedar,** is from the *Entandrophragma cylindricum,* a very large tree growing on the Ivory Coast and in Ghana and Nigeria. On the Ivory Coast it is called **aboudikro.** Another species, *E. angolense,* is called **Tiama mahogany** on the Ivory Coast, and in Nigeria is known as **brown mahogany** and **gedunohor.** A less heavy wood, from the tree *E. utile,* is known on the Ivory Coast as **Sipo mahogany** and in the Cameroons as **Assie mahogany.** It is one of the chief woods exported as mahogany from the Cameroons. The wood known on the Ivory Coast as **heavy mahogany** and **omu** in Nigeria is from the tree *E. candollei,* and is much heavier than other sapeles. **Nigerian pearwood,** from species of *Guarea,* notably *G. cedrata* and *G. thompsonii,* is also exported as African mahogany. The woods are more properly called **guarea.** The color is pale pink to reddish. The weight is about the same as sapele. The wood is of a finer texture than khaya, but is not figured like sapele or khaya. Another wood marketed as African mahogany is **lingue,** from the tree *Afzelia africana* of the west coast of Africa from Senegal to Nigeria. The wood is light brown, turning dark when seasoned, and is beautifully figured.

SAPONIN. Glucosides of the empirical formula $C_{32}H_{54}O_{18}$ which have the property of frothing with water. They are found in soap bark, soap nut, licorice, and other plants; when separated out, saponin is a white, amorphous powder of a disagreeable odor. Before the advent of the synthetic detergents saponin was important for replacing soaps in washing compounds where high sudsing was undesirable, and it was used in industrial scouring compounds, soapless shampoos, and tooth powders. It is still used in some detergents, in fire extinguishers, as an emulsifying agent, and for synthesizing other complex chemicals. Saponin is not a single compound, but is a great group of **alicyclic compounds,** or five-membered or more highly complex ring compounds having **aliphatic,** or fatty acid, properties.   The saponins occur directly in plants where they have a triterpene structure and may be either converted to or derived from a great variety of acids, vitamins, and other products by photosynthesis or catalyzation.   The are closely related to the styrols of animal life, and in both plant and animal life slight catalytic rearrangements with nitrogen produce the natural **venoms** and poisonous compounds.   The saponins thus form one of the most useful of the basic chemical groups for biological and pharmaceutical work.   Chemically, they are called **polymethylene compounds,** and can be synthesized from petroleum.   In the drug industry they are called **sapogenines.**

The saponins can be obtained from many plants.   **Soap nut** is the fruit of the trees *Sapidus mukorossi* and *S. laurifolia* of northern India known locally as **ritha.**   The soap nut has been used as a detergent in washing fabrics since ancient times.   The nut has 56% of pericarp and 44 of seed, and the saponin is found in the pericarp.   It is extracted with solvents from the dried powdered fruit.   Saponin is soluble in water but insoluble in petroleum spirits.   **Soapbark,** also called **morillo bark,** is the dried inner bark of the tree *Quillaja saponaria* of the west coast of South America.   It was used by the Incas, and the botanical name comes from the Inca word quillean meaning to wash.   The bark produces suds in water, but the powdered bark is highly sternutatory owing to fine crystals of calcium oxalate.   It is marketed in brownish white pieces, and is used as a source of saponin.   It has been used in beverages to produce froth, but is highly toxic, affecting the heart and respiration.   In medicine it is called **quillaja** and is used as an irritant and expectorant.   **Soapwort** consists of the leaves of the plant *Saponaria officinalis,* growing in North America.   The leaves contain saponin which dissolves out in water to produce a lather useful for cleaning silk and fine woolens.   **Soapberry** is the fruit of the tropical tree *Sapindus saponaria,* used in hair and toilet preparations.   The soapberry of the American Southwest consists of the fleshy berries of the small tree *S. drummondii.*   **Soaproot** is the bulb root of the plant *Chlorogalum pomeridianum* of California.   **Mexican soaproot** is the thick rootstock of the *Yucca baccata* and of the **wild date,** *Y. glauca,* growing in the dry regions of Mexico and southwestern United States.   Both plants are called **yucca,** and in Mexico they are called **amole.**   The Indians used the roots, which were called **vegetable soap** by the settlers, for washing.   In the processing of yucca leaves to obtain fiber about 20% of a powder is obtained which contains 3% saponin.   **Yucca powder** is used in scouring compounds or for the extraction of saponin. The long stout stems of the **soap plant,** *Chenopodium californicum,* also yield saponin.

SAPPHIRE. A transparent variety of the mineral corundum. When it has the beautiful blue hue for which it is noted, it ranks with the diamond, ruby, and emerald among precious gemstones. The off-color stones are cut for pointers and wearing points of instruments. The specific gravity of sapphire is 3.98, and the hardness is 9 Mohs. The blue color is from iron and titanium oxides and is rarely uniform throughout the stone in the natural material. The green is produced with cobalt, and the yellow comes from nickel and magnesium. The **pink sapphire** contains a tiny proportion of chromic oxide, and larger amounts produce the dark-red ruby. The best gem sapphires come from India. A valuable **black sapphire** comes from Thailand. Industrial stones are found in Montana. Most natural sapphires are small, but the **Star of Artaban,** in the United States National Museum, weighs 300 carats.

Synthetic sapphire is produced by flame-fusing a pure alumina powder made from calcined ammonium aluminum sulfate. The fused material forms a boule as a single crystal. The average boule is 200 carats, but sometimes they are as large as 400 carats, or about $3/4$ in. in diameter and 2 in. long. The rods are single crystals up to 0.23 in. in diameter and 18 in. long. **Sapphire balls,** for bearings and valves, are produced by Linde to great accuracy in diameters from $1/16$ to $5/8$ in. The balls are single crystals with a hardness from 1,525 to 2,000 Knoop, a coefficient of friction of 0.140, and a compressive strength of 300,000 psi. The material has a melting point of 2030°C, and is resistant to acids and alkalies. It also has a very low coefficient of expansion, and is used for ring and plug gages, and for such wear parts as the thread guides on textile machines. Stones free from strains, and as large as $3/4$ in. square, for use as lenses, prisms, and optical windows, are made by the Bell Laboratories by re-crystallization at high temperature and pressure. They transmit light better than quartz into the infrared and ultaviolet areas, and sapphire is used as an **infrared detector** in antiaircraft missiles. The dielectric constant of sapphire is also high, about 10.6.

Sapphire whiskers are alumina fibers 1 micron in diameter and $1/8$ in. long. They may be matted without bond into **ceramic papers** for electrical insulation and filters. As a reinforcement for light metals, **sapphire fibers** increase tensile and fatigue strengths. **Whiskerloy AA20,** of Melpar, Inc., is an aluminum alloy with 20% sapphire fiber. It has a tensile strength of 48,000 psi and a modulus of 18 million.

SCHEELITE. An ore of the metal tungsten, occurring usually with quartz in crystalline rocks associated with wolframite, fluorite, cassiterite, and some other minerals. It is found in various parts of the United States, Brazil, Asia, and Europe. Scheelite is **calcium tungstate,** $CaWO_4$, containing theoretically 80.6% tungsten trioxide and 19.4 lime. It is called

powellite when it contains some molybdenum to replace a part of the tungsten. It occurs massive granular or in crystals. The color is white, yellow, brown, or green, with a vitreous luster. Chinese scheelite from Kiangsi averages 65% WO_3 and can be used directly for adding tungsten to steel. **Tungstic acid** is a yellow powder of the composition H_2WO_4 made from the ore by treating with hydrochloric acid. It is not soluble in water, but is soluble in alkalies and in hydrofluoric acid, and is used as a mordant in dyeing, in plastics, and for making tungsten wire by reducing. Tungstic acid is also obtained as a by-product in the manufacture of alkalies from the brine of Owens Lake, and is a source of tungsten, 1,000 lb of acid yielding about 800 lb of metallic tungsten. **Phospho tungstic acid,** $H_3[P(W_3O_{10})_4] \cdot 5H_2O$, called **heavy acid,** is used as a catalyst in difficult synthesis operations on complex ring-compound chemicals. The molecular weight is 2,879 of which three-fourths is tungsten. The three hydrogens produce the strong acid activity. The acid is soluble in water and in organic solvents.

Pure crystals of scheelite suitable for scintillation-counter phosphors for gamma-ray detection are found, but the natural crystal is rare. Calcium tungstate is grown synthetically as a clear, water-white crystal of tetragonal structure in rods and boules with the axis oriented perpendicular to the growth axis of the rod. It has a specific gravity of 6.12, a Mohs hardness of 4.5 to 5, a melting point of 1535°C, and a refractive index of 1.9368. It has a blue luminescence under ultraviolet light. The crystals can be made in shiny crystalline scales, and the material is also used in fluorescent pigments. **Cadmium tungstate,** $CdWO_4$, is similarly grown in clear, yellowish-green monoclinic crystals with a refractive index of 2.25, and is superior to calcium tungstate for scintillation counters. The crystals can also be grown with a cleavage much like mica, and it is used in fluorescent pigments.

SCOURING ABRASIVE. Natural sand grains or pulverized quartz employed in scouring compounds and soaps, buffing compounds, and metal polishes. Federal specifications require that the abrasive grains used in grit cake soap and scouring compounds shall all pass a No. 100 screen; the grains for scouring compounds for marble floors must all pass a No. 100, and 95% pass a No. 200 screen. For ceramic floors 90% must pass a No. 80, and 95% must pass a No. 60 screen. Very fine air-floated quartz is employed in metal polishes, and all grains pass a 325-mesh screen, but the extremely fine powders of metal oxides for polishes and fine finishes are generally called soft abrasives and are not classed as scouring materials.

SCREW STOCK. A common term for soft steel with free-cutting qualities used for screws and small turned parts made in the screw machine. It usually contains a larger percentage of sulfur than ordinary soft steel. Sulfur makes steel hot-short, or brittle, at red heat, and reduces the tensile strength, but it aids machinability and is called for in steel for simple parts where strength is not important.   **SAE screw stock** specifications call for 0.08 to 0.155% sulfur, 0.09 to 0.13 phosphorus, 0.060 to 0.90 manganese, and up to 0.25 carbon.   SAE 1112 and SAE 1120 steels are produced regularly as free-cutting screw stock.   High-manganese screw stock is an open-hearth, high-sulfur steel in the medium-manganese class having good cutting and case-hardening properties and higher strength.   A grade of manganese screw stock under the name of **Ryco steel** is marketed by Joseph T. Ryerson & Son., Inc., having a tensile strength of 90,000 psi and elongation of 20%.   **Silcut steel** is a free-cutting steel produced by W. T. Flather, Ltd.   **Super-cut steel** and **Freecut steel** of the Union Drawn Steel Div., Republic Steel Corp., are high-sulfur, bessemer cold-drawn steels with tensile strengths up to 100,000 psi, elongation 18%, and hardness 196 Brinell.   **USS steel MX,** of the U.S. Steel Corp., is an SAE 1113 bessemer steel made to close control limits to give uniform machining.   **Free-cutting steels** are produced by almost all steel mills, containing sulfur, selenium, or lead.   **La-Led X steel,** of the La Salle Steel Co., is a leaded carbon steel containing also tellurium.   It can be turned at cutting speeds more than twice those used for regular sulfur steels.   Many of the regular grades of stainless and alloy steels are also obtainable with free-cutting qualities without perceptible impairment of the physical characteristics.   The 4100 Series steels containing small amounts of tellurium are marketed as free-cutting **tellurium steel.**   The machinability is increased without altering other physical properties or losing tensile strength.   The name screw stock also refers to free-cutting brass rod containing a small percentage of lead.

SEAL OIL. An oil resembling sperm oil obtained from the blubber of the **oil seal,** *Phoca vitulina,* a sea mammal native to the Atlantic Ocean. The oil has a saponification value as high as 195, and an iodine value up to 150, and was once valued for lubricating and cutting oils but is now scarce.   In the nineteenth century as many as 400 ships at a time operated from Newfoundland in seal catching, but the unrestricted catch resulted in the destruction of the herds, and North Atlantic sealing was reduced to three ships by the middle of the twentieth century.   The industry now centers around South Georgia in the South Atlantic as an adjunct to the whale industry, but considerable oil and **seal meal** come as by-products of the Alaskan fur-seal industry.

Some seal oil is obtained from Steller's sea lion, a large-eared seal occurring from Southern California to the Bering Sea.   The adult male weighs up to 2,200 lb.   The blubber is about 75% oil, with an iodine value of 143 and saponification value of 190.   From 40 to 50% of the carcass is a dense, dark-red, edible meat, but in the United States **seal meat** is used only in animal foods.   **Seal leather,** from the skin, is used for fancy specialty articles, but it has too many defects for general use.   The product known as **sealskin** is a valuable fur skin from the fur seal, about 80% of which are caught off the Pribilof Islands where they return in June to breed. No killing is now permitted at sea.   Each bull seal has as many as 50 females, and the killing is usually restricted to the surplus males.   About 30% of the skins are black fur which brings the highest price.   Next in value is the **Matara fur,** or dark-brown, which is 60% of the catch.   The **Safari fur** is light brown.

SELENIUM. An elementary metal, symbol Se, found native in cavities in Vesuvian lavas and in some shales.   The volcanic tuff of Wyoming contains 150 parts per million of selenium, and the black shale of Idaho has up to 1 lb of selenium per ton.   It also occurs in many minerals, chiefly in **cucairite,** $(AgCu)_2Se$, **naumannite,** Ag_2Se, **zorgite,** $(ZnCu)_2Se$, and in crooksite and clausthalite.   Production in the United States and Canada is largely as a by-product of copper refining, the blister copper anodes containing 0.03 to 0.14%, and the refinery slimes having a content of 8 to 9%.   The commercial recovery is 0.66 lb per ton of copper.   In England it is recovered from the residues of roasting iron sulfide ores in sulfuric acid production.

Like sulfur, selenium exists in various forms.   Six allotropic forms are recognized, but four well-defined forms are usually listed.   **Amorphous selenium,** produced by reducing selenous acid, is a finely divided, brick-red powder with a specific gravity of 4.26.   It yields the vitreous form on heating.   **Vitreous selenium** is a brownish-black, brittle, glassy mass with a specific gravity of 4.28.   It is a dielectric and is electrified by friction. The monoclinic **crystalline selenium** is produced by crystallization from carbon disulfide, and is a deep-red glass material with a specific gravity of 4.46, and a melting point of 175°C.   The hexagonal crystalline selenium is produced by heating the monoclinic.   It is a stable metal, and is a good conductor of electricity.   It has a specific gravity of 4.79, and melts at 217°C.   All of the forms become gaseous at 688°C.   Selenium is marketed as a blackish powder, the high grade being 99.99% pure, and the commercial grade 99.5% pure.

Selenium metal is odorless and tasteless, but the vapor has a putrid odor. The material is highly poisonous, and is used in insecticides and in ship-hull paints.   Foods grown on soils containing selenium may have toxic effects, and some weeds growing in the western states have high concentrations of selenium and are poisonous to animals eating them.   Selenium burns in air with a bright flame to form **selenium dioxide,** SeO_2, which is in white,

four-sided, crystalline needles.   The oxide dissolves in water to form
selenous acid, H_2SeO_3, resembling sulfurous acid but very weak.   Oxidation of this acid forms **selenic acid,** H_2SeO_4, a strong acid resembling sulfuric acid. By burning loco weed and converting to the acids, selenium has been extracted from the weeds.

The photoelectric properties of selenium make it useful for light-measuring instruments and for electric eyes. Amorphous or vitreous selenium is a poor conductor of electricity, but when heated, it takes the crystalline form and its electrical resistance is reduced, and it changes electrical resistance when exposed to light. The change of electrical conductivity is instantaneous, even the light of small lamps having a marked effect since the resistance varies directly as the square of the illumination. The pure amorphous powder is also used for coating nickel-plated steel or aluminum plates in rectifiers for changing alternating current to pulsating direct current. The coated plates are subjected to heat and pressure to change the selenium to the metallic form, and the selenium coating is covered with a layer of cadmium-bismuth alloy. Selenium rectifiers are smaller and more efficient than copper oxide rectifiers, but they require more space than silicon rectifiers and are limited to an ambient temperature of $85°C$.

Selenium is also used in steels to make them free-machining, up to 0.35% being used.   **Selenium steels** are not as susceptible to corrosion as those with sulfur and are stronger.   Up to 0.05% of selenium may also be used in forging steels to control the gas and produce a more homogenous metal.   From 0.6 to 0.85 oz of selenium per ton of glass may be used in glass to neutralize the green tint of iron compounds. Large amounts produce pink and ruby glass. Selenium gives the only pure red color for signal lenses. Pigment for glass may be in the form of the black powder, **barium selenite,** $BaSeO_3$, or as **sodium selenite,** Na_2SeO_3, and may be used with cadmium sulfide. Selenium is also used as an accelerator in rubber and to increase abrasion resistance.   **Vandex,** of R. T. Vanderbilt Co., is a selenium powder used as a rubber vulcanizer.   **Novac,** of Herron Bros. & Meyer, used for curing synthetic rubbers, is selenium dibutyl dithiocarbonate in the form of a liquid easily dispersed in the rubber.   **Selsun,** of the Abbott Laboratories, is **selenium sulfide** suspended in a detergent, used to control dandruff in hair.   In copper alloys selenium improves machinability without hot-shortness.   **Selenium copper** is a free-cutting copper containing about 0.50% selenium.   It machines easily, and the electrical conductivity is nearly equal to that of pure copper.   The tensile strength of annealed selenium copper is about 30,000 psi.   Small amounts of selenium salts are added to lubricating oils to prevent oxidation and gumming.

SEMICONDUCTORS. Materials which are capable of being partly conductors of electricity and partly insulators, and are used in rectifiers for changing alternating current to pulsating direct current, and in transistors for amplifying currents.   They can also be used for the conversion of heat energy to electrical energy, as in the solar battery.   In an electrical conductor the outer rings of electrons of the atoms are free to move and provide a means of conduction.   In a semiconductor the outer electrons, or **valence electrons,** are normally stable, but, when a **doping element** that serves to raise or lower energy is incorporated, the application of a weak electric current will cause displacement of valence electrons in the material. Silicon and germanium, each with a single stable valence of four outer electrons, are the most commonly used semiconductors.   Elements such as boron, with a lower energy level but with electrons available for bonding and thus accepting electrons into the valence ring, are called **hypoelectronic elements.**   Elements such as arsenic, which have more valence electrons than are needed for bonding and may give up an electron, are called **hyperelectronic elements.**   Another class of element, like cobalt, can either accept or donate an electron, and these are called **buffer atoms.** All of these types of elements constitute the doping elements for semiconductors.

In a nonconducting material, used as an **electrical insulator,** the energy required to break the valence bond is very high, but there is always a limit at which an insulator will break the bond and become a conductor with high current energy.   The resistivity of a conductor rises with increased temperature, but in a semiconductor the resistivity decreases with temperature rise, and the semiconductor becomes useless beyond its temperature limit.   Germanium can be used as a semiconductor to about 200°F; silicon can be used to about 400°F; and silicon carbide can be used to about 650°F.

Some materials have a complete lack of measurable electrical resistance at very low temperatures, and are called **superconductors.**   A very low power source will start a current in a superconductor, and the current will continue to flow indefinitely after the power source is removed.   Most metals except columbium lose their conductive properties in magnetic fields, and the superconductors usually contain a high percentage of columbium. The superconductors are used for magnets and memory elements in high-speed computers where space saving is important.   A **superconductive alloy** of North American Aviation, Inc., contains 75% columbium and 25 zirconium.   **Niostan,** of National Research Corp., is columbium ribbon coated with a thin layer of **columbium stannide.**   Its efficiency permits smaller units in computing equipment used in subzero temperatures.   In operation, the superconductors are kept at subzero temperatures.

Metals for use as semiconductors must be of great purity, since even minute quantities of impurities would cause erratic action.   The highly purified material is called an **intrinsic metal,** and the desired electron movement must come only from the doping element, or **extrinsic conductor,** that is introduced.   The semiconductors are usually made in single crystals, and the positive and negative elements need be applied only to the surfaces of the crystal, but methods are also used to incorporate the doping element uniformly throughout the crystal.

The process of electron movement, although varying for different uses and in different intrinsic materials, can be stated in general terms.   In the silicon semiconductor the atoms of silicon with four outer valence electrons bind themselves together in pairs surrounded by eight electrons.   When a doping element with three outer electrons, such as boron or indium, is added to the crystal it tends to take an electron from one of the pairs, leaving a hole and setting up an unbalance.   This forms the **p-type semiconductor.**   When an element with five outer electrons, such as antimony or bismuth, is added to the crystal it gives off electrons, setting up a **conductive band** which is the **n-type semiconductor.**   Fusing together the two types forms a *p-n* junction, and a negative voltage applied to the *p* side attracts the electrons of the three-valence atoms away from the junction so that the crystal resists electronic flow.   If the voltage is applied to the *n* side it pushes electrons across the junction and the electrons flow.   This is a **diode,** or **rectifier,** for rectifying alternating current into pulsating direct current.   When the crystal wafers are assembled in three layers, *p-n-p* or *n-p-n,* a weak voltage applied to the middle wafer increases the flow of electrons across the whole unit.   This is a **transistor.**   Germanium and silicon are bipolar, but silicon carbide is unipolar and does not need a third voltage to accelerate the electrons.

Semiconductors can be used for rectifying or amplifying, or they can be used to modulate or limit the current.   By the application of heat to ionize the atoms and cause movement they can also be used to generate electric current; or in reverse, by the application of a current they can be used to generate heat or remove heat for heating or cooling purposes in air conditioning, heating, and refrigeration.   But for uses other than rectifying or altering electric current the materials are usually designated by other names and not called semiconductors.   **Varistors** are materials, such as silicon carbide, the resistance of which is a function of the applied voltage.   They are used for such applications as frequency multiplication and voltage stabilization.   **Thermistors** are thermally sensitive materials. Their resistance decreases as the temperature increases, which can be measured as close as $0.001\,^{\circ}\mathrm{C}$, and they are used for controlling temperature or to control liquid level, flow, and other functions affected by rate of heat transfer.   They are also used for the production or the removal of heat in air conditioning, and may then be called **thermoelectric metals.**

Indium antimonide, InSb, has a cubic crystal structure, with three valence electrons for each indium atom and five for each antimony atom.   Between each atom and its four nearest neighbors there are four electron-pair bonds, and there is an average of four electrons per atom in the compound.   It is used for **infrared detectors** and for amplifiers in galvanomagnetic devices. **Indium arsenide,** InAs, also has very high electron mobility, and is used in thermistors for heat-current conversion since the number of electrons free to constitute the electric current increases about 3% with each 1°F rise in temperature.   It can be used to 1500°F.   Some materials can be used only for relatively low temperatures.   Copper oxide and pure selenium have been much used in current rectifiers, but they are useful only at moderate temperatures, and they have the disadvantage of requiring much space. **Indium phosphide,** InP, has a mobility higher than that of germanium, and can be used in transistors above 600°F.   **Aluminum antimonide,** AlSb, can be used at temperatures to 1000°F.   In **lead selenide,** PbSe, the mobility of the charge-carrying electrons decreases with rise in temperature, increasing the resistivity, and it is used in thermistors.

The thermoelectric generation, set up when the junction of two dissimilar thermoelectric metals is heated and which is used in thermostats for temperature measuring and control, is essentially the same as the energy conversion and heat pumping with p-type and n-type materials.   The difference is in mechanical applications.   When a semiconductor is operated thermoelectrically as a heat pump the electric charge passing through the heat-absorbing junction is carried by electrons in the n-type material and holes in the p-type material, and the charge carriers both move away from the junction and carry away heat, thus reducing temperature at the junction.   By reversing the current, heat is produced.   Each material has a definite temperature difference, or gradient, and the efficiency is proportional to the temperature difference across the material, while the power rating is proportional to the square of the temperature difference.   Thus, a material with low efficiency may have a high power rating if it can be operated at a high enough temperature, but some materials do not maintain chemical stability at high temperatures.   Also, for many uses it is undesirable to operate at advanced temperatures.

Bismuth telluride, Bi_2Te_3, maintains its operating properties between −50 and 400°F, which is the most useful range for both heating and refrigeration.   When doped as a p-type conductor it has a temperature difference of 1115°F and an efficiency of 5.8%.   When doped as an n-type conductor the temperature difference is lower, 450°F, but the efficiency within this range is more than doubled.   **Lead telluride,** PbTe, has a higher efficiency, 13.5%, and a temperature difference of 1080°F, but it is not usable below 350°F, and is employed for conversion of the waste heat from atomic reactors at about 700°F.

Gallium arsenide has high electron mobility, and can be used as a semiconductor.   When polycrystalline semiconductors are used in thin films against a metal barrier the minimum grain size of the deposited film must equal the thickness of the film so that the carrier is not intercepted by a grain boundary.   **Cadmium sulfide,** CdS, is thus deposited as a semi-conductor film for **photovoltaic cells,** or **solar batteries,** with film thickness of about 2 microns.   When radioactive isotopes are added to provide the activating agent instead of the solar rays the unit is called an **atomic battery,** and the large area of transparent backing for the semiconductor is not needed.

Manganese telluride, MnTe, with a temperature difference of 1800°F, has also been used as a semiconductor.   Many other materials can be used, and semiconductors with temperature differences at different gradients can be joined in series electrically to obtain a wider gradient, but the materials must have no diffusion at the junction.   If intermetal compounds are of such a nature as to have a p-n balance, no doping is needed, but usually they are not in perfect balance, causing scattering, and a balancing is necessary.   Materials for thermoelectric use are usually doped higher than for semiconductors, but increased doping reduces resistivity, and for high emf and low power only small amounts are used.

Cesium sulfide, CeS, has good stability and thermoelectric properties at temperatures to 2000°F, and has a high temperature difference, 2030°F. It can thus be used as a high-stage unit in conversion devices.   High conversion efficiency is necessary for **transducers,** while a high dielectric constant is desirable for capacitors.   A low thermal conductivity makes it easier to maintain the temperature gradient, but for some uses a high thermal conductivity is desirable.   **Silver-antimony-telluride,** $AgSbTe_2$, has a high energy-conversion efficiency for converting heat to electric current, and it has a very low thermal conductivity, about 1% that of germanium.

Mechanical stress as well as heat stress produces an electric charge in balanced semiconductors, and they can be used for controlling pressure. The semiconductor-type intermetals are also used in magnetic devices, since the ferroelectric phenomenon of heat conversion is the electrical analog of ferromagnetism.   **Chromium-manganese-antimonide** is nonmagnetic below about 250°C and magnetic above that temperature.   Various compounds have different critical temperatures.   Below the critical temperature the distance between the atoms is less than that which determines the line-up of magnetic forces, but with increased temperature the atomic distance becomes greater and the forces swing into a magnetic pattern.

Plastic semiconductors are organic plastic resins with conjugated double-bond systems, such as **polyacetylene** with the linkage $\cdot CH{:}CH \cdot CH{:}$, or the polycyclic aromatic compounds.   In the long-chain linear molecule of polyacetylene two of the four electrons in each double bond are in a high-energy state, permitting free migration between the two adjoining carbon atoms.   They envelop both carbon atoms, but are not attached to either.   When the double bond alternates, as in polyacetylene, these cloud-like groups of electrons overlap and make possible a free movement along the molecular chain when a voltage is applied.   The material is a semi-conductor instead of a conductor because of the resistance of the electrons to transfer from one molecule to another.

SENNA. The dried small leaves and the pods of the bushy plant *Cassia acutifolia,* the **Alexandrian senna,** and *C. angustifolia,* the **Tinnevelly senna,** of India, Arabia, and North Africa.   The plants are cultivated in India, but the Sudan material comes mostly from wild plants.   The sun-dried leaves and pods are shipped in bales.   They are used directly as a laxative by steeping in water, or the extract is used in pharmaceuticals.   It contains the yellowish noncrystalline **cathartine,** a powerful purgative.   Another species of the plant, *C. auricula,* yields **avarem bark** which is an important tanning material in India.   It is similar to algarobilla in action.

SERPENTINE. A mineral of the theoretical formula $3MgO \cdot 2SiO_2 \cdot 2H_2O$, containing 43% magnesium oxide.   It is used for building trim and for making ornaments and novelties.   The chips are employed in terrazzo and for roofing granules.   Actually, the stone rarely approaches the theoretical formula, and usually contains 2 to 8% iron oxide with much silica and aluminum.   It has an asbestoslike structure.   The attractively colored and veined serpentine of Vermont is marketed under the name of **verde antique marble.**   The massive verde antique of Pennsylvania is used with dolomite in refractories.   **Antigorite** is a form of serpentine found in California which has a platy rather than a fibrous structure. The serpentine of Columbus County, Ga., contains 36 to 38% MgO and 2 to 5 chrome ore.   It is used as a source of magnesia.

SESAME OIL. A pale-yellow, odorless, bland oil obtained from the seeds of the tropical plant *Sesamum orientale* and other species, grown in India, China, Africa, and Latin America, and used for soaps, foodstuffs, and for blending industrial oils.   It is distinct from German sesame oil. The seeds from different species and localities vary greatly in size and color, from yellowish white to reddish brown to black.   The oil from Nigeria is called **benne oil,** and the seed **benniseed.**   In India it is known as **til oil,** and the seed as **til seed.**   In Madras it is called **gingelli.**   In Mexico it is called **ajonjoli.**   The seeds contain 50% of oil of a specific gravity of 0.920 to 0.925, with saponification value 188 to 193.

   Sesame is one of the most ancient of food grains, but has been little grown in the United States because of the difficulty of harvesting and collecting the seed.   **Sesame seed** is used as a flavor garnish for breads and bakery products.   **Sesame protein,** extracted from the seed and marketed as a powder, contains the amino acids methionine and cystine which are low in other vegetable foods.   It is low in lycine.   It is valued for blending in foodstuffs.   The oil contains the natural antioxidants **sesamol** and **sesamolin,** making it very stable, and it is also highly unsaturated.   The protein is marketed as a flour containing 60% protein and less than 1% fat, and in granules containing 55% protein and up to 18% fat.   **Sesa-Lac 86,** of John Kraft Sesame Corp., is a spray-dried blend of sesame protein and whey for use in beverages, bakery products, and prepared foods, giving a more complete amino acid combination than milk powder.

SHALE. A rock formed by deposition of colloidal particles of clay and mud, and consolidated by pressure.   It is fine-grained and has a laminated structure, usually containing much sand colored by metal oxides.   Unlike sandstones, shales are not usually porous, most shales being hard, slate-like rocks.   Slate is a form of shale that has been subjected to intense pressure.   Some shales are calcareous or dolomitic and are used with limestone in making portland cement.   These are called **marlstone.   Oil shale** is a hard shale with veins of a greasy solid known as **kerogen** which is oil mixed with organic matter.   Crude **shale oil** is a black, viscous liquid containing up to 2% nitrogen and a high sulfur content.   But when oil shale is heated above 750°F, the kerogen is cracked into gases condensable to oils, gases, and coke.   Some shales also yield resins and waxes, and the **Kvarmtorp shale** of Sweden contains 220 grains of uranium oxide per ton with also vanadium and molybdenum.   The regular commercial by-products of **Swedish shale oil** recovery are sulfur, fuel gas, ammonium sulfate, tar, and lime.   Oil shales are widely distributed in many parts of the world and are regularly distilled in most of the countries of Europe, the yield varying from 15 to 100 gal per ton.   Scotch shales give an average yield of 24.5 gal crude oil and 35.7 lb ammonium sulfate per short ton.   Shale occurs in strata and is mined like coal.   The oil shales of Colorado contain **dawsonite,** a hydrated carbonate of aluminum and sodium and also **nacolite,** a sodium bicarbonate mineral. Alumina, soda ash, and other by-products can be produced from the shales. **Bituminous shale** was originally called **boghead coal** in England, and **torbane mineral** in Scotland.   In the Green River Basin of northwestern Colorado about 1,000 sq mi is underlain by oil shale 500 ft thick averaging 15 gal per ton.   The lower portion, about 100 ft thick, averages 30 gal of oil per ton.   Recovery in a continuous retort extracts 94% of the oil, which is then cracked by heat and treated with hydrogen to remove impurities and improve the quality before it is sent to the refinery.   It is estimated that the shale of the Mahogany Ledge in Colorado, extending into Utah and Wyoming, has a content of 1.2 trillion barrels of extractable oil.   No oil is visible in the shale, but it is present as the solid kerogen which yields oil when heated.   One 42-gal barrel of oil is produced from $1\frac{1}{4}$ to $2\frac{1}{2}$ tons of shale.   Other deposits occur in Nevada, Tennessee, Indiana, Ohio, and Kentucky.   **Oil sands** of Alberta, Utah, and California are free-flowing sands impregnated with bituminous oil.   A deposit on the Athabasca River covers 1,800 sq mi and is 165 ft thick. Vast quantities of oil are available from these sands.

SHARK LEATHER. A durable nonscuffing leather used for bookbindings, handbags, and fancy shoes, made from the skin of sharks.   The shark is the largest of the true fishes, but has a skin unlike fishskin.   When tanned, the surface is hard, the epidermis thicker than cowhide, and the long fibers lie in a cross weave.   The shark is split on the back instead of the belly as in cowhides, and the skins measure from 3 to 20 sq ft, averaging 10 sq ft.   The hard denticle, called the shagreen, is usually removed, after which the leather is pliable but firm, the exposed grain not pulling out.   **Shagreen leather** is a hard, strong leather with the grain side covered with globular granules made to imitate the sharkskin.   Eastern shark leather has a deep grain with beautiful markings.   The eastern shark includes about a dozen species of shark caught off the Florida and Cuban coasts except the **nurse shark** and the **sawfish** which are graded separately.   The **whale shark** attains a length of 50 ft and a weight of several tons.   It is an off-shore species, feeding on small organisms, and is harmless to man.   The **basking shark** and the **white shark** grow to 40 ft.   The white shark is very dangerous to man, but visits in shore waters only sporadically.   The nurse shark measures 6 to 10 ft.   **Olcotrop leather,** from a species of shark, has a smooth, fine grain with regular markings.   **Galuchat leather, or pearl sharkskin,** is from the Japanese ray. It is used for trim on pocketbooks.   **Boroso sharkskin, rousette leather,** or **Morocco leather,** is from a small shark of the Mediterranean, but the name is also applied to a vegetable-tanned Spanish goatskin on which a pebbly grain is worked up by hand boarding.   It is now made from ordinary goatskin by embossing.

Most of the sharkskin is now a by-product of the catch for oil, which is used for medicinal purposes.   The shark liver is about one-fourth the total weight of the animal, and **shark-liver oil** is 30 times higher in vitamin A than cod-liver oil.   The oil is also used for soap, lubricant, and heat-treating oil, though normally it is too expensive for these purposes. The Mexican shark-oil industry centers at Mazatlán, and about 25 species are caught off the West Coast.   **Vitamin oil** from South Africa is from the liver of the **stockfish,** *Merluccius capensis,* which is an important food fish.   The liver contains 30% oil.

SHEEPSKIN. The skin of numerous varieties of sheep, employed for fine leather for many uses. The best sheepskins come from the sheep yielding the poorest wool. When the hair is short, coarse, and sparse, the nourishment goes into the skin. The merino types having fine wool have the poorest pelts. Wild sheep and the low-wool crossbreds of India, Brazil, and South Africa have close-fibered firm pelts comparable in strength with some kidskin, and retain the softness of sheepskin. This type of sheepskin from the hair sheep is termed **cabretta,** and is used almost entirely for making gloves and for shoe uppers. None is produced in the United States. The lambs grown in the mountains of Wales, Scotland, and western United States also furnish good skins. The commercial difference between sheepskin and **lambskin** is one of weight only. Sheepskins usually run 3 to $3\frac{1}{2}$ lb per skin without wool, and lambskins are those below 3 lb. Sheepskins are tanned with alum, chrome, or sumac. The large and heavy skins from Argentina and Australia are often split, and the grain side tanned in sumac for bookbinding and other goods; the flesh side is tanned in oil or formaldehyde and marketed as chamois. The fine-grained sheepskins from Egypt, when skived and specially treated, are known as **mocha leather. Uda skins** and **white fulani skins,** from Nigeria sheep, are used for good-quality grain and suede glove leather. **Sheepskin shearlings** are skins taken from heavy-wooled sheep a few weeks after shearing. The wool is about an inch in length. They are tanned with the wool on, and the leather is used for aviation flying suits and for coats.

SHELLAC. A product of the *Tachardia lacca,* an insect that lives on various trees of southern Asia. The larvae of the lac insect settle on the branches, pierce the bark, and feed on the sap. The lac secretion produced by the insects forms a coating over their bodies and makes a thick incrustation over the twig. Eggs developed in the females are deposited in a space formed in the cell, and the hatched larvae emerge. This swarming continues for 3 weeks and is repeated twice a year. The incrustation formed on the twigs is scraped off, dried in the shade, and is the commercial **stick lac.** It contains woody matter, lac resin, lac dye, and bodies of insects. **Seed lac** is obtained by screening, grinding, and washing stick lac. The washing removes the lac dye. **Lac dye** was once an important dyestuff, giving about the same colors as cochineal but not as strong. It gives a fast bright-red tint to silk and to wool, but is now replaced by synthetics. **Ari lac** is stick lac collected before the young insects have swarmed, and contains living insects. Lac harvested after the swarming is called **phunki lac** and contains dead bodies of the insects. Average yield of stick lac from kusum trees is 12 lb, from the ber tree 3 lb, and from the palas tree 2 lb. About 80% of lac production is in Bihar Province, India, but it is also obtained from Bengal, the Central Provinces, and Assam.   The stick lac from Burma and Thailand is brought to India for making shellac.

Shellac is prepared from seed lac by melting or by extraction with solvents.   The molten material is spread over a hot cylinder, stretched, and the cooled sheet broken into flakes of shellac.   **Button lac** is made by dropping molten lac on a flat surface which spreads it into button-shaped cakes 3 to 4 in. in diameter.   **Kiri** is the refuse from the filtering bags.   It is marketed in pressed cakes and contains 50 to 60% lac with resin and dirt.   The yield of shellac from stick lac is about 57%.   When pure, shellac varies from pale orange to lemon yellow in color, but the color of commercial shellac may be from a high content of common rosin. **White shellac** is made by bleaching with alkalies.   **Garnet lac** is the material with lac dye left in.   Color may also be balanced with pigments. **Orange shellac** contains up to 1% powdered orpiment, and the yellow may have smaller quantities.   Shellac is composed of polyhydric acids which condense with loss of water to form long-chain esters, thus giving polyester resins in the final coating.   It also contains resin and wax. **Aleuritic acid,** $OH \cdot CH_3(CH_2)_5(CH \cdot OH)_2(CH_2)_7COOH$,   extracted from shellac, reacts with alcohols to produce odoriferous esters used in perfumes.   It is a yellowish solid melting at 101°C.   It can be made synthetically, and is also used in cellulose lacquers.

Hard lac has the soft constituents removed by solvent extraction.   For electrical use the wax content should be below $3\frac{1}{2}\%$.   By solvent extraction of the seed lac the wax may be reduced to 1%.   Shellac is graded by color and by its freedom from dirt.   The first grade contains no rosin, but other grades may contain up to 12%.   Most Indian exports of seed lac to the United States are of the special grade which has a high bleach index.   **Cut shellac** is shellac dissolved in alcohol, but usually mixed with a high percentage of rosin.   Shellac has good adhesive properties and high dielectric strength, and is used in adhesives, varnishes, floor waxes, insulating compounds, and in some molding plastics.   Hard-face wax polishes contain a high percentage of shellac, up to 80%, to conserve carnauba and other waxes.   **Shellac plastics,** usually for electrical purposes, are sold under trade names such as **Electrose,** of the Insulation Mfg. Co., and **Harvite,** of the Siemon Co.   **Shellac substitutes** are made by blending natural resins with nitrile rubber, or with modified synthetic resins.   **Beckasite P-720,** of Reichhold Chemicals, Inc., is a rosin-modified maleic resin.   It is soluble in alcohol and in water-ammonia solutions, and is used in wax emulsions.   **Waterez 1550,** of the same company, is a shellac substitute made by reacting phthalic anhydride with a polyol. It is used in self-polishing floor waxes.   It can be removed easily with alkali cleansers.   Sucrose esters are also used to replace shellac.

SHOCK-RESISTANT STEELS. A general name for steels used for tools and parts that are required to withstand much pounding. There are two general types. One type contains chromium, vanadium, and a small amount of molybdenum, with usually fairly high manganese; the other type contains up to 2% silicon, with usually some molybdenum. The silicon steels are used for pneumatic tools and for such purposes as coining dies. A **chromium-silicon steel** marketed by the Timken Steel & Tube Co. under the name of **Sicromo steel** is a combination of both types, and has high strength and resistance. It contains 2.25 to 2.75% chromium, 0.5 to 1 silicon, 0.4 to 0.6 molybdenum, and 0.15 carbon. The tensile strength, annealed, is 60,000 psi, elongation 30%, and hardness 170 Brinell. The low-alloy chromium-silicon steels with about 1% chromium, 1 silicon, 0.60 to 0.70 manganese, and 0.40 to 0.45 carbon have tensile strengths above 200,000 psi when heat-treated. They have good fatigue resistance and are also used for springs. A steel of the Allegheny Ludlum Steel Co. called **shoe die steel,** for cutting block dies, or **clicker dies,** for cutting leather and paper, contains 0.70% chromium, 0.35 molybdenum, 0.60 manganese, 0.20 silicon, and 0.53 carbon. Shoe die steel is marketed in beveled shapes. **MSM steel** of A. Milne & Co., for punches, chisels, and shear blades, has 0.50% carbon, 2.0 silicon, 0.70 manganese, and 0.25 molybdenum. **Omega steel,** of the Bethlehem Steel Co., for chisels, shear blades, and swaging tools, contains 0.60% carbon, 1.85 silicon, 0.70 manganese, 0.20 vanadium, and 0.45 molybdenum. When hardened in oil, it has a high resistance to impact. **Bearcat steel** of this company is an air-hardening, shock-resistant, nondeforming steel for rivet sets, chisels, punches, gripper dies, and die-casting dies. It contains 0.50% carbon, 0.70 manganese, 0.25 silicon, 3.25 chromium, and 1.40 molybdenum. **Hy-Tuf steel,** of the Crucible Steel Co. of America, for shock-resistant tools, gears, and parts, is an oil-hardening steel containing 1.30% manganese, 1.50 silicon, 1.80 nickel, 0.40 molybdenum, and 0.25 carbon. When heat-treated it has a tensile strength of 230,000 psi, elongation of 13%, and Rockwell C hardness of 46. **Super Hy-Tuf** contains 1.30 manganese, 2.30 silicon, 1.40 chromium, 0.20 vanadium, 0.35 molybdenum, and 0.40 carbon. When hardened it has a tensile strength of 294,000 psi, elongation of 10%, and Rockwell C hardness of 54. This steel is used for such applications as aircraft landing-gear forgings. **Halvan steel,** of this company, for chisels, punches, and rivet sets, contains 0.50% carbon, 0.80 manganese, 1 chromium, and 0.20 vanadium. A grade of Crucible's **La Belle steel,** for coining dies, jewelry dies, and cold-header dies, has 0.95% carbon, 0.35 manganese, and 0.45 silicon. It is in reality a straight carbon steel with deep-hardening characteristics capable of withstanding high impact pressures per unit area, and has been called **cold-striking steel. La Belle**

HT steel, for rivet sets, shear blades, and cold-header dies, has 2.25% silicon, 1.35 manganese, 1.35 chromium, 0.40 molybdenum, 0.30 vanadium, and 0.43 carbon.   It gives a Rockwell hardness of C58, and has high wear resistance and toughness.   Rigid melting and processing procedures in the production of these steels to ensure uniformity are more important than exact composition.   **Ludlum 602 steel,** for pneumatic tools, has 0.48% carbon, 0.70 manganese, 1.70 silicon, 0.40 molybdenum, and 0.12 vanadium, while **Seminole hard steel** of the same company has 1.3% chromium, 2 tungsten, 0.25 vanadium, and 0.48 carbon.   **Atsil steel,** of the Atlantic Steel Co., for shear blades, punches, and pneumatic tools, contains 0.50% carbon, 0.60 manganese, 0.50 tungsten, 0.30 molybdenum, and 1.30 silicon.

SILICA. A mineral of the general composition SiO_2, **silicon dioxide,** which is the most common of all materials, and in the combined and uncombined states is estimated to form 60% of the earth's crust.   Many sands, clays, and rocks are largely composed of small silica crystals.   When pure, silica is colorless to white.   The unit crystal, or molecule, of ordinary silica has the formula SiO_2, and the single crystal grains are thus molecularly cryptocrystalline with no electron bonded lattice.   But the chemical formula of fused silica and quartz is given as Si_2O_7, which is the pattern of a continuous lattice in which each silicon atom is surrounded by 4 oxygen atoms and each oxygen atom is surrounded by 4 silicon atoms.   The varieties of natural silica are **crystalline silica,** such as quartz and **tridymite; cryptocrystalline silica** (minute crystals), such as flint, chert, chalcedony, and agate; and **amorphous silica,** such as opal.   Silica is insoluble in water when anhydrous and is also insoluble in most acids except hydrofluoric. Crystallized silica in the form of quartz has a hardness of 7 Mohs and a specific gravity of 2.65.   Amorphous **silica glass** has a density of 2.21. It is a transparent fused silica.   **Vitreous silica** is a silica glass of high transparency.   When impurities are no more than 1 ppm, it is the most transparent of the glasses, and has high transmission of ultraviolet rays.

Pure **fused silica** has a melting point of 1750°C, but softens slightly at 1400°C.   In chemical and heat ware it is used up to 1100°C.   The coefficient of expansion is very low, 0.00000054 per deg C, and the dielectric strength is 500 volts per mil.   The infrared transmission of a 96% pure silica glass extends to 4 microns while retaining the lower reach of the band to 0.4 micron.   Fused silica is used for chemical parts as it withstands severe thermal shock and is resistant to acids except hydrofluoric and hot phosphoric.   The **Amersil,** of the Amersil Co., in the form of pipes and shapes, will withstand continuous temperatures to 2700°F. Fused silica parts may be made by pressing and sintering silica powder or by casting.   Large cast parts for crucibles, molds, and furnace hearths, of the Glassrock Co., are made by remelting a powder produced by melting 99.9% pure silica sand and then crushing and grinding the glass. Cast parts have a tensile strength of 1,500 psi, compressive strength of 20,000 psi, and withstand repeated heating and cooling from 2000°F. The material is white in color.

Silica flour, made by grinding sand, is used in paints, as a facing for sand molds, and for making flooring blocks. **Silver bond silica,** of the Tamms Silica Co., is a water-floated silica flour of 98.5% SiO_2, ground to 325 mesh. In zinc and lead paints it gives a hard surface. **Pulverized silica,** made from crushed quartz, is used to replace tripoli as an abrasive. **Ultrafine silica,** a white powder having spherical particles of 4 to 25 mm, is made by burning silicon tetrachloride. It is used in rubber compounding, as a grease thickener, and as a flatting agent in paints. **Aerosil,** of Cabot Corp., is this material. **Silica powder,** of Linde, is a white amorphous powder with maximum particle size of 50 millimicrons. The natural amorphous silica of the Illinois Minerals Co. comes in an average particle size of 1.5 microns with no particles larger than 10 microns. **Quso,** of the Philadelphia Quartz Co., is a soft white powder with small particles, 10 to 20 millimicrons. It is used in cosmetics and paper coatings and as an anticaking agent in pharmaceuticals. As a filler in plastics it gives a plasticizing action that aids extrusion. It comes in grades with a pH of 5.9 and 8.2. These fine silicas are also marketed as dust-free agglomerate particles which disperse easily in solution to the discrete hydrophyllic particle. **Arc silica,** of Pittsburgh Plate Glass, used as a flatting agent in clear lacquers, is produced directly from silica sand in an arc furnace at 3000°C. It has crystals of 0.015 micron agglomerated into translucent grains, 2 to 3 microns. **Valron,** of Du Pont, originally called **Estersil,** is ester-coated silica powder of 8 to 10 mm particle size, for use as a filler in silicone rubbers, printing inks, and plastics. **Ludex,** of the same company, is another **colloidal silica** with the fine particles negatively charged by the incorporation of a small amount of alkali. It forms a **sol,** or high-concentration solution, without gelling. **Min-U-Sil,** of the Pennsylvania Glass Sand Corp., for making molded ceramics, has tiny crystalline particles. **Syton,** of Monsanto, is a water dispersion of colloidal silica for treating textiles. Translucent silica particles deposited on the fibers increase the coefficient of friction, giving uniformly high strength yarns.

Silica aerogel is a fine, white, semitransparent silica powder, the grains of which have a honeycomb structure, giving extreme lightness. It weighs 2.5 lb per cu ft and is used as an insulating material in the walls of refrigerators, as a filler in molding plastics, as a flatting agent in paints, as a bodying agent in printing inks, and as a reinforcement for rubber. It is produced by treating sand with caustic soda to form sodium silicate, and then treating with sulfuric acid to form a jellylike material called

silica gel which is washed and ground to a fine dry powder. It is also called **synthetic silica. Syloid,** of the Davison Chemical Div., is this material. It is a fluffy white powder with a pH of 7.2. **Silica hydrogel,** of the same company, is a colorless, translucent, semisolid **hydrated silica** of the composition $SiO_2 \cdot xH_2O$, bulking about 44 lb per cu ft. It contains 28% solids and 72% water. It becomes fluid by mixing with water, and regels on standing. It is used for paper and textile coatings, ointments, and for water suspensions of silica. **Hi-Sil,** of Pittsburgh Plate Glass, and **Santocel,** of Monsanto, are silica gels. **Mertone WB-2,** of the same company, is silica gel used as a coating material for blueprint papers to deepen the blue and increase legibility. When silica gel is used as a pigment, the vehicle surrounds the irregular particle formation, producing greater rigidity and hardness of paint surface than when a smooth pigment is used. For insulation use, the thermal conductivity of silica gel powder is given as 0.1 Btu per hr per sq ft per in. per deg F at $-115°F$, and 0.30 Btu at $500°F$.

Silicon monoxide, SiO, does not occur naturally but is made by reducing silica with carbon in the electric furnace and condensing the vapor out of contact with the air. It is lighter than silica, having a specific gravity of 2.24, and is less soluble in acid. It is brown powder valued as a pigment for oil painting as it takes up a higher percentage of oil than ochres or red lead. It combines chemically with the oil. **Monox** is a trade name for silicon monoxide. **Fumed silica** is a fine translucent powder of the simple amorphous silica formula made by calcining ethyl silicate. It is used instead of carbon black in rubber compounding to make light-colored products, and to coagulate oil slicks on water so that they can be burned off. It is often called **white carbon,** but the "white carbon black" of Cabot Corp. called **Cab-O-Sil,** used for rubber, is a silica powder made from silicon tetrachloride. **Cab-O-Sil EH5,** a fumed colloidal form, is used as a thickener in resin coatings. The thermal expansion of amorphous fused silica is only about one-eighth that of alumina. Refractory ceramic parts made from it can be heated to 2000°F and cooled rapidly to subzero temperatures without fracture.

SILICON. A metallic element used chiefly in its combined forms; pure silicon metal is used in transistors, rectifiers, and electronic devices. It is a semiconductor, and is superior to germanium for transistors as it will withstand temperatures to 300°F and will carry more power. Rectifiers made with silicon instead of selenium can be smaller, and will withstand higher temperatures. Its melting point when pure is about 2615°F, but it readily dissolves in molten metals. It is never found free in nature, but combined with oxygen it forms silica, SiO_2, one of the most common substances in the earth. Silicon can be obtained in three modifications.

Amorphous silicon is a brown-colored powder with a specific gravity of 2.35.   It is fusible and dissolves in molten metals.   When heated in the air, it burns to form silica.   **Graphitoidal silicon** consists of black glistening spangles, and is not easily oxidized and not attacked by the common acids, but is soluble in alkalies.   **Crystalline silicon** is obtained in dark, steel-gray globules or crystals of six-sided pyramids of specific gravity 2.4. It is less reactive than the amorphous form, but is attacked by boiling water.   All these forms are obtainable by chemical reduction.   Silicon is an important constituent of commercial metals.   Molding sands are largely silica, and silicon carbides are used as abrasives.   Commercial silicon is sold in the graphitoidal flake form, or as ferrosilicon, and silicon-copper.   The latter forms are employed for adding silicon to iron and steel alloys.   Commercial refined silicon contains 97% pure silicon and less than 1 iron.   It is used for adding silicon to aluminum alloys and for fluxing copper alloys.   High-purity silicon metal, 99.95% pure, made in an arc furnace, is too expensive for common uses, but is employed for electronic devices and in making silicones.   For electronic use, silicon must have extremely high purity, and the pure metal is a nonconductor with a resistivity of 300,000 ohm-cm.   For semiconductor use it is "doped" with other atoms yielding electron activity for conducting current. **Epitaxial silicon** is highly purified silicon doped with exact amounts of impurities added to the crystal to give desired electronic properties. Thus, silicon doped with boron has resistivities in grades from 1,000 to 10,000 ohm-cm.   **Silicon ribbon** of Westinghouse, for semiconductors, consists of dendritic silicon crystals grown into thin continuous sheets $\frac{1}{2}$ in. wide, thus eliminating the need to saw slices from ingots.   Pure single-crystal silicon ribbon of Dow Chemical is as thin as 1.25 microns and is made as a membrane formed by surface tension between two growing dendritic crystals.

Silicon does not possess a metallic-type lattice structure and, like antimony, is a semimetal and lacks plasticity, but is more akin to the diamond in structure.   Because of its feeble electronegative nature, it has a greater tendency to form compounds with nonmetals than with metals.   Silicon forms **silicon hydrides** of the general formula Si_xH_{2x+2}, similar to the paraffin hydrocarbons, but they are very unstable and ignite in the air.   But a mixture of ferrosilicon and sodium hydroxide, called **hydrogenite,** which yields hydrogen gas when water is added, is used for filling balloons.   Silicon, like carbon, has a valence of 4 and links readily to carbon in SiC chain formations.   The SiC bond acts like the C-C bond of organic chemistry, but silicon does not enter into animal or plant structures.   **Silicon nitride,** used for heat-resistant ceramic parts, is made by furnace nitriding preformed shapes of silicon metal powder.   The metal in the part is completely nitrided to the composition Si_3N_4, with a density of

3.44, Rockwell hardness A99, and a compressive strength of 90,000 psi. It sublimes at 3450°F, but the parts resist oxidation to 3000°F and have high thermal shock resistance to 2200°F. The thermal expansion is low. The material is also used as a coating for corrosion resistance at high temperature. **Roydazide,** of Materials Research Corp., is silicon nitride for coatings and molded parts.

SILICON BRONZE. A name applied to two classes of copper alloys. One of these is a copper, or nearly pure copper, fluxed with silicon, in which little or no silicon remains in the final metal. This material is used for strong electric wires and has high strength and resistance to corrosion. A standard alloy of this class contains 98.55% copper, 1.40 tin, and 0.05 silicon. The tensile strength, hard-drawn, is 92,000 psi. The second class of alloy contains a considerable amount of silicon and may have nickel, tin, and other elements. This type of alloy usually depends for hardness on the formation of silicides of nickel or iron. These alloys can be heat-treated and age-hardened.

But the term silicon bronze is used frequently for many copper-base alloys, some of which may be brasses or aluminum bronzes. An early silicon bronze developed by Bridgeport Brass for overhead trolley wires and called **Phono bronze,** or **Phono electric alloys,** contained about 1.25% tin, with only small amounts of silicon and cadmium, and the balance copper. The conductivity of the grades varied from 14 to 80% that of copper, and the hard-drawn wire has a tensile strength up to 100,000 psi. It is wear-resistant and corrosion-resistant. The hard-rolled sheet has a tensile strength of 75,000 psi. **Duronze 708,** of this company, contains 91.5% copper, 6.75 aluminum, and 1.75 silicon. It is for high-strength forgings. The annealed alloy has a tensile strength of 85,000 psi, with elongation of 30%, and it retains its strength to 600°F, and also at subzero temperatures for valves for liquid oxygen. **Silnic bronze,** of the Chase Brass & Copper Co., contains 0.45 to 0.75% silicon with enough nickel, 1.6 to 2.2%, to put the nickel into solution as a nickel silicide and prevent segregation of the hard silicon crystals. It is age-hardening, by heating to 850°F, and then has a tensile strength to 100,000 psi. It comes in rod and wire, and is very corrosion-resistant.

Silicon forms solid alpha solutions in low brass up to about 2.8% silicon, above which point a beta phase is formed, and this mixed-phase structure is present in many high-silicon bronzes used for bearings. **Tombasil alloy,** developed in Germany for bearings, and marketed by the Ajax Metals Co., is tombac metal with the addition of silicon. The tensile strength is 65,000 psi, with elongation of 15% and Brinell hardness of 135. **White Tombasil,** of H. Kramer & Co., is a modification of this alloy for marine hardware which has a lustrous silver-gray finish without plating.   A very early bearing alloy, called **vulcan bronze,** contained 1% silicon, with some iron and nickel.   **P.M.G. metal,** of Vickers-Armstrong, has 2% iron, 3 to 4 silicon, 2 zinc, and the balance copper. The forged metal has a tensile strength of 94,000 psi, elongation 17%, and Brinell hardness 153.   Cast P.M.G. metal has a tensile strength of about 50,000 psi with elongation 15 to 23%, Brinell hardness 90 to 125, and specific gravity 8.44.   Castings will withstand high liquid pressures and are corrosion-resistant.

A grade of **Olympic bronze,** of the Chase Brass & Copper Co., contains 3% silicon and 1 zinc.   The tensile strength is from 56,000 to 110,000 psi and elongation 5 to 65%.   **Olympic bronze G** contains 22% zinc and 1 silicon, with the balance copper.   It is a strong **silicon brass,** and the annealed sheet has a strength of 65,000 psi with elongation 50%. **Doler brass,** of the Doehler Die Casting Co., is a silicon brass for die castings.   A group of copper-silicon-manganese alloys is produced by the American Brass Co. under the name of **Everdur metal,** originally patented by Charles Jacobs and called **Jacobs' alloy.   Everdur 1000** for castings contains about 94.9% copper, 4 silicon, and 1.1 manganese.   The tensile strength, cast, is 45,000 psi and elongation 15%.   The alloys combine high strength and toughness with acid and corrosion resistance.   The wrought alloys have some physical characteristics similar to those of mild steel, but they have the disadvantage as compared with tin bronze that they have no proportionality limit and suffer permanent deformation at a low load and low impact.   The hard-drawn rods have a minimum tensile strength of 70,000 psi.   The electrical conductivity of the cast metal is 7% that of copper, and of hard-wrought metal 12% that of copper.   A European alloy, under the name of **Kuprodur,** containing 0.5% silicon, 0.75 nickel, and the balance copper, has good strength at elevated temperatures and was used for locomotive firebox plates.

SILICON CARBIDE.   A bluish-black, crystalline, artificial mineral of the composition SiC having a hardness of 2,500 on the Knoop scale.   It is used as an abrasive as loose powder, coated abrasive cloth and paper, wheels, and hones.   It will withstand temperatures to its decomposing point of 4175°, and is valued as a refractory.   It retains its strength at high temperatures and has low thermal expansion, and its heat conductivity is 10 times that of fireclay.   Silicon carbide is made by fusing sand and coke at a temperature above 4000°F.

Unlike aluminum oxide, the crystals of silicon carbide are large, and it is crushed to make the small grains used as abrasives.   It is harder than aluminum oxide, and as it fractures less easily, it is more suited for grinding hard cast irons and ceramics.   The standard grain sizes are usually from 100 to 1,000 mesh.   The crystalline powder in grain sizes from 60 to 240 mesh is also used in lightning arrestors. **Carborundum,** of the Carborundum Co., **Crystolon,** of the Norton Co., and **Carbolon,** of the Exolon Co., are trade names for silicon carbide. Many other trade names are used, such as **Carborite, Carbolox, Carbolite, Carbobrant, Storalon, Sterbon,** and **Natalon.** **Ferrocarbo** is a silicon carbide of the Carborundum Co. in briquettes for adding to the iron cupola charge. It breaks down in the cupola above 2000°F to form nascent carbon and silicon for adding to the iron and also for deoxidizing. It produces more uniform iron castings. **Alsimag 539,** of the American Lava Corp., is a fine-grained silicon carbide in the form of molded parts for brazing fixtures and furniture for kilns for high-temperature sintering.

When used as a refractory in the form of blocks or shapes, silicon carbide may be ceramic bonded or self-bonded by recrystallization. A standard silicon carbide brick has about 90% SiC, with up to 8% silica. The density is about 3.2. It has very high resistance to spalling. The thermal conductivity of 109 Btu is about the same as that of mullite, and the coefficient of expansion is about 4.7×10^{-6} per deg C. **Carbex** is a **silicon carbide firebrick** of the General Refractories Co. **Refrax silicon carbide** of the Carborundum Co. is bonded with silicon nitride. It is used for hot-spray nozzles, heat-resistant parts, and for lining electrolytic cells for smelting aluminum. **Silicon carbide KT,** of the same company, is molded without a binder. It has 96.5% SiC with about 2.5% silica. The density is about 3.1, and it is impermeable to gases. Parts made by pressing or extruding and then sintering have a flexural strength of 24,000 psi and compressive strength of 150,000 psi. The Knoop hardness is 2,740. It is made in rods, tubes, and molded shapes, and the rough crystal surface can be diamond-ground to a smooth close tolerance. The operating temperature in inert atmospheres is to 4000°F, and in oxidizing atmospheres to 3000°F. For reactor parts, it has a low neutron-capture cross section and high radiation stability. The thermal conductivity is 2.5 times that of stainless steel. The **Crystolon R** of the Norton Co. is a stabilized silicon carbide bonded by recrystallization. It has a density of 2.5, a tensile strength of 5,500 psi, compressive strength of 25,000 psi, and Knoop hardness of 2,500. The porosity is 21%. It is for parts subject to temperatures to 4200°F, and it withstands high thermal shock. **Crystolon C** is a self-bonding silicon carbide for coating molded graphite parts to give high wear and erosion resistance. The coatings, 0.003 to 0.020 in. thick, produced by high-temperature chemical reaction, form an integral part of the graphite surface.

Silicon carbide foam is a lightweight material made of self-bonded silicon carbide foamed into shapes. The low-density foam weighs 17 lb per cu ft, has a porosity of 90%, and has a tensile strength of 30 psi, with compressive strength of 30 psi. The high-density foam of 33 lb per cu ft has a tensile strength of 85 psi and compressive strength of 750 psi. Its porosity is 80%. It is inert to hot chemicals. It can be machined.

Silicon carbide crystals are used for semiconductors for use at temperatures above 650°F. As the cathode of electronic tubes instead of a hot-wire cathode, the crystals take less power and need no warm-up. In the silicon carbide crystal both the silicon and the crystalline carbon have the covalent bond in which each atom has four near neighbors and is bonded to each of these with two electrons symmetrically placed between the atoms, but since there is an electronegative difference between silicon and carbon, there is some ionic bonding which results in a lesser mobility for lattice scattering. The silicon carbide semiconductor crystals of Westinghouse have less than 1 part of impurities in 10 million, and the junction is made by diffusing aluminum atoms into the crystal at a temperature of 3900°F, making a p-type junction.

Silicon carbide fiber is used as a reinforcement in light metals and in plastics to increase strength and stiffness. The fiber is as small as 7 microns in diameter and usually in short-length particles called whiskers. **Whiskerloy AS15,** of Melpar, Inc., is aluminum alloy 7075 with a content of 15% fiber. It has a tensile strength of 91,000 psi, and a modulus of 18 million psi. **Whiskerloy MS20** is magnesium alloy AZ31B with 20% carbide fiber. It has a modulus of 13 million psi.

SILICON CAST IRON. An **acid-resistant cast iron** containing a high percentage of silicon. When the amount of silicon in cast iron is above 10%, there is a notable increase in corrosion and acid resistance. The acid resistance is obtained from the compound Fe_3Si, which contains 14.5% silicon. The usual amount of silicon in acid-resistant castings is from 12 to 15%. The alloy casts well but is hard and cannot be machined. These castings usually contain 0.75 to 0.85% carbon; amounts in excess of this decrease the acid resistance. Too much carbon also separates out as graphite in silicon irons, causing faulty castings. Increasing the content of silicon in iron reduces the melting point progressively from 1530°C for pure iron to 1250°C for iron containing 23% silicon. A 14 to 14.5% **silicon iron** has a silvery-white structure, a compressive strength of about 70,000 psi, Brinell hardness 299 to 350, and is resistant to hot sulfuric acid, nitric acid, and organic acids. Silicon irons are also very wear-resistant, and are valued for pump parts and for parts for chemical machinery. They are marketed under many trade names. **Tantiron,** of the Bethlehem Foundry & Machine Co., contains 14 to 15% silicon, 2 to 2.5 manganese, and 1 carbon. The high manganese aids the machining properties of the metal. **Duriron,** of the Duriron Co., contains 14.5% silicon and 1 carbon and manganese. The tensile strength is 16,000 psi and weight 0.253 lb per cu in.   **Durichlor,** of the same company, is a special grade of high-silicon iron resistant to hydrochloric acid.   **Antaciron** is a 14.5% silicon iron of Antaciron, Inc., and **Corrosiron** is a similar iron of the Pacific Foundry Co.   **Thermisilid** is the original name given by the Krupp Works to high-silicon cast iron.   A heat-resistant silicon iron developed by the British Cast Iron Research Assoc. under the name of **Silal** contains only 5% silicon.   It is used for stoker and furnace parts.

SILICON-COPPER. An alloy of silicon and copper used for adding silicon to copper, brass, or bronze, and also employed as a deoxidizer of copper and for making hard copper.   Silicon alloys in almost any proportion with copper, and is the best commercial hardener of copper.   A 50–50 alloy of silicon and copper is hard and extremely brittle and black in color.   A 10% silicon, 90 copper alloy is as brittle as glass; in this proportion silicon-copper is used for making the addition to molten copper to produce hard, sound copper castings of high strength.   The resulting copper alloy is easy to run in the foundry and does not dross. Silicon-copper grades in 5, 10, 15, and 20% silicon are also marketed, being usually sold in slabs notched for breaking into smaller sections for adding to the melt.   A 10% silicon-copper melts at 1500°F; a 20% alloy melts at 1152°F.

SILICON-MANGANESE. An alloy employed for adding manganese to steel, and also as a deoxidizer and scavenger of steel.   It usually contains 65 to 70% manganese and 12 to 25 silicon.   It is graded according to the amount of carbon, generally 1, 2, and 2.5%.   For making steels low in carbon and high in manganese, silicomanganese is more suitable than ferromanganese.   A reverse alloy, called **manganese-silicon,** contains 73 to 78% silicon and 20 to 25 manganese, with 1.5 max iron and 0.25 max carbon.   It is used for adding manganese and silicon to metals without the addition of iron.   Still another alloy is called **ferromanganese-silicon,** containing 20 to 25% manganese, about 50 silicon, and 25 to 30 iron, with only about 0.50 or less carbon.   This alloy has a low melting point, giving ready solubility in the metal.

Silicon-spiegel is an alloy of silicon and manganese with iron employed for making additions of silicon and manganese to open-hearth steels, and also for adding manganese to cast iron in the cupola.   A typical analysis gives 25 to 30% manganese, 7 to 8 silicon, and 2 to 3 carbon.   Both the silicon and manganese act as strong deoxidizers, forming a thin fusible slag, making clean steel.

SILICON STEEL. All grades of steel contain some silicon and most of them contain from 0.10 to 0.35% as a residual of the silicon used as a deoxidizer.   But from 3 to 5% silicon is sometimes added to increase the magnetic permeability, and larger amounts are added to obtain wear-resisting or acid-resisting properties. Silicon deoxidizes steel, and up to 1.75%, the elastic limit and impact resistance are increased without loss of ductility. Silicon steels within this range are used for structural purposes and for springs, giving a tensile strength of about 75,000 psi and elongation 25%. A common low-silicon structural steel contains up to 0.35% silicon and 0.20 to 0.40 carbon, but the **structural silicon steels** are ordinarily **silicon-manganese steel,** with the manganese above 0.50%. Low-carbon steels used as structural steels are made by careful control of carbon, manganese, and silicon and with special mill heat treatment. **Lukens LT-75,** of Lukens Steel, contains 0.2% carbon, up to 1.35 manganese, and 0.3 silicon. The tensile strength is 90,000 psi, with elongation of 24%. European silicon structural steels contain 0.80% or more silicon, with manganese above 0.50%, and very low carbon. The silicon alone is a graphitizer, and to be most effective needs the assistance of manganese or other carbide-forming elements. It is useful in high-strength low-alloy steels, and has a wide range of utility when used with expert technique in alloy steels. Considerable addition of silicon above 1.75% increases the hardness and the corrosion resistance, but reduces the ductility and makes the steel brittle. The lower grades can be rolled, however, and silicon-steel sheet is used for electric transformer laminations. Silicon forms a chemical combination with the metal, forming an iron silicide.

The value of silicon steel as a **transformer steel** was discovered by Hadfield in 1883. Silicon increases the electrical resistivity and also decreases the hysteresis loss, making silicon steel valuable for magnetic circuits where alternating current is used. **Tran-Cor** is a high-silicon steel produced by the American Rolling Mill Co. for cores for electrical transformers. **Electrical steel,** or **electric sheet,** is sheet steel for armatures and transformers, in various grades from 1 to 4.5% silicon. **Hipersil** is a high-permeability silicon steel of Westinghouse. **Cubex,** of the same company, is a silicon steel containing 3% silicon which has been processed so that each cubical crystal of the steel structure is oriented with the faces symmetrical, giving alignment in four directions instead of the normal two. The steel is easily magnetized across as well as along the sheet. In transformers it lowers energy losses, and also gives greater flexibility in designing shapes. Westinghouse also produces a silicon iron which is double oriented, with the cubical crystals of the iron in exact alignment in all directions with the sides of the cubes parallel to the sides and ends of the sheets. It gives high permeability with low induction loss. The **relay steel,** of the Allegheny Ludlum Steel Co., used for relays and magnets, contains 0.5 to 2.75% silicon. **Orthosil,** of the Thomas & Skinner Steel Products Co., is silicon steel sheet, 0.004 in. thick, for electrical laminations.

A tough and strong tool steel for forming tools, pneumatic tools, and long punches is made with the addition of silicon and some molybdenum. **Solar steel,** of Carpenter Steel, has 1% silicon, 0.50 molybdenum, 0.40 manganese, and 0.50 carbon.   It is water-hardening, and has a breaking strength of 323,000 psi, with elongation 4.5%.   **Silman steel,** of the Vanadium Alloys Steel Co., has 2.1% silicon, 0.25 chromium, 0.30 vanadium, 0.85 manganese, and 0.55 carbon.   The silicon gives it wear-resistant properties, making it suitable for shear blades and punches; the other alloying elements give toughness and resistance to fatigue.   These steels are often referred to as **shock-resistant steel.   Black giant steel,** of the Bethlehem Steel Co., for bending, drawing, and stamping dies, has 1.4% carbon, 2.2 silicon, 0.90 manganese, 0.45 chromium, and 0.5 tungsten.   The high silicon precipitates some of the carbon in graphitic form, giving the steel a low coefficient of friction and high resistance to wear. **Dargraph steel,** of Darwin & Milner, Inc., for wear plates, gages, and cutting dies, has 1.15% silicon, 0.80 manganese, 0.25 molybdenum, 0.20 chromium, and 1.45 carbon.   It has some carbon uniformly distributed as free graphite.   Silicon steels with balanced amounts of other elements to give high strength without the normal brittleness of plain silicon steels are used for forgings for aircraft.   But the silicon-manganese steels with manganese up to 1% are tough, strong, and wear-resistant.   **SAE steel 9255,** with 2% silicon and 0.75 manganese, is such a steel.   The **Super Hy-Tuf steel,** of the Crucible Steel Co., has 2.3% silicon, 1.4 chromium, 1.3 manganese, 0.35 molybdenum, 0.20 vanadium, and 0.47 carbon. When heat-treated, it has a tensile strength of 300,000 psi with elongation 13%.

SILICONES. A group of resinlike materials in which silicon takes the place of the carbon of the organic synthetic resins.   Silicon is quadrivalent like carbon.   But, while carbon also has a valence of 2, silicon has only one valence of 4, and the angles of molecular formation are different. The two elements also differ in electronegativity, and silicon is an **amphoteric element,** having both acid and basic properties.   The molecular formation of the silicones varies from that of the common plastics, and they are designated as **inorganic plastics** as distinct from the **organic plastics** made with carbon.

In the long-chain organic synthetic resins the carbon atoms repeat themselves, attaching on two sides to other carbon atoms, while in the silicones the silicon atom alternates with an oxygen atom so that the silicon atoms are not tied to each other.   The simple **silane** formed by silicon and hydrogen corresponding to methane, CH_4, is also a gas, as is methane, and has the formula SiH_4.   But, in general, the silicones do not have the SiH radicals, but contain CH radicals as in the organic plastics.   Basically, silicon is reacted with methyl chloride and a catalyst to produce a gas mixture of silanes, $(CH_3)_x(SiCl)_{4-x}$. After condensing, three silanes are fractioned, methyl chloro silane, dimethyl dichloro silane, and trimethyl trichloro silane. These are the common building blocks of the **siloxane** chains, and by hydrolyzing them cyclic linear polymers can be produced with acid or alkali catalysts to give fluids, resins, and rubbers. **Silicone resins** have, in general, more heat resistance than organic resins, have higher dielectric strength, and are highly water-resistant. Like organic plastics, they can be compounded with plasticizers, fillers, and pigments. They are usually cured by heat.

A great variety of molecular combinations are obtainable in the silicone polymers, giving resins of varying characteristics, and those having CH radicals with silicon bonds are termed **organosilicon polymers.** **Silicon tetramethyl,** $Si(CH_3)_4$, is a liquid boiling at 26°C. **Trichloro silane,** $HSiCl_3$ is also called **silico chloroform,** and corresponds in formation to chloroform. By replacing the hydrogen atom of this compound with an alkyl group, the **alkylchloro silanes** are made which have high adhesion to metals and are used in enamels. **Methyl chloro silane,** $(CH_3)_2SiCl_2$, is a liquid used for waterproofing ceramic electrical insulators. The material reacts with the moisture in the ceramic, forming a water-repellent coating of methyl silicone resin and leaving a residue of hydrochloric acid which is washed off. **Dry-Film 9977,** of the General Electric Co., is a liquid mixture of dimethyl dichloro silane and methyl trichloro silane for this same purpose. **Silicone SC-50,** of the same company, used in concrete and in gypsum plaster and in water paints to impart water repellency, is a **sodium methyl siliconate.** **Velvasil,** of this company, is a **dimethyl siloxane** used in cosmetics as a water repellent, and in lipsticks for smear resistance. The dimethyl polysiloxanes are very stable fluids used widely in cosmetics, but valued also for use in shock absorbers, transformers and in automatic control systems. The **Sun Filter polish,** of the Westley Industries, is this material. It is resistant to sunlight and to alkaline chemicals and withstands temperatures to 300°F. The **silicone cement** of Charles Englehard, Inc., to give strong, heat-resistant bonds to metals, glass, and ceramics, is a polysiloxane with mineral fillers. The strong cements developed by the Naval Ordnance Laboratory for making chemical bonds between the glass fibers and the resin in plastic laminates are made by reacting allyl trichloro silane with phenol resorcinol, or xylenol.

Silicone insulating varnishes will withstand continuous operating temperatures at 350°F or higher. **Silicone enamels** and paints are more resistant to chemicals than most organic plastics, and when pigmented with mineral pigments will withstand temperatures up to 1000°F. For lubricants the liquid silicones are compounded with graphite or metallic soaps and will operate between −50 and 500°F. **Thermocone,** of the

Joseph Dixon Crucible Co., is a black, chemical-resistant paint which withstands temperatures to 1000°F. It is a liquid silicone containing graphite flake. The silicone liquids are stable at their boiling points, between 750 and 800°F, and have low vapor pressures, so that they are also used for hydraulic fluids and heat-transfer media. **Silicone oils,** used for lubrication and as insulating and hydraulic fluids, are methyl silicone polymers. They retain a stable viscosity at both high and low temperatures. As hydraulic fluids they permit smaller systems to operate at higher temperatures. In general, silicone oils are poor lubricants compared with petroleum oils, but they are used for high temperatures, 150 to 200°C, at low speeds and low loads.

Silicone resins are blended with alkyd resins for use in outside paints, usually modified with a drying oil. **Resin XR-807,** of Dow Corning, is such a silicone-alkyd containing 25% silicone resin, used to produce paints of high weather and sunlight resistance. A catalyst is added to give air drying. **Silicone-alkyd resins** are also used for baked finishes, combining the adhesiveness and flexibility of the alkyd with the heat resistance of the silicone. A **phenyl ethyl silicone** is used for impregnating glass-fiber cloth for electrical insulation and it has about double the insulating value of ordinary varnished cloth.

Silicone rubber is usually a long-chain **dimethyl silicone** which will flow under heat and pressure, but can be vulcanized by cross-linking the linear chains. Basically, it consists of alternate silicon and oxygen atoms with two methyl groups attached to each silicon atom. The tensile strength is 300 psi, but with fillers it is raised to 600 psi. It is usually compounded with silica and pigments. It is odorless and tasteless, is resistant to most chemicals but not to strong acids and alkalies, will resist heat to 500°F, and will remain flexible to −70°F. The dielectric strength is 500 volts per mil. **Silastic,** of Dow Corning, is a silicone rubber. It is a white rubbery material with an elongation of 70 to 150%, and has good adhesion to various materials. It is used for electric insulation, for coating fabrics, and for gaskets and other parts. **Silastic RTV 601,** used for encapsulation of electrical units, has a specific gravity of 1.29, tensile strength of 300 psi, elongation 150%, and dielectric strength of 550 volts per mil. The hardness is Shore A40.

Ordinary silicone rubber has the molecular group $(H \cdot CH_2 \cdot Si \cdot CH_2 \cdot H)$ in a repeating chain connected with oxygen linkages, but in the **nitrile-silicone rubber** of General Electric one of the end hydrogens of every fourth group in the repeating chain is replaced by a C:N radical. These polar nitrile groups give a low affinity for oils, and the rubber does not swell with oils and solvents. It retains strength and flexibility at temperatures from −100°F to above +500°F, and is used for such products as gaskets and chemical hose. This material, called **N.S. fluids** in the form of water-white to yellow liquids having 3 to 23% nitrile content, is used for solvent-resistant lubricants and as antistatic plasticizers.   As lubricants, they retain a nearly constant viscosity at varying temperatures.   **Fluoro-silicones** have fluoro alkyd groups substituted for some of the methyl groups attached to the siloxane polymer of dimethyl silicone.   They are fluids, greases, and rubbers, incompatible with petroleum oils and insoluble in most solvents.   The greases are the fluids thickened with lithium soap, or with a mineral filler.

SILK. The fibrous material in which the silkworm, or larva of the moth *Bombyx mori,* envelops itself before passing into the chrysalis state.   Silk is closely allied to cellulose and resembles wool in structure, but unlike wool it contains no sulfur.   The natural silk is covered with a wax or silk glue which is removed by scouring in manufacture, leaving the glossy **fibroin,** or raw-silk fiber.   The fibroin consists largely of the amino acid **alanine,** $CH_3CH(NH_2)CO_2H$, which can be synthesized from pyruvic acid.   **Silk fabrics** are used mostly for fine garments, but are also valued for military powder bags because they burn without a sooty residue.

The fiber is unwound from the cocoon and spun into threads.   Each cocoon has from 2,000 to 3,000 yd of thread.   One pound of raw silk is obtained from $2\frac{1}{2}$ lb of cocoons.   The chief silk-producing countries are China, Japan, India, Italy, and France.   Japanese raw silk is shipped in bales of 100 kin, $133\frac{1}{3}$ lb.   European silk bales weigh 220.5 lb, and Canton bales $106\frac{2}{3}$ lb.   The conditioned weight in shipping is the dry weight plus 11% moisture.   A book is a bundle of Asiatic silk containing 50 to 60 skeins, about 4 to 4.5 lb.   **Floss silk** is a soft silk yarn practically without twist, or is the loose waste silk produced by the worm when beginning to spin its cocoon.   **Hard silk** is thrown silk from which the gum has not been discharged.   **Soft silk** is thrown silk yarn, degummed, dyed or undyed.   **Souple silk** is dyed skein silk from which little gum has been discharged.   It is firmer but is less lustrous.   **Organizine silk** is from the best grade of cocoons.   **Marabout silk,** used for making imitation feathers, is a white silk, twisted, and dyed without discharging the gum.   **Silk waste** is silk other than that reeled from the cocoon.   It includes cocoons not fit for reeling, partly unwound cocoons, broken filaments, mill waste, and discarded noils.   It is used in the spun-silk yarn industry.   **Noils** consist of the short, staple knotty combings.

In China the cultivation of the silkworm is claimed to date back to 2640 B.C.   Silk was first woven in Rome about 50 B.C.   The eggs of the silkworm were smuggled into Europe in the year 552.   **Sericulture,** or silkworm culture, is a highly developed industry.   The larvae, which have voracious appetites, are fed on mulberry leaves for 24 days, after which they complete their cocoons in 3 to 4 days.   In from 7 to 70 days these are heated to kill the chrysalis to prevent bursting of the shell.   The reeling is done by hand and by machine.   **Wild silk** is from a night peacock moth which does not feed on the mulberry.   It is coarser and stronger, but darker in color and less lustrous.   **Tussah silk** is a variety of wild silk from South China and India.   **Charka silk** is raw silk produced in Bengal on native hand-reeling machines.   **Byssus silk** is a long fiber from a mussel of Sardinia and Corsica which spins the thread to attach itself to rocks.   The fiber is golden brown, soft, lustrous, and elastic, and not dissolved by acids or alkalies.   It was formerly used for fine garments but is no longer obtained commercially.   **Canton silk** is soft and fluffy, but is greenish in color and lacks firmness.   It is from the *B. textor,* and is used for weft yarns and in crepes.   The silk when grown in India and known as **Indian silk** is the finest of all silks with fibers 0.0004 in. compared with 0.001 in. for Japanese silk.   Before the war Japan produced most of the silk of the world from a cultivated moth of the tussah variety, *Antheria yama mai.*   **Shantung silk** is from a tussah moth, *A. pernyi,* which feeds on oak leaves.

The fabric called **shantung** is a rough-textured plain-woven silk with irregular fillings, heavier, and more bumpy than pongee.   **Grosgrain** is a heavy close-woven corded fabric of silk.   It is used for tapestry, and in narrow widths for ribbons.   **China silk, or habutai,** is an unweighted all-silk fabric of close, firm, but uneven texture woven of low quality, unthrown **raw silk** in the gum, but it is also imitated with textiles with a silk warp and a rayon filling.   The light-weight grades of 3, $3\frac{1}{2}$, and 4 momme (42, 36, 31 sq yd per lb) are classed as sheer fabrics, and are used for impregnated fabrics for umbrellas, raincoats, hospital sheetings.   Unimpregnated habutai is used for curtains, lamp shades, handkerchiefs, and caps.   Heavy-weight habutai of 12 momme, or 10 yd per lb, is used for parachutes.   **Pongee** is a rough-textured plain-woven silk fabric with irregular filling yarns.   It is made in natural color or dyed, and like China silk has a gummy feel.   **Bolting cloth,** for screening flour, is a fine, strong, silk fabric.   The yarn is a fine-thread, hard-twist tram thrown in the gum from high-quality raw silk.   The fabric has a lino weave with two warp threads swiveled around the weft.   It comes in various meshes, the finest having 166 to 200 threads per linear inch.   It is produced on hand looms in Switzerland and France.   **Cartridge cloth** is a thin strong fabric for powder bags for large-caliber guns.   It is made of silk waste and noils. The silk is consumed in the explosion without leaving residues that would cause premature explosion of the subsequent charge.   It also does not deteriorate in storage in contact with the powder.

The **kente cloth** of Ghana is a silk fabric of fine weave in delicate colors, hand-woven in long narrow strips which are sewn together to make a pattern.   **Satin** is a heavy silk fabric with a close twill weave in which the fine warp threads appear on the surface and the weft threads are covered up by the peculiar twill.   Common satin is of eight-leaf twill, the weft intersecting and binding down the warp at every eighth pick, but 16 to 20 twills are also made.   In the best satins a fine quality of silk is used.   It was originally called **zayton,** derived from the Arab name of the Chinese trading post where the fabric was produced.   Varieties of imitation satin are made with a cotton weft.   Satins are dyed to many colors, and much used for linings and trimmings.

Quiana, of Du Pont, originally called Fiber Y, produces **synthetic resin fabrics** with the feel and drape of silk.   They are resilient and take dyes readily.   The fiber is a polyamide based on an alicyclic diamine.   **A-Tell** is a Japanese textile fiber of great silkiness.   It is a polyethylene oxybenzoate, the molecule having both ester and ether linkages.   Another Japanese fiber is 50% polyvinyl chloride and 50% polyvinyl alcohol.   Called **Cordelan,** it produces fabrics with the feel of wool.

SILVER. A white metal, symbol Ag, very malleable and ductile, and classed with the precious metals.   It occurs in the native state, and also combined with sulfur and chlorine.   Copper, lead, and zinc ores frequently contain silver; about 70% of the production of silver is a by-product of the refining of these metals.   Mexico and the United States produce more than half of the silver of the world.   Canada, Peru, and Bolivia are also important producers.   Although nearly 90% of the silver produced in Arizona comes from copper ores, most of that produced in California is a by-product of gold quartz mining.   It is profitable to extract the silver from lead ores having only 3 oz per ton.   It is obtainable by chemical extraction from black calcite.   Silver is the whitest of all the metals and takes a high polish, but easily tarnishes in the air because of the formation of a silver sulfide.   It does not corrode.   It has the highest electrical and heat conductivity.   The specific gravity is 10.7, and the melting point is 1762°F.   When heated above the boiling point, it passes off as a green vapor.   It is soluble in nitric acid and in hot sulfuric acid.   The tensile strength of cast silver is 41,000 psi and Brinell hardness 59.   The metal is marketed on a troy-ounce value.

Since silver is a very soft metal, it is not normally used industrially in its pure state, but is alloyed with a hardener, usually copper.   **Sterling silver** is the name given to a standard high-grade alloy containing a minimum of 925 parts in 1,000 of silver.   It is used for the best tableware, jewelry, and electrical contacts.   This alloy of 7.5% copper work-hardens, and requires annealing between rollings.   Silver can also be hardened by alloying with other elements.   The old alloy **silanca** contained small amounts of zinc and antimony, but the name sterling silver is applied only to the specific **silver-copper alloy.**

The standard types of commercial silver are fine silver, sterling silver, and coin silver. **Fine silver** is at least 99.9% pure, and is used for plating, making chemicals, and for parts produced by powder metallurgy. **Coin silver** is usually an alloy of 90% silver and 10% copper, but when actually used for coins the composition and weight of the coin are designated by law. Silver and gold are the only two metals which fulfill all the requirements for coinage. The so-called **coins** made from other metals are really official tokens, corresponding to paper money, and are not true coins. Coin silver has a Vickers hardness of 148 compared with a hardness of 76 for hard-rolled pure silver. It is also used for silverware, ornaments, plating, for alloying with gold, and for electrical contacts. When about 2.5% of the copper in coin silver is replaced by aluminum the alloys can be age-hardened to 190 Vickers.

Silver is not an industrial metal in the ordinary sense. It derives its coinage value from its intrinsic aesthetic value for jewelry and plate, and in all civilized countries silver is a controlled metal. Under law in the United States the President is empowered when necessary to "require the delivery to the United States of any or all silver by whomsoever owned or possessed." Thus, silver used industrially is only on a lease-tenure basis, and the government has the legal power at all times to prohibit its consumption in dissipative uses or to requisition the metal.

Silver powder, 99.9% purity, for use in coatings, integrated circuits, and other electrical and electronic applications, is produced in several forms. Amorphous powder is made by chemical reduction and comes in particle size from 0.9 to 15 microns. Powder made electrolytically is in dendritic crystals with particle sizes from 10 to 200 microns. Atomized powder has spherical particles and may be as fine as 400 mesh. The silver powder of the Alloymet Mfg. Co., used for making pressed parts, is chemically precipitated. It is 99.97% pure with particle size 200 to 400 mesh. The **silver-clad powder** of Handy & Harmon, for electrical contacts, is a copper powder coated with silver to economize on silver. **Silver flake** is in the form of laminar platelets and is particularly useful for conductive and reflective coatings and circuitry. The tiny flat plates are deposited in overlapping layers permitting a metal weight saving as much as 30% without reduction in electrical properties. The **Silver flake No. 3,** of the Metz Refining Co., has an average particle diameter size of 6 microns with thickness of 0.2 micron. **Nickel-coated silver powder,** for contacts and other parts made by powder metallurgy, comes in grades with $\frac{1}{4}$, $\frac{1}{2}$, 1, and 2% nickel by weight.

The **porous silver** of the Pall Corp. comes in sheets in standard porosity grades from 2 to 55 microns. It is used for chemical filtering. **Doré metal,** used for jewelry, is silver containing some gold, but the material known as doré metal, obtained as a by-product in the production of selenium from copper slimes, is a mixture of silver, gold, and platinum. Silver plating is sometimes done with a **silver-tin alloy** containing 20 to 40 parts silver and the remainder tin. It gives a plate having the appearance of silver but with better wear resistance. Silver plates have good reflectivity in the high wavelengths, but the reflectivity falls off at about 3,500 angstroms, and is zero at 3,000, so that it is not used for heat reflectors.

Silver-clad sheet, made of a cheaper nonferrous sheet with a coating of silver rolled on, is used for food-processing equipment. It is resistant to organic acids but not to products containing sulfur. **Silver-clad steel,** used for machinery bearings, shims, and reflectors, is made with pure silver bonded to the billet of steel and then rolled. For bearings, the silver is 0.010 to 0.35 in. thick, but for reflectors the silver is only 0.001 to 0.003 in. thick. The **silver-clad stainless steel** of the American Cladmetals Co. is stainless-steel sheet with a thin layer of silver rolled on one side to give an electrically conductive surface.

Silver iodide is a pale yellow powder of the composition AgI, best known for its use as a nucleating agent and for seeding rain clouds. **Silver nitrate,** formerly known as **lunar caustic,** is a colorless, crystalline, poisonous, and corrosive material of the composition $AgNO_3$. It is used for silvering mirrors, for silver plating, in indelible inks, in medicine, and for making other silver chemicals. The high-purity material is made by dissolving silver in nitric acid, evaporating the solution and crystallizing the nitrate, and then redissolving the crystals in distilled water and recrystallizing. It is an active oxidizing agent. **Silver chloride,** AgCl, is a white granular powder used in silver-plating solutions. This salt of silver and other halogen compounds of silver, especially **silver bromide,** AgBr, are used for photographic plates and films. The image cast on the plate by the lens breaks down the atomic structure of the compound in proportion to the intensity of the light waves received and the time of exposure. Electrons gather on the positive lower side of the bromide grains, causing the formation of black threads of silver when the film is placed in a developing solution of **ferrous oxalate,** FeC_2O_4, or other reducing chemical. The comparative values, or tones, in the picture, come from the different color wavelengths in the white light and the different intensities of the incoming waves. Measured in second-units, the action of violet light, the shortest wavelength, on the compound, is more than 40 times greater than the action of the long wavelength of red light. To prevent further action by light, the film is transferred to a fixing bath of sodium thiosulfate which dissolves out the unreduced silver bromide.

Silver chloride crystals in sizes up to 10 lb are grown synthetically by the Harshaw Chemical Co. for use as radar screens and for infrared and electrical applications. The crystals are cubical, and can be heated and pressed into sheets instead of being sawed. The specific gravity is 5.56, index of refraction 2.071, and melting point 455°C. They are slightly soluble in water and soluble in alkalies. The crystals transmit more than 80% of the wavelengths from 50 to 200 microns. **Silver sulfide,** Ag_2S, is a gray-black, heavy powder used for inlaying in metal work. It changes its crystal structure at about 355°F, with a drop in electrical resistivity, and is used for self-resetting circuit breakers. **Silver potassium cyanide,** $KAg(CN)_2$, is a white, crystalline, poisonous solid used for silver-plating solutions. **Silver tungstate,** Ag_2WO_4, **silver manganate,** $AgMnO_4$, and other silver compounds are produced by Alfa Inorganics in high-purity grades for electronic and chemical uses.

SILVER SOLDER. High-melting-point solder employed for soldering joints where more than ordinary strength and, sometimes, electrical conductivity are required. The economy of silver solder is in the lower cost of labor in producing a tight, strong joint. Most silver solders are copper-zinc brazing alloys with the addition of silver, and the soldering is done with a blowtorch. They may contain from 9 to 80% silver, and the color varies from brass yellow to silver white. Cadmium may also be added to lower the melting point. Silver solders do not necessarily contain zinc, and may be alloys of silver and copper in proportions arranged to obtain the desired melting point and strength. A silver solder with a relatively low melting point contains 65% silver, 20 copper, and 15 zinc. It melts at 1280°F, has a tensile strength of 64,800 psi, and elongation 34%. The electrical conductivity is 21% that of pure copper. A solder melting at 1400°F contains 20% silver, 45 copper, and 35 zinc. **ASTM silver solder No. 3** is this solder with 5% cadmium replacing an equal amount of the zinc. It is a general-purpose solder. **ASTM silver solder No. 5** contains 50% silver, 34 copper, and 16 zinc. It melts at 1280°F, and is used for electrical work and refrigeration equipment.

Any tin present in silver solders makes them brittle; lead and iron make the solders difficult to work. Silver solders are malleable and ductile and have high strength. They are also corrosion-resistant and are especially valuable on food machinery and apparatus where lead is objectionable. Small additions of lithium to silver solders increase the fluidity and wetting properties, especially for brazing stainless steels or titanium. **Sil-Fos,** of Handy & Harmon, is a phosphor-silver brazing solder with a melting point of 1300°F. It contains 15% silver, 80 copper, and 5 phosphorus. Lap joints brazed with Sil-Fos have a tensile strength of 30,000 psi. The phosphorus in the alloy acts as a deoxidizer, and the solder requires little or no flux. It is used for brazing brass, bronze, and nickel alloys. The grade made by this company under the name of **Easy solder** contains 65% silver, melts at 1325°F, and is a color match for sterling silver. **TL silver solder** of the same company has only 9% silver and melts at 1600°F.   It is brass yellow in color, and is used for brazing nonferrous metals.   **Sterling silver solder,** for brazing sterling silver, contains 92.8% silver, 7 copper, and 0.2 lithium.   The flow temperature is 1650°F.

A **lead-silver solder** recommended by the Indium Corp. of America, to replace tin solder, contains 96% lead, 3 silver, and 1 indium.   It melts at 310°C, spreads better than ordinary lead-silver solders, and gives a strength of 4,970 psi in the joint.   The German **silberstein solder** has 97.25% lead, 2.5 silver, and 0.25 copper.   **Silver-magnesium solder,** used in Germany for brazing stainless-steel heat exchangers, contains 85% silver and 15 magnesium.   It has a melting point at 1790°F, and retains high strength up to 850°F.   **Silver-palladium alloys** for high-temperature brazing contain from 5 to 30% palladium.   With 30% the melting point is about 1232°C.   These alloys have exceptional melting and flow qualities and are used in electronic and spacecraft applications.

SISAL.   The hard, strong, light-yellow to reddish fibers from the large leaves of the sisal plant, *Agave sisalana,* and the henequen plant, *A. fourcroydes,* employed for making rope, cordage, and sacking.   About 80% of all binder twine is normally made from sisal, but sisal ropes have only 75% of the strength of Manila rope and are not as resistant to moisture. Sisal is a tropical plant, and grows best in semiarid regions.   The agave plant is native to Mexico, but most of the sisal comes from Haiti, East Africa, and Indonesia.   The retting, separation, and washing of the fiber are done by machine, and less than 5% of the weight of the leaf results in good fiber.   The plant is cut for fiber after 3 years and produces for 5 years after.   It is harvested throughout the year and yields 1,500 lb per acre.   **Mexican sisal** is classed in seven grades from the Superior white fiber 105 cm in length to the Grade C-1, short-spotted fiber 60 cm in length.   **Yucatan sisal,** or **henequen,** is from the henequen plant and is reddish in color, stiffer and coarser, and is used for binder twine.   The Indian word henequen means knife, from the knifelike leaves.   The plant is more drought-resistant than sisal.   Henequen also comes from Indonesia as the spotted or reddish grades of sisal.   Sisal is usually shipped in 400-lb bales.   **Maguey,** or **cantala,** is from the leaves of the *A. cantala* of India, the Philippines, and Indonesia.   It is used principally for binder twine.   The fibers are white, brilliant, stiff, and light in weight.   The fibers are not as strong as sisal, but have a better appearance and greater suppleness.   **Zapupe fiber,** of Mexico, is from the *A. zapupe.* The fiber is similar to sisal, finer and softer than henequen.   **Salvador sisal,** of El Salvador, is from the *A. letonae.*   The leaves are more slender than Mexican sisal, and the fiber is softer and finer.   It is used for cordage and fabrics.

The fibers of sisal are not as long or as strong as those of Manila hemp, and they swell when wet, but they are soft and are preferred for binder twine either alone or mixed with Manila hemp.   **Sisal fiber** is also used instead of hair in cement plasters for walls and in laminated plastics. **Corolite** is a molded plastic of the Columbia Rope Co. made with a mat of sisal fibers so as to give equal strength in all directions.   **Agave fibers** from other varieties of the plant are used for various purposes, notably **tampico,** from the *A. rigida,* which yields a stiff, hard, but pliant fiber employed for circular power brushes, and **istle,** a similar stiff brush fiber from several plants.   Tampico is valued for polishing wheels, as the fibers hold the grease buffing compositions, and it is not brittle but abrades with flexibility.   **Jaumave istle** is from the *A. funkiana* of Mexico.   It yields long, uniform fibers finer than tampico.   **Lechuguilla** is a type of istle from the *A. lechuguilla.*

There are at least 50 species of agave in Mexico and southwestern United States, which yield valuable by-products in addition to fiber. From some varieties saponin is obtained as a by-product.   From a number of thick-leaved species the buds are cut off, leaving a cavity from which juice exudes.   This juice is fermented to produce **pulque,** a liquor with a ciderlike taste containing about 7% alcohol.   The juice contains a sugar, **agavose,** $C_{12}H_{22}O_{11}$, which is used in medicine as a laxative and diuretic.   **Agava,** of Agava Products, Inc., is a dark-brown viscous liquid extracted from the leaves of agave plants, used as a water conditioner for boiler-water treatment.   It is a complex mixture of sapogenines, enzymes, chlorophyllin, and polysaccharides.

A fine strong fiber is obtained from the long leaves of the **pineapple,** *ananus comosus,* native to tropical America.   The plant is grown chiefly for its fruit, known in South America under its Carib name **ananá** and marketed widely as canned fruit and juice, preserves, and confections. **Pineapple concentrate** is also sold as a flavor enhancer, as much as 10% being added to apricot, cherry, or other fruit juices without altering the original flavor.   For fiber production the plants are spaced widely for leaf development and are harvested before the leaves are fully mature.   The retted fibers are long, white, and of fine texture and may be woven into water-resistant fabrics.   The very delicate and expensive **piña cloth** of the Philippines is made from **pineapple fiber.**   The fabrics of Taiwan are usually coarser and harder.

SLAG.   The molten material that is drawn from the surface of iron in the blast furnace.   Slag is formed from the earthy materials in the ore and from the flux.   Slags are produced in the melting of other metals, but iron blast-furnace slag is usually meant by the term.   Slag is used in cements and concrete, for roofing, as a ballast for roads and railways.

Finely crushed slag is used in agriculture for neutralizing acid soils.   **Blast-furnace slag** is one of the lightest concrete aggregates available.   It has a porous structure and, when crushed, is angular.   About 1,300 lb of slag is produced for every long ton of metallic iron.   It is also crushed and used for making pozzuolana and other cements.   Slag contains about 32% silica, 14 alumina, 47 lime, 2 magnesia, and small amounts of other elements.   It is crushed, screened, and graded for marketing.   **Crushed slag** weighs 1,900 to 2,100 lb per cu yd, or about 30% lighter than gravel.   **Honeycomb slag** weighs only about 30 lb per cu ft.   The finest grade of commercial slag is from $\frac{3}{16}$ in. to dust; the run-of-crusher slag is from 4 in. to dust.   **Basic phosphate slag,** a by-product in the manufacture of steel from phosphatic ores, is finely ground and sold for fertilizer.   It contains not less than 12% phosphoric oxide, P_2O_5, and is known in Europe as **Thomas slag.   Foamed slag** is a name used in England for honeycomb slag used for making lightweight, heat-insulating blocks.   A superphosphate cement is made in Belgium from a mixture of basic slag, slaked lime, and gypsum.

SLATE. A shale possessing a straight cleavage.   Most shales are of sedimentary origin, and their cleavage was the result of heavy or long-continued pressure.   In some cases slates have been formed by the consolidation of volcanic ashes.   The slaty cleavage does not usually coincide with the original stratification.   Slate is of various colors, black, gray, green, and reddish.   It is used for electric panels, blackboards, slate pencils, table tops, roofing shingles, floor tiles, and treads.   The terms **flagstone** and **cleftstone** are given to large flat sections of slate used for paving, but the names are also applied to blue sandstones cut for this purpose.   Slate is quarried in large blocks, and then slabbed and split.   The chief slate-producing states are Pennsylvania, Vermont, Virginia, New York, and Maine.   **Roofing slates** vary in size from 12 by 6 in. to 24 by 14 in., and from $\frac{1}{8}$ to $\frac{3}{4}$ in. in thickness, and are usually of the harder varieties.   The roofing slate from coal beds is black, fine-grained, and breaks into brittle thin sheets.   It does not have the hardness or weather resistance of true slate.   As late as 1915 more than 85% of all slate mined was used for roofing, but the tonnage now used for this purpose is small.   **Ribbon slate,** with streaks of hard material, is inferior for all purposes.   Lime impurities can be detected by the application of dilute hydrochloric acid to the edges and noting if rapid effervescence occurs.   Iron is a detriment to slates for electric purposes.   The average compressive strength of slate is 15,000 psi and the weight 175 lb per cu ft.   **Slate granules** are small graded chips used for surfacing prepared roofing.   **Slate flour** is ground slate, largely a by-product of granule production.   It is used in linoleum, caulking compounds, and in asphalt surfacing mixtures.   **Slate lime** is an intimate mixture of finely divided calcined slate and lime, about 60% by weight lime to 40 slate.   It is employed for making porous concrete for insulating partition walls.   The process consists in adding a mixture of slate lime and powdered aluminum, zinc, or magnesium to the cement.   The gas generated on the addition of water makes the cement porous.

SMOKE AGENTS. Chemicals used in warfare to produce an obscuring cloud or fog to hide movements.   Smokes may be harmless and are then called **screening smokes, or smoke screens,** or they may be toxic and called **blanketing clouds.**   There are two types of smokes: those forming solid or liquid particles, and those forming fogs or mists by chemical reaction. The first naval smoke screens were made by limiting the admission of air to the fuel in the boilers, and the first Army smoke pots contained mixtures of pitch, tallow, saltpeter, and gunpowder.   The British **smoke candles** contained 40% potassium nitrate, 29 pitch, 14 sulfur, 8 borax, and 9 coal dust.   They gave a brown smoke, but one that lifted too easily.

Fog or military screening may be made by spraying an oil mixture into the air at high velocity.   The microscopic droplets produce an impenetrable fog which remains for a long period.   White phosphorus gives a dense white smoke by burning to the pentoxide and changing to phosphoric acid in the moisture of the air.   Its vapor is toxic.   **Sulfuric trioxide,** SO_3, is an effective smoke producer in humid air.   It is a mobile, colorless liquid vaporizing at 45°C to form dense white clouds with an irritating effect. The French **opacite** is **tin tetrachloride, or stannic chloride,** $SnCl_4$, a liquid that fumes in the air.   When hydrated, it becomes the crystalline penta-hydrate, $SnCl_4 \cdot 5H_2O$.   The smoke is not dense, but it is corrosive and it penetrates gas masks.   **Sulfuryl chloride,** SO_2Cl_2, is a liquid that decomposes on contact with the air into sulfuric and hydrochloric acids.   **F.S. smoke** is made with a mixture of chlorosulfonic acid and sulfur trioxide. **Silicon tetrachloride,** $SiCl_4$, is a colorless liquid that boils at 60°C, and fumes in the air, forming a dense cloud.   Mixed with ammonia vapor it resembles a natural fog.   The heavy mineral known as **amang,** separated from Malayan tin ore, containing ilmenite and zircon, is used in smoke screens.   **Titanium tetrachloride,** $TiCl_4$, is a colorless to reddish liquid boiling at 136°C.   It is used for smoke screens and for skywriting from airplanes.   In moist air it forms dense, white fumes of **titanic acid,** H_2TiO_3, and hydrogen chloride.   The commercial liquid contains about 25% titanium by weight.

A common smoke for airplanes is **oleum.**   It is a mixture of sulfur trioxide in sulfuric acid, which forms fuming sulfuric acid, or **pyrosulfuric acid,** $H_2S_2O_7$.   The dense liquid is squirted in the exhaust manifold. **Zinc smoke** is made with mixtures of zinc dust or zinc oxide with various chemicals to form clouds.   **H.C. smoke** is zinc chloride with an oxidizing agent to burn up residual carbon so that the smoke will be gray and not black.   **Signal smoke** is colored smoke used for ship distress signals, and for aviation marking signals.   They are mixtures of a fuel, an oxidizing agent, a dye, and sometimes a cooling agent to regulate the rate of burning and to prevent decomposition of the dye.   Unmistakable colors are used so that the signals may be distinguished from fires, and the dyes are mainly anthraquinone derivatives.

SNAKESKINS. The snakeskins employed for fancy leathers are in general the skins of large tropical snakes which are notable for the beauty or oddity of their markings.   Snakeskins for shoe upper leathers, belts, and handbags are glazed like kid and calfskin after tanning.   Small cuttings are used for inlaying on novelties.   The leather is very thin, but is remarkably durable and is vegetable-tanned and finished in natural colors, or is dyed. **Python skins** are used for ladies' shoes.   **Regal python skins** from Borneo, the Philippines, and the Malay Peninsula sometimes measure 30 ft in length and have characteristic checked markings.   Diamond-backed rattlesnakes are raised on snake farms in the United States.   The meat is canned as food, and the skins are tanned into leather.   Only the back is used for leather, as the belly is colorless.

SOAP. A cleansing compound produced by saponifying oils, fats, or greases with an alkali.   When caustic soda is added to fat, glycerin separates out, leaving **sodium oleate,** $Na(C_{17}H_{33}O_2)$, which is soap.   But since oils and fats are mixtures of various acid glycerides, the soaps made directly from vegetable and animal oils may be mixtures of oleates, palmitates, linoleates, and laurates.   **Soap oils** in general, however, are those oils which have greater proportions of nearly saturated fatty acids, since the unsaturated fractions tend to oxidize to form aldehydes, ketones, or other acids, and turn rancid.   If an excess of alkali is used, the soap will contain free alkali, and the greater the proportion of the free alkali the coarser is the action of the soap.   ASTM standards for milled toilet soap permit only 0.17% free alkali.   **Sodium soaps** are always harder than **potassium soaps** with the same fat or oil.   Hard sodium soaps are used for chips, powders, and toilet soaps.   Soft caustic potash soaps are the liquid, soft, and semisoft pastes.   Mixtures of the two are also used. Soaps are made by either the boiled process or the cold process.   **Chip soap** is made by pouring the hot soap onto a cooled revolving cylinder from which the soap is scraped in the form of chips or ribbons which are then dried to reduce the moisture content from 30 to 10%.   **Soap flakes** are made by passing chips through milling rollers to make thin, polished, easily soluble flakes.

Powdered soap is made from chips by further reducing the moisture and grinding. **Milled soaps** are made from chips by adding color and perfumes to the dried chips and then passing through milling rollers and finally pressing in molds. Toilet soaps are made in this way. Soap is used widely in industrial processing, and much of the production has consisted of chips, flakes, powdered, granulated, and scouring powders. American consumption increased from 21.6 lb per capita in 1920 to 28.1 lb in 1940, but then an increasing proportion of synthetic detergents replaced soaps for both household and industrial uses. Soaps have definite limitations of use. They are unstable in acid solutions and may form insoluble salts. In hard waters they may form insoluble soaps of calcium or magnesium, unless a phosphate is added. Many industrial cleansers, therefore, may be balanced combinations of soaps, synthetic detergents, phosphates, or alkalies, designed for particular purposes.

About half of all soap is made with tallow, 25% with coconut oil, and the remainder with palm oil, greases, fish oils, olive oil, soybean oil, or mixtures. A typical soap contains 80% mixed oils and 20 coconut oil, with not over 0.2 free alkali. The wartime soap used in Germany called **Rif** had only 40% fat content, with the remainder sodium silicate, kaolin, or clays. Auxiliary ingredients are used in soap to improve the color, for perfuming, as an astringent, or for abrasive or harsh cleansing purposes. Phenol or chloronated compounds are used in **antiseptic soap.** The **disinfectant soap** used by the Army contained 2% "G-11" which was dihydroxyhexachloro diphenyl methane. The soft soaps and liquid soaps of USP grade have a therapeutic value and may be sold under trade names. The **Phisohex** of the Winthrop Laboratories contains 3% hexachlorophene with lanolin and cholesterols.

Solvents are added to industrial soaps for scouring textiles or when used in soluble oils in the metal industry. Zinc oxide, benzoic acid, and other materials are used in facial soaps with the idea of aiding complexion. Excessive alkalinity in soaps dries and irritates the skin, but **hand grit soap** usually has 2 to 5% alkaline salts such as borax or soda ash and 10 to 25% abrasive minerals. Softer **hand soap** may contain marble flour. Silicate of soda, used as a filler, also irritates the skin. **Face soaps,** or **toilet soaps,** contain coloring agents, stabilizers, and perfuming agents. For special purposes, **cosmetic soaps** contain medications. Transparency usually varies with the content of coconut, palm, or olive oil. **Castile soap** is a semi-transparent soap made with olive oil. **Marseilles soap** and **Venetian soap** are names for castile soap with olive oil and soda. Ordinary soft soaps used as bases for toilet soap are made with mixtures of linseed oil and olive oil. Linseed oil, however, gives a disagreeable odor. Soybean oil, corn oil, and peanut oil are also used, although peanut oil, unless the arachidic acid is removed, makes a hard soap. **Tall oil soaps** are sodium soaps made from the fatty acids of tall oil.   They are inferior to sodium oleate in detergency, but superior to sodium rosinate.

Saddle soap is any soap used for cleaning leather goods which has the property of filling and smoothing the leather as well as cleaning.   The original saddle soaps were made of palm oil, rosin, and lye, with glycerin and beeswax added.   Oils for the best soaps are of the nondrying type. High-grade **soft soap** for industrial use is made with coconut or palm kernel oil with caustic potash.   But soft soap in paste form is generally made of low titer oils with caustic soda, usually linseed, soybean, or corn oil.   The lauric acid of coconut oil gives the coconut-oil soaps their characteristic of profuse lathering, but lauric acid affects some skins by causing itching, and soaps with high coconut-oil content and low titer are also likely to break down in hot water and wash ineffectively.   Palm-kernel oil develops free acids, and upon aging the soap acquires the odor of the oil.   Palm oil produces a crumbly soap.   It does not lather freely, but is mild to the skin.   Olive oil is slow-lathering, but has good cleansing powers.   It is often used in textile soaps.   Cottonseed oil is used in some laundry soaps, but develops yellow spots in the soap.   Corn oil with potash makes a mild soft soap.   Soybean oil also makes a soft soap.   Rosin is used to make yellow laundry soaps.   ASTM standards for **bar soap** permit up to 25% rosin.   Sulfonated oils do not give as good cleansing action as straight oils, but are used in shampoos where it is desirable to have some oil or greasiness.   Blending of various oils is necessary to obtain a balance of desired characteristics in a soap.   Hand soaps may be made with trisodium phosphate or with disodium phosphate, or **sodium perborate,** $NaBO_3 \cdot H_2O$, known as **perborin,** all of which are crystalline substances which are dissolved in water solution.   **Soap powder** is **granular soap** made in a vacuum chamber or by other special processes.   It usually contains 15 to 20% soap and the balance sodium carbonate.   **Scouring powder** is an intimate mixture of soap powder and an insoluble abrasive such as pumice. **Floating soaps** are made light by blowing air through them while in the vats.   **Soapless shampoos** and tooth powders contain saponin or chemical detergents.

SOAPSTONE. A massive variety of impure talc employed for electric panels, gas-jet trips, stove linings, tank linings, and as an abrasive.   It can be cut easily and becomes very hard when heated because of the loss of its combined water.   The waste product from the cutting of soapstone is ground and used for the same purposes as talc powder.   **Steatite** is a massive stone rich in talc that can be cut readily, while soapstone may be low in talc.   When free of iron oxide and other impurities, block steatite is used for making spacer insulators for electronic tubes and for special electrical insulators.   **Block steatite** suitable for electric insulation is mined in Montana and in India and Sardinia. Steatite is also ground and molded into insulators. It can be purified of iron and other metallic impurities by electrolytic osmosis. When fluxed with alkaline earths instead of feldspar, the molded steatite ceramics have a low loss factor at high frequencies, and have good electrical properties at high temperatures. The white-burning refractory steatite of the Red Sea coast of Egypt averages 60% silica and 30.5 magnesia, with 1% iron oxide and 1.5 CaO.

Alberene stone, quarried in Virginia, is blue-gray in color. The medium-hard varieties are used for building trim and for chemical laboratory tables and sinks, and the hard varieties are employed for stair treads and flooring. Alberene stone marketed by the Alberene Stone Corp. as a basic refractory substitute for chrome or magnesite for medium temperatures has a fusion point of 2400°F. **Virginia greenstone** is a gray-green soapstone resistant to weathering, used as a building stone. **Talc crayons** for marking steel are sticks of soapstone.

SODA ASH. The common name for anhydrous **sodium carbonate,** Na_2CO_3, which is the most important industrial alkali. It is a grayish-white lumpy material, which loses any water of crystallization when heated. For household use in hydrous crystallized form, $Na_2CO_3 \cdot 10H_2O$, it is called **washing soda, soda crystals,** or **sal soda,** as distinct from **baking soda,** which is **sodium hydrogen carbonate,** or **sodium bicarbonate,** $NaHCO_3$. Sal soda contains more than 60% water. Another grade, with one molecule of water, $Na_2CO_3 \cdot H_2O$, is the standard product for scouring solutions. Federal specifications call for this product to have a total alkalinity not less than 49.7% Na_2O. Commercial high-quality soda ash contains 99% min Na_2CO_3, or 58 min Na_2O. It varies in size of particle and in bulk density, being marketed as extra-light, light, and dense. The extra-light has a density of 23 lb per cu ft, and the dense is 63 lb per cu ft. **Laundry soda** is soda ash mixed with sodium bicarbonate, with 39 to 43% Na_2O. **Modified sodas,** used for cleansing where a mild detergent is required, are mixtures of sodium carbonate and sodium bicarbonte. They are used in both industrial and household cleaners. **Tanners' alkali,** used in processing fine leathers, and **textile soda,** used in fine wool and cotton textiles, are modified sodas. **Flour bland,** used by the milling industry in making free-flowing, self-raising food flours, is a mixture of sodium bicarbonate and tricalcium phosphate.

Soda ash is made by the Solvay process, which consists in treating a solution of common salt with ammonia and with carbon dioxide and calcining the resulting filter cake of sodium bicarbonate to make **light soda ash.** **Dense soda ash** is then made by adding water and recalcination. Soda ash is less expensive than caustic soda and is used for cleansing, for softening water, in glass as a flux and to prevent fogging, in the wood-pulp industry, for refining oils, in soapmaking, and for the treating of ores. **Caustic ash,** a strong cleaner for metal scouring and for paint removal, is a mixture of about 70% caustic soda and 30 soda ash.   **Flake alkali,** of the Columbia Chemical Div., Pittsburgh Plate Glass Co., contains 71% caustic soda and 29 soda ash.   Soda ash is also used as a flux in melting iron to increase the fluxing action of the limestone, as it will carry off 11% sulfur in the slag.   **Soda briquettes,** used for desulfurizing iron, are made of soda ash formed into pellets with a hydrocarbon bond.   **Hennig purifier** is soda ash combined with other steel-purifying agents made into pellets.

The natural hydrous sodium carbonate of Egypt and Libya is called **nitron.**   Natural soda ash is obtained in Wyoming from beds 5 to 10 ft thick located 1,200 ft underground, which contain 47% Na_2CO_3 and 36 $NaHCO_3$, designated as **trona,** $Na_2CO_3 \cdot NaHCO_3 \cdot 2H_2O$.   By calcination the excess CO_2 is driven off, yielding soda ash.   The salt brine of Owens Lake, Calif., is an important source of soda ash.   The brine, which contains 10.5% Na_2CO_3 and 2.5 **sodium borate decahydrate,** is concentrated and treated to precipitate the trona.   The Salt Lake area of Utah is a source of trona.   Soda ash and sodium carbonate may be sold under trade names.   **Purite** is sodium carbonate of the Mathieson Alkali Works.

SODIUM. A metallic element, symbol Na, and atomic weight 23, occurring naturally only in the form of its salts.   The most important mineral containing sodium is the chloride, NaC', which is common salt.   It also occurs as the nitrate, Chile saltpeter, as a borate in borax, and as a fluoride and a sulfate.   When pure, sodium is silvery white, ductile, melts at 97.8°C, and boils at 883°C.   The specific gravity is 0.928.   It can be obtained in metallic form by the electrolysis of salt.   When exposed to the air, it oxidizes rapidly, and it must therefore be kept in airtight containers.   It has a high affinity for oxygen, and it decomposes water violently. It also combines directly with the halogens, and is a good reducing agent for the metal chlorides.   Sodium is one of the best conductors of electricity and heat.   The element has five isotopes, and **sodium 24,** made by neutron irradiation of ordinary sodium, is radioactive.   It has a half-life of 15 hr and decays to stable **magnesium 24** with the emission of one beta particle and two gamma rays per atom.

The metal is a powerful desulfurizer of iron and steel even in combination.   For this purpose it may be used in the form of **soda-ash pellets** or in alloys.   **Desulfurizing alloys** for brasses and bronzes are **sodium-tin,** with 95% tin and 5 sodium, or **sodium-copper.**   The **sodium-lead** of Humphrey-Wilkinson, Inc., used for adding sodium to alloys, contains 10% sodium, and is marketed as small spheroidal shot.   The same company also markets **sodium marbles** which are spheres of pure sodium up to 1 in. diameter coated with oil to reduce handling hazard.   The **sodium bricks** of Gray

Chemical contain 50% sodium metal powder dispersed in a paraffin binder. They can be handled in the air, and are a source of active sodium. Sodium in combination with potassium is used as a heat-exchange fluid in reactors and high-temperature processing equipment. A **sodium-potassium alloy** of the Mine Safety Appliances Co., containing 56% sodium and 44 potassium, has a melting point at 19°C and a boiling point at 825°C. It is a silvery mobile liquid with a heat conductivity at 200°C of 0.063. **High-surface sodium,** of U.S. Chemicals Co., is sodium metal absorbed on common salt, alumina, or activated carbon to give a large surface area for use in the reduction of metals or in hydrocarbon refining. Common salt will adsorb up to 10% of its weight of sodium in a thin film on its surface, and this sodium is 100% available for chemical reaction. It is used in reducing titanium tetrachloride to titanium metal. **Sodium vapor** is used in electric lamps. When the vapor is used with a fused alumina tube it gives a golden-white color. A 400-watt lamp produces 42,000 lumens and retains 85% of its efficiency after 6,000 hr.

Sodium compounds are widely used in industry, particularly sodium chloride, sodium hydroxide, and soda ash. **Sodium bichromate,** $Na_2Cr_2O_7 \cdot 2H_2O$, a crystalline red powder, is used in leather tanning, textile dyeing, wood preservation, and in pigments. When heated, it changes to the anhydrous form which melts at 356°C and decomposes at about 400°C. In a hot water solution with sulfuric acid, sodium bichromate gives a golden-brown brasslike finish to zinc parts. **Cronak** is the name applied to this finish by the New Jersey Zinc Co. The sodium bichromate liquor from alkali production is used for making pigments. When combined with lead compounds the bichromate precipitate is yellow. The addition of **iron blue,** or ferric cyanide, develops greens. **Sodium metavandate,** $NaVO_3$, is used as a corrosion inhibitor to protect some chemical-processing piping. It dissolves in hot water, and a small amount in the water forms a tough impervious coating of magnetic iron oxide on the walls of the pipe. **Sodium iodide** crystals are used as scintillation probes for the detection and analysis of nuclear energies. **Sodium oxalate** is used as an antienzyme to retard tooth decay. In the drug industry sodium is used to compound with pharmaceuticals to make them water-soluble salts. Sodium is a plentiful element, easily available, and is one of the most widely used.

SODIUM CYANIDE. A salt of hydrocyanic acid of the composition NaCN, used for carbonizing steel for case hardening, for heat-treating baths, for electroplating, and for the extraction of gold and silver from their ores. For carburizing steel it is preferred to potassium cyanide because of its lower cost and its higher content of available carbon. It contains 53% CN, as compared with 40% in potassium cyanide. The nitrogen also aids in forming the hard case on the steel.   The 30% grade of sodium cyanide, melting at 1156°F, is used for heat-treating baths instead of lead, but it forms a slight case on the steel.   Sodium cyanide is very unstable, and on exposure to moist air liberates the highly poisonous **hydrocyanic acid** gas, HCN.   For gold and silver extraction it easily combines with the metals, forming soluble double salts, $NaAu(CN)_2$. Sodium cyanide is made by passing a stream of nitrogen gas over a hot mixture of sodium carbonate and carbon in the presence of a catalyst. It is a white crystalline powder, soluble in water.   It is usually packed in 100- and 200-lb containers, made up in 1-oz briquettes, 4-oz eggs, or fused and broken.   **Cyanegg** is the name of Du Pont for 96 to 98% sodium cyanide in egg shape for case hardening steel.   The melting point is 1040°F.   The white **copper cyanide** used in electroplating has the composition $Cu_2(CN)_2$, containing 70% copper.   It melts at 474.5°C and is insoluble in water, but is soluble in sodium cyanide solution. **Sodium ferrocyanide,** or yellow **prussiate of soda,** is a lemon-yellow crystalline solid of the composition $Na_4Fe(CN)_6 \cdot 10H_2O$, used for carbonizing steel for case hardening.   It is also employed in paints, in printing inks, and for the purification of organic acids; and in minute quantities, it is used in salt to make it free-flowing.   It is soluble in water. **Calcium cyanide** in powder or granulated forms is used as an insecticide. It liberates 25% of hydrocyanic acid gas.   **Cyanogas,** of the American Cyanamid Co., is gaseous HCN from calcium cyanide.

SODIUM HYDROXIDE. Known commonly as **caustic soda,** and also as **sodium hydrate.**   **Lye** is an old name used in some industries and in household uses. It is a white, massive crystalline solid of the composition NaOH used for scouring and cleaning baths, for etching aluminum, in quenching baths for heat-treating steel, in cutting and soluble oils, in making soaps, and in a wide variety of other applications.   It is usually a by-product in the production of chlorine from salt.   The specific gravity is 2.13 and melting point 318°C.   It is soluble in water, alcohol, and in glycerin.   Sodium hydroxide is sold in liquid and in solid or powder forms on the basis of its Na_2O content.   A high-grade commercial caustic soda contains 98% min NaOH equivalent to 76 min Na_2O.   The liquid contains 50% min NaOH.   **Pels,** of PPG Industries, is a caustic soda in bead form.   It is less irritating to the skin when used in detergents. **Phosflake,** of Pittsburgh Plate Glass, used in washing machines, is a mixture of caustic soda and trisodium phosphate.   **Caustic potash** is **potassium hydroxide,** KOH, which has the same uses but is more expensive.   Caustic potash is a white, lumpy solid.   It is soluble in water and makes a powerful cleansing bath for scouring metals.   It is marketed as solid, flake, granular, or broken, and also in 40 and 50% liquid solutions.   It is also used in soaps and for bleaching textiles.   When used in steel-quenching baths, it gives a higher quenching rate than water alone and does not corrode the steel as a salt solution does.

SODIUM NITRATE. Also called **soda niter** and **Chile saltpeter.**   A mineral found in large quantities in the arid regions of Chile, Argentina, and Bolivia, where the crude nitrate with iodine and other impurities is called **caliche.**   It is used for making nitric and sulfuric acids, for explosives, as a flux in welding, and as a fertilizer.   The composition is $NaNO_3$. It is usually of massive granular crystalline structure with a hardness of 1.5 to 2 and specific gravity of 2.29.   It is colorless to white, but sometimes colored by impurities.   It is readily soluble in water.   In other parts of the world it occurs in beds with common salt, borax, and gypsum.   Sodium nitrate is also made by nitrogen fixation and is marketed granulated, in crystals, or in sticks.   It is colorless and odorless, and it has a specific gravity of 2.267 and a melting point of 316°C.   It has a bitter, saline taste. **Sodan,** of the Allied Chemical & Dye Corp., used for spraying on soils, is a clear liquid solution of sodium nitrate and ammonium nitrate containing 20% nitrogen.   **Norway saltpeter,** used in fertilizers and explosives, is **calcium nitrate,** $Ca(NO_3)_2$, in colorless crystals soluble in water.   Calcium nitrate of fine crystal size is used as a coagulant for rubber latex.

SODIUM SILICATE. A water-soluble salt commonly known as **water glass** or **soluble glass.**   Chemically, it is **sodium metasilicate** of the composition Na_2SiO_3 or $NaSiO_3 \cdot 9H_2O$.   Two other forms of the silicate are also available, **sodium sesquisilicate,** $3Na_2O \cdot 2SiO_2$, and **sodium orthosilicate,** $2Na_2O \cdot SiO_2$.   All of these are noted for their powerful detergent and emulsifying properties, and for their suspending power.   The material has good adhesion, and large quantities are used in water solutions for industrial adhesives.   When solid, sodium silicate is glassy in appearance and dissolves in hot water.   It melts at 1018°C.   It is obtained by melting sodium carbonate with silica, or by melting sand, charcoal, and soda.   The fused product is ground and dissolved in water by long boiling.   **Potassium silicate** is made in the same way, or a complex soluble glass is made by using both sodium and potassium carbonates.   Potassium silicate is more soluble than sodium silicate.   **Kasil,** of the Philadelphia Quartz Co., is a potassium silicate in fine powder containing 71% SiO_2 and 28.4 K_2O.   It is used in ceramic coatings and refractory cements.   The **Corlok** of the Pennsylvania Chemicals Corp. is potassium silicate free of fluorides and sodium compounds.   It is resistant to strong oxidizing acids and has good bond strength, and is used as a cement for acid tanks.   **Ammonium silicate** has an ammonium group instead of the sodium.   **Quram 220,** of the Philadelphia Quartz Co., is this material in the form of white powder or in opalescent solution.   The intermediate silica grades act like sodium silicates and are used as binders for refractory ceramics.

Sodium silicate is marketed as a viscous liquid or in powder form.   It is used as a detergent, as a protection for wood and porous stone, as a fixing agent for pigments, for cementing stoneware, for lute cements for such uses as sealing electric-light bulbs, for waterproofing walls, greaseproofing paper containers, for coating welding rods, as a filler for soaps, and as a catalyst for high-octane gasoline.   It increases the cleansing power of soaps but irritates the skin.   However, it is used in cleansing compounds because it is a powerful detergent.   **Brite Sil,** of Allegheny Industrial Chemicals, is a spray-dried sodium silicate powder which dissolves more easily and more uniformly.

Sodium silicate is also used for insulating electric wire.   It is applied in solution and the coated wire is then heated, leaving a flexible coating. Mixed with whiting, it is used as a strong cement for grinding wheels. Sodium metasilicate marketed by the Philadelphia Quartz Co. as a cleaner of metals is a crystalline powder.   Hot solutions of this salt in water are caustic and will clean grease readily from metals.   **Drymet,** of the Cowles Detergent Co., is the anhydrous sodium metasilicate.   It is a fine white powder with total alkalinity of 51% Na_2O.   It is easily soluble in water, and is used as a detergent and in soap powders to give free-flowing, non-caking properties.   The anhydrous material for a given detergent strength weighs little more than half the weight of the hydrous powder.   **Dryorth** is the anhydrous material of 60% alkalinity.   It is a powerful detergent and grease remover.   **Crystamet,** of the same company, is the material with 42% water of crystallization.   It is a free-flowing white powder. **Penchlor,** of the Pennsylvania Salt Mfg. Co., is an **acidproof cement** made by mixing cement powder with a sodium silicate solution.   It is used for lining chemical tanks and drains.   **Aquagel,** of the Silica Products Co., is a hydrous silicate of alumina, used in the same manner for waterproofing concrete.

SOLDER. An alloy of two or more metals used for joining other metals together by surface adhesion without melting the base metals as in welding alloys and without requiring a high-temperature flame as for the high-melting brazing alloys.   However, with skill in application, there is often no definite temperature line between the **soldering alloys** and the brazing alloys and a torch flame may be used for soldering.   A requirement for a true solder is that it have a lower melting point than the metals being joined, and also have an affinity for, or be capable of uniting with, the metals to be joined.

The most common solder is called **half-and-half,** or **plumbers' solder,** and is composed of equal parts of lead and tin.   It melts at 360°F.   The weight of this solder is 0.318 lb per cu in., tensile strength 5,500 psi, and the electrical conductivity 11% that of copper.   **SAE Solder No. 1** has 49.5 to 50.0% tin, 50 lead, 0.12 max antimony, and 0.08 max copper. It melts at 357.8°F.   Much commercial half-and-half, however, usually contains larger proportions of lead and some antimony, with less tin. These mixtures have higher melting points, and solders with less than 50% tin have a wide melting range and do not freeze quickly.   Sometimes a wide melting range is desired, in which case a **wiping solder** with 38 to 45% of tin is used.   **Solder No. 4663,** of Westinghouse, is a narrow-melting-range solder, melting from 183 to 185°C, while **Solder No. 1580** is a wiping solder with a melting range from 183 to 231°C.   The first contains 60% tin and 40 lead, and the second has 42% tin and 58 lead. **Slicker solder** is the best quality of plumbers' solder, containing 63 to 66% tin and the balance lead.   The earliest solders were the Roman solder called **argentarium,** containing equal parts of tin and lead, and **tertiarium,** containing 1 part tin and 2 lead.   Both alloys are still in use, and throughout early industrial times tertiarium was known as **tinman's solder.**

Good-quality solders for electrical joints should have at least 40% tin, as the electrical conductivity of lead is only about half that of tin, but conductivity is frequently sacrificed for better wiping ability, and the wiping solders are usually employed for electrical work.   **Soft solders** should not contain zinc because of poor adhesion from the formation of oxides. Various melting points to suit the work are obtained with solders by varying the proportions of the metals.   The **low-melting solders** are those that have a melting point at 230°C or lower, and the **high-melting solders** melt at higher temperatures.   The flow point, at which the solder is entirely liquid, is often considerably above the melting point.   Tin added to lead lowers the melting point of the lead until at 356°F, or 68% tin, the melting point rises with increase in tin content until the melting point of pure tin is reached.   A standard solder with 48% tin and 52 lead melts at 360°F. A 45–55 solder melts at 440°F.   Cheap solders may contain much less tin, but they have lower adhesion.   **SAE solder No. 4** contains 22.5 to 23.5% tin, 75 lead, and 2 max antimony.   It melts at 370.4°F.

Solders with low melting points are obtained from mixtures of lead, tin, cadmium, and bismuth.   **Bismuth solder** is also more fluid, as the bismuth lowers the surface tension.   Bismuth, however, hardens the alloy, although to a lesser extent than antimony.   A bismuth solder containing equal parts of lead, tin, and bismuth melts at 284°F.   The **Cerrolow alloys** of the Cerro de Pasco Corp. are bismuth solders containing sufficient indium to be designated as **indium solders.   Cerrolow 147,** which melts at 142°F, contains 48% bismuth, 25.6 lead, 12.8 tin, 9.6 cadmium, and 4 indium.   **Cerrolow 105,** melting at 100°F, contains 42.9% bismuth, 21.7 lead, 8 tin, 5 cadmium, 18.3 indium, and 4 mercury.   Cadmium solders have low melting points, are hard, and are usually cheaper than tin solders, but they have the disadvantage of blackening and corroding, and the fumes are toxic. **Cadmium zinc solders** were used in wartime because of the scarcity of tin. A solder containing 80% lead, 10 tin, and 10 cadmium has about the same strength as a 50–50 tin-lead solder and has greater ductility, but is darker in color. **Cadmium-tin solder,** with high cadmium, is used to solder magnesium alloys. Soft solders for soldering brass and copper, especially for electrical connections, may be of tin hardened with antimony. **Solder wire,** marketed by the American Brass Co. for this purpose, contains 95% tin and 5 antimony. Thallium may be used in high-lead solders to increase strength and adhesion.

Hard solder may be any solder with a melting point above that of the tin-lead solders; more specifically hard solders are the brazing solders, silver solders, or aluminum solders applied with a brazing torch. **Aluminum solders** may contain up to 15% aluminum. **Soluminium,** an early German solder, contained 55% tin, 33 zinc, 11 aluminum, and 1 copper. **Mouray's solder** contained 80 to 90% zinc, 3 to 8 copper, and 6 to 12 aluminum. A solder prepared by the National Bureau of Standards contains 87% tin, 8 zinc, and 5 aluminum. It has good strength and ductility. **Alcoa solder 805,** for joining aluminum to steel or other metals, has 95% zinc and 5 aluminum. The melting range is 715 to 725°F. For soldering aluminum to aluminum, an alloy of 91% tin and 9 zinc is used.

The solder known as **Richard's solder** is a yellow brass with 3% aluminum and 3 phosphor tin. Solders with nickel content are used for soldering nickel silver, and silver and gold solders are used for jewelry work. Silver solder in varying proportions is also used as a high-melting-point solder for general work, and small amounts of silver are sometimes used in lead-tin solders to conserve tin, but the melting point is high. **Lead-silver solders** with more than 90% lead and some silver, in use during the war emergency, had high melting points and poor spreading qualities. Indium improves these solders, and a solder with 96% lead, 3 silver, and 1 indium has a melting point at 310°C and a tensile strength of 4,970 psi. **Cerroseal 35,** of the Cerro de Pasco Corp., contains 50% tin and 50 indium. It melts at 240°F, has low vapor pressure, and will adhere to ceramics. **Alkali-resistant solders** are **indium-lead alloys.** A solder with 50% lead and 50 indium melts at 360°, and is very resistant to alkalies, but lead-tin solders with as low as 25% indium are resistant to alkaline solutions, have better wetting characteristics, and are strong. Indium solders are expensive. Adding 0.85% silver to a 40% tin soft solder gives equivalent wetting on copper alloys to a 63% tin solder, but the addition is not effective on low-tin solders. A **gold-copper solder** used for making high-vacuum seals and for brazing difficult metals such as iron-cobalt alloys contains 37.5% gold and 62.5 copper. The **silver-palladium solders** have high melting points, 1232°C for a 30% palladium alloy, good flow, and corrosion resistance. A **palladium-nickel alloy** with 40% nickel has a melting point about 1237°C. The brazing alloys containing palladium are useful for a wide range of metals, or metal to ceramic joints.

Cold solder, used for filling cracks in metals, may be a mixture of a metal powder in a pyroxylin cement with or without a mineral filler, but the strong cold solders are made with synthetic resins, usually epoxies, cured with catalysts, and with no solvents to cause shrinkage. The metal content may be as high as 80%. **Devcon F,** of the Devcon Corp., for repairing holes in castings, has 80% aluminum powder and 20 epoxy resin. It is cured by heat at 150°F, giving high adhesion. **Epoxyn solder,** of Co-Polymer Chemicals, Inc., is aluminum powder in an epoxy resin in the form of a putty for filling cracks or holes in sheet metal. It cures with a catalyst. The metal-epoxy mixtures give a shrinkage of less than 0.2%, and they can be machined and polished smooth.

SOLVENT. A material, usually a liquid, having the power of dissolving another material and forming a homogeneous mixture called a **solution.** The mixture is physical, and no chemical action takes place. A solid solution is such a mixture of two metals, but the actual mixing occurs during the liquid or gaseous state. Some materials are soluble in certain other materials in all proportions, while others are soluble only up to a definite percentage and the residue is precipitated out of solution. Homogeneous mixtures of gases may technically be called solutions, but are generally referred to only as mixtures.

The usual industrial applications of solvents are for putting solid materials into liquid solution for more convenient chemical processing, for thinning paints and coatings, and for dissolving away foreign matter as in dry-cleaning textiles. But they may have other uses, such as absorbing dust on roadways and as weed killers. They have an important use in separating materials, for example, in the extraction of oils from seeds. In such use, a **clathrate** is a solid compound added to the solution containing a difficult-to-extract material, but which is trapped selectively by the clathrate. The solid clathrate is then filtered out and processed by heat or chemically to separate the desired compound. **Antifoamers** are chemicals, such as the silicones, added to solvents to reduce foam so that processing equipment can be used to capacity without spill-over. **Antifoam 71,** of General Electric, is a silicone emulsion that can be used in foodstuffs in proportions up to 100 ppm. **Solvent-solvents** are solvents used for second-stage extraction of difficult to extract metals such as gold, uranium, and thorium. **Tributyl phosphine oxide,** $(C_4H_9)_3PO$, a white crystalline powder, is such a material used in benzene or kerosene solution for extracting metals from the acids employed in ore extraction.

The usual commercial solvents for organic substances are the alcohols, ether, benzene, and turpentine, the latter two being common solvents for paints and varnishes containing gums and resins. The so-called **coal-tar solvents** are light oils from coal tar, distilling off between 145 and 180°C, with specific gravities ranging from 0.850 to 0.890. **Solvent oils,** from coal tar, are amber to dark liquids with distillation ranges from about 150 to 340°C, with specific gravities from 0.910 to 0.980. They are used as solvents for asphalt varnishes and bituminous paints. **Shingle stains** are amber to dark grades of solvent oils of specific gravities from 0.910 to 0.930.

A valuable solvent for rubbers and many other products is **carbon bisulfide,** CS_2, also called **carbon disulfide,** made by heating together carbon and sulfur. It is flammable and toxic. When pure it is nearly odorless. The specific gravity is 1.2927 and boiling point 46.5°C. **Ethyl acetate,** $CH_3COOC_2H_5$, made from ethyl alcohol and acetic acid, is an important solvent for nitrocellulose and lacquers. It is liquid boiling at 77°C. One of the best solvents for cellulose is cuprammonium hydroxide. Amyl and other alcohols, amyl acetate, and other volatile liquids are used for quick-drying lacquers, but many synthetic chemicals are available for such use. **Dioxan,** a water-white liquid of specific gravity of 1.035 and composition $CH_2CH_2OCH_2CH_2O$, is a good solvent for cellulose compounds, resins, and varnishes, and is used also in **paint removers,** which owe their action to their solvent power. **Ethyl lactate,** used as a solvent for cellulose nitrate, is a liquid with boiling point of 150°C and specific gravity of 1.03. **Octyl alcohol,** a liquid of the composition $CH_3(CH_2)_6CH_2OH$, specific gravity 1.429, and boiling point of 195°C, has a high solvent power for nitrocellulose and resins. **Diafoam,** of the Resinous Products & Chemical Co., is a secondary octyl alcohol used as a defoaming agent in plastics and lacquers. **Methyl hexyl ketone,** $CH_3(CH_2)_5COCH_3$, is a powerful high-boiling solvent which also acts as a dispersing agent in inks, dyestuffs, and perfumes. It is a water-white liquid boiling at 173°C.

The chlorinated hydrocarbons have powerful solvent action on fats, waxes, and oils and are used in degreasing. Water is a solvent for most acids and alkalies and for many organic and inorganic materials. Acids or alkalies that decompose the material are not solvents for the material. Solvents are used to produce a solution that can be applied, as in the case of paints, and the evaporation of the solvent then leaves the material chemically unchanged. They may also be employed to separate one substance from another, by the selection of a solvent that dissolves one substance but not the other. **Dichlorethyl ether,** a yellowish liquid with a chloroformlike odor, of the composition $ClCH_2CH_2OCH_2CH_2Cl$, is a good solvent for fats and greases and is used in scouring solutions and in soaps. **Dichlorethylene** is a liquid of the composition $C_2H_2Cl_2$, specific gravity

1.278, and boiling point about 52°C. It is used as a solvent for the extraction of fats and for rubber.

Dichloro methane, known also as **methylene chloride** and **carrene,** is a colorless, nonflammable liquid of the composition CH_2Cl_2, boiling at 39.8°C. It is soluble in alcohol, and is used in paint removers, as a dewaxing solvent for oils, for degreasing textiles, and as a refrigerant. A low-boiling solvent for oils and waxes is **butyl chloride,** $CH_3CH_2CH_2$-CH_2Cl. It is a water-white liquid of specific gravity 0.8875, boiling at 78.6°C. **Isocrotyl chloride** is a liquid of the composition $CH_3 \cdot C(CH_2)_2$: $CHCl$, with specific gravity of 0.919, boiling point 68°C, used for cleaning and degreasing. **Cyclohexane,** $(CH_2)_6$, made by the hydrogenation of benzene, is a good solvent for rubbers, resins, fats, and waxes. It is a water-white highly inflammable liquid of specific gravity 0.777, boiling point 80.8°C, and flash point 10°F. This solvent is marketed in England as **Sextone.** The **Nadene** of the Allied Chemical Co. is **cyclohexanone,** $CH_2(CH_2)_4C{:}O$. It is a powerful general solvent, and is used as a coupling agent for immiscible compounds. The **Sulfolanes** of the Shell Oil Co. are selective solvents for separating mixtures having different degrees of saturation, and can be removed easily by water wash. **Dimethyl sulfolane** is produced from pentadiene by reacting with SO_2 and hydrogenation. **Cyclohexanol,** also called **hexalin** and **hexahydro phenol,** $C_6H_{11}OH$, is a solvent for oils, gums, waxes, rubber, and resins. It is made by the hydrogenation of phenol, and is a liquid boiling at 158°C.

Dichlorethyl formal, $CH_2(OCH_2 \cdot CH_2 \cdot Cl)_2$, is a water-insoluble high-boiling solvent for cellulose and for fats, oils, and resins. The boiling point is 218.1°C, and specific gravity 1.234. The **nitroparaffins** constitute a group of powerful solvents for oil, fats, waxes, gums, and resins. Blended with alcohols they are solvents for cellulose acetate, producing good flow and hardening properties for nonblushing lacquers. **Nitromethane,** CH_3NO_2, is a water-white liquid, specific gravity 1.139, boiling point 101°C, and freezing point -29°C. It is also used as a rocket fuel. At 500°F it explodes into a hot mixture of nitrogen, hydrogen, carbon monoxide, carbon dioxide, and water vapor, but with a catalyst the disintegration can be controlled into a smooth continuous explosion. **Nitroethane,** $CH_3CH_2NO_2$, has a specific gravity of 1.052, boiling point 114°C, and freezing point -90°C.

A **plasticizer** is a liquid or solid that dissolves in or is compatible with a resin, gum, or other material and renders it plastic, flexible, or easy to work. A sufficient quantity of plasticizer will result in a viscous mixture which consists of a suspension of solid grains of the resin or gum in the liquid plasticizer. The plasticizer is in that sense a solvent, but unlike an ordinary solvent the plasticizer remains with the cured resin to give added properties to the material, such as flexibility. **Dibutyl phthalate,** a water-white oily liquid of specific gravity 1.048, boiling point 340°C, and composition $C_{16}H_{22}O_4$, is a plasticizer for Buna N rubber and polyvinyl chloride plastics.   **Monoplex DOA,** of the Rohm & Haas Co., used to give flexibility to vinyl resins at low temperatures, is **diisooctyl adipate.** It has a flash point at 400°F, and freezing point at 55°C.   An **aprotic solvent** is a solvent that contains no hydrogen, such as **selenium oxychloride,** a liquid of the composition $SeOCl_2$.   Such solvents are used in electronic applications where the energy deflecting of free protons would be undesirable.   **Phosphorus oxychloride,** $POCl_3$, is an aprotic solvent used with neodymium in **liquid lasers** giving high light-beam efficiency.

SORBITOL. A **hexahydric alcohol,** $(CH_2OH)_5CHOH$, which occurs naturally in many fruits, but is now made on a large scale by the direct hydrogenation of corn sugar, or dextro glucose.   It is a white, odorless, crystalline powder of faint sweet taste.   It melts at 97.7°C, and is easily dissolved in water.   It is used as a humectant, softener, blending agent, for the production of synthetic resins, plasticizers, and drying oils, and as an emulsifier in cosmetics and pharmaceuticals.   It is digestible and nutritive and is used in confectionery to improve texture and storage life by inhibiting crystal growth of the sugar, and also in dietary foods as a substitute for sugar.   **Sorbo** and **Arlex,** of the Atlas Chemical Industries, are water solutions of sorbitol.   **Mannitol** is an isomer form of the alcohol and is produced in granular form for pharmaceuticals and foodstuffs as a binder.   In the form of a free-flowing powder it is used as an **anticaking agent** in pharmaceuticals and foodstuffs where a silica or other mineral-based agent is undesirable.   The **polysorbates** are esters of sorbitol. **Polysorbate 80,** of Hodag Chemical Corp., is such a material used as an emulsifier in prepared mixed food for improving texture and stability. **Hex,** a metal-cleaning and protective agent of Fields Paint Mfg. Co., is a phosphoric acid ester of sorbitol.

SOUND INSULATORS. Materials employed, chiefly in walls, for reducing the transmission of noise.   Insulators are used to impede the passage of sound waves, as distinct from isolators used under machines to absorb the vibrations that cause the sound.   For factory use the walls, partitions, and ceilings offer the only mediums for the installation of sound insulators.   All material substances offer resistance to the passage of sound waves, and even the glass windows may be considered as insulators.   But the term refers to the special materials placed in the walls for this specific purpose.   Insulators may consist of mineral wool, hair felt, foamed plastics, fiber sheathing boards, or simple sheathing papers.   Sound insulators are marketed under a variety of trade names, such as **Celotex,** made from bagasse, and **Fibrofelt,** made from flax or rye fiber.   Wheat straw is also used for making insulating board. Sound insulators are often also heat insulators. **Linofelt,** of Union Fiber, is a sound- and heat-insulating material used for walls. It consists of a quilt of flax fiber between tough waterproof paper. It comes in sheets $\frac{5}{16}$ to $\frac{3}{4}$ in. thick. **Torofoleum** is a German insulating material made from peat moss treated with a waterproofing agent. It will withstand temperatures up to 230°F, is porous, and weighs less than 1 lb per bd ft.

Vibration insulators, or **isolators,** to reduce vibrations that produce noises, are usually felt or fiberboards placed between the machine base and the foundation, but for heavy pressures they may be metal wire helically wound or specially woven, deriving their effectiveness from the form rather than the material. **Keldur,** of International Products, is a fibrous insulating material made up in sheets $\frac{3}{4}$ in. thick, with a resilient binder. **Korfund isolator,** of the Korfund Co., is a resilient mat of cork treated with oil and bound in a steel frame. It will take loadings up to 4,000 lb per sq ft. **Vibro-Insulator,** of B. F. Goodrich, is an isolator of Ameripol synthetic rubber. Plastic foams in sheet or flexible tape form are also used as isolators for instruments.

SOYBEAN OIL. Also known as **soya bean oil.** A pale-yellow oil obtained by expression from the seeds of the plant *Glycine soya,* native to Manchuria, but grown in the United States. It is primarily a food oil, but has an undesirable off-flavor unless highly purified. It is also used as a drying oil for linoleum, paints, and varnishes, or for mixing with linseed oil, although the untreated oil has only half the drying power of linseed oil. It is also used in core oils and in soaps. The bean contains up to 20% oil. The average yield factor is 15%, but by trichlorethylene extraction a bushel of beans will yield 11 lb of oil and 46 lb of high-protein meal containing less than 1% oil. The oil content decreases in warm climates. Southern-grown soybeans contain 2 to 5% less oil than those grown in Illinois. The usual conversion factor is 8.5 lb of oil and 48 lb of meal per bushel of beans. The oil is easy to bleach, has good consistency as a food oil, and does not become rancid easily, but has less flavor stability than many other oils. There are 280 varieties of the bean grown in the United States and 2,500 varieties listed. The pods contain two or three beans which range in color from light straw through gray and brown to nearly black. Most varieties are straw-colored or greenish yellow. The stalks and leaves of the plant contain much nitrogen, and about half of the crop is usually plowed under for fertilizer.

The specific gravity of the oil is about 0.925, iodine value 134, and it should have a maximum of not more than 1.5% free fatty acids and not more than 0.3% moisture and volatile matter. The fractionated oil yields 15% cut soybean oil of an iodine value of 70 to 90, used for soaps, lubricants, and rubber compounding; 72% selected-acid oil of an iodine value of 145 to 155, used for varnish and paint oils alone or in blends with other oils, or for glycerin making; 13% bottoms, used for soaps, lubricants, and giving a by-product pitch used in insulation and mastic flooring. **Snowflake oil** of the Archer-Daniels-Midland Co. is a heavy-bodied oxidized soybean oil for paints. It has a specific gravity of 0.986 to 0.989, and iodine number from 64 to 95. **Soyalene,** of the same company, is an alkali-refined soybean oil for varnishes. The specific gravity is 0.924, and the iodine number is 130. **Epoxidized soybean oil** is used in vinyl and alkyd resins as a plasticizer and to increase heat resistance. A very large use of soybean oil is in the making of margarine.

Soybean meal is the product obtained by grinding the soybean chips from the expeller process, or the **soybean oil cake** from the hydraulic process. The meal is marketed as stock feed or fertilizer. It is chiefly used as a protein feed for dairy cattle, but it is inferior to fish meal for poultry, as it lacks the mineral salts and vitamins of fish meal. Soybean meal hardened with formaldehyde is used as a filler with wood flour in plastics to give better flow in molding. **Gelsoy** is a protein gel extracted from soybean meal. It is used in foodstuffs as a thickening agent, and is also used as a strong adhesive.

Soybean flour for bakery food products for the American market is made from meal that has been treated by acidulated washing to remove the soluble enzymes and sugars that carry the taste. Meal produced by heat processing averages 40% protein and 20% fats, while meal from solvent extraction has 42 to 50% protein and a maximum of 2.5% fats. Further processing of the meal to remove sugars and other materials varies the final protein content of the flour, and meals from different types of beans vary in content. A soybean flour, of Power Protein, Inc., has 40% protein and 20% fats with the sugars that give easy solubility for blending. It is used as a partial replacement for milk powder and wheat flour in baked goods. The **Promax** and **Isopro** soybean flours, of Griffith Laboratories, for high-protein additions to foodstuffs, contain 70% protein with all flavor removed, and are high in lysine. They have a pH of 5.5 and 7.0, respectively. **Soy proteins,** of General Mills, used in canned soups and meat products, is toasted to eliminate all enzyme activity. It contains 50% protein with 2% lecithin and 3% lysine. **Promine,** of the Central Soya Co., is a 93% concentrate of soybean proteins, used for thickening and enriching soup mixes. **Supro 610,** of Ralston Purina Co., is a spray-dried powder, 95% protein, with a light cream color and no bitter flavor.

SPECULUM METAL. An alloy formerly used for mirrors, and also in optical instruments. It contains 65 to 67% copper and the remainder tin.   It takes a beautiful polish and is hard and tough.   Speculum metal should have a maximum of crystals of Cu_4Sn, containing 66.6% copper. An old Roman mirror contained about 64% copper, 19 tin, and 17 lead, and an Egyptian mirror contained 85% copper, 14 tin, and 1 iron.   The old Greek mirrors were carefully worked out with 32% tin and 68 copper.   They had 70% of the reflecting power of silver, with a slight red excess of reflection that gave a warm glow, without the blue of nickel or antimony.   This alloy is now plated on metals for reflectors.   A modern telescope mirror contains 70% copper and 30 tin.   **Chinese speculum** contains about 8% antimony and 10 tin.   **Speculum plate** advocated by the Tin Research Institute for electroplating, to give a hard, white, corrosion-resistant surface for food-processing equipment and optical reflectors, has 55% copper and 45 tin.   It is harder than nickel, and retains its reflectivity better than silver.

SPERM OIL.   The waxy oil extracted from the head cavity of the sperm whale, *Physeter breviceps* and *P. catadon,* and the **Bottlenose whale,** *P. macrocephalus.*   Sperm whales have teeth and feed in deep water on squid and large animal life.   The male sperm attains a length of 60 ft and the female about 38 ft.   The spermaceti is first separated out, leaving a clear yellow oil.   It is purified by being pressed at a low temperature. It is graded according to the temperature of pressing.   A good grade of sperm oil has a specific gravity of 0.875 to 0.885, and a flash point above 440°F.   Inferior grades of sperm oil may be from sperm-whale blubber. Commercial sperm oil is likely to be one-third head oil and two-thirds body oil.   Sperm oil differs from fish oil and whale oil in consisting chiefly of liquid waxes of the higher fatty alcohol esters and not fats. Sperm oil absorbs very little oxygen from the atmosphere and resists decomposition even at temperatures above 400°F, and it will pour below its cloud point of 38 to 45°F.   It wets metal surfaces easily.   It is thus a valuable lubricating oil.   It was formerly used as a lamp oil, burning with a white shining flame.   It is also an excellent soap oil.   **Sperm 42,** of Werner G. Smith, Inc., is a sperm oil with carbon chains of C_{10} to C_{22} which is emulsifiable in cold or warm water.   **Sulfonated sperm oil** is used as a wetting agent for textiles, and it is also valued for cutting oils, crankcase oil, and high-pressure lubricants.   **Smithol 25,** of the same company, is a synthetic fatty acid oil resembling sperm oil and having the same uses.   It is a light-colored odorless oil with high viscosity, a low pour point at −16°F, and an iodine value of 105.

Spermaceti is the white, crystalline flakes of fatty substance, or wax, that separate out from sperm oil on cooling after boiling.   It is **cetyl palmitate,** a true wax, and does not yield glycerin when saponified.   It is purified by pressing, and the triple-refined is snow white.   It is also separated out from **dolphin-head oil.**   Spermaceti is odorless and tasteless, has a melting point of 43°C, is insoluble in water, but soluble in hot alcohol.   It burns with a bright flame.   It was formerly used for candles but now is employed chiefly as a fine wax for ointments and compounds.   Sperm oil and spermaceti are inedible and indigestible.   **Cetyl alcohol,** $C_{16}H_{33}OH$, originally obtained from spermaceti, is now made synthetically from **ethyl palmitate.**

SPICE. An aromatic vegetable substance, generally a solid used in powdered form, employed for flavoring foods.   There is no sharp dividing line between **flavors** and spices, but in general a spice is a material that is used to stimulate the appetite and increase the flow of gastric juices. Spices are not classed as foods in themselves, having litttle food value, but as food accessories.   Pepper is distinctly a spice, though not grouped with the spices.   Some spices are also used widely as flavors and in perfumes, and also in medicine either for antiseptic or other value or to disguise the unpleasant taste of drugs.   A **condiment** is a strong spice, or a spice of sharp taste, although the word is often erroneously applied to any spice.   A **savory** is a fragrant herb or seed used for flavor in cooking. Spices are obtained from the stalks, bark, fruits, flowers, seeds, or roots of plants.   **Microground spices,** used to give uniform distribution in the quantity manufacture of foodstuffs, are spices ground to microscopic fineness in a roller mill.   The most popular spices in the United States, in the order of quantity used, are: cinnamon, nutmeg, ginger, cloves, allspice, poppy seed, and caraway seed.   Since ground spices lose flavor rapidly by the loss of the volatile oils, the particles are sometimes coated with dextrose or a water-soluble gum.   The **Spisoseals,** of Dodge & Olcott, Inc., are ground spices with the particles coated.

Allspice, also known as **pimento** and **Jamaica pepper,** is the dried unripe fruit of the small evergreen tree *Pimenta officinalis* of the myrtle family growing in the West Indies and tropical America.   The fruit is a small berry which when dried is wrinkled and reddish brown.   It has a flavor much like a combination of clove, nutmeg, and cinnamon.   **Pimento oil** is a fragrant essential oil distilled from the berries, which contain 4%. It contains eugenol and cineol and is used in flavors, in bay rum, and in carnation perfumes.   **Coriander** is the dried fruit of the perennial plant *Coriandrum sativum* grown in the Mediterranean countries and India.   It is one of the oldest of spices and has a pleasant aromatic taste. **Oil of coriander,** extracted from the dried seed, is used in medicine, beverages, and flavoring extracts.   It has a higher aromatic flavor than the fruit.   **Savory** is a fragrant herb of the mint family, *Satureia hortensis,* used in cooking, and in medicine as a carminative.   It contains **carvacrol,** a complex phenol also occurring in caraway and camphor.   The word savory also designates other herbs used directly in foods as flavors.

Celery seed, used as a savory, is from the plant *Apium graveolens.* The best-quality leafstalks, known as **celery,** are bleached white and eaten raw or cooked.   The plant is widely grown for seed in France and Spain. **Celery-seed oil** is a pale-yellow oil extracted from the seeds and used as a flavor and in perfumery.   **Fennel** is the dried oval seed of the perennial plants *Foeniculum vulgare* and *F. dulce.*   The stalks of the latter are blanched and eaten as a vegetable in Europe.   Fennel is used as a flavoring in confectionery and liqueurs, and as a carminative in medicine. **Fennel oil** is a pale yellowish essential oil with specific gravity of 0.975, distilled from the seed.   It has an aromatic odor and a camphorlike taste with a secondary sweetish, spicy taste.   It contains **fenchone,** $C_{10}H_{16}O$, an isomer of camphor, with also pinene, camphene, and **anethole,** or **anise camphor,** $C_3H_5C_6H_4OCH_3$.   The latter is used in dentifrices and pharmaceuticals.   **Fenugreek** is the seed from the long pods of the annual legume *Trigonella foenum-graecum* native to southern Europe.   It is used in curries, in medicine, and for making artificial maple flavor.   **Oregano,** used as an ingredient in chili powder and as a spice in a variety of dishes, is the pungent herb *Coleus amboinica.*

Dill seed, from the herb *Anethum graveolens,* of the parsley family, is used as a condiment for pickles.   **Dill leaves** are used as seasoning for soups, sauces, and pickles.   **Dill oil,** extracted from the whole herb, is used as a flavor in the food industry.   It resembles caraway oil and has a finer flavor than **dill-seed oil** which is more plentiful, but **dill flavor** prepared from the whole seed is stronger.   Dill is grown in the central United States and in central Europe.   **Cardamon** is the highly aromatic and delicately flavored seeds of the large perennial herb *Elettaria cardamomum,* of India, Ceylon, and Central America.   The seeds are used in pickles, curries, and cakes, and the oil is employed as a flavor.   **Garlic** is the root bulb of the lily *Allium sativum,* used as a condiment, and also used in medicine, as an expectorant under the name of **allium.**   It contains **allyl sulfide,** a liquid of the composition $(CH_2:CHCH_2)_2S$, which gives it a pungent odor and taste.   **Allicine,** extracted from garlic, is used in medicine as an antibacterial.   It is an oily liquid with a sharp garlic odor.

Cumin is the seed of the *Cuminum cyminum,* the true cumin, and *Nigella sativa,* the **black cumin,** both of India.   The seed is used in confectionery and in curries.   A kind of black cumin known as **shiah zira,** from the plant *Carum indicum* of India, is superior in taste and fragrance to ordinary cumin.   **Caraway** is the spicy seed of the biennial herb *C. carvi* of Europe and North Africa.   The seeds are used on cookies.   **Caraway**

oil, distilled from the seeds, contains carvone and limonene, and in combination with cassia gives a pleasant odor.   It is used in soap, perfumes, and mouthwashes.   **Sage** is the grayish-green hairy leaves of the shrublike plant *Salvia officinalis* used as a spice.   It is cultivated extensively in the Mediterranean region.   **Oil of sage** is used in perfumery.   **Clary sage oil** is distilled from the flowers of the *S. sclarea* of France, Italy, and North Africa.   It has the odor of a mixture of ambergris, neroli, and lavender, and is used in flavoring vermouth liquor and muscatel wines, and also in eau de cologne.   **Sassafras** is sometimes classed as a spice but is a flavor.   It is the aromatic spicy bark of the root of the tree *Sassafras albidum* which grows wild in the eastern United States.   It is used mostly for making root beer, but also for flavoring tobacco, and in patent medicines.   **Sassafras oil** is an oil extracted from the whole roots, which contain 2% of the yellow oil, and is used in medicine, perfumery, and soaps. It produces artificial heliotrope.   The oil contains **safrol,** $C_{10}H_{10}O_2$, also produced from brown camphor oil.   **Brazilian sassafras oil,** or **ocotea oil,** is distilled from the root of the tree *Ocotea cymbarum,* also of the laurel family.   The root yields about 1% of an oil which contains 90% safrol, and has the odor and flavor of American sassafras oil.   **Sarsaparilla** is an oil obtained from the long brown roots of the climbing vine *Smilax regellii* of Honduras, *S. aristolochiaefolia* of Mexico, and other species, all growing in tropical jungles.   The roots are used in medicine.   The oil is used as a flavor.   It is odorless, but has an acrid sweet taste.   It contains saponins.

Wintergreen oil is from the leaves of the small evergreen plant *Gaultheria procumbens* of the Middle Atlantic states.   The oil does not exist in the plant but is formed by the reaction between a glucoside and an enzyme when the chopped leaves are steeped in water.   It is largely **methyl salicylate,** $C_8H_8O_3$.   It is used in flavoring candies and soft drinks and in medicine.   **Hop oil,** used to give hop flavor to cereal beverages, and also in perfumes, is obtained from **lupulin,** a glandular powder found in the female inflorescence of the hop plant, *Humulus lupulus.*   **Hops** are used directly in making beer, and the oil is produced from the discard hops which contain 0.75% oil.   **Anise seed** is from the annual plant *Pimpinella anisum* grown in the Mediterranean countries and in India. The best grades come from Spain.   The seed is used in flavoring in the baking industry.   The distilled oil, **anise oil,** is used in perfumes and in soaps, and in the liqueur known as **anisette.**   The oil contains choline, and is used in medicine as a carminative and expectorant.

SPINEL. A **magnesium aluminate,** $MgO \cdot Al_2O_3$, occurring as octehedral crystals of varying colors due to impurities of iron, manganese, or chromium.   The best transparent stones are used as gems.   It is found as crystals or rolled pebbles in gem gravels with corundum stones, the **ruby spinel** often occurring with the true ruby.   It has a deep red color, but the variety **almandine** is violet.

Synthetic spinel was originally made in Germany to replace ruby and sapphire for instrument bearings because it is easier to cut and thus conserves diamond abrasive.   Spinel is produced by Linde in the forms of drawing dies, gages, wearing parts, orifices, and balls.   The composition is $MgO \cdot 3\frac{1}{2}Al_2O_3$, and the crystal structure is cubic.   The specific gravity is 3.61, the melting point is about 2040°C, and the Knoop hardness is 1,175 to 1,380, designated as Mohs 8.   Like corundum, it is not attacked by common acids or by sodium hydroxide.   The spinel powder from which the crystals are flame-grown is made by calcining a mixture of pure ammonium sulfate and ammonium magnesium sulfate.   Much synthetic spinel is used for synthetic gems, the colors being obtained with metal oxides.   Small amounts of chromic oxide give the tinted crystals of sapphire, while up to 6% is used for the dark ruby colors.   Blue is obtained with oxides of iron and titania, and green is from cobalt oxide. **Golden topaz** is colored with nickel and magnesium oxides.   The **aquamarine spinel** is tinted with a complex mixture of nickel, cobalt, vanadium, and titanium oxides.

SPODUMENE. A mineral of the composition $Li_2O \cdot Al_2O_3 \cdot 4SiO_2$, with some potassium and sodium oxides.   It is the chief ore of the metal lithium, but it requires a higher temperature for sintering than lepidolite and the sinter is more difficult to leach.   It is found in South Dakota and the Carolinas, and has an average content of 4% Li_2O, ranging from 2.9 to 7.6%.   Crystals of spodumene in South Dakota are 8 to 10 ft long and 1 ft in thickness, appearing like logs of wood, with as high as 6.5% lithium.   The specific gravity is 3.13 to 3.20, and the melting point is 1395 to 1425°C.   Spodumene is 3 times more active than feldspar as a flux in ceramics, giving fluidity, increasing surface tension, and eliminating pinholes.   A mixture of 25% spodumene with 75 feldspar is an active vitrifying agent in ceramics.   The melting point of the mixture is 1110°C, which is below the usual minimum temperature used for chinaware; it thus forms a glaze.   **Lithospar** is a name for feldspar and spodumene from the pegmatites of King's Mountain, North Carolina. In Germany lithium is obtained from the lithium mica **zinnwaldite,** which is a mixture of potassium-aluminum orthosilicate and lithium orthosilicate with some iron, and contains less than 3% Li_2O.   **Kryolithionite,** a mineral found in Greenland, has the composition $Na_3Li_3(AlF_6)_2$ and contains up to 11.5% Li_2O.   It has a crystal structure resembling garnet.   A transparent emerald-green spodumene in small crystals, known as **hiddenite,** is found in North Carolina, and is cut into gemstones.

SPONGE. The cellular skeleton of a marine animal of the genus *Spongia,* of which there are about 3,000 known species, only 13 of which are of commercial importance. It is employed chiefly for wiping and cleaning, as it will hold a great quantity of water in proportion to its weight, but it also has many industrial uses such as applying glaze to pottery. Sponges grow like plants, attached to rocks on the sea bottom. They are prepared for use by crushing to kill them, scraping off the rubbery skin, macerating in water to remove the gelatinous matter, and bleaching in the sun. Tarpon Springs, Fla., is the center of the American sponge fishing, but most of the best sponges have come from the Mediterranean and Red Seas.

The prepared sponge is an elastic fibrous structure chemically allied to silk. It has sievelike membranes with small pores leading into pear-shaped chambers. The best sponges are spheroidal, regular, and soft. Commercial sponges for the American market must have a diameter of 4.5 in. or more. Most of the Florida sponges are the **sheepswool sponge,** *Euspongia lachne,* used for cleaning and industrial sponging. The **Rock Island sponge,** from Florida, and the **Key wool sponge** are superior in texture and durability to the **Bahama wool sponge,** which is coarser, more open, and less absorbent. The **Key yellow sponge** is the finest grade. The **grass sponge,** *E. graminea,* of the Caribbean, is inferior in shape and texture. The fine **honeycomb sponge,** *Hippiospongia equina,* of the Mediterranean Sea, is of superior grade and has been preferred as a bath sponge. About 80% of the North African catch consists of honeycomb sponges, with the remainder **Turkey cup sponge,** *E. officinalis,* and **zimocca sponge,** *E. zimocca.* The Turkey cup is rated as the finest, softest, and most elastic of the sponges, but the larger of the zimocca sponges are too hard for surgical use, and are employed for industrial cleaning. Sponges for industrial and household uses have now been largely replaced by foamed rubbers and plastics.

SPONGE IRON. Iron made from ferrous sand and pressed into briquettes, which can be charged directly into steel furnaces instead of pig iron. It was originally made on a large scale in Japan where only low-grade sandy ores were available. Sponge iron is made by charging the sand continuously into a rotary furnace to drive off the light volatile products and reduce the iron oxide to metallic iron, which is passed through magnetic separators, and the finely divided iron briquetted. Unbriquetted sponge iron, with a specific gravity of 2, is difficult to melt because of the oxidation, but the briquetted material, with a specific gravity of 6, can be melted in the electric furnace. Sponge iron to replace scrap in steel-making is also made from low-grade ores by reducing the ore with coke-oven gas or natural gas. It is not melted, but the oxygen is driven off, leaving a spongy granular product. As it is very low in carbon, it is also valuable for making high-grade alloy steels.

A form of sponge iron employed as a substitute for lead for coupling packings was made in Germany under the name of **sinterit.** The reduction is carried out in a reducing atmosphere at a temperature of 1200 to 1350°C, instead of heating the iron oxide with carbon. Since the porous iron corrodes easily, it is coated with asphalt for packing use. **Iron sponge,** employed as a purifier for removing sulfur and carbonic acid from illuminating gas, is a sesquioxide of iron obtained by heating together iron ore and carbon. It has a spongy texture filled with small cells.

SPONGE RUBBER. Rubber expanded with a cellular structure and cut or molded into blocks or forms for use as a substitute for sponges or for resilient upholstery padding or insulation. Ordinary chemically blown sponge rubber is made up of interconnecting cells in a labyrinthlike formation. When made by beating latex, it may show spherical cells with the porous walls perforated by the evaporation of moisture. It is also called **foam rubber.** Special processes are used to produce celltight and gastight **cellular rubber** which is nonabsorbent. **Unicel ND,** of Du Pont, used as a blowing agent for sponge rubber, is dinitro pentamethyl tetramine. It is mixed into the rubber, and in the presence of the rubber acids it is decomposed, liberating gas during the vulcanization to form small cells. The cellular rubber of the U.S. Rubber Co., produced in sheets of a density of 3.5 to 12 lb per cu ft, for refrigeration insulation, is made with a chemical that releases nitrogen gas to produce innumerable microscopic cells during the molding. The **Rubatex** of the Rubatex Div., Great American Industries, Inc., is this type of cellular rubber. It comes in sheets of any thickness for gaskets, seals, weather stripping, vibration insulation, and refrigerator insulation.

In the form of insulation board for heat and cold, nitrogen-filled rubber has a thermal conductivity of 0.237 Btu per hr per deg F temperature difference per inch of thickness. The 5.5-lb board has a crushing strength of 33 psi. Under the name of **Royal insulation board** it is marketed in thicknesses from $\frac{3}{4}$ to $1\frac{1}{2}$ in., but most of the so-called sponge rubbers are not made of natural rubber but are produced from synthetic rubbers or plastics, and may be called by a type classification, such as **urethane foam,** or marketed under trade names. Some of these foams may be made by special processes, and some of the materials are marketed in liquid form for use as foamed-in-place insulation. The urethane foams expanded with fluorocarbon gas are 95% gas in closed microscopic pores. They are rigid, have low weight, and are used in sheets with metal, paper, felt, or other facings for wallboard and roofing, and in thermal insulation. The contained gas has very low thermal conductivity.   **Phenolic foam** is made by incorporating sodium bicarbonate and an acid catalyst into liquid phenol resin.   The reaction liberates carbon dioxide gas, expanding the plastic.

Bubblfil, of Du Pont, is **cellular cellulose acetate** expanded with air-filled cells to densities from 4 to 9 lb per cu ft, for use as insulation and as a buoyancy material for floats.   It is tough and resilient.   **Strux,** of the Strux Corp., is **cellulose acetate foam,** made by extruding the plastic mixed with barium sulfate in an alcohol-acetone solvent.   When the pressure is removed it expands into a light, cellular structure.   **Foamex,** of Firestone, is a foam rubber made from synthetic latex in several density grades.   It is stronger than that made from natural rubber and is flexible at very low temperatures.   **Styrofoam,** of Dow Chemical Co., is polystyrene expanded into a multicellular mass 42 times the original size.   It has only one-sixth the weight of cork, but will not withstand hot water or temperatures above 170°F, as it is thermoplastic.   The thermal conductivity is 0.27 Btu per hr per deg F per in.   It is used for cold-storage insulation, and is resistant to mold.   **Ensolite,** of the U.S. Rubber Co., and **Vinylaire,** of the Dura Flex Co., are foamed vinyl plastisols.   **Plasti-Cell,** of the Sponge Rubber Products Co., is an expanded polyvinyl chloride molded to densities from 2 to 12 lb per cu ft.   It is used for floats, buoys, and insulation.   **Vynafoam,** of the Interchemical Corp., used for gaskets, seals, and refrigerator doors, is a vinyl plastisol which is sprayed on and cured by heat into a foamed texture with increase in volume of 400%.   It is white in color, and has an insulating K value of 0.36, or about the same as felt.   **Permafoam,** of the Hudson Foam Plastics Corp., has only half the weight of foamed rubber with greater strength and high resistance to oxidation.   It is a foamed polyester resin, is odorless, flame-resistant, and resistant to oils and solvents.   It is used for upholstery and insulation.

Silicone foam, of Dow Corning Corp., used for insulation, is silicone rubber foamed into a uniform unicellular structure of 8 to 24 lb per cu ft density.   It will withstand temperatures above 600°F.   For structural sheets the rubber is foamed between two sheets of silicone glass laminate.   **Spongex,** of the Sponge Rubber Products Co., is a foamed silicone rubber for cushioning and damping.

Vinyl foams are widely used.   They are made from various types of vinyl resins with the general physical properties of the resin used.   Open-cell vinyl foam contains interconnecting voids and is very flexible.   It is made by mechanical foaming by absorption under pressure of an inert gas in a vinyl plastisol.   It is used for furniture and transport seating.   Closed-cell vinyl foam contains separate discrete voids.   It is made by chemical foaming, using chemical blowing agents.   It is used for impermeable insulation and marine floats.

An **epoxy foam** of the Shell Chemical Co. comes as a powder consisting of an Epon epoxy resin mixed with diamino diphenyl sulfone. When the powder is placed in a mold or in a cavity, and heat is applied, it foams to fill the space and cures to a rigid foam. The foam has a density of 16 lb per cut ft, tensile strength of 360 psi, compressive strength of 710 psi, and it will withstand temperatures to 500°F. **Lockfoam H-602,** of the Nopco Chemical Co., is a pour-in-place urethane foam that expands with a fluorocarbon to a density of 2 lb per cu ft. The insulation K factor is 0.13 Btu, and it retains its properties at subzero temperatures when used for freezer insulation. **Expandoform,** of the Armstrong Cork Co., and **Polyfoam,** of the General Tire & Rubber Co., are polyether-based urethanes that expand to a density of 2 lb per cu ft into stable, rigid foam of good strength for refrigerator insulation. **Carthane foam,** of the Carwin Co., used in aircraft and missile sandwich structures, is a polymethylene polyphenyl isocyanate that is infusible and withstands temperatures to 900°F before beginning to carbonize. **Hetrofoam,** of the Hooker Chemical Corp., is a urethane-type foam with a high chlorine content that makes it fire-resistant. The thermal conductivity K factor is 0.10, and it is used for refrigerator and building insulation. **Thurane foam board,** of the Dow Chemical Co., is a foamed urethane in the form of strong, rigid boards ¾ to 16 in. thick, with densities from 1.80 to 2.30.

SPRENGLE EXPLOSIVES. Chlorate compounds that have been rendered reasonably safe from violent explosion by separating the chlorate from the combustible matter. The potassium chlorate, made up into porous cartridges and dipped, just before use, in liquid combustible such as nitrobenzene or dead oil, was called **rack-a-rock.** Sprengle explosives were formerly used as military explosives, are very sensitive to friction and heat, and are now valued only for mining or when it is desired to economize on nitrates. **Cheddite** is a French explosive consisting of a chlorate with an oily material, such as castor oil thickened by a nitrated hydrocarbon dissolved in it. A typical cheddite has 80% potassium chlorate, 8 castor oil, and 12 mononitronaphthalene. With sodium chlorate it is less sensitive to detonation and more powerful but is hygroscopic. Potassium chlorate cheddite is a soft, yellowish, fine-grained material, and is a slow, mild explosive which will split rocks rather than shatter them. **Minelite** is a chlorate with paraffin wax. **Steelite** is a chlorate explosive with rosin. **Prométhée** is another French chlorate explosive. In this explosive the oxygen carrier consists of 95% potassium chlorate and 5 manganese dioxide, and the combustible contains 50% nitrobenzene, with turpentine and naphtha. It is extremely sensitive and will explode by friction. **Silesia** is a German high explosive used for blasting. It is potassium chlorate with rosin, with some sodium chlorate to make it less sensitive.

SPRING STEEL. A term applied to any steel used for making springs. The majority of springs are made of steel, but brass, bronze, nickel silver, and phosphor bronze are used where corrosion resistance or electrical conductivity is desired. Carbon steels, with from 0.50 to 1.0% carbon, are much used, but vanadium and chrome-vanadium steels are also employed, especially for heavy car and locomotive springs. Special requirements for springs are that the steel be low in sulfur and phosphorus, and that the analysis be kept uniform. For flat or spiral springs that are not heat-treated after manufacture, hard-drawn or rolled steels are used. These may be tempered in the mill shape. Music wire is widely employed for making small spiral springs. A much-used straight-carbon spring steel has 1% carbon and 0.30 to 0.40 manganese, but becomes brittle when overstressed. **ASTM carbon steel** for flat springs has 0.70 to 0.80% carbon and 0.50 to 0.8 manganese, with 0.04 max each of sulfur and phosphorus. Motor springs are made of this steel rolled hard to a tensile strength of 250,000 psi. **Watch spring steel,** for mainsprings, has high carbon, 1.15%, and low manganese, 0.15 to 0.25, rolled hard and giving an elastic limit above 300,000 psi.

Silicon steels are used for springs. They have high strength and impact resistance. These steels average about 0.40% carbon, 0.75 silicon, and 0.95 manganese, with or without copper, but the silicon may be as high as 2%. **Flexo steel,** of Carpenter Technology, used for automobile leaf springs and for recoil springs, contains 2% silicon, 0.75 manganese, and 0.60 carbon. The elastic limit is 100,000 to 300,000 psi, depending on the drawing temperature, with hardness 250 to 600 Brinell.

Manganese steels for automotive springs contain about 1.25% manganese and 0.40 carbon, or about 2% manganese and 0.45 carbon. When heat-treated, the latter has a tensile strength of 200,000 psi and elongation 10%. Part of the manganese may be replaced by silicon and the **silicon-manganese steels** have tensile strengths as high as 270,000 psi. The addition of chromium or other elements increases the elongation and improves the physical properties. **Uma spring steel,** of the Republic Steel Corp., is a chromium-manganese steel with 1 to 1.2% chromium, 0.80 to 1 manganese, and about 0.50 carbon. In the rolled condition it has an ultimate strength of 135,000 psi and Brinell hardness up to 332. Manganese steels are deep-hardening but are sensitive to overheating. The addition of chromium, vanadium, or molybdenum widens the hardening range.

Wire for coil springs ranges in carbon from 0.50 to 1.20%, and in sulfur from 0.028 to 0.029. Bessemer wire contains too much sulfur for spring use. Cold working is the method for hardening the wire and for raising the tensile strength. A 0.85% carbon rod, with an ultimate strength of 140,000 psi, when drawn with four or five passes through dies will have a strength of 235,000 psi. Wire drawn down to a diameter of 0.015 in.

may have an ultimate strength of 400,000 psi. The highest grades of wire are referred to as music wire. The second grade is called **hard-drawn spring wire.** The latter is a less expensive basic open-hearth steel with manganese content of 0.80 to 1.10%, and an ultimate strength up to 300,000 psi. Specially treated carbon steels for springs are sold under trade names such as **Enduria,** of Bethlehem Steel. **Resilla** is a silicon-manganese spring steel of this company.

For springs for jet engines and other applications where resistance to high temperatures is required, stainless steel and high-alloy steels are used. But, while these may have the names and approximate compositions of standard stainless steels, for spring-wire use their manufacture is usually closely controlled. For example, when the carbon content is raised in high-chromium steels to obtain the needed spring qualities, the carbide tends to collect in the grain boundaries and cause intergranular corrosion unless small quantities of titanium, columbium, or other element are added to immobilize the carbon. **Blue Label stainless,** of Carpenter Steel, is Type 302 steel of highly controlled analysis marketed in 0.0025 to 0.312 round diameters and in square and rectangular wire for coil springs. **Alloy NS-355,** of National-Standard, is a stainless steel having a typical analysis of 15.64% chromium, 4.38 nickel, 2.68 molybdenum, 1 manganese, 0.32 silicon, 0.12 copper, with the carbon at 0.14. The modulus of elasticity is 29,300,000 psi at 80°F and 24,000,000 psi at 800°F. **Armco 17-7 PH steel,** of Armco Steel, has 17% chromium, 7 nickel, 1 aluminum, and 0.07 carbon. The wire has a tensile strength up to 345,000 psi. **Spring wire** for high-temperature coil springs may contain little or no iron. **Alloy NS-25,** of National-Standard, for springs operating at 1400°F, contains about 50% cobalt, 20 chromium, 15 tungsten, and 10 nickel, with not more than 0.15 carbon. The annealed wire drawn to a 30% reduction has a tensile strength of 240,000 psi with elongation of 8%. **Matreloy,** of Materials Research Corp., for high-temperature springs, contains 39% chromium, 4 molybdenum, 2 titanium, 1 aluminum, and the balance nickel. The rolled metal has a yield strength of 275,000 psi, and at 1400°F it retains a strength of 120,000 psi.

SPRUCE. The wood of various coniferous trees of northern Europe and North America. Spruce is a leading commercial wood of north Europe. and is exported from the Baltic region as **white fir** and **white deal.** It is also called **Norway spruce** and **spruce fir.** The wood is white, and has a straight, even grain. It is tough and elastic, and is more difficult to work than pine. The weight is 36 lb per cu ft. Norway spruce is *Picea abies,* and this tree yields the **Jura turpentine** of Europe. Spruce is used for making paper pulp, for packing boxes, and as a general-utility lumber. White spruce is from the tree *P. canadensis,* of the United States and

Canada. It has quite similar characteristics. **Red spruce,** *P. rubra,* is the chief lumber spruce in the eastern United States. It is also called **yellow spruce, West Virginia spruce,** and **Canadian spruce.   Black spruce,** *P. mariana,* of New England, eastern Canada, and Newfoundland, is used for making paper pulp.   It is also called **blue spruce, bog spruce,** and **spruce pine.   White spruce,** or **shingle spruce,** is from *P. glauca.*   It is also called **skunk spruce** because of the peculiar odor of the foliage.   All of these three species are called **eastern spruce,** and they grow from Nova Scotia to Tennessee and westward to Wisconsin except that red spruce does not grow in the Lake states.   All are mountain trees and are slow-growing. **Silver spruce, yellow spruce, Sitka spruce,** or **western spruce,** is from the enormous tree, *P. sitchensis,* of the west coast of the United States and Canada.   It is soft and light in weight, but strong, close-grained, and very free from knots.   The wide sapwood is creamy white, and the heartwood pinkish to brownish.   The weight is less than eastern spruce, but it has high strength in proportion to weight.   The trees reach a height of 280 ft and a diameter of 10 ft in 600 years, but the growth is rapid in early life.   The wood is used for boxes, crates, millwork, and paper pulp.   It is particularly adapted for groundwood pulp, giving higher strength in paper than most groundwood.   The various species of commercial spruce have an average specific gravity, when kiln-dried, of 0.40, a compressive strength of 840 psi perpendicular to the grain, and a shearing strength of 750 parallel to the grain.   It combines stiffness and strength per unit weight, and has a uniform texture free from pitch.   **Japanese spruce** is from *Abies mariesii,* and **Himalayan spruce** is from *P. morinda.*   The latter resembles Norway spruce.

Spruce gum is the gum exudation of the *Picea rubra, P. mariana,* and *P. canadensis* of the northeastern United States and Canada.   It exudes from cuts in the trees as a transparent viscous liquid which hardens when it loses the volatile oil.   It occurs on all parts of the tree, and the nodules of gum are sometimes as large as an egg.   **Spruce oil** is extracted from the needles.   In Colonial days the young twigs were boiled and the liquid, mixed with molasses, was used as a beverage.   The gum is brown or reddish black in color, has a turpentinelike odor and a bitter pungent taste.   It is used in cough medicines and in chewing gum.

SQUILL. Also known as **red squill** and **sea onion.**   A reddish powder used chiefly for the control of rats in warehouses and docks.   It is obtained from the onionlike bulb of the perennial plant *Urginea maritima* growing on the beaches of Italy and other Mediterranean countries.   The bulb is pear-shaped, from 1 to 6 lb in weight and 6 to 12 in. in diameter.   The outer scales are dry, brittle, and reddish brown, and the inner scales are cream color to deep purple.   **Red squill powder** is a powerful emetic to man or animals other than rats or mice. As rats and mice do not vomit, they are poisoned by it, while it is harmless to poultry and domestic animals. It is also used in medicine. It contains calcium oxalate and in contact with the skin it gives a sensation like nettle poisoning. **White squill** is another variety used in medicine as an emetic, heart tonic, and expectorant. The substitute for red squill known as **Antu,** of Du Pont, is **naphthyl thiourea,** a gray powder of little odor or taste about 100 times more poisonous to rats than squill and not normally injurious to domestic animals. Another poison more toxic to rats than squill is **Ratbane 1080** which is **sodium fluoracetic acid** made synthetically. The poison occurs as natural fluoracetic acid in the **gifblaar** plant, *Dichapetalum cymosum,* of South Africa, which has been used locally for killing rodents. The poison, however, also kills domestic animals, and can thus be employed only in restricted places. The rodent poison known as **Warfarin** is a complex dicoumarol made under license of the Wisconsin Alumni Research Foundation. **Pival,** of the Atlantic Research Corp., is 2-pivalyl-1,3-indandione. It kills rats but is not toxic to other animals. **Pivalyn** is the material as a water-soluble sodium salt.

STAINLESS STEEL. A term now covering a wide range of iron alloys, but all characterized by having a high content of chromium which makes them highly resistant to oxidation and corrosion even at elevated temperatures. They were first produced in America in 1914 under English and German patents. The original composition was 13.5% chromium and 0.35 carbon. The original Krupp austenitic, or **KA steel,** or simple **austenitic steel,** had 20% chromium and 7 nickel, which was later balanced at 18–8. The **eighteen-eight steels,** or **chromium-nickel steels,** were called **super stainless steels** in England to distinguish them from the plain chromium steels. Austenitic stainless steels show a face-centered cubical crystal structure instead of the body-centered structure of chromium steel. They are superior in physical properties at low temperatures.

Low-carbon alloys, less subject to intergranular corrosion, were used for tank plates, pump rods, and turbine blades, under the names of **stainless iron** and **rustless iron.** **Rustless PR-11,** of the Rustless Iron & Steel Corp., had 11% chromium and 0.07 carbon. This alloy has a tensile strength of 75,000 psi, elongation 25%, and Brinell hardness 170. **Defirust,** of this company, had about 13% chromium, 0.10 carbon, and some nickel. **Defiheat,** with a scaling point at 2100°F and a tensile strength to 95,000 psi, had about 25% chromium and 0.20 carbon with some nickel. The **turbine blade steel, Lesco L,** of the Latrobe Electric Steel Co., had 11 to 13% chromium, 0.50 each of silicon and manganese, and 0.10 carbon. **Lesco M** and **Lesco H** were grades with higher chromium, up to 20%, for higher corrosion resistance.

The **Stainless iron 12,** and the **Stainless iron 18,** of the Crucible Steel Co., had a maximum of 0.12 carbon, but all of these stainless alloys are now generally called steel regardless of the carbon content. The **Delhi rustless iron,** of the Allegheny Ludlum Steel Corp., has 18% chromium, 1.5 silicon, and 0.08 carbon. **Silcrome RA,** of the same company, has 16% chromium, 1 silicon, 1 copper, and 0.12 carbon. These steels withstand temperatures above 1500°F without scaling. The chromium steels with high carbon content retain a good cutting edge, especially when they have a high silicon content, and they are used for cutlery. **Staybrite,** of the Firth-Sterling Steel Co., has 10% chromium, 3.5 silicon, and 0.45 carbon.

The **martensitic steels,** or hardenable stainless steels, are the **AISI Type 400 steels.** They are the chromium steels in various grades with chromium up to 27%, and carbon up to 1.25%. The general utility **chromium stainless steel** is AISI 410 with 12% chromium and 0.15 max carbon. These steels are ferromagnetic and air-hardening. Unless modified, they have a blue-gray color, as distinct from the whiter color of the nickel-bearing stainless steels, and they are thus not preferred for food-processing equipment. They are highly corrosion-resistant, but they stain and assume a deep-blue tinge after heating, and are thus not normally used for cooking utensils. **Armco 400** is a 13% chromium steel containing 0.5% Al, and 1% each of Si and Mn. It does not discolor easily. The **semiaustenitic steels,** or **ferritic steels,** are the chromium steels with the addition of about 4.5% nickel. When solution-annealed they contain a proportion of unhardenable delta ferrite, and are soft and easily worked. When heat-aged, carbon precipitates from the austenite to the austenite-ferrite boundaries, and they can be hardened to high tensile strengths. Even small amounts of nickel give a precipitation effect. **Uniloy 1409,** of the Universal-Cyclops Steel Corp., is a 12% chromium steel with 0.50 nickel and 0.10 carbon. The heat-treated rolled steel has a tensile strength of 105,000 psi, elongation 25%, and Brinell hardness 240. **Uniloy 1409M** is this steel with a small amount of molybdenum sulfide to give free machining, but **Uniloy 303 MA** is a free-machining Type 303 steel with lowered sulfur, and with 0.70% aluminum added to increase strength while retaining the free-machining properties.

The **precipitation-hardened steels** are produced by a controlled method of quenching with a pressure water spray uniformly distributed between the pinch rolls. It gives a deep uniform hardening that increases tensile and flexural strengths. **Bethlehem R2100B** and **Armco PH13-8Mo** are stainless steels of this type.

Free-cutting stainless steels are usually regular grades with the addition of a small amount of sulfur or selenium. Sulfur does not impair the resistance to corrosion, but it decreases ductility. **Circle L 12M,** of the Lebanon Steel Foundry Co., is a 13% chromium steel with 0.25% selenium.

E-Z stainless steel, of the Latrobe Steel Corp., is a 13.5% chromium steel with sulfur added. **Carpenter stainless No. 5** is this type of steel with the addition of 0.40 zirconium sulfide. **Ni-stainless steel,** of Latrobe, contains up to 2% nickel. It is used for pump rods and valves. **Sterling stainless FC** has 0.40 molybdenum and 0.25 sulfur.

Armco 17-4PH, of the Armco Steel Corp., is a 13.5% chromium steel with 4% nickel and 4 copper. It hardens at low heat without distortion. **Armco 15-5PH** derives increased strength from the addition of 1% each silicon and manganese, and 0.045% columbium-tantalum. When tempered at 900°F the alloy has a tensile strength of 200,000 psi with elongation of 14%. **Armco 430 ELC** is a 13% chromium steel with very low carbon, requiring no stabilizing elements.

The **AISI Type 430 steel,** with 17% chromium and 0.12 max carbon, is widely used to replace 18–8 steel when there is a need to conserve nickel, but it is not as easily worked or welded as 18–8 steel, and does not have the bright white color. **AISI Type 420 steel,** with 13% chromium, 1% each of silicon and manganese, and more than 0.15 carbon, is much used for cutlery. **E-Brite 261 steel,** of Air Reduction Co., is a chromium-type stainless steel containing 26% chromium and 1 molybdenum which is highly resistant to the corrosion and pitting of chlorine chemicals. The molten metal is passed in vacuum through an electron beam to eliminate all impurities.

Many modified grades of these steels are marketed under trade names. **Colonial stainless FMS,** of the Colonial Steel Co., has 0.12% max carbon and up to 0.35 sulfur. It is easily machined, and is used for valve parts, screws, and gun barrels. **U.S.S. steel 12A1,** of the U.S. Steel Corp., is a 13.5% chromium steel with 0.10 to 0.30 aluminum and 0.08 max carbon. It is used for pipe and tubes in refineries. The aluminum acts as a ferrite stabilizer, and it combines high strength and ductility. It requires heat treatment to obtain greatest corrosion resistance, but the steel does not harden. **U.S.S. steel 27,** for severe oxidation and reducing conditions up to 2100°F, contains 23 to 30% chromium, 0.10 to 0.25 nitrogen, and 0.20 max carbon. The nitrogen eliminates embrittlement. The steel is ferritic, and has higher physical qualities than a plain chromium steel. **Radianite steel,** of the Latrobe Steel Corp., has up to 18% chromium, 0.75 carbon, with 0.50 each of silicon and manganese. It keeps a fine cutting edge, and retains a high polish. **Lusterite** is this steel with higher carbon, and is a **keen-edge steel** for surgical instruments and knives. **Hy-Glo steel** of the same company has 17% chromium and 0.60 carbon. It has a tensile strength up to 250,000 psi and hardness to 600 Brinell. In general, the stainless steels do not hold a fine, keen-cutting edge as do the vanadium cutlery steels.

The **AISI Type 300 steels** are the chromium-nickel austenitic stainless steels in grades containing up to 30% chromium and up to 20% nickel. The standard 18–8 grade is **AISI Type 302 steel** with no more than 0.15% carbon and up to 2% manganese.   **AISI Type 303 steel** is this grade with sulfur or selenium added for free machining.   These steels do not harden by heat treatment, but can be rolled hard.   The annealed Type 302 steel has a tensile strength of 80,000 psi with elongation of 50% and Brinell hardness of 180, but when hard-rolled it has a tensile strength to 200,000 psi.   The steels are tough, ductile, and nonmagnetic.   Precipitation of chromium carbide at the grain boundaries, making them subject to inter-granular corrosion, can be eliminated by keeping the carbon very low or by adding small amounts of columbium or titanium.   Small amounts of nitrogen inhibit grain growth, and the nickel may be lowered in nitrogen-bearing steels.   Copper improves the resistance to sulfuric acid, and small amounts of molybdenum increase the resistance to hot chemicals.

The nickel-chromium stainless steels are favored for structural uses in aircraft and transport equipment because the high strength and corrosion resistance permit smaller sections to be used for weight saving.   **AISI Type 304** is most used as it is generally available in all wrought forms and is easily welded.   It contains 18% chromium, 8 nickel, 2 manganese, and 1 silicon with carbon kept below 0.08%.   Where corrosive conditions exist **AISI Type 316** is used.   It has 16% chromium, 10 nickel, 2 manganese, 1 silicon, and 2 molybdenum.   Standard specifications for these steels call for a minimum tensile strength, annealed, of 85,000 psi, and yield strength of 30,000 psi.   The cold-rolled steel tempered to $\frac{1}{2}$-hard has a tensile strength of 150,000 psi, yield strength of 110,000 psi, elongation of 16%, and Rockwell hardness C32.

The austenitic steels are normally hot-short, but small additions of the cerium metals may be used to improve hot-working.   Varying the alloying elements in these steels makes the number of possible types and grades almost unlimited.   In addition to the regular AISI grades, most producers market the steels under trade names to denote guaranteed uniformity or special characteristics.   **Sharonsteel 302,** of the Sharon Steel Corp., is an 18–8 steel that can be cold-worked to a tensile strength of 275,000 psi. **Stainless U steel,** of the Colonial Steel Co., is an 18–8 steel with the addi-tion of 1.5% molybdenum and 1.25 copper.   As rolled, it has a tensile strength of 100,000 psi and elongation of 40%.   **Cooper alloy 17SM,** of the Cooper Alloy Foundry Co., is an 18–8 steel with 1.5% silicon, 3 molybdenum, and 0.08 max carbon.   **Vickers FV 520 steel,** of Firth-Vickers Stainless Steels, Ltd., for aircraft construction, contains 16% chromium, 6 nickel, 1.5 molybdenum, 1.5 copper, 0.3 titanium, and 0.07 carbon.   It is precipitation-hardened, and has a tensile strength from 124,000 to 184,000 psi, with elongation from 23 to 45%.   The French steel, **Uranus B6,** for high resistance to hot concentrated sulfuric acid, has

20% chromium, 25 nickel, 1.5 copper, and 4.5 molybdenum.   **Maxilvry steel,** of Edgar Allen & Co., Ltd., a chromium-nickel steel with copper for deep drawing, has a tensile strength of 90,000 psi with elongation of 68%. **Bethalon steel,** of the Bethlehem Steel Co., and **Allegheny metal,** of the Allegheny Ludlum Steel Co., are 18–8 type steels in various grades.   **Sta-Gloss, Hi-Gloss,** and **Duro Gloss** are stainless steels of the Jessop Steel Co. **Stainless W steel,** of the U.S. Steel Corp., has 17% chromium, 7 nickel, 0.70 titanium, 0.20 aluminum, 0.50 silicon, 0.50 manganese, and 0.70 carbon.   When hardened to Rockwell C47 the tensile strength is 225,000 psi and elongation 10%.   **Armco 18–9 steel,** which can be swaged and cold-headed with little work-hardening, has 18% chromium, 9 nickel, 3.5 copper, 2 manganese, 1 silicon, and not over 0.10 carbon.   With a 50% cold reduction it has a tensile strength of 152,000 psi.

All of the 18–8 type steels have a brilliant luster when polished.   The heat conductivity is low, about 5% that of copper, so that where conductance is required, as for cooking utensils, they are usually laminated with copper. They are ductile and malleable, but harden rapidly with cold work.   The cast steels are varied in composition to suit particular requirements.   **Circle L22 steel,** of the Lebanon Steel Foundry, for cast parts for chemical equipment, contains 19.5% chromium, 9 nickel, 1.25 silicon, 0.75 manganese, with low carbon, 0.07 max, to prevent formation of carbides in welding. Cast parts have a tensile strength of 75,000 psi, elongation of 50%, and Brinell hardness of 135.   **Circle L22M** and **Circle L22XM** are variations of this steel with 3% of molybdenum to increase hot chemical resistance, and with a small amount of selenium to improve machining.   **Durco KA2S steel,** of the Duriron Co., is a similar steel with similar variations. Small amounts of cobalt are sometimes added to this type of steel to increase the resistance to intergranular corrosion.   For structural parts for atomic equipment, boron may be added as a neutron absorber.   Boron increases the yield strength of the steel, but decreases the corrosion resistance and drastically decreases the ductility.   Thus, only the isotope boron 10 is added, since it is 10 times more effective against neutrons than regular boron.   The chromium-nickel high alloys used for severe chemical resistance at high temperatures are often called stainless steels, but they are not steels.   **Ni-O-Nel,** of the International Nickel Co., Inc., used for chemical equipment to resist strong mixed chemicals and hot gases, contains 42% nickel, 21.5 chromium, 3 molybdenum, 2.25 copper, small amounts of silicon, manganese, titanium, and carbon, and the balance iron.   The alloy is resistant to hot sulfuric, nitric, and phosphoric acids, and to ammonium hydroxide, but such metals are expensive and are not classed with the commercial stainless steels.

Chromium-manganese steels, with manganese used to replace the nickel of the 18–8 steels, were early used in Germany to replace the chromium-nickel stainless steels, but they were difficult to work and not as corrosion-resistant as the 18–8 steels.   Modified with nickel, they now constitute the **AISI Type 200 steels,** and in general they have higher hardness and yield strength than the 300 series.   **AISI Type 201 steel** has 17% chromium, 4.5 nickel, 6.5 manganese, and 0.15 max carbon.   It has a tensile strength of 115,000 psi, yield strength 55,000 psi, and elongation 55%.   **AISI Type 202 steel** has 18% chromium, 5 nickel, 8.5 manganese, and 0.15 max carbon.   Its tensile strength is 105,000 psi and elongation 55%.   These steels are lower in cost than the 18–8 steels, and have comparable working properties and corrosion resistance.   **TRC steel,** of the Allegheny-Ludlum Steel Co., contains 15% chromium, 16.5 manganese, 1 nickel, and 0.10 carbon.   It also contains 0.15 nitrogen to stabilize the austenite.   The annealed steel has a tensile strength of 102,000 psi with elongation of 57%, and when cold-rolled the tensile strength is 150,000 psi with elongation of 12%.   It has a white color, is highly corrosion-resistant, and can be worked about the same as 18–8 steel.   It is used for railway cars and truck trailers.   **Allegheny 216** contains 19.75% chromium, 8.25 manganese, and 6 nickel.   The annealed yield strength is 108,000 psi with elongation of 51%.   The tensile and fatigue strengths at elevated temperatures are superior to those of the 18–8 steels, and cutting speeds for machining can be half those of regular stainless steels.   **Tenelon,** of U.S. Steel, is an austenitic **manganese stainless steel** with corrosion resistance about equal to that of the 18–8 steels and higher physical properties at elevated temperatures.   It contains 17% chromium, 14.5 manganese, 1 silicon, 0.10 carbon, and 0.40 nitrogen.   It has a tensile strength of 125,000 psi with elongation of 45%, and at 1000°F the tensile strength is 81,000 psi.

Diffused stainless steel is a sheet steel with a low-carbon ductile steel core and a diffused chromium-iron alloy surface.   It is produced from low-carbon steel by heating the sheets in a retort containing a chromium compound which diffuses into the metal at a temperature of about 2000°F. The chromium alloys with the steel, the alloy on the surface containing as much as 40% chromium, which tapers off to leave a ductile nonchromium core in the sheet.   **Black stainless steel,** for electronic applications, is produced by immersing sheet steel in a bath of molten potassium dichromate and sodium dichromate.   The steel has a shiny black finish. **Liquid stainless steel,** of the Lockrey Co., for producing a durable decorative finish resembling stainless steel, consists of finely flaked stainless-steel powder in a varnish vehicle of a synthetic resin and a solvent.

Metal fibers are used for weaving into fabrics for arctic heating clothing, heated draperies, chemical-resistant fabrics, and reinforcement in plastics and metals.   **Brunsmet MFA-1,** of the Brunswick Corp., is Type 304 **stainless-steel fiber** with diameters from 4 to 25 microns.   It is extremely flexible.   **Stainless-steel yarn** made from the fibers is woven into **stainless-steel fabric** that has good crease resistance and retains its physical properties to 800°F.   The fiber may be blended with cotton or wool for static control, particularly for carpeting.

STARCH. A large group of natural carbohydrate compounds of the empirical formula $(C_6H_{10}O_5)_x$, occurring in grains, tubers, and fruits.   The common cereal grains contain from 55 to 75% starch, and potatoes contain about 18%.   Starches have a wide usage for foodstuffs, adhesives, textile and paper sizing, gelling agents, fillers; in making explosives and many chemicals; and for making biodegradable detergents such as sodium tripolyphosphate.   Starch is a basic need of all peoples and all industries.   Much of it is employed in its natural form, but it is also easily converted to other forms and more than 1,000 different varieties of starch are usually on the American market at any one time.

Most of the commercial starch comes from corn, potatoes, and mandioca. Starches from different plants have similar chemical reactions, but all have different granular structure, and the differences in size and shape of the grain have much to do with the physical properties.   **Cornstarch** has a polygonal grain of simple structure.   It is the chief food starch in the Western world, although sweet-potato starch is used where high gelatinization is desired, and tapioca starch is used to give quick tack and high adhesion in glues.   **Tapioca starch** has rounded grains truncated on one side and is of lamellar structure.   It produces gels of clarity and flexibility, and, since it has no cereal flavor, it can be used directly for thickening foodstuffs.   **Rice starch** is polygonal and is lamellar, and has very small particles.   It makes an opaque stiff gel and is also valued as a **dusting starch** for bakery products, although it is expensive for this purpose. **White-potato starch** has conchoidal or ellipsoidal grains of lamellar structure.   When cooked, it forms clear solutions easily controlled in viscosity, and gives tough resilient films for coating paper and fabrics.   Prolonged grinding of grain starches reduces the molecular chain, and the lower weight then gives greater solubility in cold water.   Green fruits, especially bananas, often contain much starch, but the ripening process changes the starch to sugars.

In general, starch is a white, amorphous powder having a specific gravity from 0.499 to 0.513.   It is insoluble in cold water, but can be converted to **soluble starch** by treating with a dilute acid.   When cooked in water, starch produces an adhesive paste.   Starch is easily distinguished from dextrins as it gives a blue color with iodine while dextrins give violet and red.   The starch molecule is often described as a chain of glucose units, with the adhesive **waxy starches** as those with coiled chains.   But starch is a complex member of the great group of natural plant compounds consisting of starches, sugars, and cellulose, and originally named carbohy-drates because the molecular formula could be written as $C_n(H_2O)_x$, but not all now-known carbohydrates can be classified in this form, and many now-known acids and aldehydes can be indicated by this formula.

Starch can be fractionated into two polymers of high molecular weight. **Amylose** is a straight-chain fraction having high adhesive properties for coatings and sizings, and **amylopectin** is a branched-chain fraction best known as a suspending agent for foodstuffs.   Amylose is chemically identical with cellulose, but the chain units of the molecule have an alpha linkage and are coiled, while the cellulose molecule is rigid.   It has a molecular weight of 150,000, while amylopectin has a molecular weight above 1,000,000.   The 1–4 alpha linkage of amylopectin with random branches at the 6-carbon position makes the material easily dispersible in cold water but resistant to gelling.   Amylopectin is thus best suited for thickening, but, since it can be combined and cross-linked with synthetic resins, and is highly resistant to deterioration, it is used with resins for water-resistant coatings for paper and textiles.

The relative proportions of the two molecular forms vary in the different natural products.   Since corn yields are as high as a hundred 56-lb bushels per acre, corn is one of the most economic sources of starch.   But ordinary corn contains only about 25% of the linear polymer, amylose, and normally has about 75% of the branched-chain amylopectin.   The **amioca starch** developed during the Second World War to replace tapioca was from crossbred waxy corn, but hybrid corns are now grown to give high per-centages of either amylose or amylopectin as desired.

Tapioca is the starch from the root of the large tuber *Manihot utilissima,* now grown in most tropical countries.   It is called **cassava** in southern Asia, **manioc** in Brazil, **mandioca** in Paraguay, and **yuca** in Cuba.   It is used in enormous quantities for food in some countries, and in some areas much is used for the production of alcohol.   In the United States it is valued for adhesives and coatings, and only a small proportion in globules and flakes, known as **pearl tapioca,** is used in foodstuffs.   **Gaplek,** used for cattle feed in Asia, is not the starch, but is dried and sliced cassava root. Tapioca starch may be sold under trade names.   **Kreamgel,** of Morningstar-Paisley, Inc., used as a thickener for canned soups, sauces, and pastries, is refined tapioca that gives clear solutions without imparting odor or flavor.

Potato starch, produced from the common **white potato,** *Solanum tubero-sum,* has been the most important starch in Europe, but in the United States it is usually more expensive than cornstarch.   It forms heavier hot pastes than tapioca.   It is also free of flavor, and is used as a thickener in foods. It does not crystallize easily.   **Arogum,** of Morningstar-Paisley, Inc., is potato starch used to give tough resilient coatings on paper and textiles, and **Arojel P** is pregelatinized potato starch used as a beater additive to improve the strength and scuff resistance of kraft paper. **Sweet-potato starch** is from the tuber *Opomoea batata.* An average of 10 lb of starch is produced per bushel. The root has poor shipping qualities, and the starch is expensive, but it has excellent colloidal qualities and gelatinizes completely at 165°F. It is used in some foodstuffs. It has a pleasant sweetish flavor, and in Latin countries great quantities are marketed in the form of a stiff gel as a dessert sweet known as **dulce de batata.**

Arrowroot starch is from the tubers of the *Maranta arundinacea* of the West Indies. It is easily digested, and is used in cookies and other food products, especially baby foods. **Florida arrowroot** is from the *Zamia floridana.* **East Indian arrowroot** is from the plant *Curcuma angustifolia* which belongs to the ginger family. Arrowroot from St. Vincent, used in instant-pudding mixes and icings, is marketed as a precooked powder of about 200 mesh. It swells in cold water, and does not add flavor.

The starches do not crystallize like sugar, and they may be added to some confections to minimize crystallization. They are also used as binders in candies and in tablet sugar, but any considerable quantity in such products is considered as an adulterant. Metabolism of starch in the human system requires conversion to sugars, and the taking in of excessive quantities of uncooked starch is undesirable. **Modified starches** are starches with the molecule altered by chemical treatment to give characteristics suitable for particular industrial requirements. The modified starches and especially prepared starches are usually sold under trade names. **Superlose,** of Stein-Hall & Co., is amylose from cornstarch, and **Auperlose** is amylose from potato starch. **Ramalin,** of the same company, is amylopectin. **Amylon,** of the National Starch & Chemicals Corp., is cornstarch containing 57% amylose, and **Kosul** is cornstarch high in amylopectin. **Textaid,** of the same company, is a modified starch which reacts with water to form a grainy structure. It is used in comminuted meat products to give a firm texture. The **ColFlo** thickening agents, stable and soluble in frozen foods, are modified waxy cornstarches, high in amylopectin. **Pregelatinized starches** are pre-heat-treated starches that require no cooking for use in dry food mixes or adhesives. **Snow Flake starch,** of Corn Products Sales Co., is a cornstarch of this type.

Wheat starch is a fine white starch made by separating out the gluten of wheat flour by wash flotation. It is used in prepared mixes for foam-type cakes and pie crusts to improve texture, add volume, and reduce the amount of shortening needed. It replaces up to 30% of the wheat-flour content of the mix. **Starbake starch,** of Hercules, is wheat starch. **Paygel,** of General Mills, is also wheat starch but **alant starch,** or **inulin,** $(C_6H_{10}O_5)_6 \cdot H_2O$, is not a starch in the ordinary sense, but is an insoluble sugar which occurs as the reserve polysaccharide in many plants. It is obtained from the roots of the **artichoke,** *Helianthus tuberosis,* native to

America but now grown widely in Europe. Unlike starch, the molecule has fructose units held in glucoside linkage, and hydrolysis converts it to fructose.

Starch acetate, or **acetylated starch,** is used for textile sizing, in adhesives, and for greaseproofing paper. The insertion of acetate radicals reduces the tendency of the molecular chains to cling together. The acetylated starches are gums which gelatinize at lower temperatures than starch, and produce stable, nonlumping pastes which give strong, flexible films. **Miralloid** and **Mira-Film,** of A. E. Staley Mfg. Co., are acetylated cornstarches. **Morgum,** of Morningstar-Paisley, Inc., is a hydroxy ethyl **etherized starch** which gives high film strength in coatings. The **Kofilms** of General Mills are acetylated cornstarches which give greaseproof, craze-resistant coatings on paper and textiles.

Laundry starches are usually ordinary starches, but silicone resin emulsions may be added to starches to permit higher ironing temperatures, improve slipperiness, and improve the hand of the starched fabric. The so-called **permanent starches,** for household use, that are not removed by washing, are not starch, but are emulsions of polyvinyl acetate. **Oxidized starch,** a resistant starch for coatings, is made by the chloro-oxidation of a starch solution. **Sumstar 190,** of the Miles Chemical Co., is a **diallyl starch** made by acid oxidation of cornstarch. Small amounts of the powder added to kraft, tissue, or toweling pulp increase the wet and dry strengths and the folding endurance of the papers. An **ammoniated starch** called **Q-Tac starch,** of the Corn Products Sales Co., is cornstarch reacted with quaternary ammonium groups. A less than 1% solution improves paper strength. **Sulfonated starches** are used as dirt-suspending agents with detergents for cleaning textiles. **Nu-Film** is a starch of this type. **Clear Flo starch,** of the National Starch Products Co., is a modified starch containing a carboxyl group and a sulfonic acid group in the molecule. It has high hydrating capacity, and gelatinizes sharply at low temperatures. It is used in adhesives and water paints. **Cato starch,** of the same company, is a carboxy methyl starch used in paper sizing to add strength. **Dry Flo starch,** of the same company, is modified to contain a **hydrophobic radical,** such as $\cdot CH_2$, which makes the material insoluble in water but soluble in oils. It is used in paints.

Many enzymes hydrolize starch to maltose, but some enzymes convert the starch to the hard, tough glucosides known as **mannans,** such as the **mannose** of the ivory nut. **Phospho mannan,** produced by the fermentation of starch, is such a material used in adhesives. **Granular starch,** used in enzyme-conversion processing, is in dense granular particles produced by flash drying. **Easy-Enz starch,** of the Corn Products Co., is such a starch. **Cationic starch** is a starch with the molecules of stable negative polarity to give higher adhesion on the cellulose fibers of paper or textiles.

Molding starch, for adding to sugar candies to give sharp molding characteristics, is starch containing an edible oil.

The **phosphate starch** of the American Maize Products Co. is an orthophosphate ester of cornstarch, marketed in sodium salt form as a light-tan dry powder. It has high thickening power and makes a clearer paste than cornstarch. It has superior water-binding properties at low temperatures. Frozen foods made with it do not curdle or separate when thawed, and canned foods thickened with the starch can be stored for long periods without clouding. It is also used as a briquetting binder for charcoal.

Starch sponge is an edible starch in the form of a coarse-textured, porous, crispy, spongelike material, used for confections by impregnating with chocolate or sweets. In crushed form it is added to candy or cookies. It is produced by freezing starch paste, thawing, and pressing. The freezing insolubilizes the starch so that no soluble starch goes off when the water is pressed out. **Nitrostarch,** or **starch nitrate,** $C_{12}H_{12}O_{10}(NO_2)_3$, is a fine white powder made by treating starch with mixed acid. It is highly explosive and is used for blasting, as a military explosive, and in signal lights. **Grenite** is nitrostarch mixed with an oil binder for use in grenades. **Trojan explosive** is a mixture of 40% nitrostarch with ammonium and sodium nitrates and some inert material to reduce the sensitiveness.

STATUARY BRONZE. Copper alloys used for casting statues, plaques, and ornamental objects that require fine detail and a smooth, reddish surface. Most of the famous large bronze statues of Europe contain from 87 to 90% copper, with varying amounts of tin, zinc, and lead. Early Greek statues contained from 9 to 11% tin with as much as 5% lead added apparently to give greater fluidity for sharper casting. A general average bronze will contain 90% copper, 6 tin, 3 zinc, and 1 lead. Statuary bronze for cast plaques used in building construction contains 86% copper, 2 tin, 2 lead, 8 zinc, and 2 nickel. The nickel improves fluidity and hardens and strengthens the alloy, and the lead promotes an oxidized finish on exposure. The statuary bronze used for hardware has 83.5% copper, 4 lead, 2 tin, and 10 zinc.

STEARIC ACID. A hard, white, waxlike solid of the composition $CH_3(CH_2)_{16}COOH$, obtained from animal and vegetable fats and oils by splitting and distilling. The hard cattle fats are high in stearic acid, but other fats and oils contain varying amounts. It is also called **octo decanoic acid,** and can be made by hydrogenation of oleic acid. Stearic acid has a specific gravity of 0.922 to 0.935, a melting point at about 130°F, is soluble in alcohol but insoluble in water. It is marketed in cakes, powder, and flakes. **Emory 3101-D** is **isostearic acid** which has the solubility and physical properties of oleic acid while retaining the heat and oxidation stability of stearic acid.   **Pearl stearic acid** is the material in free-flowing bead powder.   The acid is used for making soaps, candles, paint driers, lubricating greases, and buffing compositions, and for compounding in rubbers, cosmetics, and coatings.

Successive pressings remove liquid oils, thus raising the melting point and giving a whiter, harder product of lower iodine value.   **Oleo oil** is a yellow oil obtained by cold-pressing the first-run cattle tallow.   **Tallow oil** is the oil following the first two grades of oleo oil.   **Oleostearin,** used for treating leather, is the stearin remaining after extraction of the oils.

Stearin is the glyceride of stearic acid.   **Acetostearins** are the monoglycerides acetylated with acetic anhydride.   They are closely related to fats, but are nongreasy and are plastic even at low temperatures.   The highly acetylated stearins melt below body temperature and are edible. Acetostearins are used as plasticizers for waxes and synthetic resins to improve low-temperature characteristics.   **Stearite** is a trade name for **synthetic stearic acid** made by the hydrogenation of unsaturated animal and fish oils.   It is used in rubber compounding, as it is more uniform than ordinary stearic acid.   **Hystrene,** of the Trendex Co., is purified and hardened stearic acid in grades of 70, 80, and 97% stearic acid, with the remainder palmitic acid, used for candles, cosmetics, and stearates.   **Intarvin** is a synthetic edible fat made from stearic acid by converting it to **margaric acid,** or **daturic acid,** $C_{16}H_{33}COOH$, and then esterifying with glycerin.   It is used as a fat for diabetics as it does not undergo the beta oxidation to lose two carbon atoms at a time and produce aceto acetic acid in the system as do the even-carbon food acids.

Wilmar 272, of Wilson & Co., is refined stearic acid in flake form for use in candles and coatings.   **Flexchem B,** of Swift & Co., is a **sodium stearate,** $NaC_{18}H_{35}O_2$, in the form of a water-soluble white powder, insoluble in oils.   It is used as a bodying agent in cosmetic creams. **Myvacet,** of the Distillation Products Industries, is an aceto stearin used as an edible plastic coating for poultry, cheese, and frozen fish and meats to prevent loss of the natural color and flavor.   It is a white waxy solid with melting points from 99 to 109°F, but it also comes as an oil with congealing point at 45°F for use as a release agent on bakery equipment.

Stearin pitch is a brown-to-black by-product residue obtained in the splitting and distillation of fats and oils in the manufacture of soaps, candles, and fatty acids.   While the word stearin implies that it contains only stearic acid, it usually comes from a variety of oils and has mixed acids, and it may take the name of the oil, such as **linseed pitch** or **palm pitch.**   It is used in varnishes and cold-molding compositions.

STEEL. Iron with carbon chemically dissolved in it.   When raised to a red heat and cooled suddenly, it is hardened by the formation of the hard carbide, Fe_3C.   The **eutectic point,** or the saturation point for the dissolving of the carbon in the iron, is 0.83%, above which point the excess carbon is thrown out as free graphite unless other elements are present to take it up.   Steels with less than 0.15% carbon harden only slightly, and these are technically classed as **irons,** although the name steel is used even when the carbon is very low, especially when the material is heavily alloyed.   Alloys with high proportions of other elements, and a relatively small amount of iron, are still called steel if the iron and carbon are important influencing elements.   The **Homocarb** method of Leeds & Northup gives accurate control of the carbon by forced circulation and temperature control of the applied gas.

Steel is graded according to the percentage of carbon in it, and is roughly divided into four groups: **low-carbon steel,** with 0.15 to 0.30% carbon; **medium-carbon steel,** with 0.30 to 0.60% carbon; **high-carbon steel,** with 0.60 to 0.90% carbon; and very high carbon steel, with 0.90 to 1.5% carbon.   Steel with more than 1.25% carbon is very brittle unless there are some other balancing elements.   The low-carbon steels machine easily and can be forged readily.   Those containing above 0.90% carbon are difficult to forge and machine.   In general, the low-carbon steels are used for construction parts and the high-carbon steels for tools and high-strength parts.   All steels contain some manganese, usually at least 0.30%, left after deoxidizing and desulfurizing with ferromanganese.   The latter forms MnS and MnO which pass off in the slag, but sometimes an excess of manganese is used for hard steels as the manganese is a carbide-forming element.   Manganese is added to the steels used for electromagnetic devices to retard particle growth, thus reducing magnetic aging.   Sulfur in steel forms the weak and soft sulfide FeS which weakens the steel and promotes hot-shortness or brittleness at red heat.   But sometimes a very small amount of sulfur is left in the steel to aid machinability.   Oxygen in the steel forms the embrittling compound FeO and is undesirable in any quantity.   Normally, phosphorus is considered detrimental in steels, but small amounts, up to 0.20%, in low-carbon steels increase the hardness, strength, and also increase corrosion resistance.   **Dirty steel** is steel with inclusions of iron oxide from scrap used in the converter or of aluminum oxide from the aluminum used in deoxidizing.   The melting point of steel varies with the carbon, but is always higher than that of cast iron with the same amount of combined carbon.   The average weight of carbon steel is 0.283 lb per cu in.   One of the simplest of the plain carbon steels is **AISI steel C1015,** with 0.15% carbon, and this steel has a tensile strength in the soft hot-rolled condition of 50,000 psi, elongation 28%, and Brinell hardness 100.   It is taken as a standard of relativity in comparing the strength and other physical properties of other steels and alloys.

Open-hearth steel is made by fusing cast iron with steel scrap or wrought iron in a regenerative furnace. Cementation consists in heating bars of wrought iron in contact with carbon. The product is known as **blister steel,** as the surface of the bars is covered with blisters. Blister steel has a crystalline fracture decreasing toward the center of the bar where there is less carbon. **Shear steel** is produced from this blister steel by cutting and piling together, heating to a high temperature, and rolling or hammering into bars. Shear steel was originally the only form of commercial steel.

Bessemer steel is made by decarbonizing cast iron by forcing a powerful blast of air through the molten iron. **Crucible steel** is made by melting wrought iron in a crucible with charcoal and ferromanganese, or special steel mixes in a crucible furnace. The slag separates by gravity from the molten metal in the crucibles, and the oxides combine with carbon and manganese or aluminum, and boil off. The metal is poured into ingots which are reheated and rolled into bars or other forms. The crucible process permits a high degree of control and reduces sulfur and phosphorus. **Electric steel** is made in either the induction or the arc-type furnace, and is of a uniform quality and of a higher strength and ductility than open-hearth steel of the same carbon content.

Many variations are now used in the production of steels. Oxygen may be used in the blast instead of air to give greater efficiency and better control. Calcium carbide may be used as a fuel in basic-oxygen furnaces. It permits use of more scrap and improves the efficiency of melting but shortens the life of the refractory lining. Degassing may be done in a vacuum chamber with a jet of inert gas to remove the hydrogen. Or, steel may be produced without blast-furnace reduction by compressing iron oxide in rollers at about 2200°F and then hot-strip rolling and cold-rolling. Ordinary steel has only carbon as the influencing element, except that residual manganese, sulfur, and some other elements are present in very small amounts.

Ordinary steel used for **wrought-steel pipe** has a tensile strength of 52,000 psi, yield point 30,000 psi, and elongation 20%. The tensile strength of a typical open-hearth steel varies from about 50,000 psi for a 0.12% carbon steel to 110,000 psi for a 0.55% carbon steel, with elongations of 29 and 12%, respectively. Ordinary forgings are made from steels of 0.15 to 0.30% carbon, and strong forgings from steel with 0.35 to 0.40% carbon, but most strong forgings are now made with alloy steels. Raising the carbon content from 0.40 to 0.45% will increase the possible hardness of the steel about 10%, but greater variations in strength and hardness of a steel may come from even small additions of alloying elements plus heat treatment, and very high strengths are obtainable in these steels. Very high carbon can be used to give high strength and abrasion resistance when the steel contains enough carbide-forming elements to absorb the carbon. For example, the **BR-8 die steel** of the Latrobe Steel Co., used for abrasive dies and brick molds, has 2.8% carbon, but it also contains 5.25% chromium and 4.5% vanadium to form hard carbides with heat treatment.   **Aircraft-quality steel** refers to the quality of steel, and may be of any type of steel.   It is also called **magnaflux steel,** and each bar is tested with a magnetic powder to expose any surface or subsurface irregularities.

SAE steels is the designation for the standard grades of steel approved by the Society of Automotive Engineers.   These steels are made regularly by the various mills and are known by their designating numbers. The first number indicates the class of steel, as follows: carbon steel, 1; nickel-carbon, 2; nickel-chromium, 3; molybdenum, 4; chromium, 5; chromium-vanadium, 6; tungsten, 7; nickel-chromium molybdenum, 8; and silicon-manganese steel, 9.   The second figure indicates the average percentage of the predominating alloying element.   The last two or three figures indicate the approximate carbon content in hundredths of 1%. Thus **SAE 2350 steel** is a nickel steel containing 3% nickel (2.75 to 3.25) and 0.50 carbon (0.45 to 0.55).   The manganese steels, with manganese from 1.60 to 1.90%, are designated by the letter T before the initial 1. Thus **SAE T1350 steel** contains 0.45 to 0.55% carbon and 1.60 to 1.90 manganese.   The SAE steels are made to close specifications of manganese, sulfur, and phosphorus content, and since they are very uniform in quality and usually carried in stock, they have been widely adopted for use in all kinds of products.

STEEL POWDER. Finely divided steel powder used for molding under hydraulic pressure into various parts which are then sintered at a temperature of 1075°C.   The tensile strength of the molded and sintered products is about the same as that of cast steel of the same composition.   It has the advantage that there is no metal loss in machining, and accurate gears, cams, and other parts can be made without machining.   **Sinterloy** is the name of a steel powder marketed by Charles Hardy, Inc., in compositions of 0.05, 0.40, and 0.80% carbon.   Some grades also contain nickel and chromium.   **Durex iron,** of the Moraine Products Div., General Motors Corp., is iron or steel made by compressing iron powder containing a small percentage of carbon and sintering in special furnaces with controlled atmospheres.   It can be controlled by pressure to form 70 to 95% of the density of pure iron; or with a porosity range from 5 to 30% by volume when it is desired to impregnate with oil.   It is used for mechanical parts or the porous variety for bearings.   **Porex** is a trade name of this company for porous metals made from powders and used as filters.   The production of products by the compression and sintering of powders is called **powder metallurgy.**   **P.M.P. iron,** of the Powdered Metals Corp., used for bearings, contains 90% iron and 10 copper.   With a density of 5.5 lb per cu in. it has a tensile strength of 30,000 psi and will absorb 30% of oil by volume. When compressed to a higher density, it has greater strength, and is used for cams and machine parts.

Stainless-steel powder has a typical analysis of 17.36% chromium, 8.89 nickel, 0.11 carbon, 0.47 silicon, 0.022 phosphorus, and 0.008 sulfur. It is prealloyed, and the powder has the original grain boundaries broken down. **Stay Preme,** of the Chas. Pfizer Co., Inc., is a stainless steel powder of 100 mesh for molded and sintered parts. The **prealloyed steel powders** of the Vanadium Alloys Steel Co. are in a wide variety of compositions of carbon and alloy steels. The particles are spherical and are in meshes 50 to 100. Physical properties of parts made by powder metallurgy can be controlled by choice of powder size and by the pressure. The stainless-steel powder of the American Electro Metal Corp. has spongelike particles, and it comes in mixed screen sizes from 100 to 325 mesh to give high green strength in the pressed part. The **Steelmet powders** of P. R. Mallory & Co., Inc., are prealloyed powders with controlled particle sizes to yield pressed parts with 95% of theoretical density. **Steelmet 100** has 1% manganese, 1 nickel, and the balance iron. The sintered parts have a tensile strength of 55,000 psi, elongation 25%. **Steelmet 600** has 2% copper and 0.25 nickel. The tensile strength of the parts is 95,000 psi with elongation of 16%. Practically any type of alloy powder can now be had in any particle size down to air-float powders below 150 angstroms.

STEEL WOOL. Long, fine fibers of steel used for abrasive purposes, chiefly for cleaning utensils and for polishing. It is made from low-carbon bessemer wire of high tensile strength, usually having 0.10 to 0.20% carbon and 0.50 to 1 manganese. The wire is drawn over a track and shaved by a stationary knife bearing down on it, and may be made in a continuous piece as long as 100,000 ft. Steel wool usually has three edges but may have four or five, and strands of various types are mixed. There are nine standard grades of steel wool, the finest of which has no fibers greater than 0.0005 in. thick, the most commonly used grade having fibers that vary between 0.002 and 0.004 in. Steel wool comes in batts, or in flat ribbon form on spools usually 4 in. wide. **Stainless-steel wool** is also made, and **copper wool** is marketed for some cleaning operations.

STILLINGIA OIL. A drying oil obtained from the kernels of the seeds of the tree *Stillingia sebifera,* cultivated in China. The seeds contain about 23% of a light-yellow oil resembling linseed oil but of somewhat inferior drying power. The oil has a specific gravity of 0.943 to 0.946 and iodine value of 160. It has the peculiar property of expanding with great force at the congealing point. Stillingia oil is edible, but deteriorates rapidly, becoming bitter in taste and disagreeable in odor. **Stillingia tallow,** also known as **Chinese vegetable tallow,** is obtained by pressing from the coating, or mesocarp, of the seeds.   Sometimes the whole seed is crushed, producing a softer fat than the true tallow.   The tallow contains palmitic and oleic acids and is used in soaps and for mixing with other waxes. Some stillingia trees are grown in Texas.

STRONTIUM.   A metallic element of the alkaline group.   It occurs in the minerals **strontianite,** $SrCO_3$, and **celestite,** $SrSO_4$, and resembles barium in its properties and combinations, but is slightly harder and less reactive and is not as white in color.   It has a specific gravity of 2.54 and a melting point at about 770°C, and it decomposes water.   The metal is obtained by electrolysis of the fused chloride, and small amounts are used for doping semiconductors.   Its compounds have been used for deoxidizing nonferrous alloys, and were used in Germany for desulfurizing steel.   But the chief uses have been in signal flares to give a red light, and in hard, heat-resistant greases.   **Strontium 90,** produced atomically, is used in ship-deck signs as it emits no dangerous gamma rays.   It gives a bright sign, and the color can be varied with the content of zinc, but it is short-lived. Strontium is very reactive and used only in compounds.

Strontium nitrate is a yellowish-white crystalline powder, $Sr(NO_3)_2$, produced by roasting and leaching celestite and treating with nitric acid. The specific gravity is 2.96, the melting point is 645°C, and it is soluble in water.   It gives a bright crimson flame, and is used in railway-signal lights and in military flares.   It is also used as a source of oxygen.   The **strontium sulfate** used as a brightening agent in paints is powdered celestite.   The ore of Nova Scotia contains 75% strontium sulfate.   **Strontium sulfide,** SrS, used in luminous paint, gives a blue-green glow, but it deteriorates rapidly unless sealed in.   **Strontium carbonate,** $SrCO_3$, is used in pyrotechnics, ceramics, and ceramic permanent magnets for small motors. **Strontium hydrate,** $Sr(OH)_2 \cdot 8H_2O$, loses its water of crystallization at 100°C and melts at 375°C.   It is used in making lubricating greases and as a stabilizer in plastics.   **Strontium fluoride** is produced in single crystals by Semi Elements, Inc., for use as a laser material.   When doped with samarium it gives an output wavelength around 6,500 angstroms.

STYRAX.   A grayish-brown, viscous, sticky, aromatic balsam obtained from the small tree *Liquidambar orientalis* of Asia Minor.   It is also called **Levant styrax.**   It is used in cough medicines and for skin diseases, as a fixative for heavy perfumes, and for flavoring tobacco and soaps. American styrax is obtained by tapping the sweet gum, *L. styraciflua,* of Alabama, a tree producing 8 oz of gum per year.   It is a brownish semi-solid and has the same uses as Levant styrax.   It is shipped from Central America under the name of **liquidambar,** and in the southern United States is called **sweet gum** and **storax.**   The gum is not present in large amounts in the wood, but its formation is induced by cuts.   The red gum of Louisiana yields 2.5 oz per tree per year.   **Benzoin** is another balsam obtained from several species of *Styrax* trees.   It is a highly aromatic solid with an odor like vanilla, and is used in medicine and in perfumes and incense.   **Sumatra benzoin** is from the tree *S. benzoin* and comes in reddish-brown lumps or tears.   In medicine it was originally called **gum Benjamin.   Siam benzoin,** from southern Asia, is from the trees *S. tonkinense* and *S. benzoides.*   It is in yellowish or brownish tears.   The Sumatra benzoin contains cinnamic acid, while the Asiatic gum contains benzoic acid.   **Benzoic acid,** or **phenylformic acid,** C_6H_5COOH, formerly produced from benzoin, is now made synthetically from benzol, and called **carboxy benzene.**   It is a white crystalline solid melting at 122°C, soluble in water and in alcohol, used as a food preservative, as an antiseptic, for flavoring tobacco, as a week acid mordant in printing textiles, and in the manufacture of dyestuffs, pharmaceuticals, and cosmetics.   It is poisonous, and not more than 0.1% is used in food preserving in the form of its salt, **Benzoate of soda,** or **sodium benzoate,** C_6H_5COONa, a white crystalline powder.   **Sorbic acid,** $CH_3CH:(CH)_2:CHCOOH$, a solid melting at 134°C, occurs in unripe apples, but is made synthetically.   As a preservative and antimold agent it is more effective than benzoic acid, is nontoxic, and is readily absorbed in the human system.   It is used in cheese and other foods.   For food preservation it is used in the form of the water-soluble salt, **potassium sorbate.**   In a concentration of 0.2% it does not affect taste or aroma.   **Anisic acid,** $CH_3OC_6H_4COOH$, used for pharmaceuticals, is the methyl ether of hydroxy benzoic acid.   It is produced synthetically from carbon tetrachloride and phenol, and is a solid melting at 184°C. It is also called **methoxy benzoic acid, umbellic acid,** and **dragonic acid.**

SUEDE. Also called **napped leather.**   A soft-finished, chrome-tanned leather made from calf, kid, or cowhide splits, or from sheepskin.   It is worked on a staking machine until it is soft and supple, and then buffed or polished on an abrasive wheel.   It has a soft nap on the polished side and may be dyed in any color.   Suede is used for shoe uppers, coats, hats, and pocketbooks, but is now largely imitated with synthetic fabrics. **Artificial suede,** or **Izarine,** of the Atlas Powder Co., had a base of rubberized fabric.   Fine cotton fibers dyed in colors are cemented to one side, and the underside of the sheet is beaten to make the fibers stand out until the cement hardens.   The fabric looks and feels like fine suede.   Some suede is also made by chemical treatment of sheepskins without staking. It has a delicate softness, but is not as wear-resistant as calfskin suede.

SUGAR. A colorless to white or brownish crystalline, sweet material produced by evaporating and crystallizing the extracted juice of the sugarcane or the sugar beet.   Refined sugar is practically pure **sucrose,** C_{12}-$H_{22}O_{11}$, and in addition to being a sweetening agent for many foods it is a valuable carbohydrate food, and also a food preservative.   When used with cooked fruits to make jams and jellies, it is both a preservative and an added food.   Lack of sugar in the diet develops ketosis, the disease of diabetics, and results in the wasting away of muscles, using up of reserve fats, and the production of poisonous ketones.   When the blood-sugar level is low a feeling of hunger is induced which may not be satisfied even by overeating.   A small amount of sugar curbs the appetite and obviates surplus eating of proteins and fats that create obesity.   Natural **brown sugar** contains about 2% of the minerals found in the plant, calcium, iron, phosphorus, magnesium, and potassium and, although these are valuable as foods, they are lost in the refining process.

Sugar is at present most valued as a food and for the production of by-product alcohol from the residue molasses, but the sucrose molecule is a convenient starting point for the production of many chemicals.   However, the production and distribution of sugar have been hemmed in by restrictive laws based on its use for food.   The sucrose molecule has two complex rings, a glucosido and a fructose.   It can be regarded as a type of **fructosido-glucose,** but the fructose in sucrose has a different structure, a **furanose,** five-ring form, instead of the **pyranose,** six-ring structure of ordinary fructose.   Hydrolysis of sucrose with acid gives dextrorotatory glucose and fructose, and the mixture is called **invert sugar.   Numoline,** of SuCrest Corp., is a noncrystallizing invert sugar made by hydrolizing sucrose to split the molecule into levulose and dextrose.   It is used in confectionery and bakery products.   Oxidation of sucrose produces oxalic acid and also **saccharic acid,** $(HCOH)_4(COOH)_2$, which can be reduced to adipic acid.   Glycerin can be made from sugar by hydrogenation to sorbitol and then splitting.   Thus, because of the great versatility of the sucrose molecule, and the ease with which sugar can be grown, sugar is one of the most valuable chemical raw materials.   **Sucrose benzoate** is a benzoic acid derivative of sucrose used as a plasticizer and modifier for synthetic resins for lacquers and inks.

Sugar cane, *Saccharum officinarum,* is a tropical plant, originating in Asia and first brought to the Canary Islands in 1503 and thence to the West Indies.   The plant will not withstand frost, but can be grown in a few favored regions outside of the tropics such as Louisiana.   It is now grown on plantations in Cuba, Hawaii, Brazil, the Philippines, Indonesia, Puerto Rico, Peru, and many other countries.   The cane or stalks of the plant are crushed to extract the juice, which is then concentrated by boiling, crystallized, and clarified with activated carbon or other material. The yield of sugar in Hawaii is about 14 tons of raw sugar per acre. Analysis of sugar cane gives an average of 13.4% sucrose by weight of cane.   The average yield by milling is 91% of the contained sucrose, but yields as high as 98.8% are obtained by diffusion extraction of the cut-cane chips.

The **sugar beet** is a white-rooted variety of the common beet, *Beta vulgaris,* and grows in temperate climates.   It is cut up and boiled to extract the juice, and the production and refining of the sugar are essentially the same as for cane sugar.   There is no difference in the final product, although **raffinose,** or **melitriose,** $C_{18}H_{32}O_{16}$, a tasteless trisaccharide, occurs in the sugar beet, and may not be completely changed to sucrose by hydrolysis, so that a greater quantity may sometimes be needed to obtain equal sweetening effect.   The pectins and starches of the sugar beet are not extracted by the use of the slicing and diffusion method.   With the use of single-germ seed to reduce the labor of thinning, as much as 4,820 lb of sugar per acre with 4 man-days labor have been produced from sugar beets.

Refined commercial sugar contains 99.98% sucrose, and is graded by screening to crystal size.   The best qualities are the larger crystals from the first and second runs.   The soft sugars are from further crystallizing, until the noncrystallizing brown sugars are reached.   Raw sugar testing 96° by the polariscope is the grade used as a basis for raw-sugar quotations.   About 107 lb of this grade of sugar are required to produce 100 lb of refined sugar.   Commercial sugar may have starch added.   The ultra-fine 6X **confectioners sugar** usually contains 4% cornstarch as a non-caking agent, and block sugars may contain starch as a binding agent, but starch reduces the sweetening power.

Cane syrup is the high-grade syrup or liquid sugar, while **molasses** is the heavy residual syrup left after the crystallization.   **Edible molasses** is the yellow to brownish, light purified residue syrup.   **Blackstrap molasses** is the final, inedible, unpurified residue heavy syrup, used for the production of ethyl alcohol.   It contains 50 to 60% sugar by weight, mostly sucrose but some glucose.   A purified grade which retains the minerals is marketed as an edible blackstrap molasses.

Cuban sugar mills average 48 gal of blackstrap molasses per ton of sugar, and 2.5 gal of molasses containing 50% sugar yields 1 gal of 95% alcohol.   **Molasses powder,** used for bakery products, is made by spray drying.   It is a free-flowing, noncaking powder.   **Liquid sugar,** much used in food manufacturing because it saves handling costs, comes in various liquid densities and in various degrees of invert.   The liquid sugars are usually not pure sucrose, and are called **multisugars.**   For food manufacturing the calcium and other minerals may be left in, and they then have a yellow color.   Multisugars with 90% sucrose and 10% levulose and dextrose crystallize in hard aggregate clusters, desirable in some confections.   **Flo-Sweet,** of Refined Syrups & Sugars, Inc., is liquid sugar.

Sucrodex, of the same company, is liquid sugar containing one-third dextrose and two-thirds sucrose, with a solubility of 72% compared with only 45% for dextrose and 67% for sucrose.   **Inverdex,** for canning and for fountain syrups, is about 85% invert sugar and 15 dextrose.   **Amberdex,** used for cakes and cookies, is an amber-colored 50–50 mixture of sucrose and dextrose with the edible minerals left in.   **Caramel,** used for flavoring and coloring foodstuffs and liquors, has a deep-brown color and a characteristic taste.   It is burnt sugar marketed as a liquid or powder.

The **papelon** of South America is solidified edible molasses.   **Gur** is unrefined brown sugar of India, and the **pilancillo** of Mexico is unrefined brown sugar.   **Treacle** is an English name for edible molasses.   The refuse from sugar cane, called bagasse, is used as fuel and for making paper and insulating board.   **Beet pulp,** after extraction of the juice, is marketed as cattle feed.   Despite restrictive controls over the world supply of sugar, much sucrose is now being used in the production of chemical products.   **Nonionic detergents,** which are odorless, biodegradable powders with low toxicity, are made by reacting sucrose with fatty acid esters of volatile alcohols.   Allyl sucrose is used as a shellac substitute. **Sucrose acetate butyrate,** of Eastman Chemical Products, Inc., is a clear viscous liquid boiling at 550°F, used as a plasticizer in synthetic resins to improve extrusion and to give flexibility and adhesiveness in coatings.   As much as 70% is used in nitrocellulose to give tough, flexible melt coatings. **Nitto ester,** of the Dai Nippon Sugar Mfg. Co., is a **sucrose ester** made with sugar and stearic acid.   It is used as a food additive.

A type of edible sugar syrup is also obtained from the juice of a variety of **sorghum grass,** *Sorghum vulgare,* native to South Africa, but now grown in southern United States.   The juice or syrup, called **sorghum syrup,** or **sorgo syrup,** is light in color, has a characteristic delicate flavor, and contains gums and starch, which prevent crystallization.   It also contains other sugars besides sucrose, and considerable mineral salts of value as foods.   The total sugar in the juice is from 9 to 17%, varying with the age of the plant.   It is used in some sections to replace sugar, and is employed in some confectionery to give a distinctive flavor.

Apple syrup, or **apple honey,** used as a sweetening agent in the food industry, for curing hams, and as a substitute moistening agent for tobacco, is made from cull apples.   The reduced syrup is treated to remove the bitter calcium malate.   It contains 75% solids of which 65% consists of the sugars levulose, dextrose, and sucrose.   **Palm sugar,** or **jaggary,** is the evaporated sap of several varieties of palm, including the coconut and the palms from which kittool, gomuti, and palmyra fibers are obtained.   The sap contains about 14% sugar.   It is much used in India and the Pacific Islands.   The **palm wine** known as **arrack** is made by fermenting the juice, called **taewak,** of the flower stems of the **aren palm** of

Java.   A liter of taewak yields about 0.09 kg of brown palm sugar.
Wood molasses is made by concentrating and neutralizing the dilute sugar
solution produced by pressure hydrolysis of wood chips using dilute sulfuric acid at high temperature.   The molasses has a slightly bitter taste,
but is used for stock feed and for industrial purposes.   The molasses
yield is 150 to 190 gal of 50% sugar strength per ton of wood, with 10
to 20 lb of methanol and 10 to 30 lb of furfural as by-products.   **Wood
sugars** contain **xylose,** $CHO(HCOH)_3CH_2OH$, which belongs to the great
group of **pentosans** occurring in plant life.   They have the same general
formula with different numbers of the $(HCOH)$ group.   Oxidation converts them to the respective acid, as **xylonic acid** from xylose, or arabinic
acid from the arabinose of gum arabic.   They can also be converted to
the lactones, and are related to the furanes, so that the wood sugars have
a wide utility for the production of chemicals.

Other plants yield **sweetening agents,** but few are of commercial importance.   The leaves of the **caá heé,** a small plant of Paraguay, are used
locally for sweetening Paraguayan tea.   The name, pronounced kah-áh
aye-áye, means sweet herb, and it has a more intense sweetening effect than
sugar.   **Miracle Fruit powder,** of the International Minerals and Chemical
Corp., is a complex protein-based chemical derived from the fruit pulp of
the **Agbayun** shrub, *Synsepalum dulcificum,* of West Africa.   It has a
strong sweetening effect and a pleasant natural flavor.   The 6-carbon sugar
derivative known as **glucoronic lactone,** used as an antiarthritic drug, is
derived from dextrose.   **Amino sugar,** or **glucosamine,** has an NH_2 group
in the molecule in place of the alpha hydroxyl group of glucose.   This
sugar occurs in marine animals.

Synthetic sweetening agents of no food value are used in diabetic foods
and in dietetic foods for the treatment of obesity.   Many of these synthetic sweeteners are toxic in excess and are cumulative in the human system.   Thus, **dietary foods** that depend on the substitution of chemicals
in place of sugar should be taken only with caution and under medical
direction.   **Saccharin,** produced from coal tar, is **benzoic sulfinide,** C_6H_4-
SO_2NHCO.   It is 450 times sweeter than sugar, and has no food value,
but it has a disagreeable afterflavor.   It is a water-insoluble white powder,
but its salts, **sodium saccharin** and **calcium saccharin,** are soluble in water,
and are 300 times sweeter than sugar.   Saccharin is also used as a pH
indicator, and as a brightener in nickel-plating baths.

The **cyclamates** have been widely used in beverages and diet foods, but
are now recognized as toxic drugs and are restricted.   **Sodium cyclohexyl
sulfamate,** or **sodium cyclamate,** $Na(C_6H_{12}NO_3S)_2 \cdot 2H_2O$, is used in dietetic foods and in some soft drinks as it has no food value.   It is 30 times
sweeter than sugar, but at the 25% sweetening level of sugar it has an
undesirable aftertaste, and at the sugar-sweetness level the off-taste pre-

dominates.   For both sugar-free and salt-free diets, the calcium salt, **cal-cium cyclamate,** is used.   **Sucaryl,** of the Abbott Laboratories, is sodium cyclamate, and **Cyclan,** of Du Pont, is calcium cyclamate.   **Hexamic acid,** a white crystalline powder which is cycle hexyl sulfamic acid, is used as a supplement sweetener and intensifier with the cyclamates and saccharin. **Aspartyl phenyl alanine** of Fermco Laboratories has a sweetening power higher than saccharin with a flavor more nearly like that of sucrose.   **Peryl-lartine** is the sweetest known substance, being 2,000 times sweeter than sucrose.   It is a complex aldehyde derived from **terpenylic acid** which occurs in combined forms in terpentine and many essential oils.

SUGAR PINE. The common name of the wood of the *Pinus lambertiana,* a coniferous tree growing in California and Oregon.   The tree grows ordinarily to a height from 150 to 175 ft with a diameter of 4 to 5 ft. Occasional trees are more than 200 ft in height and 12 ft in diameter, and are often free of limbs up to 75 ft from the ground.   It is the largest of the pines.   The stand is estimated to be 35 billion bd ft and is cut at the rate of 300 million feet annually.   Sugar pine is durable, has moderate strength and fairly even grain, and is not subject to excessive shrinkage or warping.   Because of the latter quality it has come into use to replace the scarcer eastern pines for patterns.   It does not darken on exposure as western pine does.   It is widely employed for construction work and for **factory lumber** for doors, frames, boxes, and wooden articles. Sugar pine is classified into three standard classes of grades according to freedom from knots and faults as select, commons, and factory, or shop. The selects are designated as No 1, and 2 clear, C select, and D select. The commons are graded as Nos. 1, 2, 3, and 4; the factory as No. 3 clear, No. 1 shop, No. 2 shop, and No. 3 shop.   The shops are judged with the idea that they will be cut up into small pieces, and are consequently classified by the area of clear cuttings that can be obtained.

SULFAMIC ACID. A white crystalline odorless solid of the composition $HSO_3 \cdot NH_2$, very soluble in water, but only slightly soluble in alcohol. The melting point is 178°C.   The acid is stronger than other solid acids, approaching the strength of hydrochloric.   It is used in bating and tanning leather, giving a silky, tight grain in the leather.   An important use is for cleaning boiler and heat-exchanger tubes.   It converts the calcium carbonate scale to the water-soluble calcium sulfamate which can then be flushed off, and combined with sodium chloride, it also converts the rust to ferric chloride and then to the water-soluble iron sulfamate.   **Cleanser 1331,** of the Ionac Chemical Co., is this material.   **Ammonium sulfamate** is the ammonia salt of the acid, used as a cleanser and anodizer of metals, as a weed killer, and for flameproofing paper and textiles.   **Lead ammo-**

nium sulfamate, $Pb(SO_3NH_2)_2$, used in lead plating, is very soluble in water and has high throwing power. **Aminoethyl sulfamic acid,** NH_2-$CH_2CH_2OSO_3H$, is used for treating paper and textile fibers to increase wet strength and water repellency. **Tobias acid,** used in making azo dyes, is **naphthylamine sulfonic acid,** $NH_2C_{10}H_6SO_3H$, in white needles decomposing at 230°C.

SULFONATED OIL. A fatty oil that has been treated with sulfuric acid, the excess acid being washed out, and only the chemically combined acid remaining. The oil is then neutralized with an alkali. Sulfonated oils are water-soluble and are used in cutting oils and in fat liquors for leather finishing. **Sulfonated castor oil** is called **Turkey red oil. Leatherlubric** is the trade name of E. F. Houghton & Co. for sulfonated sperm oil used for leather. **Solcod** is the sulfonated cod oil of the same company. **Sulfonated stearin** and **sulfonated tallow** are also used in leather dressing. They are cream-colored pastes readily soluble in hot water. **Mahogany soap** is a name for oil-soluble petroleum sulfonates used as dispersing and wetting agents, corrosion inhibitors, emulsifiers, and to increase the oil absorption of mineral pigments in paints. **Petronate,** of L. Sonneborn Sons, Inc., is a petroleum sulfonate containing 62% sulfonates, 35 mineral oil, and 3 water. **Phosphorated oils,** or their sulfonates, may be used instead of the sulfonates as emulsifying agents or in treating textiles and leathers. They are more stable to alkalies. **Phosoils,** of the Beacon Co., are phosphorated vegetable oils. **Aquasol,** of the American Cyanamid Co., is a sulfonated castor oil used as an emulsifying agent. **Cream softener** is a name used in the textile industry for sulfonated tallow.

SULFUR. One of the most industrially useful of the elements. Its occurrence in nature is little more than 1% that of aluminum, but it is easy to extract and is relatively plentiful. In economics, it belongs to the group of "S" materials—salt, sulfur, steel, sugars, starches—whose consumption is a measure of the industrialization and the rate of industrial growth of a nation. Sulfur is obtained from volcanic deposits in Sicily, Mexico, Chile, and Argentina, and along the Gulf Coast in Louisiana, Texas, and Mexico it is obtained from great deposits underground in the cap rock above salt domes. Offshore deposits worked in the Gulf of Mexico are 2,000 ft under the bottom. It is also obtained by the distillation of iron pyrites, and as a by-product of copper and other metal smelting, and from natural gas. The National Sulphur Co. produces sulfur from gypsum. The **sterri** exported from Sicily for making sulfuric acid is broken rock rich in sulfur. **Brimstone** is a very ancient name still in popular use for solid sulfur, but the District Court of Texas has ruled that sulfur obtained from gas is not subject to tax as brimstone.

Sulfur forms a crystalline mass of a pale-yellow color, with a hardness of 1.5 to 2.5 Mohs, a specific gravity of 2.05 to 2.09, and melting point at 232°F. It forms a ruby vapor at about 780°F. When melted and cast, it forms **amorphous sulfur** with a specific gravity of 1.955. The tensile strength is 160 psi, and compressive strength is 3,300 psi, and since ancient times it has been used as a lute for setting metals into stone. Sulfur also condenses into light flakes known as **flowers of sulfur,** and the **hydrogen sulfide gas,** H_2S, separated from sour natural gas, yields a sulfur powder. **Flotation sulfur** is a fine free-flowing sulfur dust with particle sizes less than 4 microns, recovered in gas production from coal. Commercial crude Sicilian sulfur contains from 2 to 11% of impurities and is sold in three grades. Refined sulfur is marketed in crystals, roll, or various grades of powder, and the Sicilian superior grade is 99.5% pure. This is the grade used in rubber manufacture. The sulfur of the Texas Gulf Sulphur Co. is 99.5% pure and is free of arsenic, selenium, and tellurium. **Crystex,** of the Stauffer Chemical Co., is a sulfur, 85% insoluble in carbon bisulfide, used in rubber compounding. The **sulfur powder** of Electronic Space Products, Inc., used for semiconductors, is 99.9999% pure.

Sulfur has twice the atomic weight of oxygen but has many similar properties and has great affinity for most metals. It has 6 valence electrons, but also has valences of 2 and 4. The **crystalline sulfur** is orthorhombic, which converts to monoclinic crystals if cooled slowly from 120°C. This form remains stable below 120°C. When molten sulfur is cooled suddenly it forms the amorphous sulfur which has a ring molecular structure and is plastic, but converts gradually to the rhombic form. Sulfur has a wide variety of uses in all industries. It is used for making gunpowder and for vulcanizing rubber, but for most uses it is employed in compounds, especially as sulfuric acid or sulfur dioxide A vast number of so-called thio compounds have been produced. The **thio alcohols,** or **mercaptans,** have an SH group instead of the OH of true alcohols, and they do not react like alcohols, but the **thio esters** are made directly from the mercaptans. **Thionyl chloride,** $SOCl_2$, a yellow liquid, is a typical compound used as a source of sulfur in synthesis. Most of the thio compounds have an offensive odor. **Vegetable sulfur** does not contain sulfur, but is **lycopodium,** a fine yellow powder from the spores of the **club moss,** a fernlike plant, *Lycopodium clavatum,* growing in North America and in Europe. It belongs to the group of **lipochromes,** or coloring matter of plants related to lycopene and carotene.

Sulfur dioxide, or **sulfurous acid anhydride,** is a colorless gas of the composition SO_2, used as a refrigerant, as a preservative, in bleaching, and for making other chemicals. It liquefies at about −10°C. As a refrigerant it has a condensing pressure of 51.7 lb at 86°F, and a pressure of vaporization of 2.9 lb at 5ZF. The gas has a pungent, suffocating odor, so that leaks are detected easily. It is corrosive to organic materials but does not attack copper or brass. The gas is soluble in water, forming **sulfurous acid,** H_2SO_3, a colorless liquid with suffocating fumes. The acid form is the usual method of use of the gas for bleaching.

SULFURIC ACID. An oily, highly corrosive liquid of the composition H_2SO_4, having a specific gravity of 1.834, and boiling at 338°C. It is miscible in water in all proportions, and the color is yellowish to brown according to the purity. It may be made by burning sulfur to the dioxide, oxidizing to the trioxide, and reacting with steam to form the acid. It is a strong acid, oxidizing organic materials and most metals. Sulfuric acid is used for pickling and cleaning metals, in electric batteries and in plating baths, for making explosives and fertilizers, and for many other purposes. In the metal industries it is called **dipping acid,** and in the automotive trade it is called **battery acid. Fuming sulfuric acid,** of 100% purity, was called **Nordhauser acid.** The grade of sulfuric acid known as **oil of vitriol,** or **vitriol,** is 66°Be, or 93.2% acid. **Sulfur trioxide,** or **sulfuric anhydride,** SO_3, is the acid minus water. It is a colorless liquid boiling at 46°C, and forms sulfuric acid when mixed with water. It is used for sulfonation. **Sulfan,** of the Allied Chemical Corp., is sulfuric anhydride. **Chlorosulfonic acid,** $HClSO_3$, has equal amounts of sulfur trioxide and hydrochloric acid, and is a vigorous dehydrating agent, used also in chlorosulfonating organic compounds. It has a specific gravity of 1.752, and boils at 311°F. Mixed with sulfur trioxide it has been called **FS smoke** for military smoke screens.

Niter cake, which is **sodium acid sulfate,** $NaHSO_4$, or **sodium bisulfate,** contains 30 to 35% available sulfuric acid and is used in hot solutions for pickling and cleaning metals. It comes in colorless crystals or white lumps, of a specific gravity of 2.435 and melting point 300°C. **Sodium sulfate,** or **Glauber's salt,** is a white crystalline material of the composition $Na_2SO_4 \cdot 10H_2O$, used in making kraft paper, rayon, and glass. It was first produced from Hungarian spring water by Johann Glauber, and when obtained from mineral springs is called **crazy water crystals.** The **burkeite,** sodium sulfate–sodium carbonate double salt, which separates out of Searles Lake brine, is used to produce sodium sulfate and other chemicals as by-products. **Salt cake,** Na_2SO_4, is impure sodium sulfate used in the cooking liquor in making paper pulp from wood. It is also used in freezing mixtures. **Synthetic salt cake,** used for making kraft pulp, is produced by sintering soda ash and sulfur. **Chrome cake** is a greenish by-product salt cake which contains some chromium as an impurity. It is used in papermaking. **Kaiseroda** is a German name for salt cake of high purity obtained as a by-product from the production of magnesium chloride from potash minerals.   **Sodium sulfite,** Na_2SO_3, or $Na_2SO_3 \cdot 7H_2O$, is a white to tan crystalline powder very soluble in water but nonhygroscopic.   **Santosite,** of Monsanto, is a grade of sodium sulfite containing 93% sodium sulfite with the balance chiefly sodium sulfate.

Sodium sulfide, Na_2S, is a pink flaky solid, used in tanneries for dehairing, and in the manufacture of dyes and pigments.   The commercial product contains 60 to 62% Na_2S, 3.5 NaCl, and other salts, and the balance water of crystallization.   **Sodium sulfhydrate,** NaSH, is in lemon-yellow flakes.   It has much less alkalinity than sodium sulfide, and is used in tanneries in unhairing solutions, and for making thiourea and other chemicals.   It contains 62.6% by weight of sulfur, and is an economical material for sulfonating.   **Sodium dithionate,** $Na_2S_2O_6 \cdot 2H_2O$, is used in leather tanning, as an assist in textile dyeing and printing, and for making other chemicals.   It comes in transparent prismatic crystals of bitter taste.   **Sodium thiosulfate,** $Na_2S_2O_3 \cdot 5H_2O$, known as **hypo,** is a white crystalline compound having a density of 1.73 and a melting point of 45°C.   It is used in photography to fix films, plates, and papers. **White vitriol** is zinc sulfate, in colorless crystals soluble in water and melting at 39°C.   It is used for making zinc salts, as a mordant, for zinc plating, and as a preservative in adhesives.

SUMAC. The dried ground leaves of the bush *Rhus coriaria* of Sicily, or *R. typhina* of eastern United States, used for tanning leather.   The Sicilian leaves contain up to 30% tannin, and the American leaves up to 38%.   It contains gallotannin and ellagitannin, and gives a rapid tan. Sumac produces a light strong leather of fine soft grain and has a bleaching action which can produce a white leather.   It is used for book and hatband leathers.   Sumac grows profusely in the eastern states, but the gathering of the leaves is not organized commercially.

SUNFLOWER OIL. A pale-yellow drying oil with a pleasant odor and taste obtained from the large seeds of the common sunflower plant, *Helianthus annuus,* of which there are many varieties.   The plant is native to Peru but is now grown in many parts of the world, particularly in California, Canada, Argentina, Chile, Uruguay, and Russia.   It requires boron in the soil.   The specific gravity of the oil is 0.925.   Sunflower oil is used in varnish and soap manufacture or as a food oil.   The by-product cake is used chiefly for cattle feed, but **sunflower meal** is also blended with wheat flour or cornmeal in foods.   It is higher in vitamin B than soybean flour.   **Sunflower seeds** are also used as poultry feed.   **Madia-seed oil** is quite similar to sunflower oil and has the same uses.   It is obtained from the seeds of the plant *Madia sativa,* native to California.   The seeds contain 35% oil, and the cold-pressed oil has a pleasant taste.   **Watermelon-**

seed oil, produced in Senegal as **bereff oil,** is an edible oil similar to sunflower.   It contains about 43% linoleic acid, 27 oleic, 19.5 stearic, and 5 palmitic acid.

The leaves of selected varieties of some species of sunflower contain from 1 to 6% **sunflower rubber** and up to 8 resin.   The *H. occidentalis, H. giganteus, H. maximiliani,* and *H. strumosus* are cultivated in Russia both for the oil seed and for the rubber in the leaves.   These perennials yield leaves up to 10 years.   A stand of 50,000 plants per hectare yields about 150 kilos of rubber and 325 kilos of resin.   Another similar rubber-bearing plant of southern Russia is the *Asclepias cornuti,* known as **vatochnik.**   It is a perennial, producing leaves for 10 to 15 years.   The leaves yield 1 to 6.5% rubber and large percentages of resin.

SUN HEMP. The bast fiber of the plant *Crotalaria juncea.*   It is used for cordage and rope in place of jute, but is lighter in color and is more flexible, stronger, and more durable than jute.   It resembles true hemp, but is not as strong.   It is more properly called **sann hemp** from the Hindu word sann.   It is also known as **sunn fiber, Indian hemp,** and **Bombay hemp.**   The plant, which is a shrub, is cultivated extensively in India.   It grows to a height of about 8 ft, with slender branches yielding the fiber.   The method of extraction is the same as for true hemp.   The best fibers are retained locally for making into cloth.   It is also used in the United States for making cigarette paper, and for oakum.   **Madras hemp** is from another species of the same plant.

SUPERBRONZE. A name applied to brasses containing both aluminum and manganese.   They are ordinarily high brasses modified with 2 to 3% manganese and 1 to 6 aluminum, with sometimes also some iron.   They have greatly increased strength and hardness over the original brasses, but the ductility is reduced and they are difficult to work and machine.   The early superbronze was known as **Heusler alloy.**   Muntz metal is also frequently modified with manganese, iron, and aluminum. The alloys are used where high strength and corrosion resistance are required, and they are often marketed under trade names.   **Tensilite,** of the American Manganese Bronze Co., is a bronze of this type.   A grade containing about 64% copper, 30 zinc, 2.5 manganese, 3 aluminum, and 1 iron has a tensile strength, cast, up to 100,000 psi and elongation 16%. **Mallory metal** is a superbronze of the P. R. Mallory Co., but **Mallory 100** metal is a high-conductivity, heat-treatable strong alloy containing 2.6% cobalt, 0.40 beryllium, and the balance copper.   It has a tensile strength of 90,000 psi and an elongation of 8 to 15%.   The name superbronze is a shop term rather than a technical classification, and thus the name is often applied to any hard, high-strength, heat-treatable copper-base alloy.

SYCAMORE. The wood of the tree *Acer pseudo-platanus,* which is also classed as a kind of maple, especially in England. The species cut as sycamore in the United States is largely *Platanus occidentalis.* The wood has a close, firm, tough texture and is yellowish in color, with a reddish-brown heartwood. The light-colored sapwood is up to 3 in. thick in commercial trees. When quartered, the wood resembles quartered oak. The weight is about 38 lb per cu ft. The surface is lustrous and takes a fine polish. It is used for veneers, flooring, furniture, cooperage, and for handles and rollers. Two other species grown in the Southwest are **California sycamore,** *P. racemosa,* and **Arizona sycamore,** *P. wrightii.*

SYNTHETIC RESINS. A large group of resinlike materials, properly called **resinoids,** although this term is now seldom used except as applied to resin bonds for grinding wheels. The resins, or **plastics,** are complex compounds produced synthetically by either polymerization or condensation of various chemicals. The physical characteristics and high molecular weights depend upon the number of repeating molecular groups that make up the resins. The basic molecule of a synthetic resin is called a **monomer,** and the recurring additions of monomers are called **polymers.** Polymerization is the chemical union of many simple molecules. The process of polymerization is achieved through the action of light, heat, pressure, or a chemical catalyst. Thus, in the polymerization of styrene, the basic formula $C_6H_5CH:CH_2$ is repeated over and over to form polymers, or polystyrene, with constantly increasing molecular weights until the process is stopped when the desired characteristics are reached. **Condensation plastics** are made by the action between two different molecules. In this fusion of two molecules, a simple molecule, such as water or ammonia, may be eliminated in the process. For example, when a **dibasic acid,** $R(COOH)_2$, is reacted with a **diamine** $R'(NH_2)_2$, as in the production of the nylons, water is eliminated, the nature of the molecule is changed, and it is increased in size. Where certain terminal groups are present, in this case $-COOH$ and $-NH_2$, polycondensation produces plastics with increasing molecular weights, but the molecular formula is different from that of either of the two original materials condensed. Styrene and butadiene can be polymerized separately to form **polymerization plastics,** but when both together are condensed, as in making Buna S rubber, the copolymer is a different product from either product formed by separate polymerization.

The chief groups of synthetic resins are **phenolaldehyde, aminoaldehyde,** and the **hydroxycarboxylic,** or alkyd, vinyl, acrylic, styrene, and indene, but the number of possible basic types and intercombinations is almost infinite. Cellulose nitrate, cellulose acetate, and the proteins such as casein are classed with the others as plastics, but they are not synthetic resins like the others.   **Molding plastics** consist of the partly polymerized resin either alone or mixed with pigment and filler, usually in powder form, for molding to the final set by heat and pressure.   A **thermosetting resin** assumes a permanent set under heat and cannot be remolded as a **thermoplastic resin** can.   The filler may be wood flour, fibers, or mineral powders, but it should have the characteristic of being wet by the resin. Some mineral fillers such as bentonite, when used in colloidal powder form, may combine chemically with the resin to give a copolymer or cross linkage of the molecule and thus give new characteristics to the plastic. Thermoplastic resins can often be made thermosetting by reacting with formaldehyde or sulfur and vulcanizing to set up cross linkages.   Most plastics become brittle at low temperatures.   The acrylic and vinyl resins lose as much as 80% of their room-temperature impact strength at near freezing point.

Cross-linking of plastic resins is done in various ways.   Polyethylene can be cross-linked by irradiation, or by adding carbon and treating with ozone.   By cross-linking polyethylene with carbon black, the tensile strength may be increased as much as 50%, and the softening point raised as much as 30°C.   Sulfur is used to cross-link some resins.   Some **cross-linking agents** may be complex chemicals which alter the properties of the plastic, as **glutar aldehyde,** $O:HC(CH_2)_3HC:O$, used to cross-link poly-hydric compounds.   Plasticizers, used to add flexibility to plastics, may increase the rate of deterioration or add fire hazard, and stabilizers are often added to the resins.   The original plasticized resins, made in Germany and called **Albertol resins,** were plasticized with natural gums and resins, but most plasticizers now are chemicals.   Chlorination gives fire retardance, but may cause acrid fumes.   Phospho nitrilic chloride, $P_3N_3Cl_3$, acts as a polymerizer and also links into the plastic to increase heat stability. The light stabilizer, **Salol,** of Monsanto, is **phenyl salicylate,** $C_6H_4(OH)$-$CO_2C_6H_5$.   **Dyphos,** of National Lead, is basic **lead phosphite,** and **Dythal** is dibasic **lead phthalate.**   **Antistatic agents** may be added, particularly in films and textile fibers, to prevent buildup or promote discharge of static electricity.   **Grafstat,** of General Aniline, used for this purpose, is a phosphorus compound having free acid radicals.

The **polysulfone resins** have three types of linkages to the carbon ring, an ether, an oxygen, and an SO_2, alternating.   They are thermoplastics which produce moldings of good physical qualities to 300°F and are resistant to chemicals and oxidation.   **Ionomer plastics** are thermoplastics characterized by a micalike molecular structure with weak metal bonds forming monoclinic layers.   The metals may be magnesium, potassium, or barium.   **Surlyn A,** of Du Pont, is this material with an ethylene base. It has a tensile strength of 5,500 psi, high flexibility, high chemical resistance, and a greater transparency than polyethylene.   **Carborane plastics** are produced from the borane molecule, a boron hydride of the composition $B_{10}H_{14}$, by replacing the four terminal hydrogens with two carbon atoms. The monomer, $C(HB_2H)_5C$, polymerizes at high heat and pressure to form rubbery solids which will withstand temperatures above 600°F; but the commercial plastics are usually copolymers with vinyls, silicones, or other plastics.

The **polyamide resins** made by the polymerization of a fatty acid and an amine are tough, hard, solvent-resistant, and have good adhesion. The simpler ones, such as that made from linoleic acid and triethylene diamine, are used as coatings and adhesives. **Polyamide resin 90,** of General Mills, is made from linoleic acid. The more complex resins for molding and fiber are in the class of nylons. **Polycarbonate resins** are made by reacting bisphenol and phosgene, or by reacting a polyphenol with methylene chloride and phosgene. The monomer may be $OC_6H_4C(CH_3)_2C_6H_4$-$OC:O$. The molecular structure is in double-linked zigzag chains that give high rigidity. The resin is thermoplastic. It is crystalline with rhombic crystals. **Lexan resin,** of General Electric, with a molecular weight of 18,000, has a tensile strength of 10,500 psi with elongation of 60%, dielectric strength to 2,500 volts per mil, Rockwell hardness M70, and the deformation temperature under load is 290°F. The specific gravity is 1.20. The material is transparent, and a $\frac{1}{8}$-in. thickness transmits 85% of the light. This material in Germany is called **Makrolon.** The **Merlon,** of the Mobray Chemical Co., is a polycarbonate resin, and the **Plestar film,** of Ansco, is polycarbonate. **Lexan 145,** of General Electric, is polycarbonate powder for use in emulsion coatings which have high strength and toughness, and are nontoxic. When this type of resin is compounded with 40% of glass fiber, its tensile strength is doubled and its coefficient of thermal expansion is greatly reduced. **Carbonate resins** are also used in mixtures with an acrylonitrile-butadiene-styrene copolymer without copolymerization. **Cycolac KM,** of Borg-Warner Corp., is this material. It retains the general characteristics of the carbonate with added flexural strength.

The **phospho-nitrile plastics** have high elasticity and high temperature resistance. They are derived from **chloro phospho nitrile,** or **phospho-nitrilic chloride,** $P_3N_3Cl_3$, which has a hexagonal ring of alternating atoms of phosphorus and nitrogen with the chlorine atoms attached. In the plastic monomers the chlorine atoms are replaced by other groups. The **PN Polymers,** of Horizons, Inc., contain OCH and C_3F_7 groups and are synthetic rubbers of high oxidation and chemical resistance. The tensile strength is up to 700 psi with elongation up to 600%. The material is used for such applications as gaskets and cratings for severe service.

The **Ryton resins,** of Phillips Petroleum Co., are **polyphenylene sulfides** with branch-chain molecules that require no cross-linking. They are used for molded parts and high-strength coatings.   The **fluorosilicone resins** of Dow Corning are copolymers of fluorocarbons and silicones.   They have the low temperature properties of the silicones and will also withstand temperatures to 500°F.   They are used as rubbers and as liquid adhesives.   The crystalline linear **acetal resins** have the repeating group, $(OCH_2)_x$, and the resins are **polyformaldehyde.**   About 50% of the weight is oxygen.   They are rigid, but do not need plasticizers for toughness.   **Delrin,** of Du Pont, is a thermoplastic acetal resin used for mechanical and electrical parts.   It has a specific gravity of 1.425, a tensile strength of 10,000 psi with elongation of 15%, dielectric strength of 500 volts per mil, and Rockwell hardness M94.   It retains its mechanical strength close to the melting point of 347°F.   **Celcon,** of the Celanese Corp., is a thermoplastic linear acetal resin produced from **trioxane,** which is a cyclic form of formaldehyde.   The specific gravity is 1.410, flexural strength 12,000 psi, hardness Rockwell M76, and dielectric strength 1,200 volts per mil.   It comes in translucent white pellets for molding.

The number of possible different synthetic resins, by variations in the monomer, copolymerization, blending, and variations in compounding, makes specific nomenclature difficult.   A trade name may represent a type of plastic with numbered grades, or it may be a company designation with the type of resin represented by the number or letter symbol. Different names may be given to the plastic by the molders, and still different names may be given to the plastics by product manufacturers.   For example, the **Plastag** used by the Camillus Cutlery Co. for knife handles is cellulose acetate pigmented to imitate antler.   **Nypene** and **Copene,** of the Neville Chem. Co., are **terpene polymers,** $(C_{10}H_{16})_x$, from turpentine, used as tack-producing agents in rubber cements and wax compounds. **Koresin,** of General Aniline, used to improve tackiness in synthetic rubbers, is a condensation product of acetylene and butyl phenol.   The **RX resins** of the Rogers Corp., for molding electrical parts, are **diallyl phthalate.**   The tensile strength is up to 9,000 psi, with dielectric strengths to 450 volts per mil, and distortion points to 525°F.   **Duracron,** of Pittsburgh Plate Glass, used to produce hard, highly resistant thermoset coatings, is an acrylic resin with amide side chains copolymerized from styrene and ethyl acrylate.   A group of liquid and solid resins is made from **fumaric acid,** a powder of the composition $HOOC(CH)_2COOH$ made by the fermentation of carbohydrates.   Food grades of these acids are soluble in water and are used as acidifiers and stabilizers.   Two parts of fumaric acid is equivalent to three parts of citric acid.   **Acetone-formaldehyde resins** are rapid-drying and give high gloss, and are used in printing inks, lacquers, and adhesives.   The **Arboneeld** of Du Pont, used for impregnating wood to increase hardness and dimensional stability, was a water-soluble **dimethylol urea resin,** a type of urea-formaldehyde.

Plastic film, usually in thicknesses from 0.0015 to 0.006 in., is used for wrapping and sealing, for waterproofing garments, for coating wood, paper, or fabrics, and for table coverings. It is made by continuous casting on an endless belt, and various resins and plasticizers are used to give the desired characteristics. **Vinyl film 7051,** of the B. F. Goodrich Co., comes in thicknesses to 0.006 in. in widths to 54 in. It is translucent, and can be printed on with vinyl inks, heat-bonded or stitched. **Reynolon film,** of the Reynolds Metals Co., is cast from a solution of polyvinyl chloride in tetrahydro furan and then stretch-oriented to thicknesses of 0.0005 and 0.001 in. It is very flexible and has high tear resistance. **Polyvinyl chloride film** and **polyethylene film** for packaging are produced regularly in thicknesses from 0.005 to 0.003 in. They are tough and transparent, and are also supplied in colors. **Trycite,** of the Dow Chemical Co., is an oriented **polystyrene film.** It has high clarity, gloss, and chemical resistance.

Laminated plastics were originally made to replace vulcanized fiber for gears, gaskets, and electrical insulation. They were made with laminations of canvas, linen, or kraft paper impregnated with 30% or more of thermosetting phenolic resin which gave good resistance to water, oils, and solvents. Rods were made by machining from strips of the molded sheets, which gave parallel cords, or the laminations were wound on wires which were withdrawn before curing. A typical laminated plastic thus made with a paper base has a tensile strength of 12,500 psi, compressive strength of 35,000 psi, and dielectric strength above 500 vpm. By using a finely woven fabric the flexural strength is increased.

While the basic process for making laminates remains much the same, the variety of choice of materials gives a very broad range of use for structural panels, machine and appliance housings, insulations, and mechanical and electrical parts. Both thermosetting and thermoplastic resins are now used, finer and especially woven fabrics give reinforcement in thinner sections, and laminations are usually cut from preimpregnated sheets to give versatility in molding. Glass fiber fabrics or asbestos may be employed for heat resistance or added electrical properties. High-modulus boron or tungsten fibers may also be used, although the ultimate strength is limited by the resin binder.

Early laminates were designated by trade names, such as **Bakelite** of Union Carbide, **Textolite** of General Electric, **Micarta** of Westinghouse, **Phenolite** of National Vulcanized Fiber Co., **Condensite** and **Dilecto** of Continental Diamond Fiber Co., **Haveg** of Haveg Corp., **Spauldite** of Spaulding Fiber Co., and **Synthane** of Synthane Corp. **Formica,** of Formica Corp., designated various types of laminates with a decorative facing layer for such uses as table tops. Trade names now usually include a number or symbol to describe the type and grade. Textolite, for example, embraces more than 70 categories of laminates subdivided into use-specification grades, all produced in many sizes and thicknesses.   **Textolite 11711** is an electronic laminate for such uses as multilayer circuit boards.   It is made with polyphenolene oxide resin, and may have a copper or aluminum cladding.   The tensile strength is up to 10,000 psi, and the dielectric strength is 400 vpm.   **Phenolyte Y240** is a paper-base laminate bonded with a polyester-modified melamine which gives high dielectric strength and arc resistance together with good punching or blanking characteristics in thicknesses up to $\frac{1}{8}$ in.   **Doryl H17511,** of Westinghouse, has glass fabric laminations bonded with a modified phenolic resin based on diphenyl oxide and polyphenyl ether.   This laminate retains a flexural strength of 27,400 psi at 480°F.   **Luxwood,** of Formica Corp., for furniture, is a $\frac{1}{16}$-in. laminate with photographic reproductions of wood grains on the face, while **Beautywood** is this material in thicker sizes for wall panels.

Laminating resins may be marketed under one trade name by the resin producer and other names by the molders of the laminate.   **Paraplex P resins,** of Rohm & Haas, for example, comprise a series of polyester solutions in monomeric styrene which can be blended with other resins to give varied qualities.   But, **Panelyte,** of St. Regis Paper Co., refers to the laminates which are made with phenolic, melamine, silicone, or other resin, for a variety of applications.   **Rockite,** of F. A. Hughes & Co., Ltd., and **Tufnol,** of Ellison Insulations, Ltd., are British phenol resins.

Plastic-bonded sheet, rods, and tubes are also made with reinforcement of dispersed or matted fibers or lightweight glass spheres, but these are classed as **composite plastics** rather than laminates.   **Weldsphere,** of Nichols & Co., is nylon with 40% glass spheres, and **Weldfibe** is nylon with 40% glass fiber.   **Metallic filaments** are used as reinforcement in composites to give added strength and heat tolerance and to control static.   Brunswick Corp. produces fibers for this purpose from stainless steel, nickel-base alloy, niobium, and tantalum.   The **Brunsmet MF-C niobium fibers** may be as small as 0.6 micron in diameter.

TALC.   A soft friable mineral of fine colloidal particles with a soapy feel. It is a **hydrated magnesium silicate,** $4SiO_2 \cdot 3MgO \cdot H_2O$, with a specific gravity of 2.8, and a hardness of 1 Mohs.   It is white when pure, but may be colored gray, green, brown, or red with impurities.   The pure white talc of Italy has been valued since ancient times for cosmetics.   Talc is now used for cosmetics, for paper coatings, as a filler for paints and plastics, and for molding into electrical insulators, heater parts, and chemical ware.   The massive block material, called **steatite talc,** is cut into electrical insulators.   It is also called **lava talc.**   **Talc dust** is a superfine, 400-mesh powder from the milling of steatite talc.   It has an oily feel and is used in cosmetics.   The more impure block talcs are used for fire-box linings and will withstand temperatures to 1700°F.   Gritty varieties contain carbonate minerals and are in the class of soapstones.   Varieties containing lime are used for making porcelain.

Talc of specified purity and particle size is marketed under trade names. **Asbestine,** of C. K. Williams & Co., is a talc powder of 325 mesh for use as a filler.   **Ceramitalc,** of the International Talc Co., Inc., is a talc powder used as a source of magnesia and to prevent crazing in ceramics. The **Sierra Fibrene** of Innis, Speiden & Co. is a California talc milled to 400 mesh.   It is white, has a platy structure, and as an extender in paints it wets easily and promotes pigment dispersion.   **French chalk** is a high-grade talc in massive block form used for marking.   The mineral occurs in the United States in the Appalachian region from Vermont to Georgia. The Georgia talc for making **crayons** is mined in blocks, and the yield of talc suitable for sawing into crayons is about 1 ton for every 8 tons of crude talc.   The crayons are made mostly in $\frac{1}{4}$-in. rounds.   The residue is marketed as ground talc.   **Attasorb** and **Permagel,** of the Minerals & Chemicals Corp., is finely powdered, cream-colored, hydrated **magnesium-aluminum silicate** from the mineral **attapulgite,** used for emulsifying and as a flatting agent and extender in paints.   The material is also used in starch adhesives to improve shear strength.   **Attacote** is the material in superfine particle size for use as an anticaking agent for hygroscopic chemicals.   **Veegum F,** of the R. T. Vanderbilt Co., is a fine white colloidal magnesium-aluminum silicate used as a suspending agent for oils and waxes.

Cordierite is a talclike mineral with a high percentage of magnesia used for refractory electronic parts.   It is found sparsely in Norway, Finland, and Connecticut, usually in granite and gneiss, or in vitrified sandstones. When heated to 1440°C it is converted to sillimanite and glass.   Synthetic cordierite is made by the Muscle Shoals Electrochemical Corp. by mixing pure silica, magnesia, and alumina in various proportions and stabilizing with calcia.   It is marketed as a powder for producing refractory insulating parts.   **Cordierite C-90** is marketed by Engineered Materials as molded parts for electronic uses. It is produced from 50.5% silica, 30.6 alumina, 13.8 magnesia, 0.1 calcia, and 0.1 iron oxide.   The parts have a density of 2.5, and good heat-shock resistance to 600°C.

Agalite is a mineral having the same composition as talc but with a less soapy feel.   It is used as a filler in writing papers, but is more wearing on the paper rolls than talc.   The talc of northern New York, known as **rensselaerite,** does not have the usual talc slip, and has a fibrous nature. The hydrous aluminum silicate **pyrophyllite,** found in California, is similar to talc but with the magnesium replaced by aluminum.   In mixtures with talc for wall tile it eliminates crazing.   It is also substituted for talc as a filler for paints and paper.   **Thix,** of the National Lead Co., used as a thickening agent in emulsion paints, in cosmetics, and in textile finishes, is a refined, hydrous magnesium silicate marketed as a 200-mesh powder. It contains 56% silica, 26 magnesia, 2.8 calcia, 2.5 NaO_2, and 1.1 lithia.

Magnesium silicate, used as a filler in rubber and plastics, and also as an alkaline bleaching agent for oils, waxes, and solvents, is a white, water-insoluble powder of the composition $MgSiO_4$, having a pH of 7.5 to 8.5. In the cosmetic trade it is known as **talcum powder. Magnesol,** of the Westvaco Chemical Co., is finely ground magnesium silicate.   **Brite-Sorb 30** of Allegheny Industrial Chemical Co. is a synthetic magnesium silicate with high adsorption and filtering power.   The **magnesium trisilicate** used in pharmaceuticals as an antacid is of extreme fineness, the super-bulking grade having 65% of the particles less than 5 microns in size. The material known as **killas** from the tin mines of Cornwall is a slaty schist.   It is finely ground and used like talc.

TALL OIL.   An oily resinous liquid obtained as a by-product of the sulfite paper-pulp mills.   The alkali saponifies the acids, and the resulting soap is skimmed off and treated with sulfuric acid to produce tall oil.   About 70 lb of crude tall oil is obtained per ton of kraft pulp.   The name comes from the Swedish **talloel,** meaning pine oil.   The crude oil is brown, but the refined oil is reddish yellow and nearly odorless.   It has a specific gravity of 0.98, flash point of 360°F, and acid number about 165.   The oil from Florida paper mills contains 41 to 45% rosin, 10 to 15 pitch, and the balance chiefly fatty acids.   The fatty acids can be obtained separately by fractionating the crude whole oil.   The oil also contains up to 10% of the phyto sterol **sitosterol,** used in making the drug cortisone.

Tall oil is used in scouring soaps, asphalt emulsions, cutting oils, insecticides, animal dips, in making factice, and in plastics and paint oils.   It is marketed in processed and concentrated form.   The **Flextal** of the Farac Oil & Chemical Co. is processed tall oil containing 60% rosin acids. Detergents are made by reacting tall oil with ethylene oxide.   Saturated alcohols are produced by high-pressure hydrogenation of tall oil.   The high linoleic acid content makes tall oil suitable for making drying oils. **Lumitol** is a German vinyl plastic produced by reacting tall oil with acetylene.   It is used for coatings.   **Smithco RT,** of the Archer-Daniels-Midland Co., used for varnishes and paints, is refined tall oil esterified with glycerin.   **Smithco PE** is tall oil esterified with pentaerythritol.   **Ardex PE,** of the same company, is a varnish oil that dries quickly to a hard film, made by esterifying tall oil with pentaerythritol.   **Sulfonated tall oil** is used to replace sulfonated castor oil in coating mixes for paper to increase folding strength.   **Opoil** is a crude tall oil of the National Southern Products Co., and **Facoil** is the refined oil with 60% fatty acid content and low rosin acid content.   **Acolin, Acosix,** and **Aconon** are grades of refined tall oil of Newport Industries, Inc.   **Pamac,** of Hercules, consists of tall oil monobasic fatty acids, used in resin coatings.

TALLOW. A general name for the heavy fats obtained from all parts of the bodies of sheep and cattle.   The best grades of internal fats, or **suet,** are used for edible purpose, but the external fats are employed for lubricants, for mixing with waxes and vegetable fats, for soaps and candles, and for producing chemicals.   The tallows have the same general composition as lard, but are higher in the harder saturated acids, with about 51% of palmitic and stearic acids, and lower in oleic acid.   The edible grades known as **premier jus,** prime, and edible, are white to pale yellow, almost tasteless, and free from disagreeable odor, but the nonedible or industrial tallows are yellow to brown unless bleached.   The best grade of industrial tallow is Packers No. 1.   **White grease, yellow grease,** and **brown grease** may be hog fat or they may be tallows with a titer below 40°C, the titer being the only commercial distinction between tallow and fat.   Tallow is thus all animal fat above 40°C titer.   **Beef tallow** is used to produce stearic acid, for leather dressing, lubricating greases, and for making soap. **Mutton tallow** contains less liquid fat and is harder, but it becomes rancid more easily.   Tallow for industrial use is generally highly purified and chemically treated, and marketed under trade names.   **Adogen 442,** of the Archer-Daniels-Midland Co., used as a softener for textiles, is a dimethyl **hydrogenated tallow.** It comes as a nearly white, odorless paste in isopropanol and water, and is dispersible in water or in organic solvents.

TANNING AGENTS. Materials, known as **tannins,** used for the treatment of skins and hides to preserve the hide substance and make it resistant to decay.   The tanned leather is then treated with fats or greases to make it soft and pliable.   Tannins may be natural or artificial.   The natural tannins are chiefly vegetable, but some mineral tanning agents are used. The vegetable tannins are divided into two color classes: the **catechol** and the **pyrogallol.** The catechol tannins are cutch, quebracho, hemlock, larch, gambier, oak, and willow.   The pyrogallol tannins are gallnuts, sumac, myrobalans, chestnut, valonia, divi-divi, and algarobilla.   Catechol tannin is distinguished by giving a greenish-black precipitate with ferric salts; the pyrogallol tannins give a bluish-black precipitate.   The catechol tannins, in general, produce leathers that are more resistant to heat and decay than the pyrogallols.   Some tannins contain considerable coloring or dye matter, but the color that a tannin imparts to leather may be lightened or darkened by raising or lowering the acidity of the tannin bath. In the ink industry the catechol tannins are known as iron-greening, and the pyrogallol tannins as iron-bluing, and the latter are used for making writing inks.   Catechol is also produced synthetically from coal tar.   It is a water-soluble **dihydric phenol** in white crystalline granules known as ortho-**dihydroxy benzene,** $C_6H_4(OH)_2$.   It is used in some inks, and for making dyestuffs, medicinals, and antioxidants.

Alum tanning is an ancient process but was introduced into Europe only about the year 1100, and the alum- and salt-tanned leather was called **Hungary leather.**   Formaldehyde is also used as a tanning agent.   Formaldehyde was patented as a tanning agent in 1898.   A later patent covered a rapid process of tanning sheepskins with alcohol and formalin and then neutralizing in a solution of soda ash.   Unlike vegetable agents, formaldehyde does not add weight to the skin.   It is often used as a pretanning agent to lessen the astringency of the vegetable tannin and increase its rate of diffusion.   Melamine resins are used for tanning to give a leather that is white throughout and does not yellow with age.   Leather may also be tanned with chromic acid or chrome salts, which make the fibers insoluble and produce a soft, strong leather.   Chrome alum, sodium or potassium dichromates, or products in which chromic acid has been used as an oxidizing agent may be used.   **Chrome tanning** is rapid and is used chiefly for light leathers.   **Tanolin** is a name for basic **chromium chloride** marketed in crystal form for use in the chrome tanning of leather.   **Santotan KR** is a trade name of Monsanto for basic **chromium sulfate,** $Cr_2(SO_4)_2(OH)_2$, used as a one-bath chrome-tanning agent.   This material is also used for treating magnesium-alloy parts to give a gray to black surface color.   **Panchrome,** an English tanning agent, is a sulfur dioxide dichromate. **Chromalin** is a glycerin-reduced dichromate.   Chrome-tanned leather is more resistant to heat than vegetable-tanned leathers, withstanding temperatures to 200°F.   Chrome tanning is used for shoe upper leathers and for gloves, belting, and packings.   **Iron-tanned leather** is produced by pretanning with formaldehyde, then tanning with ferric salts and trisodium phosphate, and neutralizing with a solution of phthalic anhydride and sodium carbonate.   The leather is soft, will absorb much oil and grease, and is suitable for use where a pliable leather is desired.   Glutar aldehyde gives a soft bulky leather suitable for garments.   It may be blended with chrome or vegetable tanning agents.

In tanning processes various supplementary materials may be used to give special properties to the leathers.   Glucose or starch may be used to make the leather more plump.   Hydrochloric acid is used in two-bath chrome tanning to enhance the feel and appearance of the leather.   Synthetic tannins, or **syntans,** are largely condensation products made by condensing sulfonated phenols with formaldehyde.   **Neradol D** is such a syntan.   **Tansyn** is the trade name of an English syntan of this kind. **Permanol,** of the Monsanto Company, is a sulfonic acid condensation syntan in liquid form used to produce light-fast white leathers.   The free sulfuric acid is completely neutralized. Syntans do not add weight to leather and are seldom used alone. They are marketed under trade names. **Leukanol,** of the Rohm & Haas Co., has a bleaching action and is used in combination with vegetable tannins to speed up the tanning and to give a light-colored leather. **Orotan,** of the same company, is a sulfonated phenol-formaldehyde which makes a good shoe leather when used alone. **Tanigan,** a German tannin, is a complex condensation product produced from waste pulp-mill liquor and formaldehyde or diphenyl methane.

TANTALUM. A white, lustrous metal resembling platinum. It is one of the most acid-resistant of the metals and is classed as a noble metal. The specific gravity is 16.6, or about twice that of steel, and the melting point is very high, 2850°C. It is very ductile and can be rolled down from 0.300 to 0.0015 in. without annealing, or drawn into extremely fine wire. Because of its high melting point the metal is not melted, but the powder obtained by chemical extraction or electrolysis is pressed into billets, sintered in vacuum, and then rolled. The metal is used especially for chemical equipment. The tensile strength of the sheet metal is 50,000 psi, and of the drawn wire 130,000 psi. The annealed metal has a hardness of 75 Brinell. It is resistant to all acids except hydrofluoric, and is not dissolved by aqua regia. It will dissolve, however, in a mixture of nitric and hydrofluoric acids, and also reacts with chlorine above 175°C. When heated in the air to about 400°C, it becomes blue; at a higher temperature, it becomes black. At very high temperatures it absorbs oxygen, hydrogen, or nitrogen, and becomes very brittle. It will absorb 740 times its own volume of hydrogen, producing a coarse, brittle substance. Tantalum can be tempered or hardened to about 600 Brinell by heating in the air to absorb gases, and will hold a fine cutting edge on tools. It can also be hardened by the addition of silicon to a hardness close to that of the diamond, but any alloying is difficult because of the high melting point.

Tantalum is used as a filament in electric-light bulbs. The metal becomes incandescent at 1700°C, or 400° below that of tungsten, so that a tantalum lamp is cooler. It is also used in radio tubes operating at high temperatures, and in vacuum tubes to absorb gases. It is lower in cost than platinum, and is used for surgical instruments and gauze, pens, instruments, and acid-resistant chemical equipment. It is also used in alloy special steels to give increased resistance to scaling at high temperatures, but since it has a large neutron cross section it must be kept very low in steels used for atomic reactors. **Tantalum-tungsten alloys,** of Stauffer Chemical Co., used for rocket motor parts, have melting points to 6150°F, and retain tensile strengths to 15,000 psi at 4500°F. **Tantalum alloy T-111,** used in fine tubing by Superior Tube Co., has 8% tungsten and 2% hafnium. The tubes, in diameters down to 0.012 in., have high corrosion resistance and a tensile strength of 90,000 psi.   **Tantalum alloy T-222,** of Westinghouse Electric Corp., contains 9.6% tungsten, 2.4 hafnium, and 0.01 carbon.   It has a tensile strength of 110,000 psi, and at 3500°F will retain a strength of 14,000 psi.   It comes in plate or rod.   Tantalum coils are used to heat acid baths.   A tube with a wall thickness of 0.020 in. will withstand operating steam pressure up to 150 psi.   The metal has the property of passing an alternating electric current in one direction only, and is thus used for current rectifiers.   As an anode, tantalum reacts instantly with oxygen in acid solutions, forming a stable oxide film which is current-blocking; this property is used in rectifiers and electrolytic condensers.

Tantalum carbide is an extremely hard, heavy, brownish, crystalline material of high melting point, 3875°C, used for the same purposes as tungsten carbide, as an abrasive and cutting material.   It has the composition TaC_2, and in hardness it ranks close to the diamond.   For use in cutting tools the carbide is ground to 325 mesh, mixed with a binder of powdered cobalt, iron, or nickel, molded to shape, and sintered at high heat.   **Ramet** is the trade name of the Fansteel Metallurgical Corp. for tantalum-carbide cutting materials, and **Tantaloy** is a name for a sintered alloy in bar form for flowing on faces of tools with a welding torch.   Tantalum-carbide filaments for incandescent lamps are used at temperatures to 6020°F, while tungsten filaments have a maximum-use temperature to 5660°F.   They give a 25% increase in light brilliance, and have longer life.   But tantalum carbide decomposes in the nitrogen-argon atmosphere used for tungsten, and a hydrogen-halogen acid atmosphere is used.   **Tantalum-hafnium carbide,** $4TaC \cdot HfC$, for refractory parts, has an extremely high melting point, 3942°C.

TANTALUM ORES.   The most important ore of the metal tantalum is **tantalite.**   When pure, its composition is $FeO \cdot Ta_2O_5$, but the American ore may contain only from 10 to 40% **tantalic oxide,** Ta_2O_5, and the Australian ore may contain as high as 70%.   The ore is marketed on the basis of 60% tantalic oxide content.   Tantalite occurs usually as a black crystalline mineral with a specific gravity up to 7.3.   It often contains manganese, tin, titanium, and sometimes tungsten; the tantalum may be replaced by columbium, which is similar to it.   When the columbium content in the ore predominates, the mineral is called **columbite.**   Tantalite also contains small amounts of germanium.   The tantalite of the Congo usually contains tin.   The ore from the Lukushi Basin contains 58% Ta_2O_5, 16.5 Cb_2O_5, 12.5 MnO, 4.5 Fe_2O_3, and 1.6 SnO_2, with some zirconium and titanium oxides.   **Thoreaulite** of that region contains 72 to 74% Ta_2O_5 and 20 to 22% SnO_2.   Tantalum metal is produced from tantalite by dissolving in acid and separating the tantalum salts from the columbium by precipitation. The tantalum salts are reduced to powdered metal, which is then compressed into rods and sintered and rolled. One pound of tantalum is produced from about $2\frac{1}{2}$ tons of American ore. The tantalite ore of Manitoba is embedded in pegmatite and the crude ore contains about 0.25% Ta_2O_5. It is crushed and concentrated to a content of 50%. Ten tons of concentrate yields 4 tons of tantalum metal.

A tantalum ore that is abundant at Wodgina, Western Australia, is **mangano tantalite** which contains about 69% tantalic oxide, 15 **columbium pentoxide,** Cb_2O_5, and 14 manganese protoxide, with a little tin oxide. The specific gravity of the ore is 6.34.   **Microlite,** an ore found at Wodgina and in the McPhee Range of Western Australia, contains 76% Ta_2O_5 and 4 to 7 Cb_2O_5.   **Tanteuxenite,** another Western Australian ore, contains 24 to 47% Ta_2O_5 and 4 to 14 Cb_2O_5.   **Tapiolite,** of Australia, contains 82% Ta_2O_5 and 2 Cb_2O_5.   **Euxenite,** of Idaho, contains about 28% columbium-tantalum oxide.   The mineral **pyrochlore,** of Canada, is composed of complex oxides of tantalum, columbium, sodium, and calcium, and the metal oxides are obtained by acid extraction.

TAR. A black solid mass obtained in the destructive distillation of coal, peat, wood, petroleum, or other organic material.   When coal is heated to redness in an enclosed oven, it yields volatile products and the residue coke. Upon cooling the volatile matter, tar and water are deposited, leaving the coal gases free.   Various types of coal yield tars of different qualities and quantities.   Anthracite gives little tar, and cannel coal yields large quantities of low-gravity tar.   In the manufacture of gas the tar produced from bituminous coal is a viscous black liquid containing 20 to 30% free carbon, and is rich in benzene, toluene, naphthalene, and other aromatic compounds.   In the dry state this tar has a specific gravity of about 1.20.   Tar is also produced as a by-product from coke ovens.

Coal tars are usually distilled to remove the light aromatics which are used for making chemicals, and the residue tar, known as **treated tar,** or **pitch,** is employed for roofing, road making, and for bituminous paints and waterproofing compounds.   **Coal-tar pitch** is the most stable bituminous material for covering underground pipes.   **Tarvia** is the trade name of a refined coal tar, marketed by the Barrett Co. in various grades.   **Tarmac** is practically the same material marketed by the Koppers Co.   **Bituplastic,** of the same company, used for coating pipes and structures, is a refined coal-tar pitch that is odorless and quick-drying.   **Bituvia** is a road tar, produced in various grades by the Reilly Tar & Chemical Corp.   **Coal-tar carbon** amounts to about 32% of the original tar.   It is marketed in lump form for chemical use.   The fixed carbon content is 92.5 to 95.6%, sulfur about 0.30, and volatile matter 3 to 6.   **Calcined carbon,** from coal tar, contains less than 0.5% sulfur and 0.5 volatile matter.

The lightest distillate of coal tar, benzol, is used as an automotive fuel. **Coal-tar oils** are used as solvents and plasticizers. They consist of various distillates or fractions up to semisolids. **Tar oil** from brown coal tars was used for diesel fuel oil by extracting the phenols with methyl alcohol. **Bardol B,** of Allied Chemical, is a clear yellow coal-tar fraction of specific gravity 1.0 to 1.04, used as a plasticizer for synthetic rubber, while **Carbonex** is a solid black tar hydrocarbon in flake form used as a rubber plasticizer. The softening point is between 205 and 220°F. **Xylol** is a water-white liquid of specific gravity 0.860 to 0.870, distilling between 135 and 185°C. It is a mixture of **xylenes,** which are dimethyl benzene, $C_6H_4Me_2$.

Naphthalene and anthracene are among the distillates. **Anthracene** is a colorless crystalline product of the composition $C_6H_4:(C_2H_2):C_6H_4$ and melting point 217°C used for the production of dyes, resins, plasticizers, tanning agents, and inhibitors. Crystals of anthracene are used for scintillation counters for gamma-ray detection. **Quinoline,** called also **benzazine** and **chinoline,** is a liquid with a tar odor. It has a double-ring molecular structure of the empirical formula C_9H_7N, and boils at 237°C. It is used for making antiseptics, pharmaceuticals, insecticides, and rubber accelerators.

Pine tar is a by-product in the distillation of pine wood. It is a viscous black mass and is much used for roofing. It is also sometimes called pitch, but pitch is the tar with the pine-tar oil removed, known as **pine pitch.** **Tarene,** of National Rosin Oil Products, Inc., is a dry, free-flowing powder made by absorbing pine tar into a synthetic hydrous calcium silicate which absorbs 4 times its own weight of liquid tar. It is used for formulating with rubbers. **Navy pitch** and **ship pitch** are names that refer to specification pine pitch for marine use. It is medium hard to solid, of a specific gravity of 1.08 to 1.10, of melting point not less than 148°F, completely soluble in benzol, and of a uniform black color, or red brown in thin layers. **Wood tar** from the destructive distillation of other woods is a dark-brown viscous liquid used as a preservative, deriving this property from its content of creosote. **Stockholm tar,** a name now out of commercial use, was a term employed in shipbuilding for the tar obtained from the crude distillation of pine stumps and roots.

TEA. The dried leaves of the shrubs *Camellia sinensis* and *Thea sinensis,* grown chiefly in southern Asia, Japan, Ceylon, Russian Transcaucasia, and Indonesia but also in Peru and in Tanzania. The plant requires a warm subtropical humid climate. Tea leaves are valued for making the beverage tea which contains the alkaloid caffeine and is stimulating. The leaves contain more caffeine than coffee berries but the flavor is different. Like coffee, also, it contains tannin, which dissolves out when the tea leaves are steeped too long, and is an astringent.   In well-prepared tea the tannins have been oxidized to the brown and red tannin which is not easily soluble and does not enter the properly steeped beverage to any great extent although it gives the color to the beverage.   The flavor and aroma of tea depend largely upon the age of the leaves when picked and the method of drying.   **Green tea** is made by drying the fresh leaves in the sun or artificially, while **black tea** is made by first fermenting the leaves and then drying.   Rolling is done to break the leaves and release the juices.   The **oolong tea** of Taiwan is partly fermented and is intermediate between green and black.   **Pouchong tea** is graded by mixing oolong with aromatic flowers such as jasmine.   Tea is also graded by the size and age of the leaf. Flowery orange pekoe is the smallest leaf, **orange pekoe tea** the second, then pekoe, pekoe souchong, and souchong.   Tea also varies with varieties grown in different climates so that Japan tea, China tea, and Ceylon have different flavors.

Commercial tea is usually a blend of different varieties to give uniformity under one trade name.   The blending of tea is considered an art.   **Brick tea,** made in China, is produced from coarse leaves and twigs which have been fermented.   They are mixed with tea dust, treated with rice water, and pressed into bricks 11 by 14 in.   **Cake tea,** or **puerh tea,** is produced in Yunnan.   The leaves are panned, sun-dried, and steamed, and then pressed into circular cakes about 8 in. in diameter.   **Tablet tea** is selected tea dust pressed into small tablets.   **Tea waste** is the final dust from the tea siftings, and is used for the production of caffeine.   **Teaseed oil,** or **sasanqua oil,** is from the seeds of another species of the tea plant, *Thea sasanqua,* of Asia.   The seeds contain 58% of a pale-yellow oil with a specific gravity of 0.916 used for lubrication, hair oil, soap, and pharmaceutical preparations.   **Paraguayan tea,** or **yerba maté,** used in immense quantities as a beverage in Argentina, Paraguay, Brazil, and some other South American countries, consists of the dried smoked leaves of the small evergreen tree *Ilex paraguayensis,* native to Paraguay and southern Brazil.   The growing region is about the Upper Paraná River.   It was an ancient beverage of the Indians, and cultivation began on a large scale under the early missionaries.   It contains a higher percentage of caffeine than tea or coffee, 3.88%, but less tannin.   The flavor of the steeped beverage is different from that of tea.   **Cassine** is a tealike beverage obtained from the twigs and leaves of two species of holly, *Ilex cassine* and *I. vomitoria,* found in the southern United States from Virginia to Texas.   It was called **Yaupon** by the Indians and used medicinally and in religious rites.   During the Civil War it was used in the South as a tea substitute.   The beverage has an odor similar to tea but is a dark color with a sharp, bitter taste.   It contains caffeine, tannin, and essential oils.

TEAK. The wood of the tree *Tectona grandis,* of southern Asia.   It resembles oak in appearance, is strong and firm, and in England is called **Indian oak.**   It contains an oil that gives it a pleasant odor and makes it immune to the attacks of insects.   It is used for boxes, chests, home furnishings, and for woodwork on ships.   The color is golden yellow, the grain is coarse and open, and the surface is greasy to the touch.   It is one of the most durable of woods, and also has small shrinkage.   The weight is 40 lb per cu ft.   In Burma large plantations grow teak for export.   Trees grow to a height of 100 ft with a diameter of 3 ft.   The growth is slow, a 2-ft tree averaging 150 years of age.   The wood marketed as **African teak,** known also as **iroko,** is from the tree *Chlorophora excelsa,* of West Africa, and is unlike true teak.   It is a firm, strong wood with a brownish color and a coarse, open grain.   The weight is somewhat less than teak, and it is harder to work, but it is resistant to decay and to termite attack, and is used in ship construction.   **Surinam teak** is the wood of the tree *Hymenea courbaril* of the Guianas and the West Indies.   It is also called **West Indian locust.**   The wood is dark brown in color, hard, heavy, and difficult to work.   It is not very similar to teak and not as durable.   **Seacoast teak,** or **bua bua,** is a hard, yellow, durable wood from species of the tree *Guettarda* of Malaya.   **Australian teak,** from New South Wales, is from the tree *Flindersia australis.*   It is yellowish red in color, close-grained, and hard with an oily feel resembling teak, but more difficult to work.   **In wood,** of Burma, also called **eng teak,** is from the in tree, *Dipterocarpus tuberculatus,* from which gurjun balsam is obtained. The wood is reddish brown; it is not as durable as teak.   Two woods of Brazil are used for the same purposes as teak: the **itaúba,** *Silvia itauba,* a tree growing to a height of about 75 ft in the upland forests of the lower Amazon, and **itaúba preta,** *Oreodaphne bookeriana,* a larger tree growing over a wider area.   The first is a greenish-yellow wood with compact texture and rough fiber, formerly prized for shipbuilding.   The second resembles teak more closely, and is used for cabinetwork.

TELLURIUM. An elementary metal, symbol Te, obtained as a steel-gray powder of 99% purity by the reduction of **tellurium oxide,** or **tellurite,** TeO_2, recovered from the residues of lead and copper refineries.   It is also marketed in slabs and sticks, and is sometimes known as **sylvanium.**   It occurs also with gold in Washington and Colorado as **gold telluride,** $AuTe_2$. The specific gravity is about 6.2 and melting point 450°C.   The chief uses are in lead to harden and toughen the metal, and in rubber as an accelerator and toughener.   Less than 0.1% tellurium in lead makes the metal more resistant to corrosion and acids, and gives a finer grain structure and higher endurance limit.   Tellurium-lead pipe, with less than 0.1% tellurium, has a 75% greater resistance to hydraulic pressure than plain lead. A **tellurium lead,** patented in England, contains 0.05% tellurium and 6 antimony.   **Tellurium copper** is a free-machining copper containing about 1.0% tellurium.   It machines 25% more easily than free-cutting brass. The tensile strength, annealed, is 30,000 psi, and the electrical conductivity is 98% that of copper.   A **tellurium bronze** containing 1% tellurium and 1.5 tin has a tensile strength, annealed, of 40,000 psi, and is free-machining.   Tellurium is used in small amounts in some steels to make them free-machining without making the steel hot-short as do increased amounts of sulfur.   But tellurium is objectionable for this purpose because inhalation of dust or fumes by workers causes garlic breath for days after exposure, although the material is not toxic.   As a secondary vulcanizing agent with sulfur in rubber, tellurium in very small proportions, 0.5 to 1%, increases the tensile strength and aging qualities of the rubber.   It is not as strong an accelerator as selenium, but gives greater heat resistance to the rubber.   **Telloy** is the trade name of the R. T. Vanderbilt Co. for **tellurium powder** ground very fine for rubber compounding.

TERNE PLATE.   Bessemer or open-hearth steel plate having on each side a thin coating of an alloy of 20% tin and 80 lead, although other proportions may be used.   Terne is an old name meaning dull and refers to the color as compared with bright tinplate.   Terne plate is made by the dip process and is used for roofing, construction work, and to replace the more expensive tinplate for uses not in contact with foodstuffs.   The coating is measured by pounds per double base box containing approximately 436 sq ft, or 112 sheets, 20 by 28 in.   **Long ternes** are those with coatings of 8, 12, and 15 lb, not heavier than No. 14 gage or lighter than No. 30 gage.   **Short ternes** are those with coatings of 8 lb or lighter, or in very heavy coatings from 15 to 40 lb for roofing.   The name long terne is also used to designate flat sheets of larger size, up to 48 by 120 in., used for manufacturing purposes.   The usual roofing material is 40 lb, and the coating is 25% tin and 75 lead.   Industrial terne plate usually comes in base boxes of 112 sheets, 14 by 20 in., furnished as standard, deep-drawing, and extra-deep-drawing.   When copper steel is specified, it has at least 0.18% copper.

Lead-coated steel is now much used instead of terne plate for building use and for stamped and formed parts.   Lead alone does not adhere well to steel, but the lead dip used contains small amounts of other elements. **Weiralead,** of the Weirton Steel Co., is a lead-coated steel in gages 16 to 28.   The lead coating contains small amounts of tin, silver, and antimony, and it will not peel when bent or deep-drawn.   **Amaloy,** of the American Machine & Foundry Co., is a lead alloy with 1% tin, used for hot-dipping iron and steel parts.   **Plate-Loy,** of the American Smelting & Refining Co., is a hot-dip plate, and the coating contains 2 to 4% tin, 1 antimony, 1.5 to 2 zinc, and the balance lead. It adheres well to the steel, and the plate can be seamed and soldered.

TERRA COTTA. A general English term applied to fired, unglazed, yellow, and red clay wares; in the United States it refers particularly to the red and brown square and hexagonal tiles made from common brick clay, always containing iron. Some special terra cottas are nearly white, while for special architectural work other shades are obtained. The clays are washed, and only very fine sands are mixed with them in order to secure a fine open texture and smooth surface. Terra cotta is used for roofing and for tile floors, for hollow building blocks, and in decorative construction work. Good, well-burned terra cotta is less than $1\frac{1}{2}$ in. thick. Terra cotta is very light, 120 lb per cu ft, and will withstand fire and frost.

TETRACHLORETHANE. A colorless liquid of the chemical formula $CHCl_2 \cdot CHCl_2$ employed as a solvent for organic compounds such as oils, resins, and tarry substances. It is an excellent solvent for sulfur, phosphorus, iodine, and various other elements. It is used as a paint remover and bleacher, as an insecticide, and in the production of other chlorine compounds. It is also called **acetylene tetrachloride,** and is made by the combination of chlorine with acetylene. Tetrachlorethane boils at 144°C, freezes at −36°C, is noninflammable, and has a specific gravity of 1.601. It is narcotic and toxic, and the breathing of the vapors is injurious. Mixed with dilute alkalies, it forms explosive compounds. In the presence of moisture it is very corrosive to metals. Mixed with zinc dust and sawdust, it is employed as a smoke screen.

THALLIUM. A soft bluish-white metal resembling lead but not as malleable. The specific gravity is 11.85, and melting point 578°F. At about 600°F it ignites and burns with a green light. The electrical conductivity is low. It tarnishes in the air, forming an oxide coating. It is attacked by nitric acid and by sulfuric acid. The metal has a tensile strength of 1,300 psi and a Brinell hardness of 2. **Thallium-mercury alloy,** with 8.5% thallium, is liquid with a lower freezing point than mercury alone, −60°C, and is used in low-temperature switches. **Thallium-lead alloys** are corrosion-resistant, and are used for plates on some chemical-equipment parts.

The metal occurs in copper pyrites and zinc ores, and the chief source is the flue dust of smelters from spalerite ores. Four rare minerals are ores of thallium: **vrbaite,** $Tl_2S \cdot 3(AsSb)_2S_3$, is found in Macedonia; **lorandite,** $Tl_2S \cdot 2As_2S_3$, is found in Macedonia and in Wyoming; **hutchinsonite,** $PbS \cdot (TlAg)_2S \cdot 2As_2S_3$, occurs in Switzerland and in Sweden; **crooksite,**

(CuTlAg)$_2$Se, is found in Sweden. The salts of thallium are highly poisonous, the sulfide being used as a rat poison. **Thallium oxysulfide** is used in light-sensitive cells. It is also sensitive to infrared rays, and is used for dark signaling. **Thallium sulfate,** Tl$_2$(SO$_4$)$_3$, is a crystalline powder used as an insecticide. It is more toxic than lead compounds. Thallium also gives high refraction to optical glass. Thallium bromide iodide crystals, grown synthetically, are used for infrared spectrometers.

The so-called **alkali-halide crystals** used in the **discriminator circuits** of **scintillators** for gamma spectrometry contain thallium. They separate the slow-decaying pulses of protons produced by fast neutrons from the electron pulses produced by gamma absorption. A French crystal, called **Scintibloc,** is **sodium iodide thallide,** NaI(Tl). The **cesium iodide thallide** crystal, CsI(Tl), gives a very blue light under electron excitation.

THERMOSTAT METALS. The metals used for indicating very high temperatures, called also **thermocouple metals** and **thermoelectric metals,** consist of two different metals or alloys joined at one end. Application of heat to the coupled end will set up an electric current in the circuit. The voltage generated is very small, usually less than 50 mv, but the electromotive force is proportional to the heat at the junction, and when connected by wires to a sensitive galvanometer will indicate the temperature on a graduated dial. Accuracy within a range of 2°F can be obtained for high-temperature readings. Copper-constantan or nickel-constantan may be used for temperatures to about 1650°F. A thermocouple wire of the Englehard Industries, Inc., for temperature indication from 1200 to 2800°C, consists of tungsten versus **tungsten-rhenium alloy** of 74% tungsten and 26 rhenium. The millivolt output at 2800°C is 43.25; at 2000°C it is 34.13 mv; and at 1200°C it drops to 18.25 mv. A thermocouple of this company that gives a higher electromotive force at lower temperatures, 48.02 mv at 1200°C, is called **Platinel,** and is used in turbojet engines for measuring temperatures from 350 to 1260°C. It consists of a gold-palladium-platinum alloy wire versus a gold-palladium alloy wire. Besides the capability of generating an electromotive force by the difference between the two metals, the metals must be capable of withstanding the high temperatures without deterioration and have a stability within an accepted drift in voltage indication of not more than 0.75%.

Various intermetallic crystals are used as thermoelectrics for transforming electric current into heat energy or, in reverse, as **heat pumps,** for refrigeration. The efficiency is proportional to the temperature difference induced across the crystal, and different crystals have their maximum efficiencies at definite temperature operating limits. Polycrystalline **bismuth telluride,** Bi$_2$Te$_3$, has a wide temperature difference, 1115°F. Some materials with low efficiency at low temperatures have high power rating at high temperatures, and others operate efficiently only at lower temperatures. Thus, the materials may be set up in parallel for heat pumps. However, the thermoelectric metals for thermostat use need to generate only slight electromotive force.

The **thermometals** used as temperature controls in electrical appliances, for temperatures from about -40 to $1000°F$, are bimetals consisting of two metals or alloys with different rates of thermal expansion welded together so that a change in temperature bends or deflects the bimetal. In heat-control or indicating devices the deflection is measured to indicate the temperature, or the deflection is utilized for mechanical or electrical action. A wide variety of metals is used for thermometals. The requirements are corrosion resistance, heat resistance, and uniform pull proportional to the temperature change. Thermometals welded at the contact surfaces are sold under trade names. **Highflex,** of the H. A. Wilson Co., is an all-steel bimetal with a temperature range of maximum sensitivity from 50 to $300°F$. **Saflex,** of the same company, is relatively inactive up to $400°F$, but has high deflection between 500 to $800°F$. **Muflex,** used where high permeability is required, has the high expanding side of pure iron and the low expanding side of Invar.

THORIUM. A soft, ductile, silvery-white metal occurring in nature to about the same extent as lead but so widely disseminated in minute quantities difficult to extract that it is considered as a rare metal. It was once valued for use in incandescent gas mantles in the form of **thorium nitrate,** $Th(NO_3)_4$, but is now used chiefly for nuclear and electronic applications. **Thorium powder** is produced by calcium reduction of thorium oxide. The impure powder burns in the air with great brilliance. Pure thorium metal in sheet form has a specific gravity of 11.7, a melting point of $3090°F$, and a tensile strength of about 35,000 psi. Even small amounts of impurities affect the physical properties greatly, and cold working increases the strength. The metal is dissolved by aqua regia or by hydrochloric acid.

Natural thorium consists largely of the alpha-emitting isotope **thorium 232,** and is a powerful emitter of alpha rays. Thorium produces fissile material, uranium 233, only when triggered by another fission material. Under neutron bombardment it forms **protactinium** which is nonfissile but decays slowly into fissile uranium 233. But, in rapid burning, the buildup of protactinium may be converted into the nonfissile uranium 234.

Thorium 230 is found in minerals that contain uranium and radium and was originally considered as a separate metal under the name of **ionium.** It is radioactive, emitting alpha rays. It has a half-life of 76,000 years, slowly converting to radium. The original production was from the fractionation of uranium ores. It was used as an additive in spark-plug wire, but is too expensive for this purpose.

The chief **thorium ore** is the mineral **monazite,** occurring as sand or in granular masses, usually as sea sand. It is the chief source of thorium oxide and of the rare-earth metals. Most of the monazite comes from Brazil, India, and the East Indies. The monazite sands of Brazil contain 8% **thorium oxide, or thoria,** ThO_2. The ore of India may have as high as 10%, but is marketed on the basis of 8% oxide and 60 rare-earth metals. Thoria has a high melting point, 3050°C, but its use as a refractory ceramic is limited because of its high cost and radioactivity. Monazite contains about 3.5 grams of **mesothorium** per 1,000 tons and usually has 30 to 35% of the oxides of lanthanum, yttrium, neodymium, and praseodymium, and a small amount of europium. Mesothorium was originally considered a separate element, but is an isotope of thorium, with an atomic weight of 228 and a half-life of 6.7 years. The radiations from mesothorium are the same as from radium, alpha, beta, and gamma rays. As it decomposes, it forms **radiothorium,** which is identical in chemical properties with thorium but emits a powerful alpha radiation. It is used in luminous paints and is a safer activator for this purpose than radium, but is scarcer and more expensive, and has a shorter life.

The type of monazite called **uranothorite,** from the Bancroft area of Canada, contains from 0.04 to 0.27% thorium oxide. The thorium is recovered from the waste liquors of the uranium-treatment plant. The rare mineral **thorite,** found in Norway, is a **thorium silicate,** $ThSiO_2$. It occurs in crystals or massive, orange to black in color, and has a resinous luster, and a specific gravity of about 5. **Thoria-urania ceramics** are used for reactor-fuel elements. They are reinforced with columbium or zirconium fibers to increase thermal conductivity and shock resistance. **Thorium-tungsten alloys** have been used for very-high-voltage electronic filaments. The **incandescent mantle,** invented by Welsbach in 1893, and widely used during the period of gas lighting, consisted of a mixture of 98 to 99% thorium nitrate and 1 to 2 cerium oxide. The nitrate is converted to thorium oxide on ignition, with an increase of 10 times its original volume, and glows in the gas flame with an intense white light.

THUYA. The wood of the tree *Thuya plicata,* also known as **western red cedar, giant arbor vitae, shinglewood,** and **Pacific red cedar.** The tree grows in cool, humid coast regions from Alaska to northern California, and the wood is widely used for shingles, poles, and tanks. It is light in weight, soft, and weak, with a straight coarse grain, but is durable. The sapwood is white and the heartwood reddish. The tree grows to great size, reaching to 200 ft in height and 16 ft in diameter at the age of 1,000 years. The stand is estimated at 53 billion bd ft. **Northern white cedar** is the wood of the tree *T. occidentalis,* of northeastern United States. It is also called **white cedar, arbor vitae, swamp cedar,** or simply cedar. The wood is soft, knotty, brittle, weak, but very durable.   It is used for shingles, poles, posts, and lumber for small boats.   The sapwood is white and the heartwood light brown.   The trees have a diameter of 1 to 3 ft, and a height of 25 to 75 ft.   **Thuya leaf oil,** used as a fixative in perfumery, is a colorless oil with a bornyl acetate odor, distilled from the leaves.

TIN. A silvery-white lustrous metal with a bluish tinge.   It is soft and malleable, and can be rolled into foil as thin as 0.0002 in.   Tin melts at 232°C.   The specific gravity is 7.298, the tensile strength 4,000 psi, the hardness slightly greater than that of lead, and the electrical conductivity about one-seventh that of silver.   It is resistant to atmospheric corrosion, but is dissolved in mineral acids.   The cast metal has a crystalline structure, and the surface shows dendritic crystals when cast in a steel mold. **Tin pest** is the breaking up of the metal into a gray powder which occurs below 19°C, and the metal is not used for applications at very low temperatures.

Tin is used in brasses, bronzes, and babbitts, and in soft solders.   One of the most important uses is for the making of tinplate, and as an electroplating material.   **Electroplated tin** has a fine white color, gives a durable protective finish, and also has a lubricating effect as a bearing surface. **Standard tin** of the London Metal Exchange must contain over 99.75% tin.   **Straits tin** is 99.895% pure.   Federal specifications for **pig tin** is 99.80% min.   **Block tin** is virgin tin cast in stone molds.   Even small traces of impurities have an influence on the physical properties of tin. Lead softens the metal; arsenic and zinc harden it.   An addition of 0.3% nickel doubles the tensile strength; 2% copper increases the strength 150%.   Pure tin melts sharply, but small amounts of impurities broaden the melting point.   **Tin powder,** used for making sintered alloys, is 99.8% pure, in powder from 100 to 300 mesh.   The **tin crystals** used in the chemical industry are **tin chloride,** or **stannous chloride,** $SnCl_2 \cdot 2H_2O$, coming as large colorless crystals or white water-soluble flakes, melting at 246°C.   They are also used for immersion tinning of metals, and for sensitizing glass and plastics before metalizing.   The chief source of tin is the mineral cassiterite, but Nigerian columbite may contain up to 6% tin oxide.   The principal tin-producing countries are Indonesia, Malaya, Bolivia, China, and Nigeria, but tin mines have been worked in Cornwall since ancient times, and tin is also found in Canada and in irregular quantities in some other areas.

Tin oxide, or **stannous oxide,** is a fine black crystalline powder of the composition SnO, made by oxidizing tin powder.   It is used as an opacifier in ceramic enamels, as a ceramic color, as an abrasive, and as a coating for conductive glass.   As a color in ceramics it is light-stable and acid-resistant.

With magnesium and cobalt oxides it gives a sky-blue color called **cerulean blue.** It is also used with copper oxide to produce ruby glass.

Stannic oxide, SnO_2, is a white powder used in ceramic glazes as an opacifier and for color. As little as 1 to 2% gives fluidity and high luster to glass. With chromates and lime it gives pinks and maroons in enamels, and with vanadium compounds it gives yellows. With gold chloride it gives brilliant-red jewelry enamels. **Protectatin** is the name of the Tin Research Institute for a thin, invisible film of oxide on tinplate to protect against sulfur staining and to give a base for paint. It is produced by dipping the tinplate in a solution of trisodium phosphate, sodium dichromate, and sodium hydroxide. **Potassium stannate,** $K_2SnO_3 \cdot 3H_2O$, or **sodium stannate,** $Na_2SnO_3 \cdot 3H_2O$, may be used for immersion tinning of aluminum. Both come as white, water-soluble crystals. The term **organotin** usually refers to butyl compounds of the metal used as catalysts, or heat and light stabilizers in vinyl polymers. **Stan-Guard 100,** of Chas. Pfizer & Co., is a liquid **butyl-tin** compound containing sulfur and used as a stabilizer in rigid PVC sheet. A **butyl-tin maleate** powder is effective as a light stabilizer. **Hollicide LT-125,** of R. M. Hollingshead Corp., is a water-soluble organo **trialkyl-tin** used as a bacteriocide in paper and textile processing. It can be used over a wide pH range.

TINPLATE. Soft-steel plate containing a thin coating of pure tin on both sides. A large proportion of the tinplate used goes into the manufacture of food containers because of its resistance to the action of vegetable acids and its nonpoisonous character. It solders easily, and also is easier to work in dies than terne plate, so that it also is preferred over terne plate for making toys and other cheap articles in spite of a higher cost. Commercial tinplate comes in boxes of 112 sheets, 14 by 20 in., and is designated by the net weight per box when below 100 lb. Heavy tinplate above 100 lb goes by number, as steel does, or by letter symbols. The weight of tin may be as high as 1.7% of the total weight of the sheet. **Coke plates** carry as little tin as is necessary to protect and brighten the plates for temporary use. The tin of the coat forms compounds of $FeSn_2$, Fe_2Sn, and $FeSn$ with the iron of the plate, and on a coke plate this compound is 0.00006 to 0.00015 in. thick. Best cokes carry more tin than do the standard cokes. **Charcoal plates** have heavier coats of tin designated by the letter A. The AAAAAA, or 6A, has the heaviest coating. Tinplate is made by the hot-dip process using palm oil as a flux, or by a continuous electroplating process. A base box contains 31,360 sq in. of tinplate, and standard-dip tinplate has $1\frac{1}{2}$ lb of tin per base box, while electrolytic plate has only $\frac{1}{4}$ lb of tin per base box and much **electrolytic tinplate** for container use has only 0.10 lb of tin per base box. Electrotinning gives intimately adherent coatings of any desired thickness, and the plate may have a serviceable coat as thin as 0.00003 in., or about one-third that of the thinnest possible dipped plate. A slight cold rolling of electrolytic tin-plate gives a bright and smooth finish.

Taggers was originally a name for tinplate that is undersized, or below the gage of the plate in the package, but the name **taggers tin** is also applied to light-gage plate. These sizes are No. 38 gage, 55 lb; No. 37, 60 lb; and No. 36 gage, 65 lb. **Ductilite,** of the Wheeling Steel Corp., is a tinplate that is not made by hot rolling in packs, but is cold-rolled from single hot-rolled strip steel. It is of uniform gage and does not have the thin edges of pack-rolled plate. It also has a uniform grain structure. **Weirite,** of the Weirton Steel Co., is cold-reduced coke tinplate. **Black plate,** used for cans in place of tinplate where the tin protection is not necessary, is not black, but is any sheet steel other than tinplate or terne plate in tinplate sizes. It may be chemically treated to resist rust or corrosion.

TITANIUM. A metallic element, symbol Ti, occurring in a great variety of minerals. It was first discovered as an element in 1791 in a black magnetic sand at Menachin, Cornwall, England, and called **menachite,** from the name of the sand, **menachinite.** Its chief commercial ores are rutile and ilmenite. In rutile it occurs as an oxide. It is an abundant element, but is difficult to reduce from the oxide. High-purity titanium metal has a yield strength of 35,000 psi with elongation of 55%. It can be produced only in protected atmospheres. Commercially pure titanium contains up to 0.3% oxygen, 0.1 nitrogen, and up to 0.2% each of carbon and iron. It is 99% min pure. This is the common aeronautical specification known as **titanium AMS 4901.** The minimum yield strength is 70,000 psi with minimum elongation of 15%. The tensile strength may be up to 105,000 psi. The specific gravity is 4.54, and melting point 1660°C. It is paramagnetic and has low electrical conductivity.

The commercial metal is produced from **sponge titanium** which is made by converting the oxide to titanium tetrachloride and then reducing with molten magnesium. One pound of titanium is produced from 4.37 lb of tetrachloride by reducing with 1.41 lb of magnesium. The metal can also be produced in dendritic crystals of 99.6% purity by electrolytic deposition from titanium carbide. Despite its high melting point, titanium reacts readily in copper and in other metals, and is much used for alloying and for deoxidizing. It is a more powerful deoxidizer of steel than silicon or manganese. An early German deoxidizing alloy known as **Badin metal** contained about 9% aluminum, 19 silicon, 5 titanium, and the balance iron. **Titanium copper,** used for deoxidizing nonferrous metals, is made by adding titanium to molten copper, and the congealed alloy is broken into lumps.

One of the chief uses of the metal has been in the form of titanium oxide as a white pigment.   It is also valued as titanium carbide for hard facings and for cutting tools.   Small percentages of titanium are added to steels and alloys to increase hardness and strength by the formation of carbides or oxides or, when nickel is present, by the formation of **nickel titanide.** The first **titanium alloys** in the United States were produced in 1945 by the Bureau of Mines.   A variety of structural alloys have been commercialized which have high strength-weight factors at ordinary temperatures, but the titanium alloys made by conventional steelmaking methods have been generally subject to catastrophic failure in structures subject to the buildup of concentrated energy-stress levels.

The crystal structure of titanium is called close-packed hexagonal, but this term is also applied to 23 other elements, each differing in bonding habits and in crystal formation.   Titanium has a 3–4 valence, and the unit molecule is unlike that of magnesium, while the cube formed when the metal is heated is unlike that of iron.   The change in the solid metal, called **alpha** and **beta structures,** occurs at about 1625°F, but the transition range is long and, unless stabilized, the metal begins to lose strength at relatively moderate temperatures.   At about 1400°F oxygen reacts with the metal causing embrittlement of the finished product.   Hydrogen and nitrogen also combine with the hot metal, affecting the physical properties. Even small amounts of sulfur react and cause grain growth, but small additions of the noble metals inhibit the reaction.   A **titanium-palladium alloy** containing 0.2% palladium, used for chemical equipment, is resistant to sulfuric acid.

The early **Rem-Cru alloys** of Remington-Crucible Steel were based on the idea of equating the two crystal structures, with aluminum to stabilize the alpha, or hexagonal, structure and manganese to stabilize the beta. In the coding system for the alloys the letter before the number indicates the structure, A for alpha, B for beta, and C for alpha-beta.   **Rem-Cru A-130-M** contains 8% manganese.   The features are good bending and welding qualities, and it has been used for structural sheet for temperatures below 700°F.   It has a tensile strength of 130,000 psi with elongation of 15%.   **Rem-Cru C-130-AMo** contains 6.5% aluminum and 3.75 molybdenum.   It maintains full strength to 800°F, but it is not used for welded structures since it is heat-hardenable at 1450°F.   **Rem-Cru A-110-AT,** with 5% aluminum and 2.5 tin, has good ductility and strength.   It can be forged below 2000°F and welds easily.   **Titanium alloy Ti-679,** of Titanium Metals Corp., for large forgings, contains 11% tin, 2.25 aluminum, 5 zirconium, 1 molybdenum, 0.2 silicon, and 0.1 oxygen, with a density of 0.174 lb per cu in.   The crystal transformation in the alloy begins at about 1400°F.   When solution treated at 1700°F the room temperature tensile strength is up to 195,000 psi with elongation of 6%.

Forgings without heat treatment have a tensile strength of 151,000 psi with elongation of 14%. **Titanium Ti-140A,** of the same company, for sheet and strip, has 2% iron, 2 chromium, 2 molybdenum, 0.05 max carbon, 0.20 max oxygen, and 0.10 max nitrogen. When annealed it has a tensile strength up to 150,000 psi with elongation of 15%. This alloy has stability to 1000°F. An English alloy, **Hylite,** containing 6% tin, 5 zirconium, 3 aluminum, 0.5 carbon, and the balance titanium, has a tensile strength of 155,000 psi, and is stable to 960°F.

Titanium tubing for aircraft and missile use is produced by the Superior Tube Co. in diameters from 0.012 to 1.125 in. It is made of **titanium alloy 3A1-2.5V,** containing 3% aluminum, 2.5 vanadium, 0.02 silicon, 0.01 manganese, 0.16 iron, 0.02 carbon, 0.015 nitrogen, and 0.011 hydrogen. It is ductile and can be cold-flared. The annealed tubing has a yield strength of 85,600 psi, while the hard-drawn tube has a yield strength of 118,000 psi. **Titanium alloy 2.5A1-16V,** of the Mallory-Sharon Metals Corp., has a high tolerance for hydrogen, and can be worked and welded easily. It has 2.5% aluminum and 16 vanadium. After aging, it has a tensile strength to 200,000 psi. **Titanium alloy 821** of the same company, for forgings for jet engines, has 8% aluminum, 2 columbium, and 1 tantalum. It can be welded easily.

Titanium alloy B-120VCA, of Crucible Steel, has a cubical crystal structure which permits severe cold working. It contains 13% vanadium, 11 chromium, and 3 aluminum. It has a yield strength of 120,000 psi. Heat treatment induces deep hardening and increases strength to 190,000 psi. **Titanium EP20-2,** of the Chicago Development Corp., has 20% aluminum and 2 vanadium. It has a specific gravity of 4.1 and a tensile strength of 190,000 psi with elongation of 6%. **Titanium sheet,** of Republic Steel, for aircraft and missiles, comes as thin as 0.010 in. and cold-forms easily. It is **Titanium alloy RS-140** containing 5% aluminum, 2.75 chromium, and 1.25 iron. It is hot-rolled and heat-treated to give a tensile strength of 190,000 psi.

One of the most commonly used alloys for aeronautical structures has been **Titanium 6Al4V.** The yield strength is about 140,000 psi, but above 500°F the strength drops off rapidly. This alloy was modified for ordnance forgings at the Watertown Arsenal by adding 2% tin, 0.5 iron, and 0.25 copper. The forgings have a yield strength of 180,000 psi and elongation to break of 9.5%. **Titanium 8Al1Mo1V,** for aircraft structural members, has a density of 0.158 lb per cu in., and a yield strength of 150,000 psi, but loses strength above 600°F. The **TiTech alloys,** of Titanium Technology Corp., are various grades of titanium casting alloys produced by controlled methods to replace forgings.

The first attempt at chemical synthesis of titanium alloys was made at the Naval Ordnance Laboratory, but the project was limited to the production of binary alloys by melt-furnace methods. The **Ti-Ni alloys** produced are intermetals, or chemical combinations of titanium and nickel. The molecule is reversible, and the alloys can be hardened or annealed by heat treatment like steel. They are suitable for cutting tools or for parts requiring high hardness and strength.

TITANIUM CARBIDE. A hard crystalline powder of the composition TiC made by reacting titanium dioxide and carbon black at temperatures above 1800°C. It is compacted with cobalt or nickel for use in cutting tools and for heat-resistant parts. It is lighter in weight and less costly than tungsten carbide, but in cutting tools it is more brittle. When combined with tungsten carbide in sintered carbide tool materials, however, it reduces the tendency to cratering in the tool. A general-purpose cutting tool of this type contains about 82% tungsten carbide, 8 titanium carbide, and 10% cobalt binder. **Kentanium,** of Kennametal, Inc., is titanium carbide in various grades with up to 40% of either cobalt or nickel as the binder, used for high-temperature, erosion-resistant parts. For highest oxidation resistance only about 5% cobalt binder is used. **Kentanium 138,** with 20% cobalt, is used for parts where higher strength and shock-resistance are needed, and where temperatures are below about 1800°F. This material has a tensile strength of 45,000 psi, compressive strength of 550,000 psi, and Rockwell hardness A90. **Kentanium 151A,** for resistance to molten glass or aluminum, has a binder of 20% nickel. **Titanium-carbide alloy** for tool bits, of the Ford Motor Co., has 80% titanium carbide dispersed in a binder of 10% nickel and 10% molybdenum. The material has a hardness of Rockwell A93, and a dense, fine-grained structure. **Ferro-Tic,** of the Chromalloy Corp., has the titanium carbide bonded with stainless steel. It has a hardness of Rockwell C55. **Machinable carbide** is titanium carbide in a matrix of Ferro-Tic C tool steel. **Titanium carbide tubing** is produced in round or rectangular form, 0.10 to 3 in. in diameter, by TEEG Research, Inc. It is made by vapor deposition of the carbide without a binder. The tubing has a hardness above 2,000 Knoop and a melting point of 5880°F.

Grown single crystals of titanium carbide of the Linde Co. have the composition $TiC_{0.94}$, with 19% carbon. The melting point is 5882°F, density 4.93, and Vickers hardness 3230.

TITANIUM ORES. The most common titanium ores are ilmenite and rutile. Ilmenite is an iron-black mineral having a specific gravity of about 4.5, and containing about 52% **titanic oxide,** or titania, TiO_2. The ore of India is sold on the basis of titanium dioxide content, and the high-grade ore averages about 60% TiO_2, 22.5 iron, and 0.4 silica. **Ilmenite** is a **ferrotitanate,** $FeO \cdot TiO_2$, but much of the material called ilmenite is

arizonite, $Fe_2O_3 \cdot 3TiO_2$.   Titanium ores are widely distributed and plentiful.   Ilmenite is found in northern New York, Florida, North Carolina, and in Arkansas, but the most extensive accessible resources are found in Canada.   The Quebec ilmenite contains 30% iron.   The concentrated ore has about 36% TiO_2, and 41% iron, and is smelted to produce pig iron and a slag containing 70% TiO_2 which is used to produce titanium oxide. The beach sands of Senegal are mixed ores, the ilmenite containing 55 to 58% TiO_2, and the **zirconiferous quartz** containing 70 to 90% zirconia. The beach sands of Brazil are washed to yield a product averaging 71.6% ilmenite, 13 zircon, and 6 monazite.   The Indian ilmenite also comes from beach sands.   The ore of New York state averages 19% TiO_2.

Rutile is a **titanium dioxide,** TiO_2, containing theoretically 60% titanium.   Its usual occurrence is crystalline or compact massive, with a specific gravity of 4.18 and 4.25 and a hardness 6 to 6.5.   The color is red to brown, occasionally black.   Rutile is found in granite, gneiss, limestone, or dolomite.   It is obtained from beach sand of northern Florida, and Espirito Santo, Brazil, and is also produced in Virginia, and in Australia and India.   Rutile, and also **brookite** and **Octahedrite,** or **anatase,** are produced in Arkansas and Massachusetts.   The best Virginia concentrates are 92.5 to 98% TiO_2, but some are 42% from rock originally showing 18.5% TiO_2 in a body of feldspar.   Rutile is marketed in the form of concentrates on the basis of 79 to 98.5% titanium oxide.   It is used as an opacifier in ceramic glazes and to produce tan-colored glass.   It is also employed for welding rod coatings.   On welding rods it aids stabilization of the arc and frees the metal of slag.   **Tanarc,** used on welding rods as a replacement for rutile, is made from slag from Canadian titaniferous hematite, and contains 70% TiO_2.

TITANIUM OXIDE. The white **titanium dioxide,** or **titania,** of the composition TiO_2, which is an important paint pigment.   The best quality is produced from ilmenite, and is higher in price than many white pigments but has great hiding power and durability.   Off-color pigments, with a light buff tone, are made by grinding rutile ore.   The pigments have fine physical qualities and may be used wherever the color is not important. Titania is also substituted for zinc oxide and lithopone in the manufacture of white rubber goods, and for paper filler.   The specific gravity is about 4.   Mixed with blanc fixe it is also marketed under the name of **Titanox.**   **Zopaque,** of the Chemical & Pigment Co., is a pure titanium oxide for rubber compounding.   The **Ti-Pure** of Du Pont is commercially pure titanium dioxide for pigment use.   **Duolith,** of this company, is titanated lithopone pigment containing 15% titanium dioxide, 25 zinc sulfide, and 60 barium sulfate.   **Titanox L,** of the Titanium Pigment Corp., is a **lead titanate,** $PbTiO_3$, used as a less costly substitute for titanium oxide.

It is yellowish in color and has only 60% of the hiding power, but is very durable and protects steel from rust.   **Butyl titanate,** of Henley & Co., Inc., is a yellow viscous liquid used in anticorrosion varnishes and for flameproofing fabrics.   It is a condensation product of the tetrabutyl ester of ortho-titanic acid, and contains about 36% titanium dioxide.

Titania crystals are produced by Linde in the form of pale-yellow, single-crystal boules for making optical prisms and lenses for applications where the high refractive index is needed.   The crystals are also used as electrical semiconductors, and for gemstones.   They have a higher refractive index than the diamond, and the cut stones are more brilliant but are much softer. The hardness is about 925 Knoop, and the melting point is 1825°C.   The refractive index of the rutile form is 2.7 and that of the anatase is 2.5, while the synthetic crystals have a refractive index of 2.616 vertically and 2.903 horizontally.   The **strontium titanate** of the Engle Mfg. Co., used as a brilliant diamondlike gemstone, is a strontium meso-tri-titanate. Stones are made up to 4 carats.   The refractive index is 2.412.   It has a cubic crystal similar to the diamond but the crystal is opaque in the X-ray spectrum.

Titanium oxide is a good refractory and electrical insulator.   The finely ground material gives good plasticity without binders, and is molded to make resistors for electronic use.   The **micro sheet** of the Glenco Corp. is titanium oxide in sheets as thin as 0.003 in. for use as a substitute for mica for electrical insulation where brittleness is not important.   **Titania-magnesia ceramics** were made in Germany in the form of extruded rods and plates and pressed parts.

TOBACCO.   The leaf of an unbranched annual plant of the genus *Nicotiana,* of which there are about 50 species and many varieties.   It is used for smoking, chewing, snuff, insecticides, and for the production of the alkaloid nicotine.   Commercial crops are grown in about 60 countries, but about a third of world production is in the United States.   Only two species are grown commercially, *N. tabacum,* a tropical plant native to the West Indies and South America, and *N. rustica,* grown by the Indians of Mexico and North America before 1492.   About 85% of world production is now from *N. tabacum,* and there are more than 100 varieties of this plant.

Tobacco was not known in Europe until it was brought from the West Indies by Columbus.   Plants for cultivation were brought to Spain in 1558, and by 1586 smoking had become a general practice in western Europe.   The first commercial shipments were made from Virginia in 1618, the growing of cultured varieties having begun in 1612.   Smoking of tobacco was practiced by the Indians from Canada to Patagonia, and the natives of Haiti used powdered tobacco leaf as **snuff** under the name of

cohoba. Like Indian corn, the tobacco plant had been domesticated for centuries and the original wild ancestor of the plant is not known. Some Indian tribes, such as the Tobacco nation of southwest Ontario, specialized in the growing of tobacco types.

The quality of the tobacco leaf varies greatly with the soil and climate, the care of the plant, and the curing of the leaf, and the nicotine content develops in the curing process. The narcotic effects are due to the alkaloid **nicotine,** $C_{10}H_{14}N_2$, a complex pyrrolidine, which is a heavy, water-white oil. The nicotine is absorbed through the mucous membranes of the nose and throat. The aroma and flavor come from the essential oils in the leaf developed during fermentation and curing. The more harmful effects to the eyes and respiratory system come from the **pyridine** C_5H_5N, a toxic aromatic compound also occurring in coal tar, and from other elements of the smoke and not from the alkaloid. The burning of the tars may also produce **carcinogen** compounds which are complex condensed benzene-ring nuclei injurious to tissues.

Although *N. tabacum* is a less hardy plant than *N. rustica,* it adapts itself to a wide variety of climates and soils, and the types generated in given areas do not normally reproduce the same type in another area. The variety developed in the Near East and known as **Turkish tobacco** and valued as an aromatic blend for cigarettes is a small plant with numerous leaves only about 3 in. long, while the American tobaccos grown from the same species have leaves up to 3 ft long. There are 60,000 Turkish tobacco plants per acre compared with 6,000 plants of Virginia tobacco. Up to 900 lb of Turkish leaf is obtained per acre, but the average yield per acre of American tobaccos is 1,200 lb. The nicotine content of Turkish tobacco is from 1 to 2%, while that of flue-cured Virginia tobacco is 2.5 to 3%, and that of burley and fire-cured American types is up to 4.5%. **Perique,** a strong black tobacco much used in French and British pipe mixtures, is cultivated only in a small area of southern Louisiana. Other tobaccos brought into the area become perique in the second year, but when transplanted back they do not thrive. *N. rustica* was the first tobacco grown in Virginia, but the tobacco now grown in the area and known as **Virginia tobacco** is *N. tabacum* brought from the West Indies, but now differing in type from West Indian tobacco. **Makhorka tobacco,** a black air-cured type grown in Russia and Poland and very high in nicotine, is from *N. rustica.* Strong, black, highly fermented tobaccos high in nicotine, and considered as inferior in the United States, are preferred in France and some other countries.

Types of tobacco are based on color, flavor, strength, and methods of curing and fermentation, while grades are based on size, aroma, and texture, but the geographical growing area also determines characteristics. Commercial purchasing is done by the area and the Department of Agriculture type classification: fire-cured, dark air-cured, flue-cured, cigar wrapper, cigar binder, cigar filler, burley, Maryland, and perique, all of which are from *N. tabacum.* Grading is done by specialists, and a single-area crop may produce more than 50 grades. In the manufacture of cigarettes, blending is done to attain uniformity, and some of the flavor and aroma may be from added ingredients. **Air-cured tobaccos** are alkaline, while **flue-cured tobaccos** are acid and the nicotine is less readily given off. *N. rustica* may contain as high as 10% nicotine, and is thus more desirable for insecticide use or for the extraction of nicotine, but some strains of *N. tabacum* have been developed for smoking with as little as 0.3% nicotine.

Tobacco is grown from seeds so small that there are about 400,000 per oz. **Tobacco seed oil** has an iodine value of 140 to 146, and is a valuable drying oil, but the production is low because the seed heads are topped in cultivation and seeds are developed only on the sucker growths. **Tobacco sauce,** used for flavoring chewing and smoking tobaccos, contains up to 10% nicotine, but since the nicotine is not desired in the flavoring it is usually extracted for industrial use. Nicotine can be oxidized easily to **nicotinic acid** and to **nicotinonitrile,** both of which are important as antipellagra vitamins. Most of the nicotine used for insecticide is marketed as **nicotine sulfate** in water solution containing 40% nicotine. It is used as a sheep dip and as a contact insecticide. **Tobacco dust** is used for the control of plant lice. **Anabasine,** obtained in Russia from the Asiatic shrub *Anabasis aphylla,* has the same chemical composition as nicotine and is an isomer of nicotine. It is marketed in the form of a solution of the sulfate as an insecticide. It can also be obtained from *N. glauca,* a wild tree tobacco native to Mexico and southeastern United States, or is made synthetically under the name of **neonicotine.**

TOLU BALSAM. A yellowish-brown semisolid gum with a pleasant aromatic odor and taste, obtained from the tree *Myroxylon balsamum,* or *Toluifera balsamum,* of Venezuela, Colombia, and Peru. It is used in medicine, chiefly in cough syrups, and also as a fixative in perfumes. **Balsam of Peru,** or **black balsam,** is a reddish-brown viscous aromatic liquid from bark of the tall tree *M. pereirae* of El Salvador. It is used in cough medicines and skin ointments, as an extender for vanilla, and as a fixative in perfumes. Some white-colored balsam is also obtained from the fruit of the tree. **Peru balsam** contains benzyl benzoate, benzyl cinnamate, and some vanillin.

TOLUOL. Also called **toluene, methyl benzene,** and **methyl benzol.** A liquid of the composition $C_6H_5CH_3$, resembling benzene but with a distinctive odor. It is obtained as a by-product from coke ovens and from coal tar. It occurs also in petroleum, with from 0.20 to 0.70% in Texas crude oil, which is not sufficient to extract. But toluol may be produced by dehydrogenation of petroleum fractions. It is used as a solvent, and for making explosives, dyestuffs, and many chemicals, and in aviation gasoline to improve the octane rating. Industrially pure toluol from coal tar distills off between 108.6 and 112.6°C, and is a water-white liquid with a specific gravity of 0.864 to 0.874, flash point 35 to 40°F, and freezing point about −95°C. The fumes are poisonous. **Monochloro toluene,** used as a solvent for rubber and synthetic resins, is a colorless liquid of the composition $CH_3C_6H_4Cl$, boiling at about 160°C and freezing at −45°C. **T oil** is a sulfur toluene condensation product made under a British patent and used as a plasticizer for chlorinated rubber. **Notol No. 1,** of the Neville Co., is a coal-tar hydrocarbon high in aromatics used as a substitute for toluol as a lacquer solvent. The specific gravity is 0.825 and the boiling point between 177 and 280°F. **Tollac,** of the same company, is another hydrocarbon substitute for toluol. **Methyl cyclohexane,** $C_6H_{11}CH_3$, is a water-white liquid with a distilling range of 100 to 103°C, produced by hydrogenating toluol. It is used as a solvent for oils, fats, waxes, and rubbers. **Methyl cyclohexanol,** $C_6H_{10}CH_3OH$, another toluol derivative, is used as a cellulose ester solvent and as an antioxidant in lubricants. It is a straw-colored viscous liquid distilling between 155 and 180°C. **Polyvinyl toluene** is a methyl form of styrene. It is polymerized with terphenyl stilbene to form plastic scintillators to count radiation isotopes.

TONKA BEAN. Called in northeastern Brazil **cumarú bean.** The kernel of the pit of the fruit of the **sarrapia tree,** *Dipteryx odorata* or *Coumarouna odorata,* of northern South America, used for the production of **coumarin** for flavoring and scenting. It has an aroma resembling vanilla. The trees often reach a height of 100 ft, and begin to bear in 3 years. The fruit is like a mahogany-colored plum, but with a fibrous pulp. The pits, or nuts, contain a single shiny black seed 1 in. or longer. The chief production is in Venezuela, Brazil, Colombia, Trinidad, and the Guianas. The tonka bean from the tree *D. oleifera* of Central America has an unpleasant odor. Before shipping, the beans are soaked in rum or alcohol to crystallize the coumarin. The ground beans are again soaked in rum, and the aromatic liquid is used to spray on cigarette tobacco. The coumarin extract is also used as a perfume or flavor in soaps, liqueurs, and confectionery. The essential oil produced from the seed is called **cumarú oil.** A substitute for tonka bean is **deer's-tongue leaf,** which is the long leaf of the herb *Trilisa odoratissima* growing wild on the edges of swamps from Carolina to Florida.   The leaf has a strong odor of coumarin when dry, and contains coumarin.   It is used in cigarette manufacture, in flavoring, and to produce synthetic vanilla.

TOOL STEEL. A high-carbon steel used for making tools.   It has the property of becoming extremely hard by quenching from a temperature of 1400 to 1800°F.   It can then be drawn to any degree of hardness by heating at lower temperatures.   The hardening properties depend upon the formation of hard reversible carbides.   The early tool steels were chance combinations in which the carbon of the fuel combined with the iron, molybdenum, or other contained elements.   One of the earliest recorded tool steels was the ancient **Chalybeate steel,** originally referring to steel from the Chalybes in Pontus.   The unqualified term tool steel does not usually include special alloy steels containing nickel, manganese, and other metals, nor high-speed steels.   However, tool steel for special purposes may contain many other elements besides carbon.   The possibilities of percentage combinations of vanadium, nickel, manganese, chromium, silicon, tungsten, and other elements in alloy tool steels are infinite; and as there are hundreds of trade-named steels on the market, the name **carbon tool steel** is used to designate tool steel containing only carbon, and with other elements below perceptible amounts.   Tool steels may be divided into two general classes, water-hardening and oil-hardening.   The **water-hardened steels,** which cool quickly in the quenching, have a hard exterior with a tough shock-resistant core.   This hard case wears off with repeated grinding.   The **oil-hardened steels** cool more slowly, thus hardening evenly throughout the metal.   In general, the oil-hardening steels contain significant amounts of manganese, chromium, tungsten, vanadium, or molybdenum.   **Desegatized steels** are tool steels that have been given special treatment to produce an even dispersion of free carbides, eliminating danger of a brittle central mass.

Tool steel may contain from 0.65 to 1.50% carbon, the lower-carbon grades, up to 0.90 carbon, being used for punches, hammers, chisels, and other tools requiring some degree of elasticity, and the high-carbon grades are used for dies, drills, and edge tools.   Files, saws, and engraving tools may contain up to 1.60% carbon.   The manganese content is 0.20 to 0.30.   **Razor steel** was steel with 1.5% carbon, but razors are now usually made of alloy steels.   **Orthopedic steel** of the Crucible Steel Co. contains 0.95% carbon, and the annealed steel has a tensile strength of 145,000 psi with elongation of 12%.   Beyond 1% carbon, there is an excess of carbon and the steels become very brittle when hardened.   Theoretically, the maximum point of solution of the Fe_3C in a plain carbon steel is at 0.85% carbon.   When other elements are present, other carbides are formed, giving greater hardness and strength above this point.   The ideal maximums of phosphorus and sulfur in a tool steel are 0.025%, with silicon at 0.20 and manganese at 0.25, but in special steels the silicon and manganese are increased. Some water-hardening carbon tool steels have higher content of silicon to give wear resistance for dies, liners, and bushings. The silicon also adds fatigue resistance. **Graph-Sil steel,** of the Timken Steel & Tube Co., has 1.5% carbon, 0.85 to 0.95 silicon, and 0.40 max manganese.

The lower temperature ranges are used for hardening high-carbon steels and thin pieces. Some steelmakers grade carbon steels by divisions as low as 5 points of carbon. **Pompton tool steel,** of the Allegheny Ludlum Steel Co., has 19 grades from 0.50 to 1.45% carbon. A free-machining steel of the same company, **Oilgraph EZ,** contains 1.15% silicon, 0.80 manganese, 0.20 chromium, 0.25 molybdenum, 0.10 sulfur, with 1.45 carbon and 0.30 graphite. The graphite, evenly dispersed in the steel, makes easy machining, gives resistance to galling, and improves the finish. Modern carbon tool steels for ordinary water hardening, with or without residual vanadium, develop remarkable physical properties. Ryerson **VD die steel,** as quenched, has a hardness of 725 Brinell, or 96 Scleroscope. **Granada steel,** of the Crucible Steel Co., is a general-purpose water-hardening tool steel containing 1% carbon, 0.30 manganese, and 0.25 silicon.

Oil-hardening tool steels usually contain about 1% manganese, but mild-alloy tool steels may contain less, with other elements. **CM** and **CMM tap steels,** of the Colonial Steel Co., are oil-hardening, keen-edge steels; CM contains 0.50% chromium, 0.60 manganese, and 1.20 carbon; CMM contains 0.50% chromium, 0.85 manganese, 0.60 molybdenum, and 1.20 carbon. These steels have high torsional strength. Additions of small amounts of molybdenum with higher silicon give oil-hardening steels of high strength and toughness. **Halcomb SS steel,** of the Crucible Steel Co., is such a steel for drills, taps, and broaches. It contains 1.20% chromium, 0.30 molybdenum, 0.35 manganese, and 1 carbon. **Versatool,** of the same company, is an intermediate steel that has high hardness and wear resistance and maintains its properties at temperatures close to those of high-speed steel. It contains 4.25% chromium, 2.5 molybdenum, 1.15 vanadium, 0.3 tungsten, 2 silicon, 0.3 manganese, and 1 carbon. It is used for shears and cutting dies. **Ketos steel** is a general-purpose steel containing 0.90% carbon, 1.35 manganese, 0.35 silicon, 0.50 chromium, and 0.50 tungsten. **BTR steel,** of Bethlehem Steel, is a general-purpose oil-hardening die and tool steel that is nondeforming and wear-resistant. It contains 1.20% manganese, 0.50 tungsten, 0.50 chromium, 0.20 vanadium, and 0.90 carbon.

Tool steel comes regularly in round, square, and octagon bars, and in flats, but drawn shapes are also available. Tool steels require more care in forging than low-carbon machinery steels, and they are more difficult to machine.   The quality of the steel is dependent upon the method of melting, rolling, and forging as well as upon the composition.   The smallest possible grain size, and freedom from nonmetallic inclusions, are the qualities sought.   **A.S.V. steel,** of Firth-Sterling Steel, is made by a patented winged ingot form of casting in order to eliminate any porosity in the center.   **Mar-aged steel** is a name given by International Nickel to high-alloy steels with high strength and ductility developed by a martensitic aging treatment.   Such a steel with 18% nickel, 7 cobalt, 5 molybdenum, 0.5 titanium, and 0.05 max carbon is resistant to corrosion cracking under stress and has a tensile strength of 400,000 psi and yield strength of 250,000 psi.   It is easily cold-formed and welded.   This composition can be varied to give different grades with differing properties.

Ceramicast steel, of the Lebanon Steel Foundry, is accurately cast steel requiring no machining.   The ceramic mold is made by pouring a liquid mixture of hydrolyzed ethyl silicate and sillimanite over the pattern, removing the pattern after the mixture has set, and firing to give a rigid ceramic mold.   **Carbon-vanadium tool steels** are produced in all carbon contents with about 0.20% vanadium.   They have a uniform fine grain, and constitute a class of "super" carbon tool steels.   Some steels for special purposes contain more vanadium.   **Colhead steel,** of the Vanadium Alloys Steel Co., for cold-heading dies, has 0.45% vanadium and 1 carbon.   **Vatool,** of Henry Disston & Sons, Inc., is a vanadium steel for taps.   **Shim steel** may be either carbon or stainless steel in gages as thin as 0.0015 in., with extra close tolerances.   **Micro-Shim steel,** of the American Silver Co., is low-carbon steel or stainless steel in thicknesses as low as 0.0005 in.   Tool steels are now usually refined alloy steels, and producers such as Carpenter Technology market them on a performance basis rather than by composition.

TRAGACANTH GUM.   An exudation of the shrub *Astragalus gummifer* of Asia Minor and Persia, used in adhesives or for mucilage, for leather dressing, for textile printing, and as an emulsifying agent.   To obtain the gum a small incision is made at the base of the shrub, from which the juice exudes and solidifies into an alteration product, not merely the dried juice.   The gum derived from the first day's incision, known as **fiori,** is the best quality, and is in clear fine ribbons or white flakes.   The second incision produces a yellow gum known as **biondo.**   The third incision produces the poorest quality, a dark gum known as **sari.**   Rainy weather during the incision period may cause a still inferior product.   Tragacanth is insoluble in alcohol but is soluble in alkalies and swells in water.   **Karaya gum** from southern Asia is from various species of *Sterculia* trees, especially *S. urens,* of India.   It is also known as **Indian gum, Indian hog gum,** and **hog tragacanth.**   The sticky gum is dried, and the chunks are broken and the pieces sorted by color. A single chunk may have colors varying from clear white to dark amber and black. The color is caused by tannin or other impurities. The No. 3 grade, the lowest, has up to 3% insoluble impurities. The gum is marketed in flakes and as a white, odorless, 150-mesh powder. The chief constituent is galactan. In general, the gum is more acid than tragacanth and is likely to form lumpy gels unless finely ground. It is widely used as a thickening and suspending agent for foodstuffs, drugs, cosmetics, adhesives, and for textile finishes.

The granules of **water-soluble gums,** such as karaya, tragacanth, and acacia, are swelled by water and dispersed in the water in microscopic particles to form cells or filamentlike structures which hold the water like a sponge and will not settle out. This type of colloidal dispersion is called a **hydrasol,** and when thick and viscous is called a **gel.** From 2 to 3% of karaya or other gum will form a gel in water. These gums will gel in cold water, while gelatin requires hot water for dissolving. In a gel there is continuous structure with molecules forming a network, while in a **sol** the particles are in separate suspension and a sol is merely a dispersion. Some dispersions, such as albumen, cross-link with heat; some, like guar gum, cross-link with alkalies; some, like pectin, link with sugar and an acid. Gums with weak surface forces form weak gels which are **pastes** or mucilage, and a high concentration is needed to produce a solid. Karaya has great swelling power, and is used in medicine as a bulk laxative. **Ghatti gum,** from the abundant tree, *Anogeissus latifolia* of India, is entirely soluble in water to form a viscous mucilage. It is twice as effective as gum arabic as an emulsifier, but is less adhesive. It comes in colorless to pale-yellow tears of vitreous fracture, called also Indian gum, and is used in India for textile finishing. **Aqualized gum,** of Glyco Products Co., Inc., is tragacanth or karaya chemically treated to give more rapid solubility. Water-soluble gums are also produced synthetically. **Polyox gum,** of the Union Carbide Chemicals Co., is a polymer of polyethylene oxide containing carboxylic groups giving water solubility when the pH is above 4.0. In paper coating with ammonia the ammonia evaporates to leave a water-insoluble, grease-resistant film that is heat-sealing. It is also used in latex paints and in cosmetics.

Another water-soluble gum which forms a true gel with a continuous branched-chain molecular network is **okra gum,** produced by Morningstar-Paisley, Inc., as a 200-mesh tan powder. It is edible, and is used for thickening and stabilizing foods and pharmaceuticals. It is also used in plating baths for brightening nickel, silver, and cadmium plates. It is extracted from the pods of the **okra,** *Hibiscus esculentus,* a plant of the cotton family. In the Southern states the pods, called **gumbo,** are used in soups. The refined gum, after extraction of the oils and sugars, contains

40.4% carbon, 6.1 hydrogen, and 2.1 nitrogen, with the balance insoluble cellulose.

TRIPOLI. A name given to finely granulated, white, porous, siliceous rock, used as an abrasive and as a filler. True tripoli is an infusorial diatomaceous earth known as **tripolite,** and is a variety of opal, or **opaline silica.** In the abrasive industry it is called **soft silica.** It is quarried in Missouri, Illinois, eastern Tennessee, and Georgia. Pennsylvania rottenstone is not tripoli, although it is often classed with it. The material marketed for oil-well drilling mud by the Corona Products, Inc., under the name of **Opalite,** is an amorphous silica. The Missouri tripoli ranges in color from white to reddish, and the crude rock has a porosity of 45%, and contains 30% or more of moisture. It is air-dried and then crushed and furnace-dried. Tripoli is used in massive form for the manufacture of filter stones for filtering small supplies of water. Missouri tripoli is also used for the manufacture of foundry parting. Tripoli finely ground, free from iron oxide, is used as a paint filler and in rubber. The grade of tripoli known as O. G. (once ground) is used for buffing composition, D. G. (double ground) for foundry partings, and the air-float product for metal polishes. Tripoli grains are soft, porous, and free from sharp cutting faces, and give a fine polishing effect. It is the most commonly used polishing agent. The word **silex,** which is an old name for silica, and is also used to designate the pulverized flint from Belgium, is sometimes applied to finely ground white tripoli employed as an inert filler for paints. Much Illinois fine-grained tripoli is used for paint, and for this purpose should be free from iron oxide. **Rottenstone** is a soft, friable, earthy stone of light-gray to olive color, used as an abrasive for metal and wood finishing. It resembles Missouri tripoli, and is derived from the weathering of siliceous-argillaceous limestone, with generally from 80 to 85% alumina, 4 to 15 silica, and 5 to 10 iron oxides. Rottenstone was largely imported from England, but a variety is found in Pennsylvania. It is finely ground and marketed either as a powder or molded into bricks. The latter form is used with oil on rag-wheel polishing. A 250-mesh powder is used as a filler in molding compounds.

TRISODIUM PHOSPHATE. A white crystalline substance of the composition $Na_3PO_4 \cdot 12H_2O$, also known as **phosphate cleaner,** used in soaps, cleaning compounds, plating, textile processing, and boiler compounds. The commercial grade is not less than 97% pure, with total alkalinity of 16 to 19% calculated as Na_2O. The anhydrous trisodium phosphate is 2.3 times as effective as the crystalline form, but requires a longer time to dissolve. **Disodium phosphate** is a white crystalline product of the composition $Na_2HPO_4 \cdot 12H_2O$ used for weighting silk, boiler treatment, cheese making, and in cattle feeds. The medicinal, or USP, grade has only 7 molecules of water and has a different crystal structure. The commercial grade is 99.4% pure, and is readily soluble in water. **Sodium tetraphosphate,** $Na_6P_4O_{13}$, contains 39.6% Na_2O and 60.4 P_2O_5. It is the sodium salt of **tetraphosphoric acid,** and is marketed in beads that are mildly alkaline and highly soluble in water. The specific gravity is 2.55, and melting point 600°C. It is used in the textile industry as a water softener and to accelerate cleansing operations. It removes lime precipitation and sludge and saves soap. **Quadrafos,** of the American Cyanamid Co., used to replace quebracho for reducing the viscosity of oil-well drilling mud, is sodium tetraphosphate, containing 63.5% of P_2O_5. It makes the calcium and magnesium compounds inactive, and 0.06% of the material controls 16.1% of water in reducing viscosity. It also gives smooth flow with minimum water in paper coating and textile printing. **Metafos,** of the same company, has a higher percentage of P_2O_5, 67%, and a lower pH, for use in textile printing where low alkalinity is needed. **Sodium pyrophosphate,** $Na_4P_2O_7$, is added to soap powders to increase the detergent effect and the lathering. It is also used in oil-drilling mud. The crystalline form, $Na_4P_2O_7 \cdot 10H_2O$, is very soluble in water and is noncaking, and is used in household cleaning compounds. **Sodium tripolyphosphate,** $Na_5P_3O_{10}$, is a water-soluble, white powder used as a detergent, a water softener, and a deflocculating agent in portland cement to govern the viscosity of the shale slurry without excessive use of water. Large quantities of these phosphates are used in the processing of chemicals, textiles, and paper; and since they are toxic containments of ground and surface waters, mill wastes must be deactivated before discharge.

TULIPWOOD. Also called **yellow poplar, whitewood,** and **canary whitewood.** The wood of the tree *Liriodendron tulipifera* of Canada and the eastern United States. The tree grows to a height of 250 ft and to diameters of more than 10 ft. It is used for furniture, veneer, millwork, toys, woodenware, boxes, crates, and pulpwood. Owing to its close texture and even coefficient of expansion it has been used for expansion blocks in humidity regulators. It is yellowish, soft, and durable. It weighs about 30 lb per cu ft. The lumber may be mixed with **cucumber magnolia,** *Magnolia acuminata,* and **evergreen magnolia,** *M. grandifolia,* but **magnolia woods** are lighter in color.

TUNG OIL. A drying oil which has almost double the rapidity of linseed oil. It is used for enamels and varnishes, in brake linings, plastic compounds, and linoleum, and for making pigment for India ink. Tung oil is pressed from the seeds of the *Aleurites montana* and *A. fordii.* The names **wood oil** or **China wood oil** are loosely and erroneously used to designate tung oils, but true wood oil is an oleoresin from the **Keruing**

tree of Malaya used for waterproofing and calking boats, while tung oil is never from the wood. The oil has a powerful purgative action, and the Chinese word tung means stomach. The **Chinese tung oil** is from the nuts of the tree *A. montana,* the China wood oil tree, and the *A. fordii.* The latter tree is more hardy than the *A. montana* which requires a hot climate. The American tung oil is from the nuts of the tree *A. fordii* of the Gulf states which gives an annual production of about 30 lb of oil per tree. The tree grows to a height of 25 ft, and bears for 5 years. The seeds, or nuts, contain 50 to 55% oil. This tree is also grown in South Africa and in Argentina.

The color of tung oil varies from golden yellow to dark brown according to the degree of heat used in extraction. It has a pungent odor resembling that of bacon fat. A good grade of raw tung oil should have a specific gravity between 0.943 and 0.940, a saponification value of 190, and an iodine value of 163. The oil contains about 72% **eleostearic acid,** which has a very high iodine value, 274, and gives to the oil a greater drying power than is indicated by the iodine value of the oil itself. The oil has the property of drying throughout at a uniform rate instead of forming a skin as linseed oil does, but it dries flat instead of glossy like linseed oil and is inclined to produce a wrinkled surface. It is mixed with rosin, since rosin has great affinity for it, and the two together are suitable for gloss varnishes. The oil from *A. montana,* or **mu oil,** has a higher percentage of eleostearic acid than that from *A. fordii.* The **Japanese tung oil** is from the nuts of the larger tree *A. cordata.* The oil is superior to Chinese tung oil and is seldom exported. It does not gelatinize like Chinese tung oil when heated. It is used in Japan for varnishes, waterproofing paper, and soaps. The saponification value is 193 to 195, iodine No. 149 to 159, and specific gravity 0.934 to 0.940. The kernels of the nuts yield about 40% oil. The tree is grown also in Brazil and thrives in hot climates. **Candlenut oil** is from the seed nuts of the *A. moluccana* of Oceania and southern Asia. It received its name from the fact that the Polynesians used the nuts as candles to light their houses. The oil is variously known as **kukui, kekune,** and **lumbang,** and as an artist's paint oil is called **walnut oil** or **artist's oil.** The nut resembles the walnut but has a thicker shell. The oil has a specific gravity of 0.923, iodine value 165, and is between linseed and soybean oil in properties. It is high in linoleic and linolenic acids. The variety known as soft lumbang oil, or **bagilumbang oil,** from the tree *A. trisperma* of the Philippines, resembles tung oil and is high in eleostearic acid. The chief production of lumbang oil is in the Fiji Islands.

The **safflower,** *Carthamus tinctorius,* is grown in California, France, and India, and in the latter country it is grown on a large scale for seeds which yield up to 35% of the clear, yellowish **safflower oil** used in paints, leather dressings, and for foods.   The oil has a high content, 73%, of linoleic acid, the highest of essential poly-unsaturated acids of any vegetable food oil.   It is odorless, with a bland taste.   **Safflower 22,** of the Pacific Vegetable Oil Corp., is a conjugated paint oil made by isomerizing safflower oil.   It has a rapid drying rate, color retention, and an ability to produce wrinkled finishes by adjustment of the amount of drier.   It can thus replace tung oil.   It takes up maleic anhydride readily, and is used for making modified alkyd finishes.   **Wecoline SF,** of Drew Chemical, is a concentrate of safflower fatty acids with 67.3% linoleic and only 0.2 linolenic acid, for compounding in coatings.   **Saff,** of Abbott Laboratories, is an emulsion of safflower oil used as a drug to lower blood cholesterol.   The heads of the plant are dried and used as food colors, for dyeing textiles, and for cosmetic rouge.

TUNGSTEN.   A heavy white metal with a specific gravity of 19.6, weighing 0.697 lb per cu in., and melting at 6152°F.   It is widely distributed in small quantities in nature, and is about half as abundant as copper, but is mostly obtained from scheelite, wolframite, and a few other ores.   The metal is usually obtained as a powder by reduction of the oxide.   It was first produced in 1783, but, because of its refractory nature, was not used alone until made into electric-lamp filaments from **tungsten paste** in 1904. Tungsten has a wide usage for alloy steels, magnets, heavy metals, electric contacts, rocket nozzles, and electronic applications.   Tungsten resists oxidation at very high temperatures, and it is not attacked by nitric, hydrofluoric, or sulfuric acid solutions.   Flame-sprayed coatings are used for nozzles and other parts subject to heat erosion.

Tungsten is usually added to iron and steel in the form of **ferrotungsten,** made by electric-furnace reduction of the oxide with iron or by reducing tungsten ores with carbon and silicon.   Standard grades with 75 to 85% tungsten have melting points from 3200 to 3450°F.   **Tungsten powder** is usually in sizes from 200 to 325 mesh, and may be had in a purity of 99.9%.   Parts, rods, and sheet are made by powder metallurgy, and rolling and forging are done at high temperature.   The rolled metal may have a tensile strength as high as 500,000 psi and hardness of Brinell 290, and drawn wire may have a tensile strength to 590,000 psi.   The tungsten powder of Kennametal, Inc., for use in spray coatings for radiation shielding has a particle size less than 40 microns and density of 165 gr per cu in. The needle-shaped powders of General Electric Co. for powder metallurgy have particle diameters of 4.8 to 5.8 microns.   The **tungsten wire** of Universal-Cyclops Steel Corp. for spark plug and electronic use is made by powder metallurgy swaging.   It has uniform density and comes in diameters from 0.02 to 0.50 in.   Tungsten wire as fine as 0.00018 in., for electronic use, has 950 miles of wire per pound.   **Tungsten whiskers,** which are extremely fine fibers, are used in copper alloys to add strength. Copper wire which normally has a tensile strength of 30,000 psi will have a strength of 120,000 psi when 35% of tungsten whiskers are added. **Tungsten yarns** of Union Carbide Corp. are as small in diameter as 0.0005 in. and are made up of fine fibers of the metal. The yarns are flexible and can be woven into fabrics. Continuous **tungsten filaments,** usually of 10 to 15 microns diameter, are used for reinforcement in metal, ceramic, and plastic structural composites. Finer filaments of tungsten are used as cores in **boron filaments.**

The metal is now also produced as arc-fused grown crystals, usually no larger than $3/8$ in. diameter and 10 in. long, and working into rod, sheet, strip, and wire. **Tungsten crystals,** 99.9975% pure, are produced by Linde and Westinghouse. Tungsten crystals are ductile even at very low temperatures, and wire as fine as 0.003 in. and strip as thin as 0.005 in. can be cold-drawn and cold-rolled from the crystal. The crystal metal has nearly zero porosity and its electrical and heat conductivity are higher than ordinary tungsten. The normal electrical conductivity is about 33% that of copper, but that of the crystal tungsten is 15% higher. In microscopy the molecules of tungsten appear as body-centered cubes, but in the pure metal the atoms normally bond uniformly in 6 directions forming a double lattice so that each grain forms a true single crystal. At elevated temperatures tungsten forms many compounds in chemicals and alloys. The **tungsten-aluminum alloy** of Du Pont is a chemical compound and is made by reducing tungsten hexachloride with molten aluminum.

Tungsten retains a tensile strength of about 50,000 psi at 2500°F, but because of its great weight is normally used in aircraft or missile parts only as coatings, usually sprayed on. It is also used for X-ray and gamma-ray shielding. Electroplates of tungsten or tungsten alloys give surface hardnesses to Vickers 700 or above. **Cobalt-tungsten alloy,** with 50% tungsten, gives a plate that retains a high hardness at red heat. **Tungsten RhC,** of Cleveland Refractory Metals, is a **tungsten-rhenium carbide alloy** containing 4% rhenium carbide. It is used for parts requiring high strength and hardness at high temperatures. The alloy retains a tensile strength of 75,000 psi at 3500°F. **Ammonium metatungstate,** used for electroplating, is a white powder of the composition $(NH_4)_6H_2W_{12}O_{40}$. It is readily soluble in water and gives solutions of 50% tungsten content. **Tungsten hexafluoride** is used for producing tungsten coatings by vapor deposition. At a temperature of 900°F the gas mixed with hydrogen deposits a tungsten plate. **Tungsten hexachloride,** WCl_6, is also used for depositing **tungsten coatings** at a temperature of 900°C in a hydrogen atmosphere. Smooth, dense **tungsten platings** can be deposited from **tungsten carbonyl,** $W(CO)_6$, at a temperature of 150°C. The carbonyl is made by reacting the hexachloride with carbon monoxide.

TUNGSTEN CARBIDE. An iron-gray powder of minute cubical crystals with a Mohs hardness above 9.5 and a melting point of about 5400°F. It is produced by reacting a hydrocarbon vapor with tungsten at high temperature. The composition is WC, but at high heat it may decompose into W_2C and carbon, and the carbide may be a mixture of the two forms. Other forms may also be produced, W_3C and W_3C_4. Tungsten carbide is used chiefly for cutting tool bits and for heat- and erosion-resistant parts and coatings.

Briquetting of tungsten carbide into usable form was first patented in Germany and produced by the Krupp Works under the name of **Widia metal.** It is made by diffusing powdered cobalt through the finely divided carbide under hydraulic pressure, and then sintering in an inert atmosphere at about 1500°C. The briquetted material is then ground to shape, and the pieces are brazed to tools. They will withstand cutting speeds from 3 to 10 times those of high-speed steel, and will turn manganese steel with a hardness of 550 Brinell, but are not shock-resistant. Pressed and sintered parts usually contain 3 to 20% cobalt binder, but nickel may also be used as a binder. The compressive strengths may be as high as 700,-000 psi with rupture strengths to 200,000 or higher.

One of the earliest of the American bonded tungsten carbides was **Carboloy,** of the General Electric Co., used for cutting tools, gages, drawing dies, and wear parts. The sintered materials are now sold under many trade names such as **Dimondite, Firthite,** and **Firthaloy,** of the Firth-Sterling Steel Co., **Armide,** of the Armstrong Bros. Tool Co., **Wilcoloy,** of the H. A. Wilson Co., and **Borium** and **Borod,** of the Stoody Co. But the carbides are now often mixed carbides. **Carboloy 608** contains 83% chromium carbide, 2% tungsten carbide, and 15% nickel binder. It is lighter in weight than tungsten carbide, is nonmagnetic, and has a hardness to Rockwell A93. It is used for wear-resistant parts, and resists oxidation to 2000°F. Titanium carbide is more fragile, but may be mixed with tungsten carbide to add hardness for dies. **Cutanit,** of Firth-Sterling, is such a mixture. **Kennametal K601,** of Kennametal, Inc., for seal rings and wear parts, is a mixture of tantalum and tungsten carbides without a binder. It has a compressive strength of 675,000 psi, rupture strength of 100,000 psi, and Rockwell hardness A94. **Kennametal K501** is tungsten carbide with a platinum binder for parts subject to severe heat erosion. **Strauss metal,** of the Allegheny Ludlum Steel Co., is tungsten carbide. **Tungsten carbide LW-1,** of the Linde Co., is tungsten carbide with about 6% cobalt binder used for flame-coating metal parts to give high-temperature wear resistance. Deposited coatings have a Vickers hardness to 1450, and resist oxidation at 1000°F. **Tungsten carbide LW-1N,** with 15% cobalt binder, has a much higher rupture strength, but the hardness is reduced to 1150. **Metco 35C** is a fine powder of tungsten carbide and cobalt for flame spraying to produce a hard wear-resistant coating of carbide in a matrix of cobalt.

TUNGSTEN STEEL. Any steel containing tungsten as the alloying element imparting the chief characteristics to the steel.   It is one of the oldest of the alloying elements in steel, the celebrated ancient Eastern sword steels having had tungsten in them.   Tungsten increases the hardness of steel, gives it the property of red hardness, stabilizing the hard carbides at high temperatures.   It also widens the hardening range of steel, and gives deep hardening.   Very small quantities serve to produce a fine grain and raise the yield point.   The tungsten forms a very hard carbide and an iron tungstite, and the strength of the steel is also increased, but it is brittle when the tungsten content is high.   When large percentages of tungsten are used in steel, they must be supplemented by other carbide-forming elements.   Tungsten steels, except the low-tungsten chromium-tungsten steels, are not suitable for construction, but they are widely used for cutting tools, because the tungsten forms hard abrasion-resistant particles in high-carbon steels.   Tungsten also increases the acid resistance and corrosion resistance of steels.   The alloys are difficult to forge, and cannot be readily welded when the tungsten exceeds 2%.   Standard **SAE tungsten steels,** SAE 71360 and SAE 71660, contain 12 to 15 and 15 to 18% tungsten, respectively, with 3 to 4 chromium and 0.50 to 0.70 carbon. **SAE steel 7260** contains 1.5 to 2% tungsten and 0.50 to 1 chromium.

When the tungsten content is high, particularly when the steel contains manganese also, the steel can be hardened by air cooling.   These alloy steels have a close, uniform texture, and tools made from them will keep an edge even when hot.   In annealing tungsten steels the hard stable carbide WC may be formed; to prevent this, chromium is used as an inhibitor.   A low tungsten steel for taps and cutters contains 1.5 to 2% tungsten, 1 to 1.3 carbon, with a small amount of chromium and vanadium. **Maxtack steel,** of A. Milne & Co., for tack and nail dies, has 10% tungsten, 2 chromium, 2.5 manganese, 1 silicon, and 2.25 carbon.   It is self-hardening.   Steels with 2 to 3% tungsten have high wear resistance and impact resistance.   They are used for cold-drawing dies, air hammers, and general tools.   **Graph-Tung,** of the Timken Steel & Tube Co., has 2.6 to 3% tungsten, 0.50 molybdenum, 0.70 silicon, and 1.5 carbon. **O. K. steel** of William Jessop & Sons, used for chisels and punches, has 2% tungsten with only 0.40 carbon.   It is hard but very shock-resisting. A chisel steel, **J-S steel,** of Firth Sterling, Inc., has 2.25% tungsten, 1.4 chromium, 0.50 carbon, and a trace of vanadium.   It is also used for cutters, punches, and shear blades for hot and cold work.   It will retain a good cutting edge.   **Wizard steel,** of the Ziv Steel & Wire Co., used for pneumatic tools, riveter dies, and swaging dies, has 1% tungsten, 1 chromium, 0.35 carbon, and a small amount of molybdenum.   At a hardness of 55 Rockwell it has great toughness and resistance to shock.   **High-Wear 64 steel,** of Carpenter Steel, which gives abrasion resistance and long life in blanking and drawing dies and in molds for compacting metals, contains 4% tungsten, 1 molybdenum, 0.90 chromium, 0.25 silicon, and 1.5 carbon.   It is air-hardened at 1550°F and is not intended for hot-work tools. **LT steel,** of Firth Sterling, Inc., for hot-forging dies, contains 9.5% tungsten, 3.5 chromium, 0.5 vanadium, and 0.33 carbon.   It is hardened in air or oil from 2150°F and tempered at 1100°F to give a hardness of Rockwell C52.   **XDL steel** of the same company, for severe hot work, has 14% tungsten, 3.4 chromium, 0.5 vanadium, and 0.38 carbon.   It is tempered to just above the maximum service heat, 1000°F giving a hardness of Rockwell C54, and 1300°F giving a hardness of C42.

TURPENTINE.   Also called in the paint industry **oil of turpentine.**   An oil obtained by steam distillation of the oleoresin which exudes when various conifer trees are cut.   Longleaf pine and slash pine are the main sources.   It also includes oils obtained by distillation and solvent extraction from stumpwood and waste wood.   Longleaf sapwood contains about 2% oleoresin, heartwood 7 to 10%, and stumpwood 25%.   Most oleoresin is obtained from the sapwood of living trees, but it is not the sap of the tree.   Heartwood resin is obtained only when the cut wood is treated with solvents.   The oleoresin yields about 20% oil of turpentine and 80 rosin; both together are known as **naval stores.**

Wood turpentine, called in the paint industry **spirits of turpentine,** is obtained from waste wood, chips, or sawdust by steam extraction or by destructive distillation.   Wood turpentine forms more than 10% of all American commercial turpentines.   Wood turpentine has a peculiar characteristic sawmill odor, and the residue of distillation has a camphorlike odor different from gum turpentine.   It differs very little in composition, however, from the true turpentine.   Steam-distilled wood turpentine contains about 90% terpenes, of which 80% is alpha pinene and 10% is a mixture of beta pinene and camphene.   Some wood turpentine is produced as a by-product in the manufacture of cellulose.   **Sulfate turpentine** is a by-product in the making of wood pulp.   It varies in composition as the less stable beta pinene is affected by the pulping process, and it is used largely in chemical manufacture.   By hydrogenation it produces cymene from which **dimethyl styrene** is made.   This material can be copolymerized to produce vinyl resins.

Turpentine varies in composition according to the species of pine from which it is obtained.   It is produced chiefly in the United States, France, and Spain.   The turpentine of India comes from the **chir pine,** *Pinus* *longifolia,* of the southern slopes of the Himalayas, also valued for lumber, and the **khasia pine,** *P. khasya.* The gum of the chir pine is different from American gum, and the turpentine, unless carefully distilled, is slower-drying and greasy. French and Spanish turpentine, or **Bordeaux turpentine,** is from the **maritime pine,** *P. pinaster,* which is the chief source, and from **Aleppo pine,** *P. halepensis,* and **Corsican pine,** *P. laricia.* In Portugal, the **stone pine,** *P. pinea,* is the source. The French maritime pine is also grown on plantations in Australia. Aleppo pine of Greece was the source of the naval stores of the ancients. **Venetian turpentine,** or **Venice turpentine,** is from the Corsican pine or European larch. It produces a harder film than American turpentine. Artificial Venice turpentine is made by mixing rosin with turpentine. European pines do not give as high a yield as American longleaf and slash pines.

American turpentine oil boils at 154°C, and the specific gravity is 0.860. It is a valuable drying oil for paints and varnishes, owing to its property of rapid absorption of oxygen from the atmosphere and transferring it to the linseed or other drying oil, leaving a tough and durable film of paint. Turpentine is also used in the manufacture of artificial camphor and rubber, and in linoleum, soap, and ink. **Gum thus,** used in artists' oil paints, is thickened turpentine, although gum thus was originally made from olibanum. Turpentine is often adulterated with other oils of the pine or with petroleum products, and the various states have laws regulating its adulteration for paint use.

The **pinene** in European turpentine is levorotatory while that in the American is dextro. **Pinonic acid** is acetyl dimethyl cyclobutane acetic acid. It is produced by oxidation of the pinene, and is a white powder used as a cross-linking agent for making heat-stable plastics.

Terpene alcohol, or **methylol pinene,** $C_{11}H_{17}OH$, is produced by condensing the beta pinene of gum turpentine with formaldehyde. **Nopol,** of the Glidden Co., is terpene alcohol. It has the chemical reactions of both a primary alcohol and pinene, and is used in making many chemicals. It is a water-insoluble liquid of specific gravity 0.963, boiling at 235°C. **Terpineol** is a name for refined terpene alcohols used largely for producing essential oils and perfumes. **Piccolyte resin,** of the Pennsylvania Industrial Chemical Corp., is a terpene thermoplastic varnish resin made from turpentine. The grades have melting points from 10 to 125°C. **Myrcene** is a polyolefin with three double bonds, which can be used as a substitute for butadiene in the manufacture of synthetic rubbers, or can be reacted with maleic anhydride or dibasic acids to form synthetic resins. It is made by isomerizing the beta pinene of gum turpentine. **Camphene** is produced by isomerizing the alpha pinene of turpentine. Camphor is then produced by oxidation of camphene in acid. Camphene was also the name of a lamp oil of the early nineteenth century made from distilled turpentine and alcohol.   It gave a bright white light, but was explosive. The insecticide known as **Toxaphene,** of Hercules Inc., is made by chlorinating camphene to 68% chlorine, or to the empirical formula $C_{10}H_{20}Cl_8$. It is a yellow waxy powder with a piney odor, melting at 65 to 90°C.   It is soluble in petroleum solvents.

TURQUOISE. An opaque blue gemstone with a waxy luster.   It is a hydrous phosphate of aluminum and copper oxides.   It is found in the western United States in streaks in volcanic rocks, but most of the turquoise has come from the Kuh-i-Firouzeh, or turquoise mountain, of Iran, which is a vast deposit of brecciated porphyry, or feldspar igneous rock. The valuable stones are the deep blue.   The pale blue and green stones were called **Mecca stones** because they were sent to Mecca for sale to pilgrims.   **Bone turquoise,** or **odontolite,** used for jewelry, is fossil bone or tooth, colored by a phosphate of iron.

TYPE METAL. Any metal used for making printing type, but the name generally refers to lead-antimony-tin alloys.   The antimony has the property of expanding on cooling, and thus fills the mold and produces sharp, accurate type.   The properties required in a type metal are ability to make sharp, uniform castings, strength and hardness, fairly low melting point, narrow freezing range to facilitate rapid manufacture in type-making machines, and resistance to drossing.   A common type metal is composed of 9 parts lead to 1 antimony, but many varieties of other mixtures are also used.   The antimony content may be as high as 30%, 15 to 20% being frequent.   A common **monotype metal** has 72% lead, 18 antimony, and 10 tin.   Larger and softer types are made of other alloys, sometimes containing bismuth; the hardest small type contains 3 parts lead to 1 antimony.   A low-melting-point, soft-type metal contains 22% bismuth, 50 lead, and 28 antimony.   It will melt at about 310°F.   Copper, up to 2%, is sometimes added to type metal to increase the hardness, but is not ordinarily used in metals employed in rapid-acting type machines.   Some monotype metal has about 18% antimony, 8 tin, and 0.1 copper, but standard **linotype metal** for pressure casting has 79% lead, 16 antimony, and 5 tin.   **Stereotype metal,** for sharp casting and hard-wearing qualities, is given as 80.0% lead, 13.5 antimony, 6 tin, and 0.5 copper.   **Intertype metal** has 11 to 14% antimony and 3 to 5 tin.   A typical formula for **electrotype metal** is 94% lead, 3 tin, and 3 antimony.   The Brinell hardness of machine-molded type ranges from 17 to 23, and that of stereotype metal is up to 30.   As constant remelting causes the separation of the tin and lead, and the loss of tin, or impoverishment of the metal, new metal must be constantly added to prevent deterioration of a standard metal into an inferior alloy.

UPHOLSTERY LEATHER. Very thin, finely finished leather once valued for upholstery, seats, and coverings for various articles, but now largely replaced by plastic-coated fabrics. It consists of split hides, tanned to a soft, even texture, and usually dyed in colors. **Chrome-tanned leather** is softer and stronger than ordinary leather tanned with barks or quebracho. In splitting, the full hide thickness of about $\frac{1}{4}$ in. can be split into three or four thicknesses. After splitting, the leather is retanned and "nourished" with cod oil. Hand buffs are top grains with the top of the grain snuffed off. The second split of $\frac{3}{64}$ in. is called deep buff, and has an artificial grain put on. The third split is called No. 2 split. What remains is called a slab and is unsuited for upholstery leather. Splitting with four cuts gives buffing, machine buff, No. 1 split, No. 2 split, and slab. Upholstery leather is finished by japanning, by coating with lacquer, by dyeing with aniline, or by combinations of the last with either of the first two methods. **Spanish leather,** used for upholstery, is made by tanning in strong quebracho liquor which draws the grain and gives a slightly wrinkled appearance.

URANIUM. An elementary metal, symbol U. It never occurs free in nature but is found chiefly as an oxide in the minerals pitchblende and carnotite where it is associated with radium. The metal has a specific gravity of 18.68 and atomic weight 238.2. The melting point is about 1133°C. It is hard but malleable, resembling nickel in color, but related to chromium, tungsten, and molybdenum. It is soluble in mineral acids. Uranium has three forms. The alpha phase, or orthorhombic crystal, is stable to 660°C; the beta, or tetragonal, exists from 660 to 760°C; and the gamma, or body-centered cubic, is from 760 to the melting point. The cast metal has a hardness of 80 to 100 Rockwell B, work-hardening easily. The metal is alloyed with iron to make **ferrouranium,** used to impart special properties to steel. It increases the elastic limit and the tensile strength of steels, and is also a more powerful deoxidizer than vanadium. It will denitrogenize steel and has also carbide-forming qualities. It has been used in high-speed steels in amounts of 0.05 to 5% to increase the strength and toughness, but because of its importance for atomic applications its use in steel is now limited to the by-product nonradioactive isotope uranium 238. The **green salt** used in atomic work is **uranium tetrafluoride,** UF_4. **Uranium hexafluoride,** UF_6, is a gas used to separate uranium isotopes.

Metallic uranium is used as a cathode in photoelectric tubes responsive to ultraviolet radiation. Uranium compounds, especially the uranium oxides, were used for making glazes in the ceramic industry and also for paint pigments. It produces a yellowish-green fluorescent glass, and a beautiful red with yellowish tinge is produced on pottery glazes. **Ura-**

nium dioxide, UO_2, is used in sintered forms as fuel for power reactors. It is chemically stable, and has a high melting point at about 2760°C, but a low thermal conductivity.   For fuel use the particles may be coated with about 0.001 in. of aluminum oxide.   This coating is impervious to xenon and other radioactive isotopes so that only the useful power-providing rays can escape.   These are not dangerous at a distance of about 6 in., and thus less shielding is needed.   For temperatures above 2300°F a coating of pyrolitic graphite is used.

Uranium has isotopes from 234 to 239, and **uranium 235,** with 92 protons and 143 neutrons, is the one valued for atomic work.   The purified natural metal contains only about one part U235 to about 140 parts of U238, and about 100,000 lb of uranium fluoride, UF_6, must be processed to obtain one pound of $U235F_6$.   **Uranium 238,** after the loss of three alpha particles of total mass 12, changes into **radium 226.**   The lead of old uranium minerals came from Ra226 by the loss of five alpha particles, and is **lead 206,** while the lead in thorium metals is **lead 208.   Lead 207** comes from the decay of actinium, and exists only in small quantities.

Natural uranium does not normally undergo fission because of the high probability of the neutron being captured by the U238 which then merely ejects a gamma ray and becomes U239.   But when natural uranium is not in concentrated form, but is embodied in a matrix of graphite or heavy water, it will sustain a slow chain reaction sufficient to produce heat.   In the fission of U235, neutrons are created which maintain the chain reaction and convert U238 to plutonium.   About 40 elements of the central portion of the periodic table are also produced by the fission, and eventually these products build up to a point where the reaction is no longer self-sustaining. The slow, nonexplosive disintegration of the plutonium yields neptunium. **Uranium 233** is made by neutron bombardment of thorium.   This isotope is fissionable and is used in thermonuclear reactors.

Uranium yellow, also called **yellow oxide,** is a **sodium diuranate** of the composition $Na_2U_2O_7 \cdot 6H_2O$, obtained by reduction and treatment of the mineral pitchblende.   It is used for yellow and greenish glazing enamels and for imparting an opalescent yellow to glass, which is green in reflected light.   **Uranium oxide** is an olive-green powder of the composition U_3O_8, used as a pigment.   **Uranium trioxide,** UO_3, is an orange-yellow powder also used for ceramics and pigments.   It is also called **uranic oxide.**   As a pigment in glass it produces a beautiful greenish-yellow **uranium glass.** The **Uranium pentoxide,** U_2O_5, is a black powder, and **uranous oxide,** UO_2, is used in glass to give a fine black color.   **Sodium uranate,** Na_2UO_4, is a yellow to orange powder used to produce ivory to yellow shades in pottery glazes.   The uranium oxide colors give luster and iridescence, but because of the application of the metal to atom work the uses in pigments and ceramics are now limited.

URANIUM ORES. The chief source of radium and uranium is **uraninite,** or **pitchblende,** a black massive or granular mineral with pitchlike luster. The mineral is a combination of the oxides of uranium, UO_2, UO_3, and U_3O_8, together with small amounts of lead, thorium, yttrium, cerium, helium, argon, and radium. The process of separation of radium is chemically complicated. Uraninite is found with the ores of silver and lead in central Europe. In the United States it occurs in pegmatite veins, in the mica mines of North Carolina, and in the carnotite of Utah and Colorado. The richest ores come from the Congo and from near Great Bear Lake, Canada. About 370 tons of Great Bear Lake ore produce 1 gram of radium and 7,800 lb of uranium, and also small amounts of polonium, ionium, silver, and radioactive lead. Numerous minor uranium ores occur in many areas. A low-grade ore of 0.1% U_3O_8 can be upgraded to as high as 5% by ion exchange. Black mud from the fjords off the coast of Norway contains up to 2 oz of uranium per long ton. **Tuyamunite,** found in Turkman, averages 1.3% U_3O_8, with radium, vanadium, and copper. **Autunite,** or **uranite,** is a secondary mineral from the decomposition of pitchblende. The composition is approximately $P_2O_5 \cdot 2UO_3 \cdot CaO \cdot 8H_2O$. It is produced in Utah, Portugal, and South Australia. **Torbernite,** or **copper uranite,** $Cu(UO_2)_2P_2O_8 \cdot 12H_2O$, is a radioactive mineral of specific gravity 3.22 to 3.6 and hardness 2 to 2.5. **Sengierite** is a copper-uranium mineral found in the Congo. It occurs in small green crystals. **Casolite** is a yellow earthy **lead uranium silicate,** $3(PbO \cdot UO_3 \cdot SiO_2)4H_2O$. **Pilbarite** is a **thorium lead uranate.** **Umohoite,** found in Utah, contains 48% uranium, with molybdenum, hydrogen, and oxygen. The name of the ore is a combination of the symbols of the contained elements. Uranium is also recovered chemically from phosphate rock. The phosphate waste rock of Florida contains from 0.1 to 0.4% of U_3O_8. Most uranium ores contain less than 0.3% U_3O_8. Solvent methods of extraction are used, 250 tons of sulfuric acid being used per ton of ore averaging 0.24% U_3O_8 for the leaching.

UREA. Also called **carbamide.** A colorless to white crystalline powder, $NH_2 \cdot CO \cdot NH_2$, best known for its use in plastics and fertilizers, but the chemistry of urea and the carbamates is very complex, and a very great variety of related products are produced. Urea is produced by combining ammonia and carbon dioxide, or from **cyanamide,** $NH_2 \cdot C:N$. It is a normal waste product of animal protein metabolism, and is the chief nitrogen constituent of urine. It was the first organic chemical ever synthesized commercially. It has a specific gravity of 1.323, and a melting point at 132°C.

The formula for urea may be considered as $O:C(NH_2)_2$, and thus as an amide substitution in **carbonic acid,** $O:C(OH)_2$, an acid which really exists only in its compounds, and the urea-type plastics are called **amino resins.** The **carbamates** can also be considered as deriving from **carbamic acid,** NH_2COOH, an **amino formic acid** that likewise appears only in its compounds. The carbamates have the same structural formula as the bicarbonates, so that **sodium carbamate** has an NH_2 group substituted for each OH group of the sodium bicarbonate. The **urethanes,** used for plastics and rubber, are **alkyl carbamates** made by reacting urea with an alcohol, or by reacting isocyanates with alcohols or carboxy compounds. They are white powders of the composition $NH_2COOC_2H_5$, melting at 50°C.

Isocyanates are esters of **isocyanic acid,** $H \cdot N:C:O$, which does not appear independently. The **dibasic di-isocyanate** of General Mills, Inc., is made from a 36-carbon fatty acid. It reacts with compounds containing active hydrogen. With modified polyamines it forms **polyurea resins,** and with other di-isocyanates it forms a wide range of urethanes. **Tosyl isocyanate,** of the Upjohn Co., for producing urethane resins without a catalyst is toluene sulphonyl isocyanate. The sulphonyl group increases the reactivity.

Urea is used with acid phosphates in fertilizers. It contains about 45% nitrogen and is one of the most efficient sources of nitrogen. Urea reacted with malonic esters produces **malonyl urea** which is the **barbituric acid** that forms the basis for the many soporific compounds such as **luminal, phenobarbital,** and **amytal.** The malonic esters are made from acetic acid, and **malonic acid** derived from the esters is a solid of the composition CH_2-$(COOH)_2$ which decomposes at about 160°C to yield acetic acid and carbon dioxide.

For plastics manufacture, substitution on the sulfur atom in thiourea is easier than on the oxygen in urea. **Thiourea,** $NH_2 \cdot CS \cdot NH_2$, also called **thiocarbamide, sulfourea,** and **sulfocarbamide,** is a white crystalline, water-soluble material of bitter taste, with a specific gravity of 1.405. It is used for making plastics and chemicals. On prolonged heating below its melting point, 182°C, it changes to **ammonium thiocyanate,** or **ammonium sulfocyanide,** a white, crystalline, water-soluble powder of the composition NH_4SCN, melting at 150°C. This material is also used in making plastics, as a mordant in dyeing, to produce black nickel coatings, and as a weedkiller. **Permafresh,** of Warwick Chemical Co., used to control shrinkage and give wash-and-wear properties to fabrics, is **dimethylol urea,** CO-$(NHCH_2OH)_2$, which gives clear solutions in warm water.

Urea-formaldehyde resins are made by condensing urea or thiourea with formaldehyde. They belong to the group known as **amino-aldehyde resins** made by the interaction of an amine and an aldehyde. An initial condensation product is obtained which is soluble in water, and is used in coatings and adhesives. The final condensation product is insoluble in water and is highly chemical-resistant. Molding is done with heat and pressure.

The urea resins are noted for their transparency and ability to take translucent colors.   Molded parts with cellulose filler have a specific gravity of about 1.50, tensile strength from 6,000 to 13,000 psi, elongation 15%, compressive strength to 45,000 psi, dielectric strength to 400 volts per mil, and heat distortion temperature to 280°F.   Rockwell hardness is about M118.   **Urea resins** are marketed under a wide variety of trade names. The **Uformite resins** of Rohm & Haas are water-soluble thermosetting resins for adhesives and sizing.   The **Urac resins,** of American Cyanamid, and the **Casco resins** and **Cascamite,** of the Borden Co., are urea-formaldehyde.   **Weldwood,** of the U.S. Plywood Corp., is a urea-formaldehyde adhesive.   Other urea-formaldehyde resins are **Polybond, Arodure, Plaskon,** and **Synvarite.**

Urethane resins, or **polyurethane,** are made by reacting isocyanates with carboxylic compounds, such as the reaction of hexane di-isocyanate with butylene glycol, resulting in a glycol-adipic polyester with the polymer chain lengthened and linked by the isocyanate.   The resins have high adhesive qualities, and are used in adhesives and coatings, and many of the molded products have high elasticity and are called **urethane rubbers.**   **Elastothane,** of the Thiokol Chemical Corp., is a urethane rubber with elongation of 200 to 600% and **Solithane** is a liquid urethane for coating or casting.   Tensile strengths are about 6,000 psi, and service temperatures range from −25 to 300°F.

Foamed urethane is made by adding a compound which produces carbon dioxide or by reaction of a di-isocyanate with a compound containing an active hydrogen.   Flexible foamed urethane is used for furniture and automobile cushions, and the rigid foam is used for insulation.   **Lockfoam,** of the Lockheed Aircraft Corp., is a phenolic-modified urethane foam. The **urethane-phenol resin** of Olin Mathieson is a phenol-blocked isocyanate-terminated polyether for hard but flexible enamels.   Coatings on metal can be bent and formed without cracking.   **Castomer resins,** of Isocyanate Products, Inc., are casting grades of urethane made with lactones.   They have high tensile strength and abrasion resistance.

Uscothane, of U.S. Rubber, produced in fabric-backed sheets for lining chutes, is an abrasion-resistant urethane produced by reacting a di-isocyanate with a polyester or a polyether.   The grades range from very soft to flexible and to rigid.   **Estane,** of the B. F. Goodrich Chemical Co., is a polyurethane rubber of high wear resistance used for shoe heels and mechanical goods.   **Texin resin,** of the Mobray Chemical Co., is a urethane rubber for molding and extrusion.   Parts made from the rubber have a hardness of Shore A60 to A65, and an elongation from 500 to 800%.   **Neothane rubber,** of Goodyear, used for solid rubber tires, is a cast polyurethane. It has good resilience and high load-bearing qualities.   **Genthane S,** of the General Tire & Rubber Co., is a urethane rubber that retains its physical properties at temperatures to 300°F, at which temperature ordinary SBR rubber loses its properties.   It has a tensile strength of 3,600 psi, elongation 590%, and Durometer hardness A66.   The urethane rubbers are resistant to oils and ordinary solvents.

Textile fibers of urethane were first made in Germany under the name of **Igamide.**   The **Fiber K,** or **Lycra,** of Du Pont, and the **Vyrene,** of the U.S. Rubber Co., are flexible **urethane fibers** used for flexible garments. They are more durable than ordinary rubber fibers or filaments, and are 30% lighter in weight.   They are resistant to oils and to washing chemicals, and also have the advantage that they are white in color.   A great variety of urea and urethane plastics are possible.   Resins made with polymethylene polyphenyl isocyanate retain their strength to about 400°F. **Biuret resin,** of the Allied Chemical Corp., is intermediate between urea and melamine.   It has the formula $NH_2(CONH_2)_2 \cdot H_2O$, and melts at 193°C.   It is used for adhesives, textile and paper coatings, and for molding.

VANADIUM.   An elementary metal, symbol V, found widely distributed, but in commercial quantities in only a few places, chiefly Peru, Rhodesia, South West Africa, and the United States.   The common ores of vanadium are carnotite, patronite, roscoelite, and vanadinite.   Much of the commercial vanadium comes from Peruvian patronite and shales.   Some Russian vanadium comes from the mineral **tyuyamunite,** the calcium analog of carnotite.   This analog also occurs in American carnotite as a greenish-yellow powder.   Titaniferous ores of South Africa also furnish vanadium. But more than 60% of the known resources are in the United States.   Carnotite occurs in Utah and Colorado, and the Arizona ore is vanadinite. The most important ore in the United States is **roscoelite.**   It is a muscovite mica in which part of the aluminum has been replaced by vanadium. It occurs in micalike scales varying in color from green to brown.   It has a specific gravity of 2.9.   The ore mined in Colorado contains about 1.5% vanadium oxide, V_2O_5, and this oxide is extracted and marketed for making ferrovanadium and vanadium compounds.   The slag from Idaho phosphorus workings contains up to 5% vanadium, which is concentrated to 13% and extracted as vanadium pentoxide.   It is now also being recovered from petroleum.   Venezuelan crude oil, containing 130 ppm vanadium, yields 2,000 lb of vanadium pentoxide per 1 million gal of oil.

Vanadium is a pale-gray metal with a silvery luster.   Its specific gravity is 6.02, and it melts at 3236°F.   It does not oxidize in the air and is not attacked by hydrochloric or dilute sulfuric acid.   It dissolves with a blue color in solutions of nitric acid.   It is marketed by the Vanadium Corp., 99.5% pure, in cast ingots, machined ingots, and buttons.   The as-cast metal has a tensile strength of 54,000 psi, yield strength of 45,000 psi, and elongation 12%.   Annealed sheet has a tensile strength of 78,000 psi, yield strength 66,000 psi, and elongation 20%, while the cold-rolled sheet has a tensile strength of 120,000 psi with elongation of 2%.   Vanadium metal is expensive, but is used for special purposes such as for springs of high flexural strength and corrosion resistance.   The greatest use of vanadium is for alloying.   **Ferrovanadium,** for use in adding to steels, usually contains 30 to 40% vanadium, 3 to 6 carbon, and 8 to 15 silicon, with the balance iron, but may also be had with very low carbon and silicon.   **Vanadium-boron,** for alloying steels, is marketed by the Vanadium Corp. as a master alloy containing 40 to 45% vanadium, 8 boron, 5 titanium, 2.5 aluminum, and the balance iron, but the alloy may also be had with no titanium.   **Van-Ad alloy,** of the Chicago Development Corp., for adding vanadium to titanium alloys, contains 75% vanadium and the balance titanium.   It comes as fine crystals.

Vanadium salts are used to color pottery and glass and as mordants in dyeing.   **Red cake,** or crystalline **vanadium oxide,** is a reddish-brown material, containing about 85% **vanadium pentoxide,** V_2O_5, and 9% Na_2O, used as a catalyst and for making vanadium compounds.   Vanadium oxide is also used to produce yellow glass; the pigment known as **vanadium-tin yellow** is a mixture of vanadium pentoxide and tin oxide.

VANADIUM STEEL. Vanadium was originally used in steel as a cleanser, but is now employed in small amounts, 0.15 to 0.25%, especially with a small quantity of chromium, as an alloying element to make strong, tough, and hard steels.   It increases the tensile strength without lowering the ductility, reduces grain growth, and increases the fatigue-resisting qualities of steels.   Larger amounts are used in high-speed steels and in special steels.   Vanadium is a powerful deoxidizer in steels, but is too expensive for this purpose alone.   Steels with 0.45 to 0.55% carbon and small amounts of vanadium are used for forgings, and cast steels for aircraft parts usually contain vanadium.   In tool steels vanadium widens the hardening range, and by the formation of double carbides with chromium makes hard and keen-edge die and cutter steels.   **Vasco vanadium steel,** of the Vanadium-Alloys Steel Co., contains 0.20% vanadium with 0.80 chromium in the various carbon grades from 0.50 to 1%.   The higher carbon steels, for gages and rollers, have somewhat more chromium.   All of these steels are classed as **chromium-vanadium steel.** The carbon-vanadium steels for forgings and castings, without chromium, have slightly higher manganese.   Plain **carbon-vanadium steel** is regularly marketed in all standard carbon grades.   It is finer-graded, tougher, and keener-edged than plain carbon steel.   **Colonial No. 7, Red star steel,** and **Elvandi,** of the Vanadium-Alloys Steel Co., are steels of this type.   **Python steel** a shock-resistant steel of the Allegheny Ludlum Steel Co., has 0.25% vanadium, 0.90 carbon, 0.30 manganese, and 0.25 silicon.   In case-hardening steels the vanadium forms an integrated bonding between the case and the core which gives shock resistance to the steel.

Vanadium steels require higher quenching temperatures than ordinary steels or nickel steels.   **SAE 6145 steel,** with 0.18% vanadium and 1 chromium, has a fine grain structure and is used for gears.   It has a tensile strength of 116,000 to 292,000 psi, when heat-treated, with a Brinell hardness 248 to 566, depending on the temperature of drawing, and an elongation 7 to 26%.   In cast vanadium steels it is usual to have from 0.18 to 0.25% vanadium with 0.35 to 0.45 carbon.   Such castings have a tensile strength of about 80,000 psi and an elongation 22%.   A nickel-vanadium cast steel has much higher strength, but high-alloy steels with only small amounts of vanadium are not usually classed as vanadium steels.

VANILLA BEANS. The seed pods of a climbing plant of the orchid family of which there are more than 50 known species.   It is native to Mexico, but now also grown commercially in Malagasy, Réunion, Mauritius, and tropical America.   It is used for the production of the flavor **vanilla.**   The species grown for commercial vanilla is *Vanilla planifolia,* a tall climbing herb with yellow flowers.   It grows in humid tropic climates.   The flowers are pollinated by hand to produce 30 to 40 beans per plant.   The green beans are cured immediately in ovens to prevent spoilage after a sweating process.   During the curing the glucoside is changed by enzyme action into **vanillin** which crystallizes on the surface and possesses the characteristic odor and flavor.   The dark-brown cured pods are put up in small packs in tin containers.   **Vanilla extract** is made by percolation of the chopped bean pods in ethyl alcohol, and then concentrated by evaporation of the alcohol at a low temperature to avoid impairing the flavor.

The species *V. pompana* is more widely distributed, but is not as fragrant.   The vanilla grown in Tahiti has an odor of heliotrope which must be removed.   At least 15 species of vanilla grow in the Amazon and Orinoco valleys.   Vanilla was used by the Aztecs for flavoring chocolate.   It is now used for the same purpose, and as a flavor for ice cream, puddings, cakes, and other foodstuffs.

Vanillin is also produced synthetically from eugenol derived from clove oil.   It is also made from **coniferin,** $C_{16}H_{22}O_8 \cdot 2H_2O$, a white crystalline material of melting point 185°C obtained from the sapwood of the northern pine.   It is produced in Wisconsin from pulp-mill waste liquors by hydrating into sugars and oxidizing to vanillin.   But the synthetic vanillin does not give the full true flavor of vanilla, as a blend of other flavors is present in the natural product.   The demand for vanilla as a flavor is always greater than the supply, so that even the grades rated as pure vanilla extract may be so adulterated or diluted as to lose the full, rich flavor.

Ethyl vanillate, $C_6H_3(OH)(OCH)_3(COOC_2H_5)$, is made from Wisconsin sulfite liquor. It is used in cheese to prevent mold, and as a preservative in tomato and apple juice. **Lioxin,** of the Ontario Paper Co., is an impure 97% vanillin made from sulfite lignin. It is not suitable for use as a flavor, but is used as an odor-masking agent, as a brightener in zinc-plating baths, as an antifoam agent in lubricating oils, and for making syntans. **Vanitrope,** of Shulton, Inc., is a synthetic aromatic with a flavor 15 times more powerful than vanillin but with a resinous note resembling that of coumarin. It differs from vanillin chemically by having no aldehyde group, and is a **propenyl guaethol** related to eugenol. It is used as a vanilla extender. A blend of Vanitrope and vanilla, called **Nuvan,** is used as a low-cost vanilla flavor. **Vanatone** and **Vanarine,** of Fritzsche Bros., Inc., are blends of vanillin with aldehydes and esters to increase the flavor tone.

VARNISH. A solution of a resin in drying oil, which when spread out in a thin film dries and hardens by evaporation of the volatile solvent, or by the oxidation of the oil, or both. A smooth, glossy coating is left on the surface. Varnishes do not contain pigments; when mixed with pigments, they become enamels. The most commonly used resin is ordinary rosin, and the most common drying oils are linseed and tung oils. **Spirit varnishes** are those in which a volatile liquid, such as alcohol or ether, is used as a solvent for the resin or oil. They dry by the evaporation of the solvent. **Oleoresinous varnishes** are those in which the resin is compounded with an oxidizable oil, such as linseed oil. The gums used in varnish, such as copal, dammar, and kauri, produce hardness and gloss to the film, and the **fossil resins,** such as kauri, give greater hardness and luster to varnishes than do the natural resins. The oils, such as tung and linseed, make it elastic and durable.

Other important ingredients of varnishes are driers, such as manganese oxide, to hasten the action of the drying oil, and thinning agents, or reducers, such as turpentine, naphtha, and benzol. Hydrated lime is added to varnishes to neutralize the acid in the resin, and to clarify and harden the varnish to prevent it from becoming sticky in warm weather. **Spar varnishes** are those made to withstand weather conditions. **Gloss oil** is a solution of hardened rosin in benzine or in turpentine with sometimes a small amount of tung oil to give a tougher film. It gives a high gloss but is not durable. **Long varnishes** are those containing 20 to 100 gal of oil to 100 lb of resin; a **short varnish** is one with less oil. The short varnishes are hard, more glossy, but not as flexible or durable. Ordinarily, quick-drying varnish made with a natural resin is less durable than slow-drying; hardness and gloss are not guarantees of good varnish.

Varnish was originally only a colorless or nearly colorless coating ma-

terial for furniture and fancy wood products to give a smooth, glossy surface for protection and to bring out the texture of the wood, and **marine
varnish** was a high grade of spar varnish.   Any color used was merely to
accent the original color of the wood or to imitate the color of another
wood of similar grain.   **Insulating varnishes** were colorless varnishes for
protecting drawings, paintings, and other products from moisture, or for
electrical insulating.   But the term varnish has come to mean any light-
bodied quick-drying glossy finish as distinct from heavily pigmented glossy
enamels.   **Synthetic varnishes** may now contain synthetic resins in oils, or
they may be made entirely with synthetic resins in solvents.   **Electrical
varnishes** are likely to be silicone, epoxy, or polyester resins that give good
dielectric strength and adhesion.

VEGETABLE FATS. When specifically used, the term refers particularly to semisolid vegetable oils that are used chiefly for food.   Vegetable
oils and fats usually contain only small quantities of the fat-soluble vitamins A, D, and E, and after refining, they are usually devoid of vitamins.
Thus, they are a better food in the producing countries.   Climate in which
the plant is grown has an effect on the nature of the oils.   Warm climates
favor the development of oleic acid while colder climates favor the less
palatable linolenic acid.   The low-melting-point oils are more easily assimilated in the body, but when these are hydrogenated to a melting point
above 45°C they become difficult to assimilate.   Most of the more edible
vegetable fats, as distinct from the more liquid food oils, are tropical
products.   **Suari fat** is a hard white fat with a pleasant taste obtained from
the kernels of the seeds of the *Caryocar brasiliense* and other species of
tropical America.   The kernels yield 60 to 70% fat of a specific gravity
of 0.989, melting point 30 to 37°C, and iodine value 41 to 50.   **Ucuhuba
tallow,** used in soaps and for candles, is a fat from the seeds of the trees
Virola surinamensis and *V. sebifera* of Brazil.   **Mahuba fat** is a hard
edible fat from the fruit of the tree *Acrodicilidium mahuba* of Brazil.
Gamboge butter, known locally as **gurgi** and **murga,** is from the seeds of
the fruit of the trees *Garcinia morella, G. hanburii,* and other species of
Ceylon and India.   The melting point is 34 to 37°C, specific gravity 0.90
to 0.913, and saponification value 196.   It is used as a soap and food oil,
and locally as an illuminant and as an ointment.   From these trees also
comes the gum resin **gamboge** used in medicine as a cathartic, and also used
as a brown dyestuff.   It is alcohol-soluble.

Sierra Leone butter, also called **kanga** or **lamy,** is a pale-yellow fat from
the seeds of the fruit of the tree *Pentadeama butyracea* of West Africa.
The melting point is about 40°C, specific gravity 0.857 to 0.860, and
saponification value 186 to 198.   It is a soap oil.   **Mafura tallow** is a
bitter-tasting heavy fat from the nuts of the tree *Trichilia emitica* of East

Africa.   It is used for soap, candles, and ointments.   The specific gravity is 0.902, melting point about 40°C, and saponification value 201.   **Shea nut oil,** also known as **shea butter, Bambuk butter, Galam butter,** and by various local names as **karité, kade,** and **kedempó,** is a fat obtained from the kernels of the fruit of the large tree *Bassia butyrospermum* of tropical West Africa.   The kernels contain 45 to 55% fat, which when refined is white, stiffer than lard, with little odor or taste.   The melting point is 33 to 42°C.   It contains oleic and stearic acids and 3 to 4% lauric acid. It is used in Europe in butter substitutes, and as a substitute for cocoa butter, and also in candles.   **Malabar tallow,** also called **dhupa fat** and **pinay tallow,** used in Europe for soap and candles, and in India for food, is from the kernels of the seed of the evergreen **pinne tree,** *Vateria indica* of south India.   The tree also yields white dammar or Indian copal.   The seeds give about 25% of a greenish-yellow, odorless, and tasteless fat of specific gravity 0.890, melting point 40°C, and saponification value 190.   The fat is extracted by grinding the roasted seed, boiling in water, and skimming off.   It is bleached by exposure.

Vegetable tallow, also called **bayberry tallow** and **myrtle wax,** used extensively in Europe for soapmaking, and in the United States for blending in candles and with waxes, is a waxy fat obtained from the outside coating of the berries of species of *Myrica* bushes of America, Europe, and Africa, by boiling the berries in water.   The berries yield 15 to 25% tallow.   The species *M. cerifera* and *M. carolinensis* grow in the eastern coastal states, and the *M. mexicana* grows in Central America.   The melting point of the tallow is 40 to 46°C, specific gravity 0.995, and saponification value 205 to 212.   The Central American product contains about 58% myristic acid, 36 palmitic, and 1.3 oleic acid.   **Ocuba wax** is a waxy fat, but not chemically a wax, obtained from the seeds of the fruit of the shrub *Myristica ocuba* of Brazil.   The seeds yield about 20% fat with a specific gravity of 0.920 and melting point of 40°C, used in candles.   The fruit nut is surrounded by a thick skin which yields a water-soluble pink dye known as **ocuba red.**

Mahubarana fat is a pale-yellow solid oil of melting point 40 to 44°C obtained from the kernels of the fruit of trees of the genus *Boldoa.* The kernels contain 65% oil.   It is used for soaps and candles.   **Mocaya butter** is a fat from the kernels of the nuts of the **Paraguayan palm,** *Acrocomia sclerocarpa,* of tropical South America.   The tree resembles a coconut palm, but the nuts grow in bunches.   The pulp of the fruit contains 60% of a yellow oil similar to palm oil.   The kernels yield 53 to 65% of the mocaya fat which is softer than palm kernel oil.   The specific gravity is 0.865, and saponification value 240.   It has the same uses as palm kernel oil.

VEGETABLE OILS. An important class of oils obtained from plants, used industrially as drying oils, for lubricants, in cutting oils, for dressing leather, and for many other purposes.   Many of the oils find wide usage in food products.   Large tracts of land are under cultivation in all parts of the world for the production of the seeds and fruits from which the oils are obtained.   Linseed, cottonseed, palm, olive, and castor beans are examples of these, and the oils are obtained by crushing.   In some cases the oil-bearing material, copra or soybean, may be dehydrated before crushing, making it simpler to extract the oil, and giving a better residue meal for animal feed.   The chief distinction between vegetable oils and fats is a physical one, oils being fluid at ordinary temperatures.   Vegetable oils can be thickened for various uses by oxidation, by blowing air through them, or they can be solidified by hydrogenation.

In the making of plastics and chemicals from fatty acids derived from vegetable oils the cost of the oil may be as much as 50% of the final cost of the product, and price economics plays an important part in the choice of the raw material.   Thus, oils produced in countries subject to political and economic disturbances may have sudden and great price fluctuations. Thus, domestic soybean oil may be substituted for castor oil in making nylon even though more chemical operations are needed, or the acids may be synthesized from petroleum hydrocarbons.

Food oils are chosen by their content of essential fatty acids, but taste is an important factor.   Linseed oil is not used for food in the United States, although it has high food value and contains both linoleic and linolenic acids.   Safflower oil, high in linoleic acid, ranks high as a food oil, only 1.35 grams of oil being required to provide 1 gram of essential fatty acids.   Olive oil, high in oleic acid with only one double bond, requires 14.2 grams of oil for 1 gram of essential acids.   But olive oil requires less linoleic acid to counteract its effect than an equivalent amount of a saturated acid with no double bond.   Butter requires the consumption of 20 grams to obtain 1 gram of essential acids, while soybean, corn, and cottonseed oils, used in margarine, rank high as food oils.

Considerable oil is extracted from the kernels of the stones or pits of cherries, apricots, and other fruits as a by-product of the canning and drying of fruits.   **Cherry kernel oil** is from cherry pits which contain 30 to 38% oil.   The cold-pressed oil is yellow and has a pleasant flavor.   It is used in salad oils and in cosmetics.   The hot-pressed oil is used in soaps.   The oil contains 47% oleic acid, 40 linoleic, 4 palmitic, 3 stearic, and some arachidic and myristic acids.   **Grapeseed oil** is obtained by pressing the by-product grape seeds from the wine industry.   The seeds contain 10 to 15% oil, valued in Europe as an edible oil, but used in the United States mostly for paints and soaps.   The oil contains about 52% linoleic acid, 32% oleic acid, and palmitic, stearic, and arachidic acids.

The hot-pressed oil is dark green and not sweet, but the cold-pressed refined oil is colorless and has a nutlike taste.   **Tomato seed oil** is from the seeds of the **tomato,** *Lycopersicon esculentum,* the seeds being by-products of the manufacture of **tomato juice** and **tomato puree,** vast quantities of which are produced in the United States from the pulp.   The tomato plant is a perennial native to Central and South America, and was grown by the Aztecs under the name of **tomatl.**   There are many varieties, and the fruits are true berries.   The common red varieties are 2 to 3 in. in diameter and contain a large number of seeds in the pulp.   The seeds yield 17% oil by cold pressing, or 33% by solvent extraction.   The cold-pressed oil is a clear liquid of 0.920 specific gravity, with an agreeable odor and bland taste.   The iodine number is 113, and saponification value 192.   It is used in salad oils, margarine, soaps, and as a semidrying oil for paints.

VELVET. A closely woven silk fabric with a short pile on one side formed by carrying the warp threads over wires and then cutting open the loops.   Velvet is made in a great variety of qualities and weights, and may have a cotton back in the cheaper grades, or be made in wool.   True velvet is all silk, but because of the number of imitations in other materials this variety is usually designated as **silk velvet.**   Velvet is dyed in various colors, the depth of color shown by the pile, giving it an air of richness.   Its largest use is in dress goods and hangings, but it is used industrially for upholstery, fancy linings, and trim.

   Plush is a name for fabrics woven of cotton, silk, linen, or wool, having a pile deeper than that of velvet.   It is used for upholstery.   Originally the pile of plush consisted of mohair or worsted yarns, but there is now no distinction except in the length of the pile.   **Upholstery plush** is made in brocade designs by burning the pile with rollers to form a lower background.   Plush is also dyed and curled to imitate furs.

   Velveteen is an imitation velvet, woven of cotton.   In the best grades the pile is of mercerized yarns.   Velveteen is woven into two systems of filling yarns and one system of warp yarns, the pile being made with the cut filling yarns instead of the warp yarns as in velvet.   It belongs to the class of **fustians** which includes also **moleskin** and **corduroy.**   The latter is a sturdy pile fabric with heavy warp rib, dyed in the piece.   It is also made in wool.   The ribs run lengthwise, while **whipcord,** a hard-woven worsted fabric, has fine ribs running diagonally on the face.   Velveteen is used for apparel, linings for jewelry and silverware boxes, shoe uppers, artificial flowers, and covering material.   It is made either plain back or twill back, the plain back having a tendency to loosen and drop the pile.

VERMICULITE. A foliated mineral employed in making plasters and board for heat, cold, and sound insulation, as a filler in calking compounds, and for plastic mortars and refractory concrete.   The mineral is an alteration product of biotite and other micas, and is found in Colorado, Wyoming, and Montana, and in the Transvaal.   It occurs in crystalline plates, specific gravity 2.3, and hardness 1.5, measuring sometimes as much as 9 in. across and 6 in. in thickness.   The color is yellowish to brown. Upon calcination at 1750°F, vermiculite expands at right angles to the cleavage into threads with a vermicular motion like a mass of small worms; hence its name.   The volume increases as much as 16 times, and the color changes to a silvery or golden hue.   It is ground into pellet form.   Plaster made with 60% vermiculite, 30 plaster of Paris, and 10 asbestos will withstand red heat without disintegrating.   **Therm-O-Flake brick,** of the Illinois Clay Products Co., is made of granules of **exfoliated vermiculite** bonded with a chemical.   It is lightweight, tough, and will withstand temperatures up to 2000°F.   The corklike pellets of vermiculite used for insulating fill in house walls are called **mica pellets.**   **Zonolite,** of W. R. Grace & Co., is an exfoliated vermiculite.   **Zonolite Verxite,** of the same company, is a spongy granular powder form of **Verxite,** a thermally expanded vermiculite.   It is used as a blending agent in animal feeds. A sound-absorbing building tile marketed by Johns-Manville under the name of **Rockoustile** is made of exfoliated mica.   An expanded vermiculite of extremely fine mesh, under the name of **Mikolite,** of the Mikolite Co., is used as an extender in aluminum paint and in lubricating oils. **Exfoliated mica** is a name for expanded vermiculite.   **Terra-Lite,** of the Zonolite Co., is fluffy powdered vermiculite for conditioning soils.   It holds water and prevents soil crusting, and helps to maintain soil temperature below the critical 80°F.

VINYL RESINS. A group of products varying from liquids to hard solids, made by the polymerization of ethylene derivatives, employed for finishes, coatings, and molding resins, or it can be made directly by reacting acetic acid with ethylene and oxygen.   In general, the term vinyl designates plastics made by polymerizing vinyl chloride, vinyl acetate, or vinylidene chloride, but may include plastics made from styrene and other chemicals.   The term is generic for compounds of the basic formula RCH:CR'CR''.   The simplest are the polyesters of vinyl alcohol, such as vinyl acetate.   This resin is light in weight, with a specific gravity of 1.18, and is transparent, but it has poor molding qualities and its strength is no more than 5,000 psi.   The vinyl resins are brittle at low temperatures. **Elvacet,** of Du Pont, and **Lemac,** of the American Monomer Corp., are vinyl acetate molding resins.   But the vinyl halides, CH_2:CHX, also polymerize readily to form **vinylite resins,** which mold well, have tensile strengths to 9,000 psi, high dielectric strength, and high chemical resistance, and a widely useful range of resins is produced by copolymers of vinyl acetate and vinyl chloride. Various grades of **Bakelite, Geon, Tygon,** and other resins are these chloride-acetate copolymers.

Vinyl alcohol, $CH_2{:}CHOH$, is a liquid boiling at 35.5°C. **Polyvinyl alcohol** is a white, odorless, tasteless powder which on drying from solutions forms a colorless and tough film. The material is used as a thickener for latex, in chewing gum, and for sizes and adhesives. It can be compounded with plasticizers and molded or extruded into tough and elastic products. **Hydrolized polyvinyl alcohol** has greater water resistance, higher adhesion, and its lower residual acetate gives lower foaming. **Soluble film,** for packaging detergents and other water-dispersible materials to eliminate the need of opening the package, is a clear polyvinyl alcohol film. Textile fibers are also made from polyvinyl alcohol, either water-soluble or insolubilized with formaldehyde or other agent. **Vinal,** of the Air Reduction Chemical Co., is a polyvinyl alcohol textile fiber which is hot-drawn by a semimelt process and insolubilized after drawing. The fiber has a high degree of orientation and crystallinity, giving good strength and hot-water resistance. Polyvinyl alcohol fibers are called **Vinylon** in Europe and **Kuravilon** in Japan.

Vinyl alcohol reacted with an aldehyde and an acid catalyst produces a group of polymers known as **vinyl acetal resins,** and separately designated by type names, as polyvinyl butyral and polyvinyl formal. The polyvinyl alcohols are called **Solvars,** and the polyvinyl acetates are called **Gelvas.** The vinyl ethers range from **vinyl methyl ether,** $CH_2{:}CHOCH_3$, to **vinyl ethylhexyl ether,** from soft compounds to hard resins. **Vinyl ether** is a liquid which polymerizes, or can be reacted with hydroxyl groups to form acetal resins. **Gantrez M,** of General Aniline & Film Corp., is a water-soluble polyvinyl methyl ether for use in paints, inks, and adhesives. **Alkyd vinyl ethers** are made by reacting acetylene with an alcohol under pressure, producing **methyl vinyl ether, ethyl vinyl ether,** or **butyl vinyl ether.** They have reactive double bonds which can be used to copolymerize with other vinyls to give a variety of physical properties. The **polyvinyl formals, Formvars,** are used in molding compounds, wire coatings, and impregnating compounds. It is one of the toughest of the thermoplastics. The Formvar of the Shawinigan Products Corp. has a specific gravity of about 1.3, a tensile strength up to 12,000 psi with elongation from 5 to 20%, Rockwell hardness M85, and dielectric strength of 450 volts per mil. This type of plastic is resistant to alkalies but is attacked by acids.

A **plastisol** is a vinyl resin dissolved in a plasticizer to make a pourable liquid without a volatile solvent for casting. The poured liquid is solidified by heating. **Plastigels** are plastisols to which a gelling agent has been added to increase viscosity. The **polyvinyl acetals, Alvars,** are used in lacquers, adhesives, and phonograph records. The transparent **poly-**

vinyl butyrals, Butvars, are used as interlayers in laminated glass.   They are made by reacting polyvinyl alcohol with **butyraldehyde,** C_3H_7CHO. **Vinal** is a general name for vinyl-butyral resin used for laminated glass.

Vinyl acetate is a water-white mobile liquid with boiling point 70°C, usually shipped with a copper salt to prevent polymerization in transit. The composition is $CH_3 \cdot COO \cdot CH:CH_2$.   It may be polymerized in benzine and marketed in solution, or in water solution for use as an extender for rubber, and for adhesives and coatings.   The higher the polymerization of the resin, the higher the softening point of the resin.   The formula for **polyvinyl acetate resin** is given as $(CH_2:CHOOCCH_3)_x$.   It is a colorless, odorless thermoplastic with density of 1.189, unaffected by water, gasoline, or oils, but soluble in the lower alcohols, benzene, and chlorinated hydrocarbons.   Polyvinyl acetate resins are stable to light, transparent to ultraviolet light, and are valued for lacquers and coatings because of their high adhesion, durability, and ease of compounding with gums and resins.   Resins of low molecular weight are used for coatings, and those of high molecular weight for molding.   **Darex** and **Everflex,** of W. R. Grace & Co., are paint and coating resins, and **Vinylite** and **Vinyloid,** of Union Carbide, are vinyl acetate resins for molding.   **Wood Glu,** of Paisley Products, Inc., is a milky water dispersion of polyvinyl acetate used as an adhesive for wood and paper.   Vinyl acetate will copolymerize with maleic acrylonitrile, or acrylic esters.   With ethylene it produces a copolymer latex of superior toughness and abrasion resistance for coatings.   **Aircoflex 500,** of Air Reduction Co., Inc., is a vinyl acetate ethylene copolymer latex.

Vinyl chloride, CH_2CHCl, called also **ethenyl chloride** and **chloro ethylene,** produced by reacting ethylene with oxygen from the air and ethylene dichloride, is the basic material for the polyvinyl chloride resins.   It is a gas.   The plastic was produced originally in Germany under the name of **Igelite** for cable insulation and as **Vinnol** for tire tubes.   The tensile strength of the plastic may vary from the flexible resins with about 3,000 psi to the rigid resin with a tensile strength to 9,000 psi and Shore hardness of 90.   The dielectric strength is high, up to 1,300 volts per mil.   It is resistant to acids and alkalies.   **Polyvinyl chloride** usually comes as a white powder for molding or extruding, but **PVC pearls,** of the Escambia Chemical Corp., is the material made by a water-suspension process in the form of white porous particles capable of absorbing easily a high proportion of plasticizer.   **Polvin** and **Opalon,** of Monsanto, are polyvinyl chloride resins, and **Ultron** is polyvinyl chloride film.   Unplasticized polyvinyl chloride is used for rigid chemical-resistant pipe.   **Kraloy D-500,** of the Kraloy Plastic Pipe Co., and **Carlon V,** of the Carlon Products Corp., are polyvinyl chloride in rigid pipe.   **Vyflex sheet,** of Kaykor Industries, Inc., is rigid unplasticized polyvinyl chloride in sheets for making acid tanks, ducts, and flumes. **Polyvinyl chloride sheet,** unmodified, may have a tensile strength of 8,200 psi, flexural strength of 12,600 psi, and a light transmission of 78%. But in bends or corners of moldings, or in folds of sheet, the resin shows opaque whitening. This can be eliminated by modifying the resin with an acrylic. The resins have improved processing qualities and flexibility, especially for blown bottles and extruded parts, but the light transmission is reduced. **Acryloid KM-607,** of Rohm & Haas, is a white acrylic powder. When used in polyvinyl sheet to a content of 20% it gives a tensile strength of 6,700 psi and a light transmission of 72%.

Vinylidene chloride plastics are derived from ethylene and chlorine polymerized to produce a thermoplastic with softening point of 240 to 280°F. The resins are noted for their toughness and resistance to water and chemicals. The molded resins have a specific gravity of 1.68 to 1.75, tensile strength 4,000 to 7,000 psi, and flexural strength 15,000 to 17,000 psi. **Saran** is the name of a vinylidene chloride plastic of the Dow Chemical Co., extruded in the form of tubes for handling chemicals, brines, and solvents to temperatures as high as 275°F. It is also extruded into strands and woven into a box-weave material as a substitute for rattan for seating. **Velon,** of the Firestone Tire & Rubber Co., is this material for screens and fabrics. **Saran latex,** a water dispersion of the plastic, is used for coating and impregnating fabrics. For coating food-packaging papers, it is waterproof and greaseproof, is odorless and tasteless, and gives the papers a high gloss. Saran is also produced as a strong transparent film for packaging. **Saranex,** of Dow Chemical Co., is **Saran film** laminated with polyethylene sheet to give heat-sealing qualities. **Saran bristles** for brushes are made in diameters from 0.010 to 0.020 in. **Zetek,** a textile fiber of the B. F. Goodrich Co., is a polyvinylidene cyanide.

Vinyl benzoate is an oily liquid of the composition $CH_2{:}CHOOCC_6H_5$, which can be polymerized to form resins with higher softening points than those of polyvinyl acetate, but are more brittle at low temperatures. These resins, copolymerized with vinyl acetate, are used for water-repellent coatings. **Vinyl crotonate,** $CH_2{:}CHOOCCH{:}CHCH_3$, is a liquid of specific gravity of 0.9434. Its copolymers are brittle resins, but it is used as a cross-linking agent for other resins to raise the softening point and to increase abrasion resistance. **Vinyl formate,** $CH_2{:}CHOOCH$, is a colorless liquid which polymerizes to form clear **polyvinyl formate resins** that are harder and more resistant to solvents than polyvinyl acetate. The monomer is also copolymerized with ethylene monomers to form resins for mixing in specialty rubbers. **Methyl vinyl pyridine,** $(CH_3)(CHCH_2)$-C_5H_3N, is produced by the Phillips Chemical Co. for use in making resins, fibers, and oil-resistant rubbers. It is a colorless liquid boiling at 64.4°C. The active methyl groups give condensation reactions, and it will copolymerize with butadiene, styrene, or acrylonitrile. **Polyvinyl carbazole,** under the name of **Luvican,** was used in Germany as a mica substitute for high-frequency insulation. It is a brown resin, softening at 150°C.

An adhesive to replace rubber cement was made in Germany by combining **Oppanol C,** a high-molecular-weight polyvinyl isobutylene ether, with **Igovin,** a low-molecular-weight polyvinyl isobutyl ether, and compounding with zinc oxide and wool grease. **Marvinol VR-10,** developed by the Glenn L. Martin Co., for coatings and impregnations, was produced by the reaction of acetylene and hydrogen chloride with a catalyst. It is also used for casting into films. The **Marvinol resins** of the U.S. Rubber Co. are polyvinyl chloride. The vinyl plastics are much used for wall tile and sheet wall coverings. They are adaptable to bright colors, are nonstaining, and easily cleaned. **Kalitex** is a vinyl sheet wall covering of the U.S. Plywood Corp., having an embossed burlap-weave pattern with colors on the reverse side. **Vinyon,** of Union Carbide, is a vinyl chloride-acetate fiber in various grades. Since it is resistant to strong acids and alkalies, **Vinyon fiber** is made into filter cloth for temperatures not above 160°C. It is also used in wool mixtures. It is produced by the copolymerization of vinyl chloride and vinyl acetate. **Vinyon N** is a vinyl chloride-acrylonitrile copolymer marketed as a fine, silklike textile fiber. The fiber has high strength, an elongation of 30%, and is nonflammable. It has a light yellow color and is easily dyed. **Carilan** is a Japanese vinyl acetate fiber.

The possibility of variation in the vinyl resins by change of the monomer, copolymerization, and difference in compounding is so great that the term vinyl resin is almost meaningless when used alone. The resins are marketed under a continuously increasing number of trade names. In general, each resin is designed for specific uses, but not limited to those uses. **Advagum,** of the Advance Solvents & Chemical Corp., is a highly plasticized vinyl copolymer used as an extender for rubbers. **Pliovac,** of the Goodyear Tire & Rubber Co., is a high-molecular-weight vinyl chloride for coatings, tiling, and extrusions. **Victron,** of the Naugatuck Chemical Co., and **Saflex,** of the Monsanto Company, are vinyl acetal resins. **Butacite,** of Du Pont, is a clear polyvinyl butyral for laminated glass. **Formex,** of the General Electric Co., is a vinyl formal resin for insulating wire. **Boltaron 6200,** of Bolta Products, Inc., is rigid unplasticized polyvinyl chloride in sheets, rods, and pipes, resisting thermal distortion below 175°F. **Ingerin** is a German polyvinyl ether, and **Cosal** is made from vinyl isobutyl ether. **Mipolam** is a German vinyl polymer for floor coverings.

Kynar, of Pennwalt, is a polymer of **vinylidene fluoride,** $CH_2:CF_2$, with a high molecular weight, about 500,000. It is a hard, white thermoplastic resin with a slippery surface, and has a high resistance to chemicals.

It resists temperatures to 650°F, and does not become brittle at low temperatures.   It extrudes easily, and has been used for wire insulation, gaskets, seals, molded parts, and piping.

VITAMINS. Organic chemical compounds which are vital building units, coenzymes, or catalyzing agents in the growth and maintenance of animal bodies.   They are produced by extraction from vegetable or animal products or made synthetically, and marketed in solid or extract form for use in foodstuffs and pharmaceuticals.   **Vitamin A,** called **carotene** because of its abundance in carrots, is an orange-yellow needle-shaped crystalline substance with a complex molecular structure having the empirical formula $C_{40}H_{56}$.   It is soluble in fats, but poorly soluble in water.   Yellow and leafy green vegetables are rich sources of carotene-bearing pigments, and carotene accompanies the green chlorophyll coloring of all plants.   The more intense the green or yellow coloring, the greater the carotene content.   **Lycopene,** the red coloring agent of tomatoes, has the same empirical formula as carotene, and both contain eight isoprene units, but it has a different structure.   The color is due to large numbers of conjugated double bonds, and different colors are from different arrangements.   **Cryptoxanthin,** one of the four yellow carotene-carrying pigments, occurs in yellow corn, egg yolk, and green grasses.   Animals convert carotene of green plants into vitamin A which is then obtained commercially from the tissues, especially from the liver.   Deficiency of vitamin A in the human body causes night blindness, muscular weakness, and defective tooth structure, but an excess can cause body deformities and stillbirth.

Vitamin B is a complex of several vitamins, including **vitamin B_1** and vitamin G.   The former cannot be formed in the normal processes of the human body and must be supplied in the diet.   Plants manufacture and store it in the seed.   Lack of vitamin B_1 causes beriberi, fatigue, stiffness, headache, nervousness, and loss of appetite and, when chronic, causes enlargement of the heart, polyneuritis, and loss of coordination of the muscular movements.   The crystalline vitamin B_1 is called **thiamin chloride,** and in Europe is called **aneurin.**   It is water-soluble, insoluble in most fats, and is destroyed by heat in the presence of moisture.   In alkaline solutions the destruction is rapid.   It is essential to the health of every living cell.   Greater amounts are needed when much starch or sugar foods are eaten in order to prevent the formation of pyruvic acid, which produces noxious breath.   **Pyruvic acid,** CH_3COCO_2H, a liquid boiling at 165°C, also called **glucic acid, pyroacemic acid,** and **propanone acid,** is **onion flavor.**   **Onions** are root plants of the genus *Allium* of which there are more than 200 species.   They constitute a valuable food product but contain varying amounts of pyruvic acid, from 5.3 micromoles per mil in the yellow **Spanish onion** to 18.6 in the strong **Ebenezer onion.**

Riboflavin is the accepted name for **vitamin B$_2$,** or **vitamin G.** The orange-yellow needle-shaped crystals have a green fluorescence. Riboflavin, $C_{27}H_{20}N_4O_6$, is water-soluble. It is gradually destroyed by exposure to light, and is destroyed by many chemicals, or by high temperatures in the presence of alkalies. It is present in meats, eggs, barley malt, yeast, milk, green leafy vegetables, and grasses. Deficiency of riboflavin results in ill health, loss of hair, and dermatosis. **Nicotinic acid,** or **niacin,** is the pellagra-preventing member of the vitamin B complex. It can be made from the nicotine of the variety of tobacco *Nicotiana rustica.* Coffee contains some niacin, and meat extracts are rich in both niacin and riboflavin. **Biotin,** originally named **vitamin H,** is also a member of the B group, and has an enzyme action on starches and sugars. It occurs widely in nature as a **phytohormone** for the growth of organisms and plants. It is extracted from yeast, egg yolk, and liver by adsorbing on carbon. **Vitamin B$_6$,** $C_8H_{11}NO_3HCl$, called **pyridoxine,** is required to enable the human system to assimilate proteins. A deficiency causes nausea, muscular weakness, and anemia. **Vitamin B$_{12}$,** or **cobalamin,** is a high-molecular-weight complex containing five-membered nitrogen nuclei. It can replace protein as a growth factor.

Vitamin C, $C_6H_8O_6$, known also as **ascorbic acid,** or **ceritamic acid,** is unstable and is easily oxidized, especially in the presence of alkalies or in iron or copper vessels, so that in foods that have been long exposed to the air or overcooked it loses its value. It is thus probably the only vitamin likely to be deficient in the American diet, but the need is easily satisfied with fresh fruits, tomato, and green vegetables, and it is now added to frozen and canned foods as it also preserves the natural color of the products. **Isoascorbic acid,** or **erythorbic acid,** has the same composition as ascorbic acid but with the OH and H reversed on one carbon. It has the same antioxidant value, and is a lower-cost chemical, but has no vitamin C activity. It is used in meats to preserve the red color, and in canned foods to prevent discoloring. **Mercate 5,** of Merck & Co., Inc., is isoascorbic acid for these purposes, and **Mercate 20** is **sodium isoascorbate. Cebicure,** for curing meats, is ascorbic acid.

The synthetic ascorbic acid is not claimed to be a complete cure for scurvy. The natural vitamin from lemons and limes contains also bioflavins which counteract the skin hemorrhage of scurvy. The juice from the **acerola plant** of Puerto Rico, used for scurvy, is 80 times richer in vitamin C than orange juice.

Vitamin D regulates the metabolism of calcium and phosphorus in the human body. Without it the body is subject to rickets, soft bones, or ill-formed bones and teeth. It is also used to counteract the germ of tuberculosis. It is found in fish and fish-liver oils and in some fruits. The vitamin D concentrate of General Mills, Inc., is made by the activation of crystalline ergosterol with low-velocity electrons, in vegetable oil. **Calciferol,** or **vitamin D$_2$,** is a synthetic antirachitic marketed in crystalline form or in solution in corn oil.   Its melting point is 116°C.   Vitamin D$_2$ is formed in the body from cholesterol by the action of sunlight on the skin.   **Vitamin E** is so widely distributed in foods taken by man that the effect is not well known.   It is also called **tocopherol** as it is a tocopherol acetate.   **Tofanin,** of Winthrop-Stearns, Inc., is vitamin E.   **Vitamin K$_5$** is very stable.   It is used in the foodstuffs industry instead of sulfur dioxide to control fermentation without affecting flavor, and in medicine to coagulate blood.

Vitamin P is found in capsicum and in lemon peel, and is used as a preventive of rheumatic fever.   Although proper quantities of vitamins are necessary in the human body, overdoses are often toxic and poisonous. An excess of vitamin C, for example, causes irritability, vertigo, and vomiting.   An excess of vitamin D causes metastatic calcification, or deposition of calcium in the arteries and kidneys, and concentrated vitamin D is classed as a toxic drug.   Since metabolism may vary with each person and is also affected by physical condition, vitamins should not be taken as supplementary drugs without medical advice.

VULCANIZED FIBER.   A wood, paper, or other cellulose fiberboard impregnated with a gelatinizing medium.   It is not vulcanized in the same sense that rubber is vulcanized.   It is made by various processes, and the medium may be sulfuric acid, zinc chloride solution, or cuproammonium solution.   It may also be made by impregnating the cellulose fiber with a phenol-furfural resin dissolved in alcohol or other solvent.   After dipping in the solution, the fiber is washed to remove excess alcohol, and then dipped in a zinc chloride solution which hydrolizes it, and it is then washed free of the chloride, dried, and rolled.   The original vulcanized fiber, patented in 1899, and called **Cellulith,** was sulfite wood pulp molded into sheets or formed parts.   The modern fiber in the hard grades is a tough, resilient, hornlike material in standard gray, red, and black colors.   Soft flexible grades are made for washers and gaskets.   The four NEMA grades are: electrical insulation, commercial, bone (high density), and trunk.   The commercial grade is in thicknesses from 0.005 to 1 in., with lengthwise tensile strength of 7,500 psi, flexural strength of 14,000 psi, compressive strength 20,000 psi, and dielectric strength of 250 volts per mil.   Unless impregnated with a synthetic resin it is not resistant to alkalies.

The bone quality is a dense material with a specific gravity of 1.4, capable of being machined.   The **hard vulcanized fiber** of the Spaulding Fibre Co. was made from cotton rags gelatinized in a zinc chloride solution and built up in layers.   The shear strength is to 15,000 psi, and compressive strength 30,000 psi.   **Codite,** of the Continental-Diamond Fibre Co., was a hard, tough fiber in the form of tubing.   **Bone fiber** is characterized by being dense and hard, while **trunk fiber** is tough and abrasion-resistant.   Because of the moderate cost vulcanized fiber still has many uses, but practically all the material for electrical use is now of the insoluble type made with synthetic resin impregnation and having higher dielectric strength.   **Fish paper,** for electrical use, was originally vulcanized fiber in thicknesses down to 0.004 in., but is now likely to be a resin impregnate. **Shoe fiber** is vulcanized fiber in leather color used for reinforcement in shoes.   It is very resilient, and can be die-cut and nailed.   Much of the fiber generally called vulcanized fiber is now impregnated with synthetic resins to meet conditions of chemical resistance, strength, and electrical properties.

VULCANIZED OILS. Vegetable oils vulcanized with sulfur and used for compounding with rubber for rubber goods, or as a rubber substitute. Castor oil, corn oil, rapeseed oil, and soybean oil are used.   Vulcanized oil is a white to brown, spongy, and odorless cake, or sticky plastic, with specific gravity of 1.04.   The material was invented in France in 1847, and was known as **factice.   Factice cake** is solidified vulcanized oils, cut in slab form.   It is an oil modifier of rubber to add softness and plasticity. It also has some elasticity.   **Brown factice** is made by treating the oil with sulfur or sulfur chloride at 160 to 200°C.   The softer grades are made with blown oils and low sulfur.   The harder grades contain up to 20% sulfur.   **White factice** is made from rapeseed oil, which is high in a characteristic acid, erucic acid, by slow addition of sulfur chloride up to 25% sulfur content.   **Erasing rubbers** are rubber compounded with white factice or the factice alone.   **Black factice** has mineral bitumen added to brown factice.   **Neophax** is the trade name of the Stamford Rubber Supply Co. for brown factice, and **Amberex** is the name for light-tan-colored factice.   **Factex** of the same company is partly vulcanized oil dispersed in water.   It produces a nontacky elastic film.   When mixed with rubber latex to the extent of 30%, it gives a velvety feel to the vulcanized product and does not decrease the strength greatly.   **Factice sheet** is made from specially processed factice made by treating warm oil with sulfur and then with sulfur chloride.   The strength and elasticity are higher.   **Mineral rubber** was a name applied to vulcanized oils mixed with bitumens, especially gilsonite.

WALNUT. A hardwood from the tree *Juglans regia,* native to Europe and Asia Minor, but now growing in many other places.   The wood is firm, with a fine to coarse, open grain, and a lustrous surface.   The weight is about 45 lb per cu ft.   The color is dark brown to black, and it takes a beautiful polish.   Walnut has great strength, toughness, and elasticity. It also has great uniformity of texture and does not split easily.   It is particularly adapted for carving.   Walnut is valued as a cabinet wood, for fine furniture, and gunstocks.   The wood from *J. regia* is called **English walnut,** and the beautifully figured wood from Iran is known as **Circassian walnut. Black walnut** or **American walnut,** is from the tree *J. nigra,* of eastern United States.   The color is darker, and it has a more uniform color than European walnut.   It is handsomely grained and has the same general characteristics and uses as European walnut.   It has a specific gravity, kiln-dried, of 0.56, a shearing strength parallel to the grain of 1,000 psi, and a compressive strength perpendicular to the grain of 1,730 psi.   **Butternut,** from the tree *J. cinerea,* resembles closely the wood of the black walnut except for its color, which is yellowish gray.   The supply of this wood is limited.

East India walnut is the wood of the tree *Albizzia lebbek* of tropical Asia and Africa, used for furniture, paneling, and interior decorative work. It is hard, dense, close-grained, and has a weight of about 50 lb per cu ft. The color is dark brown with gray streaks.   The logs come as large as 30 in. square and 20 ft long.   The shipments may be mixed with the wood of the *A. procera,* the **white siris wood** of India.   This wood has a brown walnut color, is lustrous, and resembles true walnut more than does the East India walnut.   **Mahoe,** also called **blue mahoe** and **majagua,** is the wood of the tree *Hibiscus elatus,* of tropical America.   It has been used to replace true walnut for gunstocks and in cabinetwork.   The wood has a gray-blue color, an aromatic odor, and is hard with a coarse, open grain.   **Brazilian walnut,** or **frejó,** from the tree *Cordia goeldiana,* is a strong, tough, straight-grained wood used for cooperage and cabinetwork.

African walnut, or **amonilla,** is from the tree *Lovoa klaineana* of Nigeria. The wood is brown, has a fine texture, and an interlocking grain that shows a striped figure when quartersawed.   It weighs about 40 lb per cu ft.   It is used for flooring, paneling, veneers, and cabinetwork.   The Brazilian wood known as **imbuia,** from the tree *Nectandra villosa,* is a close match to true walnut, and is valued for cabinetwork, flooring, and furniture. The heartwood has an olive to brown color and takes a high polish.   There are as many as 50 species of *Nectandra* trees in Brazil, varying widely in characteristics.   The **canela preta,** from the tree *N. mollis,* is a wood with large satiny stains on a dark-yellow background.   It has a silvery luster when polished, has a spicy scent, and is very durable.   It more resembles bleached walnut.

Walnut oil is yellowish oil obtained by pressing the nut kernels of the common walnut.   It is a good drying oil and is used especially for artists' paints.   The specific gravity is 0.919 to 0.929 and iodine value 148.   It is soluble in alcohol.   The oil from the candlenut is also called walnut

oil.   **Walnut-shell flour,** made from the refuse shells of the walnut industry of California, is used as a filler in molded plastics and in synthetic adhesives to increase bonding strength.   It contains cellulose with about
28% lignin, 5 furfural, 9 pentosans, 6 methyl hydroxylamine, and 2.5
sugars and starch.   In colonial times walnut bark was used as a cathartic.
It contains a **juglone,** or **nucin,** a complex **naphthoquinone,** $C_{10}H_6O_2$, a
reddish crystalline compound also called **lapachol** as it occurs also in
lapacho, an important hardwood of Argentina and Paraguay.

WALRUS HIDE. The skin of the walrus, a marine mammal, *Odonto-
baenus rosmarus* and *O. abesus,* native to the North Atlantic and Pacific
Oceans.   The animals sometimes have a length of 16 ft, and a weight up
to 2,000 lb, and the hide is obtainable in large pieces.   They congregate
in herds on the icebergs of the north.   The skin is tanned and makes a
leather with a beautiful natural grain.   It is also very tough and was formerly much used for coach traces.   It is now employed where a tough and
ornamental leather is needed, but the animals are now scarce and the kill
is controlled by law.   Imitation **walrus leather** is made from specially
tanned and embossed heavy sheepskins, and is used mostly for bags and
ornamental articles.

WATER. A nearly transparent liquid of the composition H_2O.   The specific gravity of pure water is taken as 1.0 at 4°C, and water is used as
the standard for measuring the specific gravity of other liquid and solid
materials.   The boiling point is 100°C, and the freezing point is 0°C.
The first essential use of water is for drinking and for the watering of
plants to sustain life, but the largest consumptive use is in industrial processing, and a large supply of water is an essential for manufacturing.
    The per capita intake of water for human drinking is taken as 1 gal per
day, but, because of wastage, the amount is larger, and the consumption of
water from the municipal systems of large American cities exceeds 150 gal
per capita per day, which includes some industrial use.   The employment
of water for hydroelectric power is not considered as a consumptive use.
Sugar refining requires up to 10,000 gal of water per ton of product produced, paper-pulp processing requires about 60,000 gal per ton, steelmaking requires about 65,000 gal per ton, viscose rayon processing needs about
200,000 gal per ton, and the processing of GR-S rubber takes as high as
600,000 gal per ton.   For such uses the water is borrowed rather than consumed, and most of it is returned to the streams or to the ground, but it is
usually contaminated.   Actually, industry consumes no more than 2% of
the water used.   Total per capita consumption of water for all purposes
is 1,800 gal per day, but the average is not a very useful figure, since the
amount used is far greater in highly industrialized centers.   About 80%

of the supply in the United States is from surface water, and about 20% from ground water.

Quality of water is important in many industrial operations.   Factories may obtain water from municipal systems, from ground water pumped from wells, or from surface water from streams.   As industries concentrate, it becomes more important to protect water supply by dams and watersheds, and by preventing the pollution of streams by the return of unclean water.   Typical municipal waters contain from 30 to 1,000 parts per million of dissolved minerals, chiefly silica, iron, calcia, magnesia, potassium, sulfates, chlorides, and nitrites.   Organic matter is also present in the water in varying amounts.   So-called pure lake water averages above 150 parts per million.   Thus, pure water for chemical processing may require ion-exchange purification after filtering.   Water for atomic reactors is thus purified to not more than 0.08 ppm.

The water molecule is one of the simplest of the chemical combinations of the natural elements, but it embraces such a vast complexity that it can be taken as an example to illustrate the basic principles of the combining habits of all the elements.   The unit molecule, $H \cdot O \cdot H$, appears to be of ovaloid shape over a wide range of temperature.   The bonding is very strong.   With active metallic inclusions in water, the disintegration of the molecule may begin at an energy equivalent of about 1000°C, but complete dissociation into its elements, hydrogen and oxygen, requires a temperature above 2000°C.   Water is a very stable **oxygen hydride.**

The molecule is too minute for measurement of hardness by any known methods, but it is deduced to be extremely hard.   When a stream of water is projected through a tiny orifice at high pressure it will cut through a tree like a power saw.   At the energy levels of the liquid stage the molecules are very mobile and roll on each other, but when water drips from a faucet or falls as rain it forms into rounded droplets.   The cause is usually given as **surface tension,** but may be the electromagnetic attraction of the exposed proton pairs on the oxygen atoms.   When the molecules are lubricated with a chemical the water flows more easily.   This property is used in fire-fighting hose.   **Polyox FRA,** of Union Carbide, is a polymer derivative of ethylene oxide used for this purpose.   When a 1% solution of the resin is injected into the line the stream of water is projected more than twice the normal distance.   Water can also be coated to form **dry water** of semisolid consistency in the form of droplets which are dry to the touch.   This property is utilized in water-based cosmetic creams by adding silicic acid. When the cosmetic is applied to the face the silicic acid dehydrolizes to leave an adherent coating of extremely fine amorphous silica on the skin, and the thin film of released water evaporates quickly to give a cool fresh feel.

Lumping and caking of flours and other powders is usually caused by absorption of water moisture from the air, but the addition of as little as 0.5% of an **anticaking agent** such as silicic acid will coat and dry the absorbed moisture and prevent caking.   The material known as **anomalous water** has properties similar to those of pure water treated with silicic acid. It forms in dry globules of low mobility, and has a wider temperature range in the liquid state.   It is produced by condensing distilled water in vacuum in a small quartz (latticed silica) tube.   The accumulation is extremely slow, requiring 18 hr to fill a tube of 0.010 in. diameter.   It is also called **polywater,** though the water molecule does not polymerize in the ordinary meaning of the term.   The water molecule can also be absorbed within the molecules of many chemicals, both solid and liquid, and such materials are called **hygroscopic.**   For example, phosphophenyl methyl phosphinic acid has a unit molecular group in the shape of an irregular toroid.   With only enough water to fill the spaces in the toroid, the unit is rounded and mobile, and the material becomes a viscous liquid which is dissimilar to a water solution of a material.   Large proportions of water may be encased in the cells and lattices of proteins or other organic materials, making the mass into a solid or semisolid in which as much as 97% of the volume is water.   This process is used in the making of puddings such as **Jello** in which a small amount of edible gelatin encases the water.   **Water-filled plastics** are usually thermoplastic resins in which 80% or more of water is used as a filler.   The water is stirred into the resin and the casting sets to a hard, firm solid which can be machined, nailed, or screwed.   The castings are used for models, ornaments, and such products as lamp stands.

There is no room within the water molecule for the containment of any other atom or molecule, but the liquid mass may be likened to the arrangement of a great pile of uniformly sized, ovaloid Danish pebbles, and the mass has comparatively large spaces between and among the units.   All natural waters contain much foreign matter including oxygen and other gases from the air, organic material from plant and animal life, minerals picked up from contact with the earth, and often high proportions of large inorganic molecules such as **astrakanite,** $Na_2SO_4 \cdot MgSO_4 \cdot 4H_2O$, and carnallite.   **Ground water,** pumped from deep wells for industrial and municipal uses, was once considered the purest of waters, containing chiefly mineral salts, but in populated areas underground waters are now contaminated with the seepage from fertilizers, insecticides, industrial chemicals, and sewage which includes froth-forming detergents.   Water in streams, in addition to the natural minerals and plant-decay matter, now usually contains high contents of industrial and agricultural chemicals and sewage, plus biological compounds from the decayed proteins and albumins of human and animal wastes.   Many of these can only be removed by costly special ion-exchange methods.   Bacteria may be inactivated by the addition of chlorine, but the skatolelike odors may remain.   The content of air in natural water, given in terms of O_2, is a minimum of 9 ppm. This contained air is a biological necessity in water for human consumption and for the maintenance of fish and other marine life. The chemical process of decay of sewage in water depletes this oxygen and thus tends to destroy marine life. **Seawater,** and water in inland lakes such as the Dead Sea where evaporation greatly exceeds runoff, contains high amounts of mineral salts. The variety and percentage content varies in different areas and at different temperatures. The density of seawater at 68°F may be 69 lb per cu ft compared with about 62 lb per cu ft for natural fresh water. About 80 elements have been found in seawater, and it is probable that all of the natural elements occur to some extent. About 30% of all commercial halite, or common salt, is now produced from seawater. By ordinary solar evaporation at about 80°F, the proportion of common salt, NaCl, precipitating after the calcite and gypsum, may be about 12% of the total salts. As much as 65% of commercial magnesium metal is produced from seawater by precipitation and reduction of contained magnesium compounds such as epsomite, kainite, kieserite, **bischofite,** $MgCl_2 \cdot 6H_2O$, and the magnesium sulfate known as **hexahydrite,** $MgSO_4 \cdot 6H_2O$. At the energy level of solidification the water molecules arrange themselves in precise order close together, and the frozen water, or **ice,** can be split in straight cleavage from a line scratched on the surface. In the solid assembly of molecules there is no available space, and the contained impurities of water are thrown out in freezing, except in the dendritic snow molecule.

WATER REPELLENTS. Chemicals used for treating textiles, leather, and paper such as washable wallpaper, to make them resistant to wetting by water. They are different from waterproofing materials in that they are used where it is not desirable to make the material completely waterproof, but to permit the leather or fabric to "breathe." Water repellents must not form acids that would destroy the material, and they must set the dyes rather than cause them to bleed on washing. There are two basic types, a durable type that resists cleaning, and a renewable type that must be replaced after the fabric is dry-cleaned. **Zelan,** a pyridinium-resin compound of Du Pont, is representative of the first type. **Quilon,** of the same company, is used for paper, textiles, and glass fabric, and forms a strong chemical bond to the surface of the material by an attachment of the chromium end of the molecule through the covalent bond to the negatively charged surface. It is a stearato chromic chloride. The second type is usually an emulsion of a mineral salt over which a wax emulsion is placed; the treatment may be a one-bath process, or may be by two separate treatments. **Aluminum acetate** is one of the most common materials for this purpose. Basic aluminum acetate is a white, amorphous powder of the composition $Al(OH)(OOC \cdot CH_3)$. It is only slightly soluble in water

but is soluble in mineral acids.   **Niaproof,** of Union Carbide, is a concentrated aluminum acetate for waterproofing textiles, and **Ramasit** of the
General Dyestuff Corp., and **Migasol** of the Ciba Co., are similar materials.
Zirconium acetate, a white crystalline material of the composition $ZrOH-$
$(C_2H_3O_2)_3$, and also its sodium salt, are used as water repellents.   **Zirconyl acetate,** $ZrO(C_2H_3O_2)_2$, a light-yellow solution containing 13%
ZrO_2, is used for both water repellency and flame resistance of textile
fibers.   **Intumescent agents** are repellent coatings that swell and snuff out
fire when they become hot.   **Latex 744B,** of the Dow Chemical Co., is a
repellent of this type.   It is a vinyl water emulsion compounded with pentaerythritol, dicyandiamide, and monosodium phosphate, and is used on
textiles, wallboard, and fiber tile.

WATER SOFTENERS. Chemical compounds used for converting soluble scale-forming solids in water into insoluble forms.   In the latter
condition they are then removed by setting or filtration.   The hardness
of water is due chiefly to the presence of carbonates, bicarbonates, and
sulfates of calcium and magnesium, but many natural waters also contain
other metal complexes which need special treatment for removal.   Temporary **hard waters** are those that can be softened by boiling; permanent
hard waters are those that require chemicals to change their condition.
Sodium hydroxide is used to precipitate magnesium sulfate.   Caustic lime
is employed to precipitate bicarbonate of magnesium, and sodium aluminate is used as an accelerator.   Barium carbonate may also be used.   Prepared water softeners may consist of mixtures of lime, soda ash, and
sodium aluminate, the three acting together.   **Sodium aluminate,** $Na_2Al_2O_4$,
is a water-soluble white powder melting at 1650°C, which is also used as
a textile mordant, for sizing paper, and in making milky glass.   Reynolds
Metals Co. produces this material in flake form with iron content below
0.0056% for paints, water softeners, and paper coatings.   Alum is used
in settling tanks to precipitate mud, and zeolite is used extensively for filtering water.   The liquids added to the washing water to produce fluffier
textiles are **fabric softeners** and not water softeners.   They are usually basic
quarternary ammonium compounds such as distearyl dimethyl ammonium
chloride with 16 and 18 carbon atoms, which are cationic, or positively
charged.   A thin coating is deposited on the negatively charged fabric,
giving a lubricated cloth with a fluffy feel.

Water is also softened and purified with **ion-exchange agents,** which may
be specially prepared synthetic resins.   **Cation-exchange agents** substitute
sodium for calcium and magnesium ions and produce soft waters.   When
the water is treated with a hydrogen derivative of a resin, the metal cations
form acids from the salts.   The carbonates are converted to carbonic acid
which goes off in the air.   When it is treated again with a basic resin

derivative, or **anion-exchange agent,** the acids are removed. Water receiving this double treatment is equal to distilled water. Salt-cycle anion-exchange substitutes chloride ions for other anions in the water, and when combined with cation exchange it produces sodium chloride in the water in place of other ions.

In electrolytic ion exchangers for converting seawater to fresh water, the basic cell is divided into three compartments by two membranes, one permeable only to cations and the other only to anions. The sodium ions migrate toward the cathode and the chlorine ions go toward the anode leaving fresh water in the center compartment. **Ion-exchange membranes** for electrodialysis (salt splitting or separation), and also used in fuel cells, are theoretically the same as powdered exchange resins but with an inorganic binder. Such a membrane resin of the Armour Research Foundation is made by the reaction of zirconyl chloride and phosphoric acid, giving a chain molecule of zirconium-oxygen with side chains of dihydrogen phosphate. **Zeo-Karb,** a sulfonated coal, and **Zeo-Rex,** a sulfonated phenol-formaldehyde resin, are cation exchangers of the Permutit Co., while **De-Acidite** and **Permutit A** of the same company are anion exchangers. **Amberlite IRA-400,** of Rohm & Haas, is a strongly basic alkyl amine which will split neutral salts in the water and also remove silica. The German **Wofatit P** exchanger is a sodium salt of a phenol-formaldehyde resin. Ion-exchange agents are also used for refining sugar, glycerin, and other products, and for the purification of acids and the separation of metals. An **eluting agent** is a solvent used to elutriate the resin beds in the separation of metals, that is, to separate the heavier from the lighter particles, causing a metal ion on the resin to change place with hydrogen or with an ammonium group in the elutriant.

WAX. A general name for a variety of substances of animal and vegetable origin, which are fatty acids in combination with higher alcohols instead of with glycerin as in fats and oils. They are usually harder than fats, less greasy, and more brittle, but when used alone do not mold as well. Chemically, the waxes differ from fats and oils in being composed of high-molecular-weight fatty acids with high-molecular-weight alcohols. The most familiar wax is beeswax from the honeybee, but commercial beeswax is usually greatly mixed or adulterated. Another animal wax is spermaceti from the sperm whale. **Vegetable waxes** include Japan wax, jojoba oil, candelilla, and carnauba wax. **Mineral waxes** include paraffin wax from petroleum, ozokerite, ceresin, montan wax. The mineral waxes differ from the true waxes and are mixtures of saturated hydrocarbons.

The animal and vegetable waxes are not plentiful materials, and are often blended with or replaced by hydrocarbon waxes or waxy synthetic resins. But waxes can be made from common oils and fats by splitting off the glycerin and reesterifying selected mixtures of the fatty acids with higher alcohols.   **Hywax 122,** of the Werner G. Smith Co., is a self-emulsifiable wax composed of cetyl, myristyl, and stearyl esters derived from animal and vegetable oils.   **Opalwax,** of Du Pont, is a **synthetic wax** produced by the hydrogenation of castor oil.   It has about the same hardness as carnauba, specific gravity of 0.98, melting point of 86 to 88°C, is odorless, and of a pearl-white color, but it lacks the luster of carnauba. It is very resistant to most solvents, and is used for insulation, coatings, candles, and carbon paper.   **Acrawax,** of Glyco Products Co., Inc., is a somewhat similar substitute for carnauba with higher melting point. **Stroba wax** of the same company is a synthetic wax with a base of stearic acid and lime.   The melting point is 103 to 106°C.   It is used in polishes, insulation, and as a flatting agent.   Synthetic wax under the name of **Pentawax 286,** of the Heyden Newport Chemical Corp., is a true wax in that it is a combination of fatty acids with an alcohol.   It is made from the long-chain acids of vegetable oils with pentaerythritol.   It has a higher melting point than carnauba, 110°F, but does not form a self-polishing liquid wax like carnauba.   **Sheerwax,** of Ru-Jac, Inc., is made by catalytic hydrogenation of vegetable oils.   It has the hardness and high-melting point of carnauba wax and can be had in white color.   Waxes are employed in polishes, coatings, leather dressings, sizings, waterproofing for paper, candles, and varnishes.   They are softer and have lower melting points than resins, are soluble in mineral spirits and in alcohol, and insoluble in water.

Some plastics have wax characteristics, and may be used in polishes and coatings or for blending with waxes.   Polyethylene waxes are light-colored, odorless solids of low molecular weight, up to about 6,000. Mixed in solid waxes to the extent of 50%, and in liquid waxes up to 20%, they add gloss and durability and increase toughness.   In emulsions they add stability.   **Alcowax,** of the Allied Chemical Corp., is a polyethylene of low molecular weight, about 2,000.   It is a translucent solid melting at about 100°C.   **Marlex 20,** of the Phillips Petroleum Co., is a methylene polymer used to blend with vegetable or paraffin waxes to increase the melting point, strength, and hardness.   **Santowax R,** of Monsanto, is a mixture of terphenols.   It is a light-buff, waxy solid, highly soluble in benzene, and with good resistance to heat, acids, and alkalies. It is used to blend with natural waxes in candles, coatings, and insulation. **Epolene wax,** of Eastman Chemical Products, Inc., is a polyethylene. Waxes are not digestible, and the so-called **edible waxes** used as water-resistant coatings for cheese, meats, and dried fruits are not waxes, but are modified glycerides.   **Monocet,** of the Glyco Products Co., Inc., is such a material.   It is a white, odorless, tasteless waxy solid melting at 40°C, and is an acetylated monoglyceride of fatty acids.

WEAR-RESISTANT STEEL. Many types of steel have wear-resistant properties, but the term usually refers to high-carbon, high-alloy steels used for press dies subject to abrasion and for wear-resistant castings. They are generally cast and ground to shape. They are mostly sold under trade names for specific purposes. The excess carbon of these steels is in spheroidal form rather than as graphite. One of the earlier materials of this kind for drawing and forming dies, **Adamite,** of the Mackintosh-Hemphill Co., was a chromium-nickel-iron alloy with up to 1.5% chromium, nickel equal to half that of the chromium, and from 1.5 to 3.5% carbon, with silicon from 0.5 to 2%. The Brinell hardness ranges from 185 to 475 as cast, with tensile strengths to 125,000 psi. The softer grades can be machined and then hardened, but the hard grades are finished by grinding. **Kinite,** of the Kinite Corp., has about 13% chromium, 1.5 carbon, 1.1 molybdenum, 0.70 cobalt, 0.55 silicon, 0.50 manganese, and 0.40 nickel. It is for blanking dies, forming dies, and cams. **Martin steel,** of the Detroit Alloy Steel Co., has 13% chromium, about 1 molybdenum, 0.80 cobalt, 0.35 vanadium, and 1.5 carbon. **Circle T15 steel,** of Firth Sterling, Inc., for extreme abrasion resistance in cutting tools, is classed as a super-high-speed steel. It has 13.5% tungsten, 4.5 chromium, 5 cobalt, 4.75 vanadium, 0.50 molybdenum, and 1.5 carbon. Its great hardness comes from the hard vanadium carbide and the complex tungsten-chromium carbides, and it has full red hardness. The property of abrasion or wear resistance in steels generally comes from the hard carbides, and is thus inherent with proper heat-treatment in many types of steel.

WELDING ALLOYS. Usually in the form of rod, wire, or powder used for either electric or gas welding, or for building up surfaces, or for hard-facing surfaces. In the small sizes in continuous lengths welding alloys are called **welding wire.** Nonferrous rods used for welding bronzes are usually referred to as **brazing rods,** as the metal to be welded is not fused when using them. Welding rods may be standard metals or special alloys, coated with a fluxing material or uncoated, and are normally in diameters from $\frac{3}{32}$ to $\frac{1}{4}$ in. Compositions of standard welding rods follow the specifications of the American Welding Society. Molded carbon, in sizes from $\frac{1}{8}$ to 1 in. in diameter, is also used for arc welding. **Intensarc** is the trade name of the National Carbon Co., Inc., for carbon rods. Low-carbon steel rods for welding cast iron and steel contain less than 0.18% carbon. High-carbon rods produce a hard deposit that requires annealing, but these are also used for producing a hard filler. High-carbon rods, with 0.85 to 1.10% carbon, will give deposits with initial hardness of 575 Brinell, whereas high-manganese rod deposits will be below 200 Brinell but will work-harden to above 500 Brinell. For high-production automatic welding operations, carbon-steel wire may have a thin coating of copper for easy operation and nonspattering.   Stainless-steel rods are marketed in various compositions.   The **Flexarc welding rods** of the Westinghouse Electric Corp. comprise a range of stainless steels with either titania-lime or straight-lime coatings.   **Stainless C,** of the Lincoln Electric Co., is an 18–8 type of stainless steel having also 3.5% molybdenum.   **Aluminumweld,** of the same company, is a 5% silicon aluminum rod for welding silicon-aluminum alloys, and the **Tungweld rods,** for hard surfacing, are steel tubes containing   fine particles of tungsten carbide.   **Kennametal KT-200,** of Kennametal, Inc., has a core of tungsten carbide and a sheathing of steel.   It gives coatings with a hardness of Rockwell C63.   **Chromang,** of the Arcos Co., for welding high-alloy steels, is an 18–8 stainless steel modified with 2.5 to 4% manganese.

The **Amsco welding rods** of the American Manganese Steel Co. are grades of high-manganese steel giving hardnesses from 500 to 700 Brinell, and **Toolface** is a high-speed steel rod of the same company for facing worn cutting tools.   **Superloy,** of the Resisto-Loy Co., used for facing surfaces where extreme hardness is required, has the alloy granules in a soft-steel tube.   The welded deposit has a composition of 30% chromium, 8 cobalt, 8 molybdenum, 5 tungsten, 0.05 boron, and 0.20 carbon.   **Tung-Alloy, Resisto-Loy,** and **Isorod** are other **hard-facing rods** of the same company; Resisto-Loy has a nonferrous content.   The **Croloy welding rods** of the Babcock & Wilcox Co., for welding alloy steels without high preheating, are low-alloy chrome-molybdenum steels.   **Stoodite** is a high-manganese steel in the form of rods marketed by the Stoody Co. for hard facing. **Chromend 9M,** of the Arcos Corp., is a rod for arc-welding hard deposits. It contains 8 to 10% chromium and 1.5 molybdenum, giving a weld with a hardness of 400 Brinell.   **Elkonite,** of the P. R. Mallory Co., is the name of a group of welding alloys made especially for welding machines.   They are, in general, sintered tungsten or molybdenum carbides, combined with copper or silver, and are electrodes for spot welding rather than welding rods.   **Tungsten electrodes** may be pure tungsten, thoriated tungsten, or zirconium tungsten, the latter two used for direct current.   **Thoriated tungsten** gives high arc stability, and the thoria also increases the machinability of the tungsten.   **Zirconium tungsten** provides adhesion between the solid electrode and the molten metal to give uniformity in the weld.

Thermit is a mixture of aluminum powder and iron oxide used for welding large sections of iron or steel or for filling large cavities.   The process, originally developed by the Goldschmidt Thermit Co., consists in the burning of the aluminum to react with the oxide, setting free the iron in molten form.   To ignite the aluminum and start the reaction a temperature of about 2800°F is required, which is reached with the aid of a gas torch or ignition powder, and the exothermic temperature is about 4600°F. **Cast-iron thermit,** used for welding cast iron, is thermit with the addition of about 3% ferrosilicon and 20 steel punchings.   **Red thermit** is made with red oxide, and **black thermit** with black oxide.   **Railroad thermit** is thermit with additions of nickel, manganese, and steel.

The **Stellite hard-facing rods,** of Union Carbide, are cobalt-based alloys that retain hardness at red heat and are very corrosion-resistant.   The grades have tensile strengths to 105,000 psi and hardnesses to Rockwell C52.   **Inco-Weld A,** of the International Nickel Co., is welding wire for stainless steels and for overlays.   It contains 70% nickel, 16 chromium, 8 iron, 2 manganese, 3 titanium, and not more than 0.07 carbon.   The annealed weld has a tensile strength of 80,000 psi with elongation of 12%. **Nickel welding rod** is much used for cast iron, and the operation is brazing, with the base metal not melted.   The **Nickel silver 828** of the American Brass Co., for brazing cast iron, contains 46.5% copper, 43.38 zinc, 10 nickel, 0.10 silicon, and 0.02 phosphorus.   The deposit matches the color of the iron.   **Colmonoy 23A,** of Wall Colmonoy Corp., is a nickel alloy **welding powder** for welding cast iron and filling blow holes in iron castings by torch application.   It has a composition of 2.3% silicon, 1.25 boron, 0.10 carbon, not over 1.5 iron, and the balance nickel, with a melting point of 1950°F.   For welding on large structures where no heat treatment of the weldment is possible, the welding rods must have balanced compositions with no elements that form brittle compounds.   **Rockide rods,** of Norton, are metal oxides for hard surfacing.

WETTING AGENTS. Chemicals used in making solutions, emulsions, or compounded mixtures, such as paints, inks, cosmetics, starch pastes, oil emulsions, dentifrices, detergents, to reduce the surface tension and give greater ease of mixing and stability to the solution.   In the food industries chemical wetting agents are added to the solutions for washing fruits and vegetables to produce a cleaner and bacteria-free product.   Wetting agents are described in general as chemicals having a large hydrophilic group associated with a smaller hydrophilic group.   Some liquids naturally wet pigments, oils, or waxes, but others require a proportion of a wetting agent to give mordant or wetting properties.   Pine oil is a common wetting agent, but many are complex chemicals.   They should be powerful enough not to be precipitated out of solutions in the form of salts, and they should be free of odor or any characteristic that would affect the solution.   **Aerosol wetting agents,** of the American Cyanamid Co., are in the form of liquids, waxy pellets, or free-flowing powders.   **Aerosol OS** is a sodium salt of an alkyl naphthalene sulfonic acid.   It is a yellowish-brown powder soluble in most organic solvents.   This salt was called **Nekal** in Germany. The **Dresinols** of Hercules are sodium or ammonium dispersions of modified rosin, with 90% of the particles below 1 micron in size.   **Polyfon,** of the West Virginia Pulp & Paper Co., is a sodium ligno sulfonate produced from lignin waste liquor.   It is used for dye and pigment dispersion, oil-well drilling mud, ore flotation, and boiler feed-water treatment.

WHALE OIL. An oil extracted by boiling and steaming the blubber of several species of whale that are found chiefly in the cold waters of the extreme north and south.   Whales are mammals, and are predaceous, living on animal food.   The blubber blanket of fat protects the body, and the tissues and organs also contain deposits of fat.   Most whale oil is true fat, namely, the glycerides of fatty acids, but the head contains a waxy fat.   In the larger animals the meat and bones yield more fat than the blubber.   Both the whalebone whales and the toothed whales produce whale oil.   The **bluehead whales** of the south, *Silbaldus musculus,* are the largest and also yield most oil per weight.   The whaling industry is under international control, and allocations are made on the basis of blue whale units averaging 20 tons of oil each.   The blue whale is about 25 ft long at birth and reaches 70 ft in 2 years.   This species often reaches 100 ft. A 100-ft whale will weigh about 150 tons, and will yield about 27 tons of oil.   The **gray whale,** or **California whale,** of the northern Pacific, is a small 50-ft species.   The **Greenland whale** of the north, *Balaena mysticetus,* and the **finback whale** of the south, *Balaenoptera physalus,* produce much oil.   The **beluga,** or **white whale,** *Delphinapterus leucas,* and the **narwhal,** *Monodon monoceros,* of the North Polar seas, produce **porpoise oil.**   Both species of porpoise measure up to 20 ft in length.

Whale oil is sold according to grade, which depends upon its color and keeping qualities.   The latter in turn depend largely upon proper cooking at extraction.   No. 0 and No. 1 grades are fine pale-yellow oils, No. 2 is amber, No. 3 is pale brown, and No. 4 is the darkest oil.   Grade 1 has less than 1% free fatty acids, while grade 4 has from 15 to 60% with a strong fishy odor.   The specific gravity is 0.920 to 0.927, saponification value 180 to 197, and iodine value 105 to 135.   Whale oil contains oleic, stearic, palmitic, and other acids in varying amounts.   But whales are now so scarce that the former uses of the oils and meat are restricted, particularly in the United States.

Whale oils of the lower grades were used for quenching baths for heat-treating steels, and also in lubricating oils.   The best oils are used in soaps and candles, or for preparing textile fibers for spinning, or for treating leather.   In Europe whale oil is favored for making margarine because it requires less hydrogen than other oils for hardening, and the grouping of the 16 to 22 carbon atom acids gives the hardened product greater plasticity over a wider temperature range.   **Sod oil** is oil recovered from the treatment of leather in which whale or other marine mammal oil was used. It contains some of the tannins and nitrogenous matter which make it more emulsifiable and more penetrant than the original oil.

Whale meat was used for food in Japan, and in dog food in the United States.   When cured in the air, the outside is hard and black, but the inside is soft.   In young animals the flesh is pale; in older animals it is dark red.   It has a slight fishy flavor, but when cooked with vegetables is almost indistinguishable from beef.   It contains 15 to 18% proteins. **Whale-meat extract** is used in bouillon cubes and dehydrated soups.   It is 25% weaker than beef extract.   **Whale liver oil** is used in medicine for its high vitamin A content.   It also contains **kitol,** which has properties similar to vitamin A but is not absorbed in all animal metabolism.   **Whale-bones** are the elastic, hornlike strips in the upper jaw of the Greenland whale and some other species.   The strips are generally from 8 to 10 ft long and number up to 600.   Those from the **bowhead whale** of the Arctic Ocean are the longest slabs, measuring up to 13 ft in length and 10 to 12 in. wide at the bottom.   **Finback whalebone** is less than 4 ft in length. The **humpback whale,** *Megaptera longimana,* of the northern Pacific, is a **baleen whale** with no teeth and with plates of baleen in the mouth to act as a sieve.   It grows to a length of 50 ft.   Whalebone is light in weight, very flexible, elastic, tough, and durable.   It consists of a conglomeration of hairy fibers covered with an enamellike fibrous tissue.   It is easily split and when softened in hot water is easily carved.   Whalebone has a variety of uses in making whips, helmet frames, ribs, and brush fibers.   **Baleen** is a trade name for strips of whalebone used for whips, and for products where great flexibility and elasticity are required.

WHEAT.   The edible seed grains of an annual grass of the genus *Triticum* of which there are many species and thousands of varieties.   Wheat was the basic food grain of the early civilizations of the Near East, and has remained the chief grain of the white races except in cold climates where rye grows better.   The plains of the United States, Canada, Argentina, Australia, southern Russia, the Danube Valley, and northern India are the great wheat areas.

The types grown commercially are chiefly common wheat and durum wheat.   **Common wheat,** *T. vulgare,* is the chief source of **wheat flour.** It has a stout head from which the grains can be separated easily.   The hundreds of varieties are divided roughly into hard wheats and soft wheats, and red wheats and white wheats.   The hard wheats usually have smaller grains, but are richer in proteins.

Spring wheat is wheat that is sown in the spring and harvested in the late summer.   **Winter wheat** is sown in the fall to develop a root system before winter, and is then harvested in the early summer.   It is more resistant and gives a higher yield.   **Durum wheat,** *T. durum,* has a thick head with long beards, and large hard grains rich in gluten.   The plant is hardy and drought-resistant, but the flour is too glutenous for American bread, and is much used for macaroni and in mixtures. Seven classes of wheat are designated in the official grain standards of the U.S. Department of Agriculture: hard red spring wheat; durum wheat; red durum wheat; hard red winter wheat; soft red winter wheat; white winter wheat; and mixed wheat. Each class permits mixtures of varieties. The minimum test weight of wheat is required to be 60 lb per bu.

Most of the wheat production is ground for edible flour. Since wheat varies with the variety, the climate, and the soil, uniformity in the flour could formerly be obtained only by blending wheats from different areas to obtain an average, but uniformity is now obtained by an air-spinning process which separates the milled flour into fractions according to protein-starch ratios, and then combining for the flour of uniform ratio. These are called **turbo-flours.** Wheat flour is not normally a uniform product even from one area, as it is made up of starch granules, fractured endosperm cells, and protein fragments. **Pregelatinized flour** is used for canned goods to reduce the time needed for dextrinizing. **Wheat-flour paste,** for textile coatings, is **hydroxy ethylated flour** made by treating wheat flour with ethylene oxide. It requires little cooking to form a starchy product.

Wheat is also used for making beer, and at times is employed for producing starch and alcohol. Some wheat is used for stock feed, but most of the wheat for this purpose is of lower and condemned grades. **Buckwheat** consists of the seed grains of the *Fagopyrum esculentum,* a plant of the same family as the rhubarb and dock. It is native to Asia and is one of the chief foods in Russia, but is used only in mixed flours in the United States. The flour is more starchy and has less protein than wheat. It is also darker in color and has a different flavor.

WHETSTONE. Stones of regular fine grains composed largely of chalcedony silica, often with minute garnet and rutile crystals. They are used as fine abrasive stones for the final sharpening of edge tools. Whetstones are also sometimes selected, fine sandstones from the grindstone quarries. The **chocolate whetstone** from New Hampshire is mica schist. The finest whetstones are called **oilstones.** A fine-grained **honestone,** known as **coticule,** comes from Belgium, and is used for sharpening fine-edged tools. It is compact, yellow in color, and contains minute crystals of yellow manganese garnet, with also potash mica and tourmaline. Coticule is often cut double with the blue-gray **phyllite** rock adhering to and supporting it. **Scythestones** are made from Ohio and Indiana sandstones, and from the schist of Vermont. **Rubbing stones** are fine-grained Indiana sandstones.

WHITE BRASS. A bearing metal which is actually outside of the range of the brasses, bronzes, or babbitt metals. It is used in various grades, the specification adopted by SAE being tin, 65%; zinc, 28 to 30; and copper, 3 to 6.   It is used for automobile bearings, and is close-grained, hard, and tough.   It also casts well.   A different alloy is known under the name of white brass in the cheap jewelry and novelty trade.   It has no tin, small proportions of copper, and the remainder zinc.   It is a high-zinc brass, and varies in color from silvery white to yellow, depending upon the copper content.   An old alloy formerly used for casting buttons, known as **Birmingham platina,** or **platina,** contained 75% zinc and 25 copper.   It had a white color but was very brittle.   A yellowish metal known as **bath metal,** once widely used for casting buttons, candlesticks, and other articles, was a brass containing 55% copper and 45 zinc.   **White nickel brass** is a grade of nickel silver.   The white brass used for castings where a white color is desired may contain up to 30% nickel.   The 60–20–20 alloy is used for white plaque castings for buildings.   The high-nickel brasses do not cast well unless they also contain lead.   Those with 15 to 20% nickel and 2 lead are used for casting hardware and valves. **White nickel alloy** is a cupronickel containing some aluminum.   **White copper** is a name sometimes used for cupronickel or nickel brass.   The nickel brasses known as **German silver** are copper-nickel-zinc white alloys used as a base metal for plated silverware, for springs and contacts in electrical equipment, and for corrosion-resistant parts.   The alloys are graded according to the nickel content.   Extra-white metal, the highest grade, contains 50% copper, 30 nickel, and 20 zinc.   The lower grade, called fifths, for plated goods, has a yellowish color.   It contains 57% copper, 7 nickel, and 36 zinc.   All of the early German silvers contained up to 2% iron which increased the strength, hardness, and whiteness, but is not desirable in the alloys used for electrical work.   Some of the early English alloys also contained up to 2% tin, but tin makes the alloys brittle. The Federal Trade Commission prohibits the use of the term German silver in the marketing of silver-plated ware, but the name still persists in other industries.

WHITE GOLD. The name of a class of jewelers' white alloys used as substitutes for platinum.   The name gives no idea of the relative value of the different grades, which vary widely.   Gold and platinum may be alloyed together to make a white gold, but the usual alloys consist of from 20 to 50% nickel, with the balance gold.   Nickel and zinc with gold may also be used for white golds.   The best commercial grades of white gold are made by melting the gold with a white alloy prepared for the purpose.   This alloy contains nickel, silver, palladium, and zinc.   The 14-carat white gold contains 14 parts pure gold and 10 white alloy.   A superior class of white gold is made of 90% gold and 10 palladium. High-strength white gold contains copper, nickel, and zinc, with the gold.

Such an alloy, containing 37.5% gold, 28 copper, 17.5 nickel, and 17 zinc, when aged by heat treatment, has a tensile strength of about 100,000 psi and an elongation 35%. It is used for making jewelry, has a fine, white color, and is easily worked into intricate shapes. **White-gold solder** is made in many grades containing up to 12% nickel, up to 15 zinc, with usually also copper and silver, and from 30 to 80 gold. The melting points of eight grades of Handy & Harman are from 695 to 845°C.

WHITE METALS. Although a great variety of combinations can be made with numerous metals to produce white, or silvery, alloys, the name usually refers to the lead-antimony-tin alloys employed for machine bearings, packings, and linings, to the low-melting-point alloys used for toys, ornaments, and fusible metals, and to the type metals. **Slush castings,** for ornamental articles and hollow parts, are made in a wide variety of soft white alloys, usually varying proportions of lead, tin, zinc, and antimony, depending on cost and the accuracy and finish desired. These castings are made by pouring the molten metal into a metal mold without a core, and immediately pouring out again, a thin shell of the alloy solidifying against the metal of the mold and forming a hollow product. A number of white metals are specified by the ASTM for bearing use. These vary in a wide range from 2 to 91% tin, 4.5 to 15 antimony, up to 90 lead, and up to 8 copper. The alloy containing 75% tin, 12 antimony, 10 lead, and 3 copper melts at 184°C, is poured at about 375°C, has an ultimate compressive strength of 16,150 psi, and a Brinell hardness of 24. The alloy containing 10% tin, 15 antimony, and 75 lead melts at 240°C, has a compressive strength of 15,650 psi and a Brinell hardness 22. The first of these two alloys contains copper-tin crystals; the second contains tin-antimony crystals. A white bearing metal produced by the American Smelting & Refining Co. under the name of **Asarcoloy** is composed of cadmium with 1.3% nickel. It contains $NiCd_7$ crystals, and is harder and has higher compressive strength than babbitt, and a low coefficient of friction. It has a melting point of 604°F. **SAE alloy 18** is such a **cadmium-nickel alloy** with also small amounts of silver, copper, tin, and zinc. A **bismuth-lead alloy** containing 58% bismuth and 42 lead melts at 123.5°C. It casts to exact size without shrinkage or expansion, and is used for master patterns and for sealing.

Various high-tin or reverse bronzes have been used as corrosion-resistant metals, especially before the advent of the chromium, nickel, and aluminum alloys for this purpose. **Trabuk** was a corrosion-resistant, high-tin bronze with about 5% nickel. **Fahry's alloy** was a **reverse bronze** containing 90% tin and 10 copper, used as a bearing metal, and the **Jacoby metal** used for machine parts had 85% tin, 10 antimony, and 5 copper. The scarcity and high cost of tin have made these alloys obsolete. The bearing alloy known in England as **motor bronze** is a babbitt with about double the amount of copper of a standard babbitt. One analysis gives tin, 84%; antimony, 7.5; copper, 7.5; and bismuth, 1. An old alloy, used in India for utensils, and known as **bidery metal,** contained 31 parts zinc, 2 lead, and 2 copper, fluxed with resins. It was finished with a velvety-black color by treating with a solution of copper sulfate. A **white metal sheet** now much used for making stamped and formed parts for costume jewelry, and electronic parts, is zinc with up to 1.5% copper and up to 0.5% titanium. The titanium with the copper prevents coarse-grain formation, raising the recrystallization temperature. The alloy weighs 22% less than copper, and it plates and solders easily. **Zilloy-20,** of the New Jersey Zinc Co., is pure zinc with no more than 1% of other elements. In rolled strip it has a tensile strength up to 27,000 psi and elongation of 35%.

WILLOW. The wood of the trees *Salix coerulea* and *S. alba,* native to Europe, but grown in many other places. It is best known as a material for cricket bats made in England. The American willows are known as **black willow,** from the tree *S. nigra,* and **western black willow,** from the tree *S. lasiandra.* The wood is also employed for making artificial limbs, and for articles where toughness and nonshrinking qualities are valued. The wood is brownish yellow in color, has a fine, open grain, and weighs about 30 lb per cu ft. It is of the approximate hardness of cherry and birch. **Japanese willow** is from the tree *S. urbaniana.* It has a closer and finer texture, and has a browner color. Black willow has a maximum crushing strength parallel to the grain of about 1,500 psi. **Salicin,** also called **salicoside** and **saligenin,** is a glucoside extracted from several species of willow bark of England and also from the American aspen. It is a colorless, crystalline material of the composition $(OH)_4C_6H_7 \cdot OO \cdot C_6H_4$-$CH_2OH$, decomposing at 201°C, and soluble in water and in alcohol. It is used in medicine as an antipyretic and tonic, and as a reagent for nitric acid. It hydrolyzes to glucose and salicyl alcohol, and the latter is oxidized to **salicylic acid,** $C_6H_4(OH)COOH$.

WIRE CLOTH. Stiff fabrics made of fine wire woven with plain loose weave, used for screens to protect windows, for guards, and for sieves and filters. Steel and iron wire may be used, either plain, painted, galvanized, or rustproofed, or various nonferrous metal wires are employed. It is usually put up in rolls in widths from 18 to 48 in. **Screen cloth** is usually 12, 14, 16, and 18 mesh, but wire cloth in copper, brass, or monel metal is made regularly in meshes from 4 to 100. The size of wire is usually from 0.009 to 0.065 in. in diameter. Wire cloth for fine filtering is made in very fine meshes. **Mesh** indicates the number of openings per inch, and has no reference to the diameter of wire. A 200-mesh cloth has 200 openings each way on a square inch, or 40,000 openings per square inch. Wire cloth as fine as 400 mesh, or 160,000 openings per square inch, is made by the Newark Wire Cloth Co., by wedge-shaped weaving, although 250 wires of the size of 0.004 in. when placed parallel and in contact will fill the space of 1 in. Very fine mesh wire cloth must be woven at an angle since the globular nature of most liquids will not permit passage of the liquid through microscopic square openings. The wire screen cloth of the Michigan Wire Cloth Co., for filtering and screening, has elongated openings. One way the 0.0055-in. wire count is 200 per inch, while the other way the 0.007-in. warp wire is 40 per inch.

Wire fabrics for reentry parachutes are made of heat-resistant nickel-chromium alloys, and the wire is not larger than 0.005 in. diameter to give flexibility to the cloth. Wire fabrics for ion engines to operate in cesium vapor at temperatures to 2400°F are made with tantalum, molybdenum, or tungsten wire, 0.003 to 0.006 in. diameter, with a twill weave. Meshes to a fineness of 350 by 2,300 can be obtained. Porosity uniformity is controlled by pressure calendering of the woven cloth, but for extremely fine meshes in wire cloth it is difficult to obtain the uniformity that can be obtained with porous sintered metals.

Where accuracy of sizing is not important, as in gravel or ore screening, wire fabric is made with oblong or rectangular openings instead of squares to give faster screening. High-manganese steel wire is used for rock screens. For window screening in tropical climates or in corrosive atmospheres plastic filaments are sometimes substituted for the standard copper or steel wire. **Lumite screen cloth,** of the Chicopee Mfg. Co., is woven of vinylidene chloride monofilament 0.015 in. in diameter in 18 and 20 mesh. The impact strength of the plastic cloth is higher than that of metal wire cloth, but it cannot be used for screening very hot materials. **Lektromesh,** of the C. O. Jelliff Corp., is copper or nickel screen cloth of 40 to 200 mesh made in one piece by electrodeposition. It can be drawn or formed more readily than wire screen, and circular or other shapes can be made with an integral selvage edge.

WIRE GLASS. A sheet glass used in building construction for windows, doors, floors, and skylights, having woven wire mesh embedded in the center of the plate. It does not splinter or fly apart like common glass when subjected to fire or shock, and has higher strength than common glass. It is made in standard thicknesses from ⅛ to ⅜ in., and in plates 60 by 110 in. and 61 by 140 in. Underwriters' specifications call for a minimum thickness of ¼ in. Wire glass is made with plain, rough, or polished surfaces, or with ribbed or cobweb surface on one side for diffusing the light and for decorative purposes. It is also obtainable in corrugated sheets, usually 27¾ in. wide.   Wire glass ¼ in. thick weighs 2.25 lb per sq ft.   Plastic-coated wire mesh may be used to replace wire glass for hothouses or skylights where less weight and fuller penetration of light rays are desired.   **Cel-O-Glass,** of Du Pont, is a plastic-coated wire mesh in sheet form.

WOLFRAMITE. The chief ore of the metal tungsten.   Its composition is $(FeMn)WO_3$.   When the manganese tungstate is low, the ore is called **ferberite;** when the iron tungstate is low, it is called **hübnerite.**   The ore is concentrated by gravity methods to a concentrate containing 60 to 65% **tungstic oxide,** WO_3.   To extract pure WO_3 from the concentrate it is fused with sodium carbonate, Na_2CO_3, to form **sodium tungstate,** Na_2WO_3, which is dissolved in water.   When an acid is added to the solution, the WO_3 precipitates out as a yellow powder.   The metallic tungsten is obtained by reducing, and is then pressed into bars and sintered.   Wolframite occurs usually bladed or columnar in form.   It has a specific gravity of 7.2 to 7.5, a hardness of 5, a black color, and a submetallic luster.   It is found in the Mountain states, Alaska, China, and Argentina, but is also widely distributed in various parts of the world in small quantities. Chinese **wolfram concentrates** contain 65% tungstic oxide; the Arizona concentrates contain an average of 67%.   California and Nevada concentrates are scheelite containing from 60 to 67% tungstic oxide.   The **sanmartinite** of Argentina is a variety containing zinc.

WOLLASTON WIRE. Any wire made by the Wollaston process of finewire drawing.   It consists in inserting a length of bare drawn wire into a close-fitting tube of another metal, the tube and core then being treated as a single rod and drawn through dies down to the required size.   The outside jacket of metal is then dissolved away by an acid that does not affect the core metal.   **Platinum wire** as fine as 0.00005 in. in diameter is made commercially by this method, and gold wire as fine as 0.00001 in. in diameter is also drawn.   Wires of this fineness are employed only in instruments.   They are marketed as composite wires, the user dissolving off the jacket.   **Taylor process wire** is a very fine wire made by the process of drawing in a glass tube.   The process is used chiefly for obtaining fine wire from a material lacking ductility, such as antimony, or extremely fine wire from a ductile metal.   The procedure is to melt the metal or alloy into a glass or quartz tube, and then draw down this tube with its contained material.   Wire as fine as 0.00004 in. in diameter is made, but only in short lengths.

WOOD. A general name applied to the cut material derived from trees. A **tree,** as distinguished from a **bush,** is designated by the United States

Forest Service as a woody plant with a single erect stem 3 in. or more in diameter at 4½ ft above the ground, and at least 12 ft high. But this definition is merely empirical since in the cold climate of northern Canada perfect, full-grown trees 10 to 15 years old may be only 6 in. high.

Timber, in general, refers to standing trees, while **lumber** is the sawed wood used for construction purposes. In construction work the word timber is often applied to large pieces of lumber used as beams. Wood is an organic chemical compound composed of approximately 49% carbon, 44 oxygen, 6 hydrogen, and 1 ash. It is largely cellulose and lignin. The wood of white pine is about 50% cellulose, 25 lignin, and the remainder sugars, resin, acetic acid, and other materials. Wood is produced in most trees by a progressive growth from the outside. In the spring when sap flows rapidly a rapid formation of large cells takes place, followed by a slower growth of hard and close cells in the summer. In some woods, such as oak, there is a considerable difference in quality and appearance between the spring and summer woods. In some long-lived trees, such as Douglas fir, there is a decreasing in strength between the outside wood with narrow rings and the wide-ringed wood of the interior. **Heartwood** is the dark center of the tree which has become set, and through which the sap has ceased to flow. **Sapwood** is the outer, live wood of the tree; unless treated, it has low decay resistance. The grain of sawed lumber results from sawing across the annual growth rings, varied to produce different grains.

Wood is seasoned either by exposing to the air to dry, or by kiln drying. The former method is considered to give superior quality, but requires more time, is expensive, and is indefinite. Numerous tests made at the United States Forest Products Laboratory did not reveal any superiority in air-dried wood when kiln drying was well done. Solvent seasoning is a rapid process consisting in circulating a hot solvent through the wood in a closed chamber. California redwood, when seasoned with acetone at 130°F, yields tannin and some other chemicals as by-products. Seasoned wood, when dry, is always stronger than the unseasoned wood. **Tank woods** are selected for resistance to the liquids to be contained. Tanks for vinegar and foodstuffs containing vinegar, such as pickles, are of white oak, cypress, or western red cedar. Beer tanks are of white oak or cypress. Tanks for aging wine are of redwood, oak, or fir.

The safe working stresses of the common construction woods in compression perpendicular to the grain are 900 to 1,300 psi. In the United States the distinction between **hardwoods** and **softwoods** is made arbitrarily by the class of tree, the evergreens being softwoods without reference to the actual hardness of the wood.

Wood decays easily when subjected to alternate wetting and drying, unless treated with creosote or zinc chloride. The largest use of wood is in building construction, but normally about 15% of all lumber produced in the United States goes into boxes and containers, and during wartime this use increases to 50% of the total.

Lumber is graded from A Select, which is practically free from defects, to D Select, which contains more defects than other selects but none detracting from a finished appearance. The common grades run from No. 1 Common, with only few and tight knots, to No. 5 Common, with coarse defects such as decay, holes, and wane. The term **log** designates the tree trunk with the branches removed. **Balk** is a roughly squared log; **plank** is a piece cut to rectangular section 11 in. wide; **deal** is a piece 9 in. wide; and **batten** is a piece 7 in. wide. Board is a thin piece of any width less than 2 in. thick. **Flitch** is half a balk cut in two lengthwise. **Scantling** is a piece sawed on all sides. **Shakes** are longitudinal splits or cracks in the wood due to shrinkage or decay. Some woods, such as fir, are obtainable in immense quantities, and can thus be used for general construction. Other woods are available only in small quantities and are used for their special characteristics. Limewood, for example, is soft, light in weight, and has a fine, close grain, cutting well in all directions, and is used for carving. Rosewood and other fine woods, when used for such purposes as cutlery handles, are impregnated with a synthetic resin to give them a hard lustrous finish and make them resistant to washing compounds. **Metalized wood** is wood treated with molten metal so that the cells of the wood are filled with the metal. Fusible alloys, with melting points below the scorching point of the wood, are used. The wood is immersed in molten metal in a closed container under pressure. The hardness, compressive strength, and flexural strength of the wood are increased, and the wood becomes an electrical conductor lengthwise of the grain. Woods are also metalized with a surface coating of metal by vacuum deposition.

Sugar pine is one of the most widely used **pattern woods** for foundry patterns. It replaces eastern white pine, which is scarcer and now usually more costly. Poplar is used for patterns where a firmer wood is desired; cherry or maple is employed where the patttern is to be used frequently or will be subject to severe treatment. Densified wood is also used for patterns required to be very wear-resistant. Mahogany is used for small and intricate patterns where a firm texture and freedom from warpage are needed. However, for small castings made in quantities on gates, aluminum or brass is more frequently used.

Excelsior is an old trade name, still used, for continuous, curly, fine wood shavings employed as a packing material for breakable articles. It is light and elastic, and it is used also as a cushioning and stuffing material. It is usually made from poplar, aspen, basswood, or cottonwood, a cord of wood producing about 1,500 lb, but it may be made as a by-product from other woodworking.   It is also called **wood fiber** and **wood wool,** but these terms more properly refer to fibers of controlled size and length used with a resin binder for molding into handles, knobs, and other **imitation wood** parts.

Some wood for special purposes comes from roots or from bushes. The **briar** used for tobacco pipes is from the root of the **white heath,** *Erica arborea,* of North Africa.   Substitutes for briar are the burls of the laurel and rhododendron.   **Yareta,** used for fuel in the copper region of Chile, is a mosslike woody plant which grows on the sunny northern mountain slopes at altitudes above 12,000 ft, requiring several hundred years to reach a useful size.   **Ironwood** is a name for several varieties of wood, and may refer to any exceedingly hard wood that is used for making bearings, gears, tool handles, or parts of machinery.   In the United States ironwood is most likely to refer to **hackia,** the wood of the hackia tree, *Ixora ferrea,* of the West Indies and of tropical South America, or it may refer to the wood of the quebracho tree.   Hackia is brown in color, has a coarse, open grain, and is very hard and tough.   The weight is about 55 lb per cu ft.   It is also used for furniture.   The Burmese tree, *Mesua ferrea,* furnishes the wood **gangaw,** which is also known as ironwood.   It is a tough, extremely hard wood of a rose-red color weighing 70 lb per cu ft.   Innumerable varieties of hardwoods occur in the tropical jungles, many unnamed or known only by native names.   Many have rich colors, shading from yellow, orange, and red to purplish-black, and in beautiful grains which can be varied by the angle of cutting.   They are generally commercialized only on a small scale for use in furniture, cabinetwork, inlays, and panel facings.

WOOD FLOUR. Finely ground dried wood employed as a filler and as reinforcing material in molding plastics and in linoleum, and as an absorbent for nitroglycerin.   It is made largely from light-colored softwoods, chiefly pine and spruce, but maple and ash flours are preferred where no resin content is desired.   Woods containing essential oils, such as cedar, are not suitable.   Wood flour is produced from sawdust and shavings by grinding in burr mills.   It has the appearance of wheat flour.   The sizes commonly used are 40, 60, and 80 mesh; the finest is 140 mesh.   Grade 1, used as a filler in rubber and plastics, has a particle size of 60 mesh and a specific gravity of 1.25, but 80 and 100 mesh are also used for plastic filler.   Since wood flour absorbs the resin or gums when mixed in molding plastics, and sets hard, it is sometimes mixed with mineral powders to vary the hardness and toughness of the molded product.   The **Hygeia wood flour,** of the Penn-Rillton Co., for use as a filler in plastics, is a dust-free 100-mesh powder made from oak.   The char point is 410°F and ignition point is 600°F.

Vast quantities of **sawdust** are obtained in the sawmill areas.   Besides being used as a fuel, it is also employed for packing, for finishing metal parts in tumbling machines, for making particle board, and for distilling to obtain resins, alcohols, sugars, and other chemicals.   Some sawdust is pulped, and as much as 20% of such pulp can be used in kraft paper without loss of strength.   Hickory, walnut, and oak sawdusts are used for meat smoking, or for the making of **liquid smoke,** which is produced by burning the sawdust and absorbing the smoke into water.   For the rapid production of bacon and other meats, immersion in liquid smoke imitates the flavor of smoked meat.   **Charsol,** of Arrow Products Corp., is maple smoke absorbed in water and refined to remove the creosote.   Some sawdust is used for agricultural mulch and fertilizer by chemical treatment to accelerate decay.   **Bark fuel,** of the Southern Extract Co., is shredded bark, flash-dried and pelletized with powdered coal.   **Kube-Kut,** of Michael Wood Products, Inc., is maple scrap wood cut into fine cubical particles for use in tumble polishing.   **Particle board,** made by compressing sawdust or wood particles with a resin binder into sheets, has uniform strength in all directions, and a smooth grainless surface.   When used as a core for veneer panels it requires no cross-laminating.   **Versacore,** of the Weyerhaeuser Co., is a veneer building board with an oak particle-board core. Mechanical pulp for newsprint can be made from sawdust, but the quantity available is usually not sufficient.   The material known as **ground wood,** of fine-mesh fibers, is made from cord wood, about one ton of fibers being produced from one cord of pulpwood.   **Plastic wood,** usually marketed as a paste in tubes for filling cavities or seams in wood products, is wood flour or wood cellulose compounded with a synthetic resin of high molecular weight that will give good adhesion but not penetrate the wood particles to destroy their nature.   The solvent is kept low to reduce shrinkage.   When cured in place the material can be machined, polished, and painted.   **Plastiplate,** of Duorite Plastics, is wood powder with a phenolic resin binder and a curing accelerator.   The cured material has a specific gravity of 1.05 and a flexural strength of 3,000 psi.

WOOL. The fine, soft, curly hair or fleece of the sheep, alpaca, vicuña, certain goats, and a few other animals.   The specific designation wool always means the wool of sheep.   **Sheep's wool** is one of the most important commercial fibers because of its good physical qualities and its insulating value, especially for clothing, but it now constitutes only about 10% of the textile fiber market.   It is best known for its use in clothing fabrics, called **woolens.**   These are designated under a variety of very old general trade names such as a loosely woven fabric called **flannel,** or the fine, smooth fabric known as **broadcloth.**   **Cheviot** is a close-napped, twill-woven fabric, and **tweed** is a woolen fabric with a coarse surface, usually with a herringbone-twill weave.   **Serge** is a twill-woven worsted fabric. **Worsteds** are wool fabrics made from combed-wool yarn, usually from long, smooth wool.   Wool is also employed for packings and for insulation, either loose or felted, and for making felts.   The average amount of wool shorn from sheep in the United States is 8.1 lb per animal.

Wool is a preferred fiber for winter clothing for both men and women, but the decreasing per-capita consumption of wool is due to the cost economics.   The raising of sheep for wool production requires very extensive grazing areas, which are not available in heavily populated countries. In the United States, also, the meat of young animals brings higher prices than that of older animals, and the sheep are slaughtered early, with wool largely as a by-product.   The less desirable synthetic fibers are thus substituted in fabrics in whole or in part.

Wool differs from hair in fineness and in its felting and spinning properties.   The latter are due to the fine scales on the wool fibers.   The finest short-staple wool has as many as 4,000 scales to the inch, and the average long-staple wool has about 2,000 scales per inch.   These scales give wool its cohesive qualities.   Some animals have both wool and hair, while others have wool only when young.   There is no sharp dividing line between wool and hair.

Wool quality is by fineness, softness, length, and scaliness.   Fiber diameters vary from 0.0025 to 0.005 in.   Long wools are generally heavy. Fibers below 3 in. in length are known as **clothing wool,** and those from 3 to 7 in. are called **combing wools.**   Long wools are fibers longer than 7 in.   The term **apparel wool** generally means clothing wool of fine weaving quality from known sources.   **Fleece wool** is the unscoured fiber. It may contain as high as 65% of grease and dirt, but this is the form in which wool is normally shipped because it then has the protection of the wool fat until it is manufactured.   Wool is very absorbent to moisture and will take up about 33% of its weight of water, and in some areas moisture and dirty grease are added to fleece wool to increase weight. **Carpet wools** are usually long nonresilient fibers from sheep bred in severe climates, such as the **Mongolian wool.**   The only breed of sheep developed for wool alone is the Merino.   In Australia the **corriedale** and the **polworth sheep** are dual-purpose animals for wool and meat.

The finest of the sheep wools comes from the **merino sheep,** but these vary according to the age of breeding of the animal.   The **Lincoln sheep** produces the longest fiber.   It is lustrous but very coarse.   Luster of wool depends upon the size and smoothness of the scales, but the chemical composition is important.   The molecular chains are linked with sulfur, and when sulfur is fed to the sheep in some deficient areas the quality of the wool is improved.   Crimpiness in wool is due to the open formation of the scales.   A fine Merino will have 24 crimps per inch; a coarse crossbred will have only 6 per inch. Strength of wool fibers often depends upon the health of the animal and the feeding.

One quarter of the world production of wool is in Australia. Argentina ranks second in production, with the United States third. But the United States is a lamb-eating nation, and a large proportion of the animals are slaughtered when 4 to 8 months old, and most of the others are kept only one season for one crop of wool. New Zealand, Uruguay, Russia, and England are also important producers. England is the center of wool-sheep breeding, with more varieties than any other country. In general, warm climates produce fine wools, and hot climates produce thin, wiry wools, but the fundamental differences come from the type of animal and the feeding. The **reused wool** from old cloth was originally called **shoddy,** but the name has an opprobrious signification in the United States, and is not used by manufacturers to designate the fabrics made from reclaimed wool. Shoddy is used in mixtures with new wool for clothing and other fabrics. **Extract wool** is shoddy that is recovered by dissolving out the cotton fibers of the old cloth with sulfuric acid. Short fibers of shoddy, less than $\frac{1}{2}$ in., are known as **mungo fibers.** They are used in woolen blends to obtain a napped effect. **Reprocessed wool** is fiber obtained from waste fabric which has not been used. **Noils** are short fibers produced in the combing of wool tops for making worsteds. They are used for woolen goods and felt. **Zeset,** of Du Pont, a shrink-proofing agent for wools, is a variant of **Surlyn T,** a terpolymer of 70% ethylene, 6 methacryloyl chloride, and 24 vinyl acetate. It prevents shrinkage and pilling under ordinary laundry methods, does not affect color, and increases the tensile strength of the fiber. But all resinous additives tend to harden the fiber and lessen the drape and feel. Conversely, each dry-cleaning of wool fabric decreases the natural oil content and hardens the fiber.

WOOL GREASE. A brownish waxy fat of a faint, disagreeable odor, obtained as a by-product in the scouring of wool. The purified grease was formerly known as **degras** and was used for leather dressing, in lubricating and slushing oils, and in soaps and ointments, but is now largely employed for the production of lanolin and its derivatives, chiefly for cosmetics. Wool grease contains **lanoceric acid,** $C_{30}H_0O_4$, **lanopalmic acid,** $C_{15}H_{30}O_3$, and **lanosterol,** a high alcohol related to cholesterol, all of which can be broken down into derivatives.

Lanolin is the purified and hydrated grease, also known as **lanain,** and in pharmacy as **lanum** and **adeps lanae.** It has a melting point at about 40°C, and is soluble in alcohol. Lanolin is basically a wax consisting of esters of sterol alcohols combined with straight-chain fatty acids, and with only a small proportion of free alcohols. It contains about 95% of fatty acid esters, but its direct use as an emollient depends on the 5% of free alcohols and acids. However, more than 30 derivatives are obtained from lanolin, and these are used in blends to give specific properties to cosmetics. They are often marketed under trade names, and some of the ingredients may be synthesized from raw materials other than wool grease, or chemically altered from wool-grease derivatives.

A variety of products used in cosmetics and pharmaceuticals are made by fractionation or chemical alteration of lanolin. They are also useful in compounding plastics and industrial coatings, but are generally too scarce and expensive for these purposes. **Ethoxylated lanolin** and ethoxylated **lanolin alcohols** are used in water-soluble emulsions and conditioners. **Solulan,** of Chemectants, Inc., is a general trade name for these materials. **Lanolin oil** and **lanolin wax** are made by solvent fractionation of lanolin. **Viscolan** and **Waxolan,** of the same company, are these products. **Isopropyl lanolates,** trade-named **Amerlate** by American Cholesterol Products, Inc., are soft hydrophylic solids which liquefy easily and are used in cosmetics as emollients, emulsifiers, and pigment dispersants. **Amerlate LFA** is derived from lanolin hydroxy acids containing iso-acids. The high hydroxyl content produces the emollient and emulsifying qualities. **Barium lanolate,** made by saponification, is used as an anticorrosion agent. It is antiphobic and is used also as an anticaking agent. In a 25% barium concentration it is used for hard lubricating grease.

Ethoxylan, of N. I. Malmstrom & Co., is an ethylene oxide derivative of lanolin, soluble in water and in alcohol, and used in shampoos. **Ceralan,** of the Robison-Wagner Co., is a waxy solid melting at 55°C to an amber-colored viscous liquid. It is a mixture of monohydroxyl alcohols, obtained by splitting lanolin, and contains 30% sterol, and free cholesterol. It forms water-in-oil emulsions, and is used in cosmetics as a dispersing and stiffening agent and as an emollient. **Acetylated lanolin,** usually sold under trade names, is made by reacting lanolin with polyoxy ethylenes. They are clear, nongreasy liquids soluble in water, oils, and in alcohol. The acetylated lanolin is hydrophobic and oil-soluble, and is used as an odorless, nontacky emollient in cosmetics.

Veriderm, of the Upjohn Co., is a substitute for lanolin as an emollient. It contains about the same percentage of triglycerol esters of fatty acids, free cholesterol, and saturated and unsaturated hydrocarbons, as occurs in the natural human skin oils. **Cholesterol** is one of the most important of the complex **sterols,** or **zoosterols,** from animal sources. It is produced from lanolin, but also from other sources, and used in drugs and cosmetics. **Amerchol L-101,** of the American Cholesterol Products, Inc., is a liquid nonionic cholesterol containing other sterols. Wool grease from the scouring of wool was originally called **Yorkshire grease. Moellon degras** is not wool grease, but is a by-product of chamois leathermaking. The sheepskins are impregnated with fish oil and, when the tanning is complete, the skins are soaked in warm water and the excess oil is pressed out to form the moellon degras.

WROUGHT IRON. Commercially pure iron made by melting white cast iron and passing an oxidizing flame over it, leaving the iron in a porous condition which is then rolled to unite it into one mass.   As thus made it has a fibrous structure, with fibers of slag through the iron in the direction of rolling.   It is also made by the Aston process of shotting bessemer iron into a ladle of molten slag.   Modern wrought iron has a fine dispersion of silicate inclusions which interrupt the granular pattern and give it a fibrous nature.

The value of wrought iron is in its corrosion resistance and ductility. It is used chiefly for rivets, staybolts, water pipes, tank plates, and forged work.   Minimum specifications for **ASTM wrought iron** call for a tensile strength of 40,000 psi, yield strength of 24,000 psi, and elongation of 12%, with carbon not over 0.08%, but the physical properties are usually higher.   **Wrought iron 4D,** of the A. M. Byers Co., has only 0.02% carbon with 0.12 phosphorus, and the fine fibers are of a controlled composition of silicon, manganese, and phosphorus.   This iron has a tensile strength of 48,000 psi, elongation 14%, and Brinell hardness 105.   **Mn wrought iron** has 1% manganese for higher impact strength.

Ordinary wrought iron with slag may contain frequent slag cracks, and the quality grades are now made by controlled additions of silicate, and with controlled working to obtain uniformity.   But for tanks and plate work, ingot iron is now usually substituted.   **Merchant bar iron** is an old name for wrought-iron bars and rods made by faggoting and forging. **Iron-fibered steel,** of the Edgar Allen Steel Co., Inc., is soft steel with fine iron wire worked into it.   **Staybolt iron** may be wrought iron, but was originally puddled charcoal iron.   **Lewis iron,** of Joseph T. Reyerson & Son, Inc., for staybolts, is highly refined, puddled iron with a tensile strength of 52,000 psi and elongation of 30%.

The **Norway iron** formerly much used for bolts and rivets was a **Swedish charcoal iron** brought to America in Norwegian ships.   This iron, with as low as 0.02% carbon, and extremely low silicon, sulfur, and phosphorus, was valued for its great ductility and toughness and also for its permeability qualities for transformer cores.   Commercial wrought iron is now usually ingot iron or fibered low-carbon steel.

YUCCA FIBER. The fiber obtained from the leaves of a number of desert plants of the genus *Yucca* of the lily family native to southwestern United States and northern Mexico.   The fiber is similar to fibers from agave plants and is often confused with them and with istle.   The heavier fibers are used for brushes, and the lighter fibers are employed for cordage and burlap fabrics.   In Mexico the word **palma** designates yucca fibers and grades of istle as well as palm-leaf fibers.   **Palma samandoca** is fiber from the plant *Samuela carnerosana,* the **date yucca.**   It is also called **palma istle.   Palmilla fiber** is from the *Y. elata.*   **Palma pita** is a fiber from the *Y. treculeana.*   **Pita fiber** used for coffee bags in Colombia and Central America is from a different plant.   Other yucca fibers come from the plants *Y. glauca, Y. baccata,* and *Y. gloriosa.*   Some varieties of the *Y. baccata* yield also edible fruits.   The roots of species of yucca yield saponin which is also obtained as a by-product in extracting the yucca fiber.

ZINC. A bluish-white crystalline metal with a specific gravity of 7.13, melting at 419.5°C and boiling at 907°C.   The commercially pure metal has a tensile strength, cast, of about 9,000 psi with elongation of 1%, and the rolled metal has a strength of 24,000 psi with elongation of 35%. But small amounts of alloying elements harden and strengthen the metal, and it is seldom used alone.   Zinc is used for galvanizing and plating; for making brass, bronze, and nickel silver; for electric batteries; for die castings; and in alloyed sheets for flashings, gutters, and stamped and formed parts.   The metal is harder than tin, and an electrodeposited plate has a Vickers hardness of about 45.   Zinc is also used for many chemicals.

The old name **spelter,** often applied to slab zinc, came from the name spailter used by Dutch traders for the zinc brought from China.   The first zinc produced in the United States in 1838 came from New Jersey ore.   **Sterling spelter** was 99.5% pure.   Special high-grade zinc is distilled, with a purity of 99.99%, containing no more than 0.006% lead and 0.004 cadmium.   High-grade zinc, used in alloys for die casting, is 99.9% pure, with 0.07 max lead.   **Brass special zinc** is 99.10% pure, with 0.6 max lead and 0.5 max cadmium.   **Prime western zinc,** used for galvanizing, contains 1.60 max lead and 0.08 max iron.   **Zinc crystals** produced by Semi-Elements, Inc., for electronic uses, are 99.999% pure metal.

Zinc has a close-packed hexagonal crystal structure, but the crystal structure differs from that of magnesium in that there is an extension in the direction of the hexagonal axis and close packing at the base, so that the electronic bonds in the hexagonal layers are stronger than those between layers, giving greater compressibility in the direction of the hexagonal axis.   The working properties of zinc are thus different from those of the hexagonal magnesium.   Zinc is very ductile at a relatively low temperature, 250°F, and can be rolled into thin sheets.

On exposure to the air, zinc becomes coated with a film of carbonate and is then very corrosion-resistant.   **Zinc foil** comes in thicknesses from 0.001 to 0.006 in.   It is produced by electrodeposition on an aluminum drum cathode and stripping off on a collecting reel. But most of the **zinc sheet** contains a small amount of alloying elements to increase the physical properties. Slight amounts of copper and titanium reduce grain size in the sheet zinc. **Hydro T Metal,** of New Jersey Zinc Co., is zinc sheet with no more than 1% combined total of other elements and with grain size kept below 0.0005 in. In cast zinc the hexagonal columnar grain extends from the mold face to the surface or to other grains growing from another mold face, and even very slight additions of iron can control this grain growth. Aluminum is also much used in alloying zinc. A high-strength **zinc wire** used in Germany in woven brake linings contains 1.1% copper and 0.8 aluminum, with a trace of iron. In zinc used for galvanizing, a small addition of aluminum prevents formation of the brittle alloy layer, increases ductility of the coating, and gives a smoother surface. Small additions of tin give bright spangled coatings.

Zinc has 12 isotopes, but the natural material consists of 5 stable isotopes, of which nearly half is **zinc 64.** The stable isotope **zinc 67,** occurring to the extent of about 4% in natural zinc, is sensitive to tiny variations in transmitted energy, giving off electromagnetic radiations which permit high accuracy in measuring instruments. It measures gamma-ray vibrations with great sensitivity, and is used in the nuclear clock. **Zinc powder,** or **zinc dust,** is a fine gray powder of 97% min purity usually in 325-mesh particle size. It is used in pyrotechnics, in paints, as a reducing agent and catalyst, in rubbers as a secondary dispersing agent and to increase flexing, and to produce **Sherardized steel.** Sherardizing consists in hot-tumbling the steel parts in a closed drum with the zinc powder. It is a form of galvanizing, and controlled zinc coatings of 0.1 to 0.4 oz per sq ft of surface give good corrosion protection. In paints, zinc powder is easily wetted by oils. It keeps the zinc oxide in suspension, and also hardens the film. **Mossy zinc,** used to obtain color effects on face brick, is a spangly zinc powder made by pouring the molten metal into the water. **Feathered zinc** is a fine grade of mossy zinc. **Photoengraving zinc** for printing plates is made from pure zinc with only a small amount of iron to reduce grain size and alloyed with not more than 0.2% each of cadmium, manganese, and magnesium. **Cathodic zinc,** used in the form of small bars or plates fastened to the hulls of ships or to underground pipelines to reduce electrolytic corrosion, is zinc of 99.99% purity and with the iron kept below 0.0014% to prevent polarization. **Merrillite,** of the Pacific Smelting Co., is high-purity zinc dust. **Foamed zinc,** of Foamalum Corp., is a lightweight structural metal with equal strength in all directions, made by foaming with an inert gas into a closed cell structure. It is used particularly for shock and vibration insulation. **Foaming agents** for metals are essentially the same as those used for plastics.   They are chemical additives that release a gas to expand the material by forming closed bubbles.   Or they may be used to cause froth as in detergents or fire-fighting foams.

ZINC-BASE ALLOYS. Alloys of zinc are mostly used for die castings for decorative parts and for functional parts where the load-bearing and shock requirements are relatively low.   Zinc die castings are not used where they may be subjected to continued stress above 100°C.   Since the zinc alloys can be cast easily in high-speed machines, producing parts of high accuracy and smooth surface that require minimum machining and finishing, and that weigh less than brass, they are widely used for such parts as handles, and for gears, levers, pawls, and other parts for small assemblies.   Zinc alloys for sheet contain only small amounts of alloying elements, with 92 to 98% zinc, and the sheet is generally referred to simply as zinc or by a trade name.   The **Modified zinc sheet** of the New Jersey Zinc Co., used for stamped, drawn, or spun parts for costume jewelry and electronics, contains up to 1.5% copper and 0.5 titanium.   The titanium raises the recrystallization temperature, permitting heat treatment without coarse grain formation.

The old **Fontainemoreau bronze,** or **reverse brass,** widely used before the development of the die-casting alloys and aluminum alloys, contained about 90% zinc, 7 to 8 copper, and small amounts of lead and iron. **Sorel's alloy,** for casting small statues and novelties, was zinc with about 1% iron and a small amount of copper.   One of the earliest die-casting alloys, **Salge's bronze,** was a white metal with 4% copper, 10 tin, 1 lead, 1 antimony, and the balance zinc.   Zinc alloys were much used in Europe for bearings.   **Leddell alloy** has 5% copper and 5 aluminum.   The German **Hartzink** had 5% iron and 2 to 3 lead, but iron forms various chemical compounds with zinc and the alloy is hard and brittle.   Copper reduces the brittleness.   **Germania bearing bronze** contained 1% iron, 10 tin, about 5 each of copper and lead, and the balance zinc.   **Fenton's alloy** had 14 tin, 6 copper, and 80 zinc, and **Ehrhard's bearing metal** contained 2.5% aluminum, 10 copper, 1 lead, and a small amount of tin to form copper-tin crystals.   **Binding metal,** for wire-rope slings, has about 2.8% tin, 3.7 antimony, and the balance zinc.   **Pattern metal,** for casting gates of small patterns, was almost any brass with more zinc and some lead added, but is now standard die-casting metal.   An early American zinc bearing metal, a grade of **Lumen bronze,** has 86% zinc, 10 copper, and 4 aluminum.   It has a compressive strength of 75,000 psi and Brinell hardness 116.   A great variety of proprietary-named zinc alloys have been marketed, some with copper as high as 60% and some with as much as 40% tin, but in general they are modified brasses, bronzes, and babbitts.

Zinc-base alloys for die castings are now quite narrowly standardized, with about 4% aluminum, with or without much copper, and with small amounts of controlling elements.   **Zinc die castings** have a wide range of use because of their low cost, good strength, ease of production of complicated shapes to accurate dimensions, and smooth surface with ease of finishing.   They are valued for gears and parts of miniature motors and instruments.   In automobiles they are used for such parts as carburetor bodies, handles, and latches.   One of the most used alloys, **zinc alloy 3,** contains 4% aluminum, 0.25 copper, 0.05 magnesium, 0.1 max iron, and the balance zinc with the impurities of lead, tin, and cadmium held to 0.005% to avoid intergranular corrosion.   This alloy has a tensile strength of 41,000 psi, compressive strength of 60,000 psi, elongation 10%, and Brinell hardness 82.   It melts at 718°F.   **Zinc alloy 5** is similar in composition but has about 1% copper, giving higher strength and hardness but lower ductility.

SAE alloy 921 contains 4% aluminum, 3 copper, up to 0.1 magnesium, and small maximums of iron, lead, cadmium, and tin.   It has a tensile strength, after aging, of about 45,000 psi, with elongation of 8% and Brinell hardness of 100.   The melting point is 715°F.   **SAE alloy 930** contains 4% aluminum, 0.10 copper, 0.05 magnesium, and small amounts of other elements.   It is a more ductile alloy with a tensile strength, after aging, of 35,000 psi and elongation of 15%.   The **Zamak alloys** of the New Jersey Zinc Co. are these alloys.   **Zamak-7,** for easier casting, has low magnesium content and a small addition of nickel.

SAE alloy 903 has a similar composition but with copper limited to 0.10 maximum.   Its physical properties are somewhat lower, but these properties are more stable, and it has better dimensional stability.   It is thus more generally used.   **Ilzro 12,** of International Lead & Zinc Research, for casting thin-walled parts such as housings for computers where the low vibration frequency of zinc gives good sound damping, contains 12% aluminum, 1 copper, and 0.02 magnesium.   The castings have a tensile strength up to 53,000 psi and elongation of 6%.   **Manganese-zinc alloys,** with up to 25% manganese, for high-strength extrusions and forgings, are really 60–40 brass with part of the copper replaced by an equal amount of manganese, and are classed with manganese bronze.   They have a bright white color and are corrosion-resistant.   **Zam metal,** of Hanson-Van Winkle-Munning Co., for zinc-plating anodes, is zinc with small percentages of aluminum and mercury to stabilize against acid attack.   **Eraydo,** of the Illinois Zinc Co., for radio shielding, is sheet zinc containing copper and silver.   **Zinc solders** are used for joining aluminum.   The **tin-zinc solders** have 70 to 80% tin, about 1.5% aluminum, and the balance zinc.   The working range is 500 to 590°F.   **Zinc-cadmium solder** has about 60% zinc and 40 cadmium.   The pasty range is between 510 and 599°F.

ZINC CHEMICALS. With the exception of the oxide, the quantities of zinc compounds consumed are not large compared with many other metals, but zinc chemicals have a very wide range of use, being essential in almost all industries and for the maintenance of animal and vegetable life. Zinc is a complex element and can provide some unusual conditions in alloys and chemicals.

Zinc oxide, ZnO, is a white, water-insoluble, refractory powder melting at about 1975°C, having a specific gravity of 5.66. It is much used as a pigment and accelerator in paints and rubbers. Its high refractive index, about 2.01, absorption of ultraviolet light, and fine particle size give high hiding power in paints, and make it also useful in such products as cosmetic creams to protect against sunburn. Commercial zinc oxide is always white, and in the paint industry is also called **zinc white** and **Chinese white.** But with a small excess of zinc atoms in the crystals, obtained by heat treatment, the color is brown to red.

In paints, zinc oxide is not as whitening as lithopone, but it resists the action of ultraviolet rays and is not affected by sulfur atmospheres, and is thus valued in outside paints. **Leaded zinc oxide,** consisting of zinc oxide and basic lead sulfate, is used in paints, but for use in rubber the oxide must be free of lead. In insulating compounds zinc oxide improves electrical resistance. In paper coatings it gives opacity and improves the finish. **Zinc-white paste** for paint mixing usually has 90% oxide and 10 oil.

Zinc oxide crystals are used for transducers and other piezoelectric devices. The crystals are hexagonal and are effective at elevated temperatures, as the crystal has no phase change up to its disassociation point. The resistivity range is 0.5 to 10 ohm-centimeters. Zinc oxide has luminescent and light-sensitive properties which are utilized in phosphors and ferrites. But the oxygen-dominated zinc phosphors used for radar and television are modifications of zinc sulfide phosphors. The **zinc sulfide phosphors** which produce luminescence by exposure to light are made with zinc sulfide mixed with about 2% sodium chloride and 0.005% of copper, manganese, or other activator, and fired in a nonoxidizing atmosphere. The cubic crystal structure of zinc sulfide changes to a stable hexagonal structure at 1020°C, but both forms have the phosphor properties. **Zinc sulfide** is a white powder of the composition $ZnS \cdot H_2O$, and is also used as a paint pigment, for whitening rubber, and for paper coating. **Cryptone,** of the New Jersey Zinc Co., is zinc sulfide for pigment use in various grades, some grades containing barium sulfate, calcium sulfide, or titanium dioxide.

Zinc is an **amphoteric element,** having both acid and basic properties, and it combines with fatty acids to form metallic soaps, or with the alkali metals or with ammonia to form **zincates.** **Sodium zincate** is used for waterproofing asbestos-cement shingles. **Zinc stearate,** $Zn(C_{18}H_{35}O_2)_2$, is a **zinc soap** in the form of a fine white powder used in paints and in rubber. A USP grade of 325 mesh is used in cosmetics. **Aquazinc,** of the Beacon Co., and **Liquizinc,** of Rubba, Inc., are zinc stearate dispersions in water used as an antitack agent in milling rubber. **Zinc acetate,** $Zn(C_2H_3O_2)_2$, is a white solid partly soluble in water, used as a mordant, as a wood preservative, in porcelain glazes, and as a mild antiseptic in pharmaceuticals.

Zinc sulfate, $ZnSO_4 \cdot 7H_2O$, is the chief material for supplying zinc in fertilizers, agricultural sprays, and animal feeds. For these purposes it is used in the form of white vitriol containing 22% zinc, or as the monohydrate, $ZnSO_4 \cdot H_2O$, containing 37% zinc. **Zinc chloride,** a white, crystalline, water-soluble powder, $ZnCl_2$, was formerly an important preservative for wood, and railway crossties treated with the material were called **Burnettized wood.** But it is highly soluble, and leaches out of the wood, and is now chromated and copperized with sodium bichromate and cupric chloride. **Copperized CZC,** of the Koppers Co., Inc., for treating wood against rot and termites, is copperized chromated zinc chloride. Zinc chloride is also used for vulcanizing fiber, as a mordant, in mercerizing cotton, in dry batteries, in disinfecting, and in making many chemicals. **Spirits of salts** and **butter of zinc** are old names for the material.

Zinc chromate, used chiefly as a pigment and called **zinc yellow** and **buttercup yellow,** is stable to light and in sulfur atmospheres, but has a lower tinting strength than chrome yellow, although it is less subject to staining and discoloration. It is a crystalline powder of specific gravity 3.40. It is only slightly soluble in water, but will absorb 24 lb of linseed oil per 100 lb. Zinc chromates are made by reacting zinc oxide with chromate solutions, and they may vary, but the usual composition is $4ZnO \cdot 4CrO_3 \cdot K_2O \cdot 3H_2O$. The **zinc bichromate,** $ZnCr_2O_7$, is an orange-yellow pigment. The **zinc peroxide** used in dental pastes and cosmetics as a mild antiseptic is a white powder, ZnO_2, containing 8.5% active oxygen.

ZINC ORES. The metal zinc is obtained from a large number of ores, but the average zinc content of the ores in the United States is only about 3%, so that they are concentrated to contain 35 to 65% before treatment. The sulfide ores are marketed on the basis of 60% zinc content, and the oxide ores on the basis of 40% zinc content. **Sphalerite,** or **zinc blende,** is the most important ore and is found in quantities in Missouri and surrounding states, and in Europe. Sphalerite is a zinc sulfide, ZnS, containing theoretically 67% zinc. It has a massive crystalline or granular structure and a hardness of about 4. When pure, its color is white; it colors yellow, brown, green, to black with impurities. The ores from New York state are ground and concentrated by flotation to an average of 58%

zinc and 32 sulfur, which is then concentrated by roasting to 68% zinc and 1 sulfur.   It is then sintered to remove lead and cadmium, and finally smelted with coke and the zinc vapor condensed.   The Silesian zinc blende, known as **wurtzite,** contains 15% zinc, 2 lead, and some cadmium.

Calamine is found in New Jersey, Pennsylvania, Missouri, and Europe. It is the ore that was formerly mixed directly with copper for making brass.   The ore usually contains only about 3% zinc, and is concentrated to 35 to 45%, and then roasted and distilled.   Calamine is **zinc silicate,** $2ZnO \cdot SiO_2 \cdot H_2O$.   It is a mineral occurring in crystal groups of a vitreous luster, and may be white, greenish, yellow, or brown.   The specific gravity is 3.4 and hardness 4.5 to 5.   It occurs in Arkansas with **smithsonite,** a **zinc carbonate** ore, $ZnCo_3$.   **Franklinite** is an ore of both the metals zinc and manganese.   Its approximate composition is $(FeZnMo)O \cdot (FeMn)_2$-O_3, but it shows wide variation in the proportions of the different elements.   It is found in the zinc deposits of New Jersey.   The zinc is converted into zinc white, and the residue is smelted to form spiegeleisen. The mineral franklinite occurs in massive granular structure with a metallic luster and an iron-black color.

The ore **zincite** is used chiefly for the production of the zinc oxide known as zinc white employed as a pigment.   Zincite has the composition ZnO, containing theoretically 80.3% zinc.   The mineral has usually a massive granular structure with a deep-red to orange streaked color.   It may be translucent or almost opaque.   Deep-red specimens from the workings at Franklin, N.J., are cut into gemstones for costume jewelry.   **Willemite** is an anhydrous silicate, Zn_2SiO_4, containing theoretically 58.5% zinc. When manganese replaces part of the zinc the ore is called **troostite.**   It is in hexagonal prisms of white, yellow, green, or blue colors; manganese makes it apple green, brown, or red.   The specific gravity is about 4, and the hardness 5.5.   The crushed ore is used in making fluorescent glass. The ore is widely dispersed in the United States.

ZIRCONIA.   A white crystalline powder which is **zirconium oxide,** ZrO_2, with a specific gravity of 5.7, hardness 6.5, and refractive index 2.2.   When pure, its melting point is about 5000°F, and it is one of the most refractory of the ceramics.   It is produced by reacting zircon sand and dolomite at 2500°F and leaching out the silicates.   The material is used as fused or sintered ceramics and for crucibles and furnace bricks. From 4.5 to 6% of CaO or other oxide is added to convert the unstable monoclinic crystal to the stable cubic form with a lowered melting point.

Fused zirconia, used as a refractory ceramic, has a melting point of 4620°F and a usable temperature to 4450°F.   The **Zinnorite** fused zirconia of the Norton Co. is a powder that contains less than 0.8% silica and has a melting point at 4900°F.   A **sintered zirconia** with a density of 5.4

has a tensile strength of 12,000 psi, compressive strength of 200,000 psi, and Knoop hardness of 1,100.   **Zircoa B,** of the Zirconium Corp., is stabilized cubic zirconia used for making ceramics.   **Zircoa A** is the pure monoclinic zirconia used as a pigment, as a catalyst, in glass, and as an opacifier in ceramic coatings.

Zirconia brick for lining electric furnaces has no more than 94% zirconia, with up to 5% calcium oxide as a stabilizer, and some silica.   It melts at about 4300°F, but softens at about 3600°F.   The **IBC 4200** brick of Ipsen Industries, Inc., is zirconia with calcium and hafnium oxides for stabilizing.   It withstands temperatures to 4200°F in oxidizing atmospheres and to 3000°F in reducing atmospheres.   **Zirconia foam** of the National Beryllia Corp. is marketed in bricks and shapes for thermal insulation.   With a porosity of 75% it has a flexural strength above 500 psi and a compressive strength above 100 psi.   For use in crucibles, zirconia is insoluble in most metals except the alkali metals and titanium. It is resistant to most oxides, but with silica it forms $ZrSiO_4$, and with titania it forms $ZrTiO_4$.   Since structural disintegration of zirconia refractories comes from crystal alteration the phase changes are important considerations.   The monoclinic material, with a specific gravity of 5.7, is stable to 1850°F, and then inverts to the tetragonal crystal with a specific gravity of 6.1 and volume change of 7%.   It reverts when the temperature again drops below 1850°F.   The cubic material, with a specific gravity of 5.55, is stable at all temperatures to the melting point which is not above 4800°F because of the contained stabilizers.   A lime-stabilized zirconia refractory with a tensile strength of 20,000 psi has a tensile strength of 10,000 psi at 2370°F.   **Stabilized zirconia** has a very low coefficient of expansion, and white hot parts can be plunged into cold water without breaking.   The thermal conductivity is only about one-third that of magnesia.   It is also resistant to acids and alkalies, and is a good electrical insulator.

Zirconia is produced from the zirconium ores known as **zircon** and **baddeleyite.**   The latter is a natural zirconium oxide, but is obtainable commercially only from Minas Gerais, Brazil.   It is also called **zirkite** and **Brazilite.**   Zircon is **zirconium silicate,** $ZrO_2 \cdot SiO_2$, and comes chiefly from beach sands.   The commercial sands are produced in Florida, Brazil, India, Ceylon, Australia, and western Africa.   The sands are also called **zirkelite** and **zirconite,** or merely **zircon sand.**   The white zircon sand from India has a zirconia content of 62%, and contains less than 1% iron.   Beach sands of New South Wales are naturally concentrated to an average of 74% zircon, but Australian zircon is shipped on a basis of 65% zirconia.   Zircon sand may be used directly for making firebricks, as an opacifier in ceramics, and for mold facings.   Clear **zircon crystals** are valued as gemstones since the high refractive index gives great brilliance.   The colorless natural crystals are called **Matura diamonds,** and the yellow-red are known as **jacinth.**

Zirconia fiber, used for high-temperature textiles, is produced from zirconia with about 5% lime for stabilization.   The fiber is polycrystalline, has a melting point of 4700°F, and will withstand continuous temperatures above 3000°F.   These fibers are produced by Union Carbide as small as 3 to 10 microns and are made into fabrics for filter and fuel cell use. **Zirconia fabrics** are woven, knitted, or felted of short-length fibers and are flexible.   **Ultratemp adhesive,** of Aremco Products, for high-heat applications, is **zirconia powder** in solution.   At 1100°F it adheres strongly to metals and will withstand temperatures to 4400°F.   **Zircar,** of Union Carbide, is zirconia fiber compressed into sheets to a density of 20 lb per cu ft.   It will withstand temperatures up to 4500°F and has low thermal conductivity.   It is used for insulation and for high-temperature filtering.

ZIRCONIUM. A silvery-white metal having a specific gravity of 6.5 and melting at about 1850°C.   It is more abundant than nickel, but is difficult to reduce to metallic form as it combines easily with oxygen, nitrogen, carbon, and silicon.   The metal is obtained from zircon sand by reacting with carbon and then converting to the tetrachloride, which is reduced to a sponge metal for the further production of shapes.   The ordinary **sponge zirconium** contains about 2.5% hafnium, which is closely related and difficult to separate.   The commercial metal usually contains hafnium, but reactor-grade zirconium, for use in atomic work, is hafnium-free.

Commercially pure zirconium is not a high-strength metal, having a tensile strength of about 32,000 psi, elongation 40%, and Brinell hardness 30, or about the same physical properties as pure iron.   But it is valued for atomic-construction purposes because of its low neutron-capture cross section, thermal stability, and corrosion resistance.   It is employed mostly in the form of alloys but may be had from Atomergic Chemetals Co. in 99.99% pure single-crystal rods, sheets, foil, and wire for superconductors, surgical implants, and vacuum tube parts.   The neutron cross section of zirconium is 0.18 barn, compared with 2.4 for iron and 4.5 for nickel.   The cold-worked metal, with a 50% reduction, has a tensile strength of about 82,000 psi, with elongation of 18% and hardness of Brinell 95.   The unalloyed metal is difficult to roll, and is usually worked at temperatures to 900°F.

The metal has a close-packed hexagonal crystal structure, which changes at 862°C to a body-centered cubic structure which is stable to the melting point.   At 300 to 400°C the metal absorbs hydrogen rapidly, and above 200°C it picks up oxygen.   At about 400°C it picks up nitrogen, and at 800°C the absorption is rapid, increasing the volume and embrittling the metal.   The metal is not attacked by nitric, sulfuric, or hydrochloric acids, but is dissolved by hydrofluoric acid.   **Zirconium powder** is very reactive, and for making sintered metals it is usually marketed as **zirconium hydride,** ZrH_2, containing about 2% hydrogen which is driven off when the powder is heated to 300°C.   For making sintered parts, alloyed powders are also used.   **Zirconium copper,** containing 35% zirconium, **zirconium nickel,** with 35 to 50% zirconium, and **zirconium cobalt,** with 50% zirconium, are marketed by Metal Hydrides, Inc., as powders of 200 to 300 mesh.

Small amounts of zirconium are used in many steels.   It is a powerful deoxidizer, removes the nitrogen, and combines with the sulfur, reducing hot-shortness and giving ductility.   **Zirconium steels** with small amounts of residual zirconium have a fine grain, and are shock-resistant and fatigue-resistant.   In amounts above 0.15% the zirconium forms zirconium sulfide and improves the cutting quality of the steel.   **Zirconium alloys** generally have only small amounts of alloying elements to add strength and resist the pickup of hydrogen.   **Zircoloy 2,** of the Westinghouse Electric Corp., for reactor structural parts, has 1.5% tin, 0.12 iron, 0.10 chromium, 0.05 nickel, and the balance zirconium.   The tensile strength is 68,000 psi, elongation 37%, and hardness Rockwell B89; and at 600°F it retains a strength of 30,000 psi.

Small amounts of zirconium in copper give age-hardening and increase the tensile strength.   Copper alloys containing even small amounts of zirconium are called **zirconium bronze.**   They pour more easily than bronzes with titanium, and they have good electrical conductivity.   Zirconium-copper master alloy for adding zirconium to brasses and bronzes is marketed in grades with 12.5 and 35% zirconium.   A **nickel-zirconium** master alloy, of the Electro Metallurgical Co., has 40 to 50% nickel, 25 to 30 zirconium, 10 aluminum, and up to 10 silicon and 5 iron.   **Zirconium-ferrosilicon,** for alloying with steel, contains 9 to 12% zirconium, 40 to 47 silicon, 40 to 45 iron, and 0.20 max carbon, but other compositions are available for special uses.   **SMZ alloy,** of the same company, for making high-strength cast irons without leaving residual zirconium in the iron, has about 75% silicon, 7 manganese, 7 zirconium, and the balance iron.   A typical zirconium copper for electrical use is **Amzirc** of the American Metal Climax, Inc.   It is oxygen-free copper with only 0.15% of zirconium added.   At 400°C it has a conductivity of 37% IACS, tensile strength of 52,000 psi, and elongation of 9%.   The softening temperature is 580°C.

Zirconium carbide, ZrC_2, is produced by heating zirconia with carbon at about 2000°C.   The cubic crystalline powder has a hardness of Knoop 2,090, and melting point of 3540°C.   The powder is used as an abrasive and for hot-pressing into heat-resistant and abrasion-resistant parts.   **Zirconium oxychloride,** $ZrOCl_2 \cdot 8H_2O$, is a cream-colored powder soluble in water that is used as a catalyst, in the manufacture of color lakes, and in textile coatings.   **Zirconium fused salt,** used to refine aluminum and magnesium, is **zirconium tetrachloride,** a hygroscopic solid with 86% $ZrCl_4$. **Zirconium sulfate,** $Zr(SO_4)_2 \cdot 4H_2O$, comes in fine, white, water-soluble crystals. It is used in high-temperature lubricants, as a protein precipitant, and for tanning to produce white leathers. **Soluble zirconium** is **sodium zirconium sulfate,** used for the precipitation of proteins, as a stabilizer for pigments, and as an opacifier in paper. **Zirconium carbonate** is used in ointments for ivy poisoning, as the zirconium combines with the hydroxy groups of the urushiol poison and neutralizes it. **Zirconium hydride** has been used as a neutron moderator, although the energy moderation may be chiefly from the hydrogen.

Zirconium alloys with high zirconium content have few uses except for atomic applications. **Zircoloy tubing** is used to contain the uranium oxide fuel pellets in reactors since the zirconium does not have grain growth and deterioration from radiation. **Zirconium ceramics** are valued for electrical and high-temperature parts and refractory coatings. The **zirconium oxide powder,** of the Norton Co., for flame-sprayed coatings comes in either hexagonal or cubic crystal forms. **Zirconium silicate,** $ZrSi_2$, comes as a tetragonal crystal powder. Its melting point is about 3000°F and hardness about 1,000 Knoop.

PART TWO

Elements of
Materials Economics

INTRODUCTION

Materials economics, or the procurement and utilization of the raw materials of the world, is a profession, that is, a deductive art. It is a profession founded on positive science, and does not embrace the compromises, expediencies, and charlatanisms of social and political economics. Like the true professions, such as medicine, materials economics seeks to eliminate personal opinions and requires basic knowledge of the sciences upon which it depends. The scope of the contributing sciences is wider than for many other professions, and includes mineralogy, botany, metallurgy, agriculture, chemistry, physics, zoology, forestry, and geography. But the materials economist need not be a specialist in any of these any more than the medical doctor need be a chemist. Yet, he must be able to finger the basic elements of all of these as the player learns to finger instinctively the keys of an instrument, to give his best attention to the broader scope of the art.

The thousands of raw materials are interlocked in their uses in hundreds of varied industries, and they come from every corner of the world; from minerals and earths; from plant leaves, stems, bark, and roots; from every part of a diverse animal life; from the seas; from the air; and from the artificial or synthetic combination of any or all of these.

It is preferable, in this scientific age, that the supervising executive, whether he be a manager, a purchasing official, or a directing economist, not be an "expert" or specialist in any one material or in any particular group of materials lest he lose perspective, but he must have a wide range of basic information. He must have an elemental knowledge of various sciences to see why materials act as they do. He must know something of all the important industries in order to form judgments on the relative values of the materials in use. He must have the economic geography of the world so implanted in his mind that he knows the relative positions of the materials and the trade routes. He must know the important characteristics of the nations that produce and market materials, and the background upon which their materials' supply depends.

Detail tends to cloud executive perspective, but the executive must know what details are necessary for proper judgment. He must fix in his mind a few figures that will serve as milestones to give a quick comparative judgment of material characteristics, because any new figure is of little value unless it brings to mind a comparison with a known value. Only a few such values in the various categories need be remembered, but acumen is the chief tool of an executive, and acumen is inoperative without basic comparative knowledge.

GEOPHYSICS OF MATERIALS

Formation of Earth Materials

It is estimated that it took at least 100 billion years for the earth to cool from the time it left the sun to a point where life could be supported. The core of the earth, called the **centrosphere,** is still a dense plastic mass, probably largely nickel and iron, just as the cores of the meteors that reach the earth are nickel-iron with the other materials burned off in penetrating the atmosphere at high speed.   The crust of the earth, composed of a **lithosphere,** or the solid matter, and a **hydrosphere,** or the water, is taken arbitrarily as 10 miles thick, and contains 93% solid matter and 7% seawater.   The sedimentary rocks and soil are only within the space of a thin veneer, igneous rocks forming at least 95%.

The height of the **atmosphere** surrounding the lithosphere and hydrosphere is more than 200 miles above sea level as proved by the phenomena of the aurora borealis and by rockets, but the barometer proves that more than half of the air, by weight, reaches not more than 3.4 miles above sea level.   As the distance from the earth increases, the air becomes colder, and because of the swift rotation of the earth the heavier colder air is thrown out in a ring around the equator. Animal and plant life are near the bottom of an atmospheric ocean with the pressure of the air at sea level 14.7 psi.   Plant life derives its carbon, and animal life its oxygen, largely from the atmosphere, some of which is again returned to the air.   Anaerobe bacteria release oxygen from solid materials.   A balance of carbon in the air is maintained partly from volcanoes.   The amount of carbon dioxide fixed at all times in the cellulose of plant life is about half the amount in the atmosphere.   A considerable amount of metallic and nonmetallic elements falls continuously on the earth in the form of dust from meteorites.   About one meteorite per 100 sq mi per year strikes the earth, most of its elements being diffused as hot gases in the air.

The oceans cover 70% of the surface of the earth with an average depth of about 2 miles.   The greatest depth is 34,219 ft, in the Pacific Ocean east of the Philippines, at which depth the pressure is more than 7.5 tons per sq in.   Water on the land areas sinks to a water table, seeping toward the seas.   A few points on the land surface are below sea level, and here any water evaporates.   Below the water tables the water gradually disappears until the deep mines are dry and dusty.   The water in and on the land areas of the earth, not counting the seas, is equivalent to a sheet of water 225 ft in depth over the continental areas.   There is a third as much water underground as there is in all the oceans, so that a simultaneous cessation of rain on all parts of the earth for even a relatively short period would cause such a rise in the surface of the oceans as to cover all port cities.   Actually, because of a balance of precipitation over the land surfaces, the changes in ocean levels have been slight.   The volume of common salt in seawater is sufficient to cover the whole surface of the land to a depth of 110 ft.

Temperatures increase below the ground surface at a little more than 1°C for each 100 ft.   At 9,000 ft the temperature is theoretically the boiling point of water, but varies at different places.   In the gold mines at Bendigo, Australia, the rock temperature at 4,600 ft is 112°F and the water is 114°F.   Pressure increases at increasing depths in the earth.   At 11 miles it is 70,000 psi, with a temperature of more than 550°C, and at increasing depths the rock is plastic. Through faults in the surface, eruptions can occur at any time, so that relatively new dikes of metal ores may be found in very old formations.

The solid crust of the earth is extremely thin compared with the diameter of the earth, relatively equivalent to a thin sheet of paper on a 20-in. globe.   This crust floats on a plastic core, and is subject at any time to minor shifts due to unbalances caused by off-center accumulations of ice at the poles.   Such minor movements can cause shifts in the position of the magnetic pole in relation to surface points, and may cause some earthquakes and local eruptions.   At the present time the center of gravity of the immense accumulation of ice at the South Pole is calculated as at about 350 miles from the pole, making an off-center centrifugal force, but, unlike an assumed prior accumulation at the North Pole, the South Pole ice is anchored largely on solid land.   Little is known of earth-crust movements except that a major shift causing a tremendous cataclysmic movement of continents occurred about 13,000 years ago, calculated from radio-activity tests on fossil trees of Wisconsin and bones of mammoths and other tropical animals buried in Siberia and Alaska.

The sway or tipping of the earth in its annual path about the sun, which brings the direct rays of the sun to a point $23\frac{1}{2}°$ north of the equator in June and $23\frac{1}{2}°$ south in December, is responsible for the seasonal climates.   These are relatively uniform, because the larger oscillation of the earth which causes the advance and retreat of polar ice is too slow to make perceptible differences, this movement being complete in about 30,000 years.   The latest ice age in Europe and North America reached its peak, with an advance of ice to about the latitude of New York City, about 10,000 B.C.   The accelerated melting of ice and the migration of forests into England were about 7,000 B.C.   The slowing of the earth in its rotation is likewise too slow to cause perceptible differences.   This slowing is about 15 min every 1,000 years.

Average Percentage of Metals in Igneous Rocks

Metal	Percentage	Metal	Percentage
Silicon	27.72	Rare earths	0.015
Aluminum	8.13	Copper	0.010
Iron	5.01	Tungsten	0.005
Calcium	3.63	Lithium	0.004
Sodium	2.85	Zinc	0.004
Potassium	2.60	Columbium, Tantalum	0.003
Titanium	0.63	Hafnium	0.003
Manganese	0.10	Thorium	0.002
Barium	0.05	Lead	0.002—
Chromium	0.037	Cobalt	0.001
Zirconium	0.026	Beryllium	0.001
Nickel	0.020	Strontium	0.001—
Vanadium	0.017	Uranium	0.001—

Relative Amounts of Engineering Materials [1]

Aluminum	4,000	Nickel	10
Iron	2,200	Copper	1
Magnesium	1,200		

[1] U.S. Geological Survey.

Occurrence of the Elements in the Earth's Crust [1]

Element	Percentage	Element	Percentage
Oxygen	47.0	Carbon	0.2
Silicon	28.0	Phosphorus	0.1
Aluminum	8.0	Sulfur	0.1
Iron	4.5	Nickel	0.02
Calcium	3.5	Copper	0.002
Magnesium	2.5	Lead and zinc	0.001
Sodium	2.5	Tin	0.00001
Potassium	2.5	Silver	0.000001
Titanium	0.4	All others	0.48
Hydrogen	0.2	Total	100.00

[1] U.S. Geological Survey.

Composition of the Seawater

The average salt content of the sea is 3.5%, with the salts divided as follows:

$NaCl$	77.76 percent
$MgCl_2$	10.88
$MgSO_4$	4.74
$CaSO_4$	3.60
K_2SO_4	2.46
$MgBr_2$	0.22
$CaCO_3$	0.34

In addition, seawater carries perceptible quantities of the following: iodine, fluorine, arsenic, gold, silver, rubidium, copper, barium, phosphorus, managanese, lithium, lead, iron, strontium, and zinc. Ammonia is also usually present, together with free oxygen, nitrogen, and other gases, and in some seas hydrogen sulfide is also present. This does not include the mineral and organic materials carried in suspension by the water especially near the mouths of great rivers.

Composition of the Atmosphere [1]

Percentage (by volume)

Nitrogen	78.03
Oxygen	20.99
Argon	0.94
Carbon dioxide	0.03
Hydrogen	0.01
Neon	0.00123
Helium	0.0004
Krypton	0.00005
Xenon	0.000006

[1] U.S. Geological Survey.

In addition, the air contains water vapor, pollens, dust, smoke, and toxic particles from the effluvia of engine fuels and industrial plants.

Basic Judgment of New Materials

To be able to judge effectively the relative values of new offerings, the industrial procurement official must have in his mind basic standards for almost instinctive comparisons, for a new figure is of no value unless it is compared to a known value.   For example, if a new steel is said to have a tensile strength of 400,000 psi, one must know instinctively that it is 10 times stronger than ordinary low-carbon steel.   But, a relatively small amount of study and reading with a perspective mind will soon fix in the consciousness important points of relativity on strengths, hardness, weights, degrees of screen fineness, and degrees of organic compositions.   With only a little effort the nonchemist can familiarize himself with the chemical groupings and characteristics of important basic chemical radicals, such as the benzene ring and the ethyl, methyl, and amine groups.

Modern chemical and metallurgical thinking requires that the materials engineer realize that all the material elements are built up from nonmaterial intangible waves or rays of energy, the actualities of which are in the realm of **metaphysics.**   Scientific judgments on these elements are made by deductions from observations of tangible measurable effects.   All the material elements have natural habits of forming and combining which, when the natural laws are determined, can be altered by environmental or other changes.   In chemistry and metallurgy, only the combining habits are normally used.

The Natural Elements

Name	Atomic number	Symbol	Atomic weight O = 16.0000	Melting point, deg C
Actinium	89	Ac	....	1800
Alabamine	85	Am	....	470
Aluminum	13	Al	26.97	660.0
Antimony	51	Sb	121.76	630.5
Argon	18	A	39.944	−189.3
Arsenic	33	As	74.91	814
Barium	56	Ba	137.36	704
Beryllium	4	Be	9.02	1280
Bismuth	83	Bi	209.00	271.3
Boron	5	B	10.82	2300
Bromine	35	Br	79.916	−7.2
Cadmium	48	Cd	112.41	320.9
Calcium	20	Ca	40.08	850
Carbon	6	C	12.00	3700
Cerium	58	Ce	140.13	600
Cesium	55	Cs	132.91	28
Chlorine	17	Cl	35.457	−101
Chromium	24	Cr	52.01	1800

The Natural Elements (*Continued*)

Name	Atomic number	Symbol	Atomic weight O = 16.0000	Melting point, deg C
Cobalt	27	Co	58.94	1490
Columbium	41	Cb	92.91	2000
Copper	29	Cu	63.57	1083.0
Dysprosium	66	Dy	162.46	
Erbium	68	Er	167.64	
Europium	63	Eu	152.0	
Fluorine	9	Fl	19.00	−223
Gadolinium	64	Gd	157.3	
Gallium	31	Ga	69.72	29.78
Germanium	32	Ge	72.60	958
Gold	79	Au	197.2	1063.0
Hafnium	72	Hf	178.6	1700
Helium	2	He	4.002	−271.4
Holmium	67	Ho	163.5	
Hydrogen	1	H	1.0078	−259.2
Illinium	61	Il	140.0	
Indium	49	In	114.76	156.4
Iodine	53	I	126.92	114
Iridium	77	Ir	193.1	2454
Iron	26	Fe	55.84	1535
Krypton	36	Kr	83.7	−157
Lanthanum	57	La	138.92	826
Lead	82	Pb	207.22	327.4
Lithium	3	Li	6.940	186
Lutecium	71	Lu	175.0	
Magnesium	12	Mg	24.32	650
Manganese	25	Mn	54.93	1260
Masurium	43	Ma	97.8	2300
Mercury	80	Hg	200.61	−38.87
Molybdenum	42	Mo	96.0	2625
Neodymium	60	Nd	144.27	840
Neon	10	Ne	20.183	−248.6
Nickel	28	Ni	58.69	1455
Nitrogen	7	N	14.008	−210.0
Osmium	76	Os	191.5	2700
Oxygen	8	O	16.0000	−218.8
Palladium	46	Pd	106.7	1554
Phosphorus	15	P	31.02	44.1
Platinum	78	Pt	195.23	1773.5
Polonium	84	Po	....	1800
Potassium	19	K	39.096	63
Praseodymium	59	Pr	140.92	940
Protoactinium	91	Pa	231	
Radium	88	Ra	226.05	700
Radon	86	Rn	222	−71
Rhenium	75	Re	186.31	3000

The Natural Elements (*Continued*)

Name	Atomic number	Symbol	Atomic weight O = 16.0000	Melting point, deg C
Rhodium	45	Rh	102.91	1966
Rubidium	37	Rb	84.44	39
Ruthenium	44	Ru	101.7	2450
Samarium	62	Sm	150.43	1300
Scandium	21	Sc	45.10	1200
Selenium	34	Se	78.96	220
Silicon	14	Si	28.06	1430
Silver	47	Ag	107.880	960.5
Sodium	11	Na	22.997	97.7
Strontium	38	Sr	87.63	770
Sulfur	16	S	32.06	119.2
Tantalum	73	Ta	180.88	3000
Tellurium	52	Te	127.61	450
Terbium	65	Tb	159.2	327
Thallium	81	Tl	204.39	300
Thorium	90	Th	232.12	1700
Thulium	69	Tm	169.4	
Tin	50	Sn	118.70	231.9
Titanium	22	Ti	47.90	1820
Tungsten	74	W	184.0	3410
Uranium	92	U	238.14	1850
Vanadium	23	V	50.95	1735
Virginium	87	Vi		
Xenon	54	Xe	131.3	−112
Ytterbium	70	Yb	173.04	1500
Yttrium	39	Y	88.92	1490
Zinc	30	Zn	65.38	419.5
Zirconium	40	Zr	91.22	1700

The new names proposed for the elements alabamine, masurium, and virginium by the scientists who first synthesized them by cyclotronic bombardment of adjacent elements are: astatine, technetium, and francium, respectively. A proposal to change the name of columbium to niobium has not been acceptable in America.

ELEMENTARY GEOLOGY OF MATERIALS

Formation and Location of Minerals

Geology and mineralogy are the sciences in which is tabulated the fundamental knowledge of the history and resources of the minerals of the earth. The 2 billion years represented in the five geologic eras are only a small part of the life span of the earth. These eras do not extend back to the time when the earth was molten, but only include the time when the earth was not significantly different in material structure than at present, that is, they extend back to little beyond the point when the first traces of life appeared.

A geologist is a historian whose archives and written documents are the rocks and formations of the earth.   The mineralogist is one who tabulates the elemental materials that are in the rocks and earths, and designates those which are ores, or from which materials may be extracted commercially.   But to a geologist a rock or earth formation is a page from the earth's autobiography.   The changes which took place, and the approximate length of time during which changes occuerd, are determined by study of the types of formations and their relative size and positions, of the animal and plant life as seen in fossil remains, and of the disintegration by erosions and by radioactive elements in the rocks.   Geology is thus not an academic science, as the practical geologist can trace the probable location of metallic ores, petroleum, coals, and nonmetallic minerals.

There are three main types of rocks: igneous, sedimentary, and metamorphic. The igneous are the mother rocks which have carried all nonorganic mineral products from the original molten condition in the depths of the earth.   Sedimentary rocks are the deposits from erosion of older rocks and from the deposits of organic matter.   Metamorphic rocks are both igneous and sedimentary rocks which have been changed by intense heat and pressure within geologic times. They include the different chemical and physical changes caused by the upheavals in the earth's crust.

Compared to the amount of rock which makes up the crust of the earth, the percentage of mineral deposits that are rated as metallic ores is small.   These deposits are found near large igneous intrusions, where they have formed from the molten rock as it cooled and crystallized, or from hot gases or hot aqueous solutions that came from the magma, and also at points of contact with their rocks into which the hot magma forced its way.   Deposits may also be found in sedimentary rocks where they came from precipitates from the seas and from beds of decayed plant life.

However, metallic mineral deposits may occur in geologic strata normally foreign to them, as in sedimentary sands or rocks, by having been forced up by earthquakes or eruptions from the earth's molten center in more recent geologic times.   Such eruptions can occur at any time, and the present Appalachian mountain chain, with the introduction of new mineral extrusions in the older geologic formations, may have been formed in the last great shift of the earth's crust about 13,000 years ago.   The time position of one metal deposit can thus be entirely unrelated to that of another deposit near it, but these irregular extrusions are readily discernible to the geologist.

The elements have played an important role in the concentration of minerals. These elements include the periods of high humidity and violent rainfall and of periodic advance and regression of polar ice, as well as the normal erosion through the ages.   During erosion, water may enrich natural deposits by dissolving out and carrying away soluble impurities, or it may form new ore veins by depositing mineral matter in the cracks of rocks as it seeps through.   It may carry nonsoluble minerals, such as gold or gemstones, to placer deposits freeing them of all soluble content.   Air has oxidized some materials near the surface, changing them to the alteration ores.   Winds have formed some deposits of heavier materials by sifting out the softer ingredients.   Chemically combined water is found only in recent metamorphic rocks.

Geology thus determines that mineral deposits of one type are likely to occur in rocks of one age or in deposits of certain types. It traces placers back to the original deposit. From the geologic formation it determines the probable size and depth of a deposit. From the folds of the strata it may determine where a continuation of the deposit is likely to occur in another area.

Definitions Relating to Minerals

Amorphous. Without definite structure.

Alluvium. Fine material or sediment deposited by streams.

Breccia. Fragmental rock with angular components.

Calcareous. Containing sufficient calcium carbonate to effervesce visibly when treated with hydrochloric acid.

Caliche. Cemented deposits of calcium carbonate materials.

Colloid. Having small particle size and high surface area per unit of mass. Colloid solutions are dispersed in particle state, not in molecular state like true solutions.

Concretions. Local concentrations of minerals in other minerals.

Detritus. Heterogeneous mass of fragments of stone.

Friable. Easily crumbled in the fingers.

Ferruginous. Said of iron-bearing materials usually containing iron oxides.

Igneous. Said of rocks produced by the cooling of melted material. Those solidified beneath the surface are **intrusive** rocks, or **magma**. Those which flowed out and cooled on the surface are **extrusive rocks.** **Volcanic rocks** are recent extrusive rocks, but may be similar to ancient igneous rocks.

Marl. Earthy crumbly deposit, chiefly of calcium carbonate and clay.

Tufa. A porous rock formed as a deposit from springs or streams.

Tuff. Rock composed of the finer kinds of volcanic detritus.

FUNDAMENTALS IN THE PRODUCTION OF PLANT AND ANIMAL MATERIALS

Determining Factors in the Production

About 55% of the land area of the earth is less than 1,500 ft above sea level, and another 18% is between 1,500 and 3,000 ft. The remaining area consists of mountains above 3,000 ft. The lands below 3,000 ft are in general most productive in agricultural, forestal, and animal products because of the climate and better soil. But large areas of the low flatlands are in the colder climates of northern Canada and Russia with short growing seasons, or in the sandy or alkaline deserts of Asia, Arabia, Africa, Australia, and Patagonia, where production is low and restricted. Multiple crops may be had in warm areas while only one is possible in cold areas.

Climatic temperatures and humidity, that is, the amount of moisture in the air, are important elements in the productivity of a region. Climate in the various zones of the earth may be considered as relatively uniform as far as the earth's movement is concerned.   But climates vary because of drifting air masses, and gradual to-and-fro shifting of great ocean currents.   The normally fertile plains of the United States, for example, may be subjected to heavy rain precipitation when moist tropical air from the Gulf of Mexico collides with dry polar air from the western Canadian plains, or there may be periods as long as four months with no rain.   Little tabulated data are yet available on the shift of ocean currents.   It is believed that the to-and-fro shift of the Gulf Stream in the Atlantic Ocean makes a cycle of about a century with a notable effect on the climate of the Eastern states in that time.

Soil is a most important element of productivity.   Although soils of great alkalinity are useful for producing some plants, they are a detriment to others. Acid soils will not produce some crops well, such as corn.   Lack of various minerals in the soil will retard or stunt the growth of plants.   Phosphorus, calcium, sulfur, boron, and other minerals must be added to the soils to produce the plants that need them.   The absence of one mineral in the soil may sometimes prevent normal growth of a plant.   Phosphorus, for example, is required for the production of the double sugar molecule in beets and cane.   Even when the soil conditions are right, plants grown in an atmosphere deficient in carbon dioxide will be deficient in starch.   The structure and color of plants, and of the animals that feed on them, may be altered if the soil lacks iron, copper, or other essential minerals.   The rarer elements, such as rubidium, are required to produce some plants.   Average land of good farming quality contains, per acre in 7 in. of surface, about 1 ton nitrogen, 1 ton phosphoric acid, 10 to 20 tons potash, 5 to 10 tons lime, 4 to 5 tons magnesia, and $\frac{1}{4}$ ton sulfur.   If not covered with grass, this plant food is washed out by erosions.

Temperature has an important effect upon the growth of plants and animals, and equality of tabulated mean annual temperatures is not always an indication of equality of climate.   Thus, corn does not grow well if the nights are cold during a part of the growing season, though the average temperature may be the same as in the corn belt.   The same species of fish will be less oily and yield less oil in warm waters than in cold waters.   Oil seeds grown in hot climates tend to have more of the saturated fatty acids while those of cooler climates have increased contents of the unsaturated fatty acids such as linolenic.

While the climate and soil set limits to what can be cultivated, the characteristics of the people who inhabit the region affect the use of the land.   On the subhumid fertile neutral soils of India the natives raise cotton, while on similar areas in Africa the Buganda natives raise cattle, and on the same type of soil and with similar climatic conditions the white inhabitants of northeastern Australia raise wheat.   Another diversion from the climatic pattern is the availability of markets.   In a belt across lower Brazil and Paraguay citrous fruits grow to the highest quality in superabundance with little or no effort, and vast tonnages go to waste, while these fruits are cultivated with difficulty within areas in the United States, not ideal for a tropic plant, because a ready market is available.

Vegetable and animal materials can normally be produced most economically where soil and climatic conditions suit their development, but they are often produced in less economic regions because of nearness of markets or for political reasons.   Sometimes high tariffs are imposed to bring the cost of the foreign material to a point as high as the cost of the material produced in the less economic region.   Quota systems, with artificial prices, may be imposed by law to protect uneconomic crops, such as the procurement quotas and the bonus price paid on imported sugar intended to protect the more costly beet-sugar and limited cane-sugar industries in the United States.

Forests cover about 22% of the land area of the earth.   Of this $7\frac{1}{2}$ billion acres, 28% is in Asia, 28 in South America, 19.3 in North America, 10.6 in Africa, 10.3 in Europe, and 3.8 in Australia and Oceania.   In the United States nearly 25% of the land is in forest, compared with 5.4 in Great Britain, 18 in France, and 27 in Germany where rigid laws have protected the forests. Wooded areas act as windbreaks, and also serve to balance atmospheric conditions and retain moisture in the soils.   The ideal condition is not extensive wild forests, but well-proportioned forest areas on farms and plantations.

The conifers, or so-called softwoods, comprise 35.4% of the total forest area. Tropical hardwood forests cover about the same percentage of area.   Most of the conifers are in the North Temperate Zone.   About 27% of the land area of North America is forest, of which 72% is composed of conifers.   In the United States 62% of the forest is coniferous and nearly 38% temperate climate hardwoods.   The northern part of the continent is predominantly coniferous with evergreen trees from Newfoundland to Alaska bordering the treeless Arctic tundra.The United States has the greatest variety of commercial woods of any of the temperate areas of the world, with more than 100 species of considerable commercial importance compared with fewer than 15 in Europe.

Although the breed or type of animal normally distinguishes the nature of the product derived from it, animal products also vary with the climate and the local feed available.   Goats feeding in the semiarid regions of north-central Argentina furnish skins that make firmer and stronger leather than that produced from skins of the same type of goat feeding on the rich pampas. Some breeds of sheep yield soft wool while others yield wiry wool, and some breeds yield more and better meats, but climate and feeding may cause variations in all these results.   Cattle grown on semiarid ranges may be shifted at a certain age to richer grasslands for development before marketing.   The overfed hogs of the prairies of the United States and Argentina yield more than twice the amount of lard obtained from the hogs grown in Canada for bacon.   The semiwild hogs of the cold and impoverished districts of North China are notable for heavy bristles and for tough skins for leather.

Classification and Naming of Plants

Species is a unit of classification, but is not a single plant type.   It is a concept of a group of individual plants having certain essential characters in common.   Thus, all oaks recognized as white oak constitute the species *Quercus alba*. In plant cultivation, species are subdivided into smaller groups known as **varieties,** and these into **subvarieties, forms,** and **strains,** which may differ only in minor characteristics such as color of the flower.

Genus, plural **genera,** is a group of related species. Thus, the plants recognized as constituting species of white oak, red oak, etc., belong to the genus *Quercus.* The chief structure of a genus is the flower and some other organs of the plant. **Family** is a group of similar and related genera. Thus, the oak genus *Quercus,* the chestnut genus *Castanea,* and the beech genus *Fagus* constitute the family *Fagaceae.* **Order** is a group of related families. Thus, the oak and the beech and the hazel constitute the order known as *Fagales.* **Class** is a group of related orders having several outstanding characteristics in common. **Subdivision** is a group of related classes resembling each other in some characteristics. **Division** is the highest general grouping of the **kingdom** of plants, each division having a common general similarity, as do seed plants, mosses, and fungi.

Commercial Trees of the United States

Trees and shrubs are both woody plants, but a tree is defined by the Department of Agriculture as a woody plant having one well-defined stem or trunk at least 2 in. in diameter at breast height, a more or less definitely formed crown of foliage, and a height of at least 10 ft. Shrubs are the smaller woody plants, usually with several branches from the ground instead of one trunk.

Without the highly variable group of hawthorns (*Crataegus*), comprising about 150 species including many shrubs, and without about 110 tropical and subtropical trees confined to Florida, there are about 585 tree species native to the United States. In addition, about 90 foreign tree species widely planted have escaped from cultivation and become naturalized, more than a third of which are tropical trees limited almost entirely to Florida. Including the foreign trees introduced for ornamental purposes, 1,027 different species of trees have been listed as growing in the 50 states, although the actual number may be much larger.

Aside from the hawthorns, the largest genera of native trees are the oaks (*Quercus*), with 57 species; the willows (*Salix*), with 33 species; and the pines (*Pinus*), with 34 species. More than 85 natural hybrids have been named by botanists among the native trees, including more than 60 hybrid oaks. The number of possible hybrids is practically unlimited, and, since hybrids do not normally reproduce themselves, the varieties of hybrid trees in any area may be subject to almost continual change.

Only 165 species, or about 30% of the 585 native tree species, have been selected by the Department of Agriculture as commercially important for their woods, although it is stated that other species furnish woods for small but important uses, and a few are important for other values. Of the 165 species, 28 are oaks and 20 pines. Sixty-four of the most important trees are designated in the following pages.

Of the total of 150 native tree species of Canada, 89 are included in the list of 165 important species of the United States. Of the 32 native tree species of Alaska, 18 occur in the list of important species of the United States.

There are more commercially important hardwood species in the eastern half of the United States, extending to the prairie plains, than in the western half, and 110 of the 165 trees designated as commercially important are native to the Eastern states. The tree species of the two regions are almost entirely different.

During the war year 1944 the cutting of saw-timber exceeded annual growth by 50%, and commercial timber in the United States is still cut at a greater rate than growth. Virgin forests have largely disappeared in the Eastern, Southern, and Lake States. Much forest acreage established by law to protect water resources is not only often in inaccessible mountain areas not suitable for economic lumbering, but also consists largely of inferior scrub trees.

Important in judging future lumber supply is the fact that a high proportion of inferior scrub growth has taken over much of the acreage still tabulated as forest land. Normally, evergreen softwoods shade out other growth, but intensive cutting of softwoods, cutting the small trees for the mature ones, permitted a preemption of the land by aspen, scrub oak, and other less desirable trees. White and red pines across the northern belt have given place to inferior hardwoods under which the pines cannot take root. In the South, much longleaf pine was succeeded by scrub oak and other inferior hardwoods.

Much of the virgin forest area in the United States was early denuded of the more valuable timber by ruthless cutting for burning to supply potash, for burning to make charcoal for iron furnaces, and by intensive stripping to supply telegraph poles, crossties, construction timbers, and pulpwood. Despite sporadic individual efforts, only at the beginning of the twentieth century were Federal and state laws enacted to promote conservation, selective cutting, forest reserves, reforestation, and tree farming.

In the first half of the twentieth century the production of lumber, plywood, and paper pulp constituted the greatest cause of the depletion of forest reserves. But more recently, the preemption of lands for the great increment of highways, power dams, and reservoirs, and the increasing expansion of urban areas have destroyed forests that are now irreplaceable. Many forest trees produced valuable products other than wood, whose loss also is irretrievable. The black walnut, now almost denuded from the Appalachian Range, furnishes one of the finest food nuts for confectionery and oil. The cutting of the sugar maple has limited greatly the supply of maple syrup and maple sugar. The **acorn,** once a valuable forage crop for hogs, is now generally inaccessible for that purpose.

(Data and following illustrations from Forest Service,
U.S. Department of Agriculture)

Longleaf pine.   Slash pine.   Loblolly pine.   Pitch pine.

Shortleaf pine.   Red pine.   Jack pine.   Virginia pine.

Spruce pine.   Eastern hemlock.   Red spruce.   White spruce.

Northern white cedar.   White fir.   Alpine fir.   Eastern white pine.

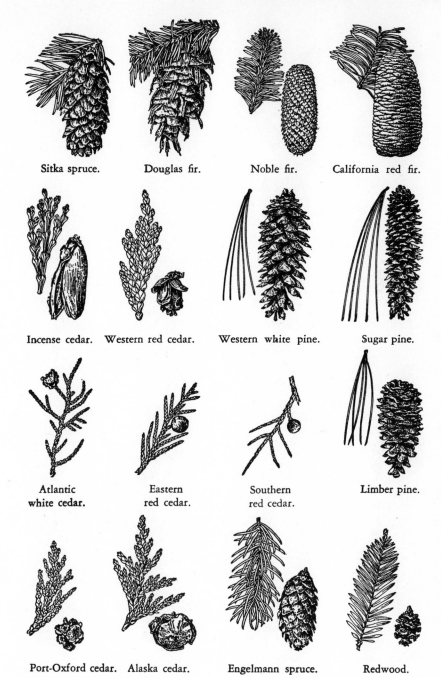

Sitka spruce.   Douglas fir.   Noble fir.   California red fir.

Incense cedar.   Western red cedar.   Western white pine.   Sugar pine.

Atlantic   Eastern   Southern   Limber pine.
white cedar.   red cedar.   red cedar.

Port-Oxford cedar.   Alaska cedar.   Engelmann spruce.   Redwood.

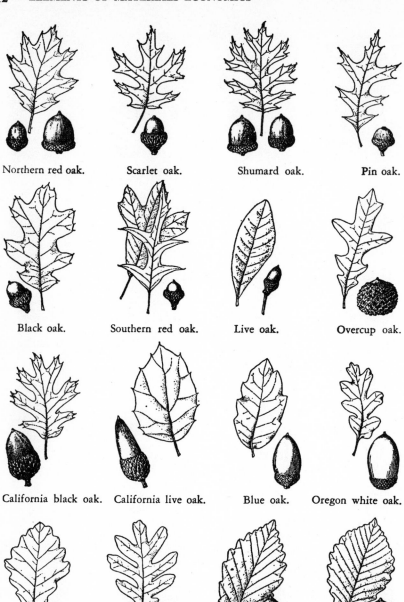

Northern red oak.   Scarlet oak.   Shumard oak.   Pin oak.

Black oak.   Southern red oak.   Live oak.   Overcup oak.

California black oak.   California live oak.   Blue oak.   Oregon white oak.

Swamp white oak.   White oak.   Chestnut oak.   Swamp chestnut oak

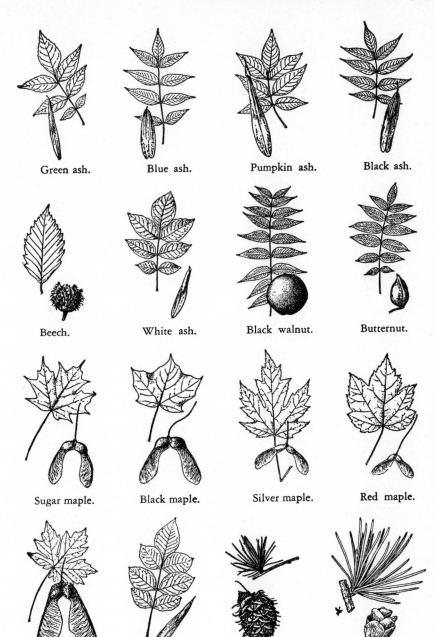

Green ash. Blue ash. Pumpkin ash. Black ash.

Beech. White ash. Black walnut. Butternut.

Sugar maple. Black maple. Silver maple. Red maple.

Bigleaf maple. Oregon ash. Western larch. Tamarack.

MATERIALS IN ENVIRONMENTAL SCIENCE

Natural Order in Environmental Science

Environmental science embraces the study and practical application of the natural laws by which mankind lives in the material universe. It is actually a profession, that is, a deductive art, in which a perspective knowledge of all the sciences is needed to visualize an orderly working balance. Everything material that we see, feel, smell, or taste is made from the 92 natural elements, which in turn are derived from natural arrangements of incorporeal energy rays.

In all this there is a highly complex interdependence. All of the material elements have intrinsic habits of arrangement and combination. All plant life, from the smallest microphytes of fungi to the giant redwood trees, incorporates both the habits of the natural elements and the instincts of their species. Animate life of the animal kingdom, from the tiniest actinomycetes of biotics to the largest mammals, has natural instincts and various gradients of intelligent action. Mankind alone of all animate material life has the additional attribute of deductive and cumulative reasoning into cause, effect, and consequence. He alone is the natural ruler of the mineral, vegetable, and animal kingdoms with the power to control, alter, recombine, or otherwise change the three material kingdoms to suit his needs. But with power there is always inexorable responsibility, in this case for the danger of destroying or seriously dislocating vital links in what is called the Universal Chain of Order.

In the **natural order** everything has reason for being; and in the balancing, every destroying influence has a counterreactant, every poison has an antidote, somewhere every disease has a preventative and a cure. But man's genius in its power of creation of new material products has superimposed new extensions and deviations of natural processes, sometimes upsetting or destroying the natural order with cumulative consequences.

Environmental science, thus, is the art of communal organization to lay out policies and regulations aiming at a wise production, employment, and disposal of materials and their products without injury to the health and welfare of the general public. It is a social art in which science and engineering are but tools of operation, and by their very nature inadaptable for the administration of the art.

Human progress is a result of evolution. The discovery of iron and the fashioning of artifacts from the wood of trees, the invention of the wheel and of surfaced roads, were first steps in the long chain of human creations that eventually produced the modern automobile, imperfect as it still is to meet the environmental needs. In corollary, only a distortion of reasoning intelligence can conceive that the interminable material universe and the complex intertwined order in the mineral, vegetable, and animal kingdoms of earth could have evolved without a creative power and reasoning intelligence of overriding vastness. The scientist and the engineer fashion their products from materials by the uncovering, or discovering, of natural laws.   Nature is not a cause but a created tool for the application of man's more limited creative genius.

Air, water, and arable land are the prime needs for the survival of mankind, and have been the first objects of consideration in **environmental control.** About 65% of the weight of the human body is oxygen, largely from water and air.   Cutting off of the oxygen supply for only a few minutes brings permanent injury to the body, a deficient supply for extended periods may cause brain injury, while a continuous oversupply is toxic to the system.   Oxygen in the atmosphere is held at a critical percentage by the action of anaerobic creatures that release the element from minerals, and by the action of marine microorganisms and other natural phenomena still little known quantitatively.

A small proportion of carbon dioxide is needed in the air for the metabolism of plant life, and the plants discharge oxygen to help balance the atmosphere. Destruction of forests disrupts this balance.   An oversupply of carbon dioxide in the air is toxic to animal life, and the heavy CO_2 gas may form tight blankets over urban areas like great gas chambers.

It takes only 6 ppm of carbon dioxide to make the air toxic, but about 40 million tons of CO_2 and hydrocarbon gases are thrown into the atmosphere annually by industrial mills, disposal plants, automobiles, and aircraft.   Sulfur dioxide from stack gas becomes sulfuric acid in moist air and destroys foliage and bird life.   One automobile traveling for 15 minutes consumes as much oxygen from the air as do 100,000 persons breathing in that time.   As gases occupy 800 times more space than liquids, dissemination is widespread, and forest trees have been killed by smog from a city 60 miles distant.

Lands around cities become increasingly sterile from the destruction of microorganisms, worms, and insects needed for maintenance of fertility and wildlife. Fertilizers are incomplete plant food and little is known of the ecology of many minor elements, but the drain-off of fertilizers, insecticides, and detergents, especially the ureas, alkalies, and phosphates, pollutes the earth, destroys marine life, and causes **eutrophication** of streams and lakes, that is, rapid growth of destructive fungi.   Stripping of forests by growth of cities and extravagant consumption of paper unbalance CO_2 and O_2 in the air and destroy wildlife havens.   No adequate plans have been devised for disposal of the increasing tonnage of solid and organic wastes from urban areas without pollution of air, water, and land. Federal policy for environmental control follows a ruling of the U.S. Supreme Court to the effect that "When the owner of property devotes it to a use in which the public has an interest, he must submit to public control to the extent of that interest."   It implies that the producers of products have the obligation to provide means of disposal of the products without injury to the public.

MATERIALS IN ECONOMIC GEOGRAPHY

Geography is a description of the face of the earth, its land and water formations and positions, and the location and nature of the areas of nations, and has long been considered a basic study in elementary schools.   But **economic geog-**

raphy primarily relates to materials, to the area conditions and the human factors under which they are produced and distributed.   In the modern world, wherein distances have been drastically lessened by rapid transportation and almost instantaneous communication, no industrial top executive, particularly if he is responsible for procurement and supply, can have a reasonable perspective unless he has a considerable background in economic geography.

Economic geography places emphasis not on industrial production as such, but on the causes of production in the various areas and the significance of the resulting production, its localized consumption, and its distribution as exports and imports.   Economic geography is the interpretation of causal influences, both material, such as growing conditions for crops and the mineral resources, and human, the natural characteristics and the inbred habits of the peoples.

Many political factors may come within the human sphere of economic geography.   For example, balance of payments is generally classed in the realm of political economy, but an unbalance of natural payments may result in laws that regulate or alter the production and trade of materials.

Résumés of the production and distribution statistics that are most useful to industrial executives are generally presented in charts.   These may show such matters as production areas by shaded representation on outline maps, manufacturing areas in relation to source of materials and distribution of markets, areas of comparative usage of materials, as of fertilizers, or trade routes for particular materials.

Because of the mathematical difficulty of representing the curved surface of the earth on a plane surface, all maps present areas in somewhat distorted forms. The commonly used **Mercator's projection** map, with meridians drawn as straight north-south lines, and the parallels drawn as straight east-west lines, has the advantages of compactness and true directions, but the distances and land areas are distorted.   On the Mercator map Greenland appears as large as Africa, although it is only one-thirteenth as large.   The homolographic, or **equal-area projections,** distort directions.   The **Mollweide projection** has parallels drawn as straight lines.   The mid-meridian is also drawn as a straight line, but the other meridians east and west of the center become more and more curved.   Each quadrangle bounded by two parallels and two meridians is equal in area, but the directions are distorted as the quadrangles become more and more elongated and distorted from the center toward the map grid.   The **conic projection** shows only slight distortions at the point of tangency of the cone with the surface of the globe of the earth, and is used for areas that have great east-west extension. Distortion increases north and south of the point of tangency.   The following charts on world production of certain agricultural and pastoral products, from the Department of Agriculture, are typical of economic-geography charts.

World corn-producing areas. Products: edible corn, corn for livestock and poultry feed, starch, glucose, corn sugar, beverage alcohols, industrial alcohol, hexahydric alcohols.

World sugar-producing areas. Products: edible sugar, edible molasses, industrial molasses, ethyl alcohol, rum, bagasse, beet pulp.

Each dot represents 25,000 short tons

World hog-producing areas. Products: pork meats, ham, bacon, lard, pigskins, bristles, gelatin, bones.

Each dot represents 100,000 head

World cattle-producing areas. Products: frozen and chilled beef, canned beef, beef extract, hides, calfskins, hair, horns, bones, oleo oils, tallow, gelatin, neatsfoot oil, glue.

World sheep-producing areas. Products: mutton and lamb meats, wool, sheepskins, lambskins, grease, lanolin, bones.

Each dot represents 200,000 head   ⁝⁝⁝ No data available

WAVES AND COLORS AS MATERIAL ELEMENTS

Electromagnetic Radiations

Tangible materials and **radiations** have a common energy origin, and thus bear a cosmic relation, but radiation is not matter in the ordinary sense of the term. Radiation is caused by vibrations, and is measured in wavelength and not in mass as is matter. Waves of high frequency and short wavelength result from the vibration of extremely small particles such as electrons of the material atom, while those of low frequency and long wavelength arise from slow vibrations such as those from a coil in a magnetic field.

Radiations are produced when materials are broken down or changed to another form, and there is then an actual loss of mass equal to the amount of energy emitted. In reverse, matter is produced when energy in the form of radiation is directed upon matter, and an actual increase in the mass of the matter results. All materials in nature are being constantly bombarded with various radiations, but it requires such an extremely large amount of energy to produce the most minute quantities of matter that the continuous changes in most materials are not noticeable in any historic period of time.

The spectrum of electromagnetic radiations extends from wavelengths of many hundred-millionths of a centimeter (1 cm equals 0.3937 in.), or infinitely small, to wavelengths of many miles, or infinitely large. The velocity of these waves is the same for all lengths of wave, 186,000 mi per sec. In the spectrum, the light waves which make objects visible to the human eye form only a small part. The human eye can see through only such materials as these light waves will penetrate. But electrical eyes can be made to operate in other wavelengths and record vision not seen by the human eye. Not all animals see with the same wavelengths, and some animals do not have normal eyes but receive vibrations through special receiving parts of the body. Different materials transmit, absorb, or reflect radiations differently. Quartz and glass, normally called transparent, transmit only a small band of light and heat waves, but will not pass very short radiations. By changing the composition of the glass the heat waves can be blocked, or some of the very short waves can be passed through. Some materials, like lead, will block the very short waves, and can be used for X-ray shields. Other materials, like beryllium, will pass only very short waves, and can be used for selective windows.

Silver will reflect 90% of visible light, while tin reflects only 70%, but silver loses reflectivity in sulfur atmospheres. Gold reflects only 61% of visible light, but has high reflectivity of infrared rays, useful for electronic purposes. All materials are sensitive to particular light waves and emit electrons when struck by those waves. Zinc is sensitive to very short ultraviolet light; cesium is sensitive to green light; potassium is sensitive to blue light. This property is the basis of electronic color selectors. It is also the basis for the operation of photoelectric cells, in which the electrons liberated constitute an electric current. Such cells are widely used as automatic switches and for conversion of light intensities to sound waves electronically.

Wavelengths and Frequencies

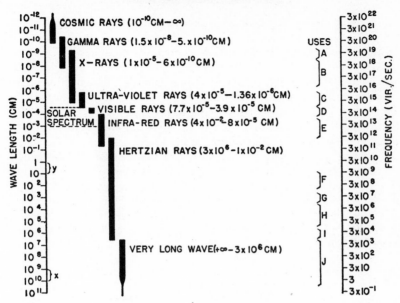

SPECTRUM OF ELECTROMAGNETIC RADIATIONS

USES:

A- RADIOLOGY, RADIOTHERAPY, X-RAY DIAGNOSIS

B- PHYSICAL AND CHEMICAL ANALYSIS OF MATTER

C- THERAPEUTIC APPLICATIONS

D- LIGHT

E- HEATING, INDUSTRIAL BAKING

F- FM, RADAR, TELEVISION, SONAR

G- SHORT WAVE RADIO

H- WIRELESS

I - LONG WAVE RADIO

J- ELECTRIC POWER, ALTERNATING CURRENT

EXPLANATION:
THE CHART IS LOGARITHMIC, THE DISTANCE X, FROM 10^9 TO 10^{10} BEING A BILLION TIMES THE DISTANCE y, FROM I TO IO

$10^1 = 10$ $10^3 = 1000$ $10^{-1} = 0.1$ $10^{-3} = 0.001$
$10^2 = 100$ $10^4 = 10000$ $10^{-2} = 0.01$ $10^{-4} = 0.0001$

From J. F. Moulton, Jr.

Light Measurement and Balancing

Visible **light waves,** like all known electromagnetic radiations, travel through space at a speed of 186,000 mi per sec. This speed is cut down perceptibly when light travels through materials. The speed through silica glass is only 122,000 mi per sec, with a bending of the light beam and a scattering of the colors. The speed through a fluoride optical glass is 146,000 mi per sec, with less color scattering than with silica glass.

The longest visible wavelength is about 0.00008 in., and the shortest is about half that length. The unit of length is the **angstrom unit,** designated as Å and equal to 0.00000001 cm. The millimicron is 10 Å.

The longest wavelengths are the reds, and the shortest are the violets. A low-intensity electric current gives a light with a yellow tint because the color composition has high percentages of red and orange-yellow. A very high-intensity current gives a higher proportion of violet, blue, and green. Adjustment of the intensity of the electric current, and incorporation of metallic elements of the proper flame color at incandescence, can flatten out the color percentage balances to give the whiteness and brilliancy desired for any particular use.

Element Colors at Incandescence

Flame colorations caused by heating materials to incandescence indicate the presence of certain elements, as the light from each element in burning has a predominance of rays or wavelengths that are characteristic of that particular element. Some elements, such as sodium, show a distinct bright color because of a predominance of wavelengths within that color range in the visible spectrum, while others show pale or intermediate colors difficult to distinguish, usually because the rays have no predominating wavelength within the visible spectrum but are mixtures of many wavelengths. Other elements, such as iron, have a predominance of rays that are not in the visible band, with wavelengths shorter or longer than those visible to the eye. Flame coloration is used in metallurgical laboratories to determine the content of alloys by burning small pieces and studying the light with a refractive prism. This property of the elements is also utilized in making carbon electrodes for electric-arc lights to give the full white light of sunshine, or short waves for therapy or industrial use, or long wavelengths for heat. For example, carbon alone gives a predominance of short wavelengths with the visible rays predominantly on the red side of the spectrum. When cerium metals are blended with the carbon, the visible light is balanced with the blue-violet to give a more even white light. When the carbon is blended with iron, nickel, and aluminum, which are all on the low-wave side of the spectrum, lower-zone ultraviolet rays are obtained.

Predominant Flame Colors of Materials

Element	Color	Element	Color
Lithium	Deep red	Antimony	Blue-green
Strontium	Crimson	Copper	Green-blue
Calcium	Yellow-red	Arsenic	Light blue
Sodium	Bright yellow	Lead	Light blue
Barium	Yellow-green	Selenium	Blue
Molybdenum	Green-yellow	Indium	Deep blue
Zinc	Light green	Potassium	Purple-red
Boron	Green	Rubidium	Violet
Tellurium	Deep green	Cesium	Bluish purple
Thallium	Greenish blue		

Reflecting Powers of Various Metal Surfaces

	White light directly reflected, percent	Color Silver = 0	
Silver	90	0	
Chromium	61	Blue-green	12 units
Nickel	50	Red	16 units
Stainless steel	49	Blue-green	3 units
White bronze speculum	70	Red	1 unit

Reflecting Power of Various Colors in Paints

Color	Light reflection, percent	Color	Light reflection, percent
Flat white	85–89	Sky blue	58
Bone white	69–70	Light orchid	57
Canary yellow	68–72	Buff	47
Light ivory	70	Pea green	40
Aluminum	70	Tan	34
Cream	65–69	Peacock blue	34
Light green	66	Steel gray	30
Ivory	61–63	Brown	9
Peach	58–59		

Heat and Light Rays from the Carbon Arc

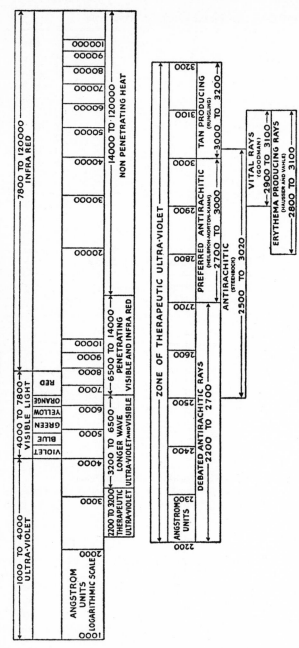

Controlled rays are obtained with arc carbons by varying the core content of the carbon. With cerium metals in the core, a light approximating sunlight is obtained. Iron in the core gives only one-quarter the visible light of the plain carbon with the same current and voltage, but gives strong ultraviolet rays. A carbon containing iron, nickel, and aluminum gives powerful ultraviolet rays between 2,500 and 3,020 angstrom units. A carbon with strontium in the core gives penetrating infrared heat rays above 6,500 angstrom units.

Chart from National Carbon Co.

Metal Melting Range and Color Scale

Chart from the Linde Air Products Co.

Terms Used in Material Color Designation

Hue is the predominant light-wave length reflected by the coloring material, and determines the **color** designation.

Brightness or **value,** or **chroma,** is the percentage of light reflected. A brilliant white approaches 100%, and a jet black approaches 0%. Black is the absence of light waves; white is a combination of all the various wavelengths. White light is broken down by refraction into separate wave bands, or hues, as in the natural rainbow.

Saturation, or **intensity,** is the percentage of reflected light which is colored, and determines the **tint.** A color, or hue, is tinted by its mixture with white.

The color circle is composed of 12 colors spaced at equal intervals: yellow, orange, red, violet, blue, green, etc., with intermediates between each. **Pigment colors** are obtained usually by **subtractive** mixing; for example, when blue and yellow are mixed, the blue absorbs the red, orange, and yellow rays, and the yellow absorbs the blue and violet rays, giving green.

Under proper illumination it is possible to detect with the eye exceedingly slight color differences, the number of distinguishable colors being estimated (U.S. Bureau of Standards) at 10,000,000.

Colors or hues vary slightly with different batches of paints, dyes, etc. For this reason products that must be matched exactly in hue are usually finished from the same batch or lot. Color matching of metals is also often important. For example, for installation of kitchens or other building equipment the stainless steel should preferably be from one lot since the color shades vary with the proportions of chromium, nickel, or manganese. These are "white" metals, but chromium has a blue tone, nickel has a yellow tone, and manganese has a purple tone. Welding alloys and solders are also matched to the color of the base metal by varying the proportions of metals with different tints.

Visibility at a distance varies with different colors. Red can be seen and recognized at long distances while blue can be seen at only short distances. The order of visibility of colors at a distance is red, green, white, yellow, blue. Legibility, however, varies also with the background. Black on yellow is more legible than black on white. Green, red, or blue on white is more legible than black on white. Visibility and legibility are important in signs, packages, or products that must be distinguished easily.

Harmony of color or **tone design** is a complicated art. It comprises the color relationship to convey pleasing emotional reaction, and includes various terms. A **rich color** is a hue at its fullest intensity. A **warm color** is one in which the red-orange predominates. A **cool color** is one in which the blue-green predominates. In general, warm colors are pleasing or exciting, while cool colors are not so pleasing or are restful to the senses. A **receding color** is one giving the illusion of withdrawing into distance by a gradation toward another tone or hue. Color, from the standpoint of harmony and design, is a sensation effect. It is not inherent in the pigments, dyes, or other materials, but is the sensation effect from those light rays reflected to the eye by the material.

PROPERTY OF FLAVOR IN MATERIALS

The quality of many materials is judged by the flavor. Flavor is the resultant of three senses: taste, smell, and feeling. Some materials, such as salt and quinine, may be detected by taste alone. Some, such as coffee and butter, depend largely upon smell. Flower perfumes are detected by smell alone. The flavor of fruits depends upon both taste and smell, and without smell would be only sour or sweet. Pepper has little or no taste, but is detected by the aroma and by the sense of feeling.

The four standard components of taste are: sweet, sour, salt, and bitter. Taste buds are located in the tongue. The tip, back, and edges of the tongue can detect all four sensations, but the center of the tongue can detect only a sour taste, and the surrounding area can detect only salty and sour. **Sour taste** is caused by hydrogen ions, and **salty taste** is due to cations from the alkali metals, accented when anions from the halogens are present. **Sweetness** and **bitterness** may or may not be from ions, and the stimuli are more complex. But all taste is electrochemical, translated to the nerves as sensations. Some materials when injected into the blood can be tasted when the blood reaches the tongue.

Odor detection is electrochemical but not entirely so, since molecules which have the same shape may have the same odor though unrelated chemically. The sense of smell is due to oscillations of the valence electrons in the molecules of the substance. The molecules of substances inhaled stimulate the tiny olfactory hairs high in the nasal cavity, and the effect is translated to the nerves as impressions or sensations. The sense of taste usually requires considerable material to register the sensation, but only the most minute molecular quantities are required to register smell. A normal person can detect a vast variety of odors, but for convenience the four fundamental odors have been designated as fragrant, acid, burnt, and caprylic. A material is then designated with a four-digit number to indicate the degree of each odor, each odor thus having ten degrees or variations, thus giving 9,999 variants. Various materials are taken as standards for the numbers, or 40 standards. The sense of smell is so discriminating that it can detect separate odors in highly complicated mixtures. Most odors are mixtures, and the art involved in the perfumery industry is to form harmonies that give a resultant pleasant sensation.

Flavors that affect the touch sensation are described as pungent, sharp, acrid, and cool. These are caused by actual pain as the biting of an acid or the cooling effect of deoxidation. **Greasiness** and **oiliness** are sensations of feel that affect taste but are not a part of it. **Texture** also is a feeling sense and not a part of flavor. The sensation of puckery of the tannin of some fruits is a definite constriction of membrane and is not taste. All of these have an effect upon the desirability of the material as a food, but in a manner apart from flavor. Too much sweetness, or sourness, or saltiness will clog the taste buds, and they must be then rested before a true flavor can be detected, but the recovery is rapid. Temperature also has an effect, and true flavors are detected only at about the temperature of the body. The judgment and grading of coffee, tea, butter, etc., are done solely by the senses of experts in comparison with standards.

FUNDAMENTALS OF BIOTIC MATERIALS

The **biotics** constitute an extensive group of organic materials that are actual living microorganisms and cannot be expressed as chemical formulas.   All of these minute bits of living matter are of plant and animal origin and may be considered as chemical factories.   It is the chemicals that certain species secrete under certain conditions that make them industrially and medicinally useful. The chemical secretions are enzymatic and catalytic in character and thus enable various chemicals to react on contact.   In industry they are used as chemical activating agents, as ferments, as leavening agents, and in various processing. In medicine they are known as **antibiotics** and are used to destroy the biotics, or bacteria, of diseases which locate themselves in the human body.

Biotics are found everywhere in myriad quantities.   A cubic centimeter of raw earth may contain as many as 50,000 **fungi,** or **microphytes,** 500 million bacteria, and 250 million **actinomycetes,** the latter being living organisms that may be ascribed, with reservations, to either the plant or the animal kingdom, and are distinguished by their mass of long silky filaments.   All these organisms lead a junglelike type of existence, attacking everything, decomposing plant debris to make humus, liberating nitrogen from proteins, liberating oxygen from rocks, liberating carbon dioxide and water from organic acids in plants and soil, and also preying on each other as jungle animals do.   Without these organisms the life cycles of all living things could not be maintained.   This same teeming population also furnishes the individual types or organisms that aid man in medicine and industry.

The number of species of these microorganisms is innumerable.   Each species has at least one enemy species that it destroys on contact or by which it is itself destroyed.   Each, apparently, has a certain definite range of activity, beyond the bounds of which it is useless.   Where one biotic is used in the manufacture of a certain product, a similar but different species used under the same conditions produces an entirely different product, or may affect the quantitative yield of the product desired.   The formation of ethyl alcohol by the fermentation of starch or sugar is caused by a biotic which is then itself killed when the alcohol produced has arrived at a certain concentration.   Other biotics may be killed by the heat that their own work produces, as at the "crisis" point of certain fevers. In general, biotics can withstand excessive cold but are usually killed by relatively low heats.

Besides the use of biotics for the medicinal and industrial applications that are now known, there are also believed to be enormous possibilities for their use in large-scale chemical processing in the future.   But the isolation of microorganisms is tedious laboratory work involving the extraction of a pure strain from cultures containing many species, and once separated, the proper conditions to promote rapid multiplication must be discovered.   Even at this stage, a biotic found to be useful in the manufacture of a certain product may simultaneously manufacture another unwanted product, difficult and costly to separate from the desired one.   But from each biotic some kind of chemical is secreted, and that chemical is the ultimate end of biotic research.

INDUSTRY TERMS

All industries have names and units peculiar to the particular industry.   The three groupings that follow are illustrative.

Terms Used in the Textile Industry

A **fiber** is the basic individual filament of raw material from which threads, cordage, or fabrics are made.

Carding consists in cleaning the particles of leaf or foreign matter from the fiber.   Originally a "card" was used—a rectangular piece of wood with wire teeth.   Carding by machine lays the cotton or wool in a continuous strand. **Drawing** consists in feeding card slivers of fibers between two pairs of rolls, the second revolving faster than the first to stretch the sliver and reduce the diameter. The first drawn slivers with slight twist are called **rovings.**   A **yarn** is the product of **spinning** the loose rovings into a continuous tight string, by running from one spool to another.   The more twists to the inch, the stronger the yarn.

Combing is a continuation of carding to eliminate short fibers, to give more evenness, and to free the fibers of all foreign matter.   The finest yarns are combed.   The eliminated short fibers are called **noils.**   At this point the yarns are dyed for yarn-dyed fabrics.   **Flock** consists of very short fibers, less than ¼ in.

Cloth or **fabric** is made by weaving, knitting, or felting.   Weaving is the interlacing of two sets of yarns at right angles.   Knitting is the looping of yarn to form rows, one row of loops being caught into the previous row.   Felting is the mass interlocking of fibers by pressure.   **Gray goods** are fabrics with no finishing treatment.

Cotton yarns are designated by numbers, or **counts.**   The standard count of cotton is 840 yd to the pound.   Number 10 yarn is therefore 8,400 yd to the pound.   A No. 80 sewing cotton is 80 × 840, or 67,200 yd to the pound.

Linen yarns are designated by the **lea** of 300 yd.   A 10-count linen yarn is 10 × 300, or 3,000 yd per lb.

The size or count of spun **rayon yarns** is on the same basis as cotton yarn. The size or count of rayon filament yarn is on the basis of the **denier,** the rayon denier being 450 meters weighing 5 centigrams.   If 450 meters (492.12 yd) of yarn weigh 5 centigrams, it has a count of 1 denier.   If it weighs 10 centigrams, it is No. 2 denier.   Rayon yarns run from 15 denier, the finest, to 1,200 denier, the coarsest.

Reeled **silk yarn** counts are designated in deniers.   The **international denier** for reeled silk is 500 meters of yarn weighing 0.05 gram.   If 500 meters weigh 1 gram, the denier is No. 20.   Spun silk count under the English system is the same as the cotton count.   Under the French system the count is designated by the number of **skeins** weighing a kilogram.   The skein of silk is 1,000 meters.

A **ply yarn** is one that has two or more yarns twisted together.   A two-ply yarn has two separate yarns twisted together.   The separate yarns may be of different materials, as cotton and rayon.   A six-ply yarn has six separate yarns.

A ply yarn may have the different plies of different twists to give different effects. Ply yarns are stronger than single yarns of the same diameter.   Tightly twisted yarns make strong, hard fabrics.   Linen yarns are not twisted as tightly as cotton because the flax fiber is longer, stronger, and not as fuzzy as the cotton.   **Filament rayon yarn** is yarn made from long, continuous rayon fibers, and it requires only slight twist.   Fabrics made from filament yarn are called **twalle. Monofilament** is fiber heavy enough to be used alone as yarn, usually more than 15 denier.   **Tow** consists of multifilament reject strand suitable for cutting into staple lengths for spinning.   Spun rayon yarn is yarn made from **staple fiber,** which is rayon filament cut into standard short lengths.

The difference between **thread** and yarn is one of more equal twist.   In thread the plies are balanced in twist so that the finished thread approximates a perfect circle.   In thread the plies are called **cords;** a six-ply thread is designated as six-cord.   **Cotton thread** comes in counts from 8 to 100, coarse to fine.

The **tex system** is the standard system of cotton yarn count in Spanish countries.   It is a direct system, the lower the count, the finer the yarn.   One thousand meters of one-tex yarn weigh 1 gram.   One thousand meters of two-tex yarn weigh 2 grams.

Group Terms Used for Drug Materials

Analgesic.   A material that diminishes the conductivity of the nerve fibers and thus relieves pain, as wintergreen.

Anodyne.   A drug that relieves pain, as opium, menthol.

Anthelmintic.   A drug that causes expulsion of intestinal worms.

Antibiotic.   A substance that destroys fungi, microbes, and other microorganisms.   Usually consists of living organisms, and not expressed by chemical formulas.

Anticatarrhal.   A drug that reduces or controls inflammation of mucous membranes of the nose or throat, as buchu.

Antiseptic.   A material that opposes or kills the microorganisms of decay, as thymol or alcohol.

Antipyretic.   A drug that reduces fever, as quinine or atabrine.

Antipyrotic.   A drug that relieves burns, as tannic acid.

Antispasmotic.   A drug that relieves convulsions or spasms, as valerian.

Antitoxin.   A chemical produced by the body, or injected into the body, which reacts with and alters poisons so that they are no longer poisonous.

Carminative.   A drug promoting the expulsion of gas to relieve colic.

Demulcent.   An oily or mucilaginous material that softens and soothes an inflamed part of the body.

Diaphoretic.   A drug that stimulates the sweat glands and causes perspiration, as aconite.

Dilatant.   A chemical that expands the muscles of the eye or other parts of the body, as belladonna.

Diuretic.   A drug that increases the renal excretions and produces increased discharge of urine, as caffeine, citrates.

Emetic.   A drug that causes vomiting to eject poisons, as zinc sulfate.

Emollient.   A drug applied externally to soften and soothe irritated or tense tissues, as zinc stearate for the skin and glycerin for throat tissues.

Expectorant.   A drug that promotes secretion of mucus from the respiratory tract, as ipecac.

Febrifuge.   A drug that reduces fever or prevents fever, as quinine.

Hemolytic.   A material that causes destruction of the red blood corpuscles, as spider poison.

Hypnotic.   A drug that produces sleep, as chloral.

Lachrymator.   A chemical that causes a copious or blinding flow of tears, as chloropicrin.

Narcotic.   A drug that produces stupor.   There are three classes: those that produce deep sleep, as opium; those that produce illusions and sleep, as cannabis; those that produce exhilaration and sleep, as alcohol.

Nutrient.   A material than can be injected to nourish the blood or a body organism, as glucose.

Peristaltic.   A drug that increases intestinal movements, as cascara.

Prophylactic.   A material given in advance to prevent disease, as quinine.

Sedative.   A material that counteracts stimulation or irritation and has a calming effect, as bromides or henbane.

Sternutator.   A chemical that causes sneezing, as diphenyl chloroarsene.

Stomachic.   A drug that increases gastric secretions and stimulates appetite, as gentian or pepper.

Vasodilator.   A material that lowers the blood pressure by dilating the arteries, as nitroglycerin or aconitine.

Vermicide. Vermifuge.   A material that expels intestinal parasites.

Terms Used in Electroplating

An **electroplate** is an adherent metal coating applied by electrodeposition to the surface of an object to improve appearance, corrosion resistance, or wear resistance.   A **composite plate** is a deposit consisting of two or more layers deposited successively.   An **alloy plate** is a composite of two or more metals deposited concurrently, such as brass.   An **anode** is an electrode in the plating bath at which metal ions are formed, negative ions are discharged, or oxidizing reactions occur.   A **cathode** is the electrode, or work parts, on which the metal ions are discharged and negative ions formed.   **Throwing power** is the ability of the bath solution to give coating distribution to all areas of the object to be plated. **Current density** is the current per unit area, usually expressed in amperes per square foot, necessary to obtain the deposit of required physical qualities.   A **cathode robber** is an auxiliary cathode so placed as to direct some current from cathode areas which otherwise might receive too high current density.   A **current shield** is a nonconductor for altering current distribution.   A **bi-polar electrode,** for altering current, is an electrode not connected to the power supply, placed in the bath between the anode and the cathode.   The area nearest the anode becomes cathodic, and the area nearest the cathode becomes anodic.

UNITS OF MEASURE

Useful Conversion Factors

1 acre = 43,560 square feet = 0.40469 hectare
1 angstrom unit = 0.0001 micron = 0.003937 millionths of an inch
1 ardeb (Egypt) = 5.44 bushels
1 arshin (Russia) = 28 inches
1 barrel (U.S.A.), cement = 376 pounds
1 barrel, oils = 42 gallons
1 berkovets (Russia) = 361.13 pounds
1 board foot = 144 cubic inches
1 bolt, cloth = 40 yards = 36.576 meters
1 buncal (Indonesia) = 1.49 troy ounces
1 bushel = 2,150.4 cubic inches
1 bushel, imperial (British) = 1.0315 U.S. bushels
1 candy (India) = 784 pounds
1 carat, metric = 0.200 gram
1 carat (U.S.A.) = 0.2056 gram
1 chittak (India) = 900 grains
1 circular mil = 0.0000007845 square inch
1 cuarteron (Spain), oil = 0.133 liquid quart
1 cuartillo (Mexico), liquid = 0.482 liquid quart
1 cubic foot = 1,728 cubic inches
1 cuffisco (Sicily), oil = 5.6 gallons
1 dram = 1.7718 grams
1 dinero (Spain) = 18.5 grains
1 drachma (Turkey) = 49.5 grains
1 ell = 48 inches
1 feddan (Egypt) = 1.038 acres
1 firkin = 9 U.S. gallons = 34.068 liters
1 flask, mercury = 75 pounds = 34.02 kilograms
1 foot = 12 inches = 0.3048 meter
1 gallon = 231 cubic inches
1 gallon, imperial (British) = 1.20094 U.S. gallons
1 gallon, proof (British) = 1.37 U.S. proof gallons
1 gill = 0.25 pint = 0.118292 liter
1 grain = 0.06480 gram
1 gram = 15.43 grains = 0.03527 avoirdupois ounce
1 gram (Libya) = 165.3 pounds
1 hamlah (Egypt) = 165.1 pounds
1 hectare = 2.471044 acres
1 hogshead = 63 U.S. gallons
1 hundred weight (British) = 112 pounds
1 inch = 0.0833 foot = 2.54005 centimeters

1 iron, leather thickness measure = $\frac{1}{48}$ inch
1 kantar (Egypt) = 99.034 pounds
1 keel (British), coal = 21.2 long tons
1 kilogram = 2.205 pounds
1 koku (Japan) = 47.65 gallons = 5.119 bushels
1 kun (Korea) = 1.323 pounds
1 kwan (Japan) = 1,000 momme = 8.267 pounds
1 ligne, metal button measure = $\frac{1}{40}$ inch
1 liter = 1.057 liquid quarts
1 lug (Bahamas) = 30 pounds avoirdupois
1 meter, square = 1.196 square yards
1 mil, square = 0.000001 square inch
1 micron = 0.001 millimeter = 0.00003937 inch
1 mil = 0.001 inch = 0.0254 millimeter
1 mile = 5,280 feet = 1.60935 kilometers
1 mile, square = 640 acres
1 millimeter = 0.03937 inch
1 ounce, avoirdupois = 28.35 grams = 0.0625 pound
1 ounce, troy = 31.1 grams
1 peck = 0.25 bushel = 8.8096 liters
1 perch = 1 square rod = 30.25 square yards
1 picul (China) = 100 catties = $133\frac{1}{3}$ pounds
1 picul (Indonesia) = 136.2 pounds
1 picul (Japan) = 132.3 pounds
1 pint, dry measure = 33.6 cubic inches
1 pint, liquid measure = 28.875 cubic inches
1 pood (Russia) = 36.11 pounds
1 pound, avoirdupois = 16 ounces = 7,000 grains = 0.4536 kilogram
1 pound, troy = 12 ounces = 0.37324 kilogram
1 pound, Venetian = 1.058 avoirdupois pounds
1 quart, dry measure = 2 pints, dry = 1.1012 liters
1 quart, liquid = 57.749 cubic inches = 0.9463 liter
1 quintal (British) = 112 pounds
1 quintal, metric = 100 kilograms = 220.5 pounds
1 ream, paper measure = 500 sheets = 20 quires
1 rod = 5.5 yards
1 scruple, apothecary weight = 20 grains = 1.296 grams
1 shih tan (China) = 50 kilograms = 110.231 pounds
1 standard (British), timber = 1,980 board feet
1 standard (U.S.A.), timber = $16\frac{2}{3}$ cubic feet
1 tank (India), gemstones and pearls = 24 rati = 0.145 ounce
1 tierce, thin-staved cask = 42 gallons, 310 to 370 pounds
1 ton, long = 2,240 pounds = 1016.047 kilograms
1 ton, metric = 1,000 kilograms = 0.9842 long ton = 1.102 short tons
1 ton, short = 2,000 pounds = 0.8929 long ton
1 vedro (Russia) = 3.249 gallons
1 yard = 3 feet = 0.9144 meter

Metal Gages in Common Use

Gage No.	Brown & Sharpe	Bir-ming-ham wire	British Impe-rial wire	Wash-burn & Moen	Music wire	U.S. Stand-ard plate	Twist drill	Stubs steel wire	Ameri-can screw	Zinc
7-0	.....	....	0.500	0.4900	.....	0.5000				
6-0	.....	....	0.464	0.4600	.....	0.4690				
5-0	.....	....	0.432	0.4300	.....	0.4380				
4-0	0.4600	0.454	0.400	0.3940	.....	0.4060				
3-0	0.4100	0.425	0.372	0.3630	.....	0.3750	.....	....	0.0315	
2-0	0.3650	0.380	0.348	0.3310	0.0085	0.3440	.....	....	0.0447	
0	0.3250	0.340	0.324	0.3070	0.0090	0.3130	.....	....	0.0578	
1	0.2890	0.300	0.300	0.2830	0.0100	0.2810	0.2280	0.227	0.0710	0.002
2	0.2580	0.284	0.276	0.2630	0.0110	0.2660	0.2210	0.219	0.0842	0.004
3	0.2290	0.259	0.252	0.2440	0.0120	0.2500	0.2130	0.212	0.0973	0.006
4	0.2040	0.238	0.232	0.2250	0.0130	0.2340	0.2090	0.207	0.1100	0.008
5	0.1820	0.220	0.212	0.2070	0.0140	0.2190	0.2055	0.204	0.1240	0.010
6	0.1620	0.203	0.192	0.1920	0.0160	0.2030	0.2040	0.201	0.1370	0.012
7	0.1440	0.180	0.176	0.1770	0.0180	0.1880	0.2010	0.199	0.1500	0.014
8	0.1290	0.165	0.160	0.1620	0.0200	0.1720	0.1990	0.197	0.1630	0.016
9	0.1140	0.148	0.144	0.1480	0.0220	0.1560	0.1960	0.194	0.1760	0.018
10	0.1020	0.134	0.128	0.1350	0.0240	0.1410	0.1940	0.191	0.1890	0.020
11	0.0907	0.120	0.116	0.1210	0.0260	0.1250	0.1910	0.188	0.2030	0.024
12	0.0808	0.109	0.104	0.1060	0.0280	0.1090	0.1890	0.185	0.2160	0.028
13	0.0720	0.095	0.092	0.0915	0.0300	0.0938	0.1850	0.182	0.2290	0.032
14	0.0641	0.083	0.080	0.0800	0.0320	0.0781	0.1820	0.180	0.2420	0.036
15	0.0571	0.072	0.072	0.0720	0.0340	0.0703	0.1800	0.178	0.2550	0.040
16	0.0508	0.065	0.064	0.0625	0.0360	0.0625	0.1770	0.175	0.2680	0.045
17	0.0453	0.058	0.056	0.0540	0.0380	0.0563	0.1730	0.172	0.2820	0.050
18	0.0403	0.049	0.048	0.0475	0.0400	0.0500	0.1695	0.168	0.2950	0.055
19	0.0359	0.042	0.040	0.0410	0.0420	0.0438	0.1660	0.164	0.3080	0.060
20	0.0320	0.035	0.036	0.0348	0.0440	0.0375	0.1610	0.161	0.3210	0.070
21	0.0285	0.032	0.032	0.0318	0.0460	0.0344	0.1590	0.157	0.3340	0.080
22	0.0254	0.028	0.028	0.0286	0.0480	0.0313	0.1570	0.155	0.3470	0.090
23	0.0226	0.025	0.024	0.0258	0.0510	0.0281	0.1540	0.153	0.3610	0.100
24	0.0201	0.022	0.022	0.0230	0.0550	0.0250	0.1520	0.151	0.3740	0.125
25	0.0179	0.020	0.020	0.0204	0.0590	0.0219	0.1500	0.148	0.3870	0.250

Metal Gages in Common Use (*Continued*)

Gage No.	Brown & Sharpe	Bir-ming-ham wire	British Impe-rial wire	Wash-burn & Moen	Music wire	U.S. Stand-ard plate	Twist drill	Stubs steel wire	Ameri-can screw	Zinc
26	0.0159	0.018	0.018	0.0181	0.0630	0.0188	0.1470	0.146	0.4000	0.375
27	0.0142	0.016	0.0164	0.0173	0.0670	0.0172	0.1440	0.143	0.4130	0.500
28	0.0126	0.014	0.0148	0.0162	0.0710	0.0156	0.1410	0.139	0.4260	1.000
29	0.0113	0.013	0.0136	0.0150	0.0740	0.0141	0.1360	0.134	0.4390	
30	0.0100	0.012	0.0124	0.0140	0.0780	0.0125	0.1285	0.127	0.4530	
31	0.0089	0.010	0.0116	0.0132	0.0820	0.0109	0.1200	0.120	0.4660	
32	0.0079	0.009	0.0108	0.0128	0.0860	0.0101	0.1150	0.115	0.4790	
33	0.0071	0.008	0.0100	0.0118	0.0900	0.0094	0.1130	0.112	0.4920	
34	0.0063	0.007	0.0092	0.0104	0.0940	0.0086	0.1110	0.110	0.5050	
35	0.0056	0.005	0.0084	0.0095	0.0980	0.0078	0.1100	0.108	0.5180	
36	0.0050	0.004	0.0076	0.0090	0.1020	0.0070	0.1065	0.106	0.5320	
37	0.0044	....	0.0068	0.0085	0.1060	0.0066	0.1040	0.103	0.5450	
38	0.0040	....	0.0060	0.0080	0.1120	0.0063	0.1015	0.101	0.5580	
39	0.0035	....	0.0052	0.0075	0.1180	.....	0.0995	0.099	0.5710	
40	0.0031	....	0.0048	0.0070	0.1250	.....	0.0980	0.097	0.5840	
41	.....	....	0.0044	0.0066	.....	.....	0.0960	0.095	0.597	
42	.....	....	0.0040	0.0062	.....	.....	0.0935	0.092	0.611	
43	.....	....	0.0036	0.0060	.....	.....	0.0890	0.088	0.624	
44	.....	....	0.0032	0.0058	.....	.....	0.0860	0.085	0.637	
45	.....	....	0.0028	0.0055	.....	.....	0.0820	0.081	0.650	
46	.....	....	0.0024	0.0052	.....	.....	0.0810	0.079	0.663	
47	.....	....	0.0020	0.0050	.....	.....	0.0785	0.077	0.676	
48	.....	....	0.0016	0.0048	.....	.....	0.0760	0.075	0.690	
49	.....	....	0.0012	0.0046	.....	.....	0.0730	0.072	0.703	
50	.....	....	0.0010	0.0044	.....	.....	0.0700	0.069	0.716	
51	.....	....	.....	.....	.....	.....	0.0670			
52	.....	....	.....	.....	.....	.....	0.0635			
53	.....	....	.....	.....	.....	.....	0.0595			
54	.....	....	.....	.....	.....	.....	0.0550			
55	.....	....	.....	.....	.....	.....	0.0520			
56	.....	....	.....	.....	.....	.....	0.0465			
57	.....	....	.....	.....	.....	.....	0.0430			
58	.....	....	.....	.....	.....	.....	0.0420			
59	.....	....	.....	.....	.....	.....	0.0410			
60	.....	....	.....	.....	.....	.....	0.0400			

Metric Length Measurements

Unit	Inches	Feet	Milli-meters	Centi-meters	Meters
One inch	1	0.0833	25.4	2.54	0.0254
One foot	12	1	304.8	30.48	0.3048
One millimeter	0.03937	0.00328	1	0.1	0.001
One centimeter	0.3937	0.0328	10	1	0.01
One meter	39.37	3.2809	1000	100	1
One yard	36	3	914.4	91.44	0.9144

Standard Metal Gages

The Brown & Sharpe, or American standard, wire gage is used for aluminum, brass, bronze, and German silver sheet, also for nonferrous wires and rod.

The Birmingham wire gage (B.W.G.), also known as the Stubs' iron wire gage, applies to seamless tubing and to sheet spring steel.

The British Imperial gage (B.I.G.), also known as the legal standard gage (L.S.G.), is used in Great Britain, and also in the United States, for copper wire.

The Washburn & Moen gage, also known as the Roebling gage, or the national wire gage, applies to all bare, galvanized, and annealed steel and iron wire, and to tinned steel wire and spring steel wire.

The music wire gage is used for "music" wire.

The U.S. Standard gage is used for steel and iron plate.

The twist drill gage, also known as the Morse gage, is used for drill-steel rod. Stubs' steel wire gage is used for steel drill rod. The American screw gage is applied to machine screws. The zinc gage is for sheet zinc.

Standard Paper Sizes

Folio note	5½ by	8½ in.
Pocket note	6 by	9½ in.
U.S. government writing	8 by	10½ in.
Commercial writing	8½ by 11	in.
Legal cap	8½ by 14	in.
Foolscap	13 by 16	in.
Denny	16 by 21	in.
Folio	17 by 22	in.
Royal	19 by 24	in.
Super royal	20 by 28	in.
Elephant	23 by 28	in.
Imperial	23 by 31	in.

Temperature Conversion Scale

To change a temperature in degrees centigrade to degrees Fahrenheit, multiply by 9/5 and add 32, thus, $F = 9/5 \ C + 32$. To change degrees Fahrenheit to degrees centigrade, subtract 32 and multiply by 5/9, thus $C = 5/9 \ (F - 32)$.

C	F	C	F	C	F	C	F	C	F
0	32	230	446	460	860	690	1274	920	1688
5	41	235	455	465	869	695	1283	925	1697
10	50	240	464	470	878	700	1292	930	1706
15	59	245	473	475	887	705	1301	935	1715
20	68	250	482	480	896	710	1310	940	1724
25	77	255	491	485	905	715	1319	945	1733
30	86	260	500	490	914	720	1328	950	1742
35	95	265	509	495	923	725	1337	955	1751
40	104	270	518	500	932	730	1346	960	1760
45	113	275	527	505	941	735	1355	965	1769
50	122	280	536	510	950	740	1364	970	1778
55	131	285	545	515	959	745	1373	975	1787
60	140	290	554	520	968	750	1382	980	1796
65	149	295	563	525	977	755	1391	985	1805
70	158	300	572	530	986	760	1400	990	1814
75	167	305	581	535	995	765	1409	995	1823
80	176	310	590	540	1004	770	1418	1000	1832
85	185	315	599	545	1013	775	1427	1005	1841
90	194	320	608	550	1022	780	1436	1010	1850
95	203	325	617	555	1031	785	1445	1015	1859
100	212	330	626	560	1040	790	1454	1020	1868
105	221	335	635	565	1049	795	1463	1025	1877
110	230	340	644	570	1058	800	1472	1030	1886
115	239	345	653	575	1067	805	1481	1035	1895
120	248	350	662	580	1076	810	1490	1040	1904
125	257	355	671	585	1085	815	1499	1045	1913
130	266	360	680	590	1094	820	1508	1050	1922
135	275	365	689	595	1103	825	1517	1055	1931
140	284	370	698	600	1112	830	1526	1060	1940
145	293	375	707	605	1121	835	1535	1065	1949
150	302	380	716	610	1130	840	1544	1070	1958
155	311	385	725	615	1139	845	1553	1075	1967
160	320	390	734	620	1148	850	1562	1080	1976
165	329	395	743	625	1157	855	1571	1085	1985
170	338	400	752	630	1166	860	1580	1090	1994

Temperature Conversion Scale (*Continued*)

C	F	C	F	C	F	C	F	C	F
175	347	405	761	635	1175	865	1589	1095	2003
180	356	410	770	640	1184	870	1598	1100	2012
185	365	415	779	645	1193	875	1607	1105	2021
190	374	420	788	650	1202	880	1616	1110	2030
195	383	425	797	655	1211	885	1625	1115	2039
200	392	430	806	660	1220	890	1634	1120	2048
205	401	435	815	665	1229	895	1643	1125	2057
210	410	440	824	670	1238	900	1652	1130	2066
215	419	445	833	675	1247	905	1661	1135	2075
220	428	450	842	680	1256	910	1670	1140	2084
225	437	455	851	685	1265	915	1679	1145	2093

Hardness Numbers

The Brinell method of determining hardness is by the indentation effect of a hard ball pressed into the surface of the metal to be tested. Tables of hardness numbers corresponding to the various indentation measurements are furnished by the makers.

The Scleroscope, or "Shore," method measures hardness by a comparison of the effect of the drop and rebound of a diamond-tipped hammer dropping by gravity from a fixed height. The resulting rebound is then read on a graduated scale.

The Rockwell hardness tester measures hardness by determining the depth of penetration under load of a steel ball or diamond cone in the material being tested. Rockwell hardness is expressed as a number, which is read on a graduated gage.

The Mohs hardness scale for abrasives and minerals is measured by scratch comparison, the mineral talc being taken as 1, and the diamond as 10 on the scale. This method is only an approximation for mineral comparison, and the Knoop indentor is used for measuring comparative hardness of hard materials.

The Vickers method is similar to the Brinell and Rockwell methods except that a diamond in the form of a pyramid is used as the penetrator. It is thus suitable for measuring metals of high hardness.

The Bierbaum microcharacter, or Bierbaum number, is used to determine the hardness by scratch. The width of a scratch made by drawing the point of a cube-shaped diamond across the surface under a 3-gram load is measured with a microscope and determines the degree of hardness.

Comparative Hardness of Hard Abrasives

(Scale: Diamond 10, corundum 9)

South American brown bort 10.00
South American Ballas 9.99
Congo yellow (cubic crystals) 9.96
Congo clear white (cubic crystals) 9.95
Congo gray opaque (cubic crystals) 9.89
South American carbonadoes 9.82
Boron carbide 9.32
Black silicon carbide 9.15
Green silicon carbide 9.13
Tungsten carbide (13% cobalt) 9.09
Fused alumina (3.14% TiO_2) 9.06
Fused alumina 9.03
African crystal corundum 9.00
Rock-crystal quartz 8.94

Approximate Relationship of Vickers, Shore (Scleroscope), Rockwell, and Brinell Hardness Numbers

Vickers or Firth	Shore or Sclero-scope	Rockwell		Brinell	Approximate tensile strength of steels, lb per sq in.	Hardness class of steel
		C	B			
1,220	96	68	...	780		
1,114	94	67	...	745		Hard
1,021	92	65	...	712	329,000–	to file
940	89	63	...	682	380,000	
867	86	62	...	653		
803	84	60	...	627		
746	81	58	...	601		
694	78	56	...	578		
649	75	55	...	555		
608	73	53	...	534		
587	71	51	...	514		
551	68	50	...	495		
534	66	48	...	477		Machining
502	64	47	...	461	165,000–	operations
474	62	46	...	444	317,000	difficult
460	60	44	...	429		
435	58	43	...	415		
423	56	42	...	401		
401	54	41	...	388		
390	52	39	...	375		
380	51	38	...	363		
361	49	37	...	352		

Approximate Relationship of Vickers, Shore (Scleroscope), Rockwell, and Brinell Hardness Numbers (*Continued*)

Vickers or Firth	Shore or Sclero-scope	Rockwell		Brinell	Approximate tensile strength of steels, lb per sq in.	Hardness class of steel
		C	B			
344	48	36	...	341		
335	46	35	...	331		
320	45	34	...	321		
312	43	32	...	311		
305	42	31	...	302		
291	41	30	...	293		
285	40	29	...	285		
278	38	28	...	277		
272	37	27	...	269		
261	36	26	...	262		
255	35	25	...	255		
250	34	24	100	248	78,000– 159,000	Commercial machine range
240	33	23	99	241		
235	32	22	99	235		
226	32	21	98	229		
221	31	20	97	223		
217	30	18	96	217		
213	30	17	95	212		
209	29	16	95	207		
197	28	14	93	197		
186	27	12	91	187		
177	25	10	89	179		
171	24	8	87	170		
154	23	4	83	156		
144	21	0	79	143		

Mohs Hardness Scale for Minerals

Original Mohs scale		Modified Mohs scale		Bierbaum number
Hardness number	Mineral	Hardness number	Material	
1	Talc	1	Talc	1
2	Gypsum	2	Gypsum	
3	Calcite	3	Calcite	15
4	Fluorite	4	Fluorite	
5	Apatite	5	Apatite	
6	Orthoclase	6	Orthoclase	
		7	Vitreous silica	
7	Quartz	8	Quartz or stellite	
8	Topaz	9	Topaz	
		10	Garnet	
		11	Fused zirconia	
9	Corundum	12	Fused alumina	
		13	Silicon carbide	
		14	Boron carbide	
10	Diamond	15	Diamond	10,000 (1 micron scratch)

Hardness Grades in Woods

1. Exceedingly hard .. Lignum-vitae, ebony
2. Extremely hard .. Boxwood, lilac, jarrah, karri
3. Very hard .... Whitethorn, blackthorn, persimmon
4. Hard .... Hornbeam, elder, yew
5. Rather hard ..... Ash, holly, plum, elm
6. Firm .... Teak, chestnut, beech, walnut, apple, oak
7. Soft .... Willow, deal, alder, Australian red cedar, birch, hazel
8. Very soft .... White pine, poplar, redwood.

Knoop Indentor Hardness of Hard Materials

Diamond 6,000–6,500
Boron carbide 2,250–2,260
Silicon carbide 2,130–2,140
Sapphire 1,600–2,100
Aluminum oxide (corundum) 1,635–1,680
Tungsten carbide (cobalt binder) 1,000–1,500
Spinel 1,200–1,400
Topaz 1,250
Quartz 710–790
Hardened steel 400–800
Glass 300–600

Specific Gravity Conversion Table

(Specific gravity multiplied by 0.036 equals the weight
in pounds per cubic inch.)

Specific gravity	Light Baumé degrees	Heavy Baumé degrees	Pounds per gal	Gallons per lb
0.6731	78	...	5.60	0.1786
0.6863	74	...	5.72	0.1748
0.7000	70	...	5.83	0.1715
0.7071	68	...	5.89	0.1698
0.7216	64	...	6.01	0.1664
0.7368	60	...	6.14	0.1629
0.7527	56	...	6.27	0.1595
0.7692	52	...	6.41	0.1560
0.7865	48	...	6.55	0.1527
0.8046	44	...	6.70	0.1493
0.8235	40	...	6.86	0.1458
0.8434	36	...	7.03	0.1422
0.8642	32	...	7.20	0.1389
0.8861	28	...	7.38	0.1355
0.9091	24	...	7.57	0.1321
0.9333	20	...	7.78	0.1285
0.9589	16	...	7.99	0.1252
0.9722	14	...	8.10	0.1235
0.9859	12	...	8.21	0.1218
1.000	10	0	8.33	0.1200
1.007	...	1	8.38	0.1193
1.014	...	2	8.46	0.1182
1.021	...	3	8.50	0.1176
1.028	...	4	8.56	0.1168
1.043	...	6	8.69	0.1151
1.058	...	8	8.81	0.1135
1.074	...	10	8.94	0.1119
1.090	...	12	9.08	0.1101
1.107	...	14	9.21	0.1086
1.124	...	16	9.36	0.1068
1.142	...	18	9.51	0.1052
1.160	...	20	9.67	0.1034
1.198	...	24	9.99	0.1001
1.239	...	28	10.32	0.0969
1.283	...	32	10.69	0.0935
1.330	...	36	11.09	0.0902
1.381	...	40	11.51	0.0869

Index of Refraction

Index of refraction indicates the relative amount of light transmitted by a material.   As the index of refraction increases, the transmitted light decreases. The amount of light reflected back may be considered as in inverse proportion to the amount transmitted, though much of the light may be dissipated.   A vacuum transmits 100% of the light and reflects 0%, and has a refractive index of 1.00.   A polished diamond with parallel sides will transmit only 83% of the light, and the reflected light makes the diamond shine.   The sparkle of angle-cut diamonds and highly refractive cut glass is caused by the dissipated or deflected light emerging from the angles.

Material	Index	Material	Index
Diamond	2.42	Nylon	1.53
Ruby	1.80	Polyethylene plastic	1.52
Sapphire (synthetic)	1.77	Pyrex (borosilicate glass)	1.52
Iceland spar	1.66	Window glass (soda-lime)	1.52
Flint glass (dense leaded)	1.66	Acrylic plastics	1.50
Flint glass (dense barium)	1.62	Cellulose acetate	1.48
Vinyledene chloride	1.61	Cellulose acetate butyrate	1.47
Polystyrene plastic	1.59	Ethyl cellulose	1.47
Flint glass (light leaded)	1.58	Fused quartz	1.46
Flint glass (light barium)	1.57	Water	1.33
Amber	1.55	Ice	1.30
Quartz crystal	1.54	Air	1.0003
Urea-formaldehyde	1.54	Vacuum	1.00

Acidity and Alkalinity Scale

The degree of acidity or alkalinity of solutions is expressed by the pH value. Water is considered neutral and is given a pH value of 7.   Values below 7 are acid, each declining value being 10 times more acid than the previous value.   A pH of 6 is 10 times more acid than a pH of 7, and a pH of 3 is 10,000 times more acid than a pH of 7.   Solutions having values from 7 to 14 are alkaline by the same multiples of 10.   A pH of 14 is 10 million times more alkaline than a pH of 7.   Chemical indicators used to indicate the acidity or alkalinity of solutions are shown in the acidity-alkalinity table.

Acidity-Alkalinity Indicators

	pH range	
Meta cresol purple	1.2–2.8	Red to yellow
Thymol blue	1.2–2.8	Red to yellow
Bromophenol blue	3.0–4.6	Yellow to blue
Bromcresol green	4.0–5.6	Yellow to blue
Chlorphenol red	5.2–6.8	Yellow to red
Bromthymol blue	6.0–7.6	Yellow to blue
Phenol red	6.8–8.4	Yellow to red
Cresol red	7.2–8.8	Yellow to red
Thymol blue	8.0–9.6	Red to blue

Viscosity of Liquids

The **viscosity** of a liquid is its resistance to change in its form, or flow caused by the internal friction of its particle components.   Thus, the higher the viscosity, the less fluid it is.   When a liquid is hot, there is less internal friction owing to the greater mobility and distance between the molecules, and a liquid will flow more readily than when it is cold.   Thus, all comparisons of viscosity should be at the same temperature.   **Kinematic viscosity** is the ratio of viscosity to density. **Specific viscosity** is the ratio of the viscosity of any liquid to that of water at the same temperature.   The reciprocal of viscosity is called **fluidity.**   Viscosity is usually expressed in poises or centipoises, a poise being equal to 1 gram per cm per sec.

Liquid	Viscosity, centipoises	Liquid	Viscosity, centipoises
Benzene (0°C)	0.906	Linseed oil (30°C)	33.1
Carbon tetrachloride (0°C)	1.35	Soybean oil (30°C)	40.6
Mercury (0°C)	1.68	Sperm oil (15°C)	42.0
Ethyl alcohol (0°C)	1.77	Sulfuric acid (0°C)	48.4
Water (0°C)	1.79	Castor oil (10°C)	2,420
Phenol (18°C)	12.7	Rape oil (0°C)	2,530

The **specific gravity** of a liquid is the relative weight per unit volume of the liquid compared with the weight per unit volume of pure water.   Water is arbitrarily assigned the value of 1.000 gram per cubic centimeter.   All liquids heavier than water thus have specific gravities greater than 1.000; liquids lighter than water have values less than 1.000.   Usually, the specific gravity of a liquid is measured at 15°C or at room temperature.   In practice, measurements are taken with a series of weighted and graduated glass cylinders called **hydrometers.** These float vertically, and the markings are usually in degrees Baumé.

Color Determination of Lubricating Oils

Color determination of lubricating oils and petrolatum is made by comparison with standard colored disks. Light is dispersed through a 4-oz sample bottle of the oil to be tested, and the color is compared visually with the gelatin colors on the glass. The colors on the standard glass disks of the National Petroleum Association are as follows:

1	Lily white	4	Orange pale
$1\frac{1}{2}$	Cream white	$4\frac{1}{2}$	Pale
2	Extra pale	5	Light red
$2\frac{1}{2}$	Extra lemon pale	6	Dark red
3	Lemon pale	7	Claret red
$3\frac{1}{2}$	Extra orange pale		

Gasoline and Fuel Oil Rating

The **cetane number** of a diesel fuel is numerically equal to the percentage by volume of cetane in a mixture of cetane and a-methylnaphthalene which will match the fuel in ignition quality. Cetane has the composition $CH_3(CH_2)_{14}CH_3$, and a-methylnaphthalene $CH_3 \cdot C_{10}H_7$. The cetane number of a fuel is given as the nearest whole number. Thus, if it required 49.8% of cetane in the mixture to match, the number would be 50.

The **octane number** of a fuel is the whole number nearest to the percentage by volume of iso-octane, $(CH_3)_3C \cdot CH_2CH(CH_3)_2$, in a blend of iso-octane and normal heptane, $CH_3(CH_2)_5CH_3$, that the fuel matches in knock characteristics.

Measurement of Impact Strength

The **impact strength** of a material is its ability to withstand a sudden hard blow, and depends upon the toughness of the material. Two standard methods are used to measure impact strength.

The **Charpy method** consists in the resultant of a single blow of a weighted pendulum at the center of the test sample which is supported at both ends and in a horizontal position. The sample may or may not be notched. The **Izod method** is similar to the Charpy method except that the test sample is held vertically at one end only. The test sample is always notched so that it will not break at the support. Impact strength is measured in foot-pounds of energy necessary to break the test sample.

Electron Micrographs

The **electron microscope** has a tungsten filament which emits electrons that are accelerated with a 50-kilovolt potential. The electrons pass through a magnetic collimating lens, through the specimen, through an electromagnetic objective lens, and finally through an electromagnetic projector lens to a screen from which a photographic enlargement is made.   Since electrons do not travel freely in air, the body of the microscope is pumped to a vacuum except the space for the insertion of the specimen.   Commercial electron microscopes will produce micrographs 25,000 times the original size.   Other methods, such as light diffraction, give higher magnification, but need much scientific skill.

Phenol Coefficient

Phenol is used as the standard for measuring the bacteria-killing power of all other disinfectants, and the relative bacteria-killing power is expressed as the **phenol coefficient.**

The phenol coefficient is the ratio of the dilution required to kill the Hopkins strain of typhoid bacillus in a specified time compared with the dilution of phenol required for the same organism in the same time.   Usually, 2.5 and 15 minute time limits are used, and the coefficient is calculated from the average of the two.   For example, if 1:80 and 1:110 dilutions of phenol kill in 2.5 and 15 minutes, respectively, as the necessary dilutions of the disinfectant under test are 1:375 and 1:650, then the phenol coefficient of the disinfectant is 5.3.

Measurement of Age

Measurement of the age of ancient bones, trees, and other organic remains, known as **radiocarbon dating,** is by measurement of the contained carbon 14 in the fossil.   It is assumed that the proportion of carbon 14 in the animal or plant during life is in direct ratio to the amount in the atmosphere.   After death the organism no longer absorbs carbon from the atmosphere, but loses the radioactive carbon 14 at a definite rate which is measurable in periods of years, thus making it possible to calculate the time of death of the organism.   Measurements are made with radiation counters.

The basic technique of the method is simple: High-energy radiation from outer space occasionally collides with nitrogen atoms in the upper atmosphere to detach a proton and capture a neutron, thus forming carbon 14; or the carbon dioxide already in the atmosphere may capture an additional neutron.   From either or both sources the carbon 14 content of the atmosphere is in a ratio of one carbon 14 atom to about one trillion atoms of ordinary carbon.   Animals and plants absorb carbon 14 in this ratio.   At death absorption ceases, but disintegration of the carbon 14 continues at a constant rate, with a half-life of 5,730 years.

In the second period of 5,730 years the carbon 14 is reduced to one-quarter of its original content.   Thus, by extension, if the carbon content of a fossil is found to be only one-sixteenth of the original, it is presumed that its age is 22,920 years.   Assuming that the composition of the atmosphere has remained stable during the period of organic life on earth, the method is considered reasonably accurate for measurements to 30,000 years or more.

PHYSICAL PROPERTIES OF MATERIALS

Definitions of Physical and Chemical Properties

Acid number. The weight in milligrams of potassium hydroxide required to neutralize the fatty acid in 1 gram of fat or fatty oil.

Aliphatic. Having a straight, chainlike molecular structure.

Aromatic. Having a ringlike molecular structure.

Anhydrous. Having no water of crystallization in the molecule.   A hydrated compound contains water of crystallization which can be driven off by heating.

Brittleness. The property of breaking without perceptible warning or without visible deformation.

Bursting strength. The measure of the ability of a material, usually in sheet form, to withstand hydrostatic pressure without rupture.

Compressibility. The extent to which a material, such as for gaskets, is compressed by a specified load.   **Permanent set** is the unit amount, in percentage of the compressibility, that the material fails to return to the original thickness when the load is removed.   **Recovery** is the amount in percentage of return to the original thickness in a given time, and is usually less under a prolonged load.

Conductivity. The relative rate at which a material conducts heat or electricity at normal temperature (60°F).   Silver is the standard of reference, as it is the best of the known conductors of both heat and electricity.

Creep rate. The rate (in./in./hr, or % hr) at which strain, or deformation, occurs in a material under stress or load.   **Creep strength** is the maximum tensile or compressive strength that can be sustained by a material for a specified time at a specified temperature without rupturing.   **Creep recovery** is a measure, in percentage, of the decrease in strain, or deformation, when the load is removed.

Ductility. The property of being permanently deformed by tension without rupture, that is, the ability to be drawn from a large to a small size.

Elasticity. The ability of a material to resume its original form after the removal of the force which has produced a change in form.   A substance is highly elastic if it is easily deformed and quickly recovers.

Elastic limit. The greatest unit stress that a material is capable of withstanding without permanent deformation.

Elongation. The increase in length of a bar or section under test expressed as a percentage difference between the original length and the length at the moment of rupture.

Factor of safety. The ratio of the ultimate strength of a material to its working stress.

Fatigue strength. The measure in pounds per square inch of the load-carrying ability without failure of a material subjected to a loading repeated a definite number of times.   Fatigue strength is usually higher than the prolonged service tensile strength.   **Fatigue life** is a measure of the useful life, or the number of cycles of loading, of a specified magnitude that can be withstood by a material without failure.

Flash point. The minimum temperature in degrees Fahrenheit at which a material or its vapor will ignite or explode.

Flow, or creep. The gradual continuous distortion of a material under continued load, usually at high temperatures.

Fusibility. The ease with which a material is melted.

Hardness. A property applied to solids and very viscous liquids to indicate solidity and firmness in substance or outline. A hard substance does not readily receive an indentation.

Hygroscopic. Readily absorbing and retaining moisture.

Impact strength. The force in foot-pounds required to break a material when applied with a sudden blow.

Iodine value. The number of grams of iodine absorbed by 100 grams of fat or fatty oil. It gives a measure of the chemical unsaturation of an oil or fat. High iodine value, 117 to 206, in vegetable oils, indicates suitability of the oil for use in paints. Low iodine value, not subject to oxidation, indicates nondrying suitable for soaps.

Malleability. The property of being permanently deformed by compression without rupture, that is, the ability to be rolled or hammered into thin sheets.

Modulus of elasticity. The ratio of the unit stress to unit strain within the elastic limit without fracture.

Modulus of rigidity. When an elastic material is subjected to a shearing stress, a displacement takes place; the ratio of the unit shearing stress to the displacement per unit length is the modulus of rigidity.

Plasticity. The property in a material of being deformed under the action of a force and not returning to its original shape upon the removal of the force.

Porosity. The ratio of the volume of the interstices of a material to the volume of its mass.

Reduction of area. The percentage difference between the area of a bar before being subjected to stress and the area of the bar after rupture.

Resilience. The energy of elasticity, that is, the energy stored in a material under strain within its elastic limit which will cause it to resume its original shape when the extreme stress is removed. The modulus of resilience is the capacity of a unit volume to store energy up to the elastic limit.

Saponification value. The number of milligrams of potassium hydroxide required to saponify 1 gram of fatty oil or grease.

Shrinkage. The diminution in dimensions and mass of a material.

Softening point. The Vicat softening point for thermoplastic materials is the temperature at which a flat-ended needle of one square millimeter area will penetrate a specimen to a depth of 1 millimeter under a load of 1,000 grams when the temperature of the specimen is raised at a constant rate of 50°C per hour.

Solubility. Capacity for being dissolved in a liquid so that it will not separate out on standing, except the excess over the percentage which the liquid (solvent) will dissolve. A **suspension** is a physical dispersion of particles sufficiently large that physical forces control their dissolution in the liquid. A **colloidal solution** is a dispersion of particles so finely divided that surface phenomena and kinetic energy control their behavior in the liquid. A colloidal solution is close to a molecular combination.

Specific gravity. The ratio of the weight of a given volume of a material to the weight of an equal volume of pure water at 4°C.

Specific heat. The number of calories required to raise 1 gram of a material 1°C in temperature.

Stiffness. The material property which is measured by the rate at which the stress in a material increases with the strain.

Strain. The distortion set up in a material by the action of an external force.

Strength. The ability to resist physical forces imposed upon a material.

Stress. Internal forces set up in a material by the action of an external force.

Tensile strength. The maximum tensile load per square unit of original cross section that a material is able to withstand. Tensile strength is the most common measure of the strength and ductility of metals.

Thermal conductivity. The number of calories transmitted per second between opposite faces of a cube, 1 cm by 1 cm by 1 cm, when the difference between the opposite faces of the cube is 1°C.

Thermal expansion. The coefficient of linear thermal expansion is the increase in unit length with each change of 1 deg in temperature.

Thermoplastic. Capable of being molded and remolded without rupture by heat and pressure at temperatures slightly above normal. When a material sets under heat and pressure into a hard solid not capable of being remolded, it is called **thermosetting.**

Toughness. The relative degree of resistance to impact without fracture; the property of a material which enables it to absorb energy while being stressed above its elastic limit but without being fractured.

Ultimate strength. The stress, calculated on the maximum value of the force and the original area of cross section, which causes fracture of the material.

Valency. The capacity of an atom or radical to combine with other atoms. A **radical** is a group of atoms so combined as to act as a single atom, such as the hydroxyl radical $-OH$. Different atoms have different valencies. Hydrogen has a valency of 1, oxygen has a valency of 2. It thus requires 2 atoms of hydrogen to combine with 1 atom of oxygen to form a stable compound H_2O.

Yield point. The minimum tensile stress required to produce continuous deformation in a solid material.

Rupture Strength of Plastic Pipe

The **design stress** of plastic pipe is defined by the Society of the Plastics Industry as the maximum tensile strength in the wall of the pipe in the circumferential orientation from hydrostatic pressure that can be applied continuously for 100,000 hours (11.43 years) without failure of the pipe. In practice, stress-rupture tests are made for only 10,000 hours, then estimated for 100,000 hours and divided by a safety factor of 2. Tests are usually at normal temperature, but for chemical-processing pipe tests are at use temperature. Maximum working pressures for plastic pipe at 73°F range from 100 psi for low-density polyethylene to 600 psi for glass-reinforced epoxy pipe. But as high as 1,000 psi may be obtained in selected special plastics such as the fluorocarbons. Still higher strengths are found in some specialty resins.

Modulus of Elasticity in Tension of Typical Materials

Lead (cast)	700,000
Lead (hard-drawn)	1,000,000
Phenolic plastic (fabric laminated)	1,000,000
Pine (static bending)	1,200,000
Ash (static bending)	1,300,000
Phenolic plastic (paper base)	2,100,000
Tin (cast)	4,000,000
Tin (rolled)	5,700,000
Glass	8,000,000
Brass	9,000,000
Aluminum (cast)	10,000,000
Duralumin	10,000,000
Copper (cast)	11,000,000
Zince (cast)	11,000,000
Zinc (rolled)	12,000,000
Cast iron (soft gray iron)	12,000,000
Brass (cast)	13,000,000
Bronze (average)	13,000,000
Prosphor bronze	13,000,000
Manganese bronze (cast)	14,000,000
Slate	14,000,000
Copper (soft, wrought)	15,000,000
Duronze	15,500,000
Cast iron (average, with steel scrap)	16,000,000
Clock brass	16,600,000
Copper (hard-drawn)	18,000,000
Cast iron (hard, white iron)	20,000,000
Meehanite metal	22,000,000
Monel metal	23,000,000
Malleable iron	23,000,000
Wrought iron	27,000,000
Carbon steel	30,000,000
Alloy steel (nickel-chromium)	30,000,000
Nickel	30,000,000
Tungsten	60,000,000

Order of Ductility of Metals

1. Gold
2. Platinum
3. Silver
4. Iron
5. Copper
6. Aluminum
7. Nickel
8. Zinc
9. Tin
10. Lead

Temperatures Available for Melting and Welding

Direct electric arc .... 4000°C
Oxygen-acetylene torch .... 3500°C
Electric furnace .... 3000°C
Aluminum-iron oxide powder .... 2800°C
Combustion furnace .... 1700°C
Oxygen-hydrogen torch ....1450°C

Thermal Conductivity of Materials [1]

Conductivity measured in British thermal units transmitted per hour per square foot of material 1 in. thick, per degree Fahrenheit difference in temperature of the two faces

Silver	2,920.0	Diatomite block	0.58
Copper	2,588.0	Magnesia, 85 percent	0.51
Steel, 1.0 carbon	328.0	Wood pulp board	0.39
Building stone	12.50	Bagasse board	0.35
Slate shingles	10.37	Cork, ground	0.31
Concrete, 1–2–4	6.10	Flax fiber	0.31
Glass, plate	5.53	Diatomite powder	0.308
Brickwork, mortar bond	4.00	Mineral wool	0.296
Gypsum plaster	2.32	Asbestos sheet	0.29
Brick, dry	1.21	Vermiculite	0.263
Air space, 3½ in.	1.10	Wool	0.261
Pine wood	0.958	Hair felt	0.26
Clay tile	0.60	Cotton, compressed	0.206

[1] From Paul M. Tyler, U.S. Bureau of Mines.

Linear Expansion of Metals

Unit length increase per degree centigrade rise in temperature

Cast iron 0.000010
Steel 0.000011
Cobalt 0.000012
Bismuth 0.000013
Gold 0.000014
Nickel 0.000014
Copper 0.000017
Brass 0.000019
Silver 0.000019
Tobin bronze 0.000021
Aluminum 0.000024
Zinc 0.000026
Tin 0.000027
Lead 0.000028
Cadmium 0.000029
Magnesium 0.000029

Melting Points of Materials
Commonly Used for Heat-treating Baths

Material	Melting points	
	Deg F	Deg C
35 percent lead ⎫ 65 percent tin ⎭	358	181
50 percent sodium nitrate ⎫ 50 percent potassium nitrate ⎭	424	218
Tin	450	232
Sodium nitrate	586	308
Lead	620	327
Potassium nitrate	642	339
45 percent sodium chloride ⎫ 55 percent sodium sulfate ⎭	1154	623
Sodium chloride (common salt)	1474	801
Sodium sulfate	1618	881
Barium chloride	1760	960

Forging Temperatures of Steels

	Maximum forging temperatures, deg F	Burning temperatures, deg F
1.5 percent carbon steel	1920	2080
1.1 percent carbon steel	1980	2140
0.9 percent carbon steel	2050	2230
0.7 percent carbon steel	2140	2340
0.5 percent carbon steel	2280	2460
0.2 percent carbon steel	2410	2680
0.1 percent carbon steel	2460	2710
Silico-manganese spring steel	2280	2460
3 percent nickel steel	2280	2500
3 percent nickel-chromium steel	2280	2500
Air-hardening Ni-Cr steel	2280	2500
5 percent nickel (case-hardening) steel	2320	2640
Chromium-vanadium steel	2280	2460
High-speed steel	2370	2520
Stainless steel	2340	2520
Austenitic chromium-nickel steel	2370	2590

Melting Range of Brazing Alloys

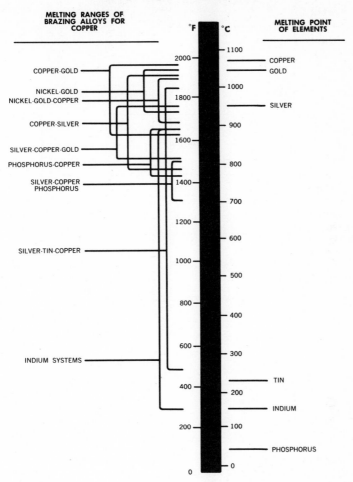

From Amax Copper, Inc.

Average Fatty Acid Composition and Constants of Fats and Oils

	Chemical formula	Coconut	Palm kernel	Tallow	Lard	Palm	Olive	Cottonseed	Corn	Peanut	Soybean	Sunflower	Linseed	Perilla	Castor	Tung	Whale	Menhaden	Sardine	Herring
Saturated acids																				
Caproic	$C_6H_{12}O_2$	0.2	Trace																	
Caprylic	$C_8H_{16}O_2$	8.0	3.0																	
Capric	$C_{10}H_{20}O_2$	7.0	6.0																	
Lauric	$C_{12}H_{24}O_2$	48.0	50.0																	
Myristic	$C_{14}H_{28}O_2$	17.5	15.0	2.0	1.0	1.0	Trace	0.5									8.0	7.0	5.0	7.0
Palmitic	$C_{16}H_{32}O_2$	8.8	7.5	30.0	26.0	42.5	9.0	21.0	7.5	7.0	6.5	3.5	5.0	7.5		4.0	11.0	16.0	14.0	8.0
Stearic	$C_{18}H_{36}O_2$	2.0	1.5	21.0	11.5	4.0	2.3	2.0	3.5	5.0	4.5	3.0	3.5	Trace	2.0	1.5	2.5	1.0	3.0	Trace
Arachidic	$C_{20}H_{40}O_2$						0.2	Trace	0.5	4.0	0.7	0.6	Trace							
Behenic	$C_{22}H_{44}O_2$									3.0	Trace	0.4								
Lignoceric	$C_{24}H_{48}O_2$					Trace			0.2											
Unsaturated acids																				
Myristoleic	$C_{14}H_{26}O_2$																1.5	Trace	Trace	Trace
Palmitoleic	$C_{16}H_{30}O_2$																17.0	17.0	12.0	18.0
Oleic	$C_{18}H_{34}O_2$	6.0	16.0	45.0	58.0	43.0	82.5	33.0	46.3	60.0	33.5	34.0	5.0	8.0	8.6	15.0	34.0	27.0	10.0	9.0
Linoleic	$C_{18}H_{32}O_2$	2.5	1.0	2.0	3.5	9.5	6.0	43.5	42.0	21.0	52.5	58.5	61.5	38.0	3.5		9.0	Trace	15.0	13.0
Linolenic	$C_{18}H_{30}O_2$										2.3		25.0	46.5			Trace			
Elaeostearic	$C_{18}H_{30}O_2$															79.5				
Ricinoleic	$C_{18}H_{34}O_3$														85.9					
C_{20} unsaturated	$C_{20}H_{2(20-x)}O_2$																5.0	20.0	22.0	20.0
C_{22} unsaturated	$C_{22}H_{2(22-x)}O_2$																12.0	12.0	19.0	25.0
Constants																				
Saponification value		251–264	240–250	196–200	195–200	196–206	185–200	192–200	188–193	185–192	189–194	189–194	189–196	188–197	175–183	189–195	185–195	189–193	189–193	179–194
Iodine number		8–10	16–23	35–44	50–69	48–58	74–94	100–115	116–130	83–95	124–148	120–136	179–204	185–206	82–86	160–170	110–136	148–185	170–190	130–144
Titer—°C		20–23°	20–23°	37–46°	36–43°	38–47°	18–25°	32–38°	18–20°	28–32°	20–21°	17–20°	19–21°	12–17°		37–38°	22–24°	31–33°	28–34°	23–27°

Relative Values of Insulating Materials

The usual comparisons of insulating values of materials are made on the basis of their dielectric strengths.   The **dielectric strength** of a material is the voltage that a material of a given thickness will resist.   It is usually given in volts per mil (1 mil equals 0.001 in.).   In any higher voltage the dielectric strength will permit a spark to pass through the material.   The quoted dielectric strengths, however, are generally the minimum for the materials.

Material	Dielectric strength, volts per mil	Material	Dielectric strength, volts per mil
Mica, muscovite	1,000	Buna rubbers	515
Glass	900	Vinylidene chloride	500
Mica, phlogopite	800	Fish paper	500
Electrical porcelain	800	Methyl methacrylate	480
Steatite	750	Cellulose acetate	400
Hard rubber	700	Casein plastic	400
Silicone rubber	600	Shellac	400
Polystyrene	600	Varnished cambric	400
Pyroxylin	600		

Electrical Conductivity of Elements Used in Alloys

Silver	100.00	Iron	14.57
Copper	97.61	Platinum	14.43
Gold	76.61	Tin	14.39
Aluminum	63.00	Tungsten	14.00
Tantalum	54.63	Osmium	13.98
Magnesium	39.44	Titanium	13.73
Sodium	31.98	Iridium	13.52
Beryllium	31.13	Ruthenium	13.22
Barium	30.61	Nickel	12.89
Zinc	29.57	Rhodium	12.60
Indium	26.98	Palladium	12.00
Cadmium	24.38	Steel	12.00
Calcium	21.77	Thallium	9.13
Rubidium	20.46	Lead	8.42
Cesium	20.00	Columbium	5.13
Lithium	18.68	Vanadium	4.95
Molybdenum	17.60	Arsenic	4.90
Cobalt	16.93	Antimony	3.59
Uranium	16.47	Mercury	1.75
Chromium	16.00	Bismuth	1.40
Manganese	15.75	Tellurium	0.001

The Electrochemical Series of Elements

In this table, the elements are electropositive to the ones which follow them, and will displace them from solutions of their salts.

1. Cesium	23. Nickel	45. Silicon
2. Rubidium	24. Cobalt	46. Titanium
3. Potassium	25. Thallium	47. Columbium
4. Sodium	26. Cadmium	48. Tantalum
5. Lithium	27. Lead	49. Tellurium
6. Barium	28. Germanium	50. Antimony
7. Strontium	29. Indium	51. Carbon
8. Calcium	30. Gallium	52. Boron
9. Magnesium	31. Bismuth	53. Tungsten
10. Beryllium	32. Uranium	54. Molybdenum
11. Ytterbium	33. Copper	55. Vanadium
12. Erbium	34. Silver	56. Chromium
13. Scandium	35. Mercury	57. Arsenic
14. Aluminum	36. Palladium	58. Phosphorus
15. Zirconium	37. Ruthenium	59. Selenium
16. Thorium	38. Rhodium	60. Iodine
17. Cerium	39. Platinum	61. Bromine
18. Didymium	40. Iridium	62. Chlorine
19. Lanthanum	41. Osmium	63. Fluorine
20. Manganese	42. Gold	64. Nitrogen
21. Zinc	43. Hydrogen	65. Sulfur
22. Iron	44. Tin	66. Oxygen

Classification of Coal [1]

Computed on an ash-free basis

Rank	Moisture, percent	Volatile matter, percent	Fixed carbon, percent	Heat value, Btu
Lignite	43.4	18.8	37.8	7,400
Subbituminous	23.4	34.2	42.4	9,720
Low-rank bituminous	11.6	41.4	47.0	12,880
Medium-rank bituminous	5.0	40.8	54.2	13,880
Cannel coal	2.2	34.8	63.0	13,250
High-rank bituminous	3.2	32.2	64.6	15,160
Low-rank semibituminous	3.0	22.0	75.0	15,480
High-rank semibituminous	5.0	11.6	83.4	15,360
Semianthracite	6.0	10.2	83.8	14,880
Anthracite	3.2	1.2	95.6	14,440

[1] U.S. Geological Survey.

Specific Gravities and Weights

For rough estimating of common construction materials

	Specific gravity	Weight, lb per cu ft
Aluminum	2.7	165
Bronze	8.0	509
Cast iron	7.2	450
Copper	8.9	556
Glass	2.5	160
Lead	11.38	710
Magnesium	1.74	109
Nickel	8.9	556
Steel	7.8	490
Zinc	7.5	440
Ash, dry	0.63	40
Cedar, dry	0.36	22
Fir, dry	0.56	32
Maple, dry	0.65	43
Redwood, dry	0.42	26
White pine, dry	0.41	26
Granite	2.6	165
Limestone	2.5	165
Sandstone	1.8	110
Pressed brick	2.2	140
Common brick	1.9	120
Terra cotta	1.9	120
Concrete	2.3	144
Portland cement	3.0	183
Mortar	1.7	103
Earth, dry, loose	.....	76
Earth, dry, packed	.....	95
Sand and gravel	.....	60
Asbestos	.....	153
Marble	2.7	170
Shale	.....	92
Tar	1.2	75
Bluestone	2.5	159

Index

Burnishing wax, 148
Burnt alum, 33
Burnt sienna, 557
Burnt umber, 558
Burr oak, 556
Burrstone, 512
Burrwood, 556
Bursting strength, 949
Bus-bar copper, 228
Bush, 874
Bush gum, 431
Bush metal, 89
Busheled iron, 420
Butacite, 851
Butadiene, 126
Butadiene rubber, 127
Butadiene-styrene rubber, 678
Butane, 595
Butane diacid, 55
Butane dicarboxylic acid, 17
Butanoic acid, 313
Butanol, 23
Butea gum, 433
Butt brass, 398
Butt oak, 556
Butta-Van, 128
Butter, 127
Butter-Aid, 128
Butter flavor, 128
Butter of zinc, 888
Buttercup yellow, 888
Butternut, 856
Button lac, 706
Buttonball wood, 615
Buttonwood, 615
Butvar, 849
Butyl alcohol, 23
Butlyl chloride, 744
Butyl ether, 300
Butyl ethyl ketone, 302
Butyl phenol, 597
Butyl rubber, 680
Butyl rubber HT, 679
Butyl tin, 810
Butyl tin maleate, 810
Butyl titanate, 816
Butyl vinyl ether, 848
Butyraldehyde, 849
Butyric acid, 313
Byrd cloth, 249

Byssus silk, 722
BZ Alloys, 631

C

C carbon, 142
C metal, 482
C oil, 281
Caá heé, 781
Cab-O-Sil, 710
Cab-O-Sil EH5, 710
Cabbage palm, 123
Cable, 236
Cable lacquer, 436
Cable lead, 63
Cable paper, 183
Cabretta, 705
Cabuya, 500
Cacahuanache oil, 560
Cacao tree, 209
Cade oil, 426
Caderite, 623
Cadmium, 129
Cadmium amalgam, 53
Cadmium bronze, 130
Cadmium copper, 130
Cadmium foil, 129
Cadmium-nickel alloy, 871
Cadmium nitrate, 130
Cadmium orange, 610
Cadmium plating, 130
Cadmium red, 610
Cadmium selenide, 130
Cadmium sulfide, 130
Cadmium sulfide crystal, 130
Cadmium sulfide film, 701
Cadmium-tin solder, 741
Cadmium yellow, 610
Cadmium-zinc solder, 741
Cadmolith, 461
Cadylite, 130
Caesium, 180
Caffeic acid, 212
Caffeine, 130
Caffeine-free coffee, 213
Cajeput bark, 131
Cajeput oil, 131
Cajeputene, 291
Cake tea, 802
Calacid salt, 686

Calam seeds, 110
Calamine, 889
Calamo, 688
Calaverite, 373
Calavo, 78
Calc spar, 131
Calcareous clay, 175
Calcareous rock, 905
Calcareous sandstone, 690
Calcene, 181
Calcia, 453
Calciferol, 854
Calcined alumina, 36
Calcined bauxite, 88
Calcined carbon, 800
Calcined coke, 214
Calcined dolomite, 273
Calcined gypsum, 385
Calcite, 131
Calcium, 132
Calcium abiotate, 503
Calcium acetate, 133
Calcium acid phosphate, 603
Calcium arsenate, 411
Calcium borate, 109
Calcium carbide, 133
Calcium carbonate, 181
Calcium caseinate, 153
Calcium chloride, 133
Calcium chloride hypo-
    chlorite, 185
Calcium cyanamide, 547
Calcium cyanide, 737
Calcium cyclamate, 782
Calcium diphosphate, 132
Calcium feldspar, 316
Calcium fluoride, 335
Calcium fluorite, 336
Calcium hydroxide, 454
Calcium hypochlorite, 186
Calcium lactate, 132
Calcium lactobionate, 132
Calcium lead, 443
Calcium-lead alloy, 443
Calcium lignosulfonate, 451
Calcium linoleate, 503
Calcium-manganese-silicon,
    134
Calcium metal, 132
Calcium metasilicate, 133
Calcium mica, 506